AWV	air-water vapor mixture
BH	Btu per hour, a heat flow rate
BHL	Btu per hour, latent heat
BHS	Btu per hour, sensible heat
BHT	Btu per hour total heat flow (where BHT = BHS
BPF	bypass factor (of a cooling coil)
Btu	British thermal units
°C	temperature in degrees centigrade or Celsius
C/B	electric circuit breaker
CCR	ceiling cavity ratio
cfh	cubic feet per hour flow rate
cfm	volume flow rate, ft^3/min
cmil	circular mils, cross-sectional area
COP	coefficient of performance
CRF	contrast rendition factor
CRI	color rendering index
CT	current transformer
CU	coefficient of utilization
DB	dry bulb temperature
dc	direct current
DE	direct expansion (of refrigerant)
DF	demand factor
DP	dew point temperature
DX	same as DE
EA	entering air
EER	energy efficiency ratio
EMF	electromotive force
EMT	electrical metallic tube (conduit)
EOM	end of main drip (for a steam main)
ESI	equivalent spherical illumination
ETD	equivalent temperature difference
°F	temperature in degrees Fahrenheit
fc or FC	footcandles, level of illumination in $lumens/ft^2$
FCR	floor cavity ratio
fpm	velocity, ft/min
fps	velocity, ft/sec
ft^3/lb	cubic feet per pound specific volume
FU	fixture units, plumbing
gpd	gallons per day flow rate
grain	unit of weight = 1/7000 lb
HID	high intensity discharge, lamps
HO	high output, lamps
hp	horsepower
HPS	high pressure sodium, lamps
HV	high velocity
HVAC	heating, ventilating, and air conditioning
Hz	hertz; cycles per second
IMC	intermediate metallic conduit
IES	Illuminating Engineering Society
INF	infiltration
IS	instant start (slimline), lamps
kVA	kilovolt-amperes
kW, kWh	kilowatts, kilowatt hours
LA	leaving air
LDD	luminaire dirt depreciation factor, lighting fixtures
LEF	lighting effectiveness factor
LLD	lamp lumen depreciation factor
lm	lumens
LPS	low pressure sodium, lamps
LPW	lumens per watt

Mechanical and Electrical Systems for Construction

McGraw-Hill Series in Construction Engineering and Project Management

Clarkson H. Oglesby, *Consulting Editor*

Barrie and Paulson: Professional Construction Management
Douglas: Construction Equipment Policy
Parker and Oglesby: Methods Improvement for Construction Managers
Shuttleworth: Mechanical and Electrical Systems for Construction

Mechanical and Electrical Systems for Construction

Riley Shuttleworth
Auburn University

McGraw-Hill Book Company

New York St. Louis San Francisco Auckland Bogotá Hamburg
Johannesburg London Madrid Mexico Montreal New Delhi
Panama Paris São Paulo Singapore Sydney Tokyo Toronto

This book was set in Press Roman by Jay's Publishers Services, Inc.
The editors were Kiran Verma and J. W. Maisel;
the production supervisor was Diane Renda.
The drawings were done by Jay's Publishers Services, Inc.
R. R. Donnelley & Sons Company was printer and binder.

MECHANICAL AND ELECTRICAL SYSTEMS FOR CONSTRUCTION

1 2 3 4 5 6 7 8 9 0   DOCDOC   8 9 8 7 6 5 4 3

ISBN 0-07-057215-1

Library of Congress Cataloging in Publication Data

Shuttleworth, Riley.
    Mechanical and electrical systems for construction.

    (McGraw-Hill series in construction engineering and project management)
    Includes index.
    1. Buildings—Mechanical equipment. 2. Buildings—Electric equipment. I. Title. II. Series.
TH6010.S48 1983   696   82-21711
ISBN 0-07-057215-1

Contents

Preface

The goal of this book is to bring to practitioners and students of construction a fairly complete but nonexhaustive study of the mechanical and electrical systems that are found in modern buildings.

The goal has also been to bring to each of the subjects treated a greater depth of examination than has been true in any of the very few texts of a similar nature available in the literature today. This has made necessary the omission, as a concession to limits of size, weight, and cost, of several secondary subjects, such as elevators, people movers, food preparation and service equipment, pneumatic tube systems, acoustics, sound and signal systems, fire extinguishing systems, and solar energy systems.

The readers that the author has in mind are people of all ages, of somewhat limited technical background, who can recall their high school and early college algebra and physics and who find themselves in one or more of the following situations:

1   A member of a mechanical and/or electrical design team, in an A/E (architect/engineer) organization, who may have extensive training in one discipline but very little training in the many other disciplines with which the team is concerned.

2   An architectural designer who needs greater knowledge of things mechanical and electrical in order to interrelate them more thoroughly with architectural designs, or to assist the designer in passing examinations leading to AIA affiliation and state registration.

3 An A/E "contact" person who in frequent meetings with clients, contracting officers, and building officials may need greater ability to speak the language of construction as it applies to mechanical and electrical work.

4 A third- or fourth-year student in one of the many developing schools of construction (building science) now coming onto the educational scene.

5 A third-, fourth- or fifth-year student of architecture.

6 A civil engineering student who plans to specialize in the field of building construction as a structural or sanitary engineer and needs to round out his background with mechanical and electrical training.

This text is arranged such that a straight-through reading and study from the first page to the last can be efficiently accomplished. However, the author has constantly borne in mind the fact that a reference text on these subjects is badly needed. An effort has therefore been made to make it possible for anyone with a somewhat limited background to jump right into any chapter and make reasonable progress on a specific subject.

To this end, an extensive index with many cross references is provided. The meanings of all symbols in all algebraic formulas are readily determinable. With only a few exceptions, no algebraic symbol is permitted to have one meaning in one chapter and another meaning elsewhere. A complete schedule is given at one location of all symbols and their meanings. To a limited extent, practical examples of the solution of typical problems are given.

A deep, rigorous treatment is not given to any of the many subjects with which this text is concerned; that is not its primary goal. However, to those who have been fully trained previously, it should give refreshment, and should begin and greatly assist the process of recall, when that becomes necessary.

This book's goal, then, is to give enlightenment on many subjects in mechanical and electrical construction, and to do this in a much more than superficial way. It is directed somewhat toward those who will spend their days (and nights) in intimate detail design, but even more toward those in the construction field who must in a secondary manner be extensively conversant and knowledgeable in things mechanical and electrical. For all readers, especially students, and for classroom use, sample problems are given at the end of most chapters.

Riley Shuttleworth

Chapter 1

HVAC Definitions and Basic Concepts

1-1 GENERALITIES

Throughout this text the expression *heating, ventilating, and air conditioning* will be abbreviated and referred to as HVAC. Everyone in the construction industry routinely uses and understands this terminology.

The HVAC systems in buildings are the most troublesome features in construction. Architects, engineers, and contractors all agree that this is so. They loudly proclaim that the headaches and worries that they suffer from difficulties with their HVAC systems are severe and unending. Difficulties with these systems are the greatest source of complaint and dissatisfaction on the part of building owners and operators.

One of the primary goals of this text is to point out the reasons for the problems and to suggest ways to solve them. A second goal is to set forth proper design principles.

Before proceeding with definitive discussions of this nature, however, it will be necessary to define all the terms and expressions that will be used, and to set forth clearly all the basic technical concepts upon which our discussion will be built.

1-2 HEAT

In HVAC practices, heat is one of the greatest problems. Rarely is heat present naturally in just the right amount. We almost always have too much or too little heat and the purpose of the HVAC system is to remedy that situation.

A basic understanding of heat is therefore mandatory. Although we discuss heat on familiar terms every day, do we really know its basic nature? Many of us do not.

Heat may be defined simply as molecular motion or activity. All matter consists of atoms and molecules, and at normal temperatures, they are in constant motion.

Energy, of which heat is but one form, has been invested in a sample of some material, and as a result, its molecules have motion. Theoretically, if all the heat could be removed from that sample of material, its molecules would fall together in a motionless heap. Add a little heat back to the sample and its molecules begin to stir. Add a lot of heat and those molecules begin to move at tremendous rates of speed, as they do at normal room temperatures.

The molecules of a material at a temperature of 70°F (Fahrenheit) have a rate of motion much greater than those of a material at 0°F whether the materials are similar or different. If brought into contact with each other, the molecular rates will tend to average out at the same rate of speed.

In other words, the warmer material will lose heat, temperature, and molecular motion, and the colder material will gain heat, temperature, and molecular motion. Given time, the heat exchange from one material to the other will result in an equalization of the temperatures and rates of molecular activity.

Swiftly moving molecules coming into physical proximity with more slowly moving molecules will cause the slower molecules to speed up, while the faster molecules, as a result, slow down. This is the process of *heat exchange,* and an understanding of this process must be achieved by the student of HVAC.

As we shall see below, however, heat may take forms other than molecular activity.

1-3 FORMS OF HEAT

In HVAC practices we are concerned with heat in three basic forms:

1 Sensible heat
2 Latent heat
3 Radiant heat

After we discuss these forms a bit, you will probably exclaim—"But two of these forms are not involved with molecular activity"—and you would be right. As we will see, latent heat and radiant heat are not really heat as such; one is vaporized water and the other is an electromagnetic radiation. However, they cause a load on a building cooling system just as sensible heat (molecular activity) does. So even though not technically correct, we do speak of them as heat.

1-4 SENSIBLE HEAT

The first form of heat, *sensible heat,* is, as indicated above, merely molecular activity. It is the form of heat most readily perceived by the human senses. When we feel a blast of warm air coming from some kind of warm air heater, we are sensing sensible heat. The high rate of molecular activity of the heated air that contacts our skin is imparted to the molecules of the tissues that make up the skin. Our senses perceive this increased molecular activity, and a sensation of warmth is transmitted to our brains.

If a person inadvertently places his or her hand on a hot stove, the extremely rapid motion of the molecules of the metal of the stove is instantly imparted to the hand. The molecules of the skin on the hand are then set into such extremely rapid motion that the skin cells cannot contain them. The cells break down and a blister forms—the result of the transfer of sensible heat.

In the same manner, sensible heat is lost from a warm building to the outside atmosphere on a cold day. The comparatively high molecular activity of the interior is transmitted right through the materials of the building walls, windows, and so on, to the comparatively low rate of molecular activity outdoors. This process of sensible heat propagation is called *conduction.* It is characterized by the physical contact of one substance with another, resulting in an exchange of molecular activity from the warmer substance to the cooler substance.

Sensible heat propagation also takes place by another process, called *convection.* In this process, a fluid such as air or water is brought into physi-

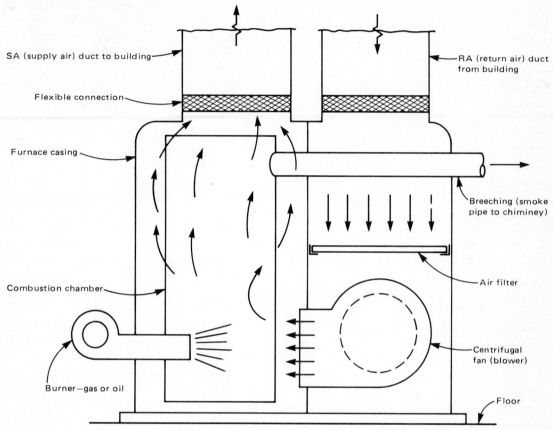

Figure 1-1 Residential warm air furnace.

cal contact with a hot surface, and the fluid is heated by conduction. The fluid is then circulated to an area of lower temperature, and in this process sensible heat is conveyed by the convection process from the hot surface to the area of low temperature.

A good example of sensible heat propagation may be seen in the typical residential warm air furnace (see fig. 1-1). Here, the steel combustion chamber is made very hot by the flame that burns within it. Air is circulated over and around the exterior of this combustion chamber by the motor-driven fan shown.

Sensible heat, molecular activity, is delivered into the moving airstream by conduction; and that heat is conveyed by convection, air move-

ment, through the supply ducts of the heating system to the house.

So sensible heat is molecular activity that is propagated by two methods—conduction and convection.

1-5 LATENT HEAT

As used in HVAC practices, the term *latent heat* has many synonyms. Some of these are: humidity, water vapor, atmospheric moisture, and low-pressure steam. These are all exact synonyms, and as such give a very good indication of the meaning of the term "latent heat."

Latent heat, then, is water which, as the result of the addition of heat to it, has become water vapor. That is what steam is—vaporized water; and the latent heat that was added, and that caused water to change state from a liquid to a vapor, is still stored in the water vapor.

Latent heat, or water vapor, is almost always present in atmospheric air. However, it is not, as is popularly assumed, absorbed by the atmospheric air. It is merely mechanically mixed with the air. The air and vapor just happen to occupy the same space at the same time. There is no chemical interaction between the molecules of the air and the vaporized water.

Latent heat or humidity should be thought of as a pressurized fluid. Consider a steam pressure cooker on the kitchen range at home. When holding pressure with the lid of the cooker tightly in place, the internal steam pressure is perfectly distributed within the cooker. It is not possible to have more steam pressure on one side of the cooker than on another. The same, to a very great extent, is true with the steam pressure (latent heat) in a room in a building. It always distributes itself evenly throughout the room.

On a cold winter day, the vapor pressure outdoors is almost always appreciably lower than the vapor pressure indoors. As a result, we find the molecules of water vapor doing their best to migrate, or escape, from the interior to the exterior—thus trying to equalize interior and exterior vapor pressures. The latent heat will migrate (that is the expression usually used) through every door and window crack, and even right through a solid wall or roof, and the rate of latent heat migration will depend on the vapor pressure differential between indoor vapor pressure and outdoor vapor pressure.

1-6   RADIANT HEAT

As mentioned earlier, radiant heat is not molecular activity. It can certainly cause molecular activity, but that is not what it is. *Radiant heat* is infrared radiation. It is part of the electromagnetic spectrum of which visible light is also a part. It is very similar to visible light except that its wavelength is much longer.

All things that surround us are emitters of radiant heat. Some objects have a dull, black surface and are excellent emitters of radiant heat. Some objects have a bright, white, shiny surface, these are very poor emitters of radiant heat.

Consider the two black spheres shown in fig. 1-2. They are of the same size, surface texture, and color. However, one is at a temperature of $150°F$ and the other is at $100°F$. Because of the temperature difference, there will be a net radiant heat exchange from the warmer sphere to the cooler sphere. However, because both spheres are appreciably warmer than the $66°F$ ambiance (surroundings), both spheres will radiate heat to the ambiance. This will be a wave form of radiant energy, and technically should not be called heat until it strikes something, such as carpeting, furniture, or people. These objects are opaque to the radiant heat; they receive it, absorb it, and convert it into sensible heat (molecular activity).

In fig. 1-2, the $100°F$ sphere will radiate heat to all surfaces of the room, all of which are at a lower temperature ($66°F$ mean). However, the $100°F$ sphere also radiates heat to the $150°F$ sphere, even though the latter is at a higher temperature. Of course, the $150°F$ sphere, being hotter, will radiate more energy to the $100°F$ sphere, so there is a *net* radiant heat exchange from the warmer to the cooler sphere.

Radiant heat, like light, is not affected by gravity, and can move in any direction—up, down, or laterally—with equal facility. For example, a ceiling in a room that is heated (by any means) until its temperature is $30°F$ or so above the other surface temperatures of the room and its furnishings will radiate heat to all parts of the room. It can "shine" downward toward the floor just as easily as it can shine in any other direction. We call it a *ceiling radiant heat panel.*

1-7   SOURCES OF INTERNAL HEAT

Let us consider now a few of the sources of heat that we might find in a typical room which impose a load on the cooling system that cools that room. Further, let us classify the heat that emanates

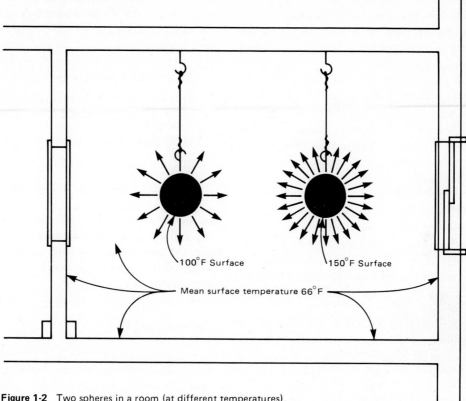

100°F Surface

150°F Surface

Mean surface temperature 66°F

Figure 1-2 Two spheres in a room (at different temperatures).

from each source as to whether it is sensible, latent, radiant, or a combination of these.

Consider first a digital computer; many of these, of considerable size and number, are found in commerce and industry. They emit lots of heat. What kind of heat? It is mainly sensible heat, as a result of the cooling air that is circulated through the computer cabinets. But the external surfaces are often warm to the touch, which means that they are radiating heat to the ambiance. So the heat output is largely sensible, with some radiant but no latent heat.

How about people? As a result of their metabolic processes, people emit heat at all times, and their rate of heat emission depends on their rate of physical and mental activity.

Although the internal body temperature of most people is 98.6°F, the usual skin surface temperature is about 85°F. Since the room surface temperatures that surround us are usually much less than that, the body radiates heat to the ambiance. Also, human beings perspire; and moisture is evaporated from the lungs as a result of respiration. So people emit latent heat.

Most of the time, the air that surrounds us and that we breathe is at a temperature below our lung and skin surface temperatures. So we lose sensible heat by physical contact with the atmosphere as well as with the furniture we sit on and the clothing that we wear. People lose heat, then, in all three forms: sensible, latent, and radiant.

A steam table or serving counter in a cafeteria also loses heat in all three forms.

Lighting fixtures emit sensible and radiant heat but no latent heat.

The sun's heat is all radiant, but that is quickly

converted to sensible heat, and sometimes to latent heat when it shines on a body of water.

The heat that transmits through walls, windows, roofs, and so on, on a hot summer day is mostly sensible.

1-8 MEASUREMENT OF HEAT

To deal adequately with heat of all types, we must know how to measure the quantities involved, and for that, we must have units of measurement.

British Thermal Unit

In the United States, the unit of thermal measurement has been, and continues to be, the British thermal unit (Btu). However, as we approach closer and closer to conversion to the metric system, Standard International (SI) units of thermal measurement will become dominant. One such SI unit is the calorie.

The Btu may be defined as that quantity of heat that must be added to or subtracted from one pound of water at 60°F to effect a temperature increase or decrease of 1°F.

Calorie

The calorie may be defined, similarly, as that quantity of heat that must be added to or subtracted from one gram of water at approximately 15°C (Centigrade or Celsius) to effect a temperature increase or decrease of 1°C.

Btu per Hour

In HVAC work we are rarely concerned with static quantities of heat, but we are constantly involved with dynamic situations—in other words, with situations where heat is moving. For example, heat is flowing out of a building in winter, and the heating system must replace that loss with an equal supply of heat. Both that heat loss and the heat supplied are measured as a time rate of heat flow. These are measured in terms of Btu per hour. The expression "Btu per hour" can be written many different ways—such as Btu/hr, Btuh, or just BH,

all meaning exactly the same thing. In this text we will generally use the expression BH to mean Btu per hour. This, and variations of it, are set forth in the following list:

BH = Btu per hour

MBH = Btu per hour in thousands;
1 MBH = 1000 BH

BHS = Btu per hour, sensible heat

BHL = Btu per hour, latent heat

BHT = Btu per hour, total heat

In the last entry above, BHT, total heat is simply the arithmetic sum of the sensible heat flow rate plus the latent heat flow rate. Therefore, BHT = BHS + BHL. Another common term for total heat is *enthalpy*.

1-9 SPECIFIC HEAT

In measuring rates of heat flow for various materials, we usually need to know what the *specific heat* of a substance might be. Specific heat may be defined as the amount of heat that must be added to or subtracted from a unit weight of a substance to cause a temperature change of one degree in whatever temperature scale is in use. This definition should sound familiar to the reader, since the thermal value of a Btu (defined above) is identical to the specific heat of water.

One value that we will need to know and to use frequently is the specific heat of air; this is 0.241 (Btu per pound of air) at ordinary room temperatures.

1-10 AIR–WATER VAPOR MIXTURE

The atmosphere almost always consists of a mechanical mixture of air and water vapor (see art. 1-5). The atmosphere normally includes many components, such as nitrogen, oxygen, water vapor, the rare gases such as argon and neon, dust, pollen, carbon dioxide, carbon monoxide, odors, and many other pollutants. However, we are concerned mostly with the air (primarily nitrogen and oxygen) and the water vapor that is mixed with it, and the behavior of these mixtures.

In this connection, there is a group of useful terms which must be carefully defined and completely understood.

1-11 DRY BULB TEMPERATURE

Dry bulb (DB) *temperature* is the temperature reading given by a dry thermometer (some thermometers are wet), which gives a direct indication of the sensible heat content of an air–water vapor mixture.

Dry bulb temperature is just the plain temperature with which you have been familiar all your life. We call it dry bulb temperature to distinguish it from the readings we get from a wet bulb thermometer.

Figure 1-3 is an illustration of a *sling psychrometer,* one of the tools of the HVAC trade. Close examination will show that it consists of two thermometers mounted on a common backing plate to which is connected a chain or a swivel handle. Notice that one thermometer has a cotton wick slid up over the mercury bulb at the bottom end. In use, the cotton wick is kept wet so that, in truth, we have a wet bulb thermometer. The other thermometer has no wick, and the bulb remains dry.

To obtain accurate readings, this instrument must be rapidly swung in a circle around the swivel handle to give the same effect as we would have if the instrument were held steady and a swiftly moving stream of air passed over it.

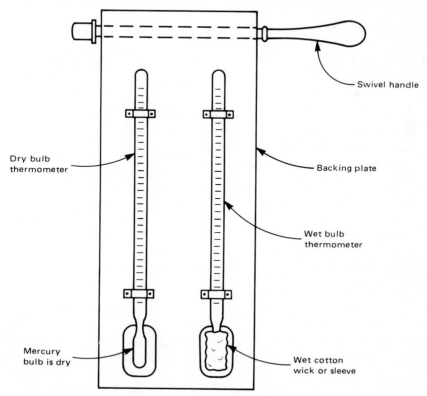

Figure 1-3 Sling psychrometer.

Obviously, from this instrument we get dry bulb and wet bulb temperature readings simultaneously.

1-12   WET BULB TEMPERATURE

Wet bulb (WB) *temperature* is the reading we get from a thermometer with a wetted bulb, immersed in a stream of rapidly moving air, which gives us a direct indication of the *total heat content* of an air-water vapor mixture.

Remember, we said in art. 1-8 that total heat is merely the arithmetic sum of the sensible heat and the latent heat content of an air-water vapor mixture. We may speak of the total heat as the Btu content per pound of a certain stationary sample of air, but more frequently we will speak of total heat as the BH (Btu per hour) in a moving stream of air. In the latter case, the total heat flow per hour (BHT) is the sum of the sensible heat flow per hour (BHS) and the latent heat flow per hour (BHL): thus, BHT = BHS + BHL.

Wet bulb temperature is so important to the study of HVAC that an effort should be made to achieve an understanding of what it basically means, as well as how wet bulb temperatures are measured. Consider a glass mercury type of wet bulb thermometer as shown in fig. 1-3, and the fact that the swiftly moving molecules of the surrounding air are beating on the wet wick and, through the wick, the glass of the thermometer and, through the glass, the mercury inside. The air molecules are trying to impart their energy to the mercury molecules and set them in more rapid motion. To the extent that this is done, the mercury molecules zip around a little faster and as a result, they require more space in which to maneuver. The volume of the mercury increases, the mercury rises higher in the stem of the thermometer, and the result is a higher temperature reading.

In opposition to this action, the water that is evaporating from the wet wick requires heat, since heat must be added to water to make it boil or evaporate from a liquid to a vapor. The necessary heat is drawn partly from the atmosphere and partly from the thermometer. Removal of heat from the thermometer cools it, causing the mercury molecules to slow down and contract—thus "trying" to give a lower temperature reading. The rate at which the water evaporates depends on the level of humidity in the atmosphere—the lower the humidity, the faster the water evaporates, and vice versa.

So we see that the wet bulb thermometer is subject to opposing forces. The sensible heat in the atmosphere tries to increase the reading up to to the dry bulb temperature as a limit, while the cooling effect of the evaporating water tries to reduce the reading down to the dew point temperature of the atmosphere as a lower limit. (Dew point temperature is defined in the following section.)

The resultant effect of the opposing forces is to balance out the thermometer reading at a point somewhat below the dry bulb reading and somewhat above the dew point temperature. It is a compromise between these two values.

It is important to realize that to the extent that moisture is constantly being evaporated from the human body's external surfaces, its nasal passages, bronchi, and lungs, the body behaves very much like a wet bulb thermometer. That is why many people feel that wet bulb temperature is a better indicator of human comfort conditions than is dry bulb temperature.

1-13   DEW POINT TEMPERATURE

Dew point (DP) *temperature* is that temperature at which an air-water vapor mixture, when cooled, will begin to yield liquid water. In other words, if a sample of an air-water vapor mixture is somehow cooled, at some point as the dry bulb temperature falls, some of the water vapor in the mixture will condense and become liquid. This is the dew point temperature of that mixture.

If in the cooling process, the dry bulb temperature fell only a few degrees before liquid water appeared, we can conclude that the moisture content of the mixture was very high. However, if the dry bulb temperature fell 30 or 40°F before visible liquid water appeared, the water content of the mixture must have been very low.

The difference in degrees between the dry bulb temperature of a mixture and its dew point temperature is known as the *dew point depression.*

1-14 RELATIVE HUMIDITY

In art. 1-5 it was stated that humidity is water vapor, and further, that it is steam at very low pressure. If we enclose a sample of an air–water vapor mixture in a closed uninsulated container of some kind, we can say that the water vapor or steam in that container has a certain *absolute pressure.* (Absolute pressure is just pressure measured above a perfect vacuum taken as zero.)

If we add water vapor to the container, the vapor pressure will rise. If we continue to add water vapor, with the dry bulb temperature held constant, we ultimately reach a condition called *saturation.* If we continue to add water vapor after we reach a saturated condition, the vapor pressure will not rise further, no matter how much steam we add. Instead, we will begin to see visible water appear as the vapor that we are adding condenses. This visible water may take the form of fog (such as we see outside on cool mornings), or we may see drops of water forming on the sides, top, and bottom of the container.

The vapor pressure in the container now is called the *saturation pressure* for that particular dry bulb temperature. For each different dry bulb temperature there is a different saturation pressure; and each vapor pressure directly represents a certain "amount" or weight of water vapor in the mixture.

If somehow we now remove exactly one-half (by weight) of the water vapor in the container, its absolute vapor pressure drops to exactly one-half its former value at saturation. We say that the air–water vapor mixture is now "50% saturated," and its *relative humidity* (RH) is 50%.

Therefore, we can loosely define relative humidity as the ratio of the vapor pressure of an air–

water vapor mixture to the vapor pressure at saturation for the same dry bulb temperature. For example, if the mixture in the container were at 70°F, its water vapor pressure at saturation happens to be 0.363 psia (pounds per square inch, absolute). If we now remove all but 30% of the water vapor, its vapor pressure will be 0.1089 psia (0.363 × 0.3 = 0.1089). The relative humidity is now 30% and may be calculated as follows:

$$\frac{0.1089 \text{ psia}}{0.363 \text{ psia}} = 0.3 \text{ or } 30\%$$

While at saturation, before we removed any moisture, its relative humidity was, of course, 100%.

1-15 SPECIFIC HUMIDITY

Specific humidity is sometimes called *humidity ratio,* and may be defined simply as the weight of the water vapor mixed with each pound of air in an air–water vapor mixture. This may be expressed as "pounds of moisture per pound of air," but it will be expressed more often as "grains of moisture per pounds of air." The term *grain* in this case is a standard unit of weight measurement and is equal to 1/7000 of a pound. In other words, 1 lb = 7000 grains.

It should be emphasized here that specific humidity is *not* grains of moisture per pound of air–water vapor mixture, but rather grains of moisture per pound of air in the mixture. It is sometimes awkwardly referred to as "grains of moisture per pound of dry air."

1-16 SPECIFIC VOLUME

Specific volume, a term we use regularly in HVAC work, can be defined simply as volume per unit weight of a substance.

We are concerned primarily with the specific volume of an air–water vapor mixture. This will vary in accordance with changes in temperature and the barometric pressure of the mixture as well as with its relative humidity. When barometric (or atmospheric) pressure increases, the specific volume of a mixture will decrease. With all other parameters (dry bulb temperature, relative humidity, specific humidity, wet bulb temperature, dew point temperature, and total heat), an increase results in an increase in specific volume.

Specific volume of an air–water vapor mixture is usually expressed in terms of cubic feet per pound (ft³/lb).

1-17 DENSITY

Density is usually expressed as mass per unit volume. An air–water vapor mixture density is measured in terms of pounds per cubic foot of volume (lb/ft³).

It is easy to see, then, that density bears an inverse relationship to specific volume—specific volume being measured in ft³/lb and density in lb/ft³.

1-18 PRESSURE

Pressure, like heat and temperature, is a fact of everyday life. We put air pressure in our automobile tires, we know there is pressure in our kitchen pressure cooker, and we hear the weather described in terms of atmospheric high- and low-pressure areas. However, in HVAC there are a few types of pressure and methods of measuring pressure that are not in general use. These must be considered and completely understood.

Few people are accustomed to thinking of pressure measurement in terms of inches of water or feet of water; however, the HVAC engineer is. In fig. 1-4 you see a vertical metallic pipe. The bottom of the pipe is closed with a welded plate, and the top end of the pipe is open to the atmosphere. Near the bottom on one side, a pressure gauge has been installed in such a way as to measure any pressure that may exist inside the pipe. It is calibrated to read in pounds per square inch (psi).

This pressure gauge gives readings in reference to the atmospheric pressure that surrounds the

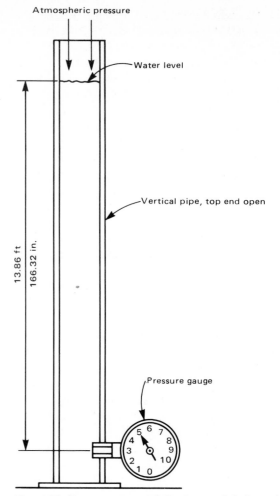

Figure 1-4 Pressure expressed in feet and inches of water.

body of the gauge and fills the case that encloses the gauge mechanism. When the pipe is filled with nothing but atmospheric air, the pressure inside the pipe is exactly the same as the pressure outside the pipe, and the gauge will give a reading of 0 psi.

Now, suppose that we begin filling the pipe with water. When water fills the pipe we see that the gauge begins to read pressures above zero. When the gauge has reached a reading of 1.0 psi, we turn the water off and measure the height of the water in the pipe. We will find that the water stands approximately 2.31 ft above the inlet to the gauge. If we filled the pipe to a height of 13.86 ft, the gauge would read 6.0 psi. Since 2.31 ft is equal to 27.7 in, we can also say that 27.7 in. of water equals 1.0 psi, and 166.32 in. of water equals 6 psi, as shown in fig. 1-4.

The diameter of the pipe has no bearing on the pressure readings indicated by the gauge, since a reading in pounds per square inch means "force per square inch of area" at the bottom and sides of the pipe. A large pipe has more downward force from the weight of a larger amount of water, but this is spread over a larger area. The pressure in terms of force per square inch of area is the same in a large pipe as in a small pipe if the height of the water is the same in both pipes.

1-19 PRESSURES AND PRESSURE LOSSES IN AIR DUCTS

Other kinds of pressure are also peculiar to HVAC work. In fig. 1-5 you will see a sketch of a centrifugal fan which is supplying air into a length of ductwork. Connected to the bottom of the duct is a U-shaped glass tube called a *manometer.*

The glass manometer is partially filled with water to the level shown. When the fan is not run-

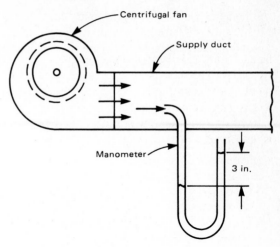

Figure 1-6 Measuring total pressure.

ning and not moving air, the water in the two sides of the manometer will stand at the same level, since the air pressure above the water is the same on both sides of the U.

When the motor that drives the fan is turned on and the fan starts running, it will build air pressures in the duct until enough pressure is developed to overcome the frictional resistance of the duct (and its dampers, registers, etc.) at the rate that air is flowing in the duct.

When air pressure builds in the duct, the manometer is no longer in a balanced condition. That is, the air pressure above the water is greater on one side (the side connected to the duct) than on the other. Therefore, the water levels will change, as shown, with one side going down and the other rising until a balanced condition is regained.

Suppose, now, that the difference in the two water levels measures 2 in., as shown; we can say that the pressure inside the duct is equal to 2 in. of water. This type of pressure is called *static pressure.*

Now, suppose that we extend one end of the glass manometer upward and bend the end of it until it faces squarely into the moving airstream as shown in fig. 1-6. The levels of the water in the

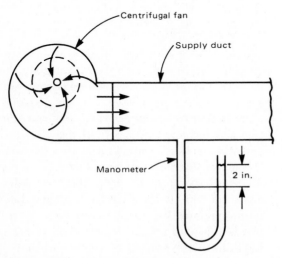

Figure 1-5 Measuring static pressure.

manometer will change again, with the water in the left side falling even more than before, and the water in the right side rising an equal amount. Now the difference in the levels is greater, and might be equal to 3 in. of water, for example.

The manometer is now measuring what we call *total pressure*. It is still sensing the 2 in. of water static pressure, but now the open end in the duct can feel the force of the air velocity. That force is called *velocity pressure*. The velocity pressure has caused our manometer reading to increase from 2 in. of water to 3 in. of water—a difference of 1 in. of water. So we can say that the manometer is measuring 2 in. of water static pressure (p_s) and 1 in. of water velocity pressure (p_v) for a total pressure (p_t) reading of 3 in. of water. Therefore, we can write the formula

$$p_t = p_s + p_v \qquad (1\text{-}1)$$

Static pressure is the type of pressure that causes the sides of the duct to distort (sometimes) outward if the static pressure is excessive. Velocity pressure cannot do this. When a child inflates a toy balloon by blowing air from his or her lungs, it is static pressure that stretches the balloon to its distended size.

To cause air to flow through a long supply duct from an air conditioner to a remote room requires the application of force. The fan in the air conditioner supplies that force, and the air moves, but the duct and everything in the duct (dampers, elbows, branch connections, size transitions, grilles, etc.) resist the flow of air through friction. It is the static pressure that the fan develops that overcomes the frictional resistance of the duct and its accessory parts.

Therefore, when an HVAC engineer writes the specifications for a centrifugal fan of the type shown in fig. 1-5, he or she will first determine the required air-moving capacity in cubic feet per minute (cfm). Then the engineer will estimate the frictional resistance expressed in inches of water static pressure, against which the fan must oper-

ate. For example, the fan in a 10-ton commercial air conditioning system might very well be required to be able to circulate 4000 cfm of air against a total SP (static pressure, system resistance) of 1.3 in WG. Here "1.3 in. WG" means a pressure of 1.3 inches of water gauge pressure.

1-20 ATMOSPHERIC PRESSURE, ABSOLUTE PRESSURE, AND GAUGE PRESSURE

Visualize, if you will, a column of atmospheric air 1 in. square and extending upward from the surface of the earth to the top of the earth's atmosphere—a distance of 100 to 150 miles or so. This column of air is part of the earth's atmosphere, but if we could somehow isolate it and weigh it, we would find that the column of air would have a certain very specific weight. That column of air, and all similar columns of air that surround it, each carrying its proportionate share of the total weight of the earth's atmosphere, bears down on the surface of the earth with a force of approximately 14.7 lb at sea level when the barometric pressure is 29.92 in. of mercury. As a result, we say that standard atmospheric pressure is about 14.7 psi. This pressure is 14.7 psi greater than absolute zero pressure, or the pressure of a perfect vacuum. So we say further that standard atmospheric pressure is about 14.7 psia (pounds per square inch, absolute).

Now, refer again to fig. 1-4 and to the pressure gauge mounted on the vertical pipe in that illustration. That gauge is sensitive to whatever pressure exists inside the pipe. However, what the gauge really does is to compare the pressure inside the pipe with the atmospheric pressure that surrounds the gauge and fills the metallic case of the gauge.

Suppose that the gauge gives a reading of 6 psi. What the gauge is really saying is that the pressure inside the pipe is 6 psi greater than the atmospheric pressure. We say that the pressure in the pipe is 6 pounds per square inch *gauge* pressure, and it is written 6 psig.

Suppose that, as before, the 6 psi pressure in the pipe resulted from 13.86 ft of water standing above the gauge level; it should be evident that the "absolute" pressure at the gauge inlet is equal to the pressure of the 13.86 ft of water plus the pressure of the atmosphere bearing down on the surface of the water. This totals 6 psi from the water plus the 14.7 psi of the atmosphere, which equals 20.7 psia.

Sometimes we will use gauge pressures in our deliberations and sometimes absolute, but we must always be careful to specify whether we mean psig or psia.

1-21 WATER CHARACTERISTICS

Because water, together with air, plays such an important part in the HVAC work, we need a thorough understanding of a few of its many, many characteristics.

Water is normally found in three states or forms:

1 The solid state (ice)
2 The liquid state (water)
3 The vapor state (steam)

Water can be easily caused to undergo a change of state merely by the addition or subtraction of heat. Visualize a cube of ice weighing 1 lb and at a temperature of $0°F$. Let us now begin to add heat to this cube. The specific heat of ice is about 0.5 (0.49), so that if we add 16 Btu of heat to this cube its temperature will rise $32°F$. (Review art. 1-9 if it is not clear to you why this is so.) The cube is still ice but is now at a temperature of $32°F$.

If we continue to add heat, the cube will now begin to melt and change from the solid state to the liquid state. After 144 Btu has been added, all the ice will be melted into 1 lb of water. The quantity of 144 Btu is called the *latent heat of fusion* of water. Latent heat of fusion can then be defined as the amount of heat that must be added to

or subtracted from a unit weight of a substance to cause a change of state from a solid to a liquid or from a liquid to a solid. The process is, of course, reversible.

If we continue heating the pound of water, we will find that, since the specific heat of liquid water is 1.0, for each Btu of heat that is added a rise of $1°F$ will result. After adding 180 Btu to the pound of water, the temperature will have risen from $32°F$ to $212°F$—a rise of $180°F$.

We now have water at the boiling point, but it will not boil, and thus change state from a liquid to a vapor, until more heat is added. We find that 970.3 Btu must be added (at standard atmospheric pressure) to cause the change of state to occur. This amount of heat—that required to change the $212°F$ liquid to a $212°F$ vapor—is called the *latent heat of vaporization.*

If we capture the steam as it boils away from the $212°F$ liquid, and contain it in some type of closed vessel so that we can continue heating it, we will find that only 0.45 Btu will now be required to raise the temperature of 1 lb of the steam $1°F$. Suppose that we add 4.5 Btu to the pound of steam; we will then see that the temperature has risen $10°F$, to $222°F$.

We say that the steam is now *superheated,* and that it has 10 degrees of superheat. So we can define superheat as the amount that a vaporized fluid is heated above its boiling point or above its saturation point. Here the saturation point represents the same condition of saturation that we discussed in art. 1-14.

1-22 TON

The word *ton* is used regularly in HVAC practices to describe cooling capacity, or a rate of heat removal from a building or a room in a building. Use of this unit derives from the very early years of the twentieth century when artificial summer cooling in buildings was first attempted. Many of the cooling systems of that day used either artificial ice or stored natural ice as the cooling medium. Usually,

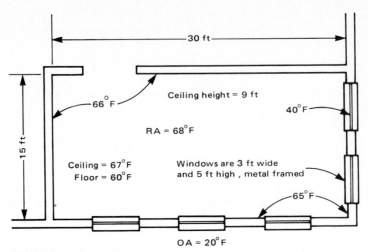

Figure 1-7   Room for MRT calculation.

a large open tank was installed in a basement or in some location where ice could be chuted into it. When filled with an adequate supply of ice, the tank would be filled with water, which soon, of course, became chilled from contact with the ice. This chilled water was then pumped around through piping to all points of the building, where cooling coils would receive the chilled water and cool a circulating stream of air.

It is not strange, then, that people began rating cooling systems in terms of the tons of ice that they could melt in a day. We still use the unit "ton" to rate our cooling and refrigerating systems.

A ton of ice, of course, weighs 2000 lb. The latent heat of fusion of ice (see art. 1-21) is, as we have seen, 144 Btu/lb. The latent heat of fusion of a ton of ice is

$$2000 \text{ lb} \times 144 \text{ Btu/lb} = 288,000 \text{ Btu/ton}$$

If a 1-ton system would melt 1 ton of ice in 1 day, this represented a heat removal rate of 288,000 Btu/day. Dividing this by the number of hours in a day, we find that 1 ton = 12,000 Btu/h.

$$288,000 \text{ Btu/day} \div 24 = 12,000 \text{ BH}$$

This is our standard unit for rating cooling and refrigerating systems today: 1 ton is equal to 12,000 BH. (Remember that BH = Btu per hour.)

1-23 MEAN RADIANT TEMPERATURE

One of the most important factors involved in the maintenance of human comfort is *mean radiant temperature* (MRT). It is also certainly one of the most neglected factors, as we shall see in chap. 2.

MRT has a somewhat involved, technical definition, concerned with such things as black body emissivity. It also has an approximate, less accurate definition with which we may, more properly, be concerned.

In common use, MRT is taken to be the weighted average of the temperatures of all the surfaces (walls, floor, etc.) that make up a room. As an example, let us consider the simple room depicted in fig. 1-7, and calculate its MRT in the following manner:

	Length, ft		Width, ft		Height, ft		Area, ft^2		Temperature, °F	
Partitions	(30	+	15)	X	9	=	405	X	66	=	26,730
Windows (5)			3	X	5	=	75	X	40	=	3,000
Outside											
Walls	(30	+	15)	X	9	=	405	–	75 ft^2 (windows)		
						=	330	X	65	=	21,450
Ceilings	30	X	15			=	450	X	67	=	30,150
Floor	30	X	15			=	450	X	60	=	27,000
Total area						=	1,710		Total	=	108,330

$$\text{MRT} = 108{,}330 \div 1{,}710 \text{ ft}^2 = 63.3°\text{F}$$

The numbers in the right-hand column are dimensionless numbers that serve merely as intermediaries leading to the final answer. The MRT developed above is a fairly close approximation of what the true MRT of this room would be. It is also about what the MRT would be in a typical room with insulated walls and ceilings, floor slab on grade, and double glass windows.

T. Napier Adlam, in his book *Radiant Heating* (New York: Industrial Press, 1947), sets forth a more accurate, but cumbersome method of calculating MRT. This involves determining the emissivity (ability to emit or receive radiant energy) of each surface in the room, the average emissivity of the entire room, and the total radiant heat emission of the room in BH. This, divided by total room area, gives mean radiant heat emission in BH per square foot of surface. From this the MRT can be determined.

MRTs calculated in this way will usually be ±2°F higher than those derived from the method utilized above.

1-24 AIR CONDITIONING DEFINED

To the general public, the term *air conditioning* is synonymous with *summer cooling*. However, that is incorrect; air conditioning may be defined as

The simultaneous control of room dry bulb temperature, humidity, air quality, air cleanliness, and air motion.

In this definition the term *air quality* refers to the chemical quality, such as carbon dioxide content, carbon monoxide content, odor level, aeriform foreign substance content, and oxygen content. *Air cleanliness* has to do with the level of filterable particulate matter (dust) in the air.

1-25 HEAT FLOW IN WATER

The HVAC practitioner has need of only a small number of very simple formulas with which to make the great majority of calculations. Most of these are concerned with heat flow in a moving stream of water, air, or refrigerant. Let us consider water first. A universal heat flow formula involving heat flow in any type of flowing medium may be written

$$\text{BH} = \text{lb/h} \times \text{specific heat} \times \Delta t \qquad (1\text{-}2)$$

where Δt represents any temperature change that occurs in the flowing medium, and the flow rate is in pounds per hour. When that medium is water, formula (1-2) may be modified as follows:

lb/hr = lb/min X 60

1 gal of water weighs 8 1/3 lb

then lb/min = gal/min X 8 1/3

or lb/min = gpm X 8 1/3

and lb/hr = gpm X 8 1/3 X 60 = gpm X 500

After dropping "specific heat" in formula (1-2) since for water it is 1.0, we may write

$$BH = gpm \times 500 \times \Delta t \qquad (1\text{-}3)$$

for heat flow in a moving stream of water. For example, consider the schematic diagram of a hot water heating system in fig. 1-8. The boiler can heat water at the rate of 200 MBH (200,000 Btu/hr), and the radiators can also deliver 200 MBH into the rooms in which they are located. Following accepted design practice, it is decided to use a 20°F Δt in the circulating water with water entering the boiler at 180°F and leaving at 200°F.

$$200°F - 180°F = 20°F \; \Delta t$$

Find the required capacity, in gpm, of the pump that causes the hot water to circulate.

Rewriting formula (1-3) as necessary, we have

$$gpm = \frac{BH}{500 \times \Delta t} \qquad (1\text{-}4)$$

and

$$gpm = \frac{200,000}{500 \times 20°F} = 20$$

The pump must be able to circulate 20 gpm.

1-26 SENSIBLE HEAT FLOW IN AIR

An HVAC supply air system is very often involved in problems where both sensible and latent heat flows are occurring. Consider first, sensible heat flow, and refer back to the universal heat flow formula (1-2).

The first term, lb/hr, may be rewritten as follows:

$$lb \; air/hr = \frac{cfm \times 60}{13.33} = cfm \times 4.5 \qquad (1\text{-}5)$$

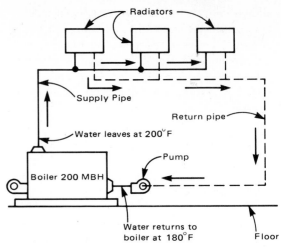

Figure 1-8 Hot water heating system.

where 60 is the number of minutes in an hour and 13.33 is the specific volume in cubic feet per pound of air at midrange temperatures near the usual room temperature. It is also the specific volume of so-called "standard" air.

Remembering that the specific heat of air is 0.24, and substituting in formula (1-2), we can write BHS = cfm $\times$ 4.5 $\times$ 0.24 $\times$ Δt, or

$$BHS = cfm \times 1.08 \times \Delta t \qquad (1\text{-}6)$$

where BHS means Btu per hour, sensible.

Notice here that the constant, 1.08, develops as a result of the use of a specific volume of 13.33 ft^3 per pound of air. But our air does not often have exactly that volume. Well, we use it anyway, and this illustrates one of the characteristics of the HVAC profession. It is not in any sense an exact science. We base all our calculations and deliberations on estimates of one kind or another, and very often these are quite rough estimates. Questions such as:

How fast will the wind be blowing?
How tightly will the windows fit?
How many people will really occupy a room?
How often will the front door be opened?
How well will a building be built?

all illustrate the fact that we are guessing much of the time. In the face of the mandatory use of such information, it would be foolish to attempt to sharpen up our formulas and calculations to within 1 or 2% of absolute accuracy. So we are satisfied with 5 to 6% accuracy, and formula (1-6) is usually used just as it is written.

1-27   LATENT HEAT FLOW IN AIR

Our formula for latent heat flow develops from the following generalized statement:

> BHL = lb air/hr × change in the specific humidity (art. 1-15) of the air-water vapor mixture (expressed in lb water/lb air) × 1061

where BHL is Btu per hour, latent, and 1061 is the latent heat of vaporization of water (art. 1-21) at a temperature of 70°F.

In the statement above the second term, specific humidity change, herein written ΔG, is very awkward if expressed in lb water/lb air because this is such a small value. So we find it convenient to express ΔG in grains (art. 1-15) of water per pound of air.

Since lb air/hr = cfm × 4.5 [formula (1-5)], we can now write

$$BHL = cfm \times 4.5 \times \frac{\Delta G}{7000} \times 1061$$

or

$$BHL = cfm \times \Delta G \times 0.68 \qquad (1-7)$$

where ΔG is the change in the specific humidity of an airstream expressed in grains of moisture per pound of air.

1-28   TOTAL HEAT FLOW IN AIR

Remembering that total heat, or enthalpy, is simply the sum of the sensible and the latent heats, you can see that we can use formulas (1-6) and (1-7) to calculate the separate BHS and BHL. Then to get BHT, we simply add the BHS and BHL. Another, and perhaps, easier method is set forth as follows:

$$BHT = (lb\ air/hr)(TH_2 - TH_1)$$

where TH_2 and TH_1 are the total heats of the air before and after some changes in the air occurs. TH is the total heat in Btu/lb air.

Substituting for "lb air/hr" [see formula (1-5)], we can write

$$BHT = cfm \times 4.5(TH_2 - TH_1) \qquad (1-8)$$

1-29   THE PSYCHROMETRIC CHART

The psychrometric chart (fig. 1-9) is drawn in such a way as to make possible the determination of all seven measurements (dry bulb, wet bulb, relative humidity, specific humidity, dew point, total heat or enthalpy, and specific volume) of an air-water vapor mixture, when enough is known to establish a point on the chart. Let us see what the foregoing sentence means.

Of the seven measurements outlined above, five are represented by lines or curves on the chart. When any two of the five are known, an intersection of two lines, or a line and a curve, results, and a point is thus established. From any point on the chart, all seven of the chart values may be read.

Looking at the chart of fig. 1-9, we may see the following:

1   The vertical lines on the chart are lines of constant dry bulb temperature, and dry bulb values may be read at the top or the bottom of the chart. For example, find the vertical line for 75°F DB temperature. Any point on that line represents 75°F DB.

2   The horizontal lines are lines of constant specific humidity, and specific humidities in *grains* of moisture per pound of air may be read at the right. On some charts this scale is called the *humidity ratio,* and is also given in *pounds* of moisture per pound of air.

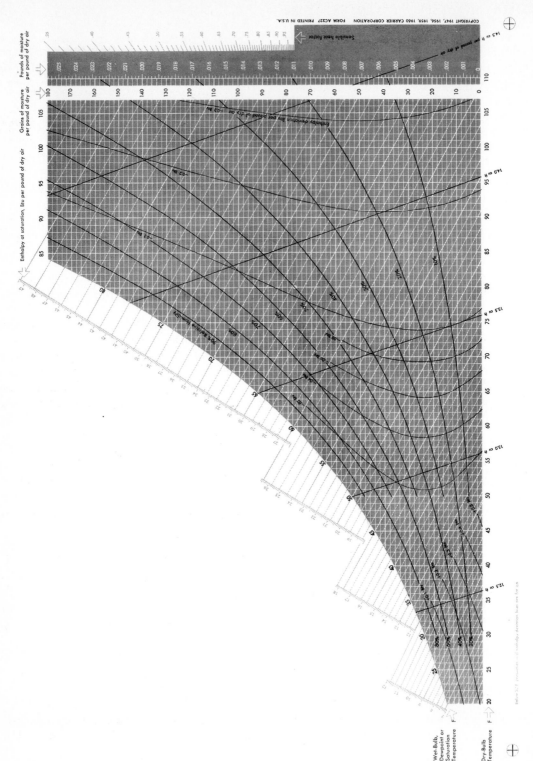

Figure 1-9

3 The lines that slope upward to the left at an angle of 30° from the horizontal are lines of constant wet bulb (WB) temperature.

4 The curving lines are curves of constant relative humidity (RH); the left hand curve is the 100% RH curve, called the *saturation* curve. Any point on the saturation curve represents an air-water vapor mixture in which the water vapor is at a vapor pressure which is the saturation pressure for that particular dry bulb temperature. (The reader might wish to review art. 1-14 at this time.)

5 The sloping lines that are nearly vertical are lines of constant specific volume, expressed in terms of cubic feet per pound of air.

6 The staggered scale just to the left of the saturation curve gives values of total heat (or enthalpy) in Btu per pound of air in the air-water vapor mixture. These values are read with reference to the wet bulb temperature lines. For example, if a mixture has a wet bulb temperature of 70°F, the total heat in that mixture is 34.1 Btu/lb.

7 Dew point temperatures may be read on the saturation curve at a point straight to the left of any point on the chart that may be under consideration. For example, consider the point on the chart for 80°F DB and 30% RH. If one follows a horizontal line straight to the left of that point, it will be seen that the horizontal line intersects the saturation curve at the 46°F point on the saturation curve. This is the DP temperature of 46°F. So an air-water vapor mixture at 80°F DB and 30% RH has a dew point temperature of 46°F.

Notice that at 46°F DP on the saturation curve, the DB and WB temperatures are also exactly 46°F. At a point on the saturation curve, these three temperatures are always identical.

Some psychrometric charts have other curves and tables on them. These are for making corrections when very great accuracy is needed in laboratory testing or for other purposes. These are not needed for the purposes of this text and are not shown.

1-30 HEAT FLOW DESIGN PROBLEM

Suppose that a lecture hall that seats 100 students needs ventilation badly. It is decided to install a ventilating unit capable of supplying 1000 cfm of outside air; this is at the rate of 10 cfm per person, a frequently used ventilation rate.

The ventilating unit would be designed and installed in such a way as to be able to bring in outside air (OA) in winter and heat this air to the required room air (RA) temperature, or in summer to cool and dehumidify the OA to the required RA temperature and humidity.

The required *design conditions* are as follows:

Room air (RA)   winter   68°F DB
Room air (RA)   summer   76°F DB and 50% RH
Outdoor air (OA) winter   5°F DB
Outdoor air (OA) summer   96°F DB and 78°F WB

Note: DB means dry bulb temperature, RH means relative humidity and WB means wet bulb temperature.

In this sample problem, we are to find the amount of heat required in winter, and the amount of sensible and latent cooling required in summer.

Since the heat provided by the ventilating unit in winter is all sensible heat, we may use formula (1-6):

$$BHS = \text{cfm} \times 1.08 \times \Delta t$$
$$= 1000 \times 1.08(68°F - 5°F)$$
$$= 68{,}040 \text{ Btu/hr}$$

The sensible heat cooling required in summer also involves the use of formula (1-6):

$$BHS = 1000 \times 1.08(96°F - 76°F)$$
$$= 21{,}600 \text{ Btu/hr}$$

The latent heat cooling required in summer involves the use of formula (1-7):

$$BHL = \text{cfm} \times \Delta G \times 0.68$$

where ΔG is the difference between the specific humidity indoors (RA) and that outdoors (OA), in grains per pound. At 96°F DB and 78°F WB (OA) we find the specific humidity to be 116 grains of moisture per pound of air (see fig. 1-10), and at 76°F DB and 50% RH it is 67 grains per pound of air. $\Delta G = 116 - 67 = 49$ grains/lb; therefore,

$$BHL = 1000 \times 49 \times 0.68 = 33,320 \text{ Btu/hr}$$

Since BHT = BHS + BHL, the total heat cooling required in summer equals 21,600 BHS + 33,320 BHL = 54,920 BHT. The cooling capacity required in summer expressed in tons is

$$54,920 \text{ BH} \div 12,000 \text{ BH/ton} = 4.58 \text{ tons}$$

Now let us check the total heat cooling capacity required using formula (1-8), BHT = cfm $\times 4.5(TH_2 - TH_1)$. In the miniature chart of fig. 1-10, the OA and RA total heats are shown; these may be used in formula (1-8):

$$BHT = 1000 \times 4.5(41.6 - 28.8) = 57,600 \text{ BH}$$

$$57,600 \text{ BH} \div 12,000 = 4.8 \text{ tons}$$

The reader will notice that there is a difference in the two calculated total heats—one yielding 4.58 tons and the other yielding 4.80 tons. Errors of this magnitude are to be expected and accepted, since the formulas used are all based on approximations.

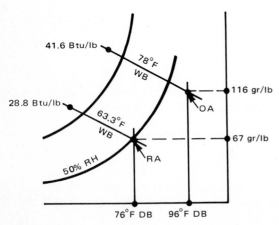

Figure 1-10

1-31 PSYCHROMETRIC CHART EXAMPLE

Let us take another example just to check the reader's use of the psychrometric chart in fig. 1-9.

Given that WB temperature = 65°F and RH = 50%, find all other readings available from the chart. These are

DB = 78°F
DP = 58°F
Specific volume = ±13.75 ft³/lb
TH = 30.1 Btu/lb
Specific humidity = 72 grains/lb

PROBLEMS

1-1   What are the three types of heat usually considered in HVAC design?

1-2   List two sources of sensible heat in an air conditioned building in summer that are not mentioned in this chapter.

1-3   List two sources of latent heat in an air conditioned building in summer that are not mentioned in this chapter.

1-4   List two sources of radiant heat in an air conditioned building in summer that are not mentioned in this chapter.

1-5   What is enthalpy?

1-6   The summertime heat gain into a certain room is 80,000 BH sensible and 40,000 BH latent. Find the enthalpy gain of this room in BH and in tons.

1-7   Will the WB temperature of an air–water vapor mixture ever be greater than its DB temperature?

1-8   If a person has a headache and takes two 5-grain aspirin tablets, what fraction of a pound of aspirin will that person take?

1-9   A municipal elevated water storage tank is open to the atmosphere and rises 130 ft above the surface of the earth. It carries water in it within 15 ft of the top. What would be the water pressure in psig in the water main coming from this tank at earth level? What is that pressure in psia?

1-10   If 50 lb of ice at 20°F is heated until it melts and then boils and becomes 232°F steam at atmospheric pressure, how much heat will be required?

1-11 Calculate the MRT of the room shown in fig. 1-7 if all surface temperatures are 5°F lower than those shown.

1-12 What is the required gpm of the pump in fig. 1-8 if heating system capacity is increased to 350 MBH and heated water leaves the boiler at 270°F and returns at 200°F?

1-13 If an air–water vapor mixture has 60°F DB and 48°F WB, find the total heat, dew point temperature, specific humidity, relative humidity, and specific volume.

1-14 If an air–water vapor mixture has 53°F DP and a specific volume of 14.0 ft³/lb, find DB, WB, total heat, specific humidity (in grains/lb), and RH. List carefully the units of each parameter.

1-15 Air enters a warm air furnace at 65°F and is heated in the furnace to 130°F. If the air flow rate is 1500 cfm, what is the heating capacity of the furnace in BH if temperatures given are DB? Is this sensible heating capacity, latent, or some of both?

1-16 Solve the problem given in art. 1-30 if OA is at 80°F WB and 98°F DB, and RA is at 65°F WB and 77°F DB.

1-17 Hot water flows through a radiator at a rate of 5 gpm. It enters at 160°F and leaves at 140°F. Find the heating capacity of the radiator.

1-18 Air flows from a room through a door into an adjacent corridor at the rate of 2000 cfm. What is this flow rate, approximately, in pounds of air per hour?

Chapter 2

Human Comfort

2-1 REQUIREMENTS FOR HUMAN COMFORT

There are many factors that contribute to human comfort or discomfort. The handling or treatment of most of these is beyond the capability of an HVAC system. In this category we find such things as noise, aesthetics, poor light levels when difficult visual tasks are being performed, and lack of order or discipline. The HVAC system can do nothing about these.

However, there are quite a few things that a well-designed HVAC system can do to promote human comfort. Some of these are:

1 Provide gentle but positive air movement in all occupied spaces of a building. Velocities of air moving over and around people must be kept within a fairly narrow range—on the order of 20 to 50 feet per minute (fpm).

2 Maintain an adequate dry bulb temperature in all occupied spaces. People have a very highly developed ability to distinguish between a comfortable temperature and one that is only 2 to 3°F away from what they perceive to be comfort.

3 Maintain a suitable relative humidity in all occupied spaces. Human beings do not readily perceive small differences in relative humidity, and these may vary by 20 to 30% without much human reaction.

4 Supply good, clean, high-quality air.

5 Assist human beings to lose their metabolic heat in proper fashion and in proper amounts.

With regard to item 5, a bit of explanation is in order. Human beings are warm-blooded animals, and as a result of our metabolic processes—simply the process of living—heat is generated and must be dissipated. If we could not get rid of our metabolic heat, we would die very quickly. Most adults, seated at rest, generate 400 to 500 Btu/hour.

People lose their heat by several methods, and are, apparently, most comfortable when all methods are in use simultaneously. A knowledge of these methods is important to the HVAC designer, and is especially important to the architect-engineer who has control over the total environment that a building provides. These methods of heat dissipation are:

1 *Loss by conduction.* By coming into physical contact with our surroundings: room air, clothing, furniture, and so on. We lose heat if the objects we touch are at temperatures lower than the surface temperature of our bodies. It is commonly estimated that body surface temperature is approximately 85°F.

2 *Loss by transpiration.* The surfaces of the human body are almost always moist, even when they seem perfectly dry. Evaporation of moisture from body surfaces is an almost continuous process. Of course, when a person is visibly perspiring, with beads of perspiration standing on the skin, the transpiration rate is greatly increased.

For moisture to evaporate from body surfaces, latent heat of vaporization must be supplied from somewhere. Most of this heat comes from the human body; this assists the body in the heat dissipation process. Of course, this process is considerably easier if the vapor pressure of the surrounding atmosphere is relatively low (in other words, if the RH is low).

3 *Loss by respiration.* When we breathe, the air that enters our lungs is usually at a temperature lower than the internal body temperature of 98.6°F. The air leaves the lungs warmer than it was when it entered, so sensible heat has been removed from the lungs.

The specific humidity of the air leaving is higher than it was when the air entered, so latent cooling of the lungs has occurred.

The body has lost both sensible and latent heat by respiration. On an exceedingly hot summer day when the dry bulb temperature is 100°F, respiration still helps to cool the human body even though there will be a small sensible heat gain to the body. The latent heat loss from the body resulting from moisture evaporation from lung surfaces will much more than offset the sensible gain and provide a net overall loss.

4 *Loss by radiation.* The radiant heat loss from the body will be in proportion to the difference between the body surface temperature and the MRT of the environment to which the body is exposed.

The MRT of our buildings falls in winter as outdoor temperatures drop. The radiation losses from the human body then increase, and even though room air temperatures may be held steady, human beings feel uncomfortably cool. They may then put on more or heavier clothing. The opposite sequence of events, of course, takes place in summer when outdoor temperatures rise.

2-2 HUMAN BODY RESPONSES

The human body has wonderful capabilities to make automatic physiological changes to increase or decrease body heat loss as necessary to maintain body temperature.

Many techniques are used by the body. For example, the respiration rate may vary. The heart rate and blood circulation rate may vary. Tiny blood capillaries near the surface of the skin receive an extra supply of blood, the skin surface temperature rises, and the skin becomes flushed and pink when the need to increase body heat loss occurs. Perspiration appears, and evaporation, as mentioned above, takes place at an increased rate.

The body has yet another technique to use if necessary. It can make a person so miserable and uncomfortable in a certain situation, that that person will, if at all possible, move to a different and possibly more favorable situation. The discomfort that a person feels is not an indication that the 98.6°F body temperature is not being maintained. Discomfort results because the body is required to make some unusual adjustments, as described above, in the process of maintaining the 98.6°F temperature.

2-3 OPTIMUM COMFORT CONDITIONS

A great amount of time, effort, and money has been spent in determining the room conditions that are most conducive to the greatest comfort in the greatest number of lightly clothed human beings.

Research by the American Society of Heating, Refrigerating and Air-Conditioning Engineers (ASHRAE), and by R. G. Nevins of the Institute for Environmental Research, Kansas State University, indicate that optimum comfort is achieved at a condition of approximately 77°F DB and 40% RH.

We will not concern ourselves extensively with the results of these research programs since the room conditions that we maintain in our buildings are greatly influenced by many extraneous factors.

Such factors as rate of occupant activity, weight of clothing, room MRT, room humidity, time of the year (winter versus summer), and need to conserve fuel and energy extensively influence thermostat settings. A room temperature of 77°F in most rooms in winter would today be very uncomfortable to most occupants.

In the last few years, concessions to energy conservation have dictated room temperatures of 68°F and lower. People are becoming adjusted physiologically, sociologically, and more important, psychologically to these reduced temperatures, and finding them healthful and refreshing.

The futility of attempting to establish and standardize one set of room design conditions is exemplified by the work the author performed many years ago on behalf of Indiana Bell Telephone Company in telephone exchange buildings throughout much of the state of Indiana. One recurrent problem was that of maintaining comfortable room conditions in the long-distance operator rooms. Here long lines of 50 to 60 operators, working shoulder to shoulder, were forced to accept one common room condition. Most of the operators made the adjustment satisfactorily. However, frequently one operator, bundled up with extra clothing and still cold, would be sitting right next to another operator who was overheated, perspiring, and removing all the clothing that propriety would permit.

We are forced to leave to the users of buildings the decisions as to where thermostats and humidi-stats are to be set. That leaves with us, the designers of HVAC systems, the responsibility of providing HVAC systems that will meet any "reasonable" demand placed on them.

It would seem reasonable today that an HVAC system be able to maintain in winter a temperature of 70°F, if relative humidities are logically expected to be 20% or higher and if the building will provide an MRT of 63°F or higher.

It would further seem reasonable today if, in summer, an HVAC system could maintain a room DB temperature of 76°F or lower, and a relative humidity of 60% or lower.

The foregoing conditions are based on the assumption that building occupants are engaged in light activities such as very light office work, and are dressed appropriately in accordance with the season of the year.

2-4 CAUSES OF DISCOMFORT

The causes of human discomfort in today's buildings are many and varied and most of them quite complicated. Many of these causes lie outside the purview of the HVAC system, but many of the causes are the direct result of the shortcomings and inadequacies of the HVAC system. Some of these causes should be enumerated.

1 *Drafts.* One of the most frequent, perhaps *the* most frequent cause of human discomfort is drafts resulting from poor distribution of air in a room. A draft is a stream of air moving at a speed in excess of 50 fpm, and usually at too low a temperature when the room is underheated and too high when the room is overheated. Drafts can be avoided by the observance of a few well-established rules of design. A more extensive discussion of this important subject is given in chap. 8.

2 *Noise.* People who are located in one particular spot, hour after hour, day after day, can become greatly irritated by the noises, if excessive, that some HVAC systems produce. Not nearly enough attention is devoted to the elimination of noise and vibration in HVAC systems. As a result, noise leading to human discomfort is a much too frequent problem.

HVAC system noise falls into two categories: air noise and mechanical noise. These two sources of noise usually are not related, and their prevention requires the application of different remedial measures. It seems that most of the noise problems result from two causes:

a *The injudicious selection and placement of HVAC equipment.* The best example of this is the use of self-contained air conditioning units in motel rooms. Here the unit is often located within 5 ft of a sleeping person's ear, the reciprocating compressor in the unit vibrates and produces much noise, and the fan and air noise level is often as high as 70 decibels. For someone not accustomed to this type of sleeping situation, sleeping may be difficult or impossible.

b *Undersizing of HVAC equipment.* In nonresidential buildings, undersizing or "on the nose" sizing of HVAC equipment is not justifiable on any basis, except that basis of saving on initial cost. Except in residential cooling systems with on-off cycling control, there is no energy saving, and the long- and well-established practice of including a factor of safety (oversizing) of 5 to 10% in load calculations is founded solidly on the successful collective experience of designers for 100 years or more.

When undersizing occurs, intentionally or inadvertently many problems arise, and one of them is noise. Air conditioner fans are necessarily speeded up. Fan wheel tip speeds become excessive and noise results. Air velocities through ductwork, grilles, registers, and diffusers become excessive and again, the result is noise. Noise, to varying degrees, makes people uncomfortable.

3 *Improper temperature and humidity.* The maintenance of improper room conditions of temperature and humidity is, of course, a big factor in human discomfort. This usually results from lack of capacity in the HVAC equipment. However, it could certainly result from improper maintenance of equipment and from improper selection and adjustment of temperature controls (thermostats, etc.).

4 *Improper room MRT.* We know that human discomfort can result if the MRT (see art. 1-23) of a room is too high or too low, even when all other comfort factors are held at normally proper levels. The architects of the world seem to give very little cognizance or acceptance to this vitally important fact. They just go merrily on their ways designing buildings with tremendously large glass areas or with poorly insulated walls, roofs, and floors. All such factors can only result in excessively low wintertime MRT values, but architects seem often oblivious of these facts.

Let us consider fig. 2-1, which portrays the same room as in fig. 1-7 (art. 1-23), and recalculate the MRT on a basis that the room construction is typical of the types that architects have habitually designed during the last 25 years.

The MRT in art. 1-23 was calculated on the assumption of very well insulated walls and roof and double glass windows. The MRT was ±63.3°F. Now let us replace that construction with a roof having 1.5 in. of insulation, suspended acoustic ceiling, masonry walls of brick and block furred with metal lath and plaster, and single glass in the windows—typical nonresidential construction. We find that the MRT is now 59°F, and this is with windows occupying 18.5% of the outside wall area. Imagine what happens to the MRT when the outside wall is 50% glass or 100% glass. With 50% glass the MRT is 55.9°F, and with 100% glass (as in some office buildings) the MRT drops to 51.0°F. Remember here that these calculated MRTs may be somewhat inaccurate. Had they been calculated by the more accurate method previously described, they would probably each be 1 to 2°F higher.

MRTs of this magnitude make human comfort very difficult on a cold day when the Δt (temperature difference) between indoors and outdoors is 70°F, as was assumed above.

2-5 OTHER CAUSES OF DISCOMFORT

There are many other causes of human discomfort in buildings; some of these are the responsibility of the HVAC system and many others definitely are not. Some of these other causes are: odors, oxygen deficiency, excess quantities of carbon monoxide and carbon dioxide, inadequate illumination when seeing tasks are being performed, ambient noise,

Walls:	$(405 \text{ ft}^2 - 75 \text{ ft}^2) 57.6°\text{F}$	19,008
Partitions:	$45 \text{ ft} \times 9 \text{ ft} \times 66°\text{F}$	26,730
Windows:	$5 \times 3 \text{ ft} \times 5 \text{ ft} \times 16.2°\text{F}$	1,215
Ceilings:	$30 \text{ ft} \times 15 \text{ ft} \times 59.8°\text{F}$	26,910
Floor:	$30 \text{ ft} \times 15 \text{ ft} \times 60°\text{F}$	27,000

$$100,863 \div 1710 \text{ ft}^2 = 59.0°\text{F}$$

50% glass

Walls:	$(405 \text{ ft}^2 - 202.5 \text{ ft}^2) 57.6°\text{F}$	11,664
Partitions:	$405 \text{ ft}^2 \times 66°\text{F}$	26,730
Windows:	$202.5 \text{ ft}^2 \times 16.2°\text{F}$	3,280.5
Ceilings:	$30 \text{ ft} \times 15 \text{ ft} \times 59.8°\text{F}$	26,910
Floor:	$30 \text{ ft} \times 15 \text{ ft} \times 60°\text{F}$	27,000

$$95,584.5 \div 1710 \text{ ft}^2 = 55.9°\text{F}$$

100% glass

Partitions:	$405 \text{ ft}^2 \times 66°\text{F}$	26,730
Windows:	$405 \text{ ft}^2 \times 16.2°\text{F}$	6,561
Ceilings:	$30 \text{ ft} \times 15 \text{ ft} \times 59.8°\text{F}$	26,910
Floor:	$30 \text{ ft} \times 15 \text{ ft} \times 60°\text{F}$	27,000

$$87,201 \div 1710 \text{ ft}^2 = 51.0°\text{F}$$

Figure 2-1 MRT modifications.

clashing colors in the room finishes, clutter or litter in the room, and poor aesthetics.

PROBLEMS

2-1 What is the range of air movement velocities in occupied rooms that permit suitable human comfort?

2-2 What is the usual range of metabolic heat production in the average adult human being?

2-3 The average human being will experience a net radiant heat exchange to the surroundings if the MRT of those surroundings is below what temperature?

2-4 From the standpoint of human comfort in a room, what is a draft that causes discomfort?

2-5 To which are human occupants of a room more sensitive—small DB temperature changes or small changes in RH?

Chapter 3

Psychrometrics

3-1 DEFINITION

Psychrometrics, or *psychrometry,* is specifically involved with the "measurements" taken in connection with mixtures of atmospheric air and water vapor; however, the general use of the word has, in this century, brought about a slightly different meaning. It can now more usefully be defined as a study of the behavior of mixtures of air and water vapor under varying conditions of heat.

A very great amount of what must be said when discussing psychrometrics has already been said in chap. 1. Discussions of such terms as sensible heat, latent heat, dry bulb temperature, wet bulb temperature, dew point temperature, relative humidity, and enthalpy are all part of a study of psychrometrics. This chapter, then, is a direct extension of the discussions begun in chap. 1.

3-2 PSYCHROMETRIC CHART

Referring to the chart of fig. 1-9, and in reviewing art. 1-29, we remember that a certain mixture of air and water vapor may be represented by a dot on the chart. For example, on the chart you will find a dot at the intersection of the vertical 80°F DB line and the 50% RH curve. From a dot such as this, all seven parameters that describe a particular mixture may be read.

In HVAC practices, our AWV (air–water vapor) mixtures are always changing, as sensible heat and latent heat content changes. When air is heated, as in a residential warm air furnace, the sensible heat content increases. If there is a humidifier in that furnace, when it turns on, the air passing through the furnace is humidified; in other words, the latent heat content increases.

3-3 SENSIBLE HEAT CHANGES

Whenever a change in the sensible or latent heat content of an AWV mixture occurs, the dot on the psychrometric chart representing the condition of that mixture will move. As it moves, it draws a line on the chart.

For example, point A on a psychrometric chart represents the condition of an AWV mixture (see fig. 3-1). If that mixture is now heated with sensible heat only, the dot will move to point B. Notice that the point has moved straight to the right, and neither up nor down, and has drawn a horizontal line.

Therefore, we can say that sensible heat changes result in horizontal movements on the chart—to the right when sensible heat is added, and to the left when sensible heat is subtracted.

In like manner, we can say that since the horizontal axis or scale of the chart is the DB temperature scale, sensible heat changes result in DB temperature changes—to the right on the chart when sensible heat is added and DB temperature rises, and to the left when sensible heat is subtracted and DB temperature falls.

3-4 LATENT HEAT CHANGES

When air passes through a humidifier, water vapor is added to the AWV mixture, and we can say that the latent heat content of the mixture has increased. Suppose that air enters a room through the supply registers, passes through the room, which is full of people, and then leaves the room through the return air grilles on its way back to an air conditioning unit. Because the people in the room are all emitting water vapor as a result of breathing and perspiring, the air leaving the room has more moisture in it than when it entered the room. In other words, the latent heat content of the AWV mixture has increased; the specific humidity has increased.

Specific humidity changes are represented by vertical movements on the psychrometric chart. For example, in fig. 3-2 is shown a psychrometric chart with the point A representing an AWV mixture at a beginning condition. If that air is somehow partially dried (water vapor removed), this represents a specific humidity decrease, and point A will move vertically downward drawing a vertical line which ends at the new, dryer condition

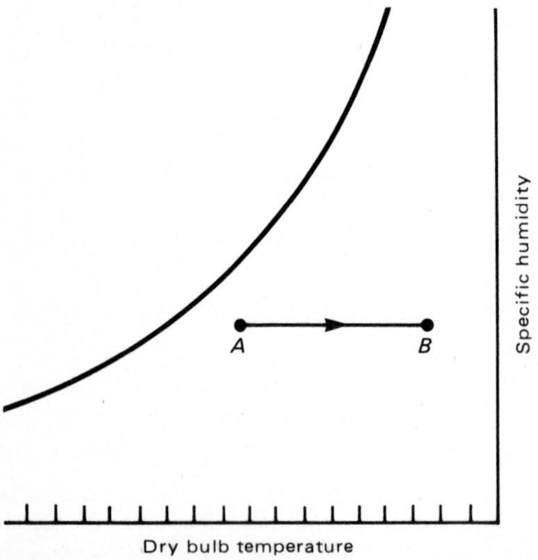

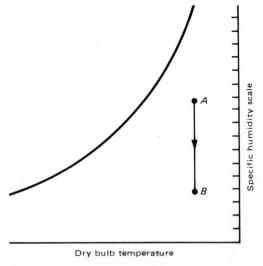

Figure 3-1   Sensible heat increase.

Figure 3-2   Latent heat decrease.

represented by point *B*. Therefore, we can say that latent heat changes result in vertical movements on the chart—upward when latent heat is added, and downward when it is subtracted. In like manner, we can say that since the vertical scale of the chart is the specific humidity scale, latent heat changes result in specific humidity changes.

3-5 CHANGES IN BOTH SENSIBLE AND LATENT HEAT

In the example cited in art. 3-4, the air passing through the heavily occupied room does, as stated, pick up latent heat. It also would, in all probability, pick up sensible heat from the occupants. In this case point *A* in fig. 3-3, at the entering condition, would move upward because of the increase in latent heat, and to the right because of the increase in sensible heat. As a result, point *A* will move upward and to the right on a sloping line as shown, which ends at *B*.

Following this line of thought further, we can see that if an AWV mixture *gains* sensible heat and *loses* latent heat, a point on the chart would move downward and to the right.

If there is a loss of sensible heat and a loss of latent heat, a point would move downward and to the left, and so on.

3-6 TOTAL HEAT (ENTHALPY) CHANGES

Since total heat, or enthalpy, is simply the arithmetic sum of the sensible heat and the latent heat in an AWV mixture (TH = SH + LH), whenever either sensible heat or latent heat alone changes, a change in total heat will always occur. We have said in art. 1-12 that wet bulb temperature is a direct indication of the total heat content of an AWV mixture. Anytime TH changes, WB temperature will change, and vice versa.

Anytime both SH and LH increase, TH will increase and WB temperature will increase. Also, anytime both SH and LH decrease, TH will decrease and WB temperature will decrease.

However, it is possible for SH to increase and LH to decrease in equal quantity with no consequent change in TH and no change in WB temperature. Figure 3-4 shows this condition where SH has increased and LH has decreased. Points *A* and *B* are on the same wet bulb temperature

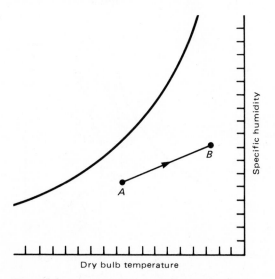

Figure 3-3 Increase in both sensible and latent heat.

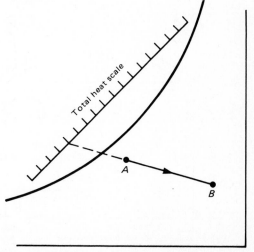

Figure 3-4 Sensible heat increase and latent heat decrease in equal quantity—an adiabatic change.

line. Therefore, the wet bulb temperature does not change and the TH content of the mixture does not change.

It should be remembered that a reading of TH can be obtained from a WB temperature reading by noting the point on the TH scale where a given WB temperature line intersects the TH scale. This process can, of course, be reversed.

3-7 ADIABATIC CHANGES

As discussed above, a psychrometric change can occur in an AWV mixture in which all parameters change except WB temperature and total heat. This type of change is called an *adiabatic change,* and fig. 3-4 depicts this.

An adiabatic change, then, is one in which an AWV mixture change takes place but no heat is added to or released from the mixture. This type of process takes place in an air washer or in an evaporative cooler. An air washer is a closed chamber through which air is circulated and which is filled completely with a dense spray of water. If no heat is added to the water as it is continuously sprayed, recirculated, and resprayed over and over, both the water and the air tend to approach the

WB temperature of the entering air as a limit. This is an adiabatic process.

3-8 EVAPORATIVE COOLERS

The principle of art. 3-7 is utilized in evaporative coolers, in common use in the arid areas of the southwestern United States. An evaporative cooler consists of an air washer chamber as described above, and a fan to circulate air from the outdoors into and through the air washer, and then into and through a building. The outside air (OA) may be quite hot, with a DB temperature of 100°F, but with a very low RH of perhaps 8%.

At this condition, the WB temperature of the OA is 62°F, and the air leaving the air washer and entering the building may be at 66°F DB and 90% RH. Air at this condition can provide considerable cooling effect. See the thermodynamic cycle portrayed in fig. 3-5.

In this adiabatic cycle, the OA enters the cooler at 100°F DB and 8% RH. It passes through the air washer sprays of the cooler, and leaves the cooler at 66°F DB and 90% RH. It then enters the building at that condition, and as it passes through the building, it picks up both sensible heat and latent

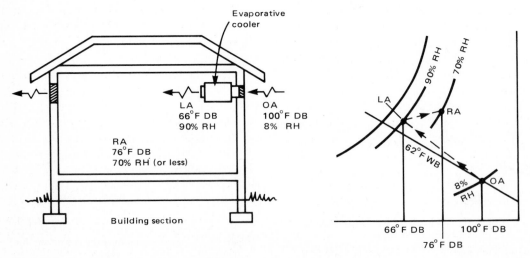

Figure 3-5   Evaporative cooler cycle—an adiabatic process.

heat and maintains the building at some RA condition such as 76°F DB and 70% RH.

Notice that in fig. 3-5 the dashed line between the OA and LA (leaving air) points does not quite coincide with the 62°F WB line. It would coincide if the air washer in the evaporative cooler were 100% efficient. The line from LA to RA represents the passage of the air through the building picking up both sensible and latent heat.

This is not an ideal room condition, but it is an improvement over the outdoor condition, and it may be improved further by moisture migration at a very substantial rate from indoors to outdoors. This would be caused by the comparatively high vapor pressure within the building and the very low vapor pressure in the outdoor atmosphere. Heavy moisture migration outward could reduce the indoor RH appreciably, with a consequent improvement in room comfort.

3-9 WARM AIR FURNACE CYCLE

The thermodynamic cycle for a warm air heating system, which has no means of humidification, can be very simply drawn as in fig. 3-6. This figure also includes a schematic detail of a typical warm air heating system of the type contemplated.

In fig. 3-6, the psychrometric chart includes a point labeled RA, representing the room air condition. This is the condition under which the air enters the furnace. As the air is heated in the furnace, the point moves straight to the right, indicating an increase in sensible heat.

Since no latent heat is added or subtracted, the point will not move either up or down, but only to the right until it reaches the LA condition, at which it leaves the furnace and enters the rooms to be heated.

As the air passes through the rooms, it gives up its sensible heat to the rooms and returns to the furnace. As the air gives up its sensible heat, the point on the chart representing the air condition moves straight back to the left to the original RA point. The two movements on the chart, first to

the right and then to the left, can be represented by two lines, which would be coincident.

3-10 WARM AIR FURNACE WITH HUMIDIFIER CYCLE

Now, suppose that some type of humidifier is installed in the outlet of the furnace shown in fig. 3-6. After the air has received its sensible heat from the hot parts of the furnace, and the point on the chart of fig. 3-6 moves from RA to LA, the air passes through the humidifier section and latent heat is added.

This would be depicted on the chart by vertical movement (see fig. 3-7). We now have a new LA point, which is both to the right and above the RA point on the chart. The line from LA to RA represents the movement of the supply air through the rooms of the building, where the air gives up both sensible and latent heat to the rooms.

3-11 COOLING CYCLE AND BYPASS FACTOR

Consider a simple window-mounted room-type cooling unit and the thermodynamic cycle that might pertain to it. This unit simply recirculates room air through the cooling coil of the unit; the air enters at room (RA) temperature and leaves approximately 15 to 20°F cooler (see fig. 3-8).

The room air (RA) returns to the cooling unit at the RA point on the psychrometric chart. As the air progresses through the cold cooling coil in the unit, it at first gives up only sensible heat, and the cycle line in fig. 3-8 runs straight to the left of the point RA. Since the cycle line neither rises nor falls, the latent heat content of the air does not, at first, change. Then as the air passes farther and farther through the depth of the cooling coil its DB temperature falls until some of the air reaches the dew point (DP) temperature and the condensation of moisture begins. At this point, the cycle line moving left from the RA point begins to

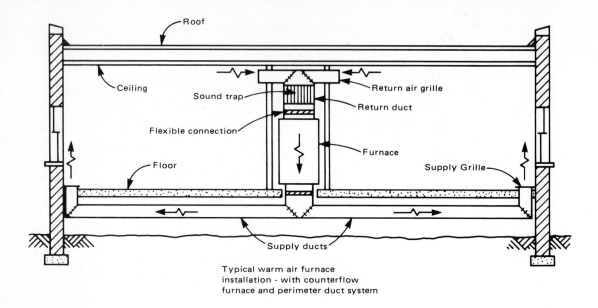

Typical warm air furnace
installation - with counterflow
furnace and perimeter duct system

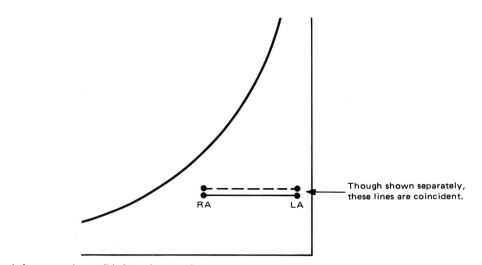

Though shown separately,
these lines are coincident.

Figure 3-6 Warm air furnace cycle, sensible heat change only.

move downward on the chart, and the straight line becomes a downward curve which ends at the LA point, where the air leaves the cooling coil.

One might think that the line to the left of point RA would run straight to the left until it reached the saturation curve and the DP temperature at that point. After all, air at the RA condition cannot yield condensation until it is cooled to the dew point temperature.

However, here we meet one of the characteristics of cooling coils; they are not 100% efficient or effective. All the air that passes through a cooling coil is not conditioned by the coil. Some of the molecules of air zigzag their way through the coil

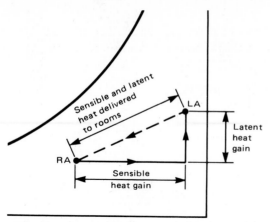

Figure 3-7 Warm air furnace with humidifier cycle—both sensible and latent heat change.

without contacting any part of the coil. As a result, they stay above the DP temperature, and the water vapor with which they are mixed does not condense. It is as though some of the air detoured or bypassed around the coil instead of passing through it. This is called the *bypass effect*.

The bypass effect can be reduced to a numerical value called the *bypass factor* (BPF). Coil manufacturers can give information as to the BPF for any of their coils; these BPF values are experimentally determined. For example, a coil might have a

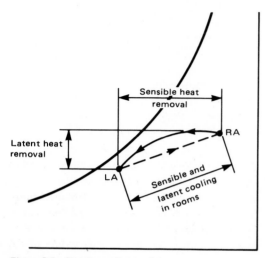

Figure 3-8 Simple cooling cycle.

BPF, at a given air velocity, of 0.22; this would mean that 22% of the air would pass through the coil, in effect, unconditioned. Also, 78% would, in effect, be fully conditioned.

Unless a coil has a BPF of zero, the cycle curve from point RA to point LA in fig. 3-8 can never reach the saturation curve because the cycle curve represents all the air flowing, not just some of it. Of course, the bypassed air and the conditioned air quickly mix as they leave the coil and represent one homogeneous condition at point LA.

3-12 COOLING CYCLE WITH OUTSIDE AIR

Almost all nonresidential buildings today need mechanical ventilation to a greater or lesser degree. This is almost always, but not always, accomplished through the introduction of outdoor air (OA) into the building at the proper places and in the proper quantities.

Also, almost always the OA is brought into the building and mixed with return air (RA) which is being returned from the conditioned spaces to the HVAC unit. This mixture is, not surprisingly, called *mixed air* (MA). The schematic diagram of fig. 3-9 shows a simplified arrangement of such an HVAC system.

Figure 3-10 shows the thermodynamic cycle of this type of HVAC system. Here we see the OA mixing with the RA to form MA, which passes through the cooling coil, as described in art. 3-11, and leaves the coil at point LA. In that condition, the supply air (SA) enters and passes through the rooms being conditioned, and leaves the rooms at the point RA. In this type of system, the air entering the coil, the EA (entering air), and the MA are identical.

3-13 OUTSIDE AIR AND RETURN AIR MIXTURES

Before the performance of any HVAC unit can be determined and a unit selected for installation, many things must be known. Two of these are the

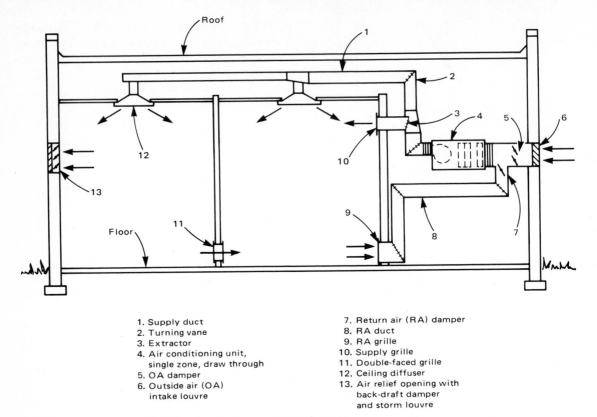

1. Supply duct
2. Turning vane
3. Extractor
4. Air conditioning unit,
   single zone, draw through
5. OA damper
6. Outside air (OA)
   intake louvre
7. Return air (RA) damper
8. RA duct
9. RA grille
10. Supply grille
11. Double-faced grille
12. Ceiling diffuser
13. Air relief opening with
    back-draft damper
    and storm louvre

Figure 3-9 Section through building showing single-zone HVAC system.

cooling coil EA and LA conditions. Since in so many HVAC systems the EA and the MA are the same, as in fig. 3-9, it is very important to be able to calculate the MA condition; this can be readily done if the OA and RA conditions are known and if the relative proportion of each in the MA is known.

In fig. 3-10, the OA and RA points are joined by a straight line. We know that the point representing the condition at which these two streams of air will meet and mix, in other words the MA point, will be somewhere on this interconnecting line. We also know that if the OA constitutes 50% (by weight) of the mixture, the RA will constitute 50% (by weight) of the mixture, and the MA point will be halfway between the OA and RA points on the interconnecting line.

In this type of problem the difference in the densities of the OA and the RA is so very slight that we find it accurate enough to use percentages of the air "volumes" rather than "weights" in describing air proportions.

The condition of a mixture of two streams of air can often be calculated by simple arithmetic proportion, although *not always*, depending on which of the characteristics (DB, WB, RH, etc.) of the airstreams are known. For example, the DB temperature of an air mixture can be determined by proportioning the DB temperatures of the airstreams being mixed; however, neither RH nor WB temperature nor DP temperature can be calculated by proportionality.

For example, suppose that we wish to circulate a mixture of air that is 20% OA at 30°F DB and

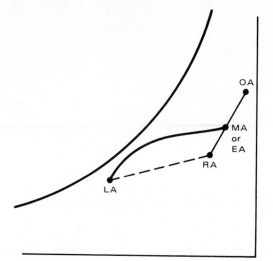

Figure 3-10 Typical cooling cycle using outside air for ventilation.

20% RH, and is 80% RA at 75°F DB and 50% RH. What would be the condition of this mixture (see fig. 3-11)?

The DB temperature of the MA is easily calculated by proportionality to be (0.2 × 30°F DB) + (0.8 × 75°F DB) = 66°F DB.

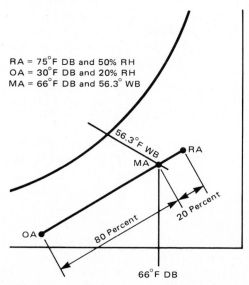

RA = 75°F DB and 50% RH
OA = 30°F DB and 20% RH
MA = 66°F DB and 56.3° WB

Figure 3-11 Determining an air mixture by plotting.

The total heat (TH) may also be calculated by proportionality, so we first find the TH at each condition. The TH of the OA is found from the psychrometric chart to be 7.8 Btu/lb, and of the RA is 28.2 Btu/lb. Proportioning these,

$$(0.2 \times 7.8) + (0.8 \times 28.2) = 24.12$$

we find the TH of the mixture to be 24.12 Btu/lb. This corresponds to a WB temperature of 56.3°F on the chart.

Knowing the 66°F DB and the 56.3°F WB temperatures of the MA enables us to establish a point on the chart and then to read from the chart all other values. These are 55% RH, specific humidity of 52.5 grains/lb, 49.2°F DP temperature, and a specific volume of 13.4 ft³/lb.

If we try to calculate WB temperature by proportionality directly we get (0.2 × 22.2°F WB) + (0.8 × 62.6°F WB) = 54.5°F WB (WB temperature of the OA is 22.2 and of the RA is 62.6°F).

But this 54.5°F WB is wrong; we can see above that it should be 56.3°F.

Similarly, if we try to calculate RH directly by proportionality, we find

$$(0.2 \times 20\% \text{ RH}) + (0.8 \times 50\% \text{ RH}) = 44\%$$

which is grossly in error. It should be 55% RH, as shown above.

The accuracy of the proper calculations in this example, and the errors in the improper calculations, may be easily checked by plotting on the psychrometric chart as shown in fig. 3-11.

Here the OA and RA points are established on the chart and are then connected by a straight line. The MA is then established by measurement such that the distance from MA to RA is 20% of the distance from OA to RA. The MA point is always closer to the RA point if there is more RA in the mixture, and vice versa.

Reading all the values from the MA point will confirm the accuracy of the proper calculations above.

In summation, then, we can say that in calculating air mixtures, the DB temperature, total heat, specific humidity, and specific volume can accurately be calculated by proportionality. However, WB temperature, RH, and DP temperature cannot be so calculated; the three latter values must be read from the psychrometric chart after the MA point is established.

PROBLEMS

3-1 A dot on a psychrometric chart (which represents the condition of an air–water vapor mixture), when it moves straight to the right on the chart, indicates what type of heat change in the mixture?

3-2 When the dot of prob. 3-1 moves straight down on the chart, this indicates what type of heat change?

3-3 When a sensible heat (only) change occurs in an AWV mixture, which of the seven psychrometric chart parameters will always change also? Which of the seven parameters will not change?

3-4 When a latent heat (only) change occurs in an AWV mixture, which of the seven psychrometric chart parameters will not change?

3-5 When an adiabatic change occurs in an AWV mixture, which of the seven psychrometric chart parameters will not change?

3-6 When an AWV mixture changes so that it gains latent heat and loses sensible heat, which direction would its dot move on the psychrometric chart as a result of the change?

3-7 If the BPF of an air conditioning system cooling coil is 0.1, what percent of the total air flowing through the coil is being fully conditioned?

3-8 If the velocity of the air flowing through a cooling coil is increased from 400 fpm to 500 fpm, would you guess that the BPF would increase or decrease?

3-9 If the depth of a cooling coil (in the direction of airflow) is increased, if the tubes through which a cold refrigerant is passing are spaced more closely together, and if the fins on those tubes are spaced more closely together (see figs. 6-6 and 6-9), would you guess that the BPF would increase or decrease?

3-10 The air entering an HVAC unit cooling coil is 25% OA at 95°F DB and 77°F WB temperature, and the RA is 75% of the total at 78°F DB and 55% RH. Plot these two points on the chart of fig. 1-9, and calculate by proportionality the mixed air DB and TH. Plot the MA point and read all other values from the chart.

Chapter 4

Heat Losses from Buildings

4-1 GENERAL

Through most of the years of this century, questions and problems of heat losses from our buildings have fallen almost exclusively within the province of the heating engineer. Even architects have routinely pushed the problems attendant thereto into the background, where they had very little influence on their building designs.

Now, all that is, hopefully, changed. The energy shortage is an everyday consideration for everyone. Building owners, faced with the painfully escalating costs of fuel and energy in any form, are insisting on energy-conservative new buildings, and on significant remedial measures for the older buildings that so clearly reflect our sins of the past.

Architects are reluctantly beginning to subordinate their flair for style and dramatic effect to the grinding reality of economic need and national conservatism. Even government officials being dragged along by this relentless tide are beginning to see, through fog-bound spectacles, the urgency of the situation.

So heat loss from buildings in winter, and heat gain into buildings in summer, is everybody's problem; and it is without apology that this author leads the reader deeply into the intricacies of those subjects. First, let us deal with heat loss considerations.

4-2 ASHRAE 90-75

One bright and shining spot in this rather dismal picture has been the American Society of Heating, Refrigerating and Air-Conditioning Engineers (ASHRAE). This old, well-established, and progressive organization has led the way for many, many decades in providing accurate information, encouragement, and guidance to all phases of the HVAC industry.

ASHRAE recognized very early that government would need to take a firm position in establishing regulations for the design of energy-conservative buildings. When government at all levels began looking around for guidance, ASHRAE was ready and waiting with good, solid recommendations.

These recommendations later developed into what is now known as ASHRAE 90-75. This guidebook is written in such a way that government at any level—municipal, county, state, or federal—can adopt it in totum, and merely by reference incorporate it into its body of laws.

Adopting such a guide into the law is the easy part, of course, and many governmental units are doing this. The difficult part is enforcement, which will require tremendous sums of money and time. But we have no choice; this program, or one like it, is mandatory.

4-3 HOW HEAT IS LOST

Heat is lost from buildings in cold weather in five ways:

1 By transmission
2 By infiltration
3 By ventilation
4 By moisture migration
5 By radiation through glass areas

4-4 TRANSMISSION HEAT LOSS

The term *transmission loss* could mean several different things; however, in HVAC practices, unless it is preceded by the world "solar," it is meant to indicate heat loss as a result of molecular activity. That is, heat will be lost when the air inside a building is warmer than the outside air. The greater rate of molecular activity in the indoor air is carried right through a solid brick wall, for example, by the "billiard ball" effect of molecules bumping into adjacent molecules (in effect). Then the higher rate of molecular activity indoors is passed from molecule to molecule until the energy is delivered to the outside air, and heat is lost by transmission.

The same type of action takes place through the glass in windows or any other homogeneous material of which a wall, ceiling, roof, or floor may be constructed.

The pattern of heat flow through a nonhomogeneous wall is much more complicated. Consider an outside wood frame wall with brick veneer, for example, as detailed in fig. 4-1.

The rapidly moving molecules of the indoor air strike the inner face of the gypsum board (drywall) and set the molecules of the gypsum board in rapid motion. This motion is transmitted, by physical contact of gypsum molecule with gypsum molecule, through the gypsum board to the outer face of this board. Here the heat, constantly arriving through the board, maintains the outer face of the board at a temperature somewhat above the

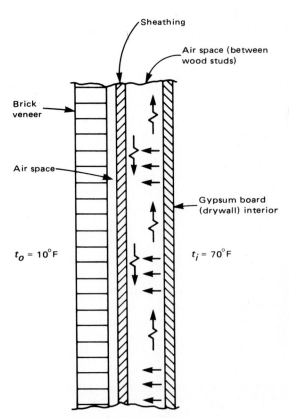

Figure 4-1 Wall section; frame wall-brick veneer.

temperature of the air in the air space between wall studs and above the temperature of the inner face of the sheathing.

Because the stud space air that touches the gypsum board receives heat from it, the air temperature rises, and the air then expands and becomes lighter in weight. Similarly, the air in contact with the comparatively cold sheathing is cooled; it then contracts and becomes heavier (more dense).

With the heavier air adjacent to the sheathing and the lighter air adjacent to the drywall, convection currents up and down, as shown in fig. 4-1, are established, and heat is delivered from the gypsum drywall to the sheathing. Heat transfer has taken place. At the same time, a net "radiant" heat exchange takes place, flowing from the gypsum board to the comparatively colder sheathing. Remember, a net radiant heat exchange will always take place from one surface to a cooler surface if they can "see" each other.

Heat also travels across the stud space by conduction, with the warmer air molecules yielding heat to adjacent cooler molecules nearer the sheathing. So heat travels across the stud space by those three methods: convection, radiation, and conduction.

The heat then flows through the sheathing by conduction (billiard ball effect), through the second air space shown by the three methods just described, and finally through the brick veneer by conduction to the outside air.

Heat is, of course, lost through ceilings, roofs, floors, and partitions in exactly the same way— utilizing the same three methods of conduction, convection, and radiation. The combined effect of these three is called *heat loss by transmission*. It is still called "transmission" if only one or two of these three methods is utilized.

4-5 AIR FILM EFFECT

In determining the rate of heat flow or the insulating value of a wall, a factor is encountered which might be unexpected. This is the air film or boundary layer effect. It has been empirically determined that the insulating value of a wall (or ceiling or floor) is greater than the combined value of all the materials that constitute a wall.

It has been learned that a very thin layer of air clings to the inner face and the outer face of a wall by adhesion and other forces and gives an insulating effect. This effect, although small, is much too large to ignore. In the case of an 8-in. solid brick wall, the insulating value of the two air films may equal 49% of the total insulating value of the wall; however, in one of today's well-insulated walls, the insulating value of the air films may be more like 5% of the total. This is still too much to ignore.

The insulating value of the film on the exterior of a wall is greatly reduced when a wind blows against the wall; apparently some of the air film is simply blown away. With a 15-mph wind blowing (the usual assumption), the insulating value of the exterior air film is about one-fourth of the value of the interior film. When an interior surface is in a horizontal position (ceiling or floor), the effect of the air film is considerably different than when the interior surface is vertical (as in a wall).

4-6 COEFFICIENTS OF HEAT TRANSMISSION

Intelligent design of an effective heating system for a building requires an accurate estimate of the amount of heat lost per hour, under given conditions of wind, usage, and temperature.

In most areas of the United States the wind velocity is assumed to be 15 mph, and most of the available empirical data are based on that assumption. However, many parts of the nation experience winds of 20 mph, 25 mph, and over so frequently in winter that higher velocities must be used as a basis for design. These areas are not described in this text, and design parameters must be determined locally. For most of our discussion a 15-mph wind will be assumed, and coefficients of heat transmission will be based thereon.

The usage that a building experiences has a great effect on the amount of heat that building loses. Usage, of course, has a great effect on the amounts of outdoor air that enter a building (infiltration); this subject will be explored later. Also, the type of building usage determines the indoor temperature required, and the amount of transmission heat loss, as a result.

Transmission heat losses may be calculated by the use of the very simple formula

$$BH = A \times U \times \Delta t \qquad (4\text{-}1)$$

where A = area (of wall, roof, glass, etc.), ft^2

$\qquad$ U = heat transfer coefficient, BH per square foot of area per degree difference in temperature [BH/ft^2/$^\circ\Delta t$]

$\qquad$ Δt = difference in temperatures in the air (on opposite sides of a wall, ceiling, window, etc.)

4-7 U COEFFICIENT

The U coefficient in formula (4-1) is calculated for a complete building element, such as a wall, including inner and outer air films as well as all other materials of which a building element is composed. Formula (4-1) expresses the rate of sensible heat flow in Btu/hr, and may be used equally well for sensible transmission heat *gains* in summer. Formula (4-1) is then a method of measuring the *ability* of a wall or other surface to *conduct* heat by transmission. It is not a measure of a wall's insulating value—just the opposite.

To calculate the U coefficients for the different elements of buildings (roofs, walls, etc.), three other coefficients are needed and regularly utilized. The first of these is *conductivity*, expressed by the symbol k.

4-8 CONDUCTIVITY k

Conductivity k is a positive term that expresses the *ability* of a homogeneous material to *conduct* heat; k is expressed in terms of BH per square foot of area of a material per inch of thickness of the material per degree difference in tem-

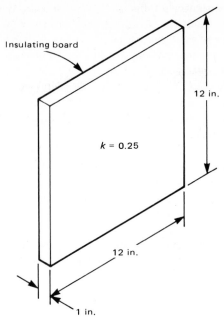

Figure 4-2 Insulating board panel.

perature between opposite faces of the material [BH/ft^2/in./$^\circ\Delta t$] .

In fig. 4-2 a piece of insulating board is shown; it is 12 in. square and 1 in. thick. The insulating value of building boards such as this varies considerably; let us assume that the conductivity k of this board is 0.25, a typical value. The value 0.25 tells us that one-fourth of a Btu will pass through this board by conduction for every $^\circ$F difference in temperature that exists between opposite faces of the board—remember that it is 1 ft square, 1 in. thick, and is homogeneous. The conductivity k of a material does not take into consideration any air film effect, only the effect of the basic material itself.

4-9 CONDUCTANCE C

The next heat transfer coefficient that we need to examine is called *conductance*, expressed by the symbol C. Conductance C is a positive term like conductivity k and expresses the ability of a nonhomogeneous building material to transmit heat. C is expressed in terms of BH per square foot (of wall or roof, etc.) area per degree difference between the temperatures of the opposite faces of the material. Notice that conductance C values are not expressed as a heat flow rate per inch of thickness of a material. Rather, C values are given for whatever thickness a material usually has when it is utilized.

For example, in fig. 4-3 is shown a section of a wall made of 4-in. bricks and 8-in. concrete blocks. A concrete block is not a homogeneous material; rather it is a composite structure composed of concrete and air arranged in a special way. The conductance C of the portion of this wall that is of concrete blocks might, for example, have a value of 0.90 if the concrete in the blocks is made with a gravel aggregate.

This 0.90 C value means that the dashed 12-in.-square area in fig. 4-3 (and every other 1-ft² area in the wall like it) will experience the passage of 0.90 BH of heat for every degree of temperature difference Δt that exists between opposite faces of the blocks. As with conductivity k, this conductance value does not take into consideration the effect of any air film that may exist on either side of the blocks.

4-10   RESISTANCE R

The last heat transfer coefficient that we need to consider is called *resistance*, expressed by the symbol R. Resistance is a negative term, with respect to heat flow, and unlike k and C, expresses the ability of a building material, homogeneous or not,

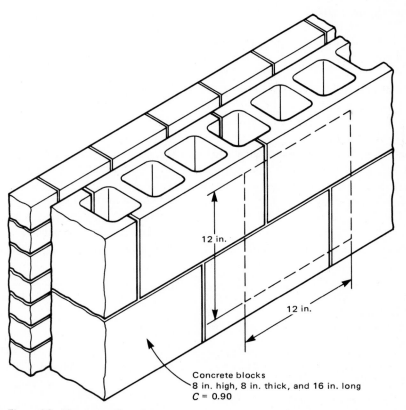

12 in.

12 in.

Concrete blocks
8 in. high, 8 in. thick, and 16 in. long
$C = 0.90$

Figure 4-3   Masonry wall section.

to resist the flow of heat. So resistance is directly proportional to insulating value—the higher the R, the higher the insulating value.

Resistance bears a reciprocal relationship to conductivity and conductance. Therefore, we can say:

$$R = \frac{x}{k} \qquad (4\text{-}2)$$

and

$$R = \frac{1}{C} \qquad (4\text{-}3)$$

where R = resistance
x = material thickness, in.
k = conductivity, $\text{BH/ft}^2/\text{in.}/°\Delta t$
C = conductance, $\text{BH/ft}^2/°\Delta t$

Consider the small piece of building board in fig. 4-2. It has a conductivity of 0.25 and is 1 in. thick. Its resistance to heat flow is

$$R = \frac{x}{k} = \frac{1 \text{ in.}}{0.25} = 4$$

We do not ascribe any units to this resistance of 4; we just use the numerical value. If the board of fig. 4-2 were 2 in. thick, its resistance would be twice as much:

$$R = \frac{2 \text{ in.}}{0.25} = 8$$

Also, consider the wall of fig. 4-3. The concrete blocks in that wall have a conductance C of 0.90 $\text{BH/ft}^2/°\Delta t$. The resistance R of the concrete blocks is then

$$R = \frac{1}{C} = \frac{1}{0.9} = 1.11$$

This resistance of 1.11 is just for the concrete blocks in the wall. Every other component in the wall of fig. 4-3 has resistance too—the brick veneer, the air space between the bricks and the blocks, the indoor air film, and the outdoor air film.

The tables in fig. 4-4*a*, *b*, and *c* list values of conductivity, conductance, and resistance for a wide range of materials that are used in the construction of buildings. Through the use of this table, the resistance of all materials and air spaces that constitute a ceiling, roof, floor, wall, or partition can easily be determined.

4-11 TOTAL RESISTANCE AND U COEFFICIENT

After the resistance of each component part of a wall, roof, or other member is determined from fig. 4-4*a*, *b*, and *c*, these resistances are simply added arithmetically to find the total resistance R_T.

Remember that resistance R measures insulating value of a material or an air space, the ability to resist heat flow—a negative term. But in making a heat loss or heat gain calculation, we need to know the positive value of the heat flowing. In other words, we need to know the magnitude of the U coefficient, which is a positive measure of the rate of heat flow.

The reader will have surely realized by now that a U coefficient is just the reciprocal of the total resistance:

$$U = \frac{1}{R_T} \qquad (4\text{-}4)$$

When the U coefficient is known, the calculation of the rate of heat flow by transmission is simple with the use of formula (4-1):

$$\text{BH} = A \times U \times \Delta t$$

Figure 4-4 Values of conductivity conductance, resistance, and heat loss. (*a* and *b* reprinted from the 1977 ASHRAE Handbook of Fundamentals with the permission of ASHRAE.) (*a*) Thermal properties of typical building and insulating materials.

Description[a]	Density lb/ft^3	Conductivity k	Conductance C	Resistance[b] (R) Per inch thickness 1/k	Resistance[b] (R) For thickness listed 1/C
Air films					
Walls, nonreflective					
Indoors			1.46		0.68
Outdoors, 15-mph wind			6.00		0.17
Outdoors, 7.5-mph wind			4.00		0.25
Ceilings, nonreflective					
Heat flow up (winter)			1.63		0.61
Heat flow down (summer)			1.08		0.92
Sloping, heat flow up			1.60		0.62
Sloping, heat flow down			1.32		0.76
Roofs—flat or sloping					
15-mph wind			6.00		0.17
7.5-mph wind			4.00		0.25
Building board					
Boards, panels, subflooring, sheathing, woodboard panel products					
Asbestos-cement board		120	4.0	. . .	0.25
Asbestos-cement board 0.125 in.	120	. . .	33.00	. . .	0.03
Asbestos-cement board 0.25 in.	120	. . .	16.50	. . .	0.06
Gypsum or plaster board 0.375 in.	50	. . .	3.10	. . .	0.32
Gypsum or plaster board 0.5 in.	50	. . .	2.22	. . .	0.45
Gypsum or plaster board 0.625 in.	50	. . .	1.78	. . .	0.56
Plywood (Douglas fir)	34	0.80	. . .	1.25	. . .
Plywood (Douglas fir) 0.25 in.	34	. . .	3.20	. . .	0.31
Plywood (Douglas fir) 0.375 in.	34	. . .	2.13	. . .	0.47
Plywood (Douglas fir) 0.5 in.	34	. . .	1.60	. . .	0.62
Plywood (Douglas fir) 0.625 in.	34	. . .	1.29	. . .	0.77
Plywood or wood panels 0.75 in.	34	. . .	1.07	. . .	0.93
Vegetable fiber board					
Sheathing, regular density 0.5 in.	18	. . .	0.76	. . .	1.32
0.78125 in.	18	. . .	0.49	. . .	2.06
Sheathing intermediate density 0.5 in.	22	. . .	0.82	. . .	1.22
Nail-base sheathing 0.5 in.	25	. . .	0.88	. . .	1.14
Shingle backer 0.375 in.	18	. . .	1.06	. . .	0.94
Shingle backer 0.3125 in.	18	. . .	1.28	. . .	0.78
Sound deadening board 0.5 in.	15	. . .	0.74	. . .	1.35
Tile and lay-in panels, plain or acoustic	18	0.40	. . .	2.50	
0.5 in.	18	. . .	0.80	. . .	1.25
0.75 in.	18	. . .	0.53	. . .	1.89
Laminated paperboard	30	0.50	. . .	2.00	
Homogeneous board from repulped paper	30	0.50	. . .	2.00	
Hardboard					
Medium density	50	0.73	. . .	1.37	
High density, service temp. service underlay	55	0.82	. . .	1.22	
High density, std. tempered	63	1.00	. . .	1.00	

Figure 4-4 *(a) (Cont.)*

Description[a]		Density lb/ft^3	Conduc- tivity k	Conduc- tance C	Resistance[b] (R)	
					Per inch thickness $1/k$	For thick- ness listed $1/C$
Particleboard						
Low density		37	0.54	. . .	1.85	
Medium density		50	0.94	. . .	1.06	
High density		62.5	1.18	. . .	0.85	
Underlayment	0.625 in.	40	. . .	1.22	. . .	0.82
Wood subfloor	0.75 in.			1.06	. . .	0.94
Building membrane						
Vapor—permeable felt		. . .	. . .	16.70	. . .	0.06
Vapor—seal two layers of mopped 15-lb felt		. . .	. . .	8.35	. . .	0.12
Vapor—seal, plastic film		. . .	. . .	. . .	. . .	Negl.
Finish flooring materials						
Carpet and fibrous pad		. . .	. . .	0.48	. . .	2.08
Carpet and rubber pad		. . .	. . .	0.81	. . .	1.23
Cork tile	0.125 in.	. . .	. . .	3.60	. . .	0.28
Terrazzo	1 in.	. . .	. . .	12.50	. . .	0.08
Tile—asphalt, linoleum, vinyl, rubber, vinyl asbestos, ceramic		. . .	. . .	20.00	. . .	0.05
Wood, hardwood finish	0.75 in.			1.47		0.68
Insulating materials						
Blanket and batt						
Mineral fiber, fibrous form processed from rock, slag, or glass						
Approximately[c] 2-2.75 in.		0.3-2.0	. . .	0.143	. . .	7[d]
Approximately[c] 3-3.5 in.		0.3-2.0	. . .	0.091	. . .	11[d]
Approximately[c] 5.50-6.5 in.		0.3-2.0	. . .	0.053	. . .	19[d]
Approximately[c] 6-7 in.		0.3-2.0		0.045		22[d]
Approximately[d] 8.5 in.		0.3-2.0		0.033		30[d]
Board and Slabs						
Cellular glass		8.5	0.38	. . .	2.63	
Glass fiber, organic bonded		4-9	0.25	. . .	4.00	
Expanded rubber (rigid)		4.5	0.22	. . .	4.55	
Expanded polystyrene extruded						
Cut cell surface		1.8	0.25	. . .	4.00	
Expanded polystyrene extruded						
Smooth skin surface		2.2	0.20	. . .	5.00	
Expanded polystyrene extruded						
Smooth skin surface		3.5	0.19	. . .	5.26	
Expanded polystyrene, molded beads		1.0	0.28	. . .	3.57	
Expanded polyurethane (R-11 exp.)		1.5	0.16	. . .	6.25	
(Thickness 1 in. or greater)		2.5				
Mineral fiber with resin binder		15	0.29	. . .	3.45	
Mineral fiberboard, wet felted						
Core or roof insulation		16-17	0.34	. . .	2.94	
Acoustical tile		18	0.35	. . .	2.86	
Acoustical tile		21	0.37	. . .	2.70	

Figure 4-4 (a) (Cont.)

Description[a]		Density lb/ft³	Conduc-tivity k	Conduc-tance C	Resistance[b] (R)	
					Per inch thickness 1/k	For thick-ness listed 1/C
Mineral fiberboard, wet molded						
Acoustical tile[f]		23	0.42	. . .	2.38	
Wood or cane fiberboard						
Acoustical tile[f]	0.5 in.	. . .	. . .	0.80	. . .	1.25
Acoustical tile[f]	0.75 in.	. . .	. . .	0.53	. . .	1.89
Interior finish (plank, tile)		15	0.35	. . .	2.86	
Wood shredded (cemented in preformed slabs)		22	0.60	. . .	1.67	
Loose fill						
Cellulosic insulation (milled paper or wood pulp)		2.3–3.2	0.27–0.32	. . .	3.13–3.70	
Sawdust or shavings		8.0–15.0	0.45	. . .	2.22	
Wood fiber, softwoods		2.0–3.5	0.30	. . .	3.33	
Perlite, expanded		5.0–8.0	0.37	. . .	2.70	
Mineral fiber (rock, slag or glass)						
Approximately[c] 3.75–5 in.		0.6–2.0				11
Approximately[c] 6.5–8.75 in.		0.6–2.0				19
Approximately[c] 7.5–10 in.		0.6–2.0				22
Approximately[c] 10.25–13.75 in.		0.6–2.0				30
Vermiculite, exfoliated		7.0–8.2	0.47	. . .	2.13	
		4.0–6.0	0.44	. . .	2.27	
Roof Insulation[g]						
Preformed, for use above deck						
Different roof insulations are available in different thicknesses to provide the design C values listed.[g] Consult individual manufacturers for actual thickness of their material				0.72 to 0.12		1.39 to 8.33
Masonry materials						
Concretes						
Cement mortar		116	5.0	. . .	0.20	
Gypsum-fiber concrete 87.5% gypsum, 12.5% wood chips		51	1.66	. . .	0.60	
Lightweight aggregates including ex-panded shale, clay or slate; expanded slags; cinders; pumice; vermiculite; also cellular concretes		120	5.2	. . .	0.19	
		100	3.6	. . .	0.28	
		80	2.5	. . .	0.40	
		60	1.7	. . .	0.59	
		40	1.15	. . .	0.86	
		30	0.90	. . .	1.11	
		20	0.70	. . .	1.43	
Perlite, expanded		40	0.93	. . .	1.08	
		30	0.71	. . .	1.41	
		20	0.50	. . .	2.00	
Sand and gravel or stone aggregate (oven dried)		140	9.0	. . .	0.11	

Figure 4-4 *(a) (Cont.)*

Description[a]		Density lb/ft³	Conductivity k	Conductance C	Resistance[b] (R)	
					Per inch thickness 1/k	For thickness listed 1/C
Sand and gravel or stone aggregate						
(not dried)		140	12.0	. . .	0.08	
Stucco		116	5.0	. . .	0.20	
Masonry units						
Brick, common[h]		120	5.0	. . .	0.20	
Brick face[h]		130	9.0	. . .	0.11	
Clay tile, hollow:						
1 cell deep	3 in.	. . .	. . .	1.25	. . .	0.80
1 cell deep	4 in.	. . .	. . .	0.90	. . .	1.11
2 cells deep	6 in.	. . .	. . .	0.66	. . .	1.52
2 cells deep	8 in.	. . .	. . .	0.54	. . .	1.85
2 cells deep	10 in.	. . .	. . .	0.45	. . .	2.22
3 cells deep	12 in.	. . .	. . .	0.40	. . .	2.50
Concrete blocks, three oval core:						
Sand and gravel aggregate	4 in.	. . .	. . .	1.40	. . .	0.71
	8 in.	. . .	. . .	0.90	. . .	1.11
	12 in.	. . .	. . .	0.78	. . .	1.28
Cinder aggregate	3 in.	. . .	. . .	1.16	. . .	0.86
	4 in.	. . .	. . .	0.90	. . .	1.11
	8 in.	. . .	. . .	0.58	. . .	1.72
	12 in.	. . .	. . .	0.53	. . .	1.89
Lightweight aggregate	3 in.	. . .	. . .	0.79	. . .	1.27
(expanded shale, clay, slate	4 in.	. . .	. . .	0.67	. . .	1.50
or slag; pumice)	8 in.	. . .	. . .	0.50	. . .	2.00
	12 in.	. . .	. . .	0.44	. . .	2.27
Concrete blocks, rectangular core.*[i]						
Sand and gravel aggregate						
2 core, 8 in. 36 lb.[j]*		. . .	. . .	0.96	. . .	1.04
Same with filled cores[k]*		. . .	. . .	0.52	. . .	1.93
Lightweight aggregate (expanded shale,						
clay, slate or slag, pumice):						
3 core, 6 in. 19 lb[j]*		. . .	. . .	0.61	. . .	1.65
Same with filled cores[k]*		. . .	. . .	0.33	. . .	2.99
2 core, 8 in. 24 lb[j]*		. . .	. . .	0.46	. . .	2.18
Same with filled cores[k]*		. . .	. . .	0.20	. . .	5.03
3 core, 12 in. 38 lb[j]*		. . .	. . .	0.40	. . .	2.48
Same with filled cores[k]*		. . .	. . .	0.17	. . .	5.82
Stone, lime or sand		. . .	12.50	. . .	0.08	. . .
Gypsum partition tile:						
3 X 12 X 30 in. solid		. . .	. . .	0.79	. . .	1.26
3 X 12 X 30 in. 4-cell		. . .	. . .	0.74	. . .	1.35
4 X 12 X 30 in. 3-cell		. . .	. . .	0.60	. . .	1.67

Figure 4-4 (a) (Cont.)

Description[a]		Density lb/ft³	Conductivity k	Conductance C	Resistance[b] (R)	
					Per inch thickness 1/k	For thickness listed 1/C
Plastering materials						
Cement plaster, sand aggregate		116	5.0	. . .	0.20	
Sand aggregate	0.375 in.	. . .	. . .	13.3	. . .	0.08
Sand aggregate	0.75 in.	. . .	. . .	6.66	. . .	0.15
Gypsum plaster:						
Lightweight aggregate	0.5 in.	45	. . .	3.12	. . .	0.32
Lightweight aggregate	0.625 in.	45	. . .	2.67	. . .	0.39
Lightweight agg. on metal lath	0.75 in.	. . .	. . .	2.13	. . .	0.47
Perlite aggregate		45	1.5	. . .	0.67	
Sand aggregate		105	5.6	. . .	0.18	
Sand aggregate	0.5 in.	105	. . .	11.10	. . .	0.09
Sand aggregate	0.625 in.	105	. . .	9.10	. . .	0.11
Sand aggregate on metal lath	0.75 in.	. . .	. . .	7.70	. . .	0.13
Vermiculite aggregate		45	1.7	. . .	0.59	
Roofing						
Asbestos-cement shingles		120	. . .	4.76	. . .	0.21
Asphalt roll roofing		70	. . .	6.50	. . .	0.15
Asphalt shingles		70	. . .	2.27	. . .	0.44
Built-up roofing	0.375 in.	70	. . .	3.00	. . .	0.33
Slate	0.5 in.	. . .	. . .	20.00	. . .	0.05
Wood shingles, plain and plastic film faced		. . .	. . .	1.06	. . .	0.94
Siding materials (on flat surface)						
Shingles						
Asbestos-cement		120	. . .	4.75	. . .	0.21
Wood, 16 in., 7.5 exposure		. . .	. . .	1.15	. . .	0.87
Wood, double, 16-in., 12-in. exposure		. . .	. . .	0.84	. . .	1.19
Wood, plus insul. backer board, 0.3125 in.		. . .	. . .	0.71	. . .	1.40
Siding						
Asbestos-cement, 0.25 in., lapped		. . .	. . .	4.76	. . .	0.21
Asphalt roll siding		. . .	. . .	6.50	. . .	0.15
Asphalt insulating siding (0.5 in. bed)		. . .	. . .	0.69	. . .	1.46
Hardboard siding, 0.4375 in.		40	1.49	. . .	. . .	0.67
Wood, drop, 1 × 8 in.		. . .	. . .	1.27	. . .	0.79
Wood, bevel, 0.5 × 8 in., lapped		. . .	. . .	1.23	. . .	0.81
Wood, bevel, 0.75 × 10 in., lapped		. . .	. . .	0.95	. . .	1.05
Wood, plywood, 0.375 in., lapped		. . .	. . .	1.59	. . .	0.59
Aluminum or steel[l], over sheathing						
Hollow-backed		. . .	. . .	1.61	. . .	0.61
Insulating-board backed nominal 0.375 in.		. . .	. . .	0.55	. . .	1.82
Insulating-board backed nominal 0.375 in., foil backed				0.34		2.96
Architectural glass		. . .	. . .	10.00	. . .	0.10

Figure 4-4 (a) (Cont.)

Description[a]		Density lb/ft^3	Conductivity k	Conductance C	Resistance[b] (R)	
					Per inch thickness $1/k$	For thickness listed $1/C$
Woods						
Maple, oak, and similar hardwoods		45	1.10	. . .	0.91	
Fir, pine and similar softwoods		32	0.80	. . .	1.25	
Fir, pine, and similar softwoods	0.75 in.	32	. . .	1.06	. . .	0.94
	1.5 in.		. . .	0.53	. . .	1.89
	2.5 in.		. . .	0.32	. . .	3.12
	3.5 in.		. . .	0.23	. . .	4.35

Densities are in lb/ft^3; k values are in BH/$^\circ$F Δt/in. thick/ft^2; C values are in BH/$^\circ$F Δt/ft^2 for given construction; U values are in BH/$^\circ$F Δt/ft^2 of complete wall, roof, E. All values are for a mean temperature of 75°F except as noted by an asterisk (*), which are for 45°F.

[a]Representative values for dry materials were selected by ASHRAE TC4.4, *Insulation and Moisture Barriers.* They are intended as design (not specifications) for materials in normal use. For properties of a particular product, use the value supplied by the manufacturer or by unbiased tests.

[b]Resistance values are the reciprocals of C before rounding off C to two decimal places.

[c]Conductivity varies with fiber diameter. Insulation is produced by different densities; therefore, there is a wide variation in thickness for the same R-value among manufacturers. No effort should be made to relate any specific R-value to any specific thickness. Commercial thicknesses generally available range from 2 to 8.5 in.

[d]Does not include paper backing and facing, if any.

[e]Values are for aged board stock.

[f]Insulating values of acoustical tile vary, depending on density of the board and on type, size and depth of perforations.

[g]The U.S. Department of Commerce, *Simplified Practice Recommendation for Thermal Conductance Factors for Preformed Above-Deck Roof Insulation* R257-55, recognizes the specification of roof insulation on the basis of the C values shown. Roof insulation is made in thicknesses to meet these values.

[h]Face brick and common brick do not always have these specific densities. When density is different from that shown, there will be a change in thermal conductivity.

[i]Data on rectangular core concrete blocks differ from the above data on oval core blocks, due to core configuration, different mean temperatures, and possible differences in unit weights. Weight data on the oval core blocks tested are not available.

[j]Weights of units approximately 7.625 in. high and 15.75 in. long. These weights are given as a means of describing the blocks tested, but conductance values are for 1 ft^2 of area.

[k]Vermiculite, perlite, or mineral wool insulation. Where insulation is used, vapor barriers or other precautions must be considered to keep insulation dry.

[l]Values for metal siding applied over flat surfaces vary widely, depending on amount of ventilation of air space beneath the siding; whether air space is reflective or nonreflective; and on thickness, type, and application of insulating backing-board used. Values given are averages for use as design guides, and were obtained from several guarded hotbox tests (ASTM C236) or calibrated hotbox (BSS 77) on hollow-backed types and types made using backing-boards of wood fiber, foamed plastic, and glass fiber. Departures of ±50% or more from the values given may occur.

Figure 4-4 (*b*) Coefficients of transmission (*U*), windows, skylights, & doors.

Windows, glass blocks	U Winter	U Summer	U Storm sash
Vertical position			
Single glass (all glass)	1.10	1.04	0.50
Wood windows, 80% single glass	0.99	0.94	0.45
Wood windows, 60% single glass	0.88	0.83	0.40
Metal windows, 80% single glass	1.10	1.04	0.60
Insulating glass—double (two panes)			
1/8 in. glass, 3/16 in. space	0.62	0.65	
1/8 in. glass, 1/4 in. air space	0.58	0.61	
1/4 in. glass, 1/2 in. air space	0.49	0.56	
Insulating glass—triple (three panes)			
1/8 in. glass, 1/4 in. air spaces	0.39	0.44	
1/4 in.-1/8 in.-1/4 in. glasses, 1/2 in. air spaces	0.31	0.39	
Plastic sheet—single			
1/8 in. sheet	1.06	0.98	
1/4 in. sheet	0.96	0.89	
1/2 in. sheet	0.81	0.76	
Plastic sheets—double (two panes)			
1/8 in sheets, 1/4 in. space	0.55	0.56	
1/2 in. air space	0.43	0.45	
Glass blocks			
6 × 6 × 4 in. thick	0.60	0.57	
8 × 8 × 4 in. thick	0.56	0.54	
8 × 8 × 4 in. with cavity divider	0.48	0.46	
12 × 12 × 4 in. thick	0.52	0.50	
12 × 12 × 4 with cavity divider	0.44	0.42	
12 × 12 × 2 in. thick	0.60	0.57	
Storm windows over single glass	0.50	0.50	
Horizontal position			
Single glass	1.23	0.83	
Insulating glass—double (two panes)			
1/8 in. glass, 3/16 in. space	0.70	0.57	
1/8 in. glass, 1/4 in. space	0.65	0.54	
1/2 in. air space	0.59	0.49	
Glass Blocks			
11 × 11 × 3 in. thick with cavity divider	0.53	0.35	
12 × 12 × 4 in. thick with cavity divider	0.51	0.34	
Plastic domes			
Single-walled	1.15	0.80	
Double-walled	0.70	0.46	
Slab doors—solid wood			
1 in.	0.64	0.61	
1 in.—wood storm door—50% glass	0.30	—	
1 in.—metal storm door	0.39	—	
1.25 in.	0.55	0.53	
1.25 in.—wood storm door—50% glass	0.28	—	
1.25 in.—metal storm door	0.34	—	
1.5 in.	0.49	0.47	
1.5 in.—wood storm door—50% glass	0.27	—	
1.5 in.—metal storm door	0.33	—	

Figure 4-4 *(b) (Cont.)*

Windows, glass blocks	*U* Winter	*U* Summer	*U* Storm sash
1.75 in.	0.46	0.45	
1.75 in.—wood storm doors—50% glass	0.26	—	
1.75 in.—metal storm doors	0.31	—	
2 in.	0.43	0.42	
2 in.—wood storm doors—50% glass	0.24	—	
2 in.—metal storm doors	0.29	—	
Slab doors—steel—1.75 in.			
Mineral fiber core (2 lb/ft³)	0.59	0.58	
Solid urethane foam core with thermal break	0.19	0.18	
Solid polystyrene core with thermal break	0.47	0.46	

Figure 4-4 *(c)* Resistances of typical air spaces in construction.

Type of air space	*R*
Stud space or furred space in wall, 3/4 to 6 in., nonreflective materials	1.1
Stud space or furred space in wall, 3/4 to 6 in., aluminum foil one side only	3.3
Stud space or furred space in wall, 3/4 to 6 in., aluminum foil both sides	3.5
Furred space above ceiling 3/4 to 12 in., nonreflective materials	0.9
Furred space above ceiling, 3/4 to 12 in., aluminum foil one side only	1.2
Attic space above ceiling, below pitched roof or flat roof, average height 4 ft, minimum ventilation, nonreflective materials	0.9
Attic space, very well ventilated, either mechanically or naturally	0.1
Furred space below floor, 3/4 to 12 in., nonreflective materials	1.2

Figure 4-4 *(d)* Heat loss through concrete floors on earth and earth-backed masonry walls in Btu/hr per ft² of area.

Location north latitude	Concrete floors poured on earth	Masonry walls below grade (earth-backed)
25°–37°	2.0	4.0
38°–50°	3.0	6.0

Example 4-1 Calculate the *U* coefficient for the wall detailed in fig. 4-3, and find the transmission heat loss through a building wall of this type 10 ft high and 60 ft long when the OA temperature is 20°F and the RA temperature is 68°F. A 15-mph wind is blowing.

Solution From fig. 4-4*a*, *b*, and *c* we select the following component resistances:

Outside air film	0.17
4-in. face brick, $R = \dfrac{x}{k} = \dfrac{4 \text{ in.}}{9.0}$	0.44
Air space between the brick and the block	1.10
8-in. gravel aggregate block	1.11
Indoor air film	0.68
Total resistance $R_T =$	3.50

From formula (4-4),

$$U = \frac{1}{R_T} = \frac{1}{3.50} = 0.29$$

Then using formula (4-1),

$$BH = A \times U \times \Delta t$$
$$= (10 \text{ ft} \times 60 \text{ ft})0.29(68°F - 20°F)$$
$$= 8352$$

The heat loss is 8352 BH.

Notice that in finding the total resistance, we started with the outside air film and worked sequentially through the wall, taking each component in order and ending with the indoor air film. It is important to follow this procedure always so that nothing is forgotten.

Example 4-2 Calculate the U coefficient of the wall detailed in fig. 4-1 if the exterior brick is 4-in. common brick, the sheathing secured to the exterior of the wood studs is 25/32-in. insulating board (vegetable fiber board), and the interior finish of the wall is 1/2-in. gypsum board (drywall).

Solution From fig. 4-4 we find the following resistances:

Outside air film	0.17
4-in. common brick $R = \dfrac{x}{k} = \dfrac{4 \text{ in.}}{5.0} =$	0.80
Air space between the brick and the sheathing	1.10
25/32-in. thick sheathing	2.06
Air space between studs	1.10
1/2-in. gypsum board	0.45
Indoor air film	0.68
Total resistance, $R_T =$	6.36

$$U \text{ coefficient} = \frac{1}{R_T} = \frac{1}{6.36} = 0.16$$

Now, suppose that we wish to add insulation to the wall of example 4-2, and decide to install a 2-in. thickness of glass fiber insulation in the stud space. If the manufacturer advises that the insulation to be used has a conductivity of 0.3, the resistance will be

$$R = \frac{x}{k} = \frac{2 \text{ in.}}{0.3} = 6.06$$

The revised R_T will now be 6.36 from example 4-2, plus the 6.06 of the insulation and $R_T = 12.42$. The revised U coefficient will now be

$$U = \frac{1}{R_T} = \frac{1}{12.32} = 0.08$$

The insulated wall is now much better, and the heat loss through this wall will be only half what it was before the insulation was added, since the U coefficient is only half as great as before.

Of course, the method of calculating U coefficients for ceilings, roofs, floors, and partitions is exactly the same as for walls. The component resistances are totaled to find R_T, which is then inverted to find the U coefficient.

4-12 RESISTANCE OF AIR SPACES

The tables in fig. 4-4a and b include data developed and published by ASHRAE; the data in these tables may be used with confidence.

The data in fig. 4-4c include data gleaned from the author's decades of field experience. These data have been used successfully by the author, but the reader must realize that the same degree of confidence cannot be placed in them that can be placed in the ASHRAE data.

Figure 4-4c includes a number of resistances for different types of air spaces. Air spaces have been a source of difficulty through the years when estimating heat losses and gains. Consider the wall section in fig. 4-5. In art. 4-4 and fig. 4-1, the three methods by which heat passes through an air space were discussed. One of the methods was by radiant means. Heat radiates in important quanti-

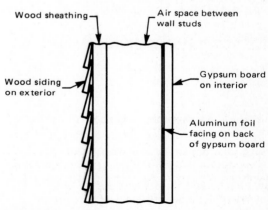

Figure 4-5 Frame wall section.

ties from one surface that bounds an air space to all other surfaces that are at a lower temperature.

In cold weather, the gypsum board would be at an appreciably higher temperature than the sheathing, and there would be a net radiant heat exchange outward toward the sheathing. With a shiny aluminum foil surface on the outer face of the gypsum board, this net radiant heat exchange would be greatly reduced.

It is easy to see that, in summer, the radiant heat flow from the sheathing to the gypsum board would be reflected back to the sheathing and the net radiant heat exchange greatly reduced. Experience has shown that a reflective surface, like the aluminum foil, which is a very poor receiver of radiant heat (being highly reflective), is also a very poor emitter of radiant heat. So the presence of the shiny surface in fig. 4-5 causes a great reduction in radiant heat exchange in both directions across the air space.

The shiny surface also causes an appreciable reduction in heat transfer across an air space by the convection and conduction processes described in art. 4-4. Therefore, the resistance of an air space bounded on one side by a reflective material is greater than that of an air space bounded by ordinary materials of construction. If both surfaces bounding an air space are reflective, the resistance is even greater yet.

The table in fig. 4-4c lists the resistances of air spaces such as stud spaces, ceiling joist and furred spaces, and so on. For example:

Stud spaces, vertical furred spaces, etc.

nonreflective	$R = 1.1$
Same, reflective one side	$R = 3.3$
Same, reflective both sides	$R = 3.5$

As we in the construction business do a better and better job of building energy-conservative buildings, the importance of the accuracy of the resistance ratings of air spaces of various types diminishes greatly. If we use a stud space air resistance of 1.1 when it should be 1.3, and the total wall resistance R_T is 14.8 instead of 15.0, the U coefficient will be 0.0675 instead of 0.0666. The error here is about 1.3%; however, both values would probably be rounded off to 0.067 or even 0.07 by the engineer. Remember also that in designing an HVAC system, the engineer will add 20 to 40% to the total calculated heat loss before beginning to size equipment.

One type of building air space that has posed especially difficult problems for the HVAC engineer is the attic space that exists between a pitched roof and a flat ceiling below. The problem is involved with the determination of the resistance of the attic air space, as well as the overall resistance of the composite ceiling and roof structure.

The solution to this problem is complicated by several factors:

1   The ratio of the roof area to the ceiling area
2   The relative area of gables that help enclose the attic space
3   The amount of ventilation, both natural and mechanical, that takes place in the attic space
4   The amount of insulation and its location and insulating value

The difficulty of placing all of these variable factors into proper perspective and deriving a dependably accurate result is just too great to justify the effort. Through the years this problem has been cut short as engineers have settled for the use of estimates not based on accurate calculations.

Fortunately, when 6 or 8 in. or more of insulation is added in the ceiling, as shown in fig. 4-6, the importance of accurately determining the attic and roof resistance is greatly minimized. Often an attic is ventilated with soffit vents and gable louvers, as shown in fig. 4-6, to the extent that the attic air temperature is very little above outdoor temperature in winter. In this case, the ceiling, the insulation above it, and the air film resistances are all that matter. The resistance of the attic air and the roof is not of much concern.

Modern buildings that have attic spaces will almost certainly have well-insulated ceilings. Where attics are essentially unventilated, the attic air could be assumed to have a resistance of 0.9; the roof resistance could also be calculated and taken into consideration.

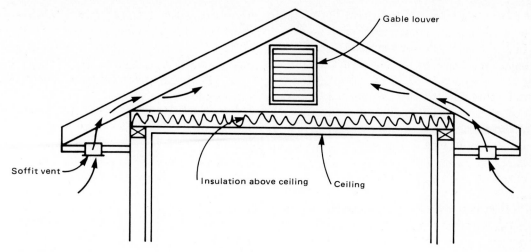

Figure 4-6 Ventilated attic with well-insulated ceiling.

4-13 TEMPERATURE GRADIENT IN A WALL

The term *resistance,* symbolized by the letter R, has several convenient uses. The most important of these is to help determine the total resistance R_T of a roof, ceiling, wall, or floor, which in turn leads to the determination of the U coefficient.

However, there are some other uses of R which are almost as important. For example, by proportional calculation, we can quite accurately predict where the dew point temperature in a wall might fall. This, of course, will tell us where condensation of moisture will occur under certain temperature conditions, and where and how provisions should be made to handle the resulting water of condensation.

Also, through the use of component resistances we can determine the inside surface temperatures of walls and all other room surfaces. These we must know if we are to predict the MRT of a room, and conceive methods of improving the MRT when that is deemed to be necessary.

Consider the frame wall with brick veneer detailed in fig. 4-1 and the calculation of its R_T in example 4-2 in art. 4-11. In that calculation, we find that $R_T = 6.36$ and that the resistance of the indoor air film is 0.68.

Suppose that RA = 70°F and OA = 10°F; Δt then equals (70°F - 10°F) = 60°F. We know that there is a temperature drop because the wall is there, separating indoors from outdoors. We also know that there is a temperature drop because the wall has resistance, and that the temperature drop in each component of the wall is proportional to the resistance of that component.

We see in example 4-2 that the 25/32-in. sheathing has a resistance of 2.06, which is 32.4% of the total resistance of 6.36: 2.06/6.36 = 0.324. Therefore, the temperature drop through the sheathing is 32.4% of the Δt of 60°F, which is 60°F × 0.324 = 19.4°F. In other words, the inner surface temperature of the sheathing is at a temperature 19.4°F higher than that of its outer surface.

The indoor air film on this wall has an R of 0.68. This R is 10.7% of R_T(0.68/6.36 = 0.107). Therefore, the temperature drop through the indoor air film is 10.7% of the Δt of 60°F and equals 0.107 × 60°F = 6.4°F; and the indoor surface temperature (of the gypsum board drywall) is 70°F RA - 6.4°F = 63.6°F. In fig. 4-7 this temperature and others throughout the wall are calculated and are shown graphically.

In the foregoing, we have inclined our discussions mostly toward walls; however, all principles

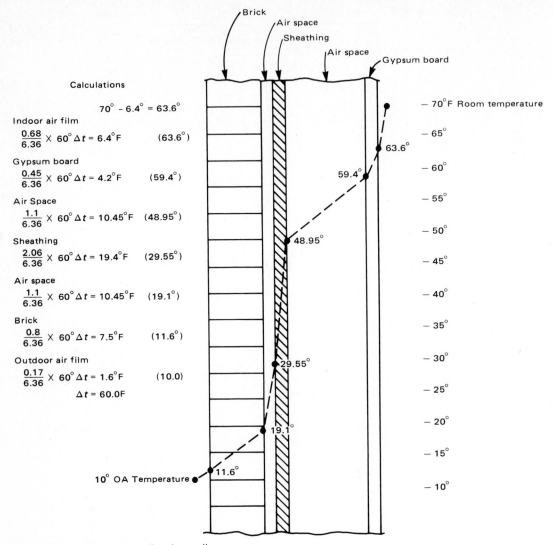

Figure 4-7 Temperature gradient in a wall.

enunciated herein apply equally to any other part of a building, such as a ceiling.

4-14   PRECALCULATED *U* COEFFICIENTS

The table in fig. 4-4 provides data that enable one to determine quickly the resistance of all the components of which a building is constituted. From these resistances it is a simple matter to calculate total resistance R_T and the resulting *U* coefficients.

However, the *U* coefficients of a large number of more-or-less standardized walls, ceilings, roofs, and floors have been precalculated. The use of these will be found to be a great convenience. While only four sets of these data are included herein (figs. 4-8, 4-9, and 4-10a, b), the *ASHRAE Handbook of Fundamentals* presents many more, and the reader is encouraged to seek these out and use them.

Figure 4-8 Coefficients of transmission (U) of frame walls. These coefficients are expressed in Btu per hour per square foot for each Fahrenheit degree difference in temperature between the air on the two sides; they are based on an outside wind velocity of 15 mph. (Reprinted with permission from the 1977 *Fundamentals Volume, ASHRAE Handbook and Products Directory*.)

Example—wall D 4				Example of substitution		
Construction		Resistance	R	Replace items 3 and 4 with insulated board		
1. Outside surface (15 mph wind)			0.17	sheathing (25/32 in.) and items 6 and 7		
2. Sliding, wood, 1/2 in. × 8 in. lapped (average R)			0.85	with gypsum wall board (1/2 in.)		
3. Building paper			0.06	Total resistance		4.12
4. Wood sheathing (25/32 in.)			0.98	Deduct 3. Building paper	0.06	
5. Air space			0.97	4. Wood sheathing (25/32 in.)	0.98	
6. Gypsum lath (3/8 in.)			0.32	6. Gypsum lath (3/8 in.)	0.32	
7. Plaster (sand aggregate) (1/2 in.)			0.09	7. Plaster (sand aggregate) (1/2 in.)	0.09	1.45
8. Inside surface (still air)			0.68			
				Difference		2.67
				Add 4. Insulated board sheathing (25/32 in.)	2.06	
Total resistance			4.12	6. } Gypsum board (1/2 in.)	0.45	2.51
U = 1/R = 1/4.12 =			0.24	7. }		
See value 0.24 in table below.				Total resistance		5.18
				U = 1/R = 1/5.18 =		0.19

Exterior Material	R	Average R	Interior finish Material	R	Type of sheathing None, building paper 0.06 U A	Gypsum board 1/2 in. 0.45 U B	Plywood 5/16 in. 0.39 U C	Wood, 25/32 in. and building paper 1.04 U D	Insulation board sheathing 1/2 in. 1.32 U E	Insulation board sheathing 25/32 in. 2.06 U F	Number
Wood siding		0.85	None	—	0.57	0.47	0.48	0.36	0.33	0.27	1
Drop (1 in. × 8 in.)	0.79		Gypsum board (3/8 in.)	0.32	0.33	0.29	0.30	0.25	0.23	0.20	2
Bevel (1/2 in. × 8 in.)	0.81		Gypsum lath (3/8 in.) and 1/2 in. plaster light weight aggregate	0.64	0.30	0.27	0.27	0.23	0.22	0.19	3
Wood shingles			Gypsum lath (3/8 in.) and 1/2 in. plaster (sand aggregate)	0.41	0.32	0.28	0.29	0.24	0.23	0.19	4
(7 1/2 in. exposure)	0.87		Metal lath and 3/4 in. plaster (light weight aggregate)	0.47	0.31	0.28	0.28	0.24	0.22	0.19	5
Wood panels (3/4 in.)	0.94		Metal lath and 3/4 in. plaster (sand aggregate)	0.13	0.35	0.31	0.31	0.26	0.24	0.21	6
			Insulated board (1/2 in.)	1.43	0.24	0.22	0.22	0.19	0.18	0.16	7
			Insulated board lath (1/2 in.) and 1/2-in. plaster (sand aggregate)	1.52	0.24	0.22	0.22	0.19	0.18	0.16	8
			Plywood (1/4 in.)	0.31	0.33	0.29	0.30	0.25	0.23	0.20	9
			Wood panels (3/4 in.)	0.94	0.27	0.25	0.25	0.22	0.20	0.18	10
			Wood lath and 1/2 in. plaster (sand aggregate)	0.40	0.32	0.28	0.29	0.24	0.23	0.19	11
Face-brick veneer	0.44	0.45	None	—	0.73	0.56	0.58	0.42	0.38	0.30	12
Plywood (3/8 in.)	0.47		Gypsum board (3/8 in.)	0.32	0.37	0.33	0.33	0.27	0.25	0.21	13
			Gypsum lath (3/8 in.) and 1/2-in. plaster (light weight aggregate)	0.64	0.33	0.30	0.30	0.25	0.24	0.20	14
			Gypsum lath (3/8 in. and 1/2 in. plaster (sand aggregate)	0.41	0.36	0.32	0.32	0.27	0.25	0.21	15
			Metal lath and 3/4 in. plaster (light weight aggregate)	0.47	0.35	0.31	0.32	0.26	0.25	0.21	16
			Metal lath and 3/4 in. plaster (sand aggregate)	0.13	0.40	0.35	0.36	0.29	0.27	0.22	17
			Insulated board (1/2 in.)	1.43	0.26	0.24	0.24	0.21	0.20	0.17	18
			Insulated board lath (1/2 in.) and 1/2 in. plaster (sand aggregate)	1.52	0.26	0.23	0.24	0.21	0.19	0.17	19
			Plywood (1/4 in.)	0.31	0.38	0.33	0.33	0.27	0.26	0.21	20
			Wood panels (3/4 in.)	0.94	0.30	0.27	0.28	0.23	0.22	0.19	21
			Wood lath and 1/2-in. plaster (sand aggregate)	0.40	0.36	0.32	0.32	0.27	0.25	0.21	22

1 2 3 4 5 6 7 8

Figure 4-9 Coefficients of Transmission (U) of masonry walls. These coefficients are expressed in Btu per hour per square foot for each Fahrenheit degree difference in temperature between the air on the two sides; they are based on an outside wind velocity of 15 mph. (Reprinted with permission from the 1977 *Fundamentals Volume, ASHRAE Handbook and Products Directory*.)

Example—wall G 1		Example of substitution	
Construction	Resistance *R*	Replace items 6 and 7 with wood panels	
1. Outside surface (15 mph wind)	0.17	(3/4 in.) and vapor barrier applied over	
2. Face brick (4 in.) (average *R*)	0.39	furring strips	
3. Cement mortar (1/2 in.)	0.10	Total resistance	3.83
4. Concrete block (cinder aggregate) (4 in.)	1.11	Deduct 6. Gypsum lath (3/8 in.)	0.32
5. Air space	0.97	7. Plaster (sand aggregate) (1/2 in.)	0.09 · 0.41
6. Gypsum lath (3/8 in.)	0.32		
7. Plaster (sand aggregate) (1/2 in.)	0.09	Difference	3.42
8. Inside surface (still air)	0.68	Add 6. Vapor barrier	0.06
		7. Wood panel (3/4 in.)	0.94 · 1.00
Total resistance	3.83		
U = 1/*R* = 1/3.83 =	0.26	Total resistance	4.42
See value 0.26 in table below.		*U* = 1/*R* = 1/4.42 =	0.23

1 2 3 4 5 6 7 8

Exterior facing			Backing		Interior finish												
					None	Plaster, 3/8 in. on wall		Metal lath and 3/4-in. plaster on furring		Gypsum lath (3/8 in.) and 1/2-in. plaster on furring			Insulated board lath (1/2 in.) and 1/2-in. plaster on furring		Wood lath 1/2 in. plaster		
						Sand aggregate 0.11	Light weight aggregate 0.39	Sand aggregate 0.13	Light weight aggregate 0.47	No plaster 0.32	Sand aggregate 0.41	Light weight aggregate 0.64	No plaster 1.43	Sand aggregate 1.52	Sand aggregate 0.40	
Material	*R*	Average *R*	Material	*R*	*U* A	*U* B	*U* C	*U* D	*U* E	*U* F	*U* G	*U* H	*U* I	*U* J	*U* K	Number
Face brick 4 in.	0.44		Concrete block Cinder aggregate													
Stone 4 in.	0.32		4 in.	1.11	0.41	0.39	0.35	0.28	0.26	0.27	0.26	0.25	0.21	0.20	0.26	1
Precast concrete		0.39	8 in.	1.72	0.33	0.32	0.29	0.24	0.22	0.23	0.23	0.21	0.18	0.18	0.23	2
(sand aggregate)			12 in.	1.89	0.31	0.30	0.28	0.23	0.21	0.22	0.22	0.21	0.18	0.17	0.22	3
4 in.	0.38		Light weight aggregate													
6 in.	0.48		4 in.	1.50	0.35	0.34	0.31	0.25	0.23	0.24	0.24	0.22	0.19	0.19	0.24	4
			8 in.	2.00	0.30	0.29	0.27	0.23	0.21	0.22	0.21	0.20	0.17	0.17	0.21	5
			12 in.	2.27	0.28	0.27	0.25	0.21	0.20	0.20	0.20	0.19	0.17	0.16	0.20	6
			Sand aggregate													
			4 in.	0.71	0.49	0.46	0.41	0.32	0.29	0.30	0.29	0.27	0.22	0.22	0.29	7
			8 in.	1.11	0.41	0.39	0.35	0.28	0.26	0.27	0.26	0.25	0.21	0.20	0.26	8
			12 in.	1.23	0.38	0.37	0.33	0.27	0.25	0.26	0.25	0.24	0.20	0.20	0.25	9
			Hollow clay tile													
			4 in.	1.11	0.41	0.39	0.35	0.28	0.26	0.27	0.26	0.25	0.21	0.20	0.26	10
			8 in.	1.85	0.31	0.30	0.28	0.23	0.22	0.22	0.22	0.21	0.18	0.18	0.22	11
			12 in.	2.50	0.26	0.25	0.24	0.20	0.19	0.19	0.19	0.18	0.16	0.16	0.19	12
			Concrete Sand aggregate													
			4 in.	0.32	0.60	0.56	0.49	0.36	0.32	0.34	0.33	0.31	0.25	0.24	0.33	13
			6 in.	0.48	0.55	0.52	0.45	0.34	0.31	0.32	0.31	0.29	0.24	0.23	0.31	14
			8 in.	0.64	0.51	0.48	0.42	0.32	0.29	0.31	0.30	0.28	0.23	0.22	0.30	15
Common brick 4 in.	0.80		Concrete block Cinder aggregate													
Precast concrete		0.72	4 in.	1.11	0.36	0.35	0.32	0.26	0.24	0.25	0.24	0.23	0.19	0.19	0.24	16
(sand aggregate)			8 in.	1.72	0.29	0.29	0.26	0.22	0.21	0.21	0.21	0.20	0.17	0.17	0.21	17
8 in.	0.64		12 in.	1.89	0.28	0.27	0.25	0.21	0.20	0.21	0.20	0.19	0.17	0.17	0.20	18
			Light weight aggregate													
			4 in.	1.50	0.32	0.30	0.28	0.23	0.22	0.22	0.22	0.21	0.18	0.18	0.22	19
			8 in.	2.00	0.27	0.26	0.25	0.21	0.20	0.20	0.20	0.19	0.16	0.16	0.20	20
			12 in.	2.27	0.25	0.25	0.23	0.20	0.19	0.19	0.19	0.18	0.16	0.16	0.19	21
			Sand aggregate													
			4 in.	0.71	0.42	0.40	0.36	0.29	0.26	0.27	0.27	0.25	0.21	0.21	0.27	22
			8 in.	1.11	0.36	0.35	0.32	0.26	0.24	0.25	0.24	0.23	0.19	0.19	0.24	23
			12 in.	1.28	0.34	0.33	0.30	0.25	0.23	0.24	0.23	0.22	0.19	0.18	0.23	24
			Hollow clay tile													
			4 in.	1.11	0.36	0.35	0.32	0.26	0.24	0.25	0.24	0.23	0.19	0.19	0.24	25
			8 in.	1.85	0.28	0.28	0.26	0.22	0.20	0.21	0.20	0.19	0.17	0.17	0.20	26
			12 in.	2.50	0.24	0.23	0.22	0.19	0.18	0.18	0.18	0.17	0.15	0.15	0.18	27
			Concrete Sand aggregate													
			4 in.	0.32	0.50	0.48	0.42	0.32	0.29	0.30	0.30	0.28	0.23	0.22	0.30	28
			6 in.	0.48	0.47	0.44	0.39	0.31	0.28	0.29	0.28	0.27	0.22	0.22	0.28	29
			8 in.	0.64	0.43	0.41	0.37	0.29	0.27	0.28	0.27	0.26	0.21	0.21	0.27	30

Figure 4-10 (a) Coefficients of transmission (U) of flat masonry roofs with built-up roofing, with and without suspended ceilings (winter conditions, upward flow). These coefficients are expressed in Btu per hour per square foot for each Fahrenheit degree difference in temperature between the air on the two sides; they are based on an outside wind velocity of 15 mph. (Reprinted with permission from the 1977 *Fundamentals Volume, ASHRAE Handbook and Products Directory.*)

Example—K 4	Resistance R	Example of substitution	
Construction (heat flow up)		Replace item 4 with 4-in. concrete slab (gravel aggregate)	
1. Outside surface (15 mph wind)	0.17	and roof insulation (C = 0.36) on top of slab	
2. Built-up roofing–3/8 in.	0.33	Total resistance	4.55
3. Roof insulation (none)	—	Deduct	
4. Concrete slab (light weight aggregate) (2 in.)	2.22	4. Concrete slab (light weight aggregate) (2 in.)	2.22
5. Corrugated metal	0		
6. Air space[a]	0.85	Difference	2.43
7. Metal lath and 3/4-in. plaster (light weight aggregate)	0.47	Add 3. Roof insulation (C = 36)	2.78
8. Inside surface (still air)	0.61	4. Concrete slab (gravel aggregate) 4 in.	0.44	3.22
Total resistance	4.65	Total resistance	5.65
U = 1/R = 1/4.65 =	0.22	U = 1/R = 1/5.65 =	0.18
See value 0.22 in table below.			

1 2 3 4 5 6 7 8

				Roof insulation no ceiling							Type of ceiling									
											Suspended ceiling									
											Gypsum board (3/8 in.) and plaster			Metal lath and plaster		Acoustical tile				
				C value of roof insulation												On furring or channels		On gypsum board (3/8 in.)		
				None	0.72	0.36	0.24	0.19	0.15	0.12	No plaster	Light weight aggregate 1/2 in.	Sand aggregate 1/2 in.	Light weight aggregate 3/4 in.	Sand aggregate 3/4 in.	1/2 in.	3/4 in.	1/2 in.	3/4 in.	
	Type of form			—	1.39	2.78	4.17	5.26	6.67	8.33	0.32	0.64	0.41	0.47	0.13	1.19	1.75	1.51	2.10	
Type of deck	Resistance			U	U	U	U	U	U	U	U	U	U	U	U	U	U	U	U	
Material	R	Material	R	A	B	C	D	E	F	G	H	I	J	K	L	M	N	O	P	Number
Concrete slab																				
Gravel aggregate																				
(4 in.)	0.32	Temporary	—	0.70	0.35	0.24	0.18	0.15	0.12	0.10	0.38	0.34	0.37	0.36	0.41	0.29	0.25	0.26	0.23	1
(6 in.)	0.48	Temporary	—	0.63	0.34	0.23	0.17	0.15	0.12	0.10	0.36	0.32	0.35	0.34	0.39	0.27	0.24	0.25	0.22	2
(8 in.)	0.64	Temporary	—	0.57	0.32	0.22	0.17	0.14	0.12	0.10	0.34	0.31	0.33	0.33	0.37	0.26	0.23	0.24	0.21	3
Light weight aggregate																				
(2 in.)	2.22	Corrugated metal	0	0.30	0.21	0.16	0.13	0.12	0.10	0.09	0.22	0.21	0.22	0.22	0.23	0.19	0.17	0.18	0.16	4
		Insulation board (1 in.)	2.78	0.16	0.13	0.11	0.10	0.09	0.08	0.07	0.14	0.13	0.14	0.13	0.14	0.12	0.11	0.12	0.11	5
		Insulation board (1 1/2 in.)	4.17	0.13	0.11	0.10	0.09	0.08	0.07	0.06	0.12	0.11	0.11	0.11	0.12	0.10	0.10	0.10	0.10	6
		Glass fiber board (1 in.)	4.00	0.14	0.11	0.10	0.09	0.08	0.07	0.06	0.12	0.11	0.12	0.12	0.12	0.11	0.10	0.10	0.10	7
(3 in.)	3.33	Corrugated metal	0	0.23	0.17	0.14	0.12	0.10	0.09	0.08	0.18	0.17	0.18	0.17	0.18	0.15	0.14	0.15	0.14	8
		Insulation board (1 in.)	2.78	0.14	0.12	0.10	0.09	0.08	0.07	0.06	0.12	0.11	0.12	0.12	0.12	0.11	0.10	0.10	0.10	9
		Insulation board (1 1/2 in.)	4.17	0.12	0.10	0.09	0.08	0.07	0.07	0.06	0.10	0.10	0.10	0.10	0.10	0.09	0.09	0.09	0.09	10
		Glass fiber board (1 in.)	4.00	0.12	0.10	0.09	0.08	0.07	0.07	0.06	0.10	0.10	0.10	0.10	0.11	0.10	0.09	0.09	0.09	11
(4 in.)	4.44	Corrugated metal	0	0.18	0.14	0.12	0.10	0.09	0.08	0.07	0.15	0.14	0.15	0.15	0.15	0.13	0.12	0.13	0.12	12
		Insulation board (1 in.)	2.78	0.12	0.10	0.09	0.08	0.07	0.07	0.06	0.11	0.10	0.10	0.10	0.11	0.10	0.09	0.09	0.09	13
		Insulation board (1 1/2 in.)	4.17	0.10	0.09	0.08	0.07	0.07	0.06	0.06	0.09	0.09	0.09	0.09	0.09	0.09	0.08	0.08	0.08	14
		Glass fiber board (1 in.)	4.00	0.10	0.09	0.08	0.07	0.07	0.06	0.06	0.09	0.09	0.09	0.09	0.09	0.09	0.08	0.08	0.08	15
Gypsum slab																				
(2 in.)	1.20	Gypsum board (1/2 in.)	0.45	0.36	0.24	0.18	0.14	0.12	0.11	0.09	0.25	0.24	0.25	0.25	0.27	0.21	0.19	0.20	0.18	16
		Insulation board (1 in.)	2.78	0.20	0.15	0.13	0.11	0.10	0.09	0.08	0.16	0.15	0.16	0.16	0.16	0.14	0.13	0.13	0.12	17
		Insulation board (1 1/2 in.)	4.17	0.15	0.13	0.11	0.09	0.09	0.08	0.07	0.13	0.13	0.13	0.13	0.13	0.12	0.11	0.11	0.11	18
		Asbestos-cement board (1/4 in.)	0.06	0.40	0.26	0.19	0.15	0.13	0.11	0.09	0.27	0.25	0.26	0.26	0.29	0.22	0.19	0.20	0.18	19
		Glass fiber board (1 in.)	4.00	0.16	0.13	0.11	0.10	0.09	0.08	0.07	0.13	0.13	0.13	0.13	0.14	0.12	0.11	0.12	0.11	20
(3 in.)	1.80	Gypsum board (1/2 in.)	0.45	0.30	0.21	0.16	0.13	0.12	0.10	0.09	0.22	0.21	0.22	0.21	0.23	0.19	0.17	0.17	0.16	21
		Insulation board (1 in.)	2.78	0.18	0.14	0.12	0.10	0.09	0.08	0.07	0.15	0.14	0.14	0.14	0.15	0.13	0.12	0.12	0.12	22
		Insulation board (1 1/2 in.)	4.17	0.14	0.12	0.10	0.09	0.08	0.07	0.06	0.12	0.12	0.12	0.12	0.12	0.11	0.10	0.11	0.10	23
		Asbestos-cement board (1/4 in.)	0.06	0.34	0.23	0.17	0.14	0.12	0.10	0.09	0.24	0.22	0.24	0.23	0.25	0.20	0.18	0.19	0.17	24
		Glass fiber board (1 in.)	4.00	0.14	0.12	0.10	0.09	0.08	0.07	0.07	0.12	0.12	0.12	0.12	0.13	0.11	0.10	0.11	0.10	25
(4 in.)	2.40	Gypsum board (1/2 in.)	0.45	0.25	0.19	0.15	0.12	0.11	0.09	0.08	0.19	0.18	0.19	0.19	0.20	0.17	0.15	0.16	0.14	26
		Insulation board (1 in.)	2.78	0.16	0.13	0.11	0.10	0.09	0.08	0.07	0.13	0.13	0.13	0.13	0.14	0.12	0.11	0.12	0.11	27
		Insulation board (1 1/2 in.)	4.17	0.13	0.11	0.10	0.08	0.08	0.07	0.06	0.11	0.11	0.11	0.11	0.12	0.10	0.10	0.10	0.09	28
		Asbestos-cement board (1/4 in.)	0.06	0.28	0.20	0.16	0.13	0.11	0.10	0.08	0.21	0.20	0.21	0.20	0.22	0.18	0.16	0.17	0.15	29
		Glass fiber board (1 in.)	4.00	0.13	0.11	0.10	0.09	0.08	0.07	0.07	0.12	0.11	0.11	0.11	0.12	0.10	0.10	0.10	0.10	30

U values would also apply if slab were poured on metal lath, paper backed wire, fabric, or asbestos-cement board (1/4 in.).
Concrete assumed to have a thermal conductivity k of 12.0 and a density of 140 lb per ft³.
Concrete assumed to have a thermal conductivity k of 0.90 and a density of 30 lb per ft³.
Gypsum slab 2 1/4 in. thick since this is recommended practice.
Gypsum fiber concrete with 12 1/2 percent wood chips (thermal conductivity k = 1.65).

Figure 4-10 (b) Coefficients of transmission (U) of wood or metal construction flat roofs and ceilings (winter conditions, upward flow). These coefficients are expressed in Btu per hour per square foot for each Fahrenheit degree difference in temperature between the air on the two sides; they are based on an outside wind velocity of 15 mph. (Reprinted with permission from the 1977 *Fundamentals Volume, ASHRAE Handbook and Products Directory.*)

Example—roof J 2

Construction (Heat flow up)	Resistance R
1. Outside surface (15 mph wind)	0.17
2. Built-up roofing 3/8 in.	0.33
3. Roof insulation (C = 0.72)	1.39
4. Wood deck (1 in.)	0.98
5. Air space[a]	0.85
6. Gypsum wall board (3/8 in.)	0.32
7. Acoustical tile (1/2 in.)—glued	1.19
8. Inside surface (still air)	0.61
Total resistance	5.84
$U = 1/R = 1/5.84$	0.17

See value 0.17 in table below.

Example of substitution

Replace item 4 with 2-in. wood deck (exposed to inside) and omit items 5, 6, and 7.

Total resistance		5.84
Deduct 4. Wood deck (1 in.)	0.98	
5. Air space	0.85	
6. Gypsum wall board (3/8 in.)	0.32	
7. Acoustical tile (1/2 in.) glued	1.19	3.34
Difference		2.50
Add 4. Wood deck (2 in.)		2.03
Total resistance		4.53
$U = 1/R = 1/4.53 =$		0.22

Type of deck (built-up roof in all cases) Material	R	Conductance of insulation C	Resistance R	None A	Gypsum board None (0.32) B	Gypsum board LW agg 1/2 in. (0.64) C	Gypsum board Sand agg 1/2 in. (0.41) D	Metal lath LW agg 3/4 in. (0.47) E	Metal lath Sand agg 3/4 in. (0.13) F	Insulation board Plain (1.43) or 1/2 in. plaster sand agg (1.52) (1.47) G	Acoustical tile on furring 1/2 in. (1.19) H	Acoustical tile on furring 3/4 in. (1.78) I	Acoustical tile on gypsum board 1/2 in. (1.51) J	Acoustical tile on gypsum board 3/4 in. (2.10) K	Number
Wood[a] 1 in.	0.98	None	—	0.48	0.31	0.28	0.30	0.29	0.33	0.23	0.24	0.21	0.22	0.20	1
		0.72	1.39	0.29	0.22	0.20	0.21	0.21	0.22	0.17	0.18	0.16	0.17	0.16	2
		0.36	2.78	0.21	0.17	0.16	0.16	0.16	0.17	0.14	0.14	0.13	0.14	0.13	3
		0.24	4.17	0.16	0.13	0.13	0.13	0.13	0.14	0.12	0.12	0.11	0.12	0.11	4
		0.19	5.26	0.14	0.12	0.11	0.12	0.12	0.12	0.10	0.11	0.10	0.10	0.10	5
		0.15	6.67	0.11	0.10	0.10	0.10	0.10	0.10	0.09	0.09	0.09	0.09	0.09	6
		0.12	8.33	0.10	0.09	0.08	0.09	0.09	0.09	0.08	0.08	0.08	0.08	0.07	7
Wood[a] 2 in.	2.03	None	—	0.32	0.23	0.22	0.23	0.22	0.24	0.18	0.19	0.17	0.18	0.16	8
		0.72	1.39	0.22	0.18	0.17	0.17	0.17	0.18	0.15	0.15	0.14	0.15	0.13	9
		0.36	2.78	0.17	0.14	0.13	0.14	0.14	0.14	0.12	0.13	0.12	0.12	0.11	10
		0.24	4.17	0.14	0.12	0.11	0.12	0.12	0.12	0.10	0.11	0.10	0.10	0.10	11
		0.19	5.26	0.12	0.10	0.10	0.10	0.10	0.11	0.09	0.10	0.09	0.09	0.09	12
		0.15	6.67	0.10	0.09	0.09	0.09	0.09	0.09	0.08	0.08	0.08	0.08	0.08	13
		0.12	8.33	0.09	0.08	0.08	0.08	0.08	0.08	0.07	0.07	0.07	0.07	0.07	14
Wood[a] 3 in.	3.28	None	—	0.23	0.18	0.17	0.18	0.18	0.19	0.15	0.16	0.14	0.15	0.14	15
		0.72	1.59	0.17	0.14	0.14	0.14	0.14	0.15	0.12	0.13	0.12	0.12	0.11	16
		0.36	2.73	0.14	0.12	0.12	0.12	0.12	0.12	0.11	0.11	0.10	0.10	0.10	17
		0.24	4.17	0.12	0.10	0.10	0.10	0.10	0.10	0.09	0.09	0.09	0.09	0.09	18
		0.19	5.26	0.10	0.09	0.09	0.09	0.09	0.09	0.08	0.09	0.08	0.08	0.08	19
		0.15	6.67	0.09	0.08	0.08	0.08	0.08	0.08	0.07	0.08	0.07	0.07	0.07	20
		0.12	8.33	0.08	0.07	0.07	0.07	0.07	0.07	0.07	0.07	0.07	0.07	0.06	21
Preformed slabs— wood fiber and cement binder 2 in.	3.60	None	—	0.21	0.17	0.16	0.17	0.17	0.18	0.14	0.15	0.14	0.14	0.13	22
3 in.	5.40	None	—	0.15	0.13	0.13	0.13	0.13	0.13	0.11	0.12	0.11	0.11	0.11	23
Flat metal roof deck	0	None	—	0.90	0.44	0.38	0.42	0.41	0.48	0.29	0.32	0.27	0.29	0.25	24
		0.72	1.39	0.40	0.27	0.25	0.27	0.26	0.29	0.21	0.22	0.19	0.21	0.18	25
		0.36	2.78	0.26	0.20	0.19	0.19	0.19	0.21	0.16	0.17	0.15	0.16	0.15	26
		0.24	4.17	0.19	0.16	0.15	0.15	0.15	0.16	0.13	0.14	0.13	0.13	0.12	27
		0.19	5.26	0.16	0.13	0.13	0.13	0.13	0.14	0.12	0.12	0.11	0.11	0.11	28
		0.15	6.67	0.13	0.11	0.11	0.11	0.11	0.11	0.10	0.10	0.10	0.10	0.09	29
		0.12	8.33	0.11	0.09	0.09	0.09	0.09	0.10	0.09	0.09	0.08	0.08	0.08	30

[a] Wood deck 1, 2, and 3 in. is assumed to be 0 in, 1 3/8, and 2 5/8 in. thick, respectively. The thermal conductivity k is assumed to be 0.80.
[b] If a vapor barrier is used beneath roof insulation it will have a negligible effect on the U value.

4-15 INFILTRATION HEAT LOSSES

When cold outside air finds its way into a building in winter, being pushed in by wind velocity, or being pulled in by the chimney effect of a tall building, or both, an equal quantity of inside heated air must find its way out. Outside air cannot invade a building unless inside air can find its way out. We call one action *infiltration* and the other action *exfiltration,* and the two actions must be equal.

The heat that is lost to the exterior when warm indoor air is replaced by cold outside air represents a very substantial percentage of the total loss of a building. It is not at all unusual for infiltration losses to equal 30% of the total loss.

With losses of this magnitude, we must know how these losses occur, how to estimate their amount, and how to minimize them. Through the years, information about infiltration has been sketchy and unconvincing. Even ASHRAE has been hard-pressed to provide dependable methods and facts for closely estimating infiltration losses. Most heating engineers have developed their own methods, and often these methods did not, in fact still do not, agree. Fortunately, substantial factors of safety have been routinely used, and most inequities have been buried thereunder.

Good, dependable information is now becoming available. It is to be hoped that in the next decade, or less, more usable infiltration data will come into widespread use. Factors of safety will then be reduced, and HVAC system designs will benefit.

There are two methods used today to estimate infiltration quantities:

1 The air change method
2 The crack method

4-16 AIR CHANGE METHOD OF ESTIMATING INFILTRATION

In using the *air change method* of estimating the possible rate of OA infiltration into a room, an assumption is made as to the number of times per hour the volume of the room would be changed,

or replaced, by the incoming OA. This assumption would be based on the amount of exposure of the outside walls to the wind.

Suppose that a room has 1000 ft^2 of floor area and the height of the ceiling is 10 ft. The room volume is then 10,000 ft^3. If 20,000 ft^3 of OA leaked into the room in 1 hr, this would amount to two air changes per hour (20,000 ft^3/hr ÷ 10,000 ft^3 = two changes per hour).

Tables are available in the HVAC literature to assist one in selecting an estimated number of air changes per hour to use for a given room. This type of information is intentionally omitted from this text because this author feels that this type of information is so inaccurate that to use it would be ridiculous. We have much better methods of estimating infiltration rates, and there seems to be no reason to use a method that is really no better than blindly picking figures out of the air.

4-17 CRACK METHOD OF ESTIMATING INFILTRATION

In the *crack method* of estimating infiltration, the lineal feet of window and door "crack" in a room is measured, and an infiltration rate per foot of crack is applied. The accuracy of this method can be very high, but it depends, of course, upon accurate knowledge of the size of the crack, or in other words, the looseness or tightness with which the windows and doors fit, and the air pressures indoors and outdoors.

One problem is in knowing how well window and door frames will be fit into their wall openings. The *ASHRAE Handbook of Fundamentals* gives some tabular guidance as to the amount of frame leakage that might be expected. The reader should review this information and give it careful consideration, primarily because it is offered by ASHRAE. The author feels that it is proper to assume that all window and door frames will be well fitted and carefully caulked, so that frame leakage will be negligible. If frames are not well caulked in a given building and difficulty arises, it is always possible to add caulking to remedy the defect. That is, this is a superficial and not an irremediable defect, so that the assumption seems to be quite safe.

Another problem is in determining maximum infiltration into a room with two or three or four exposed walls and with windows and/or doors in each exposed wall. Infiltration is caused by air pressure outside a window or door that is greater than the pressure inside. This condition can be caused by one or two or all of the following:

1 Wind pressure outdoors
2 Negative pressure indoors resulting from the action of exhaust ventilating fans, such as toilet exhaust fans
3 Negative pressure indoors resulting from chimney effect in tall buildings

In item 1, wind pressure may be calculated by the formula

$$p_v = \left(\frac{V}{4005} \right)^2 \tag{4-5}$$

where p_v = pressure, inches of water, gauge (in. WG)
V = air or wind velocity, fpm
or by the formula

$$p_v = \left(\frac{\text{mph}}{45.5} \right)^2 \tag{4-6}$$

where mph is the wind velocity in miles per hour and the air density is 0.075 lb/ft^3.

Figure 4-11 Infiltration through various types of windows in cfh per foot of crack. (All data herein taken from or based on data in the 1977 *ASHRAE Handbook of Fundamentals* with the permission of ASHRAE.)

	Wind velocity, mph		
	15	25	30
Pressure differential, Δp (in. water)[†]	0.11	0.30	0.43
Double-hung wood, locked			
Poorly fitted, not weather stripped	82	150	203
Poorly fitted, weather stripped	30	58	73
Average fit, not weather stripped	29	57	72
Average fit, weather stripped	15	30	38
ANSI-A200.1 specification*		30	
Double hung aluminum ANSI-A134.1*			
specification, types DH-A2, DH-A3 and DH-A4		30	
Aluminum awning, ANSI-A134.1			
specification,* type A-B1		45	
Aluminum casement ANSI-A134.1			
specification, types C-B1 and C-A2*		30	
Aluminum, horizontal sliding, ANSI-A134.1			
specification, types HS-B1 and HS-B2*		45	
Aluminum architectural projected, ANSI-A134.1			
specification, types P-B1 and P-A2*		30	
Aluminum vertical pivoted, ANSI-A134.1			
specification, type VP-A3*		30	
Aluminum inswinging, ANSI-A134.1			
specification, type TH-A3*		30	

Note: see fig. 4-15 for description of window types.

*American National Standards Institute specifications at 1.56 lb/ft^2 wind pressure equivalent to a 25-mph wind.

[†]Difference between total pressure p_t outdoors and static pressure p_s indoors.

Figure 4-12 Door infiltration in cfh per foot of crack with door not in use.

DOOR INFILTRATION*

	Wind Velocity, mph		
	15	25	30
Pressure differential, Δp (inches of water)[†]	0.11	0.30	0.43
Swinging doors			
Well fitted, not weather stripped[§]	82	150	203
Poorly fitted, not weather stripped[§]	164	300	406
Well fitted, weather stripped[§]	41	75	102
1/8 in. average clear crack (no doorstop or astragal)*	830	1371	1641
1/4 in. average clear crack (no doorstop or astragal)*	1660	2742	3283
1/2 in. average clear crack (no doorstop or astragal)*	3320	5484	6566
Revolving doors[‡]	104	171	205

*Assuming 100% conversion of pressure differential to velocity through door cracks and use of formula for infiltration, INF = CW $\sqrt{\Delta p}$ × 20,025,
where CW = crack width, in.
    Δp = pressure differential, in. water
    INF = infiltration rate, cfh per lin ft of crack

[†]Difference between total pressure p_t outdoors and static pressure p_s indoors.

[‡]Assuming average crack width of 1/64 in. and other assumptions as in footnote *.

[§]Based on "Air Leakage through Exterior Doors," 1977 ASHRAE Handbook of Fundamentals, page 21.8.

If wind velocity is 15 mph, its pressure may be calculated by the use of formula (4-6).

$$p_v = \left(\frac{15}{45.5}\right)^2 = 0.11 \text{ in. WG}$$

A pressure of 1.0 psi equals 27.7 in. of water (see art. 1-18), so 0.11 in. WG divided by 27.7 will equal 0.004 psig. This is an exceedingly small pressure, but it is enough to force a significant amount of air through a window or door crack. The tables in figs. 4-11, 4-12, and 4-13 show typical rates of air infiltration through various types of windows and doors.

In determining the maximum rate of air infiltration into a room having windows and/or doors in two or more walls, we must realize that the wind cannot apply pressure to more than two walls at any one time. In fig. 4-14 we see the floor plan of a room with three exposed walls and with three windows in each exposed wall. All windows are the same type and size.

Here we can have wind pressure applied to any outside wall by a broadside wind blowing straight from the north, east, or south. The west wall is protected by the remainder of the building. Or we can have two of the three walls pressurized by a quartering wind blowing from the northeast or the southeast. But there is no way that wind can pressurize all three outside walls simultaneously; the maximum is two walls.

It should be evident also that, although a quartering northeast or southeast wind will pressurize two walls, it cannot pressurize either wall as much as it could blowing broadside, or perpendicular, to a single wall. If the pressure can escape along the walls, it will not build as high as if the wind were blowing broadside.

Figure 4-13 Infiltration resulting from door operations, in cubic feet of outside air per person or per door operation.

	Wind velocity, mph		
	15	25	30
Pressure differential, Δp, in. water*	0.11	0.30	0.43
Swinging doors, 3 ft × 7 ft, with automatic closer having closing time of 8 sec	1860	3070	3680
Swinging doors 3 ft × 7 ft, manual closing time of 4 sec	930	1535	1840
Swinging doors, 3 ft × 7 ft, in vestibule, 10 ft between doors, with automatic closers	700	1150	1380
Revolving doors†	50	50	50

*Difference between total pressure p_t outdoors and static pressure p_s indoors.

†Assuming that each of the door pockets is completely filled with outside air when it is rotated to an outside position, also that only one pocket empties into the interior of the building when one person enters.

No substantial research has been conducted (and results published) to tell us what the ratio of these two pressures (quartering wind pressure and broadside wind pressure) might be. The author has estimated a quartering wind, of a given velocity, as building only approximately 70% as much pressure as a broadside wind. Therefore, only 70% as much infiltration per foot of crack will result when a quartering wind is blowing.

Suppose that in fig. 4-14, each window is 3 ft wide, 5 ft high, and is a well-fitted double-hung metal window. Each window, then, has 19 lineal feet of crack. There are three horizontal cracks of 3 ft length (including the check rail across the center of the window), and two vertical cracks of 5 ft length. So the crack is (3 × 3 ft) + (2 × 5 ft) = 19 ft. A common mistake is to overlook the check rail crack.

A south wind (blowing from the south) will cause full infiltration through all of the cracks in the south windows; 19 ft × 3 = 57 ft of full effect. The same would, of course, be true with an east wind or a north wind. However, a northeast quartering wind could not cause full infiltration through any of the window cracks that it pressurizes. It could pressurize only 70% as much, but it will pressurize six windows, not three. So the

northeast wind infiltration will be equivalent to full infiltration through 70% of 6 windows, or 4.2 windows. Total infiltration, then, is 4.2 × 19 ft crack per window × 30 cubic feet per hour (cfh) per foot (fig. 4-11) = 2394 cfh.

The quartering northeast wind will, in this case, cause more infiltration, by a ratio of 4.2:3, than a north, south, or east wind. With a northeast wind, we would have infiltration through the north and east windows, and exfiltration (outward leakage) through the south windows and through the door into the remainder of the building.

We should pause here for a moment of caution so that the reader will realize the elusive nature of the subject of infiltration. The precision implied in the use of available numbers (such as the 70% above and the tabulated values of figs. 4-11 to 4-13) cannot be sustained by their true accuracy in a real building situation.

The rate of air infiltration through window and door cracks is influenced by so many imponderable variables that the entire procedure, although better than the air change method, is sadly inaccurate. For example, the rate of infiltration into a building will depend greatly on the ability of inside air to escape from the building. In fig. 4-14, we are assuming that some of the air in the room will

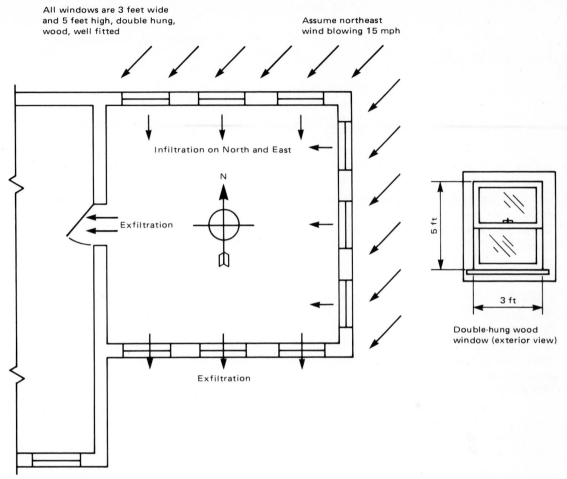

All windows are 3 feet wide and 5 feet high, double hung, wood, well fitted

Assume northeast wind blowing 15 mph

Infiltration on North and East

N

Exfiltration

Exfiltration

5 ft

3 ft

Double-hung wood window (exterior view)

Figure 4-14 Infiltration pattern with a quartering wind.

escape through the door into other parts of the building. However, if the remainder of the building has only limited avenues of escape, this assumption may be false.

Perhaps a building will have many small rooms in it through which air must pass to escape from the building. If the inside doors to these rooms are all standing open, the rooms will offer little resistance to air passage. If they are closed, a great amount of resistance will result. How many doors will be open on a windy day in winter? Who knows? The heating engineer can only guess.

Other factors difficult to evaluate are:

1 Chimney or stack effect in tall buildings
2 Operation or nonoperation of exhaust ventilation fans
3 Pressure created within a building by an HVAC system which charges outside air into the building for ventilation purposes at automatically varied rates
4 The number of times per hour that outside doors will be opened, letting air in or out
5 How well windows and doors and their weather stripping will be maintained.

The reader is also referred to art. 5-8 for further discussion on the subject of infiltration.

4-18 FACTORS OF SAFETY

The only answer to the problem outlined in art. 4-17 is to do the best we can with available data, and then apply a factor of safety (factor of ignorance) to the result. Fortunately, it has been the custom, through the years, to size the heating equipment after adding excess capacity beyond the limits of our heat loss calculations. For example, if a building has a calculated heat loss of 500,000 BH, and is to be heated with a circulating air heating system, we would normally provide a system with 20% excess capacity. The heating system would then have a gross output capacity of 500,000 BH $\times$ 1.2 = 600,000 BH. If the heating system is a steam or hot water heating system, the factor of safety must be greater, perhaps 40% to 50%.

One justification for the magnitude of these safety factors is the need to be able to heat up a cold building in cold weather in a reasonable time. Heating systems are sometimes shut down and buildings do sometimes get cold in cold weather. A major mechanical failure could occur, for example, or thermostats could be set very low during Christmas vacation. In cases such as these, recovery to normal temperatures must be accomplished in a half-day or so. Three days, for example, would not be satisfactory in most cases. Excess capacity is required to permit sufficiently rapid recovery in cold weather.

4-19 INFILTRATION TABLES

In using the infiltration tables provided herein, the designer must first decide what wind velocity should be assumed for the location of the building. He or she must then make a judgment as to what static pressure will usually be found inside the building in peak cold weather conditions.

Selecting a design wind velocity is not difficult; for decades the standard choice has been 15 mph.

However, in recent years an inclination toward higher wind velocities has become somewhat evident. As indicated in art. 4-17, wind pressure may be calculated by use of formula (4-6) as follows:

$$\text{For 15-mph wind:} \, p_v = \left(\frac{15}{45.5}\right)^2$$
$$= 0.109 \text{ in. WG}$$

$$\text{For 20-mph wind:} \, p_v = \left(\frac{20}{45.5}\right)^2$$
$$= 0.193 \text{ in. WG}$$

$$\text{For 25-mph wind:} \, p_v = \left(\frac{25}{45.5}\right)^2$$
$$= 0.302 \text{ in. WG}$$

and so on. So the determination of the design outdoor velocity pressure is quite simple. However, to calculate an infiltration rate, we must know the difference between the total pressure p_t outdoors and the static pressure p_s indoors.

$$p_t - p_s = ?$$

Total pressure is the sum of the static pressure outdoors, which in this case is the atmospheric pressure, and the velocity pressure outdoors, which is merely the wind pressure. Remember formula (1-1) from art. 1-19: $p_t = p_s + p_v$.

Static pressure p_s indoors will often be very close to the atmospheric pressure outdoors: either slightly below it, slightly above it, or equal to it. Knowing what the internal static pressure will be is the difficult part of the problem. As mentioned above, there are so many imponderables that an accurate, logical assessment of indoor static pressure is impossible. One can only review the variables in a general way and then make an intuitive estimate.

Once in a while, we can do better than guess. For example, in a windowless building or a building having fixed, gasketed windows, we may know that we can carry a slight positive pressure inside by charging appreciable quantities of OA into the building by means of an HVAC system. Any leakage of air in this case will be outward—*exfiltration*.

Most buildings having operative windows and frequent door openings cannot carry a positive pressure; and we can make the assumption that indoor static pressure and outdoor atmospheric pressure are equal. We can then select infiltration rates from the infiltration tables based on the design wind velocity. See the tables in figs. 4-11, 4-12, and 4-13 for infiltration rates.

However, in tall buildings we may not assume that indoor static pressure p_s is equal to outdoor atmospheric pressure, because the chimney or stack effect will usually create a negative pressure (below atmospheric) in the bottom half of the building and a positive pressure (above atmospheric) in the upper part of the building. For buildings over five stories in height, the reader is referred to the study of tall buildings in the *1977 ASHRAE Handbook of Fundamentals,* chap. 21.

With lower buildings (five stories or less) the infiltration values in figs. 4-11, 4-12, and 4-13 may usually be used with the assumption that the pressure differential between outdoors and indoors is equal to the velocity pressure of the wind—0.11, 0.30, and 0.43 in. WG for the 15-, 25-, and 30-mph wind velocities, respectively.

In fig. 4-11, the last seven values reflect the performance that the American National Standards Institute expects window manufacturers of the future to achieve. These values should provide a safe basis for design.

Figures 4-12 and 4-13 must be used together in estimating door infiltration. Figure 4-12 gives leakage values for doors when they are closed and not in operation. However, doors are made to be used and fig. 4-13 will give assistance in estimating the amount of outside air that will enter when one person enters or leaves a building. Therefore, values from fig. 4-13 must be added to those in fig. 4-12 to estimate total door infiltration.

Figure 4-13 requires the designer to make an estimate of the number of door openings (operations) that will occur during peak heating load conditions. This, admittedly, is difficult; often the prospective owner or user of a proposed building will have very little information about this. However, the owner's estimate should be more accurate than the HVAC designer's estimate; and the designer would be wise always to consult the owner/user on this problem. Armed with reliable information, and with the assistance of figs. 4-11, 4-12, and 4-13, the designer should be able to make reasonable estimates of window and door infiltration into buildings of modest height.

4-20 HEAT LOSS DUE TO INFILTRATION

When cold outdoor air in winter infiltrates into a building, an equal weight of warm indoor air must exfiltrate to the exterior. This, of course, represents a loss of heat—a loss that must be restored by the building heating system.

If we know the amount of the infiltration, usually expressed in terms of cfh, we can easily convert this into BH using formula (1-2) as follows:

$$BH = \text{lb air/hr} \times \text{specific heat}(t_i - t_o) \quad (1\text{-}2)$$

However,

$$\text{lb air/hr} = \frac{\text{cfh}}{\text{sp. vol.}}$$

Since the specific heat of air is 0.24, and since the specific volume can be standardized at some typical low outdoor temperature such as 15°F, where the specific volume is 12.0 ft³/lb, the expression above may be rewritten as

$$BH = \frac{\text{cfh}}{12.0} \times 0.24(t_i - t_o)$$

which gives

$$BH = \text{cfh} \times 0.02(t_i - t_o) \quad (4\text{-}7)$$

Even though the use of formula (4-7) involves some error, since infiltrating wintertime outdoor

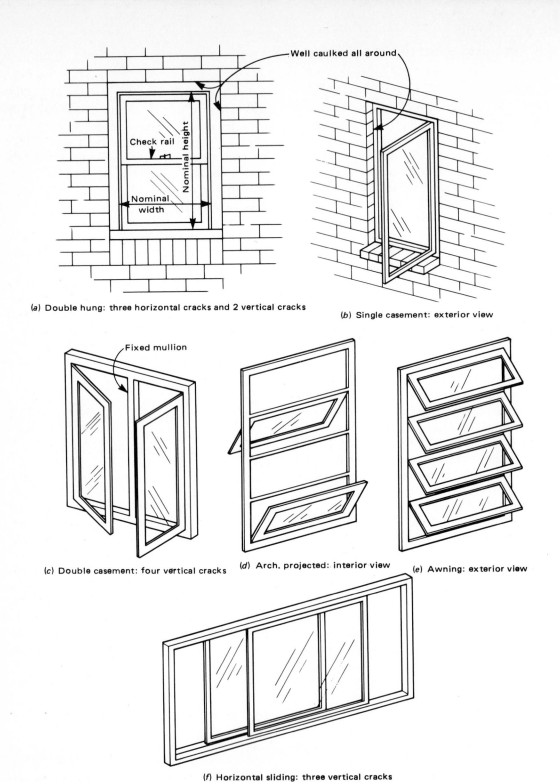

(a) Double hung: three horizontal cracks and 2 vertical cracks

(b) Single casement: exterior view

(c) Double casement: four vertical cracks

(d) Arch. projected: interior view

(e) Awning: exterior view

(f) Horizontal sliding: three vertical cracks

Figure 4-15 Types of windows.

air is not always at 15°F, the error is small compared to the safety factors (see art. 4-18) usually applied, and little damage is done.

4-21 WINDOW TYPES

In order to utilize properly the infiltration data for windows listed in fig. 4-11, an accurate understanding of the physical configuration of each window type is necessary. Figure 4-15 includes sketches of most of the window types listed.

It should be particularly observed by the reader that double-hung windows have three horizontal cracks, not two. Double casement windows, as shown, have four vertical cracks, not three, since almost all windows of this type have a fixed vertical mullion. Four-leaf awning windows, as shown, have five horizontal cracks, and the horizontal sliding window shown has three vertical cracks.

Many windows are made of welded steel construction. If these are of good quality, they should be able to meet the requirements of the ANSI specifications listed in fig. 4-11, so the infiltration rates for aluminum windows may also be applied to good-quality steel windows. Similarly, the values shown in fig. 4-11 for double-hung wood windows should also be suitable for use with good-quality double-hung steel or aluminum windows.

The aluminum vertical pivoted windows listed in fig. 4-11 would usually consist of a single pane of glass in a metal frame which is pivoted at the center point of the top and the bottom of that frame. The aluminum inswinging window listed in fig. 4-11, sometimes called a *hopper* type, is similar to the architectural projected window shown in fig. 4-15, but with only the bottom section operative.

There are many variations and modifications of the window types described herein, but the reader should have little difficulty in evaluating these if he or she will carefully determine the lineal feet of crack around the operating sections of the window, and then submit the window to a comparative quality analysis.

Super-quality windows with very precise, gas-keted construction are available. Tests show infiltration rates as low as 6 cfh per lineal foot of crack for such windows when a 25-mph wind is blowing. Even though these high-quality windows are comparatively expensive, their use can be justified in terms of fuel savings.

4-22 TYPES OF DOORS

In most commercial establishments, retail stores, offices, and so on, the doors that the public use must be easy to operate; doors that are stiff and require great effort to operate discourage their use by the public. This nearly precludes the use of tight-fitting weather-stripped doors. As a result such doors often permit tremendous rates of infiltration.

It is not unusual, even in cold northern climates, to see such doors hung in a frame with an 1/8- or 1/4-in. clear crack on all four sides (see fig. 4-16), without even a doorstop, stop strip, or close-fitting threshold to reduce infiltration. As may be seen in fig. 4-12, such construction may permit infiltration rates up to 3000 cfh per foot of crack; this is intolerable.

The HVAC engineer should certainly point these facts out to the architect before door specifications are written so that the sins of the past will not be repeated. The use of door stops, as detailed in fig. 4-16, will help greatly and does not make doors any more difficult to operate. When these stops are faced with a resilient strip, as shown, great improvement results.

When double doors are required, the use of a meeting stile is also a great help. If a meeting stile is not permissible, an overlapping astragal strip on one of the doors is of great value, although this admittedly makes use of the doors much more awkward.

4-23 STORM WINDOWS AND DOORS

Storm windows and doors have long been considered a practical necessity in the northern half of the United States; and with the present emphasis

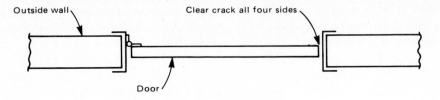

(a) Door with no doorstop, plan view

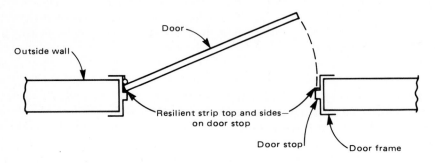

(b) Door with doorstop, plan view

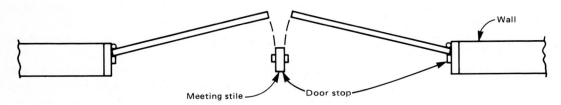

(c) Double door with meeting stile; plan view

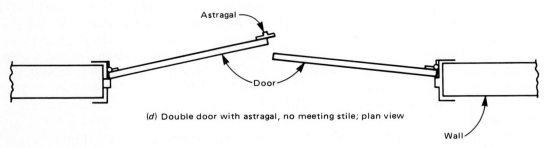

(d) Double door with astragal, no meeting stile; plan view

Figure 4-16 Door details.

on energy conservation, their use in much of the South is becoming commonplace. Both are very effective in reducing building heat loss in winter and heat gain in summer. Storm windows and doors appreciably reduce winter heat loss by transmission, and when applied to poorly fitted windows and doors, substantially reduce infiltration.

Storm sash applied to good-quality, well-fitted windows and doors reduce infiltration by only a small amount, probably no more than an average of 10%. However, when applied to poorly fitting windows and doors, a 50% reduction in infiltration can result. Figure 4-4 includes U coefficients for various types of windows and doors with storm sash applied.

4-24 HEAT LOSS THROUGH FLOORS TO CRAWL SPACES

Many buildings have unheated crawl spaces beneath their bottom floors. These crawl spaces usually vary from 2 ft in the clear, below the floor structure, to 5 or 6 ft in height. They also usually have bare earth exposed floors, exposed foundation walls, and have some means of natural ventilation. The foundation walls surrounding the crawl spaces are usually partially exposed to the weather, and partially protected by the earth outside.

The amount of heat lost through the building floor to the crawl space depends, of course, on the U coefficient of the floor and the temperature of the crawl space. Calculating U for the floor is simple and quickly accomplished, but estimating the crawl space temperature is exceedingly complicated. In fact, it is so complicated, and the floor loss is usually so small in proportion to the loss of the remainder of the building, that most heating engineers simply guess at what the crawl space temperature will be.

If the crawl space ventilation system, such as foundation wall vent openings, is such that wintertime ventilation can be controlled and minimized, the engineer will often assume that the crawl space temperature will be halfway between the indoor and outdoor temperatures, t_i and t_o. In other words,

$$t_c = \frac{t_i + t_o}{2}$$

where t_c is the crawl space temperature. The floor heat loss can then be easily calculated.

The foregoing assumption will usually be quite conservative unless the ratio of exposed foundation wall area to crawl space floor area is unusually high. In this event, an adjustment downward to the crawl space temperature must be made.

4-25 HEAT LOSS THROUGH CONCRETE FLOORS ON EARTH

Concrete floors poured on uninsulated, compacted earth are usually assumed to lose 2 BH/ft^2 of floor area at ordinary room temperature and when the earth temperature is 40 to 50°F. This is true whether the floor is poured as a basement floor well below surrounding earth level, or whether the floor is poured at or very near earth level—or in other words, at grade.

If the slab is poured at or near grade, there will also be a very appreciable loss outward from the edge of the slab, called *edge loss* or *perimeter loss*. The magnitude of the edge loss will depend on the temperature of the slab, the outdoor temperature, and the amount of insulation, if any, at the slab edge. Quite often the slab will have a warm air duct embedded in it, or the slab may be heated with warm water pipes as a radiant panel heating slab.

Figure 4-17 shows typical applications of insulation to the foundation of the outside walls of several types of wall constructions. Two of the four floor slabs at the outside walls are unheated slabs and two are heated, as shown. These details all show insulation extending downward well below outside grade, and one shows the insulation extended inward from the wall under the floor slab.

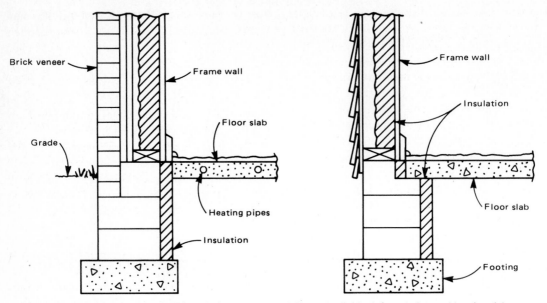

(a) Frame wall, brick veneer, block foundation, floating slab, radiant heating pipes

(b) Frame wall, block foundation and bearing slab

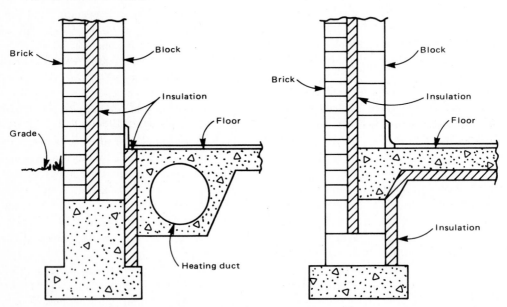

(c) Cavity wall and heating duct in floor slab

(d) Cavity wall and unheated floor

Figure 4-17 Typical applications of perimeters foundation insulation.

Figure 4-18 Heat loss of unheated concrete floor edge at or near grade level (BH per lineal foot of slab edge). (*Reprinted from 1977 ASHRAE Handbook of Fundamentals with the permission of ASHRAE.*)

Outdoor design temperature, °F	Amount of foundation insulation, in.			
	2*	1 1/2	1	None[†]
−20 to −30	50	55	60	75
−10 to −20	45	50	55	65
0 to −10	40	45	50	60

*Recommended.
[†]Not recommended.

Figures 4-18 and 4-19 give values of heat loss from concrete slabs at or near exterior grade; these are expressed in BH per lineal foot of exposed slab edge. The footnote to fig. 4-19 should be especially considered here. This footnote indicates that the values given include not only the edge loss outward from the slab, but also heat loss downward through the entire floor slab of a room. Using these values, one can estimate the entire floor loss (downward loss plus outward edge loss) by multiplying the lineal feet of exposed slab edge by the proper tabulated value.

This principle applies to the values in both figs. 4-18 and 4-19; however, this principle must be applied with great care and wisdom. Some rooms in buildings have a great amount of floor area and

very little exposed perimeter. Other rooms in non-residential buildings may be very wide for their perimeter length. Other rooms may have a large floor area and no exposed edge at all. In all three of these cases errors could result from the application of this pinciple if care is not used.

It is this author's recommendation that it be assumed that a given selected value from fig. 4-18 or 4-19 be considered to represent the heat loss through 1 foot of exposed edge plus 15 ft² of associated floor area. Any floor area in excess of 15 ft² per lineal foot of exposed edge should be estimated at 2 BH per square foot of floor (as set forth previously).

Example 4-3 A certain room has an unheated floor slab poured on compacted earth. The slab edge is insulated with 2 in. of insulation, the outdoor design temperature is 0°F, the outside wall is 50 ft long, and the room width is 30 ft. What is the total floor heat loss in BH?

Solution In fig. 4-18, for 0°F outdoor design temperature and for 2 in. of insulation, we find a value of 40 BH per lineal foot of exposed slab edge. However, this includes an allowance for the heat lost downward through 15 ft² of floor also.

Therefore, 40 BH/ft × 50 ft of exposed edge = 2000 BH heat loss through the floor edge and 750 ft² (50 ft × 15 ft²) of floor. However, the

Figure 4-19 Heat loss of concrete floor edge at or near grade level when warm air perimeter heating ducts are embedded in slabs (BH per lineal foot of slab edge).* (*Reprinted from the 1977 ASHRAE Handbook of Fundamentals with the permission of ASHRAE.*)

Outdoor design temperature, °F	Edge insulation		
	1-in. vertical extending down 18 in. below floor surface	1-in. L-type extending at least 12 in. deep and 12 in. under	2-in. L-type extending at least 12 in. deep and 12 in. under
−20	105	100	85
−10	95	90	75
0	85	80	65
10	75	70	55
20	62	57	45

*Factors include loss downward through inner area of slab.

room floor area is 50 ft × 30 ft = 1500 ft². So the total floor heat loss is

40 BH/ft × 50 ft	2000
Extra floor loss = (1500 ft² – 750 ft²)2 BH/ft²	1500
Total loss	3500 BH

4-26 DESIGN CONDITIONS, WINTER

Before a building heat loss calculation can be begun, a decision must be made as to the indoor and outdoor temperatures to be used. The heat loss from the building will, of course, be directly proportional to the Δt experienced ($\Delta t = t_i - t_o$). The choice of room temperatures (t_i) was discussed

extensively in art. 2-3, to which the reader is referred.

The OA temperature (t_o) to be used for a heat loss calculation of a given building at a given location in the United States and Canada may be chosen from the table in fig. 4-20. From these two values, t_o and t_i, the *maximum temperature difference* may be determined. However, this is not the maximum Δt that the building will experience, nor is the building heat loss calculated, using this Δt, the maximum loss that will be experienced.

For example, in Indianapolis, Indiana, the lowest temperature on record is almost –30°F; while fig. 4-20 shows a 99% wintertime design temperature of –2°F. How can the heating engineer justify

Figure 4-20 Climatic conditions for the United States and Canada. (Reprinted with permission from the 1977 Fundamentals Volume, *ASHRAE Handbook and Products Directory*.)

State and station*	Latitude Deg	Latitude Min	Winter Design dry bulb	Summer Design dry bulb and mean coincident wet bulb	Design wet bulb	Mean daily range	Average winter temperature	Degree days, winter
				(a) United States				
Alabama								
Alexander City	33	0	18	96/77	79	21		
Anniston AP	33	4	18	97/77	79	21		
Auburn	32	4	18	96/77	79	21		
Birmingham AP	33	3	17	96/74	78	21	54.2	2551
Decatur	34	4	11	95/75	78	22		
Dothan AP	31	2	23	94/76	80	20		
Florence AP	34	5	17	97/74	78	22		
Gadsden	34	0	16	96/75	78	22		
Huntsville AP	34	4	11	95/75	78	23	51.3	3070
Mobile AP	30	4	25	95/77	80	18	59.9	1560
Mobile CO	30	4	25	95/77	80	16		
Montgomery AP	32	2	22	96/76	79	21	55.4	2291
Selma-Craig AFB	32	2	22	97/78	81	21		
Talladega	33	3	18	97/77	79	21		
Tuscaloosa AP	33	1	20	98/75	79	22		
Alaska								
Anchorage AP	61	1	–23	71/59	60	15	23.0	10864
Barrow (S)	71	2	–45	57/53	54	12		
Fairbanks AP (S)	64	5	–51	82/62	64	24	6.7	14279
Juneau AP	58	2	–4	74/60	61	15	32.1	9075
Kodiak	57	3	10	69/58	60	10		
Nome AP	64	3	–31	66/57	58	10	13.1	14171

Figure 4-20 *(Cont.)*

State and station*	Latitude Deg	Latitude Min	Winter Design dry bulb	Summer Design dry bulb and mean coincident wet bulb	Design wet bulb	Mean daily range	Average winter temperature	Degree days, winter
				(a) **United States**				
Arizona								
Douglas AP	31	3	27	98/63	70	31		
Flagstaff AP	35	1	–2	84/55	61	31	35.6	7152
Fort Huachuca AP (S)	31	3	24	95/62	69	27		
Kingman AP	35	2	18	103/65	70	30		
Nogales	31	2	28	99/64	71	31		
Phoenix AP (S)	33	3	31	109/71	76	27	58.5	1765
Prescott AP	34	4	4	96/61	66	30		
Tucson AP (S)	32	1	28	104/66	72	26	58.1	1800
Winslow AP	35	0	5	97/61	66	32	43.0	4782
Yuma AP	32	4	36	111/72	79	27	64.2	974
Arkansas								
Blytheville AFB	36	0	10	96/78	81	21		
Camden	33	4	18	98/76	80	21		
El Dorado AP	33	1	18	98/76	80	21		
Fayetteville AP	36	0	7	97/72	77	23		
Fort Smith AP	35	2	12	101/75	80	24	50.3	3292
Hot Springs	34	3	17	101/77	80	22		
Jonesboro	35	5	10	96/78	81	21		
Little Rock AP (S)	34	4	15	99/76	80	22	50.5	3219
Pine Bluff AP	34	1	16	100/78	81	22		
Texarkana AP	33	3	18	98/76	80	21	54.2	2533
California								
Bakersfield AP	35	2	30	104/70	73	32	55.4	2122
Barstow AP	34	5	26	106/68	73	37		
Blythe AP	33	4	30	112/71	75	28		
Burbank AP	34	1	37	95/68	71	25	58.6	1646
Chico	39	5	28	103/69	71	36		
Concord	38	0	24	100/69	71	32		
Covina	34	0	32	98/69	73	31		
Crescent City AP	41	5	31	68/60	62	18		
Downey	34	0	37	93/70	72	22		
El Cajon	32	4	42	83/69	71	30		
El Centro AP (S)	32	5	35	112/74	81	34		
Escondido	33	0	39	89/68	71	30		
Eureka/Arcata AP	41	0	31	68/60	62	11		
Fairfield- Travis AFB	38	2	29	99/68	70	34		
Fresno AP (S)	36	5	28	102/70	72	34	53.3	2611
Hamilton AFB	38	0	30	89/68	72	28		
Laguna Beach	33	3	41	83/68	70	18		
Livermore	37	4	24	100/69	71	24		

Figure 4-20 *(Cont.)*

State and station*	Latitude Deg	Latitude Min	Winter Design dry bulb	Summer Design dry bulb and mean coincident wet bulb	Summer Design wet bulb	Mean daily range	Average winter temperature	Degree days, winter
				(a) United States				
Lompoc,								
Vandenburg AFB	34	4	35	75/61	63	20		
Long Beach AP	33	5	41	83/68	70	22	57.8	1803
Los Angeles AP (S)	34	0	41	83/68	70	15	57.4	2061
Los Angeles CO (S)	34	0	37	93/70	72	20	60.3	1349
Merced-Castle AFB	37	2	29	102/70	72	36		
Modesto	37	4	28	101/69	71	36		
Monterey	36	4	35	75/63	64	20		
Napa	38	2	30	100/69	71	30		
Needles AP	34	5	30	112/71	75	27		
Oakland AP	37	4	34	85/64	66	19	53.5	2870
Oceanside	33	1	41	83/68	70	13		
Ontario	34	0	31	102/70	74	36		
Oxnard	34	1	34	83/66	70	19		
Palmdale AP	34	4	18	103/65	69	35		
Palm Springs	33	5	33	112/71	76	35		
Pasadena	34	1	32	98/69	73	29		
Petaluma	38	1	26	94/68	72	31		
Pomona CO	34	0	28	102/70	74	36		
Redding AP	40	3	29	105/68	71	32		
Redlands	34	0	31	102/70	74	33		
Richmond	38	0	34	85/64	66	17		
Riverside-								
March AFB (S)	33	5	29	100/68	72	37		
Sacramento AP	38	3	30	101/70	72	36	53.9	2502
Salinas AP	36	4	30	74/61	62	24		
San Bernardino,								
Norton AFB	34	1	31	102/70	74	38		
San Diego AP	32	4	42	83/69	71	12	59.5	1458
San Fernando	34	1	37	95/68	71	38		
San Francisco AP	37	4	35	82/64	65	20	53.4	3015
San Francisco CO	37	5	38	74/63	64	14	55.1	3001
San Jose AP	37	2	34	85/66	68	26		
San Luis Obispo	35	2	33	92/69	73	26		
Santa Ana AP	33	4	37	89/69	71	28		
Santa Barbara MAP	34	3	34	81/67	68	24		
Santa Cruz	37	0	35	75/63	64	28		
Santa Maria AP (S)	34	5	31	81/64	65	23	54.3	2967
Santa Monica CO	34	0	41	83/68	70	16		
Santa Paula	34	2	33	90/68	71	36		
Santa Rosa	38	3	27	99/68	70	34		
Stockton AP	37	5	28	100/69	71	37		
Ukiah	39	1	27	99/69	70	40		
Visalia	36	2	28	102/70	72	38		
Yreka	41	4	13	95/65	67	38		
Yuba City	39	1	29	104/68	71	36		

Figure 4-20 *(Cont.)*

| State and station* | Latitude | | Winter | Summer | | | | Average winter temperature | Degree days, winter |
	Deg	Min	Design dry bulb	Design dry bulb and mean coincident wet bulb	Design wet bulb	Mean daily range			

(a) United States

State and station*	Deg	Min	Design dry bulb	Design dry bulb and mean coincident wet bulb	Design wet bulb	Mean daily range	Average winter temperature	Degree days, winter
Colorado								
Alamosa AP	37	3	−11	84/57	62	35	29.7	8529
Boulder	40	0	−6	93/59	64	27		
Colorado Springs AP	38	5	−3	91/58	63	30	37.3	6423
Denver AP	39	5	−5	93/59	64	28	37.6	6283
Durango	37	1	−6	89/59	64	30		
Fort Collins	40	4	−5	93/59	28	64		
Grand Junction AP (S)	39	1	2	96/59	29	64	39.3	5641
Greeley	40	3	−2	96/60	29	65		
La Junta AP	38	0	−3	100/68	31	72		
Leadville	39	2	−18	84/52	30	56		
Pueblo AP	38	2	−7	97/61	31	67	40.4	5462
Sterling	40	4	−7	95/62	30	67		
Trinidad AP	37	2	−2	93/61	32	66		
Connecticut								
Bridgeport AP	41	1	6	86/73	18	75	39.9	5617
Hartford, Brainard Field	41	5	3	91/74	22	77	37.3	6235
New Haven AP	41	2	3	88/75	17	76	39.0	5897
New London	41	2	5	88/73	16	76		
Norwalk	41	1	6	86/73	19	75		
Norwich	41	3	3	89/75	18	76		
Waterbury	41	3	−4	88/73	21	75		
Windsor Locks, Bradley Field (S)	42	0	0	91/74	22	76		
Delaware								
Dover AFB	39	0	11	92/75	18	79		
Wilmington AP	39	4	10	92/74	20	77	42.5	4930
District of Columbia								
Andrews AFB	38	5	10	92/75	18	78		
Washington National AP	38	5	14	93/75	18	78	45.7	4224
Florida								
Belle Glade	26	4	41	92/76	16	79		
Cape Kennedy AP	28	3	35	90/78	15	80		
Daytona Beach AP	29	1	32	92/78	15	80	64.5	879
Fort Lauderdale	26	0	42	92/78	15	80		
Fort Myers AP	26	4	41	93/78	18	80	68.6	442
Fort Pierce	27	3	38	91/78	15	80		
Gainesville AP (S)	29	4	28	95/77	18	80		
Jacksonville AP	30	3	29	96/77	19	79	61.9	1239
Key West AP	24	3	55	90/78	9	80	73.1	108

Figure 4-20 *(Cont.)*

State and station*	Latitude		Winter	Summer				Average winter temperature	Degree days, winter
	Deg	Min	Design dry bulb	Design dry bulb and mean coincident wet bulb	Design wet bulb	Mean daily range			
(a) United States									
Lakeland CO (S)	28	0	39	93/76	17	79		66.7	661
Miami AP (S)	25	5	44	91/77	15	79		71.1	214
Miami Beach CO	25	5	45	90/77	10	79		72.5	141
Ocala	29	1	31	95/77	18	80			
Orlando AP	28	3	35	94/76	17	79		65.7	766
Panama City, Tyndall AFB	30	0	29	92/78	14	81			
Pensacola CO	30	3	25	94/77	14	80			
St. Augustine	29	5	31	92/78	16	80			
St. Petersburg	28	0	36	92/77	16	79			
Sanford	28	5	35	94/76	17	79			
Sarasota	27	2	39	93/77	17	79			
Tallahassee AP (S)	30	2	27	94/77	19	79		60.1	1485
Tampa AP (S)	28	0	36	92/77	17	79		66.4	683
West Palm Beach AP	26	4	41	92/78	16	80		68.4	253
Georgia									
Albany, Turner AFB	31	3	25	97/77	20	80			
Americus	32	0	21	97/77	20	79			
Athens	34	0	18	94/74	21	78			
Atlanta AP (S)	33	4	17	94/74	19	77		51.7	2961
Augusta AP	33	2	20	97/77	19	80		54.5	2397
Brunswick	31	1	29	92/78	18	80			
Columbus, Lawson AFB	32	3	21	95/76	21	79		54.8	2383
Dalton	34	5	17	94/76	22	79			
Dublin	32	3	21	96/77	20	79			
Gainesville	34	2	16	93/74	21	77			
Griffin (S)	33	1	18	93/76	21	78			
La Grange	33	0	19	94/76	21	78			
Macon AP	32	4	21	96/77	22	79		56.2	2136
Marietta, Dobbins AFB	34	0	17	94/74	21	78			
Moultrie	31	1	27	97/77	20	80			
Rome AP	34	2	17	94/76	23	79		49.9	3326
Savannah-Travis AP	32	1	24	96/77	20	80		57.8	1819
Valdosta- Moody AFB	31	0	28	96/77	20	80			
Waycross	31	2	26	96/77	20	80			
Hawaii									
Hilo AP (S)	19	4	61	84/73	15	75		71.9	0
Honolulu AP	21	2	62	87/73	12	76		74.2	0
Kaneohe Bay MCAS	21	2	65	85/75	12	76			
Wahiawa	21	3	58	86/73	14	75			

Figure 4-20 *(Cont.)*

State and station*	Latitude Deg	Latitude Min	Winter Design dry bulb	Summer Design dry bulb and mean coincident wet bulb	Summer Design wet bulb	Mean daily range	Average winter temperature	Degree days, winter
				(a) United States				
Idaho								
Boise AP (S)	43	3	3	96/65	31	68	39.7	5809
Burley	42	3	−3	99/62	35	64		
Coeur d'Alene AP	47	5	−8	89/62	31	64		
Idaho Falls AP	43	3	−11	89/61	38	65		
Lewiston AP	46	2	−1	96/65	32	67	41.0	5542
Moscow	46	4	−7	90/63	32	65		
Mountain								
Home AFB	43	0	6	99/64	36	66		
Pocatello AP	43	0	−8	94/61	35	64	34.8	7033
Twin Falls (AP (S)	42	3	−3	99/62	34	64		
Illinois								
Aurora	41	5	−6	93/76	20	79		
Belleville,								
Scott AFB	38	3	1	94/76	21	79		
Bloomington	40	3	−6	92/75	21	78		
Carbondale	37	5	2	95/77	21	80		
Champaign/Urbana	40	0	−3	95/75	21	78		
Chicago, Midway AP	41	5	−5	94/74	20	77		
Chicago, O'Hare AP	42	0	−8	91/74	20	77	35.9	6639
Chicago CO	41	5	−3	94/75	15	79	38.9	5882
Danville	40	1	−4	93/75	21	78		
Decatur	39	5	−3	94/75	21	78		
Dixon	41	5	−7	93/75	23	78		
Elgin	42	0	−7	91/75	21	78		
Freeport	42	2	−9	91/74	24	77		
Galesburg	41	0	−7	93/75	22	78		
Greenville	39	0	−1	94/76	21	79		
Joliet	41	3	−5	93/75	20	78		
Kankakee	41	1	−4	93/75	21	78		
La Salle/Peru	41	2	−7	93/75	22	78		
Macomb	40	3	−5	95/76	22	79		
Moline AP	41	3	−9	93/75	23	78	36.4	6408
Mt. Vernon	38	2	0	95/76	21	79		
Peoria AP	40	4	−8	91/75	22	78	38.1	6025
Quincy AP	40	0	−2	96/76	22	80		
Rantoul,								
Chanute AFB	40	2	−4	94/75	21	78		
Rockford	42	1	−9	91/74	24	77	34.8	6830
Springfield AP	39	5	−3	94/75	21	79	40.6	5429
Waukegan	42	2	−6	92/76	21	78		
Indiana								
Anderson	40	0	0	95/76	22	79		
Bedford	38	5	0	95/76	22	79		

Figure 4-20 *(Cont.)*

| State and station* | Latitude | | Winter | Summer | | | | |
	Deg	Min	Design dry bulb	Design dry bulb and mean coincident wet bulb	Design wet bulb	Mean daily range	Average winter temperature	Degree days, winter
				(a) United States					
Bloomington	39	1	0	95/76	22	79		
Columbus,								
Bakalar AFB	39	2	3	95/76	22	79		
Crawfordsville	40	0	−2	94/75	22	79		
Evansville AP	38	0	4	95/76	22	79	45.0	4435
Fort Wayne AP	41	0	−4	92/73	24	77	37.3	6205
Goshen AP	41	3	−3	91/73	23	77		
Hobart	41	3	−4	91/73	21	77		
Huntington	40	4	−4	92/73	23	77		
Indianapolis AP (S)	39	4	−2	92/74	22	78	39.6	5699
Jeffersonville	38	2	5	95/74	23	79		
Kokomo	40	3	−4	91/74	22	77		
Lafayette	40	2	−3	94/74	22	78		
La Porte	41	3	−3	93/74	22	78		
Marion	40	3	−4	91/74	23	77		
Muncie	40	1	−3	92/74	22	76		
Peru,								
Bunker Hill AFB	40	4	−6	90/74	22	77		
Richmond AP	39	5	−2	92/74	22	78		
Shelbyville	39	3	−1	93/74	22	78		
South Bend AP	41	4	−3	91/73	22	77	36.6	6439
Terre Haute AP	39	3	−2	95/75	22	79		
Valparaiso	41	2	−3	93/74	22	78		
Vincennes	38	4	1	95/75	22	79		
Iowa								
Ames (S)	42	0	−11	93/75	23	78		
Burlington AP	40	5	−7	94/74	22	78	37.6	6114
Cedar Rapids AP	41	5	−10	91/76	23	78		
Clinton	41	5	−8	92/75	23	78		
Council Bluffs	41	2	−8	94/76	22	78		
Des Moines AP	41	3	−10	94/75	23	78	35.5	6588
Dubuque	42	2	−12	90/74	22	77	32.7	7376
Fort Dodge	42	3	−12	91/74	23	77		
Iowa City	41	4	−11	92/76	22	80		
Keokuk	40	2	−5	95/75	22	79		
Marshalltown	42	0	−12	92/76	23	78		
Mason City AP	43	1	−15	90/74	24	77		
Newton	41	4	−10	94/75	23	78		
Ottumwa AP	41	1	−8	94/75	22	78		
Sioux City AP	42	2	−11	95/74	24	78	34.0	6951
Waterloo	42	3	−15	91/76	23	78	32.6	7320
Kansas								
Atchison	39	3	−2	96/77	23	81		
Chanute AP	34	4	3	100/74	23	78		

Figure 4-20 *(Cont.)*

State and station*	Latitude		Winter	Summer					
				Design dry bulb and mean coincident wet bulb			Mean daily range	Average winter temperature	Degree days, winter
	Deg	Min	Design dry bulb		Design wet bulb				
				(a) United States					
Dodge City AP (S)	37	5	0	100/69		25	74	42.5	4986
El Dorado	37	5	3	101/72		24	77		
Emporia	38	2	1	100/74		25	78		
Garden City AP	38	0	−1	99/69		28	74		
Goodland AP	39	2	−5	99/66		31	71	37.8	6141
Great Bend	38	2	0	101/73		28	78		
Hutchinson AP	38	0	4	102/72		28	77		
Liberal	37	0	2	99/68		28	73		
Manhattan, Fort Riley (S)	39	0	−1	99/75		24	78		
Parsons	37	2	5	100/74		23	79		
Russell AP	38	5	0	101/73		29	78		
Salina	38	5	0	103/74		26	78		
Topeka AP	39	0	0	99/75		24	79	41.7	5182
Wichita AP	37	4	3	101/72		23	77	44.2	4620
Kentucky									
Ashland	38	3	5	94/76		22	78		
Bowling Green AP	37	0	4	94/77		21	79		
Corbin AP	37	0	4	94/73		23	77		
Covington AP	39	0	1	92/73		22	77	41.4	5265
Hopkinsville, Campbell AFB	36	4	4	94/77		21	79		
Lexington AP (S)	38	0	3	93/73		22	77	43.8	4683
Louisville AP	38	1	5	95/74		23	79	44.0	4660
Madisonville	37	2	5	96/76		22	79		
Owensboro	37	5	5	97/76		23	79		
Paducah AP	37	0	7	98/76		20	79		
Louisiana									
Alexandria AP	31	2	23	95/77		20	80	57.5	1921
Baton Rouge AP	30	3	25	95/77		19	80	59.8	1560
Bogalusa	30	5	24	95/77		19	80		
Houma	29	3	31	95/78		15	81		
Lafayette AP	30	1	26	95/78		18	81		
Lake Charles AP (S)	30	1	27	95/77		17	80	60.5	1459
Minden	32	4	20	99/77		20	79		
Monroe AP	32	3	20	99/77		20	79		
Natchitoches	31	5	22	97/77		20	80		
New Orleans AP	30	0	29	93/78		16	81	61.0	1385
Shreveport AP (S)	32	3	20	99/77		20	79	56.2	2184
Maine									
Augusta AP	44	2	−7	88/73		22	74		
Bangor, Dow AFB	44	5	−11	86/70		22	73		
Caribou AP (S)	46	5	−18	84/69		21	71	24.4	9767
Lewiston	44	0	−7	88/73		22	74		

Figure 4-20 *(Cont.)*

State and station*	Latitude Deg	Latitude Min	Winter Design dry bulb	Summer Design dry bulb and mean coincident wet bulb	Summer Design wet bulb	Mean daily range	Average winter temperature	Degree days, winter
				(a) United States				
Millinocket AP	45	4	−13	87/69	22	72		
Portland (S)	43	4	−6	87/72	22	74		
Waterville	44	3	−8	87/72	22	74		
Maryland								
Baltimore AP	39	1	10	94/75	21	78	43.7	4654
Baltimore CO	39	2	14	92/77	17	80	46.2	4111
Cumberland	39	4	6	92/75	22	77		
Frederick AP	39	3	8	94/76	22	78	42.0	5087
Hagerstown	39	4	8	94/75	22	77		
Salisbury (S)	38	2	12	93/75	18	79		
Massachusetts								
Boston AP (S)	42	2	6	91/73	16	75	40.0	5634
Clinton	42	2	−2	90/72	17	75		
Fall River	41	4	5	87/72	18	74		
Framingham	42	2	3	89/72	17	74		
Gloucester	42	3	2	89/73	15	75		
Greenfield	42	3	−7	88/72	23	74		
Lawrence	42	4	−6	90/73	22	76		
Lowell	42	3	−4	91/73	21	76		
New Bedford	41	4	5	85/72	19	74		
Pittsfield AP	42	3	−8	87/71	23	73	32.6	7578
Springfield, Westover AFB	42	1	−5	90/72	19	75		
Taunton	41	5	5	89/73	18	75		
Worcester AP	42	2	0	87/71	18	73	34.7	6969
Michigan								
Adrian	41	5	−1	91/73	23	76		
Alpena AP	45	0	−11	89/70	27	73	29.7	8506
Battle Creek AP	42	2	1	92/74	23	76		
Benton Harbor AP	42	1	1	91/72	20	75		
Detroit (City) AP	42	2	3	91/73	20	76	37.2	6232
Escanaba	45	4	−11	87/70	17	73	29.6	8481
Flint AP	42	0	−4	90/73	25	76	33.1	7377
Grand Rapids AP	42	5	1	91/72	24	75	34.9	6894
Holland	42	5	2	88/72	22	75		
Jackson AP	42	2	1	92/74	23	76		
Kalamazoo	42	1	1	92/74	23	76		
Lansing AP	42	5	−3	90/73	24	75	34.8	6909
Marquette CO	46	3	−12	84/70	18	72	30.2	8393
Mt Pleasant	43	4	0	91/73	24	76		
Muskegon AP	43	1	2	86/72	21	75	36.0	6696
Pontiac	42	4	0	90/73	21	76		
Port Huron	43	0	0	90/73	21	76		

Figure 4-20 *(Cont.)*

| State and station* | Latitude | | Winter | Summer | | | | | |
	Deg	Min	Design dry bulb	Design dry bulb and mean coincident wet bulb	Design wet bulb	Mean daily range	Average winter temperature	Degree days, winter
				(a) United States				
Saginaw AP	43	3	0	91/73	23	76		
Sault								
Ste. Marie AP (S)	46	3	−12	84/70	23	72	27.7	9048
Traverse City AP	44	4	−3	89/72	22	75		
Ypsilanti	42	1	1	92/72	22	75		
Minnesota								
Albert Lea	43	4	−17	90/74	24	77		
Alexandria AP	45	5	−22	91/72	24	76		
Bemidji AP	47	3	−31	88/69	24	73		
Brainerd	46	2	−20	90/73	24	75		
Duluth AP	46	5	−21	85/70	22	72	23.4	10000
Fairbault	44	2	−17	91/74	24	77		
Fergus Falls	46	1	−21	91/72	24	76		
International								
Falls AP	48	3	−29	85/68	26	71		
Mankato	44	1	−17	91/72	24	77		
Minneapolis/								
St Paul AP	44	5	−16	92/75	22	77	28.3	8382
Rochester AP	44	0	−17	90/74	24	77	28.8	8295
St Cloud AP (S)	45	4	−15	91/74	24	76		
Virginia	47	3	−25	85/69	23	71		
Willmar	45	1	−15	91/74	24	76		
Winona	44	1	−14	91/75	24	77		
Mississippi								
Biloxi, Keesler AFB	30	2	28	94/79	16	82		
Clarksdale	34	1	14	96/77	21	80		
Columbus AFB	33	4	15	95/77	22	80		
Greenville AFB	33	3	15	95/77	21	80		
Greenwood	33	3	15	95/77	21	80		
Hattiesburg	31	2	24	96/78	21	81		
Jackson AP	32	2	21	97/76	21	79	55.7	2239
Laurel	31	4	24	96/78	21	81		
McComb AP	31	2	21	96/77	18	80		
Meridian AP	32	2	19	97/77	22	80	55.4	2289
Natchez	31	4	23	96/78	21	81		
Tupelo	34	2	14	96/77	22	80		
Vicksburg CO	32	2	22	97/78	21	81	56.9	2041
Missouri								
Cape Girardeau	37	1	8	98/76	21	79		
Columbia AP (S)	39	0	−1	97/74	22	78	42.3	5046
Farmington AP	37	5	3	96/76	22	78		
Hannibal	39	4	−2	96/76	22	80		
Jefferson City	38	4	2	98/75	23	78		

Figure 4-20 *(Cont.)*

State and station*	Latitude Deg	Latitude Min	Winter Design dry bulb	Summer Design dry bulb and mean coincident wet bulb	Summer Design wet bulb	Mean daily range	Average winter temperature	Degree days, winter
				(a) United States				
Joplin AP	37	1	6	100/73	24	78		
Kansas City AP	39	1	2	99/75	20	78	43.9	4711
Kirksville AP	40	1	−5	96/74	24	78		
Mexico	39	1	−1	97/74	22	78		
Moberly	39	3	−2	97/74	23	78		
Poplar Bluff	36	5	11	98/78	22	81		
Rolla	38	0	3	94/77	22	78		
St Joseph AP	39	5	−3	96/77	23	81	40.3	5484
St Louis AP	38	5	2	97/75	21	78	43.1	4900
St Louis CO	38	4	3	98/75	18	78	44.8	4484
Sedalia, Whiteman AFB	38	4	−1	95/76	22	79		
Sikeston	36	5	9	98/77	21	80		
Springfield AP	37	1	3	96/73	23	78	44.5	4900
Montana								
Billings AP	45	5	−15	94/64	31	67	34.5	7049
Bozeman	45	5	−20	90/61	32	63		
Butte AP	46	0	−24	86/58	35	60		
Cut Bank AP	48	4	−25	88/61	35	64		
Glasgow AP (S)	48	1	−22	92/64	29	68	26.4	8996
Glendive	47	1	−18	95/66	29	69		
Great Falls AP (S)	47	3	−21	91/60	28	64	32.8	7750
Havre	48	3	−18	94/65	33	68	29.8	8182
Helena AP	46	4	−21	91/60	32	64	31.1	8129
Kalispell AP	48	2	−14	91/62	34	65	31.4	8191
Lewiston AP	47	0	−22	90/62	30	65		
Livingston AP	45	4	−20	90/61	32	63		
Miles City AP	46	3	−20	98/66	30	70		
Missoula AP	46	5	−13	92/62	36	65	31.5	8125
Nebraska								
Beatrice	40	2	−5	99/75	24	78		
Chadron AP	42	5	−8	97/66	30	71		
Columbus	41	3	−6	98/74	25	77		
Fremont	41	3	−6	98/75	22	78		
Grand Island AP	41	0	−8	97/72	28	75	36.0	6530
Hastings	40	4	−7	97/72	27	75		5864
Kearney	40	4	−9	96/71	28	74		
Lincoln CO (S)	40	5	−5	99/75	24	78	38.8	5684
McCook	40	1	−6	98/69	28	74		
Norfolk	42	0	−8	97/74	30	78		
North Platte AP (S)	41	1	−8	97/69	28	74	35.5	6684
Omaha AP	41	2	−8	94/76	22	78	35.6	6612
Scottsbluff AP	41	5	−8	95/65	31	70	35.9	6673
Sidney AP	41	1	−8	95/65	31	70		

Figure 4-20 *(Cont.)*

State and station*	Latitude Deg	Latitude Min	Winter Design dry bulb	Summer Design dry bulb and mean coincident wet bulb	Summer Design wet bulb	Summer Mean daily range	Average winter temperature	Degree days, winter
				(a) United States				
Nevada								
Carson City	39	1	4	94/60	42	63		
Elko AP	40	5	−8	94/59	42	63	34.0	7433
Ely AP (S)	39	1	−10	89/57	39	60	33.1	7733
Las Vegas AP (S)	36	1	25	108/66	30	71	53.5	2709
Lovelock AP	40	0	8	98/63	42	66		
Reno AP (S)	39	3	5	95/61	45	64	39.3	6332
Reno CO	39	3	6	96/61	45	64		
Tonopah AP	38	0	5	94/60	40	64		
Winnemucca AP	40	5	−1	96/60	42	64	36.7	6761
New Hampshire								
Berlin	44	3	−14	87/71	22	73		
Claremont	43	2	−9	89/72	24	74		
Concord AP	43	1	−8	90/72	26	74	33.0	7383
Keene	43	0	−12	90/72	24	74		
Laconia	43	3	−10	89/72	25	74		
Manchester, Grenier AFB	43	0	−8	91/72	24	75		
Portsmouth, Pease AFB	43	1	−2	89/73	22	75		
New Jersey								
Atlantic City CO	39	3	10	92/74	18	78		
Long Branch	40	2	10	93/74	18	78		
Newark AP	40	4	10	94/74	20	77	42.8	4589
New Brunswick	40	3	6	92/74	19	77		
Paterson	40	5	6	94/74	21	77		
Phillipsburg	40	4	1	92/73	21	76		
Trenton CO	40	1	11	91/75	19	78	42.4	4980
Vineland	39	3	8	91/75	19	78		
New Mexico								
Alamagordo, Holloman AFB	32	5	14	98/64	30	69		
Albuquerque AP (S)	35	0	12	96/61	27	66	45.0	4348
Artesia	32	5	13	103/67	30	72		
Carlsbad AP	32	2	13	103/67	28	72		
Clovis AP	34	3	8	95/65	28	69		
Farmington AP	36	5	1	95/63	30	67		
Gallup	35	3	0	90/59	32	64		
Grants	35	1	−1	89/59	32	64		
Hobbs AP	32	4	13	101/66	29	71		
Las Cruces	32	2	15	99/64	30	69		
Los Alamos	35	5	5	89/60	32	62		
Raton AP	36	5	−4	91/60	34	65	38.1	6228

Figure 4-20 *(Cont.)*

| State and station* | Latitude | | Winter | Summer | | | | | |
	Deg	Min	Design dry bulb	Design dry bulb and mean coincident wet bulb	Design wet bulb	Mean daily range	Average winter temperature	Degree days, winter
				(a) United States					
Roswell,								
Walker AFB	33	2	13	100/66	33	71	47.5	3793
Santa Fe CO	35	4	6	90/61	28	63		
Silver City AP	32	4	5	95/61	30	66	48.0	3705
Socorro AP	34	0	13	97/62	30	67		
Tucumcari AP	35	1	8	99/66	28	70		
New York								
Albany AP (S)	42	5	−6	91/73	23	75	34.6	6875
Albany CO	42	5	−4	91/73	20	75	37.2	6201
Auburn	43	0	−3	90/73	22	75		
Batavia	43	0	1	90/72	22	75		
Binghamton AP	42	1	−2	86/71	20	73	33.9	7286
Buffalo AP	43	0	2	88/71	21	74	34.5	7062
Cortland	42	4	−5	88/71	23	74		
Dunkirk	42	3	4	88/73	18	75		
Elmira AP	42	1	−4	89/71	24	74		
Geneva (S)	42	5	−3	90/73	22	75		
Glen Falls	42	2	−11	88/72	23	74		
Gloversville	43	1	−8	89/72	23	75		
Hornell	42	2	−4	88/71	24	74		
Ithaca (S)	42	3	−5	88/71	24	74		
Jamestown	42	1	−1	88/70	20	74		
Kingston	42	0	−3	91/73	22	76		
Lockport	43	1	4	89/74	21	76		
Massena AP	45	0	−13	86/70	20	73		
Newburg-								
Stewart AFB	41	3	−1	90/73	21	76		
NYC-Central Park (S)	40	5	11	92/74	17	76	42.8	4871
NYC-Kennedy AP	40	4	12	90/73	16	76	41.4	5219
NYC-LaGuardia AP	40	5	11	92/74	16	76	43.1	4811
Niagara Falls AP	43	1	4	89/74	20	76		
Olean	42	1	−2	87/71	23	74		
Oneonta	42	3	−7	86/71	24	73		
Oswego CO	43	3	1	86/73	20	75		
Plattsburg AFB	44	4	−13	86/70	22	73		
Poughkeepsie	41	4	0	92/74	21	77		
Rochester AP	43	1	1	91/73	22	75	35.4	6748
Rome-Griffiss AFB	43	1	−11	88/71	22	75		
Schenectady (S)	42	5	−4	90/73	22	75	35.4	6650
Suffolk County AFB	40	5	7	86/72	16	76		
Syracuse AP	43	1	−3	90/73	20	75	35.2	6756
Utica	43	1	−12	88/73	22	75		
Watertown	44	0	−11	86/73	20	75		

Figure 4-20 *(Cont.)*

State and station*	Latitude		Winter	Summer				Average winter temperature	Degree days, winter
	Deg	Min	Design dry bulb	Design dry bulb and mean coincident wet bulb	Design wet bulb	Mean daily range			
				(a) United States					
North Carolina									
Asheville AP	35	3	10	89/73	21	75			
Charlotte AP	35	0	18	95/74	20	77		50.4	3191
Durham	36	0	16	94/75	20	78			
Elizabeth City AP	36	2	12	93/78	18	80			
Fayetteville, Pope AFB	35	1	17	95/76	20	79			
Goldsboro, Seymour-Johnson AFB	35	2	18	94/77	18	79			
Greensboro AP (S)	36	1	14	93/74	21	77		47.5	3805
Greenville	35	4	18	93/77	19	79			
Henderson	36	2	12	95/77	20	79			
Hickory	35	4	14	92/73	21	75			
Jacksonville	34	5	20	92/78	18	80			
Lumberton	34	4	18	95/76	20	79			
New Bern AP	35	1	20	92/78	18	80			
Raleigh/Durham AP (S)	35	5	16	94/75	20	78		49.4	3393
Rocky Mount	36	0	18	94/77	19	79			
Wilmington AP	34	2	23	93/79	18	81		54.6	2347
Winston-Salem AP	36	1	16	94/74	20	76		48.4	3595
North Dakota									
Bismarck AP (S)	46	5	-23	95/68	27	73		26.6	8851
Devil's Lake	48	1	-25	91/69	25	73		22.4	9901
Dickinson AP	46	5	-21	94/68	25	71			
Fargo AP	46	5	-22	92/73	25	76		24.8	9226
Grands Forks AP	48	0	-26	91/70	25	74			
Jamestown AP	47	0	-22	94/70	26	74			
Minot AP	48	2	-24	92/68	25	72			
Williston	48	1	-25	91/68	25	72		25.2	9243
Ohio									
Akron-Canton AP	41	0	1	89/72	21	75		38.1	6037
Ashtabula	42	0	4	88/73	18	75			
Athens	39	2	0	95/75	22	78			
Bowling Green	41	3	-2	92/73	23	76			
Cambridge	40	0	1	93/75	23	78			
Chillicothe	39	2	0	95/75	22	78			
Cincinnati CO	39	1	1	92/73	21	77		45.1	4410
Cleveland AP (S)	41	2	1	91/73	22	76		37.2	6351
Columbus AP (S)	40	0	0	92/73	24	77		39.7	5660
Dayton AP	39	5	-1	91/73	20	76		39.8	5622
Defiance	41	2	-1	94/74	24	77			
Findlay AP	41	0	2	92/74	24	77			

Figure 4-20 *(Cont.)*

State and station*	Latitude Deg	Latitude Min	Winter Design dry bulb	Summer Design dry bulb and mean coincident wet bulb	Summer Design wet bulb	Mean daily range	Average winter temperature	Degree days, winter
				(a) United States				
Fremont	41	2	−3	90/73	24	76		
Hamilton	39	2	0	92/73	22	76		
Lancaster	39	4	0	93/74	23	77		
Lima	40	4	−1	94/74	24	77		
Mansfield AP	40	5	0	90/73	22	76	36.9	6403
Marion	40	4	0	93/74	23	77		
Middletown	39	3	0	92/73	22	76		
Newark	40	1	−1	94/73	23	77		
Norwalk	41	1	−3	90/73	22	76		
Portsmouth	38	5	5	95/76	22	78		
Sandusky CO	41	3	1	93/73	21	76	39.1	5796
Springfield	40	0	−1	91/74	21	77		
Steubenville	40	2	1	89/72	22	74		
Toledo AP	41	4	−3	90/73	25	76	36.4	6494
Warren	41	2	0	89/71	23	74		
Wooster	40	5	1	89/72	22	75		
Youngstown AP	41	2	−1	88/71	23	74	36.8	6417
Zanesville AP	40	0	1	93/75	23	78		
Oklahoma								
Ada	34	5	10	100/74	23	77		
Altus AFB	34	4	11	102/73	25	77		
Ardmore	34	2	13	100/74	23	77		
Bartlesville	36	5	6	101/73	23	77		
Chickasha	35	0	10	101/74	24	78		
Enid-Vance AFB	36	2	9	103/74	24	79		
Lawton AP	34	3	12	101/74	24	78		
McAlester	34	5	14	99/74	23	77		
Muskogee AP	35	4	10	101/74	23	79		
Norman	35	1	9	99/74	24	77		
Oklahoma City AP (S)	35	2	9	100/74	23	78	48.3	3725
Ponca City	36	4	5	100/74	24	77		
Seminole	35	2	11	99/74	23	77		
Stillwater (S)	36	1	8	100/74	24	77		
Tulsa AP	36	1	8	101/74	22	<u>79</u>	47.7	3860
Woodward	36	3	6	100/73	26	78		
Oregon								
Albany	44	4	18	92/67	31	69		
Astoria AP (S)	46	1	25	75/65	16	65	45.6	5186
Baker AP	44	5	−1	92/63	30	65		
Bend	44	0	−3	90/62	33	64		
Corvallis (S)	44	3	18	92/67	31	69		
Eugene AP	44	1	17	92/67	31	69	45.6	4726
Grants Pass	42	3	20	99/69	33	71		

Figure 4-20 *(Cont.)*

State and station*	Latitude		Winter Design dry bulb	Summer			Mean daily range	Average winter temperature	Degree days, winter
	Deg	Min		Design dry bulb and mean coincident wet bulb	Design wet bulb				
(a) United States									
Klamath Falls AP	42	1	4	90/61	36		63		
Medford AP (S)	42	2	19	98/68	35		70	43.2	5008
Pendleton AP	45	4	−2	97/65	29		66	42.6	5127
Portland AP	45	4	17	89/68	23		69	45.6	4635
Portland Co	45	3	18	90/68	21		69	47.4	4109
Roseburg AP	43	1	18	93/67	30		69	46.3	4491
Salem AP	45	0	18	92/68	31		69	45.4	4754
The Dalles	45	4	13	93/69	28		70		
Pennsylvania									
Allentown AP	40	4	4	92/73	22		76	38.9	5810
Altoona CO	40	2	0	90/72	23		74		
Butler	40	4	1	90/73	22		75		
Chambersburg	40	0	4	93/75	23		77		
Erie AP	42	1	4	88/73	18		75	36.8	6451
Harrisburg AP	40	1	7	94/75	21		77	41.2	5251
Johnstown	40	2	−3	86/70	23		72		
Lancaster	40	1	4	93/75	22		77		
Meadville	41	4	0	88/71	21		73		
New Castle	41	0	2	91/73	23		75		
Philadelphia AP	39	5	10	93/75	21		77	41.8	5144
Pittsburgh AP	40	3	1	89/72	22		74	38.4	5987
Pittsburgh CO	40	3	3	91/72	19		74	42.2	5053
Reading CO	40	2	9	92/73	19		76	42.4	4945
Scranton/ Wilkes-Barre	41	2	1	90/72	19		74		
State College (S)	40	5	3	90/72	23		74		
Sunbury	40	5	2	92/73	22		75		
Uniontown	39	5	5	91/74	22		76		
Warren	41	5	−2	89/71	24		74		
West Chester	40	0	9	92/75	20		77		
Williamsport AP	41	1	2	92/73	23		75	38.5	5934
York	40	0	8	94/75	22		77		
Rhode Island									
Newport (S)	41	3	5	88/73	16		76		
Providence AP	41	4	5	89/73	19		75	38.8	5954
South Carolina									
Anderson	34	3	19	94/74	21		77		
Charleston AFB (S)	32	5	24	93/78	18		81		
Charleston CO	32	5	25	94/78	13		81	57.9	1794
Columbia AP	34	0	20	97/76	22		79	54.0	2484
Florence AP	34	1	22	94/77	21		80	54.5	2387
Georgetown	33	2	23	92/79	18		81		
Greenville AP	34	5	18	93/74	21		77	51.6	2980

Figure 4-20 *(Cont.)*

State and station*	Latitude Deg	Latitude Min	Winter Design dry bulb	Summer Design dry bulb and mean coincident wet bulb	Summer Design wet bulb	Summer Mean daily range	Average winter temperature	Degree days, winter
				(a) United States				
Greenwood	34	1	18	95/75	21	78		
Orangeburg	33	3	20	97/76	20	79		
Rock Hill	35	0	19	96/75	20	78		
Spartanburg AP	35	0	18	93/74	20	77	51.6	2980
Sumter-Shaw AFB	34	0	22	95/77	21	79		
South Dakota								
Aberdeen AP	45	3	-19	94/73	27	77		
Brookings	44	2	-17	95/73	25	77		
Huron AP	44	3	-18	96/73	28	77	28.8	8223
Mitchel	43	5	-15	96/72	28	76		
Pierre AP	44	2	-15	99/71	29	75		
Rapid City AP (S)	44	0	-11	95/66	28	71	33.4	7345
Sioux Falls AP	43	4	-15	94/73	24	76	30.6	7839
Watertown AP	45	0	-19	94/73	26	76		
Yankton	43	0	-13	94/73	25	77		
Tennessee								
Athens	33	3	13	95/74	22	77		
Bristol-								
Tri City AP	36	3	9	91/72	22	75	46.2	4143
Chattanooga AP	35	0	13	96/75	22	78	50.3	3254
Clarksville	36	4	6	95/76	21	78		
Columbia	35	4	10	97/75	21	78		
Dyersburg	36	0	10	96/78	21	81		
Greenville	35	5	11	92/73	22	76		
Jackson AP	35	4	11	98/76	21	79		
Knoxville AP	35	5	13	94/74	21	77	49.2	3494
Memphis AP	35	0	13	98/77	21	80	50.5	3232
Murfreesboro	35	5	9	97/75	22	78		
Nashville AP (S)	36	1	9	97/75	21	78	48.9	3578
Tullahoma	35	2	8	96/74	22	77		
Texas								
Abilene AP	32	3	15	101/71	22	75	53.9	2624
Alice AP	27	4	31	100/78	20	82		
Amarillo AP	35	1	6	98/67	26	71	47.0	3985
Austin AP	30	2	24	100/74	22	78	59.1	1711
Bay City	29	0	29	96/77	16	80		
Beaumont	30	0	27	95/79	19	81		
Beeville	28	2	30	99/78	18	82		
Big Springs AP (S)	32	2	16	100/69	26	74		
Brownsville AP (S)	25	5	35	94/77	18	80	67.7	600
Brownwood	31	5	18	101/73	22	77		
Bryan AP	30	4	24	98/76	20	79		
Corpus Christi AP	27	5	31	95/78	19	80	64.6	914

Figure 4-20 *(Cont.)*

State and station*	Latitude Deg	Latitude Min	Winter Design dry bulb	Summer Design dry bulb and mean coincident wet bulb	Summer Design wet bulb	Summer Mean daily range	Average winter temperature	Degree days, winter
				(a) United States				
Corsicana	32	0	20	100/75	21	79		
Dallas AP	32	5	18	102/75	20	78	55.3	2363
Del Rio,								
Laughlin AFB	29	2	26	100/73	24	79		
Denton	33	1	17	101/74	22	78		
Eagle Pass	28	5	27	101/73	24	78		
El Paso AP (S)	31	5	20	100/64	27	69	52.9	2700
Fort Worth AP (S)	32	5	17	101/74	22	78	55.1	2405
Galveston AP	29	2	31	90/79	10	81	62.2	1274
Greenville	33	0	17	101/74	21	78		
Harlingen	26	1	35	96/77	19	80		
Houston AP	29	4	27	96/77	18	80	61.0	1396
Houston CO	29	5	28	97/77	18	80	62.0	1278
Huntsville	30	4	22	100/75	20	78		
Killeen-Gray AFB	31	0	20	99/73	22	77		
Lamesa	32	5	13	99/69	26	73		
Laredo AFB	27	3	32	102/73	23	78	66.0	797
Longview	32	2	19	99/76	20	80		
Lubbock AP	33	4	10	98/69	26	73	48.8	3578
Lufkin AP	31	1	25	99/76	20	80		
McAllen	26	1	35	97/77	21	80		
Midland AP (S)	32	0	16	100/69	26	73	53.8	2591
Mineral Wells AP	32	5	17	101/74	22	78		
Palestine CO	31	5	23	100/76	20	79		
Pampa	35	3	7	99/67	26	71		
Pecos	31	2	16	100/69	27	73		
Plainview	34	1	8	98/68	26	72		
Port Arthur AP	30	0	27	95/79	19	81	60.5	1447
San Angelo,								
Goodfellow AFB	31	2	18	101/71	24	75	56.0	2255
San Antonio AP (S)	29	3	25	99/72	19	77	60.1	1546
Sherman Perrin AFB	33	4	15	100/75	22	78		
Snyder	32	4	13	100/70	26	74		
Temple	31	1	22	100/74	22	78		
Tyler AP	32	2	19	99/76	21	80		
Vernon	34	1	13	102/73	24	77		
Victoria AP	28	5	29	98/78	18	82	62.7	1173
Waco AP	31	4	21	101/75	22	78	57.2	2030
Wichita Falls AP	34	0	14	103/73	24	77	53.0	2832
Utah								
Cedar City AP	37	4	-2	93/60	32	65		
Logan	41	4	-3	93/62	33	65		
Moab	38	5	6	100/60	30	65		
Ogden AP	41	1	1	93/63	33	66		

Figure 4-20 *(Cont.)*

State and station*	Latitude		Winter	Summer				Average winter temperature	Degree days, winter
	Deg	Min	Design dry bulb	Design dry bulb and mean coincident wet bulb	Design wet bulb	Mean daily range			
				(a) United States					
Price	39	4	−2	93/60	33	65			
Provo	40	1	1	98/62	32	66			
Richfield	38	5	−2	93/60	34	65			
St George CO	37	1	14	103/65	33	70			
Salt Lake City AP (S)	40	5	3	97/62	32	66		38.4	6052
Vernal AP	40	3	−5	91/61	32	64			
Vermont									
Barre	44	1	16	84/71	23	73			
Burlington AP (S)	44	3	−12	88/72	23	74		29.4	8269
Rutland	43	3	−13	87/72	23	74			
Virginia									
Charlottesville	38	1	14	94/74	23	77			
Danville AP	36	3	14	94/74	21	77			
Fredericksburg	38	2	10	96/76	21	78			
Harrisonburg	38	3	12	93/72	23	75			
Lynchburg AP	37	2	12	93/74	21	77		46.0	4166
Norfolk AP	36	5	20	93/77	18	79		49.2	3421
Petersburg	37	1	14	95/76	20	79			
Richmond AP	37	3	14	95/76	21	79		47.3	3865
Roanoke AP	37	2	12	93/72	23	75		46.1	4150
Staunton	38	2	12	93/72	23	75			
Winchester	39	1	6	93/75	21	77			
Washington									
Aberdeen	47	0	25	80/65	16	65			
Bellingham AP	48	5	10	81/67	19	68			
Bremerton	47	3	21	82/65	20	66			
Ellensburg AP	47	0	2	94/65	34	66			
Everett-Paine AFB	47	5	21	80/65	20	67			
Kennewick	46	0	5	99/68	30	70			
Longview	46	1	19	88/68	30	69			
Moses Lake, Larson AFB	47	1	1	97/66	32	67			
Olympia AP	47	0	16	87/66	32	67		44.2	5236
Port Angeles	48	1	24	72/62	18	64			
Seattle-Boeing Fld	47	3	21	84/68	24	69			
Seattle CO (S)	47	4	22	85/68	19	69		46.9	4424
Seattle- Tacoma AP (S)	47	3	21	84/65	22	66		44.2	5145
Spokane AP (S)	47	4	−6	93/64	28	65		36.5	6655
Tacoma- McChord AFB	47	1	19	86/66	22	68			
Walla Walla AP	46	1	0	97/67	27	69			
Wenatchee	47	2	7	99/67	32	68			
Yakima AP	46	3	−2	96/65	36	68		39.1	5941

Figure 4-20 *(Cont.)*

State and station*	Latitude Deg	Latitude Min	Winter Design dry bulb	Summer Design dry bulb and mean coincident wet bulb	Design wet bulb	Mean daily range	Average winter temperature	Degree days, winter
(a) United States								
West Virginia								
Beckley	37	5	−2	83/71	22	73		
Bluefield AP	37	2	−2	83/71	22	73		
Charleston AP	38	2	7	92/74	20	76	44.8	4476
Clarksburg	39	2	6	92/74	21	76		
Elkins AP	38	5	1	86/72	22	74	40.1	5675
Huntington CO	38	2	5	94/76	22	78		
Martinsburg AP	39	2	6	93/75	21	77		
Morgantown AP	39	4	4	90/74	22	76		
Parkersburg CO	39	2	7	93/75	21	77	43.5	4754
Wheeling	40	1	1	89/72	21	74		
Wisconsin								
Appleton	44	2	−14	89/74	23	76		
Ashland	46	3	−21	85/70	23	72		
Beloit	42	3	−7	92/75	24	78		
Eau Claire AP	44	5	−15	92/75	23	77		
Fond du Lac	43	5	−12	89/74	23	76		
Green Bay AP	44	3	−13	88/74	23	76	30.3	8029
La Crosse AP	43	5	−13	91/75	22	77	31.5	7589
Madison AP (S)	43	1	−11	91/74	22	77	30.9	7863
Manitowoc	44	1	−11	89/74	21	76		
Marinette	45	0	−15	87/73	20	75		
Milwaukee AP	43	0	−8	90/74	21	76	32.6	7635
Racine	42	4	−6	91/75	21	77		
Sheboygan	43	4	−10	89/75	20	77		
Stevens Point	43	0	−15	92/75	23	77		
Waukesha	43	0	−9	90/74	22	76		
Wausau AP	44	6	−16	91/74	23	76		
Wyoming								
Casper AP	42	5	−11	92/58	31	63	33.4	7410
Cheyenne AP	41	1	−9	89/58	30	63	34.2	7381
Cody AP	44	3	−19	89/60	32	64		
Evanston	41	2	−9	86/55	32	59		
Lander AP (S)	42	5	−16	91/61	32	64	31.4	7870
Laramie AP (S)	41	2	−14	84/56	28	61		
Newcastle	43	5	−17	91/64	30	69		
Rawlins	41	5	−12	86/57	40	62		
Rock Springs AP	41	4	−9	86/55	32	59		
Sheridan AP	44	5	−14	94/62	32	66	32.5	7680
Torrington	4	0	−14	94/62	30	66		
(b) Canada								
Alberta								
Calgary AP	51	6	−27	84/63	25	65		9703

Figure 4-20 *(Cont.)*

| State and station* | Latitude | | Winter | Summer | | | | Average winter temperature | Degree days, winter |
	Deg	Min	Design dry bulb	Design dry bulb and mean coincident wet bulb	Design wet bulb	Mean daily range			
				(b) Canada					
Edmonton AP	53	34	−29	85/66	23	68			10268
Grande Prairie AP	55	11	−39	83/64	23	66			
Jasper	52	53	−31	83/64	28	66			
Lethbridge AP (S)	49	38	−27	90/65	28	68			8644
McMurray AP	56	39	−41	86/67	26	69			
Medicine Hat AP	50	1	−29	93/66	28	70			
Red Deer AP	52	11	−31	84/65	25	67			
British Columbia									
Dawson Creek	55	44	−37	82/64	26	66			
Fort Nelson AP (S)	58	50	−43	84/64	23	67			
Kamloops CO	50	43	−21	94/66	29	68			
Nanaimo (S)	49	11	16	83/67	21	68			
New Westminster	49	13	14	84/68	19	69			
Penticton AP	49	28	0	92/68	31	70			
Prince George AP (S)	53	53	−33	84/64	26	66			9755
Prince Rupert CO	54	17	−2	64/59	12	60			7029
Trail	49	8	−5	92/66	33	68			
Vancouver AP (S)	49	11	15	79/67	17	68			5515
Victoria CO	48	25	20	77/64	16	64			5579
Manitoba									
Brandon	49	52	−30	89/72	25	74			
Churchill AP (S)	58	45	−41	81/66	18	67			16728
Dauphin AP	51	6	−31	87/71	23	74			
Flin Flon	54	46	−41	84/68	19	70			
Portage la Prairie AP	49	54	−28	88/73	22	76			
The Pas AP (S)	53	58	−37	85/68	20	71			
Winnipeg AP (S)	49	54	−30	89/73	22	75			10679
New Brunswick									
Campbellton CO	48	0	−18	85/68	21	72			
Chatham AP	47	1	−15	89/69	22	72			
Edmundston CO	47	22	−21	87/70	21	73			
Fredericton AP (S)	45	52	−16	89/71	23	73			8671
Moneton AP (S)	46	7	−12	85/70	23	72			
Saint John AP	45	19	−12	80/67	19	70			
Newfoundland									
Corner Brook	48	58	−5	76/64	17	67			8978
Gander AP	48	57	−5	82/66	19	69			9254
Goose Bay AP (S)	53	19	−27	85/66	19	68			11887
St. John's AP (S)	47	37	3	77/66	18	69			8991
Stephenville AP	48	32	−3	76/65	14	67			
Northwest Territory									
Fort Smith AP (S)	60	1	−49	85/66	24	68			

Figure 4-20 *(Cont.)*

	Latitude		Winter	Summer				
				Design dry bulb and mean coincident wet bulb				
State and station*	Deg	Min	Design dry bulb	Design dry bulb and mean coincident wet bulb	Design wet bulb	Mean daily range	Average winter temperature	Degree days, winter
(b) Canada								
Frobisher AP (S)	63	45	−43	66/53	14	54		
Inuvik (S)	68	18	−56	79/62	21	64		
Resolute AP (S)	74	43	−50	57/48	10	50		
Yellowknife AP	62	28	−49	79/62	16	64		
Nova Scotia								
Amherst	45	49	−11	84/69	21	72		
Halifax AP (S)	44	39	1	79/66	16	69		
Kentville (S)	45	3	−3	85/69	22	72		
New Glasgow	45	37	−9	81/69	20	72		
Sydney AP	46	10	−1	82/69	19	71		8049
Truro CO	45	22	−8	82/70	22	73		
Yarmouth AP	43	50	5	74/65	15	68		7340
Ontario								
Belleville	44	9	−11	86/73	20	75		
Chatham	42	24	0	89/74	19	76		
Cornwall	45	1	−13	89/73	21	75		
Hamilton	43	16	−3	88/73	21	76		
Kapuskasing AP (S)	49	25	−31	86/70	23	72		
Kenora AP	49	48	−32	84/70	19	73		
Kingston	44	16	11	87/73	20	75		
Kitchener	43	26	−6	88/73	23	75		11572
London AP	43	2	−4	87/74	21	76		7349
North Bay AP	46	22	−22	84/68	20	71		
Oshawa	43	54	−6	88/73	20	75		
Ottawa AP (S)	45	19	−17	90/72	21	75		
Owen Sound	44	34	−6	84/71	21	73		
Peterborough	44	17	−13	87/72	21	75		
St. Catharines	43	11	−1	87/73	20	76		
Sarnia	42	58	0	88/73	19	76		
Sault Ste. Marie AP	46	32	−17	85/71	22	73		
Sudbury AP	46	37	−22	86/69	22	72		
Thunder Bay AP	48	22	−27	85/70	24	72		
Timmins AP	48	34	−33	87/69	25	72		
Toronto AP (S)	43	41	−5	90/73	20	75		
Windsor AP	42	16	0	90/74	20	77		
Prince Edward Island								
Charlottetown AP (S)	46	17	−7	80/69	16	71		
Summerside AP	46	26	−8	81/69	16	72		
Quebec								
Bagotville AP	48	20	−28	87/70	21	72		
Chicoutimi	48	25	−26	86/70	20	72		
Drummondville	45	53	−18	88/72	21	75		
Granby	45	23	−19	88/72	21	75		

Figure 4-20 *(Cont.)*

State and station*	Latitude		Winter	Summer					
				Design dry bulb and mean coincident wet bulb					
	Deg	Min	Design dry bulb	Design dry bulb and mean coincident wet bulb	Design wet bulb	Mean daily range	Average winter temperature	Degree days, winter
(b) Canada								
Hull	45	26	–18	90/72	21	75		
Mégantic AP	45	35	–20	86/71	20	74		
Montréal AP (S)	45	28	–16	88/73	17	75		8203
Québec AP	46	48	–19	87/72	20	74		9372
Rimouski	48	27	–16	83/68	18	71		
St. Jean	45	18	–15	88/73	20	75		
St. Jéirome	45	48	–17	88/72	23	75		
Sept. Iles AP (S)	50	13	–26	76/63	17	67		
Shawinigan	46	34	–18	86/72	21	74		
Sherbrooke CO	45	24	–25	86/72	20	74		
Thetford Mines	46	4	–19	87/71	21	74		
Trois Rivières	46	21	–17	88/72	23	74		
Val d'Or AP	48	3	–32	85/70	22	72		
Valleyfield	45	16	–14	89/73	20	75		
Saskatchewan								
Estevan AP	49	4	–30	92/70	26	72		
Moose Jaw AP	50	20	–29	93/69	27	71		
North Battleford AP	52	46	–33	88/67	23	69		
Prince Albert AP	53	13	–42	87/67	25	70		11630
Regina AP	50	26	–33	91/69	26	72		10806
Saskatoon AP (S)	52	10	–35	89/68	26	70		
Swift Current (AP (S)	50	17	–28	93/68	25	70		
Yorkton AP	51	16	–35	87/69	23	72		
Yukon Territory								
Whitehorse AP (S)	60	43	–46	80/59	22	61		

*AP indicates airport readings; CO indicates city office readings.

the use of this –2°F OA design temperature when he or she knows that OA temperatures frequently will fall as low as –10 to –15°F and occasionally much lower? Aren't buildings required to stay warm under these extreme conditions?

Of course, buildings are required to stay reasonably warm, but the American public has fully accepted the fact that under extremely cold conditions (such as –25 to –30°F in Indianapolis)

room temperatures will fall from 70°F to 60°F, or even lower. This, in other words, is reasonable.

It is not economically feasible to design heating systems for the extremes, and the OA design temperature of –2°F for Indianapolis is, in the opinion of ASHRAE (which provided the data), a reasonable basis for design. One saving grace in this situation is that safety factors are universally used.

If a building has a calculated heat loss of 1,000,000 BH, and a circulating warm air type of heating system is to be installed, the designer of that system will probably add a 20% factor of safety and specify a system that will have a gross output capacity of 1,200,000 BH.

In essence, then, that heating system designed to maintain a t_i of 70°F when t_o is -2°F, a Δt of 72°F, could maintain an 86.4°F Δt (72°F × 1.2 = 86.4°F) if a 20% factor of safety is included. This would represent usual practice in HVAC design.

The reader is referred to art. 4-18 for more discussion of factors of safety.

4-27 HEAT LOSS CALCULATION PROBLEM

Example 4-4 In fig. 4-21 is shown the floor plan of a one-story office building. A heat loss calculation has been made for each room in this building, and the totals have been tabulated below. However, the details of the individual room calcu-

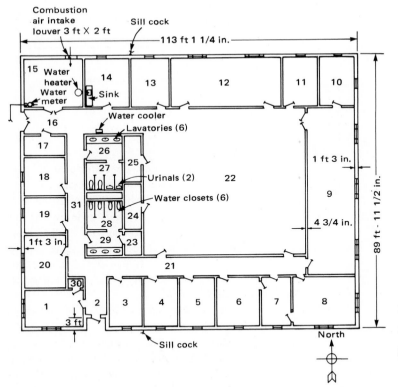

Room schedule and sizes
1. Display room, 20′ × 12′
2. Entry, 7′4″ × 12′
3. Receptionist, 11′4″ × 16′
4. Office, 11′4″ × 16′
5. Office, 11′4″ × 16′
6. Office, 14′8″ × 16′
7. Office, 10′ × 16′
8. Office, 20′8″ × 16′
9. Office, 16′ × 54′8″
10. Office, 12′ × 16′
11. Office, 11′4″ × 16′
12. Accounting, 37′4″ × 16′
13. Office, 12′8″ × 16′
14. Snack room, 15′4″ × 16′
15. Equipment room, 20′ × 16′
16. Rear entry, 40′8″ × 8′
17. Storage, 14′ × 6′8″
18. Office, 14′ × 12′8″
19. Office, 14′ × 12′
20. Office, 14′ × 18′
21. Corridor, 74′ 6″ × 6′
22. General office, 54′8″ × 48′8″
23. Rest room, 6′8″ × 7′4″
24. Storage, 6′8″ × 14′6″
25. Storage, 6′8″ × 14′6″
26. Men's lavatory, 12′ × 8′
27. Men's toilet, 12′ × 9′4″
28. Ladies toilet, 12′ × 9′4″
29. Ladies lavatory, 12′ × 8′
30. Closet, 5′4″ × 3′
31. Corridor, 6′ × 47′4″

Figure 4-21 Floor plan, one-story office building.

lations are shown for only four of the rooms—rooms 8, 12, 16, and 22. The reader should, for purposes of practice and familiarization, calculate the heat loss of the remaining rooms in the building and compare the results for each room with the room totals shown below. The reader's room totals should agree within ±5% of those calculated by the author.

The conditions under which these calculations are to be made are as follows:

Building Location: Indianapolis, Indiana.
Design temperatures: $t_i = 70°F$, $t_o = -2°F$.

Walls: 4-in. face brick veneer; 2-in. cavity filled with insulation ($k = 0.30$); 8-in. sand and gravel aggregate, two-core concrete blocks; 2 in. × 2 in. wood furring strips which create an air space; and interior finish of 3/4-in. lightweight aggregate gypsum plaster on metal lath; see the section below.

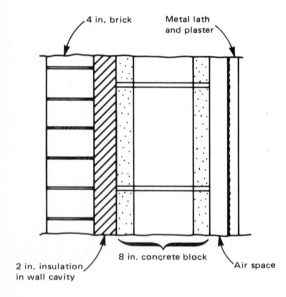

Roof: built-up roof, 1/4-in. high-density (55-lb) hardboard, 6-in. thickness of 6-lb density glass

fiber insulating board, metal roof deck, and 3/4-in. lay-in acoustic 18-lb-density ceiling tile as shown below.

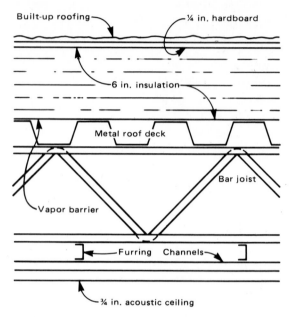

Floor: concrete floor on compacted fill with 2-in. Styrofoam insulation at perimeter.

Windows: double aluminum, well-fitted casement (ANSI-A134.1 spec.) 3 ft wide by 3 ft high with two operating sections and no fixed glass and with overall storm windows; also same type of window 6 ft wide × 3 ft high with 3-ft-wide fixed glass section, two operating sections, and overall storm window.

Doors: 1 3/4-in.-thick solid-core well-fitted unweather stripped swinging doors, one 3 ft × 7 ft single and one 6 ft × 7 ft double with no meeting stile. The double door is opened four times per hour (closes in 8 sec), and the single door opens 20 times per hour and is closed manually in 4 sec.

Wind: 15 mph.

Solution *Wall U_w coefficient calculation:*

Totaling resistances R:

R_o, outdoor film (see fig. 4-4)	0.17
4-in. face brick (fig. 4-4)	0.44
2-in. cavity insulation ($k = 0.3$): $R = \dfrac{x}{k} = \dfrac{2 \text{ in.}}{0.3}$	6.67
8-in. concrete block (fig. 4-4)	1.04
Air space, nonreflective (fig. 4-4)	1.10
Lath and plaster (fig. 4-4)	0.47
R_i, indoor air film (fig. 4-4)	0.68
Total resistance R_T	10.57

$$\text{Wall } U_w = \frac{1}{R_T} = \frac{1}{10.57} = 0.095$$

Roof U_R coefficient calculation:

Totaling resistances R:

R_o, outdoor air film	0.17
Built-up roof (fig. 4-4)	0.33
1/4-in. hardboard, $k = 0.82$ (fig. 4-4): $R = \dfrac{x}{k} = \dfrac{0.25 \text{ in.}}{0.82}$	0.30
6-in. insulation, $k = 0.25$ (fig. 4-4): $R = \dfrac{x}{k} = \dfrac{6 \text{ in.}}{0.25}$	24.00
Metal deck, resistance nil	00.00
Air space, nonreflective (fig. 4-4)	0.90
Ceiling tile (vegetable fiber board, fig. 4-4)	1.89
R_i, indoor air film (fig. 4-4)	0.61
Total resistance R_T	28.20

$$\text{Roof } U_R = \frac{1}{R_T} = \frac{1}{28.20} = 0.035$$

Window glass U_G coefficient: windows are single glass with overall storm sash applied, U_G (fig. 4-4) = 0.50
Remember, heat loss in BH = $A \times U \times \Delta t$ [formula (4-1)]

Heat loss calculation, room 8 (20 ft 8 in. $\times$ 16 ft):

Glass: 2 $\times$ 6 ft $\times$ 3 ft $\times$ 0.5[70 – (–2)]	1296
Wall: [20 ft 8 in. + 16 ft)9 ft – (2 $\times$ 6 ft $\times$ 3 ft)] 0.095 $\times$ 72°F Δt	2011
Roof: (20 ft 8 in. $\times$ 16 ft)0.035 $\times$ 72°F Δt	833
Floor edge: (20 ft 8 in. + 16 ft) 67 (fig. 4-19 and interpolating)	2457
Extra floor: [(20 ft 8 in. $\times$ 16 ft) – (20 ft 8 in. $\times$ 15 ft) – (1 $\times$ 15)]2 (see art. 4-25)	11
Infiltration [(formula (4-7)] : two windows at 18 ft crack/window $\times$ 30 cfh/ft (fig 4-11) $\times$ 0.02 $\times$ 72°F $\Delta t \times$ 0.70 (art. 4-17) $\times$ 0.9 (storm sash)	980
Heat loss room 8	7588 BH

In the foregoing heat loss for room 8, a quartering southeast wind would cause infiltration through both windows, 36 ft crack (18 ft crack for each window); however, the infiltration rate for a quartering wind is only 70% as much as for a broadside wind; hence the 0.7 factor in the infiltration calculation above.

The window crack length is computed as shown here:

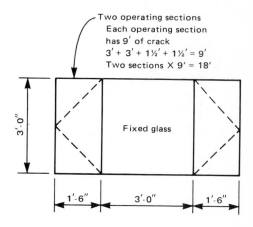

A south wind would cause infiltration through only one window, or 18 ft crack: one window $\times$ 18 ft $\times$ 30 $\times$ 0.02 $\times$ 72°F $\times$ 0.9 = 700 BH.

Here the 0.02 factor is the constant in formula (4-7); and the 0.9 factor accounts for the 10%

reduction in infiltration resulting from the use of storm windows covering well-fitted windows.

For an explanation of the "extra floor" loss, see example 4-3 in art. 4-25.

Heat loss calculation room 12:

Glass: 2 × 6 ft × 3 ft × 0.5 × 72°F Δt	1296
Wall: [(37 ft 4 in. × 9 ft) – (2 × 6 ft × 3 ft)]0.095 × 72°F	2052
Roof: (37 ft 4 in. × 16 ft)0.035 × 72°F	1505
Floor edge: 37 ft 4 in. × 67	2501
Extra floor: 37 ft 4 in.(16 ft – 15 ft)2 BH/ft² floor	75
Infiltration: 2 × 18 ft × 30 × 0.02 × 72°F Δt × 0.9	1400
	8829 BH

In room 12, the 0.7 multiplier was not used, since a broadside wind from the north represents our worst condition.

Heat loss calculation, room 16:

Door: 6 ft wide × 7 ft high × 0.46 × 72°F Δt	1,391
Wall: [(8 ft × 9 ft) – (6 ft × 7 ft)] 0.095 × 72°F	205
Roof: (40 ft 8 in. × 8 ft)0.035 × 72°F	820
Floor edge: 8 ft × 67	536
Extra floor: [(40 ft 8 in. × 8 ft) – (8 ft × 15 ft)]2	411
Infiltration: 33 ft crack × 82 (fig. 4-12) × 0.02 × 72°F	3,897
Infiltration (door openings): two doors × four openings per hour × 1860 (fig. 4-13) × 0.02 × 72°F	21,427
	28,687 BH

Heat loss calculation, room 22:

Roof: (54 ft 8 in. × 48 ft 8 in.) 0.035 × 72°	6,705
Floor: (54 ft 8 in. × 48 ft 8 in.)2	5,322
Total heat loss	12,027 BH

The individual room heat losses have been calculated by the author, but only those for rooms 8,

12, 16, and 22 are shown here. The heat losses for all other rooms should be calculated by the reader and the room totals compared with the room totals tabulated below.

Room	BH	Room	BH
1	6,933	18	3,038
2	28,185	19	2,928
3	3,285	20	4,174
4	2,899	21	2,020
5	2,899	22	12,027
6	3,469	23	221
7	2,671	24	437
8	7,639	25	437
9	13,016	26	434
10	5,589	27	506
11	2,899	28	506
12	8,829	29	434
13	3,127	30	72
14	3,583	31	1,284
15	5,442		
16	28,687	Total	158,763 BH
17	1,093		

The author hastens to point out that the total heat loss of 158,763 BH calculated above is not the proper total heat loss of this building. It is considerably too high! Each individual room heat loss has been calculated including infiltration under the worst, or maximum, wind condition for that room. This involves winds blowing from almost all directions, but the wind can blow from only one direction at a time, so an error has been made.

For example, room 12 has been calculated for a broadside wind perpendicular to the north wall—a north wind, the worst wind for room 12. However, room 8 has been calculated for a quartering wind from the southeast—the worst wind for room 8. However, the wind cannot blow from the north and the southeast simultaneously, so we have an error. The heat loss for each room is correct, but the total heat loss of all rooms is not correct. To calculate the correct total loss for this building, we must make a *block load calculation.*

4-28 BLOCK LOAD CALCULATION

A block load calculation may be made for winter heat loss or summer heat gain. What we need here is a *heating block load calculation.* Many heating engineers will omit the block load calculation and use the erroneously high total (similar to the one totaled above). They then add a factor of safety which is perhaps somewhat less than they would otherwise use to derive a total heat loss to be used for equipment sizing.

This procedure obviously involves appreciable error, but the error is on the side of safety and conservatism. However, it is better to follow the more accurate procedure and make a block load calculation. To do this we must find the one wind condition that gives the greatest amount of infiltration for the entire building as a unit—or as a block.

Often a superficial examination will tell, almost at a glance, which wind will give the greatest infiltration into the building; sometimes a fairly extensive study will be required to determine this. In our building it is easy to see that rooms 2 and 16, the rooms with outside doors, have much greater heat losses than any other rooms. It is also easy to see that most of the heat loss of these rooms is caused by infiltration. So one can tell very quickly that the worst wind condition will be a south wind, a west wind, or a southwest wind. A simple study will tell which of these is worst.

South wind infiltration will be:

1 Seven windows in south wall × 18 ft crack per window × 30 cfh/ft (fig. 4-11) = 3780 cfh
2 South door (room 2) has 20 ft crack × 82 cfh/ft (fig. 4-12) = 1640 cfh
3 South door operations 20 times per hour × 930 cfh per operation (fig. 4-13) = 18,600 cfh
4 Total south wind infiltration = 3780 cfh + 1640 cfh + 18,600 cfh = 24,020 cfh

West wind infiltration will be:

1 Four windows × 18 ft × 30 cfh ft = 2160 cfh

2 West door (room 16) 33 ft crack × 82 cfh/ft (fig. 4-12) = 2706 cfh
3 West door operations four times per hour × 1860 cfh per operation (fig. 4-13) = 7440 cfh
4 Total west wind infiltration = 2160 cfh + 2706 cfh + 7440 cfh = 12,306 cfh

Southwest wind infiltration will be:

70% of the sum of the south and the west winds = (24,020 cfh + 12,306 cfh)0.7 = 25,428 cfh

Therefore, the southwest wind gives the most infiltration, 25,428 cfh.

The question that must now be raised is whether 25,428 cfh can exfiltrate or escape from the building; if not, that much air cannot infiltrate. At first glance it would seem that with air entering through 11 windows and two doors (in the south and west walls), not that much could escape through the 11 windows in the north and west walls. However, it must be remembered now that our building has two toilet rooms, 27 and 28. These two rooms must have ventilation, and will probably get this at the rate of 3 cfm/ft^2 of floor. (Ventilation is discussed in a later chapter.) Each room has 112 ft^2 of floor and total exhaust will then be:

2 × 112 ft^2 × 3 = 672 cfm, and 672
cfm × 60 = 40,320 cfh

40,320 cfh × 0.02 × 72°F = 58,061
BH loss due to infiltration

This amount will then be greater than the normal infiltration rate, and will be the controlling factor. Of course, this will not always be true in all buildings, and comparative calculations must always be made.

Therefore, in the case of the building in this example, we must find the total heat loss without any infiltration and then add infiltration at the rate of 58,061 BH, as noted above.

In the author's calculations, the building heat loss exclusive of infiltration is 99,090 BH (not shown herein). Total building heat loss, including the infiltration rate due to toilet ventilation, is then 99,090 BH + 58,061 BH = 157,151 BH.

If the toilet exhaust fans were turned off, the infiltration rate would then be reduced to the 25,428 cfh value shown above calculated for the southwest wind; and the total building loss would be 99,090 BH (as above) + (25,428 × 0.02 × 72°F) = 135,706 BH.

Since the exhaust fans certainly will often run when the design winter conditions prevail (t_i = 70°F and t_o = 2°F), we must use the greater heat loss above (157,151 BH) as a basis for designing the heating system.

Suppose that our building is to be heated with a circulating air system having a furnace or other type of heating unit located in equipment room 15. This heating unit should have approximately 20% spare capacity. Its gross heat output capacity would then be 157,151 BH × 1.2 = 188,581 BH.

If we decided to supply heated air into the building at a temperature of 110°F, a reasonable choice, the total heated air quantity that the heating system must be able to supply may be calculated with the use of formula (1-5), BHS = cfm × 1.08 × Δt.

Solving for CFM, we may rewrite formula (1-5) as

$$\text{cfm} = \frac{\text{BHS}}{1.08 \times \Delta t} = \frac{188,581}{1.08(110°F - 70°F)} = 4365$$

Therefore, we need for our building a warm air heating system capable of supplying heat at the rate of 188,581 BH, and circulating air at the rate of 4365 cfm.

This total circulating air quantity must now be divided up and apportioned to each room in accordance with its percentage of the total heat loss. In the room-by-room heat loss tabulation above, room 1 has a loss of 6933 BH; this is 4.37% of the total of that tabulation, 158,763 BH. Therefore, room 1 should receive 4.37% of the total air quantity, or 4365 cfm × 0.0437 = 919 cfm.

By this method, all of the room supply air

quantities may be determined. These air quantities are tabulated below.

Room	cfm	Room	cfm
1	191	17	30
2	775	18	83
3	90	19	80
4	80	20	115
5	80	21	55
6	95	22	330
7	73	23	6
8	210	24	12
9	358	25	12
10	154	26	12
11	80	27	14
12	243	28	14
13	86	29	12
14	100	30	–
15	150	31	35
16	790		

The HVAC designer may now proceed to select suitable heating equipment, design a ductwork air distribution system, and finalize the heating system design. These subjects are discussed in other chapters.

4-29 VENTILATION HEAT LOSSES

Most nonresidential buildings have a considerable need for ventilation with fresh outdoor air. This need is usually met in one or both of two ways:

1 By supplying outdoor air into the building by and through the HVAC systems that heat and cool a building

2 By operating exhaust fans of various types that pull air from a building and discharge it to the outdoors

Both methods place a heavy load on the heating system in winter and represent an appreciable heat loss. Therefore, the use of outdoor air for ventilation should be carefully and continuously monitored to ascertain that, at all times, minimum amounts of outside air are utilized.

Subsequent chapters deal extensively with the

subject of ventilation so that outside air requirements may be intelligently established. At the moment, we are concerned with the amount of load that may be placed on a heating system as those requirements are met.

It should be realized that the air that is exhausted from a building by the exhaust ventilating systems may be partially or fully replaced by air that has infiltrated into the building and would have done so even if the exhaust fans were not operating.

To the extent that this is so, the exhaust ventilation system does not increase the load on the building heating system. A study must, of course, be made of each building with anticipated infiltration quantities balanced off against exhaust air quantities to determine the extent to which heating system loads are increased.

When there is an increase, or an excess of exhaust quantities over expected infiltration quantities exists, the heat load attendant thereto may be calculated with the use of formula (1-6); BH = cfm $\times$ 1.08 $\times$ Δt (see art. 1-26).

This formula is suitable for use here since exhaust air quantities are based on usual room temperatures, not outside air temperatures; formula (1-6) and its constant 1.08 are also based on ordinary room temperatures.

It must also be realized that when infiltration is induced by the stack or chimney effect in a tall building, the offsetting effect mentioned above would probably not take place. In this case, exhaust ventilation action would add materially to the heat load of the heating system.

PROBLEMS

4-1 The insulating concrete roof deck on a building has a conductivity k of 5.5 and is 2.5 in. thick. Find the resistance R of this roof deck.

4-2 The conductance C of a certain masonry block in a wall is 0.60. Find the resistance R of this block.

4-3 Find the U coefficient of the wall in fig. 4-1 and example 4-2 if the brick veneer is made

of 4-in. face brick, if the sheathing is made of 1/2-in. Douglas fir plywood, and if the interior finish of the wall is 5/8-in. of lightweight aggregate gypsum plaster.

4-4 If the wall in prob. 4-3 has a U coefficient of 0.22, what would be the heat loss through 700 ft^2 of this wall in BH if outdoor temperature is 15°F and the indoor temperature is 66°F?

4-5 The uninsulated flat roof on a building has an overall U coefficient of 0.25. What would be the U coefficient of this roof if 4 in. of insulation having a conductivity k of 0.20 is added? Find the resistance R of the uninsulated roof, the resistance of the insulation that is added, and the resistance of the roof after the insulation is added.

4-6 Find the conductance and the resistance of a 4-in. cinder aggregate, three-core concrete block.

4-7 Find the wintertime U coefficient of window glass which consists of three 1/8-in.-thick panes with 1/4-in. air spaces. How much heat would be lost per hour through 300 ft^2 of this glass when $\Delta t = 80$°F?

4-8 Find the U coefficient of a 1 3/4-in.-thick solid wood door with a metal storm door.

4-9 A building located at 40° north latitude has 5000 ft^2 of basement floor, and 7000 ft^2 of basement wall, all below grade. There is no other heat loss from this basement. Find its total heat loss in BH.

4-10 The roof and ceiling of a single-story building has an R_T of 15. When OA = 5°F and RA = 67°F, what is the temperature of the ceiling surface? The ceiling surface is nonreflective. What would be the ceiling surface temperature if the roof were insulated until $R_T = 25$?

4-11 If the room drawn in fig. 4-14 has 4-ft-wide by 6-ft-high double aluminum casement windows (see fig. 4-15) instead of the type shown, what would be the approximate "maximum" infiltration rate in cfh when a 25-mph wind is blowing? What would be the approximate infiltration rate when an east wind is blowing at 25 mph?

4-12 Calculate the heat loss due to infiltration in BH, for the two conditions listed in prob. 4-11, if Δt is 55°F.

Chapter 5

Heat Gains into Buildings

5-1 GENERALITIES

Not too many years ago, in the 1930s for example, few buildings were cooled in the summer; building owners did not consider summer cooling necessary. Through all the millennia of human existence it had been so. Certainly, buildings had, for centuries, been adequately heated; that was a necessity. But summer cooling? No!

A few buildings had been artificially cooled by one means or another before the 1930s. The New York Stock Exchange building was cooled with ice water starting in about the year 1905. However, it was not until the period following World War II that summer cooling became commonplace.

For any kind of commercial establishment that catered directly to the public—theaters, restaurants, department stores, and so on—summer cooling became mandatory; no longer was it a matter of choice.

Now, of course, summer cooling is no longer a luxury, afforded only by the very rich and by commercial and industrial establishments. To most of the middle and upper classes in the United States, summer cooling is a "necessity," without which life in summer would seem to be unbearable. Most of us hurry from mechanically cooled homes to mechanically cooled autos to mechanically cooled schools and places of business.

Since summer cooling is an everyday fact of life, it is exceedingly important for all of us in the construction industry to learn all that we can about summer cooling practices—how it should be accomplished, the scientific principles involved, how we can avoid the mistakes of the past, how we can make cooling systems less wasteful of energy, and how we can design buildings to conserve energy and accommodate themselves most gracefully and efficiently to our needs for summer cooling.

To perform the latter task effectively, we must first learn how buildings gain heat in warm weather. Only then can we do a good job of planning and constructing comfortable, energy-conservative buildings.

So first we must know how to make a heat gain (cooling load) calculation.

5-2   HEAT GAINS VERSUS HEAT LOSSES

In chap. 4 we studied the subject of heat losses from buildings in cold weather. Much that we learned there is applicable to a study of heat gains. Heat *loss U* coefficients, conductivities *k*, and conductances *C* are usable for summertime heat gains with very little or no revision. However, there are many differences that greatly outnumber the similarities.

Heat gain calculations are much more complicated and difficult than heat loss calculations. In winter, the sun, building lights, appliances, people, and all things that emit heat in or around a building help materially to heat that building. They minimize fuel consumption, and are, in general, all beneficial.

In summer, all this is changed. The sun and all these other sources of heat are now working against us, and since they are, we must now be able to measure accurately their quantities, intensity, timing, and controllability.

5-3   BUILDING EVALUATION

If a building or a space in a building is to be cooled properly in summer, many design steps and procedures must be carefully and properly undertaken. A heat gain calculation, estimating the magnitude of the cooling load, must be made as one of the first steps in the procedure. However, even before this is begun, a careful evaluation of the subject building must be made.

With the shortage of energy that exists today, and considering the extremely high cost of this energy, no cooling load estimate should be made until a building has been subjected to the closest scrutiny. This scrutiny should, of course, determine how "energy wasteful" or "energy conservative" the planned building will be. There is no excuse for permitting an energy-wasteful building to come into existence.

A partial list of the steps that should be taken in evaluating a planned building follows.

Insulation

As mentioned earlier, the days are gone when an architect or engineer can design a building with no insulation or minimum insulation. A well-proven statement advises that "insulation does not cost—it pays." Often the cost of extra insulation in a building will be fully offset by a reduction in the initial cost of the HVAC system. Additionally, then, the operating cost savings resulting from energy savings accrue as net profit for the life of the building.

We should have as our goal building walls with a *U* coefficient of 0.05 or better, and roofs (or ceiling-roof combinations) with a *U* coefficient of 0.03 or better. This is a realizable goal. Before making load calculations the HVAC engineer should suggest to the architect ways in which this practical goal can be achieved.

Fenestration

It is probably outside the province of the HVAC engineer to discuss with the architect the question of how much window area a building should have. However, it is certainly within the engineer's province to point out the magnitude of the effect that large window areas have. Many architects are not familiar with the amount of solar transmission (direct sunshine) that a large window permits, nor are they able, usually, to translate solar transmission into HVAC system initial cost or operating cost.

The types of windows—double glass versus single glass, heat absorbing glass versus clear glass, and so on—must also be evaluated in the light of their effect on HVAC system costs. The HVAC engineer must also be fully armed with data concerning the effect of such sun screening devices as:

1 Venetian blinds of various colors
2 Sunshade screening material for windows (consisting of very thin metal strips set at an angle which serve both as an insect screen and a sun screen)
3 Reflective draperies
4 Transparent metallic films applied to window glass surfaces, which reject most of the sun's rays
5 Outside shading devices such as awnings, vertical fins on the building beside the windows, and building overhanging features

ASHRAE 90-75

This guideline specification drafted by ASHRAE gives overall performance data showing what a properly designed building can do in the matter of energy conservation; building designs *must* in the future provide construction that equals or exceeds these specifications. The HVAC engineer must be able to guide the architect through the intricacies of these specifications; this should be done before building designs are finalized and before the heat gain calculation is begun.

External Shade

The HVAC designer must carefully survey the proposed building site to determine the extent to which surrounding buildings, trees, and other fixed structure will cast shade on the proposed building. A note of caution should be advanced here, however. Some trees and many buildings may not always be there to protect the new building from the sun. Trees do fall or are removed intentionally. Also, many older buildings cannot compete economically, so they make way for parking lots; and parking lots cast very little shade. Therefore, the proposed owner of any new building should be brought into the decision as to whether credit should be allowed for present shading features.

Type of HVAC System

Before starting a heat gain calculation, the HVAC designer must have in mind a clear and complete picture of what the HVAC system design will be. A centrally located HVAC unit will have air distribution ductwork that carries conditioned air to the various areas of the building. Some of these ducts may be installed in very hot spaces (such as unventilated attics or furred spaces) or in very cold spaces. In a very hot space, a cool air duct will pick up large quantities of heat; this must be recognized in the heat gain calculation.

Lighting

Since in some buildings, such as office buildings, the heat from the lighting system may constitute the largest segment of the cooling load, careful attention must be paid to the selection and design of the building lighting system. To the extent possible, the more efficient sources of light should be utilized. It is recognized that very often the more efficient sources of light cannot be appropriately applied in a given building situation; however, very often the possibility of utilizing high-efficiency lamps is not thoroughly considered.

Figure 5-1 shows comparative electrical efficiencies of various lamps in common use today. Notice the tremendous variation or range of efficiencies that exist.

Usually, when the preliminary evaluation of a building is being made, or even later when the heat gain calculation is being made, the lighting layout

Figure 5-1 Comparative light source efficiencies.

Type of lamp	Light output, lumens/watt*
Incandescent	12–20
Tungsten halogen	12–16
Fluorescent	72–88
Mercury vapor	30–60
Metal halide	60–90
Sodium vapor	100–105

*Based on initial lumens output.

and design has not been begun. In order to have some basis on which to estimate roughly the magnitude of the heat load from the lighting system, the following factors may be utilized:

With fluorescent lights:

$$BH/ft^2 \text{ of floor} = \frac{fc}{6.8}$$

where fc = footcandles of light required.

With incandescent lights:

$$BH/ft^2 \text{ of floor} = \frac{fc}{1.6}$$

The factors 6.8 and 1.6 shown above are constants based on a coefficient of utilization (CU) of light of 0.4 and a maintenance factor (MF) of 0.75. They are rough approximations only and must not be used for final design purposes.

Example 5-1 A given room has 500 ft^2 of floor and is to be illuminated to a maintained lighting level of 60 footcandles. Find the heat load on the building cooling system that would result from the use of either a fluorescent or an incandescent lighting system.

Solution With fluorescent lights, the heat load would equal 60 fc ÷ 6.8 (as shown above) = 8.82

BH/ft^2 of floor. The heat load from fluorescent lights is 8.82 × 500 ft^2 of floor = 4410 BH.

With incandescent lights, the heat load would equal 60 fc ÷ 1.6 (as shown above) = 37.5 BH/ft^2 of floor. The heat load from incandescent lights is then 37.5 × 500 ft^2 of floor = 18,750 BH.

Notice in the example above how much more heat load the building cooling system must carry when it is illuminated with incandescent lights—more than four times as much load.

During this preliminary evaluation of the building the HVAC designer should now investigate the possibility of exhausting or removing the heat of the lights before it can travel into the occupied areas of the rooms and thus become internal heat load. In other words, if the sensible heat generated directly by the lighting fixtures can be exhausted upward before it gets down into the room, it will not be necessary to introduce cool air into the room to absorb this heat.

Further, if a certain percentage of this heat-laden air returning from lighting fixtures (see fig. 5-2) is exhausted from the building (as is usually done to make possible the introduction of outside air into the building for ventilation purposes), this percentage of the heat of the lights is vented to the outdoors and does not become a load on the cooling system.

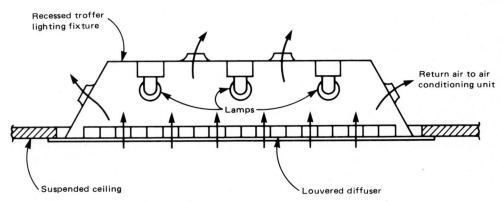

Figure 5-2 Return air type of lighting fixture.

Figure 5-2 shows a recessed fluorescent troffer type of lighting fixture, but other types of fixtures may also be installed to permit return air passage.

5-4 DESIGN CONDITIONS

Before a heat gain (cooling load) calculation can be started, a set of design conditions must be established. In other words, the designer must now decide what temperature and humidity conditions are to be maintained in the various areas or zones of the building. The designer must also decide what outdoor conditions should be assumed to exist (for design purposes) while those indoor conditions are being maintained.

As was the case with heating system design, the cooling system will not be designed to maintain the selected indoor conditions at those times when outdoor temperature and humidity are equal to or near those of the hottest day on record.

It is not practical to design for the hottest day on record; something less than this should be used. Further, the designer must think of outdoor dry bulb temperature and outdoor wet bulb temperature independently of each other.

It is not usually true that peak outdoor dry bulb temperature and peak outdoor wet bulb temperature occur simultaneously. The tables in fig. 4-20 give the ASHRAE recommended summer outdoor design conditions for hundreds of cities throughout the United States and Canada. These tables show the recommended outdoor design dry bulb temperature and the wet bulb temperature that will probably prevail while that dry bulb temperature exists. The tables also show a separate design wet bulb temperature that should be used when water evaporative devices such as cooling towers, evaporative coolers and condensers, and air washers are being considered.

The outdoor design conditions, then, should be those shown, for a given location, in the column in fig. 4-20 headed "Design dry bulb and mean coincident wet bulb." These summertime design conditions are not reached on a given day in the early morning hours, and often will not be reached until

midafternoon. However, design conditions are very frequently reached by noon or even before; and it is not safe to base an HVAC system design on any other premise.

Some HVAC designers have held that at 10:00 A.M., the outdoor design dry bulb temperature may be reduced by 50% of the daily range (see art. 5-5). This may be true on the average, but there are so many departures from the average pattern that to follow this procedure would result in too many HVAC system failures—that is, failures to maintain proper indoor design conditions.

The indoor design conditions for human comfort have been very well stabilized through years of experience, and the agreement among people is surprisingly complete. There seems to be no reason, then, to run more laboratory tests to determine optimum human comfort conditions, or even to waste space in publishing the results of tests that have already been run.

The operators and occupants of buildings will surely continue setting their thermostats at 74 to 78°F DB, and when humidistats are available, these will continue to be set at approximately 50%. The author recommends the use of 76°F DB and 50% RH as indoor design conditions in the usual building situation. Of course, the U.S. federal government has requested a setting of 78°F.

5-5 MEAN DAILY RANGE—t_d

Another aspect of design conditions is the *daily range*, which may be peculiar to a given building location. Daily range is the summertime difference that will usually be experienced between the high daytime dry bulb temperature and the low nighttime dry bulb temperature. *Mean daily range* is the weighted average difference taken hour by hour and day by day. See the daily range values listed in fig. 4-20.

Daily range is important, since a lower dry bulb temperature at night (with a high daily range value) means that the exterior surfaces of a building are cooled to a lower temperature. As a result, the sun and high temperatures of the succeeding day must be applied to the building for a longer time before their heat begins to be felt on the inside of the building.

There is a net equivalent effect on the temperature difference between outside air and indoor air—either to increase this difference or decrease it. We will see later in the chapter how this effect is calculated.

5-6 APPLIANCE LOADS

Any type of device that we may find in our conditioned buildings and which emits heat either intermittently or continuously is called an *appliance* in HVAC parlance. This includes all sorts of heat-producing devices which we usually think of as kitchen appliances (coffee makers, toasters, etc.), but it also includes any other device that liberates heat. An electric typewriter has a very small motor which produces a little heat and motion, which is soon converted into heat—that is an appliance. A big, sophisticated electronic computer produces large amounts of heat—that is also an appliance. In a manufacturing plant having motors and machines humming and thumping on all sides, the appliance load may very well be by far the greatest component in the total cooling load.

The appliance load in a building is sometimes very difficult to evaluate; yet this must be done, and done reasonably accurately. Figure 5-3 will give considerable assistance in evaluating the sensible and latent heat gain from commercial cooking appliances and a few miscellaneous appliances. However, the data shown in fig. 5-3 will not go far in answering all the questions regarding appliance loads that will arise. The HVAC designer is left mostly to his or her own devices in determining these, and the solution to this problem is not always easily found.

Often the designer must obtain the needed data from appliance equipment manufacturers. If the items in question are available for inspection, the equipment nameplates will usually give much information.

It must always be remembered in this context that appliances are rarely in use continuously, so a diversity or use factor must be applied. Often the owner or user of the equipment can be of help in assigning a use factor.

5-7 HUMAN OCCUPANCY LOADS

As stated previously, human beings continuously liberate heat as a result of their metabolic processes. The amount of heat released depends greatly on an individual's rate of activity.

People emit both sensible and latent heat, and in heavily occupied spaces, the latent portion of this load causes some very special problems for the HVAC designer. These problems are dealt with extensively in a subsequent chapter dealing with the selection and design of HVAC systems.

In making preliminary evaluations of a building, the designer will often have difficulty in finding a dependable figure representing the number of people that may occupy a room. Again, it is suggested that the owner or user of the building be consulted; however, it is surprising how often the owner or user will not have this information available.

The information appearing in fig. 5-4 will give some guidance as to the number of people that might be expected to occupy the various types of rooms in buildings that are frequented by the public. Also, fig. 5-5 gives information as to the rate of heat emission of adult human beings engaged in various activities in various types of building situations.

One frequently severe problem associated with human occupancy is the room or space in a building where many people gather quickly and stay for a short period of time—1 or 2 hours. Rooms of this type are typified by conference rooms, dining rooms, cafeterias, and auditoriums. When such a room fills with people, the body heat can build up quickly. If the human comfort in such rooms is controlled by a thermostat located in some other room, only discomfort can result. However, if a room thermostat is located in the heavily occupied space, which also controls comfort in adjacent

Figure 5-3 (a) Recommended rate of heat gain from commercial cooking appliances located in the air-conditioned area. (Reprinted with permission from the 1977 Fundamentals Volume, *ASHRAE Handbook and Products Directory*.)

(a) Appliances Located in the Air-Conditioned Area[a]

Appliance	Capacity	Overall dimension, in. width × depth × height	Miscellaneous data (dimension in inches)	Manufacturer's input rating — Boiler, hp or W	Manufacturer's input rating — Btu/hr	Probable maximum hourly input Btu/hr	Without hood — Sensible	Without hood — Latent	Without hood — Total	With hood — All sensible
Gas-burning, counter type										
Broiler-griddle		31 × 20 × 18			36,000	18,000	11,700	6,300	18,000	3,600
Coffee brewer per burner			With *warm* position		5,500	2,500	1,750	750	2,500	500
Water heater burner			With storage tank		11,000	5,000	3,850	1,650	5,500	1,100
Coffee urn	3 gal		12 in. diameter		10,000	5,000	3,500	1,500	5,000	1,000
	5 gal		14 in. diameter		15,000	7,500	5,250	2,250	7,500	1,500
	8 gal twin		25 in. wide		20,000	10,000	7,000	3,000	10,000	2,000
Deep fat fryer	15 lb fat	14 × 21 × 15			30,000	15,000	7,500	7,500	15,000	3,000
Dry food warmer per ft² of top					1,400	700	560	140	700	140
Griddle, frying, per ft² of top					15,000	7,500	4,900	2,600	7,500	1,500
Short order stove, per burner			Open grates		10,000	5,000	3,200	1,800	5,000	1,000
Steam table per ft² of top					2,500	1,250	750	500	1,250	250
Toaster, continuous	360 slices/hr	19 × 16 × 30	Two slices wide		12,000	6,000	3,600	2,400	6,000	1,200
	720 slices/hr	24 × 16 × 30	Four slices wide		20,000	10,000	6,000	4,000	10,000	2,000
Gas-burning, floor-mounted type										
Broiler, unit		24 × 26 grid	Same burner heats oven		70,000	35,000				7,000
Deep fat fryer	32 lb fat		14 in. kettle		65,000	32,500				6,500
	56 lb fat		18 in. kettle		100,000	50,000				10,000
Oven, deck, per sq ft² of hearth area			Same for 7 and 12 high decks		4,000	2,000	Exhaust hood required	Exhaust hood required	Exhaust hood required	400
Oven, roasting		32 × 32 × 60	Two ovens—24 × 28 × 15		80,000	40,000				8,000
Range, heavy duty										
Top section		32 × 42 × 33	32 wide × 39 deep		64,000	32,000				6,400
Oven			25 × 28 × 15		40,000	20,000				4,000
Range, jr., heavy duty										
Top section		31 × 35 × 33	31 wide × 32 deep		45,000	22,500				4,500
Oven			24 × 28 × 15		35,000	17,500				3,500
Range, restaurant type										
Per two burner section			12 wide × 28 deep		24,000	12,000				2,400
Per oven			24 × 22 × 14		30,000	15,000				3,000
Per broiler-griddle			24 wide × 26 deep		35,000	17,500				3,500

Item	Capacity	Size (in.)	Description							
Coffee brewer										
Per burner				625	2,130	1,000	770	230	1,000	340
Per warmer				160	545	300	230	70	300	90
Automatic	240 cups/hr			5,000	17,000	8,500	6,500	2,000	8,500	1,700
Coffee urn	3 gal	27 × 21 × 22	Four burner + water heater	2,000	6,800	3,400	2,550	850	3,400	1,000
	5 gal			3,000	10,200	5,100	3,850	1,250	5,100	1,600
	8 gal twin			4,000	13,600	6,800	5,200	1,600	6,800	2,100
Deep fat fryer	14 lb fat	13 × 22 × 10		5,500	18,750	9,400	2,800	6,600	9,400	3,000
	21 lb fat	16 × 22 × 10		8,000	27,300	13,700	4,100	9,600	13,700	4,300
Dry food warmer, per ft² of top				240	820	400	320	80	400	130
Egg boiler	2 cups	10 × 13 × 25		1,100	3,750	1,900	1,140	760	1,900	600
Griddle, frying, per ft² of top				2,700	9,200	4,600	3,000	1,600	4,600	1,500
Griddle-grill		18 × 20 × 13	Grid, 200 in.²	6,000	20,400	10,200	6,300	3,600	10,200	3,200
Hotplate		18 × 20 × 13	Two heating units	5,200	17,700	8,900	5,300	3,600	8,900	2,800
Roaster		18 × 20 × 13		1,650	5,620	2,800	1,700	1,100	2,800	900
Roll warmer		18 × 20 × 13		1,650	5,620	2,800	2,600	200	2,800	900
Toaster, continuous	360 slices/hr	15 × 15 × 28	Two slices wide	2,200	7,500	3,700	1,960	1,740	3,700	1,200
	720 slices/hr	20 × 15 × 28	Four slices wide	3,000	10,200	5,100	2,700	2,400	5,100	1,600
Toaster, pop-up	4 slice	12 × 11 × 9		2,540	8,350	4,200	2,230	1,970	4,200	1,300
Waffle iron		18 × 20 × 13	2 grids	1,650	5,620	2,800	1,680	1,120	2,800	900

Item	Capacity	Size (in.)	Description							
Griddle[c]		36 × 32 × 37	36 × 25 cooking surface	16,800	57,300	20,500				2,060[b]
Broiler, no oven		23 wide × 25 deep grid		12,000	40,900					6,500
with oven		23 × 27 × 12 oven		18,000	61,400	30,700				9,800
Broiler, single deck[c]		36 × 36 × 54		16,000	54,600	20,500				10,800
Deep fat fryer	28 lb fat	20 × 38 × 36	14 wide × 15 deep kettle	12,000	40,900					6,500
	60 lb fat	24 × 36 × 36	20 wide × 20 deep kettle	18,000	61,400	30,700				9,800
Fryer[c]		15 × 32 × 36	13 × 23 cooking surface	22,000	75,000					730
Oven, baking, per ft² of hearth			Compartment 8-in. high	500	1,700	850	Exhaust hood required	Exhaust hood required	Exhaust hood required	270
Oven, roasting, per ft² of hearth			Compartment 12-in. high	900	3,070	1,500				490
Range, heavy duty[c]										
Top section		38 × 36 × 37	36 × 24 cooking surface	15,000	51,200					19,100
Oven				6,700	22,900					1,700
Range, medium duty										
Top section		30 × 32 × 36		8,000	27,300	13,600				4,300
Oven				3,600	12,300	6,200				1,900
Range, light duty										
Top section		30 × 29 × 36		6,600	22,500	11,200				3,600
Oven				3,000	10,200	5,100				1,600
Convection oven[c]		38 × 36 × 55		11,000	37,500					1,540
Charbroiler[c]		36 × 24 × 34	30 × 18 cooking surface	16,500	56,300					4,320
Steam cooker, two sections[c]		36 × 29 × 64		24,000	81,900					3,140

Appliances Located in the Air-Conditioned Area[a]

Appliance	Capacity	Overall dimension, in. width × depth × height	Miscellaneous data (dimension in inches)	Manufacturer's input rating		Probable maximum hourly input Btu/hr	Recommended rate of heat gain, Btu/hr			
				Boiler, hp or W	Btu/hr		Without hood			With hood
							Sensible	Latent	Total	All sensible
Steam heated										
Coffee urn	3 gal			0.2	6,600	3,300	2,180	1,120	3,300	1,000
	5 gal			0.3	10,000	5,000	3,300	1,700	5,000	1,600
	8 gal twin			0.4	13,200	6,600	4,350	2,250	6,600	2,100
Steam table, per ft^2 of top			With insets	0.05	1,650	825	500	325	825	260
Bain marie, per ft^2 of top			Open tank	0.10	3,300	1,650	825	825	1,650	520
Oyster steamer				0.5	16,500	8,250	5,000	3,250	8,250	2,600
Steam kettles, per gal capacity			Jacketed type	0.06	2,000	1,000	600	400	1,000	320
Compartment steamer per compartment		24 × 25 × 12 compartment	Floor mounted	1.2	40,000	20,000	12,000	8,000	20,000	6,400
Compartment steamer	3 pans 12 × 20 × 2.5		Single counter unit	0.5	16,500	8,250	5,000	3,250	8,250	2,600
Plate warmer, per ft^3				0.05	1,650	825	550	275	825	260

[a] The data in this table (except as noted in c below) were determined by assuming the hourly heat input was 0.50 times the manufacturer's energy input rating. This is felt to be conservative on the average but could result in heat gain estimates higher or lower than actual heat gains depending on the appliance.

[b] For poorly designed or undersized exhaust systems the heat gains in this column should be doubled and half of the increase assumed as latent heat.

[c] Based on measured heat gain at typical idle conditions. For open island canopies multiply values by 1.32.

Figure 5-3 (b) Recommended rate of heat gain from miscellaneous appliances. (Reprinted with permission from the 1977 Fundamentals Volume, *ASHRAE Handbook and Products Directory*.)

(b) Miscellaneous Appliances

Electrical appliances

Appliance	Miscellaneous data	Manufacturer's rating		Recommended rate of heat gain, Btu/hr		
		Watts	Btu/hr	Sensible	Latent	Total
Hair dryer	Blower type	1580	5400	2300	400	2700
Hair dryer	Helmet type	705	2400	1870	330	2200
Permanent wave machine	60 heaters @25 W. 36 in normal use	1500	5000	850	150	1000
Neon sign, per linear ft of tube	0.5 in. diameter			30		30
	0.375 in. diameter			60		60
Sterilizer, instrument		1100	3750	650	1200	1850

Gas-burning appliances

Appliance	Miscellaneous data	Manufacturer's rating		Recommended rate of heat gain, Btu/hr		
		Watts	Btu/hr	Sensible	Latent	Total
Lab burners Bunsen	0.4375-in. barrel		3000	1680	420	2100
Fishtail	1.5 in. wide		5000	2800	700	3500
Meeker	1 in. diameter		6000	3360	840	4200
Gas light, per burner	Mantle type		2000	1800	200	2000
Cigar lighter	Continuous flame		2500	900	100	1000

Figure 5-4 Rate of human occupancy in public buildings. (Extracted from the Indiana State Ventilating Code, vol. 4, 1969.)

Use of occupancy	Basis of occupancy
Arenas and field houses	4 ft^2 per person; use seated areas only
Assembly halls	6 ft^2 per person
Banquet halls	15 ft^2 per person
Churches and other places of worship	6 ft^2 per person
Dance halls	12 ft^2 per person
Dining halls	15 ft^2 per person
Dormitories	40 ft^2 per person
General offices	75 ft^2 per person
Gymnasiums	6 ft^2 per person for seated space, 15 ft^2 for space not seated
Hospitals	Depends on usage
Laboratories	Depends on usage
Lecture halls	6 ft^2 per person
Library reading rooms	25 ft^2 per person
Lodge halls	6 ft^2 per person for seated space, 12 ft^2 per person not seated
Penal institutions	Depends on usage
Places of employment	Depends on usage
Recreational room	15 ft^2 per person
Restaurants	15 ft^2 per person
Retail establishments and shops	Basement—20 ft^2 per person
(a) Department stores and similar occupancies	First floor—30 ft^2 per person; second floor and above—60 ft^2 per person
(b) Shops and other retail establishments	Basement—40 ft^2 per person; first floor and above—60 ft^2 per person
School auditoriums	6 ft^2 per person
School cafeterias	10 ft^2 per person
School classrooms	Minimum of 225 ft^3 per occupant or:
Elementary: academic	25 ft^2 per person
Elementary: integrated activities	29 ft^2 per person
High school	25 ft^2 per person
Kindergarten	35 ft^2 per person
Lecture	12 ft^2 per person
School project rooms	
Art or drawing	25 ft^2 per person
Music—instrumental	20 ft^2 per person
Music—vocal	16 ft^2 per person
Laboratories	35 ft^2 per person
Taverns	20 ft^2 per person
Theaters	6 ft^2 per person of all seated areas
Vocational instruction and research	
Business education	30 ft^2 per person
Commercial art	29 ft^2 per person
Home economics	40 ft^2 per person
Laboratories	Depends on usage
Shop general	50 ft^2 per person
Shop specialized	Depends on usage
School playroom	15 ft^2 per person

Figure 5-5 Rates of heat gain from occupants of conditioned spaces. (Reprinted with permission from the 1977 Fundamentals Volume, *ASHRAE Handbook and Products Directory*.)

Degrees of activity	Typical application	Total heat adults, male			Total heat adjusted[b]			Sensible heat			Latent heat		
		Watts	Btu/hr	kcal/hr	Watts	Btu/hr	kcal/hr	Watts	Btu/hr	kcal/hr	Watts	Btu/hr	kcal/hr
Seated at rest	Theater, movie	115	400	100	100	350	90	60	210	55	40	140	38
Seated, very light work writing	Offices, hotels, apts	140	480	120	120	420	105	65	230	55	55	190	50
Seated eating	Restaurant[c]	150	520	130	170	580[c]	145	75	255	60	95	325	80
Seated, light work, typing	Offices, hotels, apts	185	640	160	150	510	130	75	255	60	75	255	65
Standing, light work or walking slowly	Retail store, bank	235	800	200	185	640	160	90	315	80	95	325	80
Light bench work	Factory	255	880	220	230	780	195	100	345	90	130	435	110
Walking 3 mph, light machine work	Factory	305	1040	260	305	1040	260	100	345	90	205	695	170
Bowling[d]	Bowling alley	350	1200	300	280	960	240	100	345	90	180	615	150
Moderate dancing	Dance hall	400	1360	340	375	1280	320	120	405	100	255	875	220
Heavy work, heavy machine work, lifting	Factory	470	1600	400	470	1600	400	165	565	140	300	1035	260
Heavy work, athletics	Gymnasium	585	2000	500	525	1800	450	185	635	160	340	1165	290

[a]*Source:* Tabulated values are based on 78°F room dry-bulb temperature. For 80°F room dry-bulb, the total heat remains the same, but the sensible heat value should be decreased by approximately 8% and the latent heat values increased accordingly.

[b]Adjusted total heat gain is based on normal percentage of men, women and children for the application listed, with the postulate that the gain from an adult female is 85% of that for an adult male and that the gain from a child is 75% of that for an adult male.

[c]Adjusted total heat value for eating in a restaurant, includes 60 Btu/hr for food per individual (30 Btu sensible and 30 Btu latent).

[d]For bowling figure one person per alley actually bowling, and all others as sitting (400 Btu/hr) or standing and walking slowly (790 Btu/hr).

All values rounded to nearest 5 watts or kcal/hr or to nearest 10 Btu/hr.

rooms with normal occupancy, the adjacent rooms will almost certainly be overcooled and thus be very uncomfortable when the conference room is fully occupied. The answer, of course, lies in having a room thermostat in the heavily occupied room which has control over that room only.

In making the preliminary building evaluation, the HVAC designer must recognize such problems and make advance plans to solve them properly.

5-8 INFILTRATION LOADS

As discussed earlier, building infiltration in winter is a very serious problem which is often exceedingly difficult to evaluate. This is not usually so in summer.

The wind does, of course, blow in summer—sometimes with tornadic force. However, on that peak load summer day when the sun is shining fiercely and the outdoor temperature is very high, there is usually very little wind stirring, and the infiltration resulting from wind is negligible.

Infiltration in summer can result if a negative static pressure exists in a building; this might happen if exhaust fans of various types (kitchen exhaust, toilet exhaust, process exhaust, etc.) draw more air out of a building than is being supplied into it.

Infiltration can occur in the upper half of very tall buildings when indoor air is much cooler and more dense than surrounding outdoor air. In this case the denser indoor air tends to settle downward in the building, leaking outward through windows and doors located below the *static median* (see fig. 5-6), and drawing outdoor air inward through window cracks located above the static median. The static median is, as can be seen in fig. 5-6, the horizontal dividing line between areas of infiltration and areas of exfiltration. In winter, the pattern of air movement is reversed. Air movement is upward, as in a chimney, with infiltration below the static median, and exfiltration above it.

In tall buildings, these air currents represent a powerful force, especially in winter. The HVAC designer should, in the original study and evalua-

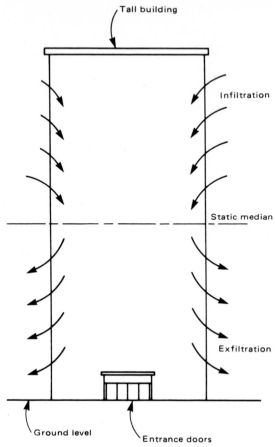

Figure 5-6 Infiltration and exfiltration in tall buildings in summer.

tion, recognize the greatly adverse effect that these air currents have on building comfort, operating economy, and HVAC system design. The designer should recommend to the architectural designer methods by which this problem can be minimized. Some of these are:

1 Use revolving doors instead of swinging doors wherever possible at exterior entrances. Revolving doors greatly reduce air movement through the door since the building interior is never opened to the exterior (see fig. 5-7).

2 Use closed elevator lobbies as shown in fig. 5-8. The elevator shafts in any tall building cause tremendous updrafts in winter and downdrafts in

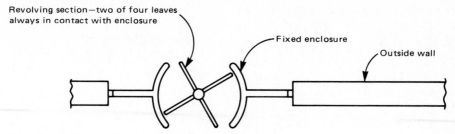

Figure 5-7   Plan detail—revolving door.

summer. Elevator doors must, of necessity, be very loose fitting, and they offer very little resistance to airflow into or out of the elevator shafts.

However, air cannot enter an elevator shaft at one point if it cannot escape at another point (or points). If we can discourage air movement by effectively sealing the elevator lobbies on each floor of the building, the problem is greatly minimized.

Sealing elevator lobbies is not a difficult task. It does require the use of well-fitted automatically closing doors at all openings leading from each lobby. It further requires that all lobby walls be extended up to the floor structure or roof structure above and sealed thereto.

3 All openings in all floor structures (usually concrete slabs) must be sealed. Where pipes, ducts, conduits, and so on, run vertically through a tall building, openings are formed when the floor slabs are poured. Later, the pipes, ducts, and conduits are installed through these openings. The floor openings are always appreciably larger than the pipe, duct, or conduit that passes through. In other words, an annular space remains around the pipe through which air can easily move up or down.

It is not a difficult or expensive task to seal all such annular spaces with some resilient packing material which will permit pipe movement result-

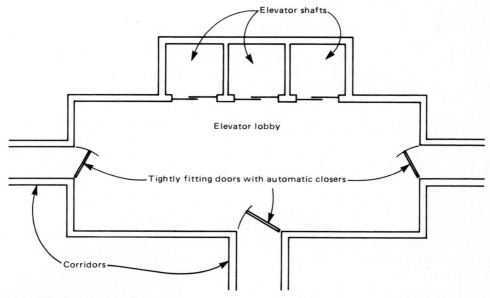

Figure 5-8   Plan—elevator lobby.

ing from expansion and contraction. All floor openings of all types must somehow be sealed.

4 The use of pipe and duct shafts must be discontinued. Very often an architect will try to facilitate the installation of mechanical and electrical systems by providing vertical, masonry shafts extending the full height of a building. Such a utility shaft does often provide convenient containment for the vertical pipes, ducts, and so on; however, it also adds materially to the problem of vertical air movement. The concrete floor slabs should always extend completely through such vertical utility shafts to break them up into short segments and to permit the sealing recommended in item 3.

5-9 INFILTRATION RECOMMENDATIONS

It is recommended that the problems of summertime infiltration be solved in the light of the following:

1 For five-story buildings and less (this must cover 99+% of the buildings in the world) of fairly new construction, with well-fitting windows and doors, infiltration may be ignored.

2 The HVAC system should be designed to supply outside air into the building, during all occupied periods, in quantities somewhat in excess of those quantities expected to be withdrawn from the building by its exhaust ventilation systems; this will maintain a slight positive pressure in the building which will discourage infiltration. (Even though no exhaust ventilation is planned, provisions should be made for OA supply—at least 7% of the total quantity of air circulated by the HVAC systems.)

3 In tall buildings, summertime infiltration may be ignored in the lower 50% of the building (below the static median). In the upper half of the building, use the 15-mph values for infiltration in fig. 4-11.

4 Check with the National Weather Service, other local weather agencies, and local HVAC designers for known local wind conditions that may lie outside usual wind patterns; such information would negate or moderate recommendations 1, 2, and 3.

Building heat gains resulting from infiltration may be easily calculated with the use of formulas (1-6) and (1-7):

$$BHS = cfm \times 1.08 \times \Delta t \qquad (1\text{-}6)$$

and

$$BHL = cfm \times \Delta G \times 0.68 \qquad (1\text{-}7)$$

where BHS and BHL = Btu/hr sensible and latent

cfm = infiltration air quantity, ft^3/min

Δt = temperature difference between outdoors and indoors, dry bulb

ΔG = specific humidity difference, grains per pound of air between outdoors and indoors

5-10 HEAT GAINS THROUGH GLASS AREAS

Heat is gained through the glass areas of a building for two reasons:

1 Because there is a temperature difference (Δt) between the high outdoor dry bulb temperatures that occur in summer and the comparatively lower indoor temperatures that are desirable; this is called *conduction heat gain*.

2 Because of the direct (or reflected) sunshine, or solar impingement, that passes through glass areas into a building interior.

Conduction heat gain, for the first reason given above, can be easily calculated with the use of formula (4-1):

$$BH = A \times U \times \Delta t \qquad (4\text{-}1)$$

where BH = heat flow, Btu/hr

A = area, ft^2

U = heat transfer coefficient, BH per square foot of area per degree difference in temperature between indoors and outdoors, °F [$BH/ft^2/°\Delta t$]

Δt = temperature difference between indoors and outdoors, °F

Necessary U coefficients may be selected from the table in fig. 4-4B.

Heat gain resulting from direct solar transmission can be determined through the use of empirical data on the "insolation" rate at various times of the day in various parts of the world. However, this solar incidence rate is almost always greatly reduced, for a given room in a given building, by shading devices and other building features. The insolation rate is always greatly reduced, first, by the earth's atmosphere.

Then, of course, solar radiation flow through glass areas into buildings is interrupted or diminished by such features as awnings, building overhangs, vertical building fins adjacent to windows, solar screens on the exterior of buildings, venetian blinds, roller shades, draperies, and transparent metallic films on the interior of the glass of building windows.

When direct solar radiation passes uninterrupted through glass areas into buildings, the solar rays are finally received by the interior surfaces of the building (walls, floors, and ceilings) and by the building furnishings. At these surfaces, the sun's rays are converted mostly to sensible heat, and that heat is mostly absorbed by those surfaces. As a result, the temperature of those surfaces rises.

When those surface temperatures have risen appreciably above the automatically controlled room air temperature, heat will begin to flow into the room air and thus become load on the building cooling system. So there is a time lag between the time that the sun begins to shine into a room and the time that heat, in appreciable quantities, begins to flow into the room air. In other words, there is a difference, sometimes, between heat gain and cooling load.

The amount of time lag, in the situation just described, depends on the mass of the building structure and its furnishings. With a heavy structure and furnishings, the time lag between heat gain and the perception of cooling load will be greater than when these are lightweight. The effect of a heavy structure may be offset by very light furnishings, and vice versa.

It probably is not possible for the HVAC designer to accurately predict, for the life of the building, the character of the building furnishings and the color of the building interior surfaces (which affect their solar receptivity).

It must be further realized that when interior shading of some type, such as draperies or blinds, is used, most of the direct solar rays are intercepted by this interior shading. These rays are then converted to sensible heat very quickly, and the solar heat gain becomes cooling load with very little time lag. Interior shading devices might later be added to most any building, even though the original design did not contemplate such.

It is therefore this author's recommendation that, with very few exceptions, such calculations be based on the assumption of medium-weight buildings and furnishings, and the inclusion of interior shading devices. This assumption will usually fall on the side of conservatism and safety.

The table in fig. 5-9 has been prepared on this assumption, and lists values of solar heat gain in BH per square foot of net glass area (total window area minus window framing, mullions, muntins, check rails, etc.). Solar values are given in fig. 5-9 for different north latitudes, during the month of July, at various hours of the day, for vertical glass areas with various compass orientations, and for horizontal glass surfaces such as skylights.

Values for other earth latitudes and other months of the year may be found in the *1977 ASHRAE Handbook of Fundamentals*, from which the values in fig. 5-9 were excerpted.

The total "heat gain" (now considered here to be practically synonymous with "cooling load") through glass areas may then be calculated by adding the "solar heat gain" to the "conduction heat gain due to temperature difference." This procedure is illustrated by the following example.

Example 5-2 A corner room in a building has windows in each of its two exposed walls. A south wall has three windows, and a west wall has two windows. All five windows are 4 ft wide and 5 ft high. Each window is 80% glass and 20% wood framing. Find the peak heat gain through the

Figure 5-9 Solar heat gain through glass (BH/ft^2 of net glass area) with interior shading and medium-weight construction. (Calculated from data in the 1977 Fundamentals Volume *ASHRAE Handbook and Products Directory* with the permission of ASHRAE.)

Solar time									

Glass orientation at 40° N latitude in July

Solar time	N	NE	E	SE	S	SW	W	NW	Horizontal
5	3	3	4	3	3	5	6	5	8
6	28	91	102	51	10	12	13	11	31
7	25	124	156	95	17	19	19	18	71
8	25	121	173	126	24	24	24	23	115
9	28	95	164	138	41	27	28	28	155
10	30	60	134	134	63	32	32	31	189
11	33	47	89	116	82	37	35	33	212
12	34	44	58	83	90	65	37	34	223
13	34	42	52	56	87	100	67	36	223
14	33	39	48	48	74	128	114	49	212
15	31	36	43	43	55	141	156	85	186
16	29	33	37	37	38	138	177	119	152
17	30	26	30	31	29	117	175	134	110
18	35	20	24	22	21	77	132	112	66
19	9	10	13	14	12	26	35	26	37

Glass orientation at 32° N latitude in July

Solar time	N	NE	E	SE	S	SW	W	NW	Horizontal
5	3	3	4	3	2	5	6	5	8
6	29	94	101	45	6	11	13	12	33
7	26	127	155	84	12	17	19	18	74
8	26	124	172	111	16	21	24	23	120
9	29	97	163	122	27	24	28	28	161
10	32	62	133	119	42	29	32	32	197
11	34	48	88	102	54	33	34	33	221
12	36	45	58	74	60	57	37	35	232
13	36	43	52	50	58	89	67	37	232
14	34	40	47	42	49	113	114	50	221
15	33	37	43	38	36	125	155	87	194
16	30	33	37	33	25	122	178	122	158
17	31	27	30	27	19	104	174	137	115
18	36	20	24	20	14	68	131	115	68
19	10	10	13	11	8	23	34	27	38

Glass orientation at 24° N latitude in June

Solar time	N	NE	E	SE	S	SW	W	NW	Horizontal
5	4	4	4	2	1	4	6	6	8
6	41	103	100	35	4	8	13	13	33
7	37	140	153	66	7	13	19	20	75
8	36	136	170	87	9	16	23	26	123
9	41	107	161	95	16	19	28	31	165
10	45	68	131	92	25	22	32	35	201
11	48	53	87	80	32	26	34	37	226
12	50	50	57	57	36	44	36	39	237
13	50	48	51	39	34	69	66	40	237
14	48	44	47	33	29	88	112	55	226
15	46	40	42	29	22	97	153	96	198
16	42	37	36	26	15	95	174	134	162
17	44	29	30	21	12	81	172	151	117
18	51	22	23	15	8	53	129	127	70
19	13	11	13	9	5	18	34	29	39

Figure 5-9   *(Cont.)*

Glass orientation at 24° N latitude in July									
Solar time	N	NE	E	SE	S	SW	W	NW	Horizontal
5	3	4	4	3	1	4	6	5	8
6	33	99	100	39	4	9	13	12	33
7	30	134	153	72	7	14	19	19	75
8	29	130	170	95	10	18	23	25	122
9	33	102	162	104	17	21	28	30	164
10	36	65	132	102	27	25	32	33	200
11	39	51	87	88	35	28	34	35	225
12	40	48	58	63	38	49	36	37	236
13	40	46	51	43	37	76	66	39	236
14	39	42	47	36	31	97	113	53	225
15	37	39	43	32	23	107	153	92	197
16	34	35	36	28	16	104	175	128	161
17	35	28	30	23	12	89	173	144	117
18	41	21	23	17	9	58	130	121	70
19	11	11	13	10	5	19	34	28	39

windows in this room in the month of July if the building is located at a north latitude of 40°. The windows have 1/8-in.-thick single glass, the outdoor design temperature is 94°F, and the indoor design temperature is 78°F.

Solution *Conduction heat gain* (due to temperature difference):

$$BH = A \times U \times \Delta t = 5 \times 4 \text{ ft} \times 5 \text{ ft}$$
$$\times 0.94(94°F - 78°F)$$
$$= 1504$$

Here the 0.94 factor is the summertime U factor for 80% glass windows found in the table of fig. 4-4*b*.

Solar heat gain: Using values from fig. 5-9, we see that peak solar heat gain through the south windows occurs at 12:00 solar time; and

$$BH = 3 \text{ windows} \times 4 \text{ ft} \times 5 \text{ ft} \times 0.8$$
$$\times 90 \text{ BH/ft}^2 = 4320$$

where the 0.8 is for 80% glass and the 90 is from fig. 5-9 for 40° north latitude in July at 12:00 o'clock.

The peak solar gain through the west windows occurs at 16:00 solar time, and

$$BH = 2 \times 4 \text{ ft} \times 5 \text{ ft} \times 0.8 \times 177 = 5664$$

However, the peak solar heat gain for all windows is not the sum of these two calculated values. The solar gain through the west windows at 12:00 is

$$BH = 2 \times 4 \text{ ft} \times 5 \text{ ft} \times 0.8 \times 37 \text{ BH/ft}^2$$
$$= 1184$$

Therefore, at 12:00 the solar gain through all five windows = 4320 BH + 1184 BH = 5504 BH.

Similarly, at 16:00, the solar gain through the south windows is

$$BH = 3 \times 4 \text{ ft} \times 5 \text{ ft} \times 0.8 \times 38 \text{ BH/ft}^2$$
$$= 1824$$

Then total gain at 16:00 for all five windows = 5664 BH (see above) + 1824 BH = 7488 BH.

However, a simple investigation shows that the peak load for all five windows taken simultaneously occurs at 15:00 solar time, and is

BH (south)
$$= 3 \times 4 \text{ ft} \times 5 \text{ ft} \times 0.8 \times 55 \text{ BH/ft}^2 \quad 2640$$
BH (west)
$$= 2 \times 4 \text{ ft} \times 5 \text{ ft} \times 0.8 \times 156 \text{ BH/ft}^2 \quad \underline{4992}$$

Total solar gain   7632 BH

The total peak heat gain through these five windows occurs, then, at 15:00 solar time and is the sum of the peak solar gain of 7632 BH and the conduction gain calculated above at 1504 BH.

$$7632 + 1504 = 9136 \text{ BH}$$

In the foregoing example, the use of fig. 5-9 assumed that some type of draperies were in use inside the glass areas. The solar gain could be appreciably reduced if venetian blinds were installed, or if heat-absorbing glass of some type were installed, or if a reflective film were applied to the inside of the glass.

The tables that are included in figs. 5-10 through 5-15, and figs. 5-17 and 5-18, show the effect of these and other shading or reflective devices. In these tables a *shading coefficient* (SC) is given which serves as a reducing multiplier that may be applied to values of solar transmission heat gain. These SC values are all unity or less and are expressed as a decimal. Therefore, solar heat gain in BH = net glass area $\times$ solar heat gain (SHG) in BH/ft^2 (from fig. 5-9) $\times$ the shading coefficient: BH = $A \times$ SHG $\times$ SC. In example 5-2, the SC from fig. 5-10 was 1.0 and thus did not enter the calculation.

Figure 5-10 shows the solar shading coefficients (SC) for various types of single glass and double glass (two panes—insulating). All window

Figure 5-10 Shading coefficients for single glass and insulating glass. (Reprinted with permission from the 1977 Fundamentals Volume, *ASHRAE Handbook and Products Directory*.)

Type of glass	Nominal thickness,[a] in.	Solar transmittance[a]	Shading coefficient $h_o = 4.0$[e]	Shading coefficient $h_o = 3.0$[e]
A. Single glass				
Clear	1/8	0.84	1.00	1.00
	1/4	0.78	0.94	0.95
	3/8	0.72	0.90	0.92
	1/2	0.67	0.87	0.88
Heat absorbing	1/8	0.64	0.83	0.85
	1/4	0.46	0.69	0.73
	3/8	0.33	0.60	0.64
	1/2	0.24	0.53	0.58
B. Insulating glass (see Note)				
Clear out, clear in	1/8[b]	0.71[d]	0.88	0.88
Clear out, clear in	1/4	0.61	0.81	0.82
Heat absorbing[c] out, clear in	1/4	0.36	0.55	0.58

Note: Refers to factory-fabricated units with 3/16-, 1/4-, or 1/2-in. air space or to prime windows plus storm sash.

[a]Refer to manufacturer's literature for values.

[b]Thickness of each pane of glass, not thickness of assembled unit.

[c]Refers to gray-, bronze-, and green-tinted heat-absorbing float glass.

[d]Combined transmittance for assembled unit.

[e]h_o is the outer glass surface heat transfer coefficient in BH/ft^2/$^\circ\Delta t$ and is 4.0 for 7.5-mph wind and 3.0 for lower wind velocities.

Figure 5-11 Solar optical properties and shading coefficients of transparent plastic sheeting. (Reprinted with permission from the 1977 Fundamentals Volume, *ASHRAE Handbook and Products Directory*.)

Type of plastic	Transmittance Visible	Transmittance Solar	SC
Acrylic			
Clear	0.92	0.85	0.98
Gray tint	0.16	0.27	0.52
	0.33	0.41	0.63
	0.45	0.55	0.74
	0.59	0.62	0.80
	0.76	0.74	0.89
Bronze tint	0.10	0.20	0.46
	0.27	0.35	0.58
	0.49	0.56	0.75
	0.61	0.62	0.80
	0.75	0.75	0.90
Reflective*	0.14	0.12	0.21
Polycarbonate			
Clear (1/8-in.)	0.88	0.82	0.98
Gray (1/8-in.)	0.50	0.57	0.74
Bronze (1/8-in.)	0.50	0.57	0.74

*Aluminum metallized polyester film on plastic.

glasses pass most of the solar radiation right on through to the building interior, where it becomes cooling load. However, many types of glass, to a greater or less extent, absorb some solar radiation. The resulting rise in glass temperature enables the glass to conduct, convey, and radiate a portion of this absorbed heat back out to the exterior. Figure 5-10 shows the extent to which this occurs.

Figure 5-11 gives shading coefficients SC for various types of plastic sheet that might be used in place of glass in a window or door. Notice in fig. 5-11 the tremendous reduction in solar transmission that results from the use of an aluminum metallized polyester film applied to the inside of a plastic sheet.

Figure 5-12 gives shading coefficients SC for various types of indoor shading devices, such as venetian blinds and roller shades, applied to single glass sheets of different types.

Figure 5-13 lists shading coefficients SC for

Figure 5-12 Shading coefficients for single glass with indoor shading by venetian blinds or roller shades. (Reprinted with permission from the 1977 Fundamentals Volume, *ASHRAE Handbook and Products Directory*.)

			Type of shading				
			Venetian blinds		Roller shade		
					Opaque		Translucent
	Nominal thickness[a]	Solar transmit- tance[b]	Medium	Light	Dark	White	Light
Clear	3/32 to 1/4	0.87 to 0.80					
Clear	1/4 to 1/2	0.80 to 0.71					
Clear pattern	1/8 to 1/2	0.87 to 0.79	0.64	0.55	0.59	0.25	0.39
Heat-absorbing pattern	1/8	. . .					
Tinted	3/16, 7/32	0.74, 0.71					
Heat-absorbing[c]	3/16, 1/4	0.46					
Heat-absorbing pattern	3/16, 1/4	. . .	0.57	0.53	0.45	0.30	0.36
Tinted	1/8, 7/32	0.59, 0.45					
Heat-absorbing or pattern	. . .	0.44 to 0.30	0.54	0.52	0.40	0.28	0.32
Heat-absorbing[c]	3/8	0.34					
Heat-absorbing or pattern	. . .	0.29 to 0.15 0.24	0.42	0.40	0.36	0.28	0.31
Reflective coated glass SC[d]							
0.30			0.25	0.23			
0.40			0.33	0.29			
0.50			0.42	0.38			
0.60			0.50	0.44			

[a] Refer to manufacturer's literature for values.

[b] For vertical blinds with opaque white and beige louvers in the tightly closed position, SC is 0.25 and 0.29 when used with glass of 0.71 to 0.80 transmittance.

[c] Refers to grey, bronze, and green tinted heat-absorbing glass.

[d] SC for glass with no shading device.

Figure 5-13 Shading coefficients for insulating glass with indoor shading by venetian blinds or roller shades. (Reprinted with permission from the 1977 Fundamentals Volume, *ASHRAE Handbook and Products Directory*.)

Type of glass[a]	Nominal thickness, in., each light	Solar transmittance[b] Outer pane	Solar transmittance[b] Inner pane	Venetian blinds[c] Medium	Venetian blinds[c] Light	Roller shade Opaque Dark	Roller shade Opaque White	Roller shade Translucent Light
Clear out	3/32, 1/8	0.87	0.87					
Clear in	. . .	. . .	. . .	0.57	0.51	0.60	0.25	0.37
Clear out	. . .	. . .	. . .					
Clear in	1/4	0.80	0.80					
Heat-absorbing[d] out clear in	1/4	0.46	0.80	0.39	0.36	0.40	0.22	0.30
Reflective coated glass SC[e]								
0.20	. . .	. . .	. . .	0.19	0.18			
0.30	. . .	. . .	. .	0.27	0.26			
0.40	. . .	. . .	. .	0.34	0.33			

[a]Refers to factory-fabricated units with 3/16-, 1/4-, or 1/2-in. air space, or to prime windows plus storm windows.

[b]Refer to manufacturer's literature for exact values.

[c]For vertical blinds with opaque white or beige louvers, tightly closed, SC is approximately the same as for opaque white roller shades.

[d]Refers to bronze, or green tinted, heat-absorbing glass.

[e]SC for glass with no shading device.

Figure 5-14 Shading coefficients for double glazing with between-glass shading. (Reprinted with permission from the 1977 Fundamentals Volume, *ASHRAE Handbook and Products Directory*.)

Type of glass	Nominal each pane, in.	Solar transmittance[a] Outer pane	Solar transmittance[a] Inner pane	Description of air space	Venetian blinds Light	Venetian blinds Medium	Louvered sun screen
Clear out Clear in	3/32, 1/8	0.87	0.87	Shade in contact with glass or shade separated from glass by air space	0.33	0.36	0.43
Clear out Clear in	1/4	0.80	0.80	Shade in contact with glass-voids filled with plastic	. . .	. . .	0.49
Heat-absorbing[b] out				Shade in contact with glass or shade separated from glass by air space	0.28	0.30	0.37
Clear in	1/4	0.46	0.80	Shade in contact with glass-voids filled with plastic	. . .	. . .	0.41

[a]Refer to manufacturer's literature for exact values.

[b]Refers to grey, bronze, and green tinted heat-absorbing glass.

insulating, double-glazed windows with indoor shading consisting of venetian blinds and roller shades.

Figure 5-14 gives shading coefficients SC for double-glazed windows of various types with venetian blinds or louvered sun screen installed in the space between the glass sheets. Double glazing is now commercially available with the enclosed venetian blinds externally adjustable.

When louvered sun screen is installed in the enclosed space between glass sheets it consists of a metallic screen in which the horizontal strands

consist of thin strips of metal set at an angle to simulate a venetian blind partially open. This permits vision outward, but intercepts the direct rays of the sun and reflects them outward.

Figure 5-15 lists shading coefficients SC for various types of louvered sun screen when it is applied as an insect screen on the exterior of a window. Notice that the footnotes to fig. 5-15 describe the construction details of the several groups of sun screens listed in the table. Figure 5-16 explains some of these construction details so as to make fig. 5-15 more understandable.

In an examination of fig. 5-16 it is easy to see that, whenever the *profile angle* exceeds the *cutoff angle*, there can be no direct solar radiation striking the window pane. However, there will be indirect solar transmittance, which increases as the profile angle decreases. The shading coefficients SC listed in fig. 5-15 take these factors into consideration.

Figure 5-15 Shading coefficients for louvered sun screens. (Reprinted with permission from the 1977 Fundamentals Volume, *ASHRAE Handbook and Products Directory*.)

Profile angle, deg	Group 1		Group 2	
	Transmittance	SC	Transmittance	SC
10	0.23	0.35	0.25	0.33
20	0.06	0.17	0.14	0.23
30	0.04	0.15	0.12	0.21
40 and above	0.04	0.15	0.11	0.20
	Group 3		**Group 4**	
10	0.40	0.51	0.48	0.59
20	0.32	0.42	0.39	0.50
30	0.21	0.31	0.28	0.38
40 and above	0.07	0.18	0.20	0.30
	Group 5		**Group 6**	
10	0.15	0.27	0.26	0.45
20	0.04	0.11	0.20	0.35
30	0.03	0.10	0.13	0.26
40	0.03	0.10	0.04	0.13

Group 1, black, width over spacing ratio 1.15/1; 23 louvers per inch.

Group 2, light color; high reflectance, otherwise same as group 1.

Group 3, black or dark color; w/s ratio 0.85/1; 17 louvers per inch.

Group 4, light color or unpainted aluminum; high reflectance; otherwise same as group 3.

Group 5, same as group 1, except two lights of 0.25-in. clear glass with 0.5-in. air space.

Group 6, same as group 3, except two lights of 0.25-in. clear glass with 0.5-in. air space.

U value = 0.85 Btu/hr/(ft^2)($^\circ$F) for all groups when used with single glazing.

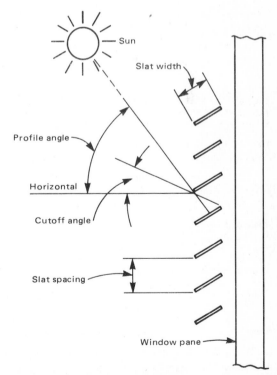

Figure 5-16 Louvered sun screen details.

Figure 5-17 Shading coefficients for single and insulating glass with draperies. (Reprinted with permission from the 1977 Fundamentals Volume, *ASHRAE Handbook and Products Directory*.)

Glazing	Glass transmittance	Glass SC*	A	B	C	D	E	F	G	H	I	J
Single glass												
1/4 in. clear	0.80	0.95	0.80	0.75	0.70	0.65	0.60	0.55	0.50	0.45	0.40	0.35
1/2 in. clear	0.71	0.88	0.74	0.70	0.66	0.61	0.56	0.52	0.48	0.43	0.39	0.35
1/4-in. heat-absorbing	0.46	0.67	0.57	0.54	0.52	0.49	0.46	0.44	0.41	0.38	0.36	0.33
1/2-in. heat-absorbing	0.24	0.50	0.43	0.42	0.40	0.39	0.38	0.36	0.34	0.33	0.32	0.30
Reflective-coated (see	—	0.60	0.57	0.54	0.51	0.49	0.46	0.43	0.41	0.38	0.36	0.33
manufacturers' literature for	—	0.50	0.46	0.44	0.42	0.41	0.39	0.38	0.36	0.34	0.33	0.31
exact values)	—	0.40	0.36	0.35	0.34	0.33	0.32	0.30	0.29	0.28	0.27	0.26
	—	0.30	0.25	0.24	0.24	0.23	0.23	0.23	0.22	0.21	0.21	0.20
Insulating glass (1/2-in. air space)												
Clear out and clear in	0.64	0.83	0.66	0.62	0.58	0.56	0.52	0.48	0.45	0.42	0.37	0.35
Heat-absorbing out and clear in	0.37	0.56	0.49	0.47	0.45	0.43	0.41	0.39	0.37	0.35	0.33	0.32
Reflective-coated (see	—	0.40	0.38	0.37	0.37	0.36	0.34	0.32	0.31	0.29	0.28	0.28
manufacturers' literature for	—	0.30	0.29	0.28	0.27	0.27	0.26	0.26	0.25	0.25	0.24	0.24
exact values)	—	0.20	0.19	0.19	0.18	0.18	0.17	0.17	0.16	0.16	0.15	0.15

*For glass alone, with no drapery.

Figure 5-17 gives shading coefficients for single and double glazing of various types with many types of draperies hung inside the windows. The column headings A through J in fig. 5-17 represent different types of drapery materials, and the use of these data will require some judgment and familiarity with such materials.

Columns A and B give shading coefficients for use when drapery material is of a comparatively open weave (over 25% open space in the weave) and a comparatively dark color, with low light reflectance characteristics.

Columns I and J list shading coefficients for use when the drapery fabric is of a closed weave (less than 7% open space in the weave) and a comparatively light color with high light reflectance.

Columns C through H list shading coefficients that may be used when the drapery fabric weave and color fall somewhere in between the extremes listed above for columns A and B and for columns I and J.

Notice that for comparative purposes in fig. 5-17, the third column lists SC values, for the various types of glass shown, when no draperies are in use.

For the purposes of using fig. 5-17, closed weave, semiopen weave, and open weave fabrics may be defined as follows:

Closed weave: no objects are visible looking through the drapery fabric, but large light and dark areas may show.

Semiopen weave: these fabrics do not permit details to be seen through them, but large objects are clearly defined.

Open weave: these fabrics allow details to be seen through them, and the general view is relatively clear with no confusion of vision.

Figure 5-18 lists values of SC for domed skylights of the type and relative proportioning shown. Notice that values are given for skylights both with and without the light diffuser panel near the bottom of the skylight assembly. Notice also the *U* factors are given; these are summertime-only factors, and would not be suitable for wintertime calculations.

Example 5-3 In the corner room of example 5-2, if the five windows in the south and west walls are protected from the sun by:

Figure 5-18 Shading coefficients for domed skylights. (Reprinted with permission from the 1977 Fundamentals Volume, *ASHRAE Handbook and Products Directory*.)

Dome	Light diffuser (translucent)*	Curb		Shading coefficient	U factor
		Height, in.	Width-to-height ratio		
Clear	yes	0	∞	0.61	0.46
$\tau = 0.86$	$\tau = 0.58$	9	5	0.58	0.43
		18	2.5	0.50	0.40
Clear		0	∞	0.99	0.80
$\tau = 0.86$	None	9	5	0.88	0.75
		18	2.5	0.80	0.70
Translucent	None	0	∞	0.57	0.80
$\tau = 0.52$		18	2.5	0.46	0.70
Translucent	None	0	∞	0.34	0.80
$\tau = 0.27$		9	5	0.30	0.75
		18	2.5	0.28	0.70

*τ = transmittance.

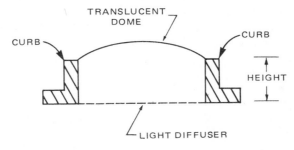

1   Group 4 louvered sun screen on the south windows (exterior) and

2   Light-colored venetian blinds on the interior of the west windows.

Find the total heat gain through all five windows at 15:00 solar time.

Solution   As shown in example 5-2, at 15:00 solar time, the solar gain is 7632 BH and the conduction heat gain (due to temperature difference between outdoors and indoors) is 1504 BH. Of the solar gain, 2640 BH is through the south glass (3 windows $\times$ 4 ft $\times$ 5 ft $\times$ 0.8 $\times$ 55 BH/ft^2 = 2640 BH), and 4992 BH is through the west glass

(2 windows $\times$ 4 ft $\times$ 5 ft $\times$ 0.8 $\times$ 156 BH/ft^2 = 4992).

From fig. 5-15 we see that a group 4 sun screen is made of light color or unpainted aluminum with a slat width which is 85% of the slat spacing (see fig. 5-16). Also, we see in fig. 5-19 that for 15:00 solar time, the solar altitude angle at 40° north latitude is 76° in July. (Solar altitude angle in fig. 5-19 and the profile angle of fig. 5-15 are the same.) The 76° solar altitude angle is greater than the 40° listed in fig. 5-15, so we find in fig. 5-15 that the shading coefficient SC is 0.30 for the south windows.

Similarly, we see in fig. 5-12 that the shading

Figure 5-19 Solar altitude and azimuth angles for 32° and 40° north latitude. (Reprinted with permission from the 1977 Fundamentals Volume, *ASHRAE Handbook and Products Directory*.)

Date,* Month	Solar time A.M.	Solar time P.M.	32° N latitude Solar position Altitude†	32° N latitude Solar position Azimuth‡	40° N latitude Solar position Altitude†	40° N latitude Solar position Azimuth‡
December	8	16	10	54	5	53
	9	15	20	44	14	42
	10	14	28	31	21	29
	11	13	33	16	25	15
	12		35	0	27	0
January	7	17	1	65		
and	8	16	13	56	8	55
November	9	15	22	46	17	44
	10	14	31	33	24	31
	11	13	36	18	28	16
	12		38	0	30	0
February	7	17	7	73	4	72
and	8	16	18	64	15	62
October	9	15	29	53	24	50
	10	14	38	39	32	35
	11	13	45	21	37	19
	12		47	0	39	0
March	7	17	13	82	11	80
and	8	16	25	73	23	70
September	9	15	37	62	33	57
	10	14	47	47	42	42
	11	13	55	27	48	23
	12		58	0	50	0
April	7	17	19	92	19	89
and	8	16	31	84	30	79
August	9	15	44	74	41	67
	10	14	56	60	51	51
	11	13	65	37	59	29
	12		70	0	62	0
May	7	17	23	100	24	97
and	8	16	35	93	35	87
July	9	15	48	85	47	76
	10	14	61	73	57	61
	11	13	72	52	66	37
	12		78	0	70	0
June	7	17	24	103	26	100
	8	16	37	97	37	91
	9	15	50	89	49	80
	10	14	62	80	60	66
	11	13	74	61	69	42
	12		81	0	73	0

*As of the twenty-first day of each month.

†Angle of the sun above the horizon, in degrees.

‡Angular position of the sun, away from south, in degrees.

coefficient for clear single glass with light-colored venetian blinds is 0.55 for the west windows.

The solar heat gain through these five windows is now reduced from the values shown above by the application of the SC values as follows:

South glass:

$$3 \times 4 \text{ ft} \times 5 \text{ ft} \times 0.8 \times 55 \times 0.30 = 792 \text{ BH}$$

West glass:

$$2 \times 4 \text{ ft} \times 5 \text{ ft} \times 0.8 \times 156 \times 0.55 = 2746 \text{ BH}$$

The total heat gain through these five windows is now:

South solar	792
West solar	2746
Conduction gain	1504
Total gain	5042 BH

The total heat gain is thus reduced from 9136 BH to 5042 BH by the rather inexpensive expedient of adding solar protection.

In example 5-3, the cooling load for the room in question is reduced 0.34 ton:

$$\frac{9136 \text{ BH} - 5042 \text{ BH}}{12,000 \text{ BH}} = 0.34 \text{ ton}$$

It is a good guess that the 0.34-ton reduction in the capacity of the cooling system would result in a cost saving equal to the cost of the solar protection. Therefore, the net cost of the solar protection sun screening and venetian blinds is zero; and for the life of the building, there is a savings in operating cost.

5-11 HEAT GAINS THROUGH WALLS

The problems of summertime heat gains, like wintertime heat losses, through building walls can be, in general, solved with the use of the basic conduction heat flow formula:

$$BH = A \times U \times \Delta t \qquad (4\text{-}1)$$

The wall area A is, of course, the same summer and winter, and the U factor is only very slightly different. (Many HVAC designers do not wish to bother with the slight U-factor difference and use wintertime U factors all year around.) However, when we consider the Δt, the outdoor-indoor temperature difference, $t_o - t_i$, we encounter a very substantial variation in procedure.

In winter, the greatest heat flow through walls occurs at night when OA temperatures are lowest. Also, in winter the OA temperature usually varies very little for many hours between bedtime and the following morning. Temperature conditions become fairly stabilized, and heat flow is very closely proportional to temperature difference. Of course, the sun is not shining and is not a factor.

In summer, the situation is really very different. Now we have a continuously changing pattern of daytime temperature differences, building uses, solar position, solar angles, and solar intensities; and the heat gains through walls are influenced by all of these.

Now, with comparatively rapid changes in the building environment, we become concerned not only with the wall U factor, but with the type of wall construction as well. A lightweight frame wall, with very little mass, may almost change its internal temperatures as fast as outdoor temperature changes. As the sun rises and shines on this lightweight wall, its temperature may rise very quickly and deliver such heat to the building interior very quickly. In other words, it has very little *thermal inertia* or time lag.

Compare this with the thick, heavy masonry wall of a church. This wall cools off during the long hours of the night, and even though outdoor air temperature rises quickly the following day, and the sun beats on it, the heat resulting from this attack may not reach the building interior and become cooling load until late afternoon or early evening. This wall has much thermal inertia, and the time lag between temperature and solar attack and the appearance of resultant heat flow indoors is great.

We say that a heavy wall has great *storage effect*; that is, it can store great quantities of heat before its temperature rises to the point that it begins to deliver heat to the interior.

It is easy to see that heat flow through a wall cannot be estimated with the use of the formula above unless we can apply some "experience factors" to the selection of the Δt in this very complicated situation. Fortunately, ASHRAE has come to our rescue again and provided us with good, solid, empirical data on the basis of which we may select *equivalent temperature differences* (ETDs) to substitute in the heat flow formula for the Δt term. We may now write

$$BH = A \times U \times ETD \qquad (5\text{-}1)$$

ASHRAE calls these ETDs by the term CLTD, meaning "cooling load temperature difference." However, the term ETD is also used extensively in the HVAC business and seems to give a more meaningful expression of the situation that really prevails. These empirical factors are really "air" temperature differences which are "equivalent" to a situation that involves a somewhat different actual air temperature difference as well as the effect of the sun and the thermal inertia of the building.

For example, a given wall might be exposed to the summer afternoon sun at a time when the outdoor temperature is 95°F and room air is 78°F. Even though the actual air temperature difference, Δt, is 17°F (95°F - 78°F = 17°F), the amount of heat flow is equivalent to a much higher Δt, such as 35°F, for example.

Suppose that a given building wall was exposed, for many hours, on an overcast, sunless day to the conditions 95°F OA and 78°F RA and the resulting 17°F Δt. A certain amount of heat would pass through this wall. On the following day, the same conditions prevail except that now the sun shines brightly all day. Everyone will surely agree that

more heat will pass through the wall on the second day when the sun beats on the wall all day. The heat that flows in on the sunny day is "equivalent" to a greater Δt; this greater Δt is the ETD.

However, the impression should not be given that ETDs are always greater than actual air temperature differences, Δt; they are not. In the case of the church with the heavy masonry walls, during morning hours the ETD would probably be less than the actual air Δt.

When one is making a heat gain calculation for a glass area, as shown in the preceding article, one must make two separate calculations: one for conduction heat gain and one for direct solar transmission. With walls and roofs this is not the case; after the ETD is determined, only one calculation using the formula BH = $A \times U \times$ ETD is necessary.

Since wall areas and U factors are very easily determined, the problem devolves into one of determining the proper ETD. Figure 5-20 lists ETD values for many different types of walls, at all the different hours of the day solar time, for the eight standard compass orientations. Figure 5-20 is based on the assumption that walls are dark colored (dark blue, red, brown, and green), that the date is July 21, that the building location is at 40° north latitude, that outdoor design temperature is 95°F, that indoor temperature is 78°F, and that the summertime daily range t_d is 21°F. The reader is referred to the footnotes of fig. 5-20, where instructions are given for making corrections for:

1 Design conditions other than those shown in the footnotes and listed above
2 Building locations at or near 32° north latitude instead of 40° north latitude
3 Wall exterior colors other than the dark colors mentioned

Inspection of the table in fig. 5-20 quickly reveals that its use requires the selection of one of the seven wall groups shown (groups A through G). To make a choice among these groups, one must consult fig. 5-21, which describes in some detail the

Figure 5-20 Equivalent temperature differences (ETDs) for calculating cooling load from sunlit walls; for 40° north latitude, July 21, and design temperatures of 95.5°F t_o, 78°F t_i, and 21°F t_d. (Reprinted with permission from the 1977 Fundamentals Volume, *ASHRAE Handbook and Products Directory*.)

North latitude wall facing	\multicolumn{24}{c}{Solar time, hr}																								Hour of maximum ETD	Minimum ETD	Maximum ETD	Difference ETD
	1	2	3	4	5	6	7	8	9	10	11	12	13	14	15	16	17	18	19	20	21	22	23	24				
\multicolumn{29}{c}{Group A walls}
N	14	14	14	13	13	13	12	12	11	11	10	10	10	10	10	10	11	11	12	12	13	13	14	14	2	10	14	4
NE	19	19	19	18	17	17	16	15	15	15	15	15	16	16	17	18	18	18	19	19	20	20	20	20	22	15	20	5
E	24	24	23	23	22	21	20	19	19	18	19	19	20	21	22	23	24	24	25	25	25	25	25	25	22	18	25	7
SE	24	23	23	22	21	20	20	19	18	18	18	18	18	19	20	21	22	23	23	24	24	24	24	24	22	18	24	6
S	20	20	19	19	18	18	17	16	16	15	14	14	14	14	14	15	16	17	18	19	19	20	20	20	23	14	20	6
SW	25	25	25	24	24	23	22	21	20	19	19	18	17	17	17	17	18	18	19	20	22	23	24	25	25	24	17	25	8
W	27	27	26	26	25	24	24	23	22	21	20	19	19	18	18	18	18	19	20	22	23	25	26	26	1	18	27	9
NW	21	21	21	20	20	19	19	18	17	16	16	15	15	14	14	14	15	15	16	17	18	19	20	21	1	14	21	7
\multicolumn{29}{c}{Group B walls}
N	15	14	14	13	12	11	11	10	9	9	9	8	9	9	9	10	11	12	13	14	14	15	15	15	24	8	15	7
NE	19	18	17	16	15	14	13	12	12	13	14	15	16	17	18	19	19	20	20	21	21	21	20	20	21	12	21	9
E	23	22	21	20	18	17	16	15	15	15	17	19	21	22	24	25	26	26	27	27	26	26	25	24	20	15	27	12
SE	23	22	21	20	18	17	16	15	14	14	15	16	18	20	21	23	24	25	26	26	26	26	25	24	21	14	26	12
S	21	20	19	18	17	15	14	13	12	11	11	11	12	14	15	17	19	20	21	22	22	22	21		23	11	22	11
SW	27	26	25	24	22	21	19	18	16	15	14	14	13	13	14	15	17	20	22	25	27	28	28	28	24	13	28	15
W	29	28	27	26	24	23	21	19	18	17	16	15	14	14	14	15	17	19	22	25	27	29	29	30	24	14	30	16
NW	23	22	21	20	19	18	17	15	14	13	12	12	12	11	12	12	13	15	17	19	21	22	23	23	24	11	23	9
\multicolumn{29}{c}{Group C walls}
N	15	14	13	12	11	10	9	8	8	7	7	8	9	10	12	13	14	15	16	17	17	17	17	16	22	7	17	10
NE	19	17	16	14	13	11	10	10	11	13	15	17	19	20	21	22	22	23	23	23	23	22	21	20	20	10	23	13
E	22	21	19	17	15	14	12	12	14	16	19	22	25	27	29	29	30	30	30	29	28	27	26	24	18	12	30	18
SE	22	21	19	17	15	14	12	12	12	13	16	19	22	24	26	28	29	29	29	29	28	27	26	24	19	12	29	17
S	21	19	18	16	15	13	12	10	9	9	9	10	11	14	17	20	22	24	25	26	25	25	24	22	20	9	26	17
SW	29	27	25	22	20	18	16	15	13	12	11	11	11	13	15	18	22	26	29	32	33	33	32	31	22	11	33	22
W	31	29	27	25	22	20	18	16	14	13	12	12	12	13	14	16	20	24	29	32	35	35	35	33	22	12	35	23
NW	25	23	21	20	18	16	14	13	11	10	10	10	10	11	12	13	15	18	22	25	27	27	27	26	22	10	27	17
\multicolumn{29}{c}{Group D walls}
N	15	13	12	10	9	7	6	6	6	6	6	7	8	10	12	13	15	17	18	19	19	19	18	16	21	6	19	13
NE	17	15	13	11	10	8	7	8	10	14	17	20	22	23	23	24	24	25	25	24	23	22	20	18	19	7	25	18
E	19	17	15	13	11	9	8	9	12	17	22	27	30	32	33	33	32	32	31	30	28	26	24	22	16	8	33	25
SE	20	17	15	13	11	10	8	8	10	13	17	22	26	29	31	32	32	32	31	30	28	26	24	22	17	8	32	24
S	19	17	15	13	11	9	8	7	6	6	7	9	12	16	20	24	27	29	29	29	27	26	24	22	19	6	29	23
SW	28	25	22	19	16	14	12	10	9	8	8	8	10	12	16	21	27	32	36	38	38	37	34	31	21	8	38	30
W	31	27	24	21	18	15	13	11	10	9	9	9	10	11	14	18	24	30	36	40	41	40	38	34	21	9	41	32
NW	25	22	19	17	14	12	10	9	8	7	7	8	9	10	12	14	18	22	27	31	32	32	30	27	22	7	32	25
\multicolumn{29}{c}{Group E walls}
N	12	10	8	7	5	4	3	4	5	6	7	9	11	13	15	17	19	20	21	23	20	18	16	14	20	3	22	19
NE	13	11	9	7	6	4	5	9	15	20	24	25	25	26	26	26	26	26	25	24	22	19	17	15	16	4	26	22
E	14	12	10	8	6	5	6	11	18	26	33	36	38	37	34	33	32	30	28	25	22	20	17		13	5	38	33
SE	15	12	10	8	7	5	5	8	12	19	25	31	35	37	37	36	34	33	31	28	26	23	20	17	15	5	37	32
S	15	12	10	8	7	5	4	3	4	5	9	13	19	24	29	32	34	33	31	29	26	23	20	17	17	3	34	31
SW	22	18	15	12	10	8	6	5	5	6	7	9	12	18	24	32	38	43	45	44	40	35	30	26	19	5	45	40
W	25	21	17	14	11	9	7	6	6	6	7	9	11	14	20	27	36	43	49	49	45	40	34	29	20	6	49	43
NW	20	17	14	11	9	7	6	5	5	5	6	8	10	13	16	20	26	32	37	38	36	32	28	24	20	5	38	33
\multicolumn{29}{c}{Group F walls}
N	8	6	5	3	2	1	2	4	6	7	9	11	14	17	19	21	22	23	24	23	20	16	13	11	19	1	23	23
NE	9	7	5	3	2	1	5	14	23	28	30	29	28	27	27	27	27	26	24	22	19	16	13	11	11	1	30	29
E	10	7	6	4	3	2	6	17	28	38	44	45	43	39	36	34	32	30	27	24	21	17	15	12	12	2	45	43
SE	10	7	6	4	3	2	4	10	19	28	36	41	43	42	39	36	34	31	28	25	21	18	15	12	13	2	43	41

Figure 5-20 *(Cont.)*

North latitude wall facing	1	2	3	4	5	6	7	8	9	10	11	12	13	14	15	16	17	18	19	20	21	22	23	24	Hour of maximum ETD	Minimum ETD	Maximum ETD	Difference ETD
S	10	8	6	4	3	2	1	1	3	7	13	20	27	34	38	39	38	35	31	26	22	18	15	12	16	1	39	38
SW	15	11	9	6	5	3	2	2	4	5	8	11	17	26	35	44	50	53	52	45	37	28	23	18	18	2	53	48
W	17	13	10	7	5	4	3	3	4	6	8	11	14	20	28	39	49	57	60	54	43	34	27	21	19	3	60	57
NW	14	10	8	6	4	3	2	2	3	5	8	10	13	15	21	27	35	42	46	43	35	28	22	18	19	2	46	44
Group G walls																												
N	3	2	1	0	-1	2	7	8	9	12	15	18	21	23	24	24	25	26	22	15	11	9	7	5	18	-1	26	27
NE	3	2	1	0	-1	9	27	36	39	35	30	26	26	27	27	26	25	22	18	14	11	9	7	5	9	-1	39	40
E	4	2	1	0	-1	11	31	47	54	55	50	40	33	31	30	29	27	24	19	15	12	10	8	6	10	-1	55	56
SE	4	2	1	0	-1	5	18	32	42	49	51	48	42	36	32	30	27	24	19	15	12	10	8	6	11	-1	51	52
S	4	2	1	0	-1	0	1	5	12	22	31	39	45	46	43	37	31	25	20	15	12	10	8	5	14	-1	46	47
SW	5	4	3	1	0	0	2	5	8	12	16	26	38	50	59	63	61	52	37	24	17	13	10	8	16	0	63	63
W	6	5	3	2	1	1	2	5	8	11	15	19	27	41	56	67	72	67	48	29	20	15	11	8	17	1	72	71
NW	5	3	2	1	0	0	2	5	8	11	15	18	21	27	37	47	55	55	41	25	17	13	10	7	18	0	55	55

1. Application: These values may be used for all normal air-conditioning estimates; usually without correction (except as noted below) when the load is calculated for the hottest weather.

2. Corrections: The values in the table were calculated for an inside temperature of 78°F and an outdoor daily range of 21°F. The table remains approximately correct for other outdoor maximums (93 to 102°F) and other outdoor daily ranges (16 to 34°F), provided the outdoor daily average temperature remains approximately 85°F. ETD_c (corrected ETD) = ETD from table + $(78° - t_i) + (t_o - t_d/2 - 85°)$. The table values will be approximately correct for the east or west wall in any latitude (0° to 50° north or south) during the hottest weather.

3. Color of exterior surface of wall: For light colors, multiply the wall-cooling load temperature difference in the table by 0.65. Use temperature differences for light walls only when the permanence of the light wall is established by experience. For cream colors, use the light wall values. For medium colors, interpolate halfway between the dark and light values. Medium colors are medium blue and green, bright red, light brown, unpainted wood, and natural color concrete. Dark blue, red, brown, and green are considered dark colors.

4. 32° N latitude: For locations at 32° N latitude, tabulated ETDs must be adjusted plus or minus as follows: North: no change; Northeast: +1°F; East: -1°F; Southeast: -2°F; South: -4°F; Southwest: -1°F; West: no change; Northwest: no change.

types of wall construction included in each group. Further information is given concerning wall construction in fig. 5-22, which gives thicknesses and thermal properties of the various wall component materials.

Example 5-4 A building is located at 32° north latitude and has in it a southwest room that is 30 ft long along its south wall and 20 ft wide along its west wall. Its ceiling height is 9 ft and it has five windows 4 ft wide by 5 ft high—three in the south wall and two in the west wall.

Both outside walls are constructed of: 4-in. face brick exterior, 2-in. insulation with a conductivity k of 0.3, 8-in. heavy-weight (gravel aggregate)

concrete block, and 3/4-in. gypsum plaster and metal lath on 3/4-in. furring strips on the interior.

Find the heat gain through these walls on a sunny day in July, at 15:00 solar time, if the outdoor temperature (OA or t_o) is 95°F DB, the indoor room temperature (RA or t_i) is 76°F DB, and the daily range t_d for the location is 20°F.

Solution The heat gain through these walls can be estimated with the use of formula (5-1): BH = $A \times U \times$ ETD. Because of differing solar exposures, the south wall must be calculated independently of the west wall.

South wall:

Wall area = (30 ft long $\times$ 9 ft high)
$$-(3 \text{ windows} \times 4 \text{ ft} \times 5 \text{ ft}) = 210 \text{ ft}^2$$

Figure 5-21 Wall construction group description. (Reprinted with permission from the 1977 Fundamentals Volume, *ASHRAE Handbook and Products Directory*.)

Group no.	Description of construction	Weight, lb/ft^2	U value Btu/hr/ft^2/°F	Code numbers of layer (see fig. 5-22)
4-in. face brick + brick				
C	Air space + 4-in. face brick	83	0.358	A0, A2, B1, A2, E0
D	4-in. common brick	90	0.415	A0, A2, C4, E1, E0
C	1-in. insulation or air space + 4-in. common brick	90	0.174–0.301	A0, A2, C4, B1/B2, E1, E0
B	2-in. insulation + 4-in. common brick	88	0.111	A0, A2, B3, C4, E1, E0
B	8-in. common brick	130	0.302	A0, A2, C9, E1, E0
A	Insulation or air space + 8-in. common brick	130	0.154–0.243	A0, A2, C9, B1/B2, E1, E0
4-in. face brick + heavy-weight concrete				
C	Air space + 2-in. concrete	94	0.350	A0, A2, B1, C5, E1, E0
B	2-in. insulation + 4-in. concrete	97	0.116	A0, A2, B3, C5, E1, E0
A	Air space or insulation + 8-in. or more concrete	143–190	0.110–0.112	A0, A2, B1, C10/11, E1, E0
4-in. face brick + light-weight or heavy-weight concrete block				
E	4-in. block	62	0.319	A0, A2, C2, E1, E0
D	Air space or insulation + 4-in. block	62	0.153–0.246	A0, A2, C2, B1/B2, E1, E0
D	8-in. block	70	0.274	A0, A2, C7, A6, E0
C	Air space or 1-in. insulation + 6-in. or 8-in. block	73–89	0.221–0.275	A0, A2, B1, C7/C8, E1, E0
B	2-in. insulation + 8-in. block	89	0.096–0.107	A0, A2, B3, C7/C8, E1, E0
4-in. face brick + clay tile				
D	4-in. tile	71	0.381	A0, A2, C1, E1, E0
D	Air space + 4-in. tile	71	0.281	A0, A2, C1, B1, E1, E0
C	Insulation + 4-in. tile	71	0.169	A0, A2, C1, B2, E1, E0
C	8-in. tile	96	0.275	A0, A2, C6, E1, E0
B	Air space or 1-in. insulation + 8-in. tile	96	0.142–0.221	A0, A2, C6, B1/B2, E1, E0
A	2-in. insulation + 8-in. tile	97	0.097	A0, A2, B3, C6, E1, E0
Heavy-weight concrete wall + finish				
E	4-in. concrete	63	0.585	A0, A1, C5, E1, E0
D	4-in. concrete + 1-in. or 2-in. insulation	63	0.119–0.200	A0, A1, C5, B2/B3, E1, E0
C	2-in. insulation + 4-in. concrete	63	0.119	A0, A1, B6, C5, E1, E0
C	8-in. concrete	109	0.490	A0, A1, C10, E1, E0
B	8-in. concrete + 1-in. or 2-in. insulation	110	0.115–0.187	A0, A1, C10, B5/B6, E1, E0
A	2-in. insulation + 8-in. concrete	110	0.115	A0, A1, B3, C10, E1, E0
B	12-in. concrete	156	0.421	A0, A1, C11, E1, E0
A	12-in. concrete + insulation	156	0.113	A0, C11, B6, A6, E0
Light-weight and heavy-weight concrete block + finish				
F	4-in. block + air space insulation	29	0.161–0.263	A0, A1, C2, B1/B2, E1, E0
E	2-in. insulation + 4-in. block	29–37	0.105–0.114	A0, A1, B3, C2/C3, E1, E0
E	8-in. block	47–51	0.294–0.402	A0, A1, C7/C8, E1, E0
D	8-in. block + air space insulation	41–57	0.149–0.173	A0, A1, C7/C8, B1/B2, E1, E0
Clay tile + finish				
F	4-in. tile	39	0.419	A0, A1, C1, E1, E0
F	4-in. tile + air space	39	0.303	A0, A1, C1, B1, E1, E0
E	4-in. tile + 1-in. insulation	39	0.175	A0, A1, C1, B2, E1, E0
D	2-in. insulation + 4-in. tile	40	0.110	A0, A1, B3, C1, E1, E0
D	8-in. tile	63	0.296	A0, A1, C6, E1, E0
C	8-in. tile + air space/1-in. insulation	63	0.151–0.231	A0, A1, C6, B1/B2, E1, E0
B	2-in. insulation + 8-in. tile	63	0.099	A0, A1, B3, C6, E1, E0
Metal curtain wall				
G	With/without air space + 1-in./2-in./3-in. insulation	5–6	0.091–0.230	A0, A3, B5/B6/B12, A3, E0
Frame wall				
G	1-in. to 3-in. insulation	16	0.081–0.178	A0, A1, B1, B2/B3/B4, E1, E0

Note: A frame wall with brick veneer and 1 to 3 in. of insulation may be considered to be a group E wall.

Figure 5-22 Thermal properties and code numbers of layers used in calculations of coefficients for roof and wall. (Reprinted with permission from the 1977 Fundamentals Volume, *ASHRAE Handbook and Products Directory*.)

Description	Code number	Thickness, in.	Conductivity (k)	Density, lb/ft^3	Specific heat	Resistance R	Weight per ft^2
Outside surface resistance	AO	. . .	. . .	. . .	. . .	0.333	. . .
1-in. stucco (asbestos cement or wood siding plaster, etc.)	A1	1.0	4.8	116	0.20	0.208	9.66
4-in. face brick (dense concrete)	A2	4.0	9.0	130	0.22	0.444	43.3
Steel siding (aluminum or other lightweight cladding)	A3	0.06	312	480	0.10	0.0002	2.40
Outside surface resistance	. . .	. . .	. . .	. . .	. . .	0.333	. . .
0.5-in. slag, membrane	A4	0.50	9.96	55	0.40	. . .	. . .
0.375-in. felt	. . .	0.375	1.32	70	0.40	. . .	. . .
Finish	A6	0.50	2.88	78	0.26	0.174	3.25
4-in. face brick	A7	4.0	9.24	125	0.22	0.433	41.6
Air space resistance	B1	. . .	. . .	. . .	. . .	0.91	. . .
1-in. insulation	B2	1.0	0.30	2.0	0.2	3.32	0.17
2-in. insulation	B3	2.0	0.30	2.0	0.2	6.68	0.33
3-in. insulation	B4	3.0	0.30	2.0	0.2	10.0	0.50
1-in. insulation	B5	1.0	0.30	5.7	0.2	3.33	0.47
2-in. insulation	B6	2.0	0.30	5.7	0.2	6.68	0.95
1-in. wood	B7	1.0	0.84	37.0	0.6	1.19	3.08
2.5-in. wood	B8	2.5	0.84	37.0	0.6	2.98	7.71
4-in. wood	B9	4.0	0.84	37.0	0.6	4.76	12.3
2-in. wood	B10	2.0	0.84	37.0	0.6	2.39	6.18
3-in. wood	B11	3.0	0.84	37.0	0.6	3.58	9.25
3-in. insulation	B12	3.0	0.30	5.7	0.2	10.0	1.42
4-in. clay tile	C1	4.0	3.96	70.0	0.2	1.01	23.3
4-in. light-weight concrete block	C2	4.0	2.64	38.0	0.2	1.51	12.7
4-in. heavy-weight concrete block	C3	4.0	5.64	61.0	0.2	0.71	20.3
4-in. common brick	C4	4.0	5.04	120	0.2	0.79	40.0
4-in. heavy-weight concrete	C5	4.0	12.0	140	0.2	0.333	46.6
8-in. clay tile	C6	8.0	3.96	70	0.2	2.02	46.7
8-in. light-weight concrete block	C7	8.0	3.96	38.0	0.2	2.02	25.4
8-in. heavy-weight concrete block	C8	8.0	7.20	61.0	0.2	1.11	40.7
8-in. common brick	C9	8.0	5.04	120	0.2	1.59	80.0
8-in. heavy-weight concrete	C10	8.0	12.0	140	0.2	0.667	93.4
12-in. heavy-weight concrete	C11	12.0	12.0	140	0.2	1.00	140.0
2-in. heavy-weight concrete	C12	2.0	12.0	140	0.2	0.167	23.4
6-in. heavy-weight concrete	C13	6.0	12.0	140	0.2	0.50	70.0
4-in. light-weight concrete	C14	4.0	1.20	40	0.2	3.33	13.3
6-in. light-weight concrete	C15	6.0	1.20	40	0.2	5.0	20.0
8-in. light-weight concrete	C16	8.0	1.20	40	0.2	6.67	26.7
Inside surface resistance	E0	. . .	. . .	. . .	. . .	0.685	. . .
0.75-in. plaster; 0.75-in. gypsum or other similar finishing layer	E1	0.75	5.04	100	0.2	0.149	6.25
0.5-in. slag or stone	E2	0.50	9.96	55	0.40	0.050	2.29
0.375-in. felt and membrane	E3	0.375	1.32	70	0.40	0.285	2.19
Ceiling air space	E4	. . .	. . .	. . .	. . .	1.0	. . .
Acoustic tile-3/4 in.	E5	0.75	0.42	30	0.20	1.786	1.88

Wall U factor U_w: In fig. 5-22 the thermal resistances R of the various component wall materials may be found:

Code A0, outside surface film R_o	0.333
Code A7, 4-in. face brick	0.433
Code B3, 2-in. insulation	6.68
Code C8, 8-in. heavy concrete block	1.11
Code B1, air space between furring strips	0.91
Code E1, 3/4-in. plaster	0.149
Code E0, inside surface film R_i	0.685
Total resistance R_T	10.300

$$U_w = \frac{1}{R_T} = \frac{1}{10.300} = 0.097$$

ETD (equivalent temperature difference): From fig. 5-21 we see that, constructed as it is, this wall is a group B type of wall. From fig. 5-20 we select an ETD of 14 for group B south wall at a solar time of 15:00. However, this ETD must be corrected for nonstandard design conditions as instructed in footnote 2 of fig. 5-20 as follows:

$$\text{ETD}_c = \text{ETD} + (78°F - t_i) + (t_o - \frac{t_d}{2} - 85)$$

$$= 14 + (78°F - 76°F) + (95°F - \frac{20}{2} - 85)$$

$$= 14 + 2 + 0$$

$$= 16°F$$

Also, this corrected ETD_c must be further corrected because our building is at 32° north latitude and not 40° north latitude. Footnote 4 of fig. 5-20 shows this further correction for a south wall to be $-4°F$; therefore, our final $\text{ETD}_c = 16°F - 4°F = 12°F$.

Now, using formula (5-1), we have

$$\text{BH} = A \times U \times \text{ETD}$$
$$= 210 \text{ ft}^2 \times 0.097 \times 12°F$$
$$= 244.4 \text{ for the south wall}$$

West wall:

$$\text{Area} = (20 \text{ ft} \times 9 \text{ ft}) - (2 \times 4 \text{ ft} \times 5 \text{ ft})$$
$$= 140 \text{ ft}^2$$

U_w is same as the south wall = 0.097. ETD from fig. 5-20 is 14 for a group B west wall at 15:00 solar time.

$$\text{ETD}_c = 14 + 2°F \text{ correction (as above)} = 16°F$$

From footnote 4 of fig. 5-20 we see that the further correction for a west wall at 32° north latitude is zero—no change; and the ETD_c remains at 16°F.

Now, using formula (5-1) again, we have

$$\text{BH} = 140 \text{ ft}^2 \times 0.097 \times 16°F$$
$$= 217 \text{ for the west wall}$$

5-12 HEAT GAINS THROUGH ROOFS

Similar to heat gains through walls, heat gains through roofs may be calculated in one operation, using formula (5-1): $\text{BH} = A \times U \times \text{ETD}$, where the ETD, the equivalent temperature difference, is proportional to the combined effect of the conduction heat gain due to temperature difference $(t_o - t_i)$, and the heat gain due to sun effect. As before, the ETD also takes into account the thermal inertia, or time lag, of the roof.

As is true for walls, the roof area and U factor are usually very easily determined, but the ETD is a little more difficult. Figure 5-23 gives ETDs for 13 basic types of roofs both with and without suspended ceilings hung below the roofs.

The ETD values given are prepared for the standard design conditions of 95°F DB outdoors, 78°F DB indoors, and a daily range temperature t_d of 21°F. If nonstandard design conditions are in use, a correction may be easily made as instructed in footnote 2 of fig. 5-23 with the ETD_c correction formula listed.

Figure 5-23 Equivalent temperature differences (ETDs) for calculating cooling load from flat roofs. (Reprinted with permission from the 1977 Fundamentals Volume, *ASHRAE Handbook and Products Directory*.)

Roof no	Description of construction	Weight, lb/ft²	U value Btu/hr/ft²/°F	1	2	3	4	5	6	7	8	9	10	11	12	13	14	15	16	17	18	19	20	21	22	23	24	Hour of maximum ETD	Minimum ETD	Maximum ETD	Difference ETD
															Solar time, hr																
															Without suspended ceiling																
1	Steel sheet with 1-in. (or 2-in.) insulation	7 (8)	0.213 (0.124)	1	-2	-3	-3	-5	-3	6	19	34	49	61	71	78	79	77	70	59	45	30	18	12	8	5	3	14	-5	79	84
2	1-in. wood with 1-in. insulation	8	0.170	6	3	0	-1	-3	-3	-2	4	14	27	39	52	62	70	74	74	70	62	51	38	28	20	14	9	16	-3	74	77
3	4-in. light-weight concrete	18	0.213	9	5	2	0	-2	-3	-3	1	9	20	32	44	55	64	70	73	71	66	57	45	34	25	18	13	16	-3	73	76
4	2-in. heavy-weight concrete with 1-in. (or 2-in.) insulation	29	0.206 (0.122)	12	8	5	3	0	-1	-1	3	11	20	30	41	51	59	65	66	66	62	54	45	36	29	22	17	16	-1	67	68
5	1-in. wood with 2-in. insulation	19	0.109	3	0	-3	-4	-5	-7	-6	-3	5	16	27	39	49	57	63	64	62	57	48	37	26	18	11	7	16	-7	64	71
6	6-in. light-weight concrete	24	0.158	22	17	13	9	6	3	1	1	3	7	15	23	33	43	51	58	62	64	62	57	50	42	35	28	18	1	54	63
7	2.5-in. wood with 1-in. insulation	13	0.130	29	24	20	16	13	10	7	6	6	9	13	20	27	34	42	48	53	55	56	54	49	44	39	34	19	6	56	50
8	8-in. light-weight concrete	31	0.126	35	30	26	22	18	14	11	9	7	7	9	13	19	25	33	39	46	50	53	54	53	49	45	40	20	7	54	47
9	4-in. heavy-weight concrete with 1-in. (or 2-in.) insulation	52 (52)	0.200 (0.120)	25	22	18	15	12	9	8	8	10	14	20	26	33	40	46	50	53	53	52	48	43	38	34	30	18	8	53	45
10	2.5-in. wood with 2-in. insulation	13	0.093	30	26	23	19	16	13	10	9	8	9	13	17	23	29	36	41	46	49	51	50	47	43	39	35	19	8	51	43
11	Roof terrace system	75	0.106	34	31	28	25	22	19	16	14	13	13	15	18	22	26	31	36	40	44	45	46	45	43	40	37	20	13	46	33
12	6-in. heavy-weight concrete with 1-in. (or 2-in.) insulation	75 (75)	0.192 (0.117)	31	28	25	22	20	17	15	14	14	16	18	22	26	31	36	40	43	45	45	44	42	40	37	34	19	14	45	31
13	4-in. wood with 1-in. (or 2-in.) insulation	17 (18)	0.106 (0.078)	38	36	33	30	28	25	22	20	18	17	16	17	18	21	24	28	32	36	39	41	43	43	42	40	22	16	43	27
															With suspended ceiling																
1	Steel sheet with 1-in. (or 2-in.) insulation	9 (10)	0.134 (0.092)	2	0	-2	-3	-4	-4	-1	9	23	37	50	62	71	77	78	74	67	56	42	28	18	12	8	5	15	-4	78	82
2	1-in. wood with 1-in. insulation	10	0.115	20	15	11	8	5	3	2	3	7	13	21	30	40	48	55	60	62	61	58	51	44	37	30	25	17	2	62	60

Figure 5-23 *(Cont.)*

No.	Construction	Code No.	U	Equivalent temperature differences, °F
3	4-in. light-weight concrete	20	0.134	19 14 10 7 4 2 0 0 4 10 19 29 39 48 56 62 65 64 61 54 46 38 30 24 17 0 65 65
4	2-in. heavy-weight concrete with 1-in. insulation	30	0.131	28 23 20 17 15 13 13 14 16 20 25 30 35 39 43 46 47 46 44 44 41 38 35 32 18 13 47 34
5	1-in. wood with 2-in. insulation	10	0.083	25 20 16 13 10 7 5 5 7 12 18 25 33 41 48 53 57 57 56 52 46 40 34 29 18 5 57 52
6	6-in. light-weight concrete	26	0.109	32 28 23 19 16 13 10 8 7 8 11 16 22 29 36 42 48 52 54 54 51 47 42 37 20 7 54 47
7	2.5-in. wood with 1-in. insulation	15	0.096	34 31 29 26 23 21 18 16 15 16 18 21 25 30 34 38 41 43 44 44 42 40 37 37 21 15 44 29
8	8-in. light-weight concrete	33	0.093	39 36 33 29 26 23 20 18 15 14 15 17 20 25 29 34 38 42 44 45 46 45 44 42 21 14 46 32
9	4-in. heavy-weight concrete with 1-in. (or 2-in.) insulation	53 (54)	0.128 (0.090)	30 29 27 26 24 22 20 21 22 24 27 29 32 34 36 38 38 38 37 36 34 33 33 33 19 20 38 18
10	2.5-in. wood with 2-in. insulation	15	0.072	35 33 30 28 26 24 22 20 18 18 20 22 25 28 32 35 38 40 41 41 40 39 37 37 21 18 41 23
11	Roof terrace system	77	0.082	30 29 28 27 26 25 24 23 22 22 22 23 25 26 28 29 31 32 33 33 33 33 32 32 22 22 33 11
12	6-in. heavy-weight concrete with 1-in. insulation	77 (77)	0.125 (0.088)	29 28 27 26 25 24 23 22 21 22 23 25 26 28 30 32 33 34 34 34 33 32 31 31 20 21 34 13
13	4-in. wood with 1-in. (or 2-in.) insulation	19 (20)	0.082 (0.064)	35 34 33 32 31 29 27 26 24 23 22 22 22 24 25 27 30 32 34 35 36 37 36 36 23 21 37 16

1. Application: These values may be used for all normal air-conditioning estimates; usually without correction (except as noted below) in latitude 0° to 50° north or south when the load is calculated for the hottest weather.

2. Corrections: The values in the table were calculated for an inside temperature of 78°F and an outdoor maximum temperature of 95°F, with an outdoor daily range of 21°F. The table remains approximately correct for other outdoor maximums (93 to 102°F) and other outdoor daily ranges (16 to 34°F), provided the outdoor daily average temperature remains approximately 85°F. If the room air temperature is different from 78°F and/or the outdoor daily average temperature is different from 85°F, the following rules apply: (a) For room air temperature less than 78°F, add the difference between 78°F and room air temperature; if greater than 78°F, subtract the difference. (b) For outdoor daily average temperature less than 85°F, subtract the difference between 85°F and the daily average temperature; if greater than 85°F, add the difference; or otherwise, $ETD_C = ETD$ from above $+ (78° - t_i) + (t_o - t_d/2 - 85)$.

3. Attics or other spaces between the roof and ceiling: If the ceiling is insulated and a fan is used for positive ventilation in the space between the ceiling and roof, the total temperature difference for calculating the room load may be decreased by 25%. If the attic space contains a return duct or other air plenum, care should be taken in determining the portion of the heat gain that reaches the ceiling.

4. Light colors: Multiply the ETDs in the table by 0.5. Credit should not be taken for light-colored roofs except where the permanence of light color is established by experience, as in rural areas or where there is little smoke.

5. Solar transmission in other months: The table values of temperature differences calculated for July 21 will be approximately correct for a roof in the months as shown in table continuation, page 136.

6. For details of construction of the above roofs, see schedule of code numbers below and fig. 5-22.

Figure 5-23 *(Cont.)*

Roof Construction Code

Roof no.	Description	Code numbers of layers (see fig. 5-22)
1	Steel sheet with 1-in. insulation	A0, E2, E3, B5, A3, E0
2	1-in. wood with 1-in. insulation	A0, E2, E3, B5, B7, E0
3	4-in. light-weight concrete	A0, E2, E3, C14, E0
4	2-in. heavy-weight concrete with 1-in. insulation	A0, E2, E3, B5, C12, E0
5	1-in. wood with 2-in. insulation	A0, E2, E3, B6, B7, E0
6	6-in. light-weight concrete	A0, E2, E3, C15, E0
7	2.5-in. wood with 1-in. insulation	A0, E2, E3, B5, B8, E0
8	8-in. light-weight concrete	A0, E2, E3, C16, E0
9	4-in. heavy-weight concrete with 1-in. insulation	A0, E2, E3, B5, C5, E0
10	2.5-in. wood with 2 in. insulation	A0, E2, E3, B6, B8, E0
11	Roof terrace system	A0, C12, B1, B6, E2, E3, C5, E0
12	6-in. heavy-weight concrete with 1-in. insulation	A0, E2, E3, B5, C13, E0
13	4-in. wood with 1-in. insulation	A0, E2, E3, B5, B9, E0

Latitude	Months	Latitude	Months
	North latitude		South latitude
0°	All months	0°	All months
10°	All months	10°	All months
20°	All months except November, December, January	20°	All months except May, June, July
30°	March, April, May, June, July, August, September	30°	September, October, November, December, January, February, March
40°	April, May, June, July, August	40°	October, November, December, January, February
50°	May, June, July	50°	November, December, January

It should be noted that the values listed in fig. 5-23 are usable in most north and south latitudes without correction. Figure 5-23 also includes a schedule of code numbers representing the materials that are used in construction of the 13 basic types of roofs listed. Detailed information is given in fig. 5-22 to describe the physical and thermal characteristics of the roof materials considered. Cross-reference is made between figs. 5-23 and 5-22 through the use of alphanumeric code numbers shown in both figures.

Example 5-5 The same building considered in examples 5-1 through 5-4, located at 32° north latitude, has a southwest room which is 30 ft long and 20 ft wide. It has a flat roof of normal, dark color (most flat roofs either are or become dark in color) with a 3/4-in. acoustic ceiling suspended beneath it. The roof is constructed with a 4-in. lightweight concrete roof deck, and is similar to roof number 3 of fig. 5-23.

Find the heat gain through this roof at 15:00 solar time on July 21 if design conditions are 95°F DB outside air, 76°F DB room air, and 20°F daily range.

Solution As in example 5-4, we again use formula (5-1), BH = $A \times U \times$ ETD.

$$\text{Area } A = 30 \text{ ft} \times 20 \text{ ft} = 600 \text{ ft}^2$$

U-factor calculation: fig. 5-23 advises that this roof utilizes materials with code numbers A0, E2, E3, C14, and E0. In addition, it has a 3/4-in. suspended acoustic ceiling and an air space between the roof and the ceiling. The resistance R of each of these components is:

A0, outside surface film	0.333
E2, 1/2-in. slag or stone	0.050
E3, 3/8-in. felt and membrane	0.285
C14, 4-in. lightweight concrete	3.333
E4, ceiling air space	1.000
E5, 3/4-in. acoustic tile	1.786
E0, inside surface film	0.685
Total resistance R_T	7.472

$$U \text{ factor} = \frac{1}{R_T} = \frac{1}{7.472} = 0.134$$

The ETD may now be selected from fig. 5-23 for roof 3, with suspended ceiling, at 15:00 solar time; this value is 56. This value must be corrected for nonstandard design conditions as follows:

$$\text{ETD}_c = \text{ETD} + (78°\text{F} - t_i) + (t_o - \frac{t_d}{2} - 85)$$

$$= 56 + (78°\text{F} - 76°\text{F}) + (95°\text{F} - \frac{20}{2} - 85)$$

$$= 56 + 2 + 0 = 58°\text{F}$$

No correction is needed for the 32° north latitude building location.

The roof heat gain is then

$$\text{BH} = 600 \text{ ft}^2 \times 0.134 \, U \text{ factor} \times 58°\text{F}$$

$$= 4663$$

PROBLEMS

5-1 A large room in an office building is 50 ft long and 25 ft wide and has in it:

  1 Fifty office workers, both men and women, seated and doing light work.
  2 Twenty-five 100-watt (W) lighting fixtures (1 W = 3.42 BH).
  3 Two 625-W electric coffee brewers which are counter-mounted with no exhaust hood.

  4 A water cooler with a 1/4-horsepower (hp) motor which runs 60% of the time. Power consumption of small motors may be estimated at 1500 W/hp.
  5 Sixteen electric typewriters which draw 65 W of power and operate 45% of the time.

Find the total heat load in BH (or Btuh) and in tons that the listed items of internal load constitute.

5-2 The seating area of a movie theater is 75 ft wide and 120 ft long. Calculate the tons of cooling load that the people in this theater constitute; find the separate sensible heat and latent heat loads as well as the total heat load.

5-3 A tall building acts like a chimney in winter, with vigorous movement of air upward in the building. Does this phenomenon also take place in the summer? Discuss your answer briefly.

5-4 The use of vertical, enclosed shafts in tall buildings to enclose ducts, piping, and conduits is a good idea, but what must be done in these shafts to prevent them from operating like a chimney?

5-5 An institutional building has a 200-ton HVAC system in it which is designed to circulate as much as 80,000 cfm total quantity of air. What would be the minimum amount of outside air that the HVAC system should supply for general building ventilation?

5-6 In the building of prob. 5-5, what would be the load in MBH that the calculated amount of OA would add to the heating system load when OA = 10°F and RA = 68°F?

5-7 In the building of prob. 5-5, what would be the OA latent heat load when OA is 96°F DB and 77°F WB and RA is 77°F DB and 40% RH?

5-8 Find the heat gain of example 5-2 in art. 5-9 if the building is located at 32° north latitude, if the glass in the windows is 1/4-in. heat-absorbing glass ($h_o = 4.0$) if OA temperature is 97°F and RA temperature is 76°F.

5-9 Find the heat gain through the windows of example 5-2 in art. 5-9 and prob. 5-8 if the windows were made of acrylic plastic sheet with an added film of reflective aluminum metallized polyester. Notice the dramatic reduction achieved by this change.

5-10 A one-piece picture window in a house faces south. Its bottom edge is 2 ft above the earth and its top edge is 8 ft above the earth. The roof eave above this window is 10 ft above the earth (to its underside) and extends 1 ft out from the window. How much of this window would be lit by the sun on a July day at noon at 32° north latitude? Plot this on graph paper to find your answer.

5-11 A building located at 40° north latitude has a room with a light-colored south wall that is 70 ft long and 9 ft high. The windows and outside door of this room have a gross area of 130 ft^2. The wall is constructed of 4-in. face brick, an air space, insulating sheathing board with a resistance R of 2.06, 2-in. X 4-in. wood studs, and 3/4-in. lightweight aggregate gypsum plaster on metal lath. The stud space has 2 in. of insulation ($k = 0.25$) in it which leaves an air space of 1 1/2 in. OA design temperature is 97°F, and RA design temperature is 76°F. If the daily range is 18°F, find the heat gain in BH, through this wall at 17:00 o'clock on a clear day in July. Observe the footnotes in figs. 5-20 and 5-23.

Chapter 6

HVAC System Components

6-1 GENERALITIES

In the preceding chapters we have given much thought and attention to the heating and cooling needs of buildings, and methods of estimating and evaluating the magnitude and basic nature of those needs.

We have not, thus far, given much thought to the needs of buildings for ventilation. Ventilation is a very basic requirement in almost all buildings, and ample space will be devoted to this subject in a later chapter.

Sometimes the ventilation system of a building is completely independent and separate from the heating and cooling systems of that building. However, much more often than not, the heating and cooling systems are fully integrated with the ventilating system, and the outside air that is needed for ventilation purposes is conditioned by this integrated HVAC system and distributed by it throughout the building.

Although our basic purpose in this chapter is to examine the components that comprise an integrated HVAC system, there are a few thoughts that must first be advanced about HVAC systems in general.

6-2 HVAC SYSTEMS: TWO BASIC TYPES

HVAC systems may be divided into two very broad categories; this must be recognized here, because the equipment components required in each category vary widely in basic nature. The two broad categories are:

1 Central station systems
2 Unitary systems

As the name implies, *central station systems* consist of centrally located air conditioning units (often called *air handling units*) (see fig. 6-1).

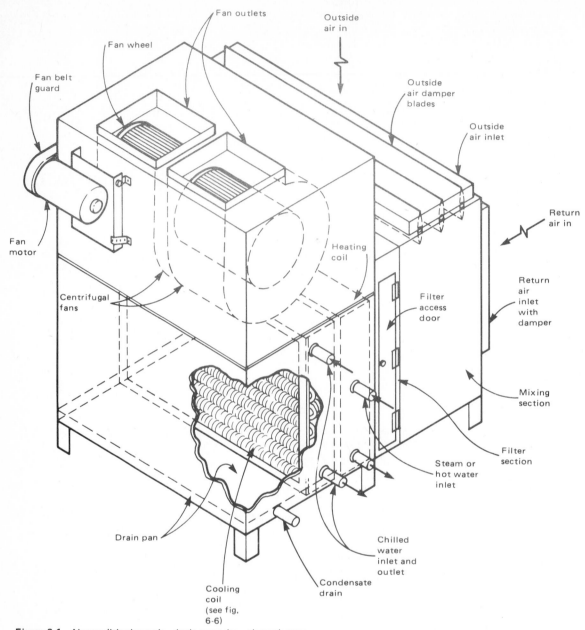

Figure 6-1 Air conditioning unit—single-zone draw-through type.

Fan outlets

Fan wheel

Outside air in

Fan belt guard

Outside air damper blades

Outside air inlet

Fan motor

Heating coil

Return air in

Centrifugal fans

Filter access door

Return air inlet with damper

Mixing section

Steam or hot water inlet

Filter section

Drain pan

Chilled water inlet and outlet

Cooling coil (see fig. 6-6)

Condensate drain

These centrally located units are installed in an equipment room of some type, or even on the roof exposed to the weather, and are located at points remote from the rooms being conditioned. Conditioned air is supplied from the air conditioning unit to the rooms through supply ductwork.

In *unitary systems* air is conditioned by a multiplicity of very small air conditioning (a/c) units, with one or more of these small units located within each room that is being conditioned. In this case, the a/c units are often fully exposed to view (see fig. 6-2).

HVAC systems are usually one or the other of these two basic types; however, they are very, very often a combination of the two types in an effort to utilize the inherent advantages of each.

6-3 HEATING SYSTEMS: FOUR BASIC TYPES

Heating systems, which meet only the wintertime needs of a building, may be divided into four broad categories:

1 Circulating air systems
2 Hot water systems
3 Steam systems
4 Radiant panel systems

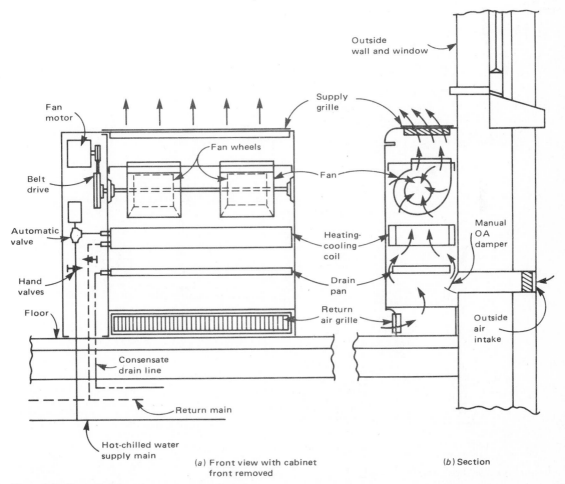

(a) Front view with cabinet front removed

(b) Section

Figure 6-2 Fan-coil unit.

The reader will probably recognize quickly that many heating systems are combinations of the four basic types, and further that there is much overlapping between the several categories enumerated above.

Circulating Air Systems

Circulating air systems usually consist of a remotely located heating unit, usually called a *furnace*, which burns oil, coal, or gas or uses electricity to generate heat. This heat is distributed by a circulating stream of air moving through the heating unit and through a supply duct system to deliver heat throughout a building as needed (see fig. 6-3).

Hot Water Heating Systems

In this type of heating system, water is heated in one or more hot water heating boilers (see fig. 6-4) and is pumped by centrifugal pumps through pipelines to all parts of the building needing heat. In the spaces to be heated, heat is extracted from the hot water by a wide range of heating devices, such as fan-coil units, radiators, unit heaters, or a/c unit heating coils. A very high percent of the nonresidential heating that is done in the United States is done with hot water.

Even though the heart of this system is the fuel-fired *boiler*, which heats the circulating water, the water does not at any time boil because it is kept under high enough pressure to prevent this.

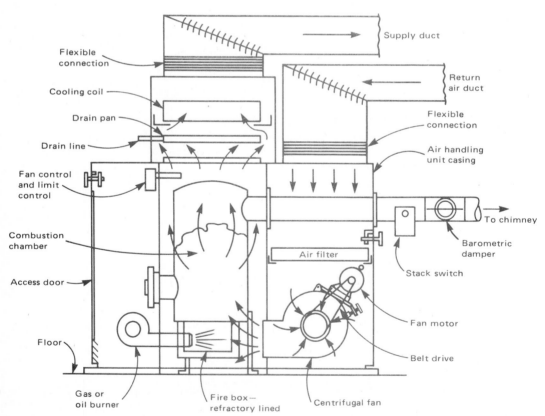

Figure 6-3 Section through warm air furnace.

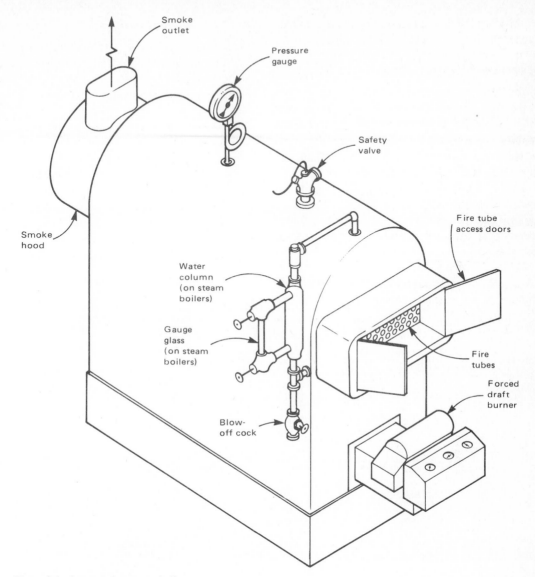

Figure 6-4   Steam or hot water boiler.

Steam Heating Systems

In steam heating systems, water is boiled in fuel-fired boilers (fig. 6-4) or electric boilers until a small amount of steam pressure is generated. This pressure causes the steam to flow through piping systems to all parts of a building. Heat is extracted from the steam in the same wide range of heating devices mentioned above for hot water heating systems. As heat is removed from the steam by these devices, it condenses back to water, in which form it flows by gravity or is pumped back to the boiler.

Like hot water, a tremendous amount of non-residential construction is heated with steam; and though some of our very earliest central heating systems were steam systems, it is not in any sense an obsolete heating medium for nonresidential applications.

Radiant Panel Heating Systems

In this type of heating system, a large surface area, or panel, in a room is heated by some means. This panel, which may be part or all of the ceiling, wall, or floor, radiates and convects heat into the room because it is warmer than other surfaces in the room and warmer than the air in the room.

There are many methods utilized to make these room surfaces warm enough to perform their heating function. Plastered ceilings and concrete floors are warmed by embedded copper tubes carrying hot water, for example (see fig. 6-5).

Of course, many heating systems are combinations of two or more of the four basic types listed above. One very popular combination involves the

use of a central station circulating air system supplemented by a perimeter wall radiation hot water system.

6-4 COOLING SYSTEMS: TWO TYPES

There is basically only one type of summer cooling system—the circulating air system, whether central station or unitary. However, there are two major divisions in this category, based on the cooling medium utilized:

1 Direct expansion
2 Chilled water

Practically all a/c units that cool air utilize a refrigerated cooling coil which makes contact with the circulating air and removes heat from it (see

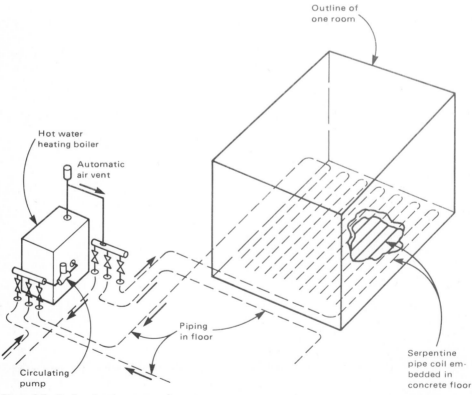

Figure 6-5 Radiant heating system, floor type.

fig. 6-6). However, we do utilize two different media for refrigerating the cooling coil.

Direct Expansion

The first medium which is utilized in the direct expansion system, uses a chemical refrigerant which under the proper conditions of temperature and pressure boils or evaporates. This is a process often referred to as *expansion*. In this process, the refrigerant enters the tubes of the cooling coil as a liquid and expands, or boils, into a vapor as heat, from the circulating air passing over the coil, is added to it. The use of a chemical refrigerant to cool the cooling coil also involves the use of a compressor to compress the refrigerant vapor, a condenser to condense it back to a liquid, and a

goodly number of miscellaneous controls and accessories.

Chilled Water

The cooling coil may also be refrigerated by low-temperature chilled water passing through the tubes of the coil. The chilled water may be at a temperature of approximately 45°F as it enters the coil, and it may leave the coil 8 to 12°F warmer after it has picked up heat from the circulating air.

The chilled water is refrigerated by a *water chiller* unit, which itself incorporates some type of refrigerating system, perhaps a direct expansion system (see fig. 6-7).

The use of direct expansion cooling coils has, according to best practice, been limited to fairly small HVAC systems. It is not impossible to service very large buildings with a large number of these smaller direct expansion systems, but in this case it would be difficult to find suitable locations for the large number of *condensing units* required. A condensing unit is an assembly consisting of a refrigeration compressor, a motor to drive it, a condenser coil, and necessary accessories (see fig. 6-8). Chapter 10 discusses refrigeration equipment and its functions.

6-5 TEMPERATURE CONTROL: THREE BASIC METHODS

The subject of temperature control is exceedingly complex and will be dealt with in a subsequent chapter. However, there are a few broad concepts of control that should be discussed here in a preliminary fashion.

HVAC systems may be divided into three broad categories according to the methods by which they operate and are controlled:

1 Constant volume–variable temperature
2 Variable air volume (VAV)
3 Cycling

Method 1, as its name implies, is applied to a system in which the fan or blower that circulates the air throughout a building (or a portion of a

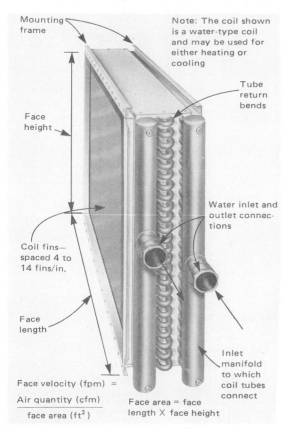

Figure 6-6 Typical cooling coil (four-row). (© The Trane Company, used by permission.)

Mounting frame

Note: The coil shown is a water-type coil and may be used for either heating or cooling

Tube return bends

Face height

Water inlet and outlet connections

Coil fins— spaced 4 to 14 fins/in.

Face length

Inlet manifold to which coil tubes connect

Face velocity (fpm) =

$$\frac{\text{Air quantity (cfm)}}{\text{face area (ft}^2)}$$

Face area = face length × face height

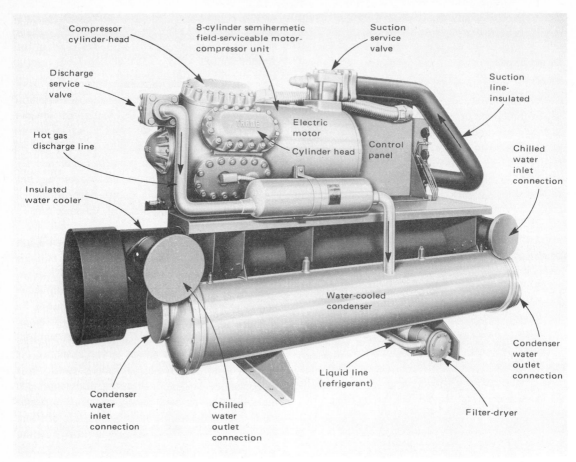

Figure 6-7   Direct expansion water chiller unit. (© The Trane Company, used by permission.)

building) is started manually and runs continuously. The temperature and relative humidity of the supply air are then automatically varied to meet the changing needs of the building. This concept has almost always been embodied in the design of the HVAC systems in nonresidential buildings.

Method 2, commonly referred to as VAV, refers to a control concept in which the supply air condition (temperature and humidity) is held constant, or nearly so, and the quantity of the supply air is gradually varied so that the heating or cooling effect of the HVAC system is matched to the needs of the building. The variation in air quantity is achieved by modulating the position of dampers in the supply ducts or at the fan inlet, or by varying the speed of the fan(s).

Method 3, cycling control, involves automatically turning the circulating air fan on and off as necessary to supply the required amounts of heat or cooling effect. Control method 3 has been used extensively in residential applications almost to the exclusion of the other two methods; its use normally results in the lowest initial cost and operating cost. However, the results of the use of method 3 have been considered to be inferior to the results required of first-class nonresidential HVAC systems.

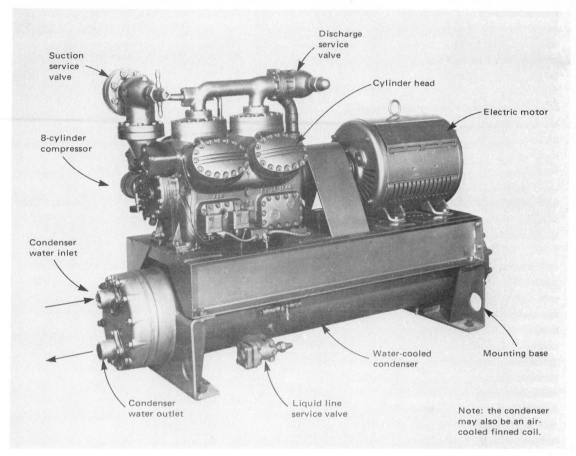

Figure 6-8 Refrigeration condensing unit. (Reproduced by permission of Carrier Corp., © 1980 Carrier Corp.)

Method 2, VAV, is comparatively new in popularity, having been in frequent use only in the last 10 years. Compared to the more popular control method 1, it seems to result in reduced initial costs as well as operating costs.

6-6 CENTRAL STATION SYSTEM COMPONENTS

We may now proceed to a closer examination of the basic components that make up central station HVAC systems. For this purpose, the components have been divided into seven broad categories:

1 A/c units (air handling units)
2 Supply duct systems
3 Supply grilles, registers, and diffusers
4 Return air grilles, registers, and diffusers
5 Return duct systems
6 Outside air intake and relief systems
7 Temperature control systems

In the foregoing list, no inclusion has been made for steam or hot water heating boilers, or for water chillers or refrigerating machines. These sources of heat and cooling effect are necessary, of course, in any central station HVAC system, but they are not peculiar to, or limited to central station systems. These heat and cooling sources are used by unitary systems as well. They will be dealt with separately, and individual chapters on these subjects are included later.

6-7   A/C UNITS

First, let us examine central station air conditioning or air handling units. These units are, in most cases, required to perform six functions:

1   Produce heat in winter
   a   By direct firing—burning gas, oil, coal, wood, and so on, directly inside the a/c unit enclosing cabinet; such a unit is shown in fig. 6-3. This unit is complete with combustion chamber (where the fuel burns), cooling coil, fan, fan motor and V-belt drive, air filters, and humidifier.
   b   By indirect firing—receiving steam or hot water from a remotely located boiler (such a unit is shown in fig. 6-1), and is complete with heating coil (see fig. 6-9), cooling coil, fan, fan motor and V-belt drive, air filters, and humidifier, all contained in an enclosing metal cabinet.
   c   By using an electric resistance heating coil (see fig. 6-10); otherwise similar to the unit shown in fig. 6-1 and described in paragraph b.
2   Produce cooling in summer with the use of a cooling coil (see fig. 6-6), which, as mentioned, utilizes either chilled water or expanding refrigerant as a cooling medium.
3   Produce air circulation with a fan (sometimes

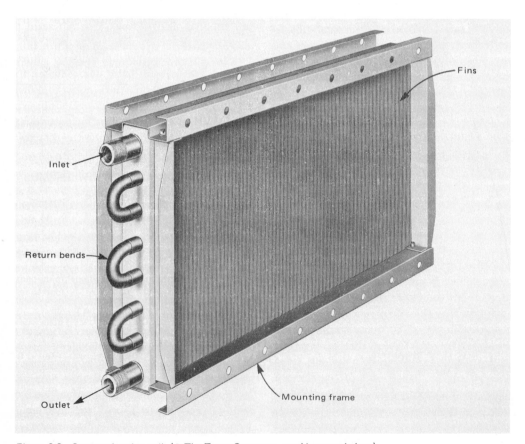

Figure 6-9   One-row heating coil. (© The Trane Company, used by permission.)

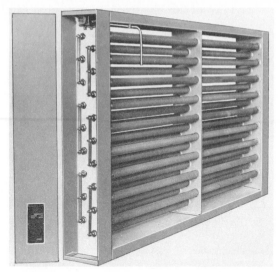

Figure 6-10 Electric resistance heating coil. [Photo provided courtesy of Industrial Engineering and Equipment Co. (Indeeco).]

called a blower), which is driven by an electric motor through a variable-pitch V-belt drive. The fan is of the centrifugal type (sometimes called a *squirrel cage* fan), which is designed to circulate the required amount of air against the considerable airflow resistance (frictional resistance) of coils, filters, ductwork, and so on (see fig. 6-11).

4 Produce air cleanliness by passing the full moving airstream through properly designed and selected air filters to remove airborne particulate matter (dust).

5 Produce humidification when that is required—mostly in wintertime—through the use of:

a Steam injectors. These are steam nozzle assemblies, or perforated pipe manifolds wrapped with asbestos wool, which are mounted inside the a/c unit and which inject the steam directly into the moving airstream (see fig. 6-12).

b Water spray nozzles. These are arranged in banks inside the a/c unit; they are connected to the water supply of the building, and automatically inject finely atomized water mist into the moving airstream. These nozzles have sometimes taken the form of "target nozzles," which direct a high-velocity jet of water against

a hard, flat target where the water is broken up into a fine mist.

c Evaporating pans. These are large metal pans 8 to 12 in. deep in which water is maintained at a fixed level by float valves. Immersed in the water of such a pan is a serpentine pipe coil through which steam is flowing. The heat and high temperature of the steam causes the water in the pan to boil. Since the pan is located inside the a/c unit, the steam from the pan is carried away by the moving airstream (see fig. 6-12).

d Evaporative surface humidifiers. These also include a metal pan in which water is maintained at the desired level by means of a float valve. In addition, a metal rack lying on the bottom of the pan supports a series of parallel, porous plates. These plates stand on edge with one end in the water, and soak up water from the pan until the entire plate is wet. The circulating airstream passes over, around, and between these plates and the very great area of the wet plates yields water to the airstream (see fig. 6-12).

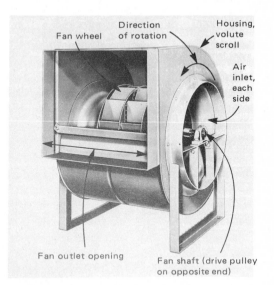

Note: The fan shown has a backwardly inclined blade wheel and is of the double inlet, double width, top horizontal discharge (DIDW, THD) type

Figure 6-11 Centrifugal fan (blower). (© The Trane Company, used by permission.)

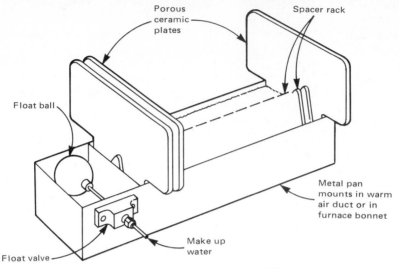

(a) Evaporative surface humidifier

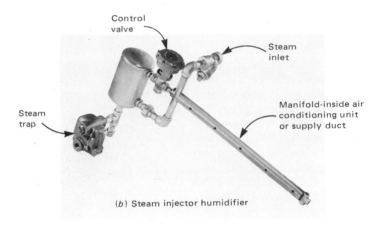

(b) Steam injector humidifier

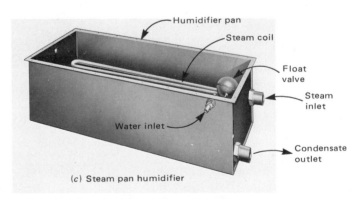

(c) Steam pan humidifier

Figure 6-12 Humidifier types. (b and c, Johnson Controls, Inc.)

6 Produce dehumidification. Dehumidification in buildings is achieved by three methods; and of these three, the first method listed below is used almost to the complete exclusion of the other two in building HVAC systems. These three methods are:

a Condensing on a cooling coil. With the use of a cooling coil, the external surfaces of which are maintained well below the dew point temperature of the air flowing over the coil surfaces, great quantities of moisture can be wrung out of the air. This is dehumidification.

b Chemical absorption (notice that the second letter of absorption is a "b"). This process involves bringing the air to be dehumidified into intimate contact with a spray of liquid solution, such as lithium chloride. If such a solution is at a temperature of 83°F or lower, and is comparatively anhydrous (free of moisture), it will have a high affinity for water and will extract moisture from the moving airstream. In this system, the liquid absorbent is continuously circulated through a heater and then through a cooler, after which it is returned to the dehumidifier sprays in the a/c unit. When the absorbent is heated, most of the moisture chemically absorbed is driven off and discarded. When the absorbent is then cooled, it recovers its high affinity for moisture and its ability to extract moisture from atmospheric air.

c Chemical adsorption (here the second letter is a "d"). This process involves moving the stream of air to be dehumidified through a bed of granular material which under proper conditions has a high affinity for moisture. The granular material used is a material such as silica gel or activated alumina. These materials are often carried in a revolving drum, on one side of which moisture is extracted from the circulating airstream, and on the other side of which the granular material is first heated to drive off the adsorbed moisture and then cooled to return to it its high affinity for atmospheric moisture.

Chemical absorbers and adsorbers are extensively used in commercial and industrial processes but are rarely used in comfort air conditioning systems.

6-8   A/C UNITS CLASSIFIED

Air conditioning units may be classified or categorized in several ways, both as to function and as to physical properties, as follows:

Configuration

A/c units are manufactured in many different physical configurations so as to gracefully fit into the space available in the building, and most conveniently permit the connection of ductwork, piping, and electrical circuits. Human access for service and operating control is also a matter of a/c unit configuration.

As shown in fig. 6-13, a/c units are available in a straight-through horizontal pattern in which the air enters at one end and passes straight through to exit horizontally at the opposite end. Such units may stand on the floor, or may be suspended overhead at or near the ceiling to conserve floor space.

Also, as shown in fig. 6-15, a/c units are made for vertical pattern of airflow, either up or down. Vertical pattern a/c units are made for floor mounting or may be bolted to a wall well above the floor.

With both horizontal and vertical pattern a/c units, the inlet and outlet connections may be such that the air turns through 90° immediately after entering the unit or immediately before leaving (see fig. 6-1).

Pressure and Duty

A/c units are manufactured for high-pressure (heavy-duty) or low-pressure (light-duty) in accordance with the type of duct system to be utilized.

Supply duct systems may be designed for high velocity, to minimize the sizes of ducts and the space required for their installation, or they may be designed for low velocity. In high-velocity systems, the force required to drive the required amount of air through the small ducts is comparatively great; and the pressure that the a/c unit fan must build is correspondingly great.

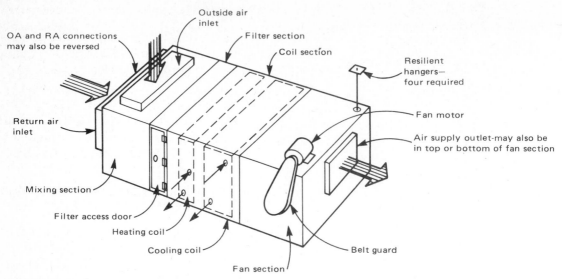

Figure 6-13 Single-zone draw-through horizontal pattern air conditioning unit.

This pressure may cause a bursting force in the a/c unit as high as 40 lb/ft^2 of internal surface area. Therefore, this type of unit must be very ruggedly constructed; it is, as a result, quite expensive, and the fan and fan motor are quite expensive.

Contrastingly, low-pressure units are comparatively lightweight and inexpensive.

Single Zone or Multizone

Some a/c units are designed to condition several or many different areas, or zones, of a building simultaneously. Since the different zones regularly call for air at greatly differing conditions (some requiring heat while others call for cooling), a multizone a/c unit must be capable of supplying many separate streams of air under widely varying conditions.

Other a/c units are installed to serve only one zone of a building and thus are required to supply air at only one condition at any one time. These are called single-zone units. Figure 6-1 shows an external view of a single-zone a/c unit and fig. 6-14 shows some details of a double-deck multizone unit. Triple-deck units, having hot, cold, and neutral (or bypass) decks, are available also.

Draw-Through and Blow-Through Units

A/c units may further be classified as to the type of fan action that is utilized. Some units are constructed with the fan at the leaving end of the unit—in effect, pulling or drawing the air through the unit, and then pushing the air out into the supply duct system. This, called a *draw-through* a/c unit, is shown in figs. 6-13, 6-15, and 6-16.

In contrast to the draw-through unit, the *blow-through* unit has its fan located near the inlet to the a/c unit; and the fan, in effect, pushes the air through the cooling and heating coils and then out into the supply ductwork. Notice that the multizone unit in fig. 6-14 is of the blow-through type.

It should be noted here that the fan that circulates the conditioned air throughout the building does involve considerable power—in other words, heat. For example, a fairly modestly sized a/c unit might have a fan that requires a 3-hp motor to drive it. Most of the electrical energy that this motor consumes is converted to mechanical energy by the motor; this is then transferred through the fan drive into the fan and from the

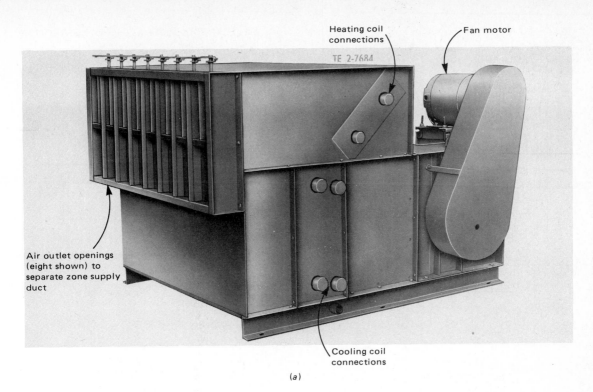

(a)

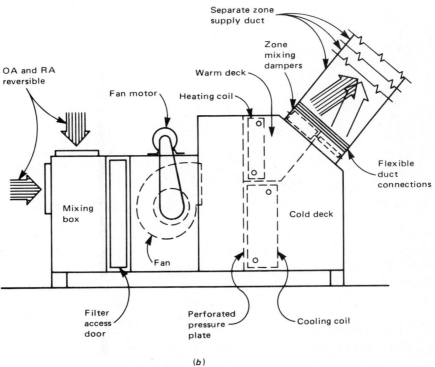

(b)

Figure 6-14 AC unit—multizone blow-through, horizontal pattern, double deck. (*a*, photo courtesy Aladdin Heating Corp., San Leandro, Calif.)

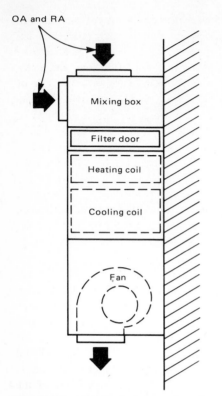

Figure 6-15 AC unit—single-zone, draw-through, vertical.

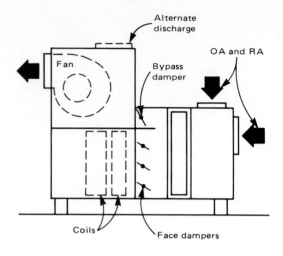

(a) Vertical pattern

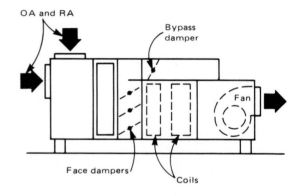

(b) Horizontal pattern—single-zone draw-through
Figure 6-16 AC unit—face-and-bypass damper type.

fan into the circulating air. In the airstream this mechanical energy is converted into sensible heat at the rate of 2540 BH/hp.

The 3-hp motor then delivers 7640 BH into the airstream. Note that the blow-through a/c unit does this at a point upstream of the cooling coil, so that the cooling coil can intercept this heat before it leaves the a/c unit. However, notice that in the draw-through unit this is not the case; the heat of the fan does get out into the supply duct, and thus becomes internal load. This is an important difference, as the reader will see in later discussions.

Bypass Control and Valve Control

A/c units may further be classified as to the type of basic temperature control utilized.

Some a/c units have a built-in bypass arrangement by means of which some or all of the circulating air is routed around the heating and cooling coils instead of passing through these coils in the usual manner. Figure 6-16 shows this arrangement in two different a/c units in which face dampers (that cover the face of the coils) can partially or fully close while a bypass damper, in the bypass duct shown, partially or fully opens. If this action of bypassing air around the coil is under the control of a thermostat, it can be seen how the bypassing action can provide more or less heating or more or less cooling in accordance with the needs of the rooms being conditioned by the a/c unit.

Face-and-bypass damper control (or just bypass control) requires, of course, that the a/c unit be manufactured specifically for this purpose, and as such is then a basic a/c unit type.

An alternative to the foregoing type of temperature control is called *valve control*. This is a very simple type of control which requires only a standard type of unit without face and bypass dampers. Here the steam or hot water supplied to the heating coil is controlled by a modulating motorized valve. The chilled water supplied to the cooling coil is controlled by a similar valve.

It can be seen, then, that with these two motorized valves operating under the control of a room thermostat, room temperature can be maintained as required. Here the a/c unit is of a basically different type than the unit used with bypass control.

6-9   SUPPLY DUCT SYSTEMS

The supply duct system is, of course, the system by means of which conditioned air is conveyed from a central station a/c unit to the spaces of the building to be conditioned. The power or motive force that causes the air to move through the supply ducts is supplied by the fan in the a/c unit and the electric motor that drives the fan.

Duct Frictional Resistance

Any type of duct system offers frictional resistance to the movement of the supply air. If the air moves at high speed, as would be the case if a duct is quite small, the frictional resistance and the required fan horsepower are much higher than would be true if we moved the same quantity of air at lower velocity in a larger duct.

The frictional resistance of a supply duct varies in proportion to the "square" of the ratio of the velocity at two different velocities, and the fan power varies as the cube of this ratio. For example, if a supply duct is carrying 5000 cfm of standard air at a velocity of 1000 fpm, and a second supply duct is also carrying 5000 cfm of standard air at a velocity of 2000 fpm, the frictional resistance of the second duct per foot of duct length will be four times as much: (2000 fpm/1000 fpm)^2 = 4; and the power required to overcome this frictional resistance will be eight times as much, (2000 fpm/1000 fpm)^3 = 8.

Therefore, in the light of today's extreme need to save energy, it is our patriotic duty to keep duct velocities as low as is practical. Fortunately, it almost always makes good economic sense to do so.

The reader should begin to think of frictional resistance of ductwork in terms of the pressure that the a/c unit fan must develop to overcome this resistance. This pressure, called static pressure, is measured in inches of water. The reader may wish to review art. 1-19 and figs. 1-5 and 1-6, where static pressure is defined and explained.

It should be helpful to give some idea of the magnitude of typical static pressure values in the usual low-velocity duct system. (Low velocity versus high velocity will be discussed later in this chapter.) Every foot of duct in the duct system, every damper, elbow, grille, turning vane, and so on, as well as the a/c unit itself, offers frictional resistance to the air movement, and each causes a certain amount of static pressure "drop" to result. For example, in the duct shown in fig. 6-17, the static pressure in the duct upstream of the elbow shown is 1.37 in. WG (inches of water, gauge pressure), whereas the static pressure downstream from the elbow is 1.31 in. WG. There has been a static pressure drop or loss resulting from the frictional resistance (and some turbulence loss) of the elbow; the amount of this loss is 0.06 in. WG (1.37 in. - 1.31 in. = 0.06 in.).

The following tabulation will give a rough idea of the magnitude of the static pressure losses one might find in the usual small, commercial HVAC

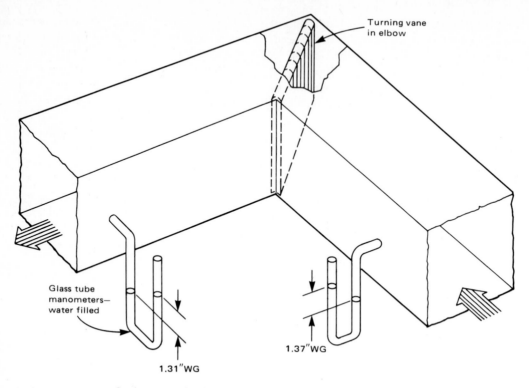

Static pressure loss in the elbow = 1.37″ - 1.31″ = 0.06″ WG

Figure 6-17   Static pressure loss due to friction.

system. See fig. 6-18, and identify the various components listed, starting with the supply duct:

1. Supply duct system, 60 ft actual length, probably 90 ft equivalent length, at 0.1 in. WG pressure drop per 100 ft (usual design parameter).   0.09

   Equivalent length is the length of plain, perfectly straight, uncluttered duct that has the same frictional resistance, and resulting static pressure loss, as has another duct of the same size and air quantity which has elbows, offsets, branch connections, dampers, and so on. In this case, the 60 ft of installed duct, having elbows, dampers, and so on, is assumed to have as much pressure loss as a straight, uncluttered duct 50% longer, or 90 ft long.

   The term *equivalent length* is applied in the same manner to pipe as

well as ductwork. There are methods of accurately calculating equivalent lengths, although many engineers are able to estimate this superficially.

2. Supply grille or diffuser	0.07
3. Double-faced grille between rooms	0.08
4. Return air grille	0.04
5. Return air duct, 28 ft actual length, probably 42 ft equivalent length, at 0.07 in. WG pressure drop per 100 ft	0.03
6. Return air damper	0.07
7. A/c unit	
Air filter	0.20
Heating coil	0.25
Cooling coil	0.60
Cabinet	0.10
Total static pressure loss	1.53 in. WG

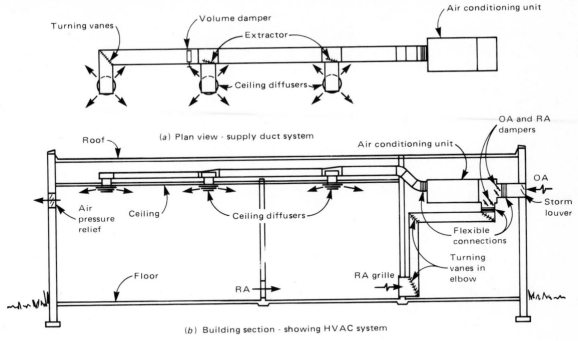

Figure 6-18   Building section showing HVAC system.

In the tabulation above, the first six items total 0.38 in. WG; this is called *external static pressure loss* since all the items constitute losses that are external to the a/c unit. The internal static loss consists of the four items listed in item 7; these total 1.15 in. WG. Of course, the sum of the internal and the external is the total static pressure loss, in this case 1.53 in. WG.

In a very large building, the lengths of the supply and return ducts would probably be much greater than in the illustration above, and the external static pressure loss would then be much greater. However, the internal loss might very well be about the same.

6-10   DUCTWORK CATEGORIES

Supply duct systems are designed and constructed in many different ways, and may be categorized as follows:

1   Round ducts versus rectangular
2   Metallic ducts versus nonmetallic
3   Low velocity versus high velocity

Round Ducts Versus Rectangular

Both round and rectangular ducts have their advantages and disadvantages, and both find applications where one is definitely superior to the other. Many duct designers use one type routinely to the exclusion of the other without much hard logic to support their attitude.

Many ductwork contractors prefer round ducts to rectangular, or vice versa, depending somewhat on how their fabricating shop is equipped. A round duct is more efficient than a rectangular duct in performing the same task; it is also smaller in cross-sectional area and has less duct wall exposed to the moving air. For example, as shown in fig. 6-19, an 18-in.-diameter round duct has the same air-carrying capacity (equal in friction) as a

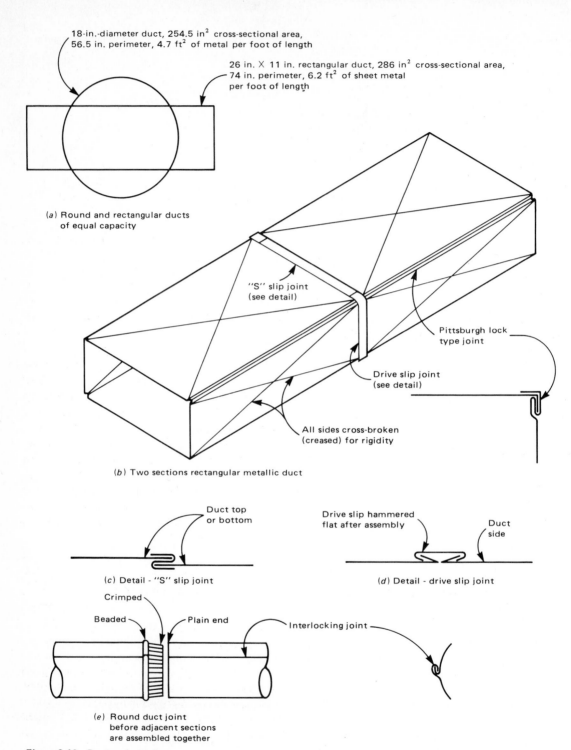

18-in.-diameter duct, 254.5 in^2 cross-sectional area,
56.5 in. perimeter, 4.7 ft^2 of metal per foot of length

26 in. × 11 in. rectangular duct, 286 in^2 cross-sectional area,
74 in. perimeter, 6.2 ft^2 of sheet metal
per foot of length

(a) Round and rectangular ducts
of equal capacity

"S" slip joint
(see detail)

Pittsburgh lock
type joint

Drive slip joint
(see detail)

All sides cross-broken
(creased) for rigidity

(b) Two sections rectangular metallic duct

Duct top
or bottom

Drive slip hammered
flat after assembly

Duct
side

(c) Detail - "S" slip joint

(d) Detail - drive slip joint

Crimped

Beaded   Plain end

Interlocking joint

(e) Round duct joint
before adjacent sections
are assembled together

Figure 6-19 Ductwork details.

rectangular duct 26 in. wide and 11 in. high. The round duct has a cross-sectional area of 254.5 in.² while the rectangular duct has 286 in.² area.

Also, the round duct has a perimeter of 4.7 ft and a duct wall area, then, of 4.7 ft² per lineal foot of duct. The rectangular duct has a perimeter of 6.2 ft and thus has a duct wall area of 6.2 ft² per lineal foot of duct. The rectangular duct has 32% more metal in it, and should cost proportionately more. These two ducts are equal in friction and static pressure loss.

Figure 6-19 also shows details of duct construction that are typical for round and rectangular galvanized steel ducts. In these details it may be seen that sections or lengths of rectangular ductwork are joined together by means of *S slips* on the top and bottom of a duct, and by *drive slips* on the sides. The drive slips are driven into place last, hammered flat, and then bent over on the top and bottom to make a fairly tight seal, which is adequate for the needs of low-velocity low-pressure ducts.

The joints between sections of round duct are exceedingly simple and inexpensive. They consist merely of crimping one end of a section of duct; this reduces the diameter of the end so that it will slide into the open end of the adjoining duct section.

The longitudinal joints in square or rectangular ducts are usually made with a *Pittsburgh Lock*, as detailed in fig. 6-19. Longitudinal, or lengthwise, joints in round ducts are made with a simple interlocking joint as shown.

One big disadvantage of round ducts is their height. If the net clear height of a furred space above a suspended ceiling is 14 in., an 18-in.-diameter duct cannot be installed therein; however, its equivalent 26-in.-wide by 11-in.-high rectangular duct will fit the space easily.

When the appearance of ducts is important, as when the ducts are exposed to view and not concealed, there is again considerable difference of opinion among designers as to which looks better, round or rectangular. The appearance of larger rectangular ducts, where the greatest dimension

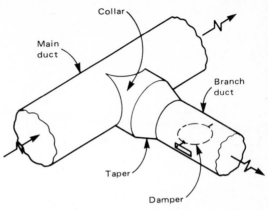

Figure 6-20 Efficient branch connection—round branch to round main.

(width or height) exceeds 30 in., is considerably worsened by the installation of the necessary angle iron stiffeners that give these ducts adequate strength and rigidity.

With round ducts, many of the methods utilized in making branch connections to the side of a main duct have left much to be desired in appearance. These have included "Y," 45°, and radius-type connections.

Research has shown that a 90° branch connection to a round main duct, made with a slightly tapered transition piece between the main and the branch, is equally efficient aerodynamically and has a much smoother, even, and streamlined appearance. A detail of this type of connection is shown in fig. 6-20.

When an *extractor*, an adjustable turning vane device, is added to a rectangular branch connection, optimum appearance and efficiency results. See the details of a turning vane and an extractor in figs. 6-21 and 6-22.

Metallic Ducts

Supply ducts may be further categorized according to the material of which the ducts are made. These may be divided into two broad categories: metallic and nonmetallic. Metallic ducts use many different metals; however, the great majority of metal-

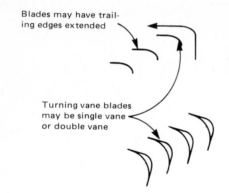

Blades may have trailing edges extended

Turning vane blades may be single vane or double vane

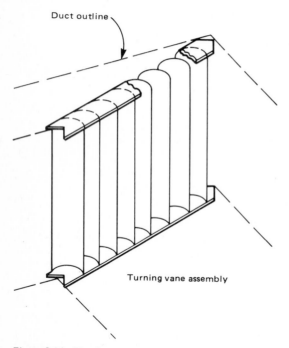

Duct outline

Turning vane assembly

Figure 6-21 Turning vane details.

expansion and contraction as do galvanized steel ducts.

However, aluminum has never achieved the popularity that was once expected of it. Of course, its biggest disadvantage is its high basic cost per pound.

Other metals, such as copper and stainless steel, are used for ductwork, but only under very special circumstances. These might be used in spite of their high cost to give special appearance in commercial use when exposed to full public view, or they might be used to resist some type of chemical attack.

Steel ducts with special coatings designed to resist acid, or other chemical attack, are often found to be effective. One of these has the commercial designation "PVS," for polyvinyl steel, where a tough vinyl coating is applied to steel. This particular material is suitable for ducts that are to be buried directly in the earth. Plain galvanized steel is often used for buried ductwork, but is surrounded by concrete as shown in fig. 6-23. In this case, the concrete is really the duct material, and the steel, made of very thin gauge metal, is only a form for the concrete.

Nonmetallic Ducts

Nonmetallic ducts are available in six different basic materials:

1 Glass fiber
2 Compressed paper
3 Plastic
4 Cement-asbestos
5 Vitrified clay
6 Concrete

Glass Fiber Ducts Glass fiber ducts are made of glass wool insulating material in which the stranded fiber wool is compressed until a fairly rigid insulating board results (see fig. 6-24). Glass fiber ducts are available prefabricated in either round or rectangular form. The ducts are faced on the outside with a noncombustible, aluminum foil scrim vapor barrier jacketing material. The alumi-

lic ducts are made of galvanized steel in HVAC systems.

Next in popularity in metal ducts is aluminum. Aluminum ducts are light in weight, which makes them less expensive to install. Aluminum ducts are easily formed and are quieter in operation. They have somewhat better noise attenuation characteristics, and do not crack and pop as much with

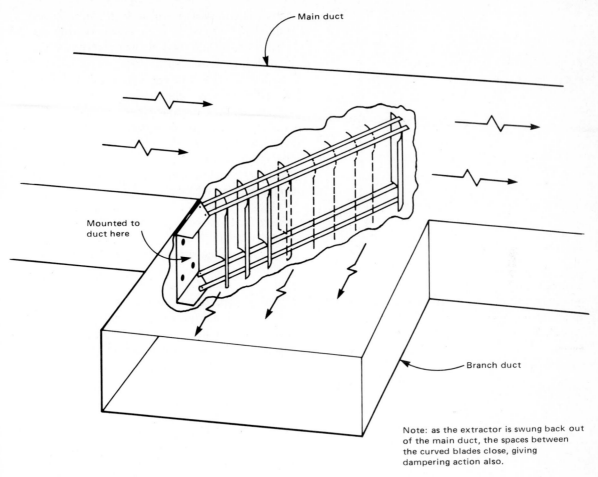

Main duct

Mounted to
duct here

Branch duct

Note: as the extractor is swung back out
of the main duct, the spaces between
the curved blades close, giving
dampering action also.

Figure 6-22 Extractor detail.

num foil jacketing is reinforced with tough glass fiber strands so as to make an ideal finish. The smoke production and flame spread ratings of this finish material is nearly zero.

Prefabricated rectangular glass fiber ducts are shipped in flat sheets with the glass fiber material grooved along the lines where the board is to be folded to form it into a rectangular shape. Round ducts are formed into a round shape before shipment.

Because the interior surface of glass fiber ducts is much rougher than that of galvanized steel, the friction factor is appreciably higher and the static pressure loss is greater. For duct systems using glass fiber ducts, it is recommended that the system be designed and sized with galvanized steel duct sizing charts. The calculated static pressure loss, of the ductwork only, should then be increased by 20%. The total static pressure loss of the system may then be determined by adding this increased "ductwork only" loss to the losses of all other components (coils, filters, grilles, etc.) that make up the HVAC system.

Fittings such as elbows, tees, branch takeoffs,

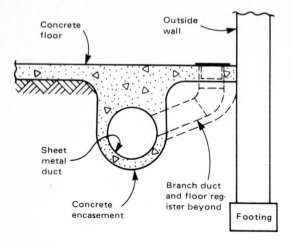

Figure 6-23 Detail of buried duct encased in concrete.

and so on, in rectangular ducts are quite simply and economically made. Elbows are simply 90° mitered elbows with turning vanes fitted inside. Branch connections are made with a perpendicular 90° attachment of a branch duct through an open-ing cut in the side of a main duct. An extractor (adjustable turning vane) is assembled into the connection and makes an efficient branch fitting.

Each end of each length or section of duct has a molded shiplap edge with one end of male con-figuration and the opposite end female. Adjacent sections of duct then merely slide together, and when taped with properly designed tape at this joint, make a very secure, leakproof connection. Metal sleeves are often slid into the ends of ad-jacent sections of round duct to make a secure connection and then taped.

Glass fiber ducts are more expensive than gal-vanized steel ducts, but are less expensive than steel ducts with insulation added. Glass ducts give very good sound attenuation and can often be justified for that reason alone.

Compressed Paper Ducts Compressed paper, or cardboard, ducts are round tubes made of very strong, thick-walled paper. These rigid tubes are available in a wide range of diameters (2 to 36 in.)

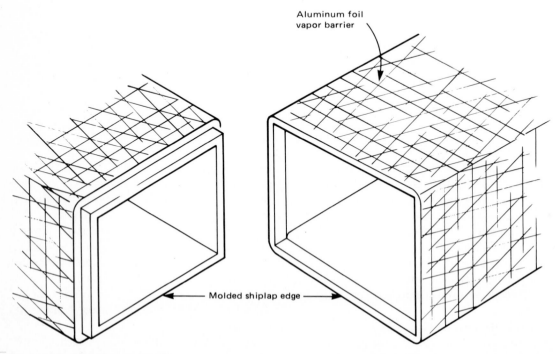

Figure 6-24 Glass fiber duct details.

and are used as a form in buried ducts around which concrete is poured. Galvanized steel fittings and connectors are usually used with paper ducts. The coefficient of friction is approximately equal to that of galvanized steel. Duct sizing tables and charts for galvanized steel may also be used for this type of paper duct.

Plastic Ducts To a limited extent HVAC duct-work is made of plastics such as polyvinyl chloride (PVC). The use of such ducts is limited to small sizes of approximately 12 in. diameter and less and of round configuration.

Plastic ducts are available as both flexible and rigid types. Flexible plastic ducts have corrugated walls which cause the fairly lightweight plastic wall to hold its shape very well. The reader may recognize this duct as the type that is often used to connect the vent connection of a residential clothes dryer to a vent fitting in an outside wall.

Round plastic ducts often utilize a spirally wound helix of stiff wire on which a vinyl or glass fiber fabric is assembled outside the wire helix to make a fairly tough, flexible duct (see fig. 6-25). Flexible ducts of both types, insulated or not, are extensively used to make connections from a

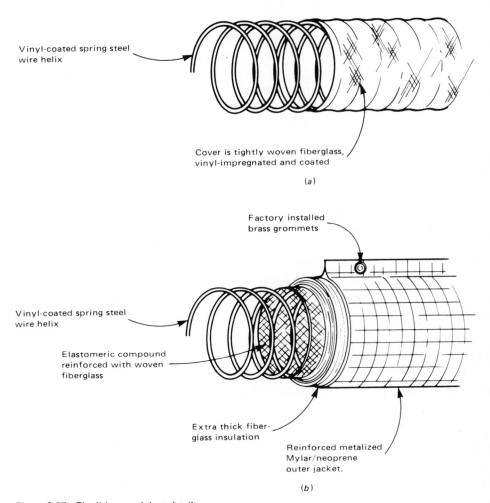

Figure 6-25 Flexible round duct details.

main supply duct installed above a suspended ceiling to supply air diffusers mounted in the ceiling. This is an important use.

Rigid plastic ducts, in small sizes, are often used for direct burial ducts laid in the earth below a concrete floor slab and connecting to grilles or registers in the floor. These ducts will withstand the attack of ground acids and other substances and do not need to be encased in concrete.

Cement-Asbestos Ducts   Cement-asbestos ducts are made of hard, dense, impervious material compounded of asbestos fibers and cement; this cement is of the type that is used in concrete. This material is used extensively in sheet form, 1/4 to 1/2 in. and more in thickness, which is used in building boards. The same material is used in making round air ducts and high- and low-pressure piping for water supply and drainage purposes.

Since the material is very dense and very heavy, its major use as air ductwork has been limited almost exclusively to buried ductwork located beneath a concrete floor. Joints between sections of pipe are made with a rubber gasketed coupling into which the plain ends of the sections of pipe are pushed.

Cement-asbestos ducts can be cut with a saw to make openings for branch connections and other features. These ducts may be used for direct burial, and do not require encasement in concrete. The material is quite expensive, and because of this, and its weight and the difficulty of fabricating it into a duct system, it has not found much use in HVAC systems.

Vitrified Tile and Concrete Ducts   Vitrified clay tile and concrete tile are sometimes used as air ducts. They are almost always round, and are exactly the same material as is used in underground drain lines.

Both materials are suitable for direct underground burial, and when complete, a duct system made of these materials is very permanent and trouble free. Like cement-asbestos ducts, it is not practical to install dampers and balancing devices

inside the ducts. These are limited to installation in branch connections to grilles and registers.

Joints in vitrified tile ducts are usually of the bell-and-spigot type cemented with cement mortar. In concrete ducts the joints may be of the bell-and-spigot type or may be gasketed tongue-and-groove type. The major disadvantage to the use of both of these materials is the great difficulty of making branch connections.

6-11   LOW-VELOCITY DUCTS

Low-velocity ducts are characterized by air velocities in the range 400 to 2500 fpm, but not usually in excess of 2000 fpm. The vast majority of supply ducts in this world, certainly more than 90% (probably more than 98%), have been designed for low-velocity performance. That is as it should be, because low-velocity (LV) ducts, compared to high-velocity (HV) ducts, have all the advantages except one—they are larger for a given air quantity, and do require more space for their installation.

Low-velocity systems do enjoy the very important advantages of lower initial installed cost and much lower energy consumption, which results, of course, in lower operating costs. LV ducts do not need to be fabricated with great care, and usually some air leakage out of the ducts is experienced. The amount of this leakage may be assumed to be 1 to 3% of the air volume circulating, depending on the length of the duct runs in a given system. Some details of LV duct construction are shown in fig. 6-19. Figure 6-26 gives further information regarding joints in round and rectangular metallic ducts, and also gives information as to metal thicknesses (sheet metal gauges) required.

The design of LV duct systems is quite simple and can be quickly learned with just a little experience. It is a fully developed fact that LV duct systems may be designed on the basis of 0.1 in. WG static pressure loss per 100 ft of equivalent length. "Equivalent length" was defined in art. 6-9.

This design parameter, 0.1 in. WG per 100 ft

Figure 6-26 Recommended construction for low-pressure ducts. (Reprinted with permission from the 1967 Systems and Equipment Volume, *ASHRAE Handbook and Products Directory*.)

Dimensions of longest side, in.	Sheet metal gage (all four sides)[a] — Steel gage	Aluminum alloy[b] thickness, in.	Copper, oz/ft²	Between joints[d] — Minimum reinforcing angle size and maximum longitudinal spacing	Flat S slip / Drive slip — Minimum gage	Standing S slip — Minimum gage	Standing S slip — Minimum angle size	Standing seam joint / Pocket lock — Minimum gage for pocket lock or standing S slip	Pocket lock — Minimum angle size	Alternate standing S slip — Minimum height, in.
Up thru 12	26	0.020	16	None required	26	24	None required	24	None required	1
13–18	24	0.025	24	None required	24	24	None required	24	None required	1
19–30	24	0.025	24	1 × 1 × 1/8 at 60 in.	...	24	None required	24	None required	1
31–42	22	0.032	32	1 × 1 × 1/8 at 60 in.	...	22	None required	22	None required	1
43–48	22	0.032	32	1 1/2 × 1 1/2 × 1/8 at 60 in.[f]	...	22	1 1/2 × 1 1/2 × 1/8	22	None required	1 1/2
49–54	22	0.032	32	1 1/2 × 1 1/2 × 1/8 at 48 in.	...	22	1 1/2 × 1 1/2 × 1/8	22	None required	1 1/2
55–60	20	0.040	36	1 1/2 × 1 1/2 × 1/8 at 48 in.	...	22	1 1/2 × 1 1/2 × 1/8	22	None required	1 1/2
61–84	20	0.040	36	1 1/2 × 1 1/2 × 1/8 at 24 in.	...	22	1 1/2 × 1 1/2 × 1/8	22	1 1/2 × 1 1/2 × 1/8	1 1/2
85–96	18	0.050	48	1 1/2 × 1 1/2 × 3/16 at 24 in.	...	22	1 1/2 × 1 1/2 × 3/16	22	1 1/2 × 1 1/2 × 3/16	1 1/2
97–120	18	0.050	48	2 × 2 × 1/4 at 24 in.	...	22	2 × 2 × 1/4	22	2 × 2 × 1/4	1 1/2
121 and over	18	0.050	48	2 × 2 × 1/4 at 24 in. with tie rods at 120 in. along angle	...	...	...	22	2 × 2 × 1/4 with tie rods at 120 in. along joint	1 1/2

[a]Flat areas of duct over 18 in. wide shall be stiffened by crossbreaking unless duct will have nonconductive covering or sound absorbing lining.

[b]Suitable aluminum alloys are: Commercial designation 3003 temper H14 and duct sheet.

[c]Transverse reinforcing size is determined by dimension of side to which angle is applied. Angle sizes are based on mild steel. Reinforcing made in other shapes or of other materials must be of equivalent strength and rigidity.

[d]There is no restriction on the length of duct sections between joints. Ducts are normally made in sections of 4, 8, 10, or 12 ft in length. The longitudinal spacing of the transverse reinforcing between joints may necessarily be less than the spacing recommended in the table in order to conform to the selected length module.

[e]Other joint types of equivalent strength, rigidity and air tightness may be used.

[f]For aluminum or copper ducts 43 in. through 48 in. maximum dimensions, the maximum longitudinal spacing of transverse reinforcing is 48 in.

Duct diameter, in.	Steel—galvanized sheet gage — Low pressure ducts and fittings	Medium and high-pressure ducts — Spiral lock seam duct	Longi- tudinal seam duct	Welded fittings	Girth reinforcing — Minimum reinforcing angle size and maximum longitudinal spacing	Girth joints* Continuously welded or as below — Low-pressure ducts	Girth joints* — Medium- and high-pressure ducts
Up through 8	26	26	24	22	None required	Crimped and beaded joint	2-in. long slip joint
9–13	26	24	22	20	None required	Crimped and beaded joint	4-in. long slip joint
14–22	24	24	22	20	None required	Crimped and beaded joint	4-in. long slip joint
23–36	→	22	20	20	None required	...	4-in. long slip joint
37–50	→	20	20	18	1 1/4 × 1 1/4 × 1/8 at 72 in.	...	1 1/4 × 1 1/4 × 1/8 angle flanged joint
51–60	→	...	18	18	1 1/4 × 1 1/4 × 1/8 at 72 in.	...	1 1/4 × 1 1/4 × 1/8 angle flanged joint
61–84	→	...	16	16	1 1/2 × 1 1/2 × 1/8 at 48 in.	...	1 1/2 × 1 1/2 × 1/8 angle flanged joint

*Flanged joints may be considered as girth reinforcing.   → = use next recommended construction.

of equivalent length, has evolved through the decades as a result of HVAC designers' search for a practical basis of design which balances duct size and cost against operating cost. Obviously, the initial cost and amortized cost of a duct system may be reduced by reducing duct sizes throughout the system; however, the power and its cost required to force air through this undersized system, for the life of a building, would probably make such a system much too expensive in overall cost and much too wasteful of energy.

Using 0.1 in. WG per 100 ft of equivalent length has proven to be a very practical basis for design; if any deviation from this value is made, it should be in the direction of less static pressure loss per unit length, such as perhaps 0.08 in. WG per 100 ft. This will be a concession to our national need to save energy.

When using this method, there is one problem that must never be overlooked—that problem is noise. The pressure drop method will in some cases result in a duct velocity which is excessive, and which will result in unsuitable duct air noise. This noise, generated in a duct, will usually emanate from the grilles, registers, and diffusers that connect to the duct; noise is the product of excessive velocity. Therefore, to be certain that air noise will remain within acceptable levels, we must *always* check the velocities that will result when a given duct size is selected.

Duct sizes may be easily selected from the sizing charts in figs. 6-27, 6-28, and 6-29. For example, suppose that a certain LV main supply duct is to carry 4250 cfm. It is to be installed in a ceiling furred space which is 18 in. high, so that it is desirable to limit the duct height to 15 in.

From fig. 6-28, where we enter the chart on the left at 4250 and move horizontally to the right to the vertical 0.1 in. line, we see that a 24-in.-diameter round duct will be required. However, this duct exceeds the 15 in. height limitation, and it is apparent that a rectangular duct must be used. Consulting fig. 6-29, which is a chart of circular equivalents, we see that a rectangular duct 15 in.

high and 20.6 in. wide is equivalent to a 24-in. round duct. We would probably decide to use, then, a 21 in. × 15 in. duct, if the velocity is not too great. Figure 6-28 shows that the velocity in this case will be 1400 fpm.

Figure 6-30 includes a table of recommended and maximum velocities suitable for various locations within an HVAC system. In this chart, on the line for "main ducts," we see that following "recommended" practice, our 1400-fpm velocity is a little too high for the commercial building range (1000 to 1300 fpm), is well within the industrial building range (1200 to 1800 fpm), and is much too high for the "quiet" building range (700 to 900 fpm).

If we decide that for a given building the duct velocity is too high, we arbitrarily increase the duct size until its velocity is suitable. Its rate of static pressure loss will now fall below our design parameter of 0.1 in. WG per 100 ft but this must be done, and a satisfactory result should be obtained.

In fig. 6-30 the term "face velocity" may be seen in many locations; this is the velocity in fpm at some point in the system based on the overall area through which air is passing, and is not based on "net free" area. For example, a sidewall supply register is supplying 375 cfm of air into a room; the duct to which the register is connected is 18 in. wide by 6 in. high (this is also the nominal register size), and the register has 60% free area.

This 18 in. × 6 in. register has an overall area of 108 in.^{2} (18 in. × 6 in. = 108 in.^{2}), or 0.75 ft^2. We may, of course, say that air quantity in cfm is equal to cross-sectional area A in ft^2 (of a duct or register, etc.) multiplied by velocity V in fpm; or

$$\text{cfm} = A \times V \quad \text{or} \quad V = \frac{\text{cfm}}{A} \quad (6\text{-}1)$$

The *face velocity* of the register above is equal to 375 cfm ÷ 0.75 ft^2 = 500 fpm because the *face area* (18 in. × 6 in.) is equal to 0.75 ft^2. Since this register has 60% free area (or open space), of the 0.75 ft^2 face area, 60%, or 0.45 ft^2, is open and

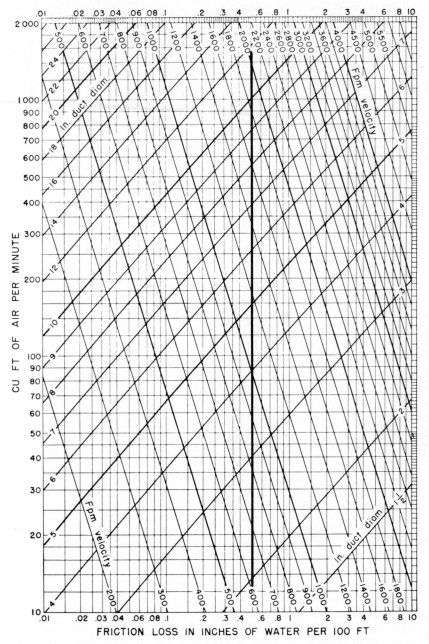

Figure 6-27 Lost head due to friction for galvanized steel ducts. (Reprinted with permission from the 1972 Fundamentals Volume, *ASHRAE Handbook and Products Directory*.)

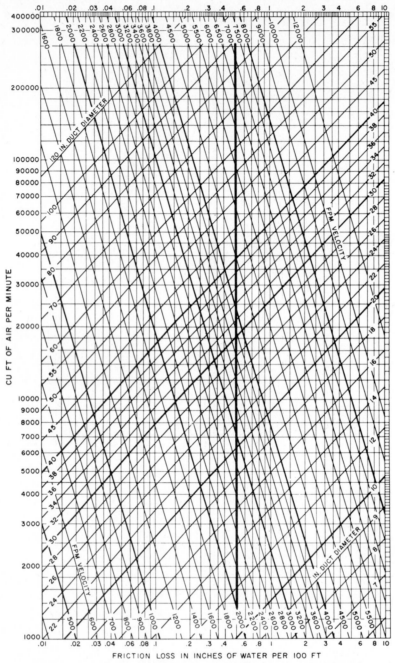

Figure 6-28 Lost head due to friction for galvanized steel ducts. (Reprinted with permission from the 1972 Fundamentals Volume, *ASHRAE Handbook and Products Directory* .)

Figure 6-29 Circular equivalents of rectangular ducts for equal friction and capacity. Dimensions in inches, feet, or meters. (Reprinted with permission from the 1972 Fundamentals Volume, *ASHRAE Handbook and Products Directory*.)

Side rectangular duct	6	7	8	9	10	11	12	13	14	15	16	17	18	19	20	22	24
6	6.6																
7	7.1	7.7															
8	7.5	8.2	8.8														
9	8.0	8.6	9.3	9.9													
10	8.4	9.1	9.8	10.4	10.9												
11	8.8	9.5	10.2	10.8	11.4	12.0											
12	9.1	9.9	10.7	11.3	11.9	12.5	13.1										
13	9.5	10.3	11.1	11.8	12.4	13.0	13.6	14.2									
14	9.8	10.7	11.5	12.2	12.9	13.5	14.2	14.7	15.3								
15	10.1	11.0	11.8	12.6	13.3	14.0	14.6	15.3	15.8	16.4							
16	10.4	11.4	12.2	13.0	13.7	14.4	15.1	15.7	16.3	16.9	17.5						
17	10.7	11.7	12.5	13.4	14.1	14.9	15.5	16.1	16.8	17.4	18.0	18.6					
18	11.0	11.9	12.9	13.7	14.5	15.3	16.0	16.6	17.3	17.9	18.5	19.1	19.7				
19	11.2	12.2	13.2	14.1	14.9	15.6	16.4	17.1	17.8	18.4	19.0	19.6	20.2	20.8			
20	11.5	12.5	13.5	14.4	15.2	15.9	16.8	17.5	18.2	18.8	19.5	20.1	20.7	21.3	21.9		
22	12.0	13.1	14.1	15.0	15.9	16.7	17.6	18.3	19.1	19.7	20.4	21.0	21.7	22.3	22.9	24.1	
24	12.4	13.6	14.6	15.6	16.6	17.5	18.3	19.1	19.8	20.6	21.3	21.9	22.6	23.2	23.9	25.1	26.2
26	12.8	14.1	15.2	16.2	17.2	18.1	19.0	19.8	20.6	21.4	22.1	22.8	23.5	24.1	24.8	26.1	27.2
28	13.2	14.5	15.6	16.7	17.7	18.7	19.6	20.5	21.3	22.1	22.9	23.6	24.4	25.0	25.7	27.1	28.2
30	13.6	14.9	16.1	17.2	18.3	19.3	20.2	21.1	22.0	22.9	23.7	24.4	25.2	25.9	26.7	28.0	29.3
32	14.0	15.3	16.5	17.7	18.8	19.8	20.8	21.8	22.7	23.6	24.4	25.2	26.0	26.7	27.5	28.9	30.1
34	14.4	15.7	17.0	18.2	19.3	20.4	21.4	22.4	23.3	24.2	25.1	25.9	26.7	27.5	28.3	29.7	31.0
36	14.7	16.1	17.4	18.6	19.8	20.9	21.9	23.0	23.9	24.8	25.8	26.6	27.4	28.3	29.0	30.5	32.0
38	15.0	16.4	17.8	19.0	20.3	21.4	22.5	23.5	24.5	25.4	26.4	27.3	28.1	29.0	29.8	31.4	32.8
40	15.3	16.8	18.2	19.4	20.7	21.9	23.0	24.0	25.1	26.0	27.0	27.9	28.8	29.7	30.5	32.1	33.6

40% is metal grillage. The free area velocity is equal to 375 cfm ÷ (0.75 ft² × 0.6) = 833.33 fpm. We very often speak in terms of face velocity, but we very rarely speak in terms of free area velocity. This is true of heating and cooling coils, air intake louvers, and so on.

In completing our discussion of fig. 6-30, attention should be called to the "remarks" column. These remarks tell us that on lines 4 and 6, the type of a/c unit under consideration is of the central station type remotely located an appreciable distance from the conditioned spaces, and utilizing much supply ductwork. Such ductwork

gives considerable noise attenuation and permits higher a/c unit fan outlet velocities and higher fan tip speeds.

Fan tip speeds refer to the peripheral velocity of the tips of the blades in the cylindrical squirrel cage fan wheel (see fig. 6-11). For example, a fan wheel in this type of fan, having a diameter of 1 ft and rotating at a speed of 1000 rpm, would have a tip speed of 3141.6 fpm (1000 rpm × 1 ft diameter × π = 3141.6 fpm).

The remarks on lines 5 and 7 refer to the type of a/c unit that is located directly in the occupied space.

Figure 6-30 Recommended and maximum air velocities for low velocity air distribution systems.

	Recommended			Maximum			
	Commercial buildings	Industrial buildings	Churches, homes, etc. (quiet)	Commercial buildings	Industrial buildings	Churches, homes, etc. (quiet)	Remarks
1. Outside air intake louvers	500	500	500	500	500	500	Face velocity
2. Heating coil face velocity	500	500	500	700	700	700	
3. Cooling coil face velocity	500	500	500	550	550	550	
4. Air conditioning unit fan outlet	1200	1800	1200	1500	2000	1200	Remotely located unit
5. Air conditioning unit fan outlet— no ducts	1000	1500	1000	1000	1500	1000	Located in occupied space
6. Air conditioning unit fan tip speed	5000	6000	5000	5000	6000	5000	Remotely located unit
7. Air conditioning unit fan tip speed— no ducts	3000	5000	3000	3000	5000	3000	Located in occupied space
8. Main ducts	1000–1300	1200–1800	700–900	1100–1500	1400–2200	800–1200	
9. Branch ducts*	600–800	800–1000	600	800–1200	1000–1400	700–900	
10. Supply registers	300–600	300–800	300–500	300–600	500–1000	300–500	Face velocities
11. Diffuser necks	400–700	600–1000	400–600	500–900	800–1200	400–600	
12. Corridors	100	100	100	100	150	100	When used for return
13. Return grilles	400	600–800	400	500	600–800	500	Face velocities
14. Relief openings	600–700	700–900	600	600–700	700–900	600	Face velocities

Note: All velocities in feet per minute.
*Within 15 ft of a supply grille, register, or diffuser.

Duct Equivalent Length

As may be seen above, it is necessary, in designing a duct system, to know what the equivalent length of the system will be. When a preliminary layout of the supply duct system has been made, it is easy to measure, by scaling the drawing, the "actual" length of the longest duct run to the most remote supply grille, register, or diffuser. However, the actual measured length is only the beginning. To this must be added extra length in proportion to the frictional resistance of all the fittings (duct elbows, tees, branch connections, etc.) and all the accessories in the ducts (dampers, extractors, etc.).

A method is available for estimating the equivalent length, expressed in feet of straight duct, of each item of resistance. When this is done for each item offering airflow resistance, these are totaled and then added to the actual measured length. The final total is the equivalent length needed for design purposes.

The method to be used in doing this is set forth in detail in the ASHRAE guidebooks and is not included herein. Many HVAC designers do not follow this complicated and time-consuming process. Instead, they study the preliminary duct layout, developing a feeling for the relative complexity of same, and after measuring the "actual" length, they make an intuitive estimate of the percentage of the actual length that must be added to find the total equivalent length.

Rarely will the percentage to be added to the actual length be less than 40%, and rarely will it exceed 100%. In most cases it will fall in this range; therefore, we may write

$$TEL = L + (C \times L) \qquad (6\text{-}2)$$

where TEL = total equivalent length
     L = actual measured length, ft
     C = a coefficient of duct system complexity which will be of the order of 0.4 for simple duct systems and 1.0 or more for very complex duct systems

The reader may fear that such an approximate method of estimating duct friction may introduce too much error. In this case, the ASHRAE method is always available. However, as may be seen in the typical static pressure loss tabulation included herein near the end of art. 6-9, the static pressure loss of the supply ducts is only a small fraction of the total static pressure loss of the entire system. This is rarely in excess of 10% for a low-velocity system; therefore, substantial errors may be made in estimating such a system without having any appreciable effect on overall design.

When the total static pressure loss of the entire system, including all "external" static pressure

loss and all "internal" SP loss, is finally totaled, a preliminary selection of an a/c unit may be made.

To do this, two facts must be known: the total system cfm (which by now would be known) and the total SP loss. The designer would now consult several manufacturers' a/c unit rating catalogs. Knowing the specific type of a/c unit required (whether floor mounted or ceiling hung, single zone or multizone, using bypass control or valve control, etc.), the designer may now make a preliminary selection. Having reached this point, many other unknowns in the system may now be determined.

Sometimes, when larger a/c systems are involved, the designer may need to custom design the a/c unit, it being too large to obtain as a standard manufactured unit. Knowing the total system cfm and the total SP loss, the designer may now begin to select system components, such as coils, fans, fan motor, and filters, and the design of the field-erected unit can proceed.

An example of a low-velocity duct design is shown in figs. 6-31 and 6-32; the method used for this design follows.

Example 6-1 The building shown in fig. 6-31 is a one-story office building. For HVAC design purposes, the building has been divided into five temperature control zones: a north zone including four rooms along the north wall, a south zone including rooms 1 through 8 along the south wall, an east zone including two rooms along the east wall, a west zone including five rooms along the west wall, and a center or interior zone which includes all interior rooms that do not border on an outside wall.

Each zone would have its own temperature control thermostat, and would have its own individual air supply duct delivering air to that zone only at conditions of temperature and humidity required by that zone.

As shown in fig. 6-31, a multizone air conditioning unit is installed in room 15, the equipment room. This a/c unit is like the one detailed in fig.

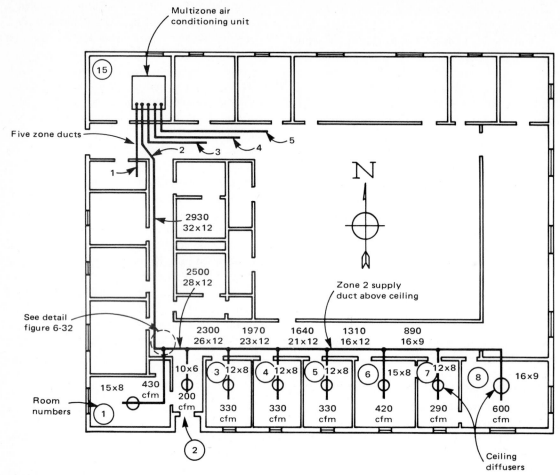

Figure 6-31 Building plan showing typical zone duct layout. (Scale = 1/16 = 1ft.)

6-14, and for this building, is able to produce air at five widely varying conditions as called for by the five different zone thermostats mentioned above.

The zone 2 (south zone) supply duct is the one detailed in fig. 6-31. Here we assume that heating and cooling load calculations (not included herein) have been made and the required air quantities have been determined for each room, as shown. The total air quantity for all eight rooms is 2930 cfm as noted. Notice that in the small-scale drawing of fig. 6-31, the ductwork is indicated by a single line. In a larger scale drawing, the ductwork should always be fully detailed, with the actual width of all ducts drawn to scale.

Zone 2 duct connects to the a/c unit and then runs above the corridor ceilings to the south zone with a branch duct extended to a round ceiling diffuser in each office, as shown. Figure 6-32 shows an enlarged detail of one portion of this zone duct, and includes details of an elbow and a branch connection to the main duct.

In this building, an acoustic ceiling is suspended from the roof structure so that a duct space is provided which has a net height of 16 in. Therefore, the maximum height of ducts in this space can be only 12 in. When insulated with a 1-in. thickness of insulation, such ducts would be 14 in. high.

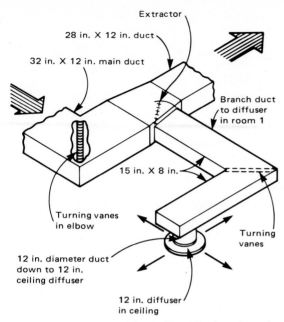

Extractor

28 in. X 12 in. duct

32 in. X 12 in. main duct

Branch duct
to diffuser
in room 1

15 in. X 8 in.

Turning vanes
in elbow

Turning
vanes

12 in. diameter duct
down to 12 in.
ceiling diffuser

12 in. diffuser
in ceiling

Figure 6-32 Detail of portion of supply duct shown in Fig. 6–31.

Consulting the duct sizing chart in fig. 6-28, we find that a duct carrying 2930 cfm (the total zone air quantity), at a static pressure friction loss of 0.1 in. WG per 100 ft, would need to be 21 in. in diameter and would have a velocity of approximately 1280 fpm. Now, consulting fig. 6-29 we can select a rectangular duct size equivalent to the 21-in. round duct required. Figure 6-29 shows that a duct 12 in. high and 32 in. wide is equivalent to a 20.8-in. round duct. This is very close, and a 32 in. X 12 in. main duct leading to zone 2 is chosen.

A study of ceiling diffuser manufacturers' catalogs now shows that the following ceiling diffusers would be required:

Rooms 3, 4, 5, and 7	10-in. diffusers
Rooms 1 and 6	12-in. diffusers
Room 2	8-in. diffuser
Room 8	14-in. diffuser

Figure 6-42 shows some details of ceiling diffusers; the nominal sizes listed above are the diameters of the round necks through which the air

enters the diffusers. Notice that the connecting supply ducts are, in each case, somewhat larger than the diffusers.

Having chosen the main duct size of 32 in. X 12 in., we now proceed to size the duct connecting to the last diffuser in the zone—in room 8. This diffuser is a 14-in. size, and a 16-in. wide duct (somewhat larger) is chosen. In figure 6-27, with 600 cfm at 0.1 in. WG friction loss rate, an 11.4-in.-diameter duct is chosen. In fig. 6-29 this 11.4-in.-diameter converts to a 16 in. X 7 in. rectangular size.

Now, the main duct sizing may be completed, section by section, according to the total air required in each section of duct. The 12-in. duct height may be retained with the width progressively reducing, as shown in fig. 6-31, until a 16-in. width is reached (the width chosen for the last section of duct). Now the 16-in. width is retained and the duct height permitted to reduce as necessary until the size of the last section is reached.

In sizing the branch ducts leading to each diffuser, we find that the use of 0.1 in. WG (friction loss per 100 ft) as a basis for design now gives us velocities that are too high. Our study of ceiling diffuser manufacturers' performance data (mentioned above) has shown us that approach velocities and diffuser neck velocities should be 500 to 700 fpm. Therefore, our branch ducts must be sized on the basis of velocity rather than pressure drop (friction), and the branch duct sizes shown in fig. 6-31 are the result.

The supply duct shown is the longest of any of the five that connect to the a/c unit shown, and it measures an actual installed length of approximately 160 ft. An overall examination reveals that the first 60 ft section of the 160 ft is an almost straight, uncluttered duct with no branch connections and other features. The remaining 100 ft section is straight and simple but does have the seven branch takeoff connections shown.

This is a comparatively simple duct system and the equivalent length could not exceed 150% of the actual length. The equivalent length would then be 160 ft actual X 150% = 240 ft equivalent length. All but the last 10 ft or so of this duct has been sized to have a friction loss of 0.1 in. WG per 100 ft of equivalent length, so the static pressure loss of the entire duct will be 0.1 in. $\times$ 240/100 = 0.24 in. WG.

Suppose, for example, that the static pressure loss of everything in the system except the supply duct is 1.4 in. WG. The total SP loss is then 1.4 in. + 0.24 in. = 1.64 in. WG. Suppose that we had, perchance, underestimated the SP loss of the supply duct badly and it should have been 200% of the actual length instead of the 150% used above. The SP loss of the duct is now 160 ft $\times$ 200% = 320 ft equivalent length. At 0.1 in. WG per 100 ft the duct loss is 0.32 in. WG. Adding this to the 1.4 in. SP loss of the remainder of the system, the total SP loss is 0.32 + 1.40 = 1.72 in. WG. The error in the 1.64 in. WG figure amounts to 4.9% [(1.72 – 1.64)/1.64 = 0.049]; this is well within reasonable design tolerances for a duct system.

One can easily see why practicing HVAC designers so often do not bother with the detail calculation of static pressure losses in low velocity duct systems.

6-12 High-Velocity Duct Systems

High-velocity duct systems are air supply systems that utilize air velocities in the range 2500 to 7000 fpm, although normally velocities do not exceed 6000 fpm. Velocities as high as these represent a very dramatic change from those that have traditionally been used. In fact, high-velocity design represents such a radical departure from tradition that the reasons supporting such a departure should be carefully called into question and given closest scrutiny whenever such design is contemplated.

Obviously, when in an existing building a certain, fixed space is available for supply duct installation, and no means are available to increase this space, a high-velocity system could, if necessary, be justified. However, even in this inflexible case, alternative HVAC systems that would require no ductwork or minimum ductwork should be thoroughly considered.

High-velocity systems, including the extra-heavy-duty a/c units required to supply them, are much more expensive in initial installed cost, and the cost disadvantage is even greater with regard to operating cost. The inescapable conclusion, then, is that high-velocity air distribution systems should be used only when all alternatives have been thoroughly considered and rejected.

It is entirely possible that when a new high-rise building is being planned, enough building height reduction could be realized, through the use of high-velocity ducts and less resulting floor-to-floor heights, to effect a substantial savings in building cost. Suppose that, in a 40-story building, a reduction in duct space height of 5 in. per floor could be realized, the 16 ft 8 in. overall reduction in building height results in an impressive saving in building cost. It is easy to see how an architect or building owner could yield to the temptation of effectuating such a cost saving.

But is the saving as much as it seems? Or is there any saving at all? Only an extensive life-cycle cost study can reveal the true answer, and, of course, the answer will vary from building to building and from owner to owner.

In the case of the 40-story building above, the overall height reduction might be 4% with perhaps a reduction of 1.5 to 2% in the cost of the building shell. The increased cost of a high-velocity duct system would offset only a small part of this reduction. However, the very substantial increase in the operating cost of the high-velocity system (as compared to a low-velocity system or a system with no ducts) would, in most cases, offset building shell cost reduction sooner or later.

To some building owners, the initial cost of the building is the major consideration. If the building is to be leased to others who will pay the operating costs, the decision may be in favor of a high-velocity system, unpatriotic though it may be in terms of our national need to save energy.

Since so much emphasis has been placed in this chapter on the limitation of duct velocities as a means of noise control, the reader may be wondering about the feasibility of 6000-fpm duct velocities in a quiet building. Duct velocities of

3000 to 6000 fpm would be intolerable if applied in the usual way. However, high-velocity systems are very satisfactorily quiet because positive steps are taken to make them quiet.

Acoustic Chambers and Terminals

Usually, some type of *acoustic chamber* is installed near the outlet of the high-speed fan that drives the air. This acoustic chamber is inserted in the main supply duct and consists of a box lined with sound-absorbing material and filled with acoustic boards set parallel to each other and spaced so that the air can flow between them (see fig. 6-33). There are several types of acoustic chambers available from manufacturers; but these are also often locally fabricated as required.

In addition to acoustic chambers, every high-velocity duct system is fitted with *acoustic terminals,* sometimes referred to as "attenuators" or "terminal boxes," located at the extreme end of each high-velocity duct run. Therefore, HV duct systems are not noisy, because the noise is effectively trapped out by the acoustic treatment always provided.

In fig. 6-34 is shown a detail of a typical acoustic terminal such as might be used in a con-

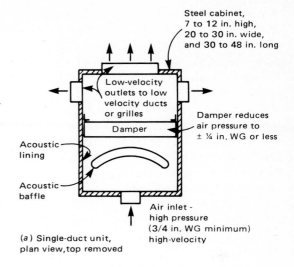

(a) Single-duct unit, plan view, top removed

Steel cabinet, 7 to 12 in. high, 20 to 30 in. wide, and 30 to 48 in. long

Low-velocity outlets to low velocity ducts or grilles

Damper

Damper reduces air pressure to ± ¼ in. WG or less

Acoustic lining

Acoustic baffle

Air inlet - high pressure (3/4 in. WG minimum) high-velocity

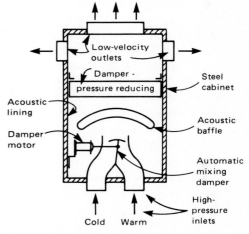

(b) Double-duct unit, plan view, top removed

Low-velocity outlets

Damper - pressure reducing

Steel cabinet

Acoustic lining

Acoustic baffle

Damper motor

Automatic mixing damper

High-pressure inlets

Cold   Warm

Figure 6-34 High velocity acoustic terminals.

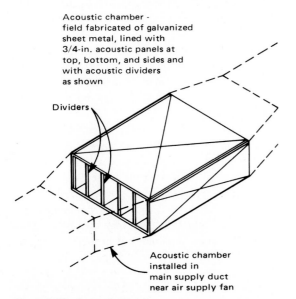

Acoustic chamber - field fabricated of galvanized sheet metal, lined with 3/4-in. acoustic panels at top, bottom, and sides and with acoustic dividers as shown

Dividers

Acoustic chamber installed in main supply duct near air supply fan

Figure 6-33 Acoustic chamber.

ventional single-duct high-velocity system. Double-duct systems (which will be discussed later), in which a warm air supply duct main and a cold air supply main run side by side throughout a building, utilize double-inlet high-velocity acoustic terminals. These make provision for branch duct connections from both the warm supply main and the cold supply main. The double-inlet acoustic terminal then automatically mixes warm air and cold air in proper proportions to deliver just the correct temperature air to the occupied spaces.

Acoustic terminals, then, are available as single-inlet or double-inlet boxes. They reduce the high pressure of the high-velocity system down to a more manageable pressure of 0.15 in. WG or so, but most important, they trap out the noise of the high-velocity air.

The air that leaves the acoustic terminal is at low pressure and low velocity. It may pass directly into a supply grille, register, or diffuser and into the room to be conditioned, or it may pass into a very short low-velocity duct system which supplies air to several grilles, registers, or diffusers.

High-Velocity-Duct Construction

Because high-velocity ducts carry much higher static pressures than do low-velocity ducts, they must be much more heavily constructed and must be leakproof. At the higher pressures carried, even a very small leak can waste a great quantity of conditioned air; in addition, a pinhole-sized leak may often squeal and hiss and be objectionably noisy.

Of course, the heavier, leakproof construction makes high-velocity ducts quite expensive. This is especially true when the height of the ducts is severely limited, and wide, flat ducts must be used. If round ducts can be used, the cost penalty will not be nearly so great.

One type of duct now finding extensive acceptance in high-velocity systems is made of a strip of steel of proper thickness which is spirally wound to form a round duct. The spiral seam made where the edges of the steel strip meet is a double-locked standing seam which gives the duct rigidity, and leakage is negligible.

This spirally wound duct is also flattened to form an oval cross section that permits larger ducts to fit into a limited height space. Joints in spiral ducts are easily and tightly made and a wide range of fittings (elbows, branch takeoffs, transitions, etc.) are available.

In conventional, rectangular high-velocity ducts, the girth joints, where adjacent sections of duct meet, are expensive and difficult to make leakproof. These joints are welded or soldered or flanged and gasketed; as a result, they are quite costly.

Some of the materials that are used in low velocity systems, such as glass fiber ducts, are not suitable for high-velocity use; however, other materials, such as vitrified tile, concrete tile, cement-asbestos, and concrete encased paper or plastic, are eminently suited to high-velocity work.

Low-velocity systems depend to a great extent on the use of dampers, extractors, splitters, and other directional devices to cause the conditioned air to go in proper quantity to the proper places. High-velocity systems do not do this. They use a minimum of dampers and similar devices but depend upon maintaining a comparatively high static pressure throughout a duct system. This pressure then will cause an adequate amount of flow out through any opening that may exist.

The acoustic terminals, which are always required, trap out the noise that exists within the system, as mentioned above; but in addition, they provide volume control either automatically or through manual adjustment. They are usually automatic, however.

High-Velocity-Duct Design

In high-velocity systems, the duct design must be more precise and careful than in LV duct design. Because of the much higher velocities utilized, poorly designed and constructed fittings can result in an unexpectedly high static pressure loss, with the result that the entire operation may be faulty. A LV design, as we have seen, can be very forgiving, and although serious errors in design and construction may be made, the effect on the overall system total resistance may be very small percentagewise.

Therefore, with HV system design we must carefully estimate the airflow resistance of each fitting and each section of ductwork. As with LV duct design, we will start with the longest duct run, or the one expected to have the greatest pressure loss. When it is carefully designed for minimum pressure loss, all other duct runs may then be designed with a bit more freedom, but in such a way that pressure loss does not exceed that of the longest run.

Each duct run must be fitted, close to the a/c unit, with a sound trap to remove fan noise. Some multizone blow-through a/c units have acoustically lined hot and cold discharge plenums which also serve as sound traps.

There are several methods in current use in duct design, such as the equal friction method, the static regain method, the constant velocity method, the velocity reduction method, and the constant friction method. The latter method was used in the LV duct design example given above.

The static regain method is one that is quite frequently and satisfactorily used in HV system design. This method is based on the principle, previously set forth herein, that total pressure p_t in a duct is equal to the sum of the static pressure p_s and the velocity pressure p_v. This was discussed in art. 1-19 and is expressed by formula (1-1):

$$p_t = p_s + p_v$$

From this it is obvious that, for a given total pressure, if the velocity pressure in a duct is reduced, the static pressure must increase in equal amount. Of course, velocity pressure can fall only when duct velocity is reduced.

In the static regain method, at each branch takeoff from the main duct a transition is provided which is so designed that the main duct velocity decreases. The design is such that the static pressure increase, resulting from the velocity pressure decrease, is just enough to overcome the total pressure loss in the succeeding section of ductwork (leading to the next branch connection).

Since the total pressure p_t must progressively fall from the a/c unit outlet to the end of each duct run, the velocity pressure, and hence the air velocity, should be continuously reduced from beginning to end. There will usually be an appreciable static pressure reduction in a duct run, but there must be enough static pressure maintained to the end of the longest run to operate the acoustic terminal located there. Most acoustic terminals require approximately 3/4 in. WG of static pressure to permit them to control and function properly.

Once the decision has been made to design for high velocity the question of how high the velocities should be must be answered. Current practice seems to favor velocities that result from designing on a constant friction basis of 0.5 in. WG per 100 ft of equivalent duct length. In other words, we may enter our duct sizing charts in fig. 6-27 and 6-28 at the vertical 0.5 line and select a duct size where the proper horizontal cfm line crosses the vertical 0.5 line. However, we should limit duct velocities to 6000 fpm which means that for extremely large air quantities of 140,000 cfm and more we should select duct sizes on the 6000-fpm velocity line.

Since in HV systems we must carefully select our fittings and evaluate them for pressure loss, we must have pressure loss data for the various fittings to be used. Again, the ASHRAE handbooks come to our assistance, and the several tables shown in fig. 6-35 have been taken from that source.

Figure 6-35 shows 12 different types of fittings and the pressure loss characteristics of each. These tables give values of C, which is a *loss coefficient*. The C values are multipliers that may be applied to the velocity pressure at a given point in the system. Remember, velocity pressure may be calculated by the use of formula (4-5), which states that

$$p_v = \left(\frac{V}{4005}\right)^2 \tag{4-5}$$

where p_v = velocity pressure, in. WG
  V = duct velocity, fpm

For example, if a duct has in it a square, mitered elbow with single-thickness turning vanes, and is a rectangular duct carrying air at 3500 fpm velocity, what is the airflow resistance of this elbow? Assuming that the turning vanes have no trailing edges, that the radius of each turning vane is 4.5 in., and that the spacing between vanes is 2.25 in., we may use table 3-8 in fig. 6-35 and see that the coefficient, C_0, is 0.15. Then using formula (4-5), we calculate that the loss in pressure when the velocity is 3500 fpm is

$$\Delta p = 0.15 \left(\frac{V}{4005}\right)^2 = 0.15 \left(\frac{3500}{4005}\right)^2$$
$$= 0.115 \text{ in. WG}$$

Figure 6-35 Pressure loss in ductwork fittings. (Reprinted with permission from the 1977 Fundamentals Volume, *ASHRAE Handbook and Products Directory*.)

1-10 Hood, tapered, flanged, or unflanged

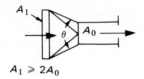

$$A_1 \geq 2A_0$$

θ is a major angle for rectangular hoods

					Round				
θ	$0°$	$20°$	$40°$	$60°$	$80°$	$100°$	$120°$	$140°$	$160°$	$180°$
C_0	1.0	0.11	0.06	0.09	0.14	0.18	0.27	0.32	0.43	0.50

					Square or rectangular				
θ	$0°$	$20°$	$40°$	$60°$	$80°$	$100°$	$120°$	$140°$	$160°$	$180°$
C_0	1.0	0.19	0.13	0.16	0.21	0.27	0.33	0.43	0.53	0.62

3-4 Elbows, 30°, Z-shaped, round

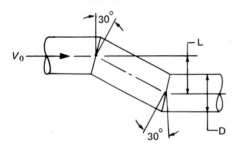

L/D	0	0.5	1.0	1.5	2.0	2.5	3.0
C_0	0	0.15	0.15	0.16	0.16	0.16	0.16

3-8 Elbow, mitered, with single-thickness vanes, rectangular

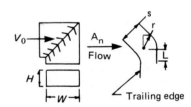

	Dimensions			
No.	r	s	L	C_0
1*	2.0	1.5	0.75	0.12
2	4.5	2.25	0	0.15
3	4.5	3.25	1.60	0.18

*When extension of trailing edge is not provided for this vane, losses are approximately unchanged for single elbows in series but increase considerably for elbows in series.

Figure 6-35 *(Cont.)*

Local loss coefficients, elbows

3-1 Elbow, smooth radius, round

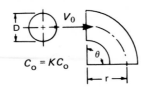

$$C_o = KC_o$$

Coefficients for $90°$ elbows:

r/D	0.5	0.75	1.0	1.5	2.0	2.5
C_o	0.71	0.33	0.22	0.15	0.13	0.12

For angles other than $90°$ multiply by the following factor:

θ	0	20	30	45	60	75	90	110	130	150	180
K	0	0.31	0.45	0.60	0.78	0.90	1.00	1.13	1.20	1.28	1.40

3-5 Elbow, smooth radius without vanes, rectangular

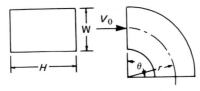

$$C_o = KC_o'$$

Coefficients for $90°$ elbows:

$$c_o'$$

	H/W										
r/W	0.25	0.5	1.0	1.5	2.0	3.0	4.0	5.0	6.0	7.0	8.0
0.5	1.3	1.0	0.93	0.95	0.99	1.1	1.2	1.3	1.4	1.5	1.6
0.75	0.61	0.46	0.39	0.38	0.39	0.41	0.43	0.46	0.49	0.51	0.54
1.0	0.36	0.26	0.21	0.20	0.20	0.20	0.21	0.22	0.23	0.23	0.24
1.5	0.18	0.12	0.09	0.08	0.08	0.07	0.07	0.08	0.08	0.08	0.08
2.0	0.11	0.07	0.05	0.04	0.04	0.04	0.04	0.04	0.04	0.04	0.04
2.5	0.07	0.04	0.03	0.03	0.02	0.02	0.02	0.02	0.02	0.02	0.02
3.0	0.05	0.03	0.02	0.02	0.02	0.01	0.01	0.01	0.01	0.01	0.01

For angles other than $90°$ multiply by the following factor:

θ	$0°$	$20°$	$30°$	$45°$	$60°$	$75°$	$90°$	$110°$	$130°$	$150°$	$180°$
K	0	0.31	0.45	0.60	0.78	0.90	1.0	1.13	1.20	1.28	1.40

Figure 6-35 *(Cont.)*

Local loss coefficients,
transitions (converging flow)

5-1 Contraction, gradual, round and rectangular

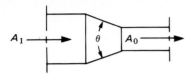

A_0	C_o					
	θ degrees					
A_1	10	20	30	40	50	60
0.1	0	0.01	0.02	0.03	0.05	0.07
0.2	0	0.01	0.02	0.03	0.05	0.07
0.3	0	0.01	0.02	0.03	0.05	0.06
0.4	0	0.01	0.02	0.03	0.04	0.06
0.5	0	0.01	0.01	0.02	0.04	0.05
0.6	0	0.01	0.01	0.02	0.03	0.04
0.7	0	0	0.01	0.02	0.03	0.04
0.8	0	0	0.01	0.01	0.02	0.03
0.9	0	0	0	0.01	0.01	0.01

7-5 Damper, rectangular, parallel blades

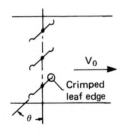

L/R is the sum of lengths of all leafs divided by
perimeter of duct

L	C_o								
	θ, degrees								
R	10	20	30	40	50	60	70	80	90
0.3	116	32	14	9.0	5.0	2.3	1.4	0.79	0.52
0.4	152	38	16	9.0	6.0	2.4	1.5	0.85	0.52
0.5	188	45	18	9.0	6.0	2.4	1.5	0.92	0.52
0.6	245	45	21	9.0	5.4	2.4	1.5	0.92	0.52
0.8	284	55	22	9.0	5.4	2.5	1.5	0.92	0.52
1.0	361	65	24	10	5.4	2.6	1.6	1.0	0.52
1.5	576	102	28	10	5.4	2.7	1.6	1.0	0.52

6-5 Diverging wye, round

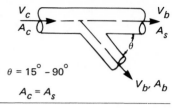

$$\theta = 15° - 90°$$

$$A_c = A_s$$

Branch, $C_{c,b}$

$\dfrac{V_b}{V_c}$	θ, degrees				
	15	30	45	60	90
0	1.0	1.0	1.0	1.0	1.0
0.1	0.92	0.94	0.97	1.0	1.0
0.2	0.65	0.70	0.75	0.84	1.0
0.4	0.38	0.46	0.60	0.76	1.1
0.6	0.20	0.31	0.50	0.65	1.2
0.8	0.09	0.25	0.41	0.80	1.3
1.0	0.10	0.25	0.52	0.90	1.3
1.2	0.11	0.32	0.67	1.1	1.4
1.4	0.22	0.63	0.88	1.4	1.6
1.6	0.41	0.72	1.2	1.8	1.8
2.0	0.99	1.4	1.9	2.7	2.2
2.6	2.5	2.9	2.7	4.6	—
3.0	6.5	6.7	7.0	7.3	—

Main

V_s/V_c	0	0.1	0.2	0.3	0.4	0.5	0.6	0.8	1.0
$C_{c,s}$		0.40	0.32	0.26	0.20	0.15	0.10	0.06	0.02	0

7-6 Damper, rectangular, opposed blades

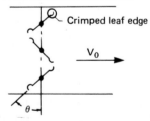

L/R is the sum of lengths of all leafs divided by perimeter by duct

L	C_o								
	θ, degrees								
R	10	20	30	40	50	60	70	80	90
0.3	807	284	73	21	9.0	4.1	2.1	0.85	0.52
0.4	915	332	100	28	11	5.0	2.2	0.92	0.52
0.5	1045	377	122	33	13	5.4	2.3	1.0	0.52
0.6	1121	411	148	38	14	6.0	2.3	1.0	0.52
0.8	1299	495	188	54	18	6.6	2.4	1.1	0.52
1.0	1521	547	245	65	21	7.3	2.7	1.2	0.52
1.5	1654	677	361	107	28	9.0	3.2	1.4	0.52

Figure 6-35 *(Cont.)*

6-6 Diverging wye, rectangular

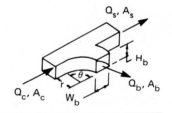

$\theta = 90°$

$r/W_b = 1.0$

Branch, $C_{c,b}$

$\dfrac{A_b}{A_s}$	$\dfrac{A_s}{A_c}$	$\dfrac{A_b}{A_c}$	Q_b/Q_c								
			0.2	0.3	0.4	0.5	0.6	0.7	0.8	0.9	1.0
0.25	1.0	0.25	0.50	0.60	0.85	1.2	1.8	3.1	4.4	6.0	6.7
0.33	0.75	0.25	0.35	0.50	0.80	1.3	2.0	2.8	3.8	5.0	6.5
0.5	1.0	0.5	0.48	0.40	0.40	0.48	0.60	0.78	1.1	1.5	2.0
0.67	0.75	0.5	0.40	0.32	0.30	0.34	0.44	0.62	0.92	1.4	2.0
1.0	0.5	0.5	0.38	0.38	0.41	0.52	0.68	0.92	1.2	1.6	2.0
1.0	1.0	1.0	0.55	0.46	0.37	0.32	0.29	0.29	0.30	0.37	0.50
1.33	0.75	1.0	0.60	0.51	0.42	0.34	0.28	0.26	0.26	0.29	0.37
2.0	0.5	1.0	0.52	0.43	0.33	0.24	0.17	0.15	0.17	0.21	0.25

Main, $C_{c,s}$

$\dfrac{A_b}{A_s}$	$\dfrac{A_s}{A_c}$	$\dfrac{A_b}{A_c}$	Q_b/Q_c								
			0.2	0.3	0.4	0.5	0.6	0.7	0.8	0.9	1.0
0.25	1.0	0.25	−.03	−.01	0.05	0.13	0.21	0.29	0.38	0.46	0.54
0.33	0.75	0.25	0	−.02	−.01	0.02	0.08	0.16	0.24	0.34	0.45
0.5	1.0	0.5	−.06	−.05	0	0.06	0.12	0.19	0.27	0.35	0.43
0.67	0.75	0.5	−.02	−.04	−.03	−.01	0.04	0.12	0.23	0.37	0.50
1.0	0.5	0.5	0.48	0.28	0.13	0.05	0.04	0.09	0.18	0.30	0.50
1.0	1.0	1.0	−.04	−.04	−.01	0.06	0.13	0.22	0.30	0.38	0.45
1.33	0.75	1.0	0.01	−.03	−.03	−.01	0.03	0.10	0.20	0.30	0.42
2.0	0.5	1.0	0.38	0.23	0.13	0.08	0.05	0.06	0.10	0.20	0.40

Local loss coefficients, obstructions

7-1 Damper, butterfly, round

θ, deg	0	5	10	15	20	25	30
C_o	0.17	0.24	0.52	0.90	1.6	2.5	3.9
θ, deg	35	40	50	60	65	70	90
C_o	7.4	11	33	118	256	751	∞

7-2 Damper, butterfly, rectangular

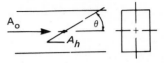

θ, deg	0	5	10	15	20	25	30
A_h/A_o	1.00	0.91	0.83	0.74	0.66	0.58	0.50
C_o	0.17	0.28	0.45	0.77	1.4	2.2	3.5
θ, deg	35	40	50	60	65	70	90
A_h/A_o	0.43	0.36	0.23	0.13	0.09	0.06	0
C_o	6.4	9.3	25	77	158	368	∞

This 0.115 in. WG is total pressure loss, but since there is no change in velocity in this elbow, there is no change in the velocity pressure p_v and the entire pressure loss is static pressure p_s.

Let us now proceed to a high-velocity duct system design problem, which illustrates the constant friction method of HV duct design.

Example 6-2 The *1977 ASHRAE Handbook of Fundamentals* advises that a major disadvantage of the static regain method is that excessively large ducts (low velocities) result at the ends of long

duct runs. This disadvantage is not as pronounced using the constant friction method, as may be seen from this example.

Consider the HV duct system detailed in fig. 6-36. As may be seen, the duct shown is one of several zone ducts supplied by a high-velocity high-pressure multizone a/c unit. This zone duct supplies 16,000 cfm through a duct that is approximately 525 ft long, and supplies 1000 cfm to each of 16 round ceiling diffusers. There are eight acoustic terminals, each of which receives 2000 cfm of HV air. These terminals remove the noise, the

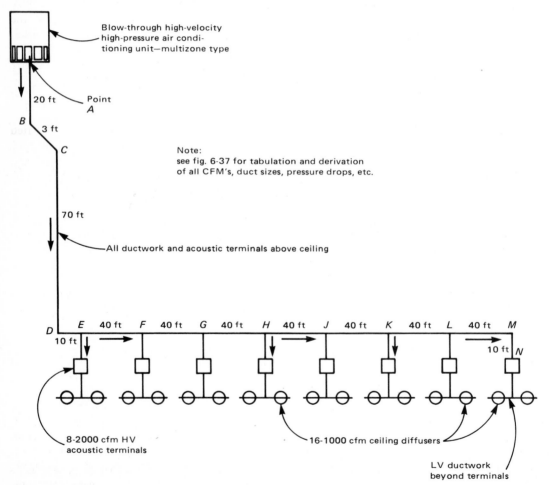

Figure 6-36 Single-line high velocity duct layout. See fig. 6-37 for tabulation and derivation of all cfm's, duct sizes, pressure drops, etc.

velocity, and the pressure from the incoming air, and deliver that air into a short LV duct leading to two ceiling diffusers.

This duct is shown as a single line for simplicity in this example, and the actual length of each section of duct is noted. Elbows are of the mitered turning vane type shown in table 3-8 of fig. 6-35; and branch takeoff connections are of the type shown in table 6-6 of fig. 6-35.

Turning vane elbows are not as good as radius elbows in very high velocity systems, where velocities reach 6000 fpm or even higher. However, in this system the highest velocity is 3650 fpm, and the air noise, rattle, and wear should not be objectionable at this velocity.

The results of the calculations in this example are tabulated in fig. 6-37. Notice that in column 10, the pressure loss in inches of water, gauge pressure, the total loss of the duct run is 3.046 in. WG. The loss values listed in column 10 result from two types of calculations. The first, as in location line A (the top line of fig. 6-37) involves finding a loss coefficient C of 0.15 in fig. 6-35, table 3-8 (see column 11), and applying this as a multiplier to the main duct velocity pressure, 0.83 in. WG (see column 6): 0.83 × 0.15 = 0.125 in. WG (column 10). The 0.83 in. WG in column 6, line A, results from selecting a 40 in. × 18 in. duct (column 4) to handle 16,000 cfm at a velocity of 3650 fpm (column 5). This selection was made from figs. 6-28 and 6-29 on or near the vertical 0.5 line of fig. 6-28. With a velocity of 3650 fpm, the velocity pressure

$$p_v = \left(\frac{V}{4005}\right)^2 = \left(\frac{3650}{4005}\right)^2 = 0.83 \text{ in. WG}$$

This procedure is used with all fittings such as elbows, duct offsets, and branch takeoff connections.

The second type of calculation involves finding the total net pressure loss value in column 10, where a straight run of duct is being considered, as on line A-B of fig. 6-37. Here the pressure loss per 100 ft of duct, 0.52, from fig. 6-28 is applied as a multiplier to the 20-ft length of that section

of duct = 0.52 in. WG per 100 ft × 20 ft/100 ft = 0.104 in. WG loss.

Note that the calculations for the sections of duct from fitting H to fitting L have been omitted from fig. 6-37 since they were merely repetitive. However, the calculations were made; and the pressure loss for that section, 0.545 in. WG, is shown in column 10, and is included in the total loss 3.046 in. WG.

For practice, the reader should make the calculations that were omitted and verify that value 0.545 shown in column 10.

Had the supply duct of fig. 6-36 been calculated and sized using the static regain method instead of the constant friction method, the ducts in the last half of the duct run would have been considerably larger, the velocities less, and the pressure loss less than the 3.046 in. WG shown. The proper choice of method must be left to the HVAC designer, who must balance first cost against operating cost.

To complete the picture that has been started in example 6-2, we might estimate the pressure losses in the remaining parts of the HVAC system. These might typically be of the approximate magnitudes shown in the tabulation below:

1. LV ducts between the acoustic terminals and the diffusers	0.12
2. Door louvers permitting airflow from rooms to a corridor	0.02
3. Return air through corridors	Nil
4. Return air grille near a/c unit	0.04
5. Return duct and RA damper	0.07
6. Air filter in a/c unit	0.20
7. Cooling coil at 500 fpm face velocity	0.60
8. Cabinet of the a/c unit	0.15
9. Zone mixing dampers at the a/c unit outlet	0.08
Total	1.28 in. WG

If this 1.28 in. WG pressure loss is added to the 3.046 in. WG loss of the HV supply ducts, we find a total system pressure loss of 1.28 + 3.046 = 4.326 in. WG. Consulting manufacturers' a/c unit rating catalogs, we find that 15 hp would be required to drive the fan to deliver 16,000 cfm against a resistance of 4.326 in. WG.

Figure 6-37 Calculations for Example 6-2, HV duct design.

Location	Item	Cfm	Duct size, in.	Velocity, fpm	Velocity pres., in. WG	Duct length, ft	Loss per 100 ft, in. WG	Fitting loss coefficient C	Net loss, in. WG	Reference	Quantity ratio $\frac{Q_b}{Q_c}=\frac{\text{branch cfm}}{\text{main cfm}}$	Area ratio $\frac{A_b}{A_c}=\frac{\text{branch area}}{\text{main area}}$
A	Elbow above air conditioning unit	16,000	40×18	3650	0.83	...	...	0.15	0.125	fig. 6-35, table 3-8, figs. 6-28		
A-B	Main duct	16,000	40×18	3650	0.83	20	0.52	...	0.104	and 6-29		
B-C	Offset	16,000	40×18	3650	0.83	...	...	0.15	0.125	fig. 6-35, table 3-4		
C-D	Main duct	16,000	40×18	3650	0.83	70	0.52	...	0.36	figs. 6-28 and 6-29		
D	Elbow	16,000	40×18	3650	0.83	...	...	0.15	0.125	fig. 6-35, table 3-8 figs. 6-28		
D-E	Main duct	16,000	40×18	3650	0.83 — 0.83 in. main	10	0.52	...	0.052	and 6-29		
E	Branch takeoff	2,000	18×8	2300		...	...	−0.03	−0.025	fig. 6-35, table 6-6 figs. 6-28	$\frac{2,000}{16,000}=0.125$	$\frac{18\times8}{40\times18}=0.2$
E-F	Main duct	14,000	36×18	3450	0.74 — 0.74 in. main	40	0.50	...	0.20	and 6-29		
F	Branch takeoff	2,000	18×8	2300		...	...	−0.03	−0.022	fig. 6-35, table 6-6 figs. 6-20	$\frac{2,000}{14,000}=0.14$	$\frac{18\times8}{36\times18}=0.22$
F-G	Main duct	12,000	32×18	3400	0.72 — 0.72 in. main	40	0.52	...	0.21	and 6-29		
G	Branch takeoff	2,000	18×8	2300		...	...	−0.03	−0.022	fig. 6-35, table 6-6 figs. 6-28	$\frac{2,000}{12,000}=0.17$	$\frac{18\times8}{32\times18}=0.25$
G-H	Main duct	10,000	28×18	3180	0.63	40	0.50	...	0.20	and 6-29		
L-M	Main duct	2,000	18×8	2300	0.33	40	0.54	...	0.216	figs. 6-28 and 6-29		
M	Elbow	2,000	18×8	2300	0.33	...	...	0.15	0.05	fig. 6-35, table 3-8		
M-N	Main duct	2,000	18×8	2300	0.33	10	0.53	...	0.053	figs. 6-28 and 6-29		
N	Acoustic terminal	2,000	...	...	...	...	...	...	0.75	Given in text		

Note:
Lines H, H-J, J, J-K, K, K-L, and L were calculated but omitted for brevity. Total net loss of these seven items = 0.545

Total net loss = 3.046 in. WG

184

Had we been able to use a low-velocity supply duct system, the pressure loss in the supply ducts might have been approximately 0.64 in. WG instead of 3.046 in. WG (425 ft actual length × 1.5 estimated = 638 ft equivalent length, which at 0.1 in. WG per 100 ft = 0.638 in. WG). The total loss would then be 1.28 in. WG + 0.638 in. WG = 1.918 in. WG. With this lower pressure loss (less frictional resistance), we find that a 7 1/2-hp fan motor would be adequate. Only 44% as much power would be required with the low-velocity duct system. Of course, the power requirements for other HVAC components, refrigeration compressor, pumps, cooling tower, and so on, would be the same with either HV or LV duct systems.

In chap. 1, in our discussion on pressure, we found that we could express pressure in terms of feet and inches of water instead of the more familiar term, pounds per square inch (psi). We also found that 1.0 psi is equivalent to 2.31 ft of water or 27.7 in. of water. Another useful conversion factor shows that 69.33 ft of standard air is equivalent to 1.0 in. WG.

With the latter conversion factor we can easily calculate the a/c unit fan horsepower requirement if we know the pressure drop of the entire system and use the following expression:

$$\text{hp} = \frac{\text{lb air/min} \times \text{pressure (in. WG)} \times 69.33}{33,000 \times \text{efficiency}}$$

By definition, 1.0 hp is equal to 33,000 ft-lb/min. In other words, if we lift a 33,000-lb weight a height of 1 ft in 1 min, we are performing work at a 1.0-hp rate.

When divided by the specific volume of 13.33 ft^3/lb (see chap. 1), 16,000 cfm of standard air equals 16,000/13.33 = 1200.30 lb/min.

When our pressure loss, as shown above, is 4.326 in. WG, and fan efficiency is assumed to be 70%, then

$$\text{hp} = \frac{1200.3 \times 4.326 \times 69.33}{33,000 \times 0.7} = 15.58$$

Comparatively, when our pressure loss, also as shown above, is 1.918 in. WG, and fan efficiency is 70%, then

$$\text{hp} = \frac{1200.3 \times 1.918 \times 69.33}{33,000 \times 0.7} = 6.91$$

It is easy to see the implications here where energy conservation is at issue.

6-13 DUCT INSULATION

There are four primary reasons for insulating the ductwork in an HVAC system:

1 To conserve energy—to prevent undesirable heat loss from a duct or heat gain into a duct
2 To prevent condensation on the outer surfaces of a duct carrying cool air
3 To provide noise attenuation—or to minimize noise transmission either into or out from the ducts
4 To improve appearance

Normally, to prevent condensation on a duct carrying cool air requires less thickness of insulation than to conserve energy. The amount of insulation required to conserve energy depends, of course, on the temperature difference between the air inside the duct and the air surrounding it, as well as the quality of the insulation to be used.

Figure 6-38 shows a table of recommended duct insulation thicknesses for three different insulation conductivity values k. The values listed are based on energy conservation needs. Where ducts are exposed in the conditioned spaces so that the heat lost or gained helps to heat or cool the spaces, many HVAC designers properly omit duct insulation. However, when ducts are installed in unconditioned spaces, insulation is almost always required; and fig. 6-38 will be of assistance in selecting thickness.

During the summertime cooling cycle when ducts are carrying air as cold as 50 or 55°F, insulation may be considered necessary even when ducts

Figure 6-38 Recommended duct insulation thicknesses (inches) for energy conservation purposes.

Temperature difference, °F*	Insulation conductivity (k)		
	0.25	0.30	0.35
20	1/2	1/2	1/2
25	1/2	1/2	3/4
30	1/2	3/4	3/4
40	3/4	1	1
50	1	1	1 1/4
60	1	1 1/4	1 1/2
70	1 1/4	1 1/2	1 1/2
80	1 1/2	1 3/4	2

*Temperature difference between air inside duct and surrounding air, °F.

are located in conditioned spaces. The problem here is that many buildings are shut down on weekends, holidays, and periods of equipment failure. At these times, the building temperature may rise to a very high value in summer. If a building should rise to a condition of 90°F DB and 75°F WB and the cooling system turned on, all ducts carrying air at temperatures of 65 or 66°F or so, or colder, will have outer surface temperatures below the surrounding air dew point and condensation on and dripping from these ducts will occur. With 55°F air passing through an uninsulated duct, condensation might occur with the surrounding air condition as low as 80°F DB and 50% RH. If only a 1/2-in. thickness of insulation is added to the duct, the possibility of condensation is virtually eliminated. Other benefits will pertain, and this is highly recommended.

For calculations of insulated duct heat gain and heat loss, the U coefficient of the duct wall and insulation must be determined. Knowing this, the duct area and the Δt pertaining, the heat transfer can be easily calculated by methods previously described. For this purpose fig. 6-39 has been included here; this chart gives U coefficients when insulation thickness and conductivity k are known.

One big problem involved with the exterior insulation of ducts that carry cold air in summertime is that of keeping the exterior surface of the insulation vaporproof. Because the air between

the duct and the insulation, as well as the air in the interstitial spaces between insulation fibers close to the duct is cold, its vapor pressure is relatively low. Wherever ambient water vapor can enter the insulation, which is porous and permeable, it will do so and travel inward until it reaches the cold duct. There it will condense, and cause trouble.

Therefore, the exterior surfaces of exterior duct insulation must be made vaporproof to prevent the

Figure 6-39 Heat loss coefficients for insulated ducts. (Reprinted with permission from the 1977 Fundamentals Volume, *ASHRAE Handbook and Product Directory*.)

Thickness of insulation, in.	0.5	1	1.5	2
12-to-21-in. duct diameter	3%	5%	7%	9%
21-to-30-in. duct diameter	1%	2%	3%	4%

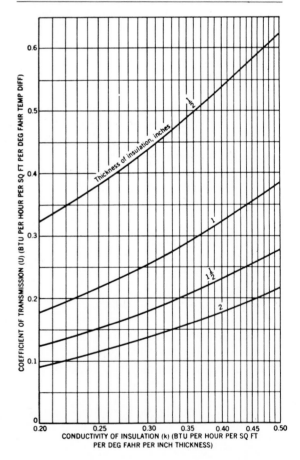

entrance of moisture. There are some very good vaporproof insulations available, and these should always be used. One of these is a fibrous insulation, which has a very tough exterior jacketing material, on the outside of which is secured a reinforced aluminum foil cladding. In addition to having a tough, vapor-proof finish, such a covering has an excellent *flame spread* rating and an excellent *smoke production* rating. Requirements for flame spread prevention and smoke prevention are set forth in *NFPA* (National Fire Protective Association) *Bulletin 90A*. Obviously, duct insulation must be "self-extinguishing" when a flame is applied to it, and its production of smoke under fire conditions must be very low, as specified in *NFPA Bulletin 90A* (also called *NBFU Bulletin 90A*).

Since moisture will enter through the slightest fault in the vapor-proof covering of cold duct insulation, and since this moisture condenses and quickly renders the insulation useless, it is mandatory that such vaporproof covering be maintained in good, faultless condition. This is not easy. Workers often walk on such insulated ducts both during and after construction, breaking the vapor barrier. However, the worst offenders are the methods utilized to hang or support insulated ducts overhead.

Too often ducts are hung on metal hangers, band iron, or angle iron or round rods, secured to the sides of the duct before the covering (insulation) is applied. This means that the hangers are inside the covering on the sides of a duct but must penetrate through the covering at the top in order to extend upward to points of support (see fig. 6-40, detail B). Since HVAC ducts are always heating and cooling, changing temperature, they are continually expanding and contracting and, in effect, swinging on their hangers. This makes it nearly impossible to keep the points of hanger penetration sealed. As a result, moisture enters and the insulation is ruined. If the hangers are rigidly

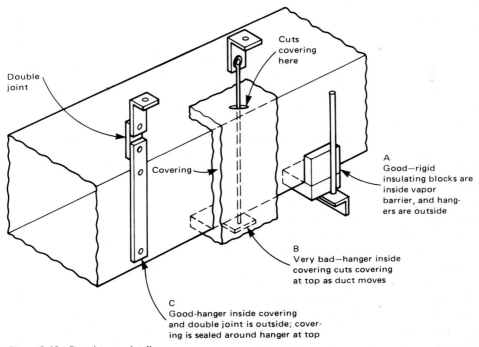

Figure 6-40 Duct hanger details.

secured at top and bottom to the sides of the duct so that they cannot move in the insulation, the latter may then be sealed around the hangers and kept sealed. Then the hangers must be flexibly hung in some manner at two pivot points (see fig. 6-40, detail C).

Sometimes a trapeze hanger of the type shown in detail A, fig. 6-40, is used with the hanger on the outside of the covering, and the covering between the hanger and the duct. In this case, the weight of the duct seriously compresses the covering across the bottom of the duct, and ultimately cuts the vapor barrier; moisture enters and the covering is ruined.

However, as shown in detail A of fig. 6-40, a trapeze-type hanger on the outside of the covering can be very satisfactory if rigid insulation blocks of materials such as polyurethane or cork, located inside the vapor barrier jacketing, are used. Of course, in all cases, the vapor barrier is only as good as the tape that is used to seal the joints in the covering. Some excellent tapes are available, and only the highest-quality tapes should be utilized; this is one place where the installer should not attempt to skimp and save a few dollars.

Sometimes duct insulation is applied to the interior of the ducts and usually makes a very satisfactory installation. Here, the metal duct serves as an excellent vapor barrier if all joints can be adequately sealed. This can usually be accomplished with good-quality tape if standing seam or bolted angle iron joints are not utilized. Flat seams can be satisfactorily taped.

Care should be used in installing flexible blanket insulation inside wide rectangular ducts. Here the blanket tends to sag away from the top of the duct; this reduces the cross-sectional area of the duct, and the loose, sagging blanket vibrates and often falls. The insulation at the top and sides should therefore be made secure with adhesive or metal clip fasteners. Internally insulated ducts, of course, give excellent sound attenuation; this may be their major advantage.

If internal insulation is used, the duct friction will be somewhat greater than with metal interiors. As set forth above for glass fiber ducts, the pressure loss with lined ductwork will be approximately 20% greater than with metal interiors.

Materials used for duct lining must be carefully selected for low flame spread and low smoke production ratings. Further, since duct linings will be subject to high-velocity air movement, the inner surface of the lining must be specially prepared to prevent wind erosion. Of course, internally lined ducts will be somewhat more expensive; because of the difficulty of installing the lining and because the metal size of the duct must be greater to allow for the insulation thickness. For example, a 24 in. × 12 in. duct with a 1-in.-thick lining must be 24 in. × 12 in. inside the lining, and the metal exterior will then be 26 in. × 14 in.

6-14 GRILLES, REGISTERS, AND DIFFUSERS

In this discussion there are, first of all, many terms that must be defined.

Grille

A supply grille is a metal or plastic grilled facing that covers the end of a branch duct to conceal the rough opening of the duct, and to give direction to the air as it passes through the grille into a room. A return air grille, through which air leaves a room or space, is essentially the same as a supply grille except that it merely covers an opening and is not required to give directional quality to the air.

Grilles do not, and cannot, give a dampering or volume control effect, because grilles are not equipped with any type of damper—by definition.

Register

A register is exactly the same as a grille except that it does have a dampering device, and can give control of the volume of the air that passes through it. Registers are not normally used for return air purposes, but are used to some extent on exhaust ventilating systems to balance out the airflow through each of several or many exhaust registers that may be a part of such a system. For example, a toilet exhaust system, having many points of air exhaust, may have lock louver-type registers, which include lockable louver (multiblade) dampers in their makeup.

Diffusers

An air supply diffuser is a device that pours air into a room and spreads it out so that the air becomes diffuse. Strictly speaking, grilles and registers are diffusers; but in the common parlance of the HVAC industry, a distinction is made. Almost exclusively the term *diffuser* is meant to indicate a ceiling-mounted device, usually round, square, or linear, which receives air from a duct located above the ceiling and diffuses air in a radial pattern in all directions.

Although most ceiling diffusers are round or square supplying a radial air pattern, there are many exceptions to this. We see today many long, slender, linear slot-type ceiling diffusers worked into an integrated ceiling of some very special nature which deliver air outward in only one or two directions. There is also available from many manufacturers a whole family of rectangular ceiling diffusers which supply air in a wide range of directional patterns: one-way, two-way, three-way, four-way, and so on.

Throw

The throw of an air supply device is the distance that the air travels before it slows down to a velocity of 50 fpm. The reader may remember that 50 fpm is the upper limit of the comfort range of room air movement at or below the breathing level of a room.

If a sidewall grille is supplying air across a room that is 20 ft wide, that grille should be selected to have a throw of approximately 4 ft less than the room width, or 16 ft in this case. Like grilles and registers, ceiling diffusers are also rated as to their throw characteristics.

Drop

As air proceeds outward from a grille, register, or diffuser it is presumed to drop vertically in the room; and the distance, measured vertically from the centerline of the device, that the air falls by the time it reaches the end of its throw is called its drop. Ideally, the drop will be such that the air is just entering the breathing zone 6 ft above the floor, when its velocity is reduced to 50 fpm.

In wintertime, when supply air is quite warm, it may have a tendency to rise when it leaves a sidewall grille, but with proper air quantities in motion and properly selected air supply devices in use, an air circulation pattern can be established in a room that will carry the warm air downward as required.

Aspect Ratio

The aspect ratio of an air supply device is merely the ratio of its width to its height, and is a term usually applied to sidewall grilles and registers. However, aspect ratio is a generalized term and may be applied to anything where the ratio of one dimension to another is important—as in an air duct.

Aspiration Ratio

As supply air leaves any type of supply outlet it has a certain volume flow rate expressed in cfm; this is called *primary air*. As soon as the primary air leaves the outlet, it begins attracting air from the room surrounding the primary airstream, and this room air, called *secondary air*, joins the primary air, mixes with it, and is carried along with it. The moving airstream now has a much greater volume by the time it reaches the end of its throw. This total volume divided by the primary air volume is called *aspiration ratio* or *entrainment ratio*.

A high aspiration ratio is good, because this means that a greater quantity of room air is kept in motion, with less chance of stagnation in parts of the room and with less chance of temperature stratification within the room.

A stream of air that converges as it leaves the supply outlet will entrain less room air, and have a lower aspiration ratio than will a supply stream that is caused, by the design of the outlet, to diverge or spread as it leaves (assuming that its throw is adequate). Supply grilles that have a high aspect ratio will, to a very limited extent, have a higher aspiration ratio than will a more square grille, since its area of contact with the room air will be greater.

Air Change

If all the air in a room is removed and replaced with different air, that is one air change. If this happens in 1 hr, we have one air change per hour. If, for example, a room has a volume of 10,000 ft^3, and is conditioned with a supply air volume of 1000 cfm, the room will experience six air changes per hour:

$$\frac{1000 \text{ cfm} \times 60 \text{ min/hr}}{10,000 \text{ ft}^3} = 6.0 \text{ changes/hr}$$

We also will quite often refer to an airflow rate in terms of the number of minutes required for one air change. In the example above, six air changes per hour, or six air changes in 60 min, equals one air change in 10 min. We would then say that the room has a 10-min air change.

$$\frac{10,000 \text{ ft}^3 \text{ room volume}}{1000 \text{ cfm flow rate}} = 10 \text{ min air change}$$

There are some general rules that will give guidance in the selection of the quantities of air to be supplied into a room. Considerable variation in the air change rate may be found to be quite satisfactory, with this rate falling within the range of six air changes per hour (10-min air change) to 15 changes per hour (4-min air change). However, unless well-designed and selected grilles and diffusers are utilized, six air changes per hour could give many stagnant areas in a room, and 15 changes per hour could give many areas of excessive air movement. The air quantities to be supplied into a room are not determined usually by figures such as these (as we shall see later); air change values should, however, always be used as a cross-check to be certain that design results are reasonable.

Airflow Patterns

In all cases, the HVAC designer must have an airflow pattern in mind when air supply outlets (grilles, etc.) are selected and placed in a room.

Architectural considerations will usually determine where outlets can be located, whether high in a sidewall or end wall, or in the ceiling or perhaps in the floor near an outside wall (perimeter location).

Realizing the importance of the aspirating effect (aspiration ratio) of an outlet, the designer must conceive a room flow pattern that will bring air movement to all parts of the room and yet not cause excessive air movement at any point in the room. The location of the return air grille or opening will have a small effect on the overall room pattern, but the types of supply outlets and their locations will be the controlling factors.

When high sidewall grilles are to be used, the desired room pattern will be as shown in fig 6-41a. Here it is important that the throw of the grilles be such as to carry the air across the room to the vicinity of the outside wall, but not to hit that wall. If this is accomplished, the pattern shown will not be difficult to establish whenever the supply air is cooler than room air.

During the heating cycle when supply air is warm, it will tend to rise at the end of its throw. To counter this, a definite downward pitch must be given to the air at the supply grille.

If the ceiling height and the grille mounting height are great enough, this may be effective. If not, the pattern will not be as shown, warm air will rise to the ceiling, especially in coldest weather, when supply air is hottest, and temperature stratification will result. Temperatures at the ceiling may be 6 to 10°F warmer than at the floor. This can be minimized by keeping supply air quantities high and resulting warm air supply temperatures correspondingly low. Benefits will also result from maintaining constant air circulation, and not using cycling or "on-off" fan operation, and not using a variable air volume type of control.

In fig. 6-41b is shown a plan view of the same room shown in part a. Here may be seen the spreading pattern required of each supply grille to blanket the outside wall effectively. Grille manufacturerers' rating data will give good information concerning the distance air will be thrown from a given size grille, with a given air quantity,

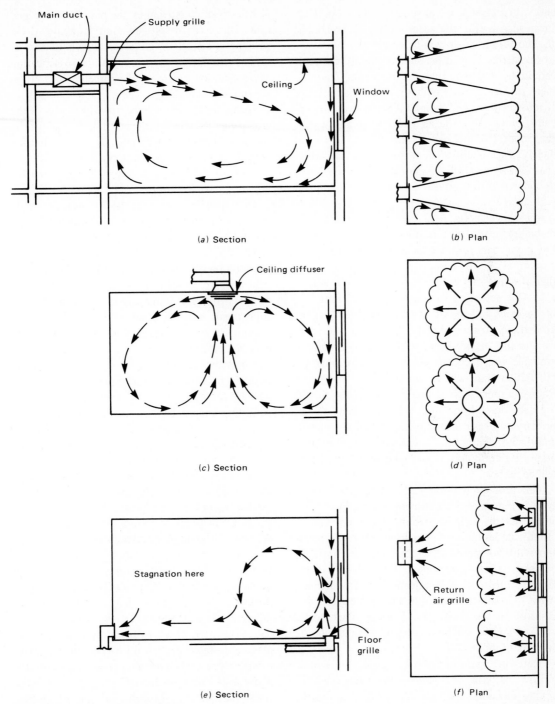

Figure 6-41 Room airflow patterns.

and with a given angle of spread to the air pattern. From such a grille, the wider the angle of spread is, the shorter the throw will be.

From this brief discussion of supply grilles, it should be apparent that one mandatory requirement of such a device is that it must be adjustable. It must be possible to direct air downward or upward, or to cause the air to converge as it enters the room (to increase its throw) or to spread widely. High-quality, yet reasonably priced grilles are available that will do all of this. They are called *double deflection grilles* (or registers if equipped with dampers).

As shown in fig. 6-42, this grille consists of a metal frame into which are mounted two sets of flat metal bars—one set is vertical and one set is horizontal. All of these bars are set in place with a tight friction fit, but each is individually adjustable. One set of bars lines up with the front face of the grille and the other set is mounted just behind these. In fig. 6-42, the "face" bars are vertical and the "back" bars are horizontal. Grilles are available with face bars either vertical or horizontal. Grilles that will be installed high above the floor in a room with unusually high ceilings should normally have horizontal face bars, because the primary emphasis is in directing the air downward, and the horizontal face bars slanted downward will be most able to do this. In that case, the back bars will be vertical.

One problem with fully adjustable grilles of this type is that unauthorized people can adjust them and upset the airflow pattern in a room. This is usually undesirable, although not always. Sometimes the occupants of a room, such as an office, can request grille adjustments that will help them. How fortunate it is if adjustments can be made when the airflow patterns in a room are giving discomfort to the occupants. There is much to be said, of course, on both sides of this question of easy adjustability.

Referring again to fig. 6-41, we see the typical airflow patterns that might be established by ceiling diffusers and by floor-mounted grilles. In fig. 6-41c it may be seen how the cold air downdraft at the outside wall in wintertime can be picked up and tempered by the basic room circulation. This is accomplished even more positively with perimeter floor grilles as shown in part *e*. Part *e* also shows how temperature stratification and stagnation can result if perimeter floor grilles are applied in too large a room.

In fig. 6-41b one may see how the spread of the grilles may be adjusted to just fill the length of the room to eliminate dead spots. In rooms that are quite long and narrow, the spread may need to be as much as 45° on each side of a centerline (or 90° total included angle).

One question that the HVAC designer must resolve is whether to use grilles (which have no dampers) or to use registers (which have dampers). Much difference of opinion exists in the HVAC industry on this question. In the author's experience, there is some small advantage in having dampers to give some degree of local volume adjustment, but the disadvantage resulting from room occupants tampering with air volume adjustment is tremendous.

Permitting adjustment of volume control devices, such as the built-in dampers in supply registers, by room occupants or ordinary maintenance personnel should be very strictly forbidden. For that reason, grilles and diffusers without integral dampers should be used and "registers" should never be used. Volume control and balancing should be accomplished through the use of lockable and comparatively inaccessible dampers, extractors, and splitters located in the supply ductwork. Extractors and splitters are volume control devices which will be described later.

It has been firmly stated here that supply pattern adjustability for a supply grille is a very necessary feature; this is equally true for ceiling diffusers. Most commercially available ceiling diffusers are not adjustable, and this is unfortunate. However, most diffuser manufacturers do make adjustable pattern diffusers, and in spite of a small extra cost, these should be chosen for use. Many a defective air distribution system has been made satisfactory through the use of pattern adjustability. See fig. 6.42b for ceiling diffuser details.

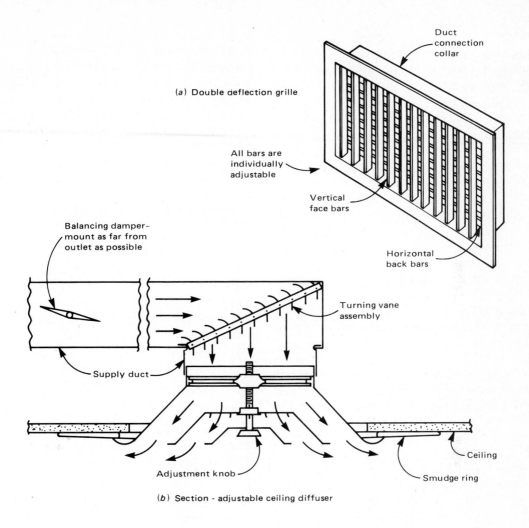

(a) Double deflection grille

Duct connection collar

All bars are individually adjustable

Vertical face bars

Horizontal back bars

Balancing damper—mount as far from outlet as possible

Turning vane assembly

Supply duct

Ceiling

Adjustment knob

Smudge ring

(b) Section - adjustable ceiling diffuser

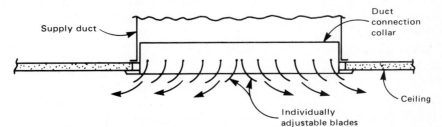

Supply duct

Duct connection collar

Ceiling

Individually adjustable blades

(c) Section - curved blade diffuser

Figure 6-42 Air supply outlets.

Smudging

With grilles, registers, and diffusers, one serious operational problem is the ring of dirt that collects on a ceiling or wall around a supply air outlet. This is called smudging; it is a problem that is much more severe with ceiling diffusers than with sidewall grilles and registers.

The cause of smudging is not well understood, and efforts to eliminate the problem have met with very limited success. The dirt that so seriously soils the surface surrounding an air outlet comes mainly from room air which is recirculated from the room back to the immediate vicinity of the outlet by the aspirating action of the outlet. To a much lesser extent the dirt comes from the primary air entering from the supply duct.

Since a high aspiration ratio for a grille or diffuser is highly desirable, we dare not attack the problem by minimizing aspiration. Efforts thus far have consisted mainly in the use of wide metal rings or extenders that surround round or square ceiling diffusers. The metal surfaces, which may extend out along the ceiling 6 to 8 in., catch most of the dirt, and may be easily cleaned. These rings are, not surprisingly, called *smudge rings*; and while soil does certainly collect on the ceiling beyond the smudge rings, they are a very worthwhile investment (see fig. 6-42).

There is one particular type of ceiling diffuser which, in this author's experience, has very little difficulty with smudging. This is a square diffuser made to simulate the appearance of perforated acoustical ceiling tile. It does not extend at all below the surrounding ceiling, and has quite favorable airflow characteristics. Soil does collect quickly on the perforated metal face, but this is easily removed.

Other Air Supply Outlets

Although a very high percentage of our air supply problems are solved with the use of ceiling diffusers, sidewall grilles, and floor grilles and registers, there are other types of supply outlets that deserve mention.

Linear diffusers are long, narrow slot-type devices which may be only a few inches wide and perhaps 8 ft long. They consist of one to four or more parallel slots and are very often coordinated into an integrated ceiling system (which provides ceiling closure, acoustic treatment, illumination, air supply, and air return in one package). Linear diffusers supply air effectively in one direction, or two opposite directions, and because of their tremendously high aspect ratios give very high aspiration ratios (or entrainment ratios).

Curved blade diffusers are air supply devices, usually mounted in ceilings, which consist of curved metal blades set into aluminum frames. The blades are made of long metal strips about 1 1/2 in. wide and definitely curved around their lengthwise axis. They are pivoted along one lengthwise edge and are mounted in groups to give a louver effect (see fig. 6-42c). This type of diffuser is available with one set of blades, two sets of blades (as shown in fig. 6-42), three sets of blades, or four sets of blades to discharge air in one, two, three, or four directions, respectively.

Noise and Vibration

Noise emanating from a supply outlet is one of the biggest problems that the HVAC engineer must face—and defeat. There are many causes of this noise; some of these are:

1 Excessively high tip speed of the fan in the a/c unit (see fig. 6-30)

2 Excessively high outlet velocity of the a/c unit fan (see fig. 6-30)

3 Excessive duct velocities causing high duct friction (air rubbing noise) and turbulence at dampers, fittings, and so on

4 The use of air supply "registers" with their dampers nearly closed

5 Buffeting or pulsation noises resulting from fans operating under unstable conditions or from improperly reinforced rectangular ducts whose tops and bottoms vibrate with a diaphragming action

In general, this noise is just the result of the use of excessive air velocities, and the recommendations set forth in fig. 6-30 should be carefully considered in all HVAC design.

Of course, noise resulting from the vibrations of rotating and reciprocating machinery, such as a/c units, refrigerating machines, pumps, exhaust fans, and fuel burners, may transmit directly through the building structure to occupied spaces or may be carried airborne through ductwork. All such machines must be carefully mounted on scientifically designed vibration eliminators of some type. Some of the precautions that can be taken are listed below.

1 Use "flexible connections" at all points where ductwork connects to air conditioning units, fans, and so on. This involves leaving a 1- to 2-in. break or gap in the ducts, which is then closed with a strong, heavily reinforced vinyl fabric.

2 All ceiling-hung a/c units, fans, and so on, should be hung on vibration eliminator hangers or mounted on wooden platforms which are hung on resilient hanger rods.

3 Floor- or roof-mounted machines of all types, including compressors, pumps, fans, a/c units, evaporative condensers, air-cooled condensers, water chillers, and cooling towers, must be mounted on rubber, cork, or spring-type vibration eliminators.

4 Where pipes or electrical conduits connect to vibrating machines, final connections to such machines must be made with sections of flexible pipe and conduits made especially for this purpose.

Where high-velocity air noise is unavoidable, such noise must be trapped out by the use of air duct mufflers and acoustic terminals as mentioned previously. Often when such a noise problem can be anticipated, an acoustic lining in a 10- to 20-ft length of supply duct will avoid the problem. Incidentally, where the situation permits, greater sound attenuation will result if instead of acoustically lining all four sides of a duct, only two sides are lined but for twice the distance—the same amount of lining material being used in both cases.

For example, instead of lining all four sides of a duct for a distance of 15 ft, greater sound attenuation would result from lining 30 ft of duct on the bottom and one side. This also makes possible the omission of the lining of the top of the duct; this is desirable since the top lining gives much trouble from sagging and pulling loose from the duct.

Often the air that is returned from a given room back to an a/c unit must pass through a corridor or an adjacent room on the way. A door louver or wall grille communicating directly with those adjacent spaces will permit much noise to pass and *cross-talk* to occur. This is usually objectionable and may be solved two ways:

1 Ceiling grilles may be installed in the ceilings of the subject room and the adjacent room. These grilles are then connected by an acoustically lined duct located above the ceiling.

2 Two wall grilles may be installed in the common wall between the adjacent spaces, with one grille near the baseboard and the other near the ceiling on the opposite side of the wall. An acoustically lined duct running vertically in the wall then connects the two grilles.

The problem of grille, register, and diffuser noise must always be solved with care. This can usually be accomplished with the observance of a few basic rules. First, observe the noise limitations of each room in light of the activity expected and the sound level that can be tolerated. Second, air supply outlets must be carefully selected in accordance with the noise criteria (NC) ratings listed in manufacturers' catalogs.

Manufacturers' NC ratings are usually based on the assumption that the average room will have a sound absorptance of 18 decibels (dB; a unit of comparative sound measurement) referenced to a reference power of 10^{-13}. Sound power level in decibels is calculated by the simple formula

$$dB = 10 \log_{10} \frac{W}{10^{-13}}$$

where W is the sound power produced by a source of sound, in watts.

Manufacturers' NC ratings in decibels may be judged for suitability by comparing them with the recommended NC values for various types of rooms shown below:

Broadcasting studios	20–25
Concert halls	20–25
Legitimate theaters	20–30
Schoolrooms	30–40
Apartments and hotels	30–40
Assembly halls (amplification)	30–35
Homes (sleeping areas)	25–35
Conference rooms	25–35
Motion picture theaters	30–35
Hospitals	25–35
Churches	20–30
Courtrooms	30–40
Libraries	30–40
Small private offices	30–40
Restaurants	35–45
Coliseum for sports only	30–40
Stenographic offices	35–50
Factories	40–65

The data above were reprinted by permission from *ASHRAE Handbook and Product Directory— Systems 1973.*

6-15 VENTILATING CEILINGS

The term *ventilating ceiling* is used to designate a suspended acoustic ceiling in a room, above which the furred space is a sealed chamber or plenum. Air is supplied into this sealed chamber above the ceiling by a supply duct which has an open end and which just stubs into the chamber. The acoustic panels that make up the ceiling are perforated by many small holes through which air can pass from the sealed plenum, or chamber, into the conditioned room.

The number and size of the perforations in the acoustic panels is carefully controlled in such a way that the air supply is more than the perforations can release into the room without a small static pressure being developed in the plenum. This pressure is very slight, on the order of 0.01 in. WG; but it is very necessary, since this is what

causes the supply air to properly distribute itself throughout the ceiling plenum.

The result of this type of installation is an air supply system which has excellent ability to distribute air throughout a room in a quiet, draft-free manner. With this system it is literally impossible for a room occupant to determine from the feel of air movement, or from any auditory clues or visual clues what the source of the air supply might be.

Air movements in the occupied zones of the room are typically in the range 15 to 30 fpm— nearly ideal. The temperature gradient in the occupied zone, 6 in. to 5 ft 6 in. above the floor, runs approximately $2.5°F$ in wintertime during the heating cycle, and 1 to $1.5°F$ during the cooling cycle. Temperature gradients are therefore very good also.

The noise level resulting from air supply in a room with a ventilating ceiling will, of course, be negligible. In fact, one complaint that has been made about rooms conditioned in this manner is that they are too quiet when they (the rooms) have no noise-generating activities of their own. This should be considered when designing for rooms which are inherently quiet; an air supply system with a slightly audible noise level may be desirable. In this case, a ventilating ceiling system may be too quiet.

A ventilating ceiling properly installed and maintained will give excellent results, in general, in terms of human comfort; one primary reason for this is that the ceiling panel becomes a radiant heating panel in winter and a radiant cooling panel in summer. In winter the MRT (mean radiant temperature) is appreciably increased, and this is highly desirable in most cases. On a cold winter day when the supply air temperature may be 110 to $120°F$, the ceiling surface temperature may be $100°F$ and the total heat input into the room may be 30 to 40% pure radiant energy. This radiant heat is directed mainly downward so that most of it shines on the floor. Here the radiant heat is converted to sensible heat as the floor is warmed; rising air currents from the floor then carry heat upward through the occupied zone of the room.

In summer, with 55 to 60°F air passing through the ceiling plenum and down through the ceiling perforations, the ceiling is cooled, the MRT of the room is lowered, and the problem of achieving human comfort is appreciably minimized.

In outside rooms, a greater input of air is often required into the areas near the windows. This is easily accomplished by using perforated ceiling panels near the outside walls, and using solid, unperforated panels, which look exactly the same, in other parts of the room. Successful use has also been made of directional registers installed in the ceiling near large areas of glass (windows) to offset their cold or hot effect. Such registers should have lockable dampers to prevent unauthorized adjustment.

There are some difficulties in connection with the use of ventilating ceilings and steps must be taken in the design stage to forestall these.

1 With some types of construction, it may be too difficult or too expensive to effectively seal the plenums above the ceilings. Partition walls must be taken up to the floor or roof structure above to create a plenum; and all pipes, ducts, and conduits that pass through these walls must be carefully sealed. When a wall is built up under or around a bar joist, there may be considerable difficulty in sealing the joist to be air tight. These types of problems must be completely evaluated before deciding to use ventilating ceilings.

2 The HVAC system must have high-quality air filtration equipment; because excessive airborne dust quantities can plug the perforations in the ceiling panels. It is strongly recommended that only "lay-in" types of ceiling panels be used; these can then be easily removed and vacuum cleaned from the upper side in case plugging should ever become a problem.

3 It should be remembered that temperatures in the ceiling plenum will be at times very high (120°F in winter), and at other times very low (55°F in summer). Adequate insulation should be added to the sides and tops of such plenums if such insulation is not already planned. It must also be realized that in a multistory building, the floor above the plenum may be quite warm, re-

leasing considerable heat to the rooms above, or may be quite cold during the cooling season. It is possible for the floor above to have an upper surface temperature below the dew point temperature in the rooms above. In that event, moisture would form on the floor above, which could damage floor finishes or present a hazardous, slippery condition. A small amount of spray-on insulation applied to the underside of the floor structure can inexpensively preclude such problems. Since the ductwork for such a system is much less expensive than for other systems, and since grilles and diffusers are largely eliminated, there is a cost savings which can very well offset much of the extra cost of plenum sealing, insulation, and so on.

Ventilating ceilings were quite popular and extensively used in the years of the 1960s, but for some reason unknown to this author they have lost popularity. This seems to be unjustified, and it is recommended that ventilating ceilings be considered, together with all other possible systems, on every building project where high-quality results are required.

PROBLEMS

6-1 What are the usual major component parts of a refrigeration "condensing unit" and a compression cycle water chiller?

6-2 The a/c unit in fig. 6-14a, as drawn, can supply conditioned air to how many different building zones? May the temperature of the air being delivered to the various zones be different; or must it be the same for all zones?

6-3 What is a temperature control zone in a building?

6-4 A fully loaded, 40-hp electric motor drives the fan in a large single-zone draw-through a/c unit. How much energy, in BH, does this motor deliver to the fan? Trace the flow of this energy as far as you can through the HVAC system.

6-5 In a blow-through HVAC unit, does the heat from the fan get out into the supply duct system?

6-6 The longest branch of an HVAC supply duct system is 400 ft long equivalent length. Following accepted practice in the sizing and design of low-velocity ductwork, what would be the static pressure loss of this duct system in inches of water gauge pressure?

6-7 After sizing a duct system on the unit static pressure loss basis (in. WG per 100 ft), what one cross-check must always be made before duct sizes are finalized?

6-8 The main supply duct leading from a single-zone HVAC unit must carry 16,000 cfm in a commercial application. What would be the maximum allowable velocity for recommended practice? What would be a typical size for a rectangular duct, and what would be a suitable round duct size?

6-9 What is the recommended tip speed of the fan in an air conditioning unit located directly in the occupied space of a large room in a commercial building without supply air or return air ductwork?

6-10 A remotely located air conditioning unit supplies air through ductwork to a large department store. The supply fan in this a/c unit is 15 in. in diameter and runs at 1200 rpm. What is the tip speed of this fan, and does it exceed the maximum allowable tip speed for a low-velocity air distribution system?

6-11 Why are high-velocity duct systems not noisy?

6-12 The fan in an air conditioning unit delivers 42,000 cfm of standard air against a total static pressure resistance of 2.2 in. WG. If the motor that drives this fan is 87% efficient, what size must this fan motor be?

6-13 A heating supply duct carrying air at $110°F$ runs through an unheated attic which is at a temperature of $38°F$. The duct is 24 in. wide and 12 in. high and is 92 ft long. It is insulated with 1.5 in. of insulation having a conductivity of 0.34. Find the heat loss from this duct in BH.

Chapter 7

Automatic Control Fundamentals

7-1 GENERAL

The HVAC industry as we know it today would be completely impossible were it not for the scientific and progressive nature of those engaged in the automatic controls business. Their complete understanding of the operational problems of HVAC systems and the equipment that makes up those systems, and their ability to provide automatic controls to solve those problems, has, more than any other factor, permitted the tremendous development that the HVAC industry has experienced in the last 50 years.

The art of automatic control has progressed to such a point that it seems safe to state that controls and control techniques are now available to perform any task that HVAC equipment manufacturers and system designers wish to have done.

The complexity of HVAC control systems is tremendous, well beyond anything that most lay persons can imagine. In fact, it is a rare HVAC system designer who will attempt to design, in all its details, a control system for an extensive nonresidential temperature control system.

Fortunately, the three or four leading manufacturers of automatic controls have branch offices located in almost every state in the United States and in most major cities. These offices are manned by highly trained experts, and capable guidance is always available. Any engineer or architectural engineering (A/E) firm that is frequently engaged in specifying HVAC systems should find the one manufacturer that, in its locality, has the best qualified control specialists. The engineer should then submit *all* control problems to this one office. This will result in a consistently high level of control efficacy for all projects. However, in following this procedure the engineer must be very careful to write control specifications in such a way that all control manufacturers can competitively bid.

This chapter deals only with the basic fundamentals of automatic control; however, the subject will be reintroduced in later chapters whenever discussions of specific HVAC systems are presented.

Control systems can be divided into two broad categories:

1 *Constant volume-variable temperature systems.* In this group, the flow of the heating or cooling medium (water, steam, air, etc.) is held at a constant rate and temperatures are varied as necessary to meet changing load conditions. This category includes systems which cycle on and off but which use a constant flow rate whenever the system is on.

2 *Variable volume systems.* In this group the primary method of control is to vary the quantity of water, steam, or air to meet changing load conditions. Temperatures of these media may be held constant or, in secondary fashion, may be caused to vary.

Control systems may be said to consist basically of four components:

1 *Controllers.* These include such devices as thermostats and humidistats having elements sensitive to temperature, humidity, pressure, and so on.

2 *Controlled devices.* These include automatic valves that regulate the flow of such media as water, steam, and refrigerant. Also included are automatic dampers, to regulate airflow, and many other types of devices.

3 *Control signal media.* These include fluids and electric pulses used for the purpose of conveying control signals from the controllers. Control media are largely limited to compressed air, electric signals, and electronic signals.

4 *Control accessories.* These include equipment such as air compressors (in pneumatic systems), switches, relays, transformers, thermometers, gauges, etc.

As noted in item 3, control systems utilize three media for transmitting control signals. There are other media in use, but the extent of such use is very limited, and will not be considered herein.

There is also another category of automatic controls in fairly extensive use in the HVAC business; these are called *self-contained controls.* These include controlled devices which have their own built-in sensing elements. An example of this is a valve that controls the flow of hot water into some kind of radiator. This valve assembly includes a thermal bulb consisting of an 8-in. length of 5/8-in. copper tubing sealed on one end, and connected at the opposite end to a 5- to 20-ft length of 1/8-in. copper tubing. This 1/8-in. tube extends to a 2- to 6-in.-diameter sealed metal chamber one flat side of which is a flexible metal diaphragm as shown in fig. 7-6. The thermal bulb and diaphragm chamber are filled with a volatile liquid such as ether.

As the temperature around the thermal bulb varies, the pressure of the ether inside the bulb varies; this results in a flexing movement of the diaphragm which is connected to the valve stem of a valve. As the temperature around the thermal bulb falls, its pressure falls, the diaphragm flexes, the valve opens, and more heat is admitted to the radiator and the space it heats.

Pneumatic, electric, and electronic systems are all in very extensive, successful use. Although the equipment utilized with these three control media varies widely, the basic techniques of control are nearly identical. The control cycles used with pneumatic systems may be closely duplicated with electric or electronic systems.

Space does not permit a full treatment of the details of all three systems; and all discussions (here and in later chapters) will be constructed around the use of pneumatic (compressed air) control. In the light of the preceding paragraph, this seems reasonable, especially since in larger nonresidential buildings (with which this text is mainly concerned), pneumatic control systems are clearly dominant. A diagram of a very simple pneumatic control system is shown in fig. 7-1.

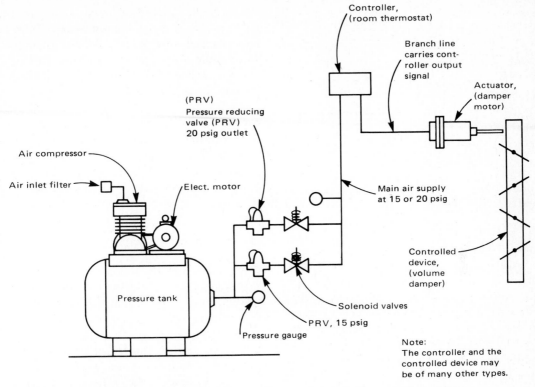

Figure 7-1 Schematic diagram of a simplified pneumatic control system. The controller and the controlled device may be of many other types.

7-2 CONTROL ACTIONS

The combination of *controllers* (see above) and *controlled devices* working in unison produces different control *actions,* or results, which may be characterized and categorized as follows:

1 Closed loop
2 Open loop
3 Two-position (on-off)
4 Floating
5 Proportioning (modulating)
6 Relaying

These various control actions make possible an exceedingly wide range of control systems which meet the greatly varying needs of the HVAC industry. Let us examine separately each of the control actions listed above.

7-3 CLOSED-LOOP ACTION

Most control systems in use today are of the closed-loop type, which is typified by fig. 7-2. Here the controller is, for example, a room thermostat which is sensitive to controlled space. (The term *controlled space* will be used throughout this discussion to mean that which is the ultimate concern or responsibility of a controller. Controlled space may be many things—a room or rooms in a building, air in a supply duct, or water flowing in a pipe.)

If controlled space temperature climbs too high, the controller sends a signal (for example, a

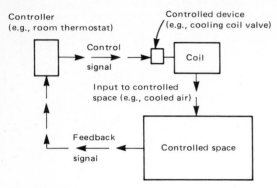

Figure 7-2 Schematic diagram of a system with closed-loop control action.

surge of higher-pressure compressed air) to the controlled device. This might, for example, be an automatic valve with a pneumatic operator. This valve, responding to the control signal, opens a little wider to increase the flow of cooling medium, perhaps chilled water, through a cooling coil. This results in a revised input (cooler supply air) to the controlled space, and the controlled space temperature is modified as necessary. Finally, the controller, which is sensitive to controlled space temperature (is perhaps mounted in the controlled space), receives a *feedback* signal, resulting from revised space temperature, and governs accordingly.

The point of importance here is that the room thermostat senses and is influenced by the result of its own control signal. If the control signal were not quite adequate, it could issue further signals until accurate control results. The feedback signal is the final section of the control loop, which makes it a *closed loop.* All control systems do not have this feedback feature.

7-4 OPEN-LOOP ACTION

Open-loop control action may be diagrammed as in fig. 7-2, with one exception. The feedback signal is not included; thus the control loop is not complete; it is open.

Open-loop control might be used, for example, with an outdoor thermostat, which is sensitive

only to outdoor air temperature. It controls, perhaps, a steam valve that supplies steam to the heating system of a building. When outdoor air (OA) temperature drops, the OA thermostat opens the steam valve wider and admits more steam heat to the building heating system, and vice versa.

In this case, there is no feedback signal. The OA thermostat does not sense exactly what the results of its control actions are. In certain types of buildings, heat loss in winter weather is almost exactly in proportion to the difference between OA temperature and room air (RA) temperature. Open-loop control action is then quite satisfactory.

7-5 TWO-POSITION ACTION

Two-position control action results in an on-off cycling type of control. Here a controller senses a need for heat or cooling, humidification or dehumidification, and so on, and transmits a control signal, which sets an HVAC system into operation at its full capacity. This is typified by a warm air heating system in a residence. When heat is needed a room thermostat starts a furnace to supplying heat at full capacity; and when heat is no longer needed, the furnace stops. This is two-position, on-off cycling control. A graph of this type of control cycle is plotted in fig. 7-3.

In fig. 7-3, time, on the horizontal scale, is plotted against controlled space temperature (room temperature, etc.) for a controller such as a room thermostat. The curve of fig. 7-3 would vary considerably with changing demands (such as changing weather conditions). In very cold winter weather, the on-cycle of the heating equipment would be very long, and the off-cycle would be very short, timewise, with the slope of the on-cycle portion of the curve being reduced, and the curve of the off-cycle being nearly vertical. In this case, the number of cycles per hour would probably be reduced.

In fig. 7-3, the *differential* of an on-off controller is graphically portrayed. It is shown to be the difference between the temperatures at which the controlled device is turned on and at which it

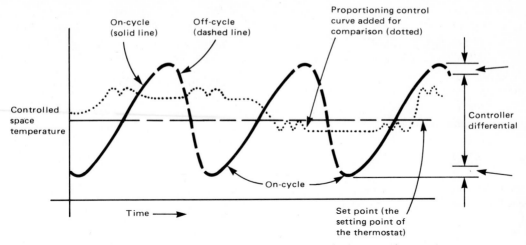

Figure 7-3 Typical cycle of a system with on-off two-position control using room thermostat.

is turned off. In many controllers the differential is adjustable.

It may also be noted in fig. 7-3 that the controlled temperature experiences *overtravel* and *undertravel;* these are especially noticeable when on-off cycling control is utilized. For example, in a warm air heating system, when a heater is firing and producing heat, it will be turned off by the controller when room temperature rises to the top of the differential. However, even though the heater burner is off, the system has residual heat stored in it; this residual heat continues to flow into the heated space and causes the room temperature to rise above the top of the differential range. This is called overtravel. Undertravel of room temperature occurs in a similar fashion at the bottom of the differential range when the fuel burner in the heater is cycled "on."

Excessive overtravel and undertravel can, of course, result in discomfort for human beings and must not be accepted in high-quality HVAC systems. Overtravel can be minimized by several different methods. One of these involves the use of electric *heat-anticipating*-type two-position thermostats; these are sometimes also called *heat accelerated* thermostats.

This type of thermostat has a very small, built-in electric heater. This heater is so connected that during the heating cycle, when the heating system is on and room temperature is rising, this small heater begins heating the temperature-sensitive element in the thermostat. This results in the thermostat opening the electric circuit and stopping the heating system action before the room temperature rises to the top of the differential range shown in fig. 7-3.

Two-position heating-cooling thermostats also use this very small electric heater to prevent overtravel on the summer cooling cycle. Here the electric heater accelerates the action of the temperature-sensitive element during the off-cycle when room temperature is rising. The thermostat then closes its electric contacts and starts the cooling system operation slightly before the room temperature rises to the top of the differential range.

7-6 FLOATING ACTION CONTROL

Floating action control is of a type in which a controller slowly repositions a controlled device in response to the reaction of the controller to the temperature of whatever is being controlled. The controlled device (valve, damper, etc.) moves very slowly and continuously in the required direction until it reaches the end of its travel (wide open or fully closed), or until the controller signals the controlled device to stop moving. This it may do at any point between wide open and fully closed if the controller finds the controlled room temperature (for example) to fall within the limits of its differential. When the controlled space temperature rises or falls to a point outside the controller's differential, the controller will again start the controlled device moving slowly.

7-7 PROPORTIONING CONTROL ACTION

In proportioning control, the controller is capable of transmitting an infinite number of varying signals, the magnitude of which is in proportion to the temperature, pressure, humidity, and so on, of the controlled space. For example, a pneumatic room thermostat may sense an increase in room temperature. As a result, it permits the pressure in a small plastic tube leading to a controlled device to rise very slightly—perhaps only a small fraction of a pound.

In proportioning control systems, all controlled devices are capable of receiving and responding to very small changes in the control signal. A valve might close just a little or a damper might open just a little upon receiving a very light increase in pneumatic control signal pressure.

With proportioning control, a steam valve is not limited to its fully open and fully closed positions. It may assume an infinite number of positions between these two extremes. Such a valve is not continually opening and closing to supply the proper amount of steam; it will find an intermediate position at which the steam flow rate exactly meets the need for steam, and there the valve may remain for an hour or two. This is vastly different from *two-position control,* in which the valve is either fully open or fully closed; and it greatly differs from *floating control,* in which the valve continues to open or to close until it reaches its fully open or fully closed position or until feedback from the controlled space signals it to stop at some intermediate position.

Proportioning or *modulating control,* as it is often called, can give better and more accurate control in most situations than can either "two-

position" or floating control. The curve of typical proportioning control is drawn in fig. 7-3 to show its comparison with typical on-off cycling control.

7-8 RELAY ACTION CONTROL

Relay action is not a separate type of control system as such; rather, it is an auxiliary type of function which can be an integral part of any of the three major control system types (pneumatic, electric, and electronic), and can be used with two-position systems, floating action systems, and proportioning systems.

However, even though relay action is only auxiliary in nature, it is special enough and important enough to deserve separate treatment. Relay action, as a control technique, is certainly not limited to the automatic control of HVAC systems, but is used extensively in electric power distribution, radio and television practices, aircraft control, automotive, and almost every phase of our technological world.

A relay, as contemplated here, is a device that uses one type of primary signal to trigger and control a secondary signal or power flow. Very often the primary signal is a very simple weak or low level signal that is able, through relay action, to control, regulate, modulate, or amplify a very complex and powerful flow of power. The range of relay practices is so extensive as to defy a complete listing of them all here or in any one information source. Therefore, only a few will be mentioned, in an effort to set forth the basic principles of relay action.

Consider a simple low-voltage [24-volt (V)] two-position electric room thermostat. Even though the trickle of electric power that passes through its contacts may be a very small flow of watts, that tiny signal can actuate, for example, the solenoid coil of a magnetic starter, which is one form of relay, to close the heavy-duty electrical contacts that deliver the 480-V power to a 500-hp compressor motor. Here a control signal of less than 100 W can control a power flow of nearly 500,000 W to a large power consumer such as a huge motor.

A vacuum tube in a radio can also illustrate relay action. Here an infinitesimally small electric current results from the passage of radio waves, broadcast from a commercial radio station, across an antenna wire. The antenna wire is connected to a radio receiver, and this small current passes through the radio's vacuum tubes. The small antenna current here triggers and controls a heavier secondary flow of electric current (from a battery or building wiring system) which is exactly the same in frequency and other characteristics as the antenna current. The secondary current flow can be made as powerful as necessary to actuate the radio speakers. This represents relay action.

Relays are also available in which an electric current controls a pneumatic signal. This is called an *electropneumatic* (E-P) *relay,* and provides an interconnection between an electric or electronic system and a pneumatic system. As the reader might guess, pneumatic-electric (P-E) relays are also available in which a pneumatic signal controls an electric signal.

7-9 CONTROLLERS

A controller is that part of an automatic control system that is sensitive to conditions in the controlled space. It is also capable of transmitting signals which result in the control of the equipment of HVAC systems. Controllers include devices such as thermostats, humidistats, pressurestats, etc.

Controllers, in general, include two elements: a *measuring element* (which senses changes in the controlled space) and a *control element* (which translates the signal from the measuring element into a signal that can be used by the controlled devices).

7-10 TEMPERATURE-MEASURING ELEMENTS

Temperature-measuring elements are, in general, of five types:

1 Bimetal elements
2 Rod and tube elements
3 Sealed bellows
4 Remote bulb bellows and diaphragms
5 Electric resistors

These are separately described as follows:

1 Bimetal elements consist of two thin strips of dissimilar metal bonded together. One popular bimetal element consists of a flat strip of brass bonded to a similarly sized strip of Invar (a nickel-steel alloy). Brass has a very high coefficient of expansion. That is, for every degree of temperature change, its length will change a comparatively great amount. Invar has almost no change in dimension with temperature changes. A bimetal element of this type, then, will experience a bending deformation as its temperature changes (see fig. 7-4).

In fig. 7-4 the position of the bimetal element controls the pressure in the air chamber in a thermostat by opening or closing the control port. This control pressure is transmitted to a controlled device as a pneumatic control signal. The air pressure in the air chamber will be *modulated,* or proportionally varied throughout the range of pressures available to it, usually 0 to 15 psig.

Therefore, the controlled device, whatever it may be, will respond to the thermostat's control signal in a proportional manner. Since the control port in fig. 7-4 can bleed pressure from the air chamber faster than the inlet restrictor can permit air to enter, it is possible for the air chamber pressure and the resulting control signal to be reduced to zero. When the control port is partially closed by the bimetal element, air chamber pressure then rises; and when the control port is closed completely, air chamber pressure will rise to the full supply pressure.

This type of *bleed-port* control action can be used with other types of controllers, such as humidistats and pressurestats. In a humidistat, a moisture-sensitive element would change its dimensions with changing humidities to vary the degree of throttling at the control port.

In fig. 7-4 the lower half of the bimetal strip is made of the metal with the greater rate of expansion. Therefore, it may be seen that as ambient temperature rises, the bimetal will deflect upward, the control port will be opened more widely, and the air chamber and control signal pressure will fall. This is called *reverse action control* when con-

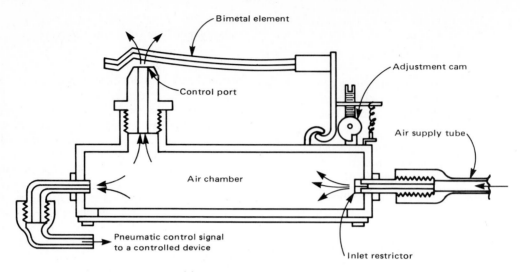

(a) Schematic—bimetal sensing element
in pneumatic room thermostat

(b) Thermostat exterior view

Figure 7-4   Room thermostat details. (b, Johnson Controls, Inc.)

trol signal pressure falls as ambient temperature rises.

It should be easily perceived, then, that if the bimetal were to be turned over, it would deflect downward with increasing ambient temperature. This would result in greater throttling of the control port as temperature rises and an increase in control signal pressure. Increasing control signal pressure as temperature rises is called *direct action control*. The action of the controller must be carefully matched with the type of action built into the controlled device (which may also be either direct or reverse acting) to be certain that proper overall control will result.

2 *Rod-and-tube* elements consist of a metal rod with a very low coefficient of expansion located within and secured to the free end of a high-expansion metal tube as shown in fig. 7-5. The opposite end of the tube is securely connected to the heavy metal backplate of the control case, while the free end of the rod is joined to the control linkage inside the control case. As the tube expands and contracts, the resulting movement of the rod can actuate many different control mechanisms.

Rod-and-tube controllers are usually made for insertion-type mounting, with the temperature-sensitive metal tube inserted in through the side of

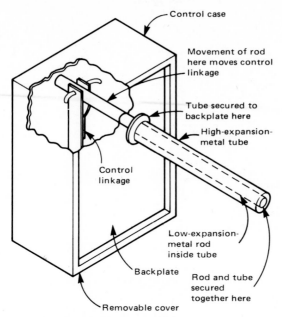

Figure 7-5 Rod-and-tube controller.

Control case

Movement of rod
here moves control
linkage

Tube secured to
backplate here

High-expansion-
metal tube

Control
linkage

Low-expansion-
metal rod
inside tube

Backplate

Rod and tube
secured
together here

Removable cover

an air duct, the hot bonnet of a warm air furnace, the hot and cold decks of a multizone air conditioner, into the breeching (smoke pipe) of any fuel-fired furnace or boiler, or into pressurized water tanks or piping or boilers.

This type of controller can be made to actuate any of the usual types of control signals: pneumatic, electric, or electronic.

3 *Sealed bellows* elements consist of a corrugated brass or copper flexible bellows approximately 2 in. in diameter, with both ends sealed shut and with a charge of some volatile fluid contained within. One end of the bellows is solidly secured to a stationary mounting plate while the other end is permitted to move. The movement of the free end of the bellows, as ambient temperature varies, can actuate a control signal: pneumatic, electric, or electronic (see fig. 7-6a).

4 *Remote-bulb-type bellows and diaphragm* elements are used in conjunction with a remotely located thermal bulb to give positive control action. Details of these are shown in fig. 7-6b and c.

Here the thermal bulb, which is usually a sealed copper tube approximately 5/8 in. in diameter and 8 in. or so long, is charged with a volatile fluid

which expands and contracts as ambient temperature changes. The bulb is connected by a long, very small copper tube, called a capillary tube, which transmits changing pressure from the thermal bulb to the flexible bellows or diaphragm. The resulting movement provides control action which may be pneumatic, electric, or electronic.

5 *Electrical-resistor*-type temperature-sensing elements consist of a coil of special electric wire whose electrical resistance changes as ambient temperature changes. The temperature-sensitive coil is wired into a balanced *Wheatstone bridge* circuit in such a way that as its electrical resistance changes, it unbalances the circuit. The unbalancing causes a controlled device to *move* so as to rebalance the circuit. This movement of the controlled device accomplishes the necessary control action. This type of control action is used only in electronic control systems.

7-11 HUMIDITY-MEASURING ELEMENTS

Humidity-measuring (sensing) elements are in general of two basic types:

1 Organic, or polymeric, hygroscopic elements which experience an appreciable change in physical dimension when space humidity changes. These elements are made of:
a Human hair
b Wood
c Paper
d Nylon
e Animal membrane
f Cellulose acetate butyrate (CAB)
2 Electric resistors whose resistance changes appreciably as ambient humidity changes. These are used in electronic systems.

In the hygroscopic type mentioned above, the change in physical dimension provides an action that can easily be translated into operation of some type of controlled device.

Control of humidity during the heating season is usually quite simple. When relative humidity is

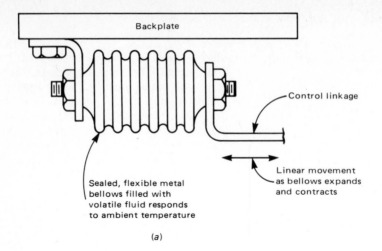

Backplate

Control linkage

Sealed, flexible metal
bellows filled with
volatile fluid responds
to ambient temperature

Linear movement
as bellows expands
and contracts

(a)

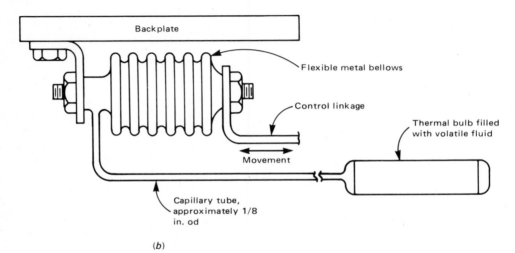

Backplate

Flexible metal bellows

Control linkage

Thermal bulb filled
with volatile fluid

Movement

Capillary tube,
approximately 1/8
in. od

(b)

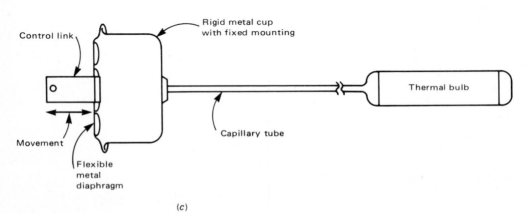

Rigid metal cup
with fixed mounting

Control link

Thermal bulb

Capillary tube

Movement

Flexible
metal
diaphragm

(c)

Figure 7-6 Controller actions with flexible bellows and diaphragms.

too low, a humidistat merely activates some type of humidifier until the relative humidity is satisfactory. However, during the summer cooling cycle, when dehumidification is needed, the problem is much more complicated.

Dehumidification is almost always accomplished by condensing moisture on the cold surfaces of a cooling coil as the circulated air passes through it. The cold coil, of course, provides dehumidification (latent cooling) as this happens; but it also provides sensible cooling simultaneously. Many times, during mild summer weather or during early morning or late evening operation, latent cooling is required at a maximum rate, but sensible cooling is required at a minimum rate.

Keeping the cooling coil cold enough to provide adequate dehumidification under such conditions will, of course, result in too much sensible cooling. The dry bulb temperature in controlled spaces then falls to too low a value for comfort.

If the coil is kept cold enough to provide only the required amount of sensible cooling inadequate removal of latent heat will result. The relative humidity in controlled spaces then rises to too high a value for comfort.

The usual answer to the predicament described above is to keep the cooling coil cold enough to provide the necessary latent cooling and then to reheat the supply air to a higher dry bulb temperature so that excessive sensible cooling in controlled spaces will not result. To overcool the supply air and then reheat it is, of course, very wasteful of energy, and must not be permitted unless absolutely necessary.

Sometimes, however, it is necessary to maintain accurate control of both dry bulb temperature and relative humidity, and the above described procedure must be followed and the energy waste must be tolerated. This waste can be somewhat minimized if rejected heat, from the refrigerating machine that is providing the cooling, is utilized in the "reheat" process. If properly planned for in the original HVAC system design, this use of rejected heat for reheating is not difficult.

7-12 PRESSURE-MEASURING ELEMENTS

In almost all HVAC control systems of any appreciable extent or complexity, many needs arise for pressure-measuring (sensing) controllers. A few of these needs for pressure controllers may be listed as follows:

1 To measure and control steam pressure or vacuum in a steam boiler or a steam piping system.
2 To measure and control pressure in a hydraulic system using water, oil, or other liquids.
3 To measure and control refrigerant pressure in a cooling system.
4 To measure and control static pressure in a building or rooms within a building.
5 To measure and control static pressure or velocity pressure in the ductwork of an HVAC system.
6 To measure and control pressure differences between two points in a hydraulic system, or an air supply and return system. One frequent use of this type of control is in the safety protection of a large water chiller that provides cooling for a large building. Here it is vitally important that before the refrigerating compressor is started, a positive flow of water through the chiller is established. Otherwise, if the compressor is permitted to run without adequate water flow, the water passages will quickly freeze, with serious damage resulting.

A *differential pressure* controller can be so installed here as to measure the water pressures at the chiller inlet and the chiller outlet. An adequate *difference* between these two readings will prove that adequate water flow exists and that compressor operation is safe. The controller then closes its electrical contacts and the compressor is permitted to run.

Pressure can be sensed with many types of devices, but these usually are bellows and diaphragms and *Bourdon tubes*. In fig. 7-6b and c it may be seen that, if the thermal bulbs are omitted and the capillary tubes are connected to some type of pressure system, control movement at the linkage end of the bellows or diaphragm will result. In other words, changing pressures will cause the

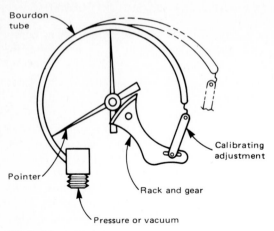

Figure 7-7 Bourdon tube, pressure control element.

diaphragm or bellows to flex, and control movement will result.

A Bourdon tube, as shown in fig. 7-7, is a small metal tube of 1/4 to 3/8 in. in diameter which is partially flattened and then bent into a circular form on a 1- to 2-in. radius. One end of the tube is sealed shut and connected to a control linkage. The other end is rigidly fixed and connected to some pressure system. As pressure in the system and the tube rises, the bent tube unbends a small amount, and the sealed end moves the control linkage to provide control movement. Falling pressure reverses the action and the control movement direction.

7-13 ENTHALPY-MEASURING ELEMENTS

The reader should first remember that the term *enthalpy* means *total heat* in an air–water vapor mixture—the sum of the sensible heat and the latent heat in the mixture.

Enthalpy-measuring (sensing) devices, and the modern controllers that incorporate them, are fairly new in the HVAC industry. Although available in one form or another for many decades, their popularity today results from today's heavy demand for energy conservation.

In public buildings, places of employment, and so on, the requirements for ventilation with outside air are very heavy. These requirements are imposed primarily by state ventilating codes and by the Public Health Service of the federal government. The resulting *ventilating load* placed on HVAC systems and the energy consumed in carrying this load constitute a very great percentage of the total load and the total energy consumption. This percentage may easily be 20 to 50% for a given building.

Temperature control systems have been called upon to maximize the benefits of outside air (OA) ventilation when OA conditions are favorable, and to minimize the use of OA when conditions are unfavorable. An *economizer cycle* has long been utilized for this purpose. In this cycle, the OA and RA dampers of the HVAC system are automatically positioned to admit great quantities of OA into a building when OA temperatures are favorable, but to minimize OA usage when OA temperatures are too high in summer or too low in winter.

In other words, the economizer cycle will cause the introduction of great quantities of OA (as much as 100% of the total HVAC system air quantity) when, for example, OA temperature is 55 to 65°F and when cooling is needed in the building. The cooling effect of the OA then reduces the need for mechanical cooling. Energy is thereby saved.

However, there has been one serious problem with the economizer cycle as used in the past. Most control systems have ignored the fact that even though the OA dry bulb temperature may be low, the OA wet bulb temperature may be higher than the wet bulb temperature desired and maintained inside the building. The introduction of OA under this condition will not reduce the cooling load; it will increase the load and waste energy.

To circumvent this possibility, a type of controller that is sensitive to the total heat or enthalpy content of the OA is being used increasingly. Now we do not use more than the minimum required amount of OA if its enthalpy content is higher than that of the interior air.

Enthalpy controllers in present use are of two

types. One type has separate temperature and humidity sensors, and the separate signals from these two sensors are blended into one enthalpy signal. These sensing units are standard temperature- and humidity-sensing elements as described earlier in this chapter. The other type of enthalpy controller uses a single sensing unit which responds directly to total heat.

7-14 NORMALLY OPEN VERSUS NORMALLY CLOSED

Pneumatic control systems sometimes lose their air pressure, and sometimes electric and electronic control systems lose their supply of electric power. When the power supply, pneumatic or electric, is lost, various types of control equipment will assume their "power-off" position, called the *normal position.*

For example, an automatic pneumatic steam valve will assume either a wide open or a fully closed position when its supply of compressed air is lost, depending on the construction of the valve. If its pneumatic control pressure falls to zero and the valve opens wide, the valve is said to be *normally open,* and vice versa.

Whether a valve or a damper is normally open or normally closed usually depends on safety considerations. An outside air damper which admits outside air in cold weather would always be selected to be normally closed when control power is lost. If an OA damper were permitted to open wide when control power is lost, great quantities of freezing, outside air could enter the HVAC system and the building. The result might be heavy damage due to freezing of such things as hot water and steam heating coils, water lines, and plumbing fixtures.

7-15 TRANSDUCERS

A transducer is a proportional relay type of device which can receive a varying input signal from one control medium and convert it to a proportional control output signal in a different control medium. For example, an electropneumatic transducer can convert a 1- to 15-V direct current input signal from an electronic controller and deliver a proportionally variable pneumatic output signal to a pneumatic controlled device.

7-16 MASTER/SUBMASTER CONTROL

Master/submaster control involves a two-step control sequence in which a master thermostat controls a controlled device (motorized valve or damper, etc.) by resetting an intermediate thermostat, the submaster, which then transmits the final controlled signal to the controlled device.

For example, a steam valve that regulates the flow of steam into a heating coil in an a/c unit is positioned by a discharge thermostat. This discharge thermostat is of the type that mounts on the side of the supply duct that carries the heated air leaving the a/c unit; it has a remote-type thermal bulb located inside this duct. In addition, there is a room thermostat in the controlled space, connected so as to send a control signal to the discharge thermostat. Suppose that the discharge thermostat is adjusted to maintain 100°F in the supply duct. It will then modulate the steam valve open or closed as necessary to deliver 100°F in the duct. However, if 100°F supply air does not heat the controlled space adequately and room temperature slowly falls, the room thermostat will send a signal (falling pneumatic pressure through a plastic tube) to the submaster discharge thermostat. This signal will cause the submaster to revise its control temperature, or set point, upward until the discharge air temperature is maintained at a higher temperature, perhaps 102°F instead of 100°F.

By the use of master/submaster control, improved regulation results. Undertravel and overtravel of controlled space temperature is greatly minimized, and the oscillating curve of space temperature shown in fig. 7-2 becomes more nearly a straight line.

7-17   STEP CONTROLLERS

A step controller is a device designed to operate a series of electric switches in a fixed series sequence. Usually, a rotating camshaft, driven by a pneumatic or electric actuator, closes a series of electric switches in a preprogrammed sequence. In the programming, cams on the camshaft are set to close and open the switches in proper sequence and at proper time intervals, all of which are adjustable. The rotation of the camshaft, and the positions it assumes, are under the control of a primary controller.

For example, a series of separate electric heaters, arranged in a large heating bank, might be brought into action one at a time through the action of a step controller. The step controller might be under the control of a room thermostat, which turns the step controller camshaft. As the need for heat around the room thermostat increases, the camshaft is driven to close more of the electric switches and bring more electric heating elements into action. This action would be reversed as the need for heat subsided.

There are many such situations in HVAC systems where step controllers are profitably utilized.

7-18   SUMMER-WINTER CHANGEOVER

In many HVAC automatic control systems, the primary control signal and the resulting control action in winter must be opposite to that required in summer.

For example, if an a/c unit has a single coil which receives warm water for heating in winter, and receives chilled water for cooling in summer, a single motorized valve may be positioned by a room thermostat to control this a/c unit.

In winter when the controlled space temperature rises too high, the direct-acting thermostat transmits an increasing air pressure signal to the valve. This causes the valve to *close* partially or fully, reducing the flow of warm water into the coil, and less heat is delivered to the controlled space. So an *increase* in room temperature closes the valve.

This is just fine for the heating season, but it is exactly wrong for the cooling season. In summer, when controlled space temperature rises, it is necessary for the valve to *open* and permit more chilled water to flow through the coil, thus delivering more cooling effect. What we must do is to provide a thermostat that will reverse its signal as the season changes from heating to cooling and back.

In small inexpensive systems where only one or a few thermostats are involved, it may be satisfactory to add a switch or manual lever on the thermostat to cause it to reverse its action. However, in large systems where many hundreds of thermostats are involved, manual changeover is not practical. Changeover must be accomplished by a change at one point, or a few points, in the building.

With pneumatic control systems, this can be accomplished by using thermostats that provide direct action (increasing signal pressure with increasing room temperature) when compressed air at one supply pressure is delivered to the thermostats, and which provide reverse action when air supply pressure is at a different value. With reverse action, the thermostat signal (outgoing) pressure is reduced when room air temperature rises.

Now, with this type of control system, when room temperature rises in winter, the increasing signal pressure from the thermostat closes the coil valve. Then, in summer, when room temperature rises the falling signal pressure opens the valve and cooling begins or is increased.

It is possible to install an outdoor thermostat, set in such a way that as OA temperature rises above a certain point, it causes the main supply control air pressure to be delivered to the thermostats at, for example, 20 psig. Then when OA temperature falls below that certain changeover point, the main air supply pressure is reduced to, for example, 15 psig.

Now, the control system will automatically change its main supply air pressure, and controlled space thermostats will automatically reverse their action as necessary. No manual changeover is then required. However, automatic changeover has never been completely satisfactory. It is difficult, for one thing, to select one outdoor temperature at which changeover should occur. For this and other reasons, manual changeover, which can be accomplished from one point in a building, is recommended.

In some HVAC systems, such as those using multizone a/c units, or double-duct air distribution systems, seasonal changeover is never required. These systems are discussed in a subsequent chapter.

7-19 CONTROLLED DEVICES

In general, controlled devices are the items of mechanical or electrical equipment which, as parts of an HVAC system, are controlled by controllers, such as thermostats, humidistats, pressurestats, etc. In the simplified diagram of fig. 7-1, the damper with its pneumatic actuator is the controlled device.

Although most HVAC controlled devices are automatic valves and dampers, there are many other types of controlled devices, such as electric motors, steam turbines, engines, fuel burners, fans, contactors, magnetic starters, and electric heaters. The list goes on and on, but a great majority of controlled devices fall in the general categories of valves and dampers.

7-20 AUTOMATIC VALVES

Automatic valves control the flow of the fluids that are used in HVAC: steam, water, oil, antifreeze solutions, refrigerants, and so on. They operate in an on-off cycling fashion (either fully open or fully closed) and they also operate in a modulating or proportioning action, stopping at any degree of openness.

Automatic valves consist of two parts: the valve body, and the operator. The body is usually made of cast metal—cast iron, brass, bronze, or aluminum—and may also be made of plastic. The valve body consists of a valve seat (an opening through which the controlled fluid flows) and a valve plug which closes or opens the seat (see fig. 7-8).

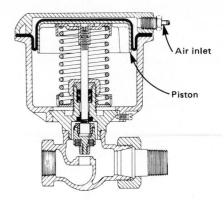

(*a*) Piston top valve operator on a normally open valve

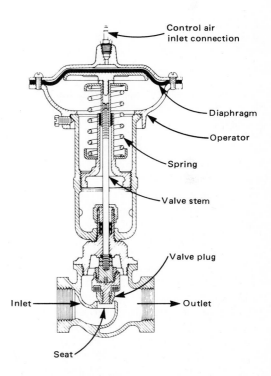

(*b*) Rubber diaphragm operator on a normally open valve

Figure 7-8 Pneumatic, globe pattern, automatic valves. (Johnson Controls, Inc.)

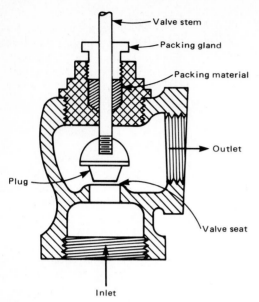

Figure 7-9 Valve body, angle pattern (with operator removed).

Valve bodies are available in many different designs and vary in accordance with the demands placed on them. Some of the more popular types of bodies are:

1 *Globe pattern.* This type is shown in fig. 7-8.

2 *Angle pattern.* As shown in fig. 7-9, this is basically a globe valve with a 90° angle between inlet and outlet openings.

3 *Gate pattern.* As shown in fig. 7-10, this valve has a tapered plug which moves straight up and down (in the position shown in fig. 7-10) and when all the way down closes a matching tapered seat. This type of valve is not often used for automatic operation, and should not be used for throttling control.

4 *V-port pattern.* These valves are basically similar to the globe valve shown in fig. 7-8, except that the plug is like a small inverted cup with V-shaped notches cut in its sides (see fig. 7-11). As the valve stem rises, more and more of the V-shaped notches in the plug open and permit increased flow.

5 *Butterfly pattern.* In these valves the valve stem rotates instead of raising and lowering. A nearly round metal disk on the end of the stem

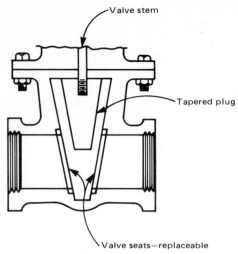

Figure 7-10 Gate valve body.

turns in the valve opening. When the disk is positioned so as to be crosswise of the direction of flow, the valve is closed; it seals around the perimeter of the disk. When the valve stem is then turned 90°, the disk is aligned with the direction of flow, and the valve is wide open.

6 *Three-way valves.* All of the valves described above are two-way valves; that is, they have two openings for pipe connections—one inlet and one outlet. Three-way valves have three openings, as

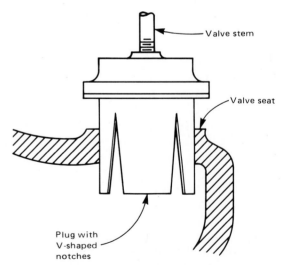

Figure 7-11 Seat and plug, V-port valve.

shown in fig. 7-12. The controlled fluid may enter at one opening and divide in the valve and leave at two openings; this is called a *diverting valve.* Or the fluid may enter at two openings and leave at one opening; this is called a *mixing valve* because the two fluid streams do mix in the valve and become a single fluid stream.

Valve operators, like valve bodies, are of many types, but in most frequent use are basically as follows:

1 *Electric motors.* These motors, driving through a train of high reduction gears, slowly turn an arm that moves a valve stem to open or close a valve. When required by the controller, the motor then moves the valve stem in the opposite direction to reverse itself. Also, another type of drive uses a very small motor to drive an equally small gear pump, which pumps hydraulic oil from

a reservoir into a pressure chamber above a sealed diaphragm. As the oil pressure above the diaphragm rises, the diaphragm is pushed down; this moves a valve stem downward and compresses a stiff spring. To reverse the valve stem motion, oil pressure is gradually released back to the reservoir, and the compressed spring pushes the diaphragm and valve stem up.

2 *Pneumatic actuators.* The actuators of fig. 7-8 are of this type. When some type of pneumatic controller increases the control air pressure above the diaphragm, it descends and pushes the valve closed. At the same time it compresses the spring shown in fig. 7-8. When control air pressure above the diaphragm is reduced, the spring pushes the diaphragm upward and opens the valve.

The arrangement of the valve seat and plug in a valve body may be such that raising the valve stem and plug opens the valve, as in fig. 7-8. However, very often raising the valve stem and plug closes the valve. The valves in fig. 7-8 are normally open valves, because releasing the control pressure above the diaphragm back to zero (as would be the case when a power failure occurs) permits the valves to open wide.

3 *Solenoid actuators.* A solenoid is an electromagnet; it consists of a cylindrical coil of electric wire so arranged that when an electric current is passed through the coil, a short bar of soft iron is magnetically pulled up inside the coil. This lifting action can be made to open a valve. When the electric current is switched off, the magnetic action ceases, the iron bar falls, and the valve closes. Solenoid valves are two-position valves, either fully open or fully closed. They can be made to be normally closed (closed when the electric current is turned off) or normally open. The magnetic action of a solenoid can be used to perform many functions in addition to operating valves.

4 *Self-contained actuators.* As mentioned previously, valves may be actuated by the control movement resulting from the expansion and contraction of bellows and diaphragms (see fig. 7-6). These actuators are not triggered or powered by any remote controller or remote source of power. The action results simply from the expansion and contraction of the fluid, enclosed inside the thermal bulb or bellows, as ambient temperatures change.

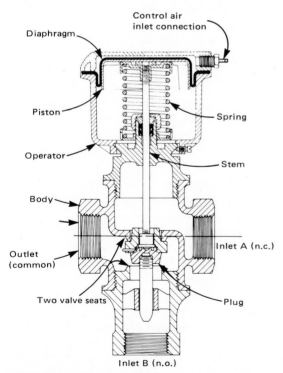

Figure 7-12 Three-way mixing valve with piston-top operator. (Johnson Controls, Inc.)

7-21 AUTOMATIC DAMPERS

Since HVAC systems, in the final analysis, do their work by conditioning, circulating, and controlling air, all of which extensively involve dampers, the importance of automatic and manual dampers cannot be overstated. In the past, many of the dampers upon which we placed great dependence were sadly inadequate. They were leaky, rattled, and had unpredictable performance characteristics.

Fortunately, today's good-quality dampers are fully capable of performing their assigned tasks. They can provide 99% tight shutoff at pressures up to 4 in. of water pressure differential. Resilient edging on all four sides of damper blades not only make tight shutoff possible but provide rattle-free operation as well. Damper shaft bearings are oil impregnated for permanent freedom of movement.

HVAC dampers are of many different types, as listed below and shown in fig. 7-13:

1   Single blade, center pivoted
2   Single blade, edge pivoted
3   Barometric dampers
4   Backdraft dampers
5   Parallel multiblade
6   Opposed multiblade
7   Vortex or inlet vane dampers

Single-blade dampers are, more often than not, manually operated. If so, they are provided with a locking device, called a *locking quadrant,* by means of which they may be fixed in the desired position. However, they may also be automatically positioned, as shown in fig. 7-13.

Barometric dampers and backdraft dampers are essentially the same. Barometric dampers are usually made with more sensitive or fine-tuned adjustment features; they are often used in the breeching (smoke pipe) of a furnace or boiler to stabilize draft conditions and permit close adjustment of fuel burners. The adjustable counterweight, shown in fig. 7-13, if slid outward on its mounting shaft would make the damper more difficult to open (by the air and gases trying to push it open). As a result, airflow is reduced through the burner and boiler (or furnace).

Backdraft dampers are usually used to relieve excess air pressure from within a building. They permit building air to escape, but prevent outside air from entering the building. Excessive building air pressure makes in-swinging exterior doors difficult to open, and makes outswinging doors difficult to close—often to the extent that automatic door closers cannot close them. Often backdraft dampers are replaced in high quality HVAC systems with automatic dampers and operators under the control of *static pressure regulators.* A static pressure regulator is a pressure-sensitive controller which constantly compares two static pressures (for example, building indoor pressure and outdoor pressure) and maintains a fixed differential between them.

Multiblade dampers are used for control of large volumes of HVAC system air moving at high or low velocities in large duct systems. These are of two types, parallel blade and opposed blade dampers, as shown in fig. 7-13.

In parallel blade dampers all blades are linked together in such a way that when one blade is rotated by a damper operator, all blades rotate in the same direction. Unless fully open, this type of damper imparts a definite crosswise direction to the air as it leaves the damper. This is almost always undesirable because it causes turbulence and static pressure loss. The turbulence may persist for a great distance down the duct and cause problems in succeeding elbows and points where air is to be diverted from the duct.

Opposed blade dampers do not have these unfortunate operating difficulties and should be utilized at all points where smooth, nonturbulent flow is important. This is especially important where air in a duct is approaching a supply grille, register, or diffuser. Also where air passes through a face damper located at the inlet to a heating or cooling coil, that damper must be of the opposed blade type.

Where the volume of air that is circulated in an

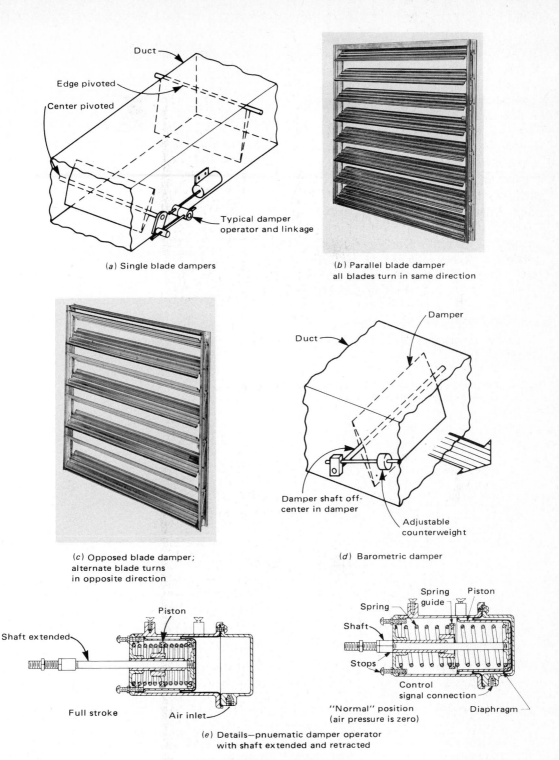

(a) Single blade dampers

Duct

Edge pivoted

Center pivoted

Typical damper operator and linkage

(b) Parallel blade damper all blades turn in same direction

(c) Opposed blade damper; alternate blade turns in opposite direction

(d) Barometric damper

Damper

Duct

Damper shaft off-center in damper

Adjustable counterweight

Shaft extended

Piston

Full stroke

Air inlet

Spring   Piston

Spring guide

Shaft

Stops

Control signal connection

Diaphragm

"Normal" position (air pressure is zero)

(e) Details—pnuematic damper operator with shaft extended and retracted

Figure 7-13 Damper details. (b, c, and e, Johnson Controls, Inc.)

HVAC system is subject to frequent or continual change, automatic dampers of all types have been utilized. This is true in variable air volume (VAV) systems especially, and in larger systems, the multiblade types are in greatest use.

One type of multiblade damper that has been found very effective in VAV use is the *vortex damper*, also called *inlet vane damper*. This type of damper is fitted into the round inlet opening through which air enters into a centrifugal fan. Each damper blade is pie shaped, and all blades together completely fill the fan inlet opening. Each blade turns on a radially positioned damper rod which receives support from a metal cone at the center and from bearing points around the perimeter of the air inlet opening. Perfectly tight shutoff is not required of a vortex damper because it is never required to reduce airflow to less than 25 to 30% of maximum design air quantity.

7-22 AIR COMPRESSORS

In pneumatic temperature control systems, a source of compressed air of excellent quality is necessary. Usually, this is provided by an air compressor unit which is supplied and installed by the temperature control system contractor. This unit must, of course, be of the highest quality since a great amount of dependence will be placed on it. Its malfunction and failure can cause great disruption and economic loss. For this reason air compressor units are often of the duplex type, in which two motor-compressor units are included in the compressor assembly (see fig. 7-14).

In keeping with the effort to provide great dependability in the compressed air supply system, the following measures are frequently taken:

1 Only filtered outdoor air is permitted to enter the compressor unit.

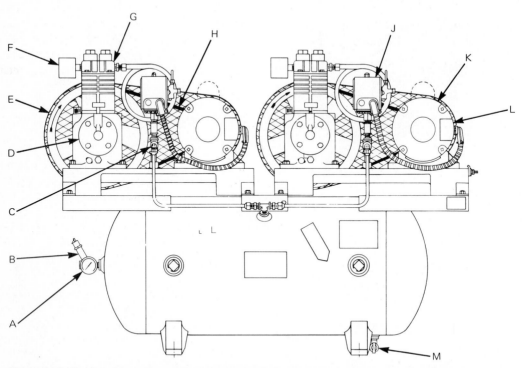

Figure 7-14 Duplex air compressor. A, pressure gauge; B, pop safety valve; C, check valve; D, compressor; E, flywheel; F, air inlet filter; G, cylinder head; H, drive belt; J, pressure switch; K, motor pulley (behind motor); L, electric motor; M, drain cock.

2 Oil separators are installed in the compressor discharge line to ascertain that supply air is completely oil free.

3 If compressors are electric motor driven, a standby motor-generator unit is provided to supply electric power during periods of general power failure.

4 Since moisture in the compressed air supply system is the cause of frequent operational difficulties, air dryers are installed in the main air supply line. These dryers are of two types: the desiccant type, which passes the air through a cannister of chemical adsorber such as silica gel or activated alumina, and a refrigeration-type dryer

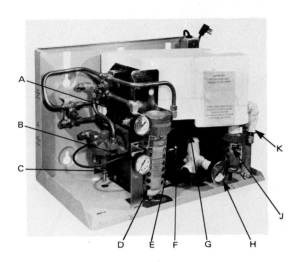

Item	Name of part
A	Gage, 0-100 psig
B	Gage, 0-30 psig
C	Pressure reducing valve
D	Filter complete
	Filter cartridge
E	Overload and relay 115 v
F	Condensing unit, 115 v
	(includes items e and g)
G	Fan motor, 115 v
H	Gage, 0-60 psig
J	Drain trap
K	Expansion valve
	Pop valve (not shown)
	Air dryer (not shown)
	Insulating tape (not shown)
	(order in multiples of 30 ft)

Figure 7-15 Refrigeration-type air dryer. (Johnson Controls, Inc.)

(see fig. 7-15), which uses a hermetic refrigeration condensing unit to cool the compressed air below its dew point temperature and thus remove much of its moisture.

7-23 COMPUTERIZED BUILDING AUTOMATION

Computerized building automation systems are now available to integrate all of the mechanical and electrical systems and their operation. The range of such systems extends far beyond the limits of the HVAC system; in fact, they can produce benefits in terms of energy savings, cost reductions, and improved safety that are little short of miraculous.

A central computer command console may be installed in a given building or, for smaller buildings, a tie-in with a remotely located computer, perhaps 100 miles or more away, can be made. The operation and maintenance of all mechanical and electrical systems of any nature can be monitored, integrated, and with full intercommunion, be accurately controlled. Figure 7-16 shows details of such a computer console installation.

The following is a summary of *some* of the activities that may be processed by such equipment:

1 HVAC

a Save on energy consumption by taking into account and utilizing waste heat available from equipment, lights, people, exhausted building air, and so on.

b Save energy by monitoring and closely controlling the amounts of outside air brought into a building for ventilation purposes.

c Save energy by limiting the running time of HVAC machinery to the very minimum.

d Save maintenance costs by issuing instructions to maintenance crews when malfunctions are imminent or occur, when filters need cleaning, when equipment needs lubrication, and so on.

e Project system diagrams on a television screen to pinpoint the location at which service or maintenance is required.

Figure 7-16　Computer console installation. (Johnson Controls, Inc.)

f Indicate temperatures, humidities, and other conditions at locations all over the entire building; these may be read and adjusted, when necessary, from the central console location. Also, fans may be started and stopped either manually or automatically according to an easily modified program.

g Adjust control point settings automatically according to program to account for changing building needs during nighttime and weekends and according to season.

2 Electrical systems

a Save energy by programming lighting systems to be on only when occupancy exists,

security needs must be met, aesthetic lighting is apt to be seen, and so on. The changing patterns of lighting systems are modified according to changing hours of darkness.

b Reduce electrical *demand charges* by load shedding to minimize peak electrical demand. The simultaneous starting of large motors is prevented, and the starting of these motors is delayed when power demand is high.

c Operation of domestic water heaters is prevented when the need for hot water is improbable.

3 Fire safety

   a Close building doors to isolate a fire or to establish a fire-safe area.

   b Close fire dampers in ducts to prevent the spread of fire.

   c Control HVAC blower and damper operation so as to evacuate smoke from the building or to supply fresh air into a contaminated area.

   d Since building elevators are often unsafe in fire conditions, elevators are controlled to prevent unsafe use or to expedite escape of occupants by a safe route when that is feasible.

   e Activate prerecorded public address system instructions in times of fire.

   f Contact the municipal fire department and give information as to the nature and location of a fire.

4 Building security

   a Respond to intrusion of unauthorized persons by closing certain doors, turning on lights, indicating on the computer display screen the place of intrusion, sounding a local alarm, and notifying the police.

   b Monitor critical areas with television cameras for unauthorized activity in occupied areas inside and outside buildings.

   c Provide motion detectors in unlighted areas.

PROBLEMS

7-1 Sometimes in the cooling cycle, air is cooled and then reheated before it is supplied into the controlled space. When would it be necessary to do this?

7-2 What is the economizer cycle as applied to the use of OA for building ventilation? Why is the use of an enthalpy controller necessary in this cycle?

7-3 A steam valve controls the flow of steam into a tempering coil that raises the temperature of ventilation OA to a point well above freezing before it enters a building. Should this steam valve be a normally open or a normally closed type? Why?

Chapter 8

Hot Water Heating Systems and Boilers

8-1 GENERALITIES

Heating buildings through the medium of circulating heated water is one of the oldest methods known; yet, viewing the modern scene, we see that its popularity through the years has only increased.

On the residential scene, the popularity that this method once enjoyed has waned considerably. Until the early 1950s, hot water heating systems in residences were gaining in popularity, especially after the tremendous boost given by the use of radiant panel heating systems in homes. Radiant panel heating became very popular in the early to middle 1940s. In 1947 at Levittown, New York, a housing project involving more than 1000 homes, all heated with hot water floor panel radiant heating systems, was completed. At Windsor Village in Indianapolis, a similar project of 800 homes was completed in 1948.

In the early decades of this century, most of the high-quality homes built in New England were heated with some type of "wet heat"—hot water or steam systems. Almost all nonresidential buildings used some form of wet heat system, and as the early years of this century passed, hot water heating gained in popularity even at the expense of steam heat.

Then in the 1950s, summer cooling in residences began to pass from the luxury category to that of a necessity. Today that is certainly the case; summer cooling in good-quality residences is certainly a necessity. Summer cooling requires a circulating air system; and as the use of summer cooling became universal, the use of circulating air heating systems grew in proportion. Circulating air systems providing both heating and cooling became the most economical expedient in the residential field. In these all-air systems the air is heated directly by some type of warm air furnace; no water or steam is involved.

In the nonresidential field, especially in buildings of greater size, wet heat is still king. Very little direct warm air furnace heating is used; and in probably 75% or more of the larger nonresidential structures, wet heat is utilized. However, now it is different than it was 40 years ago. Then, we used a great amount of *radiator*-type heat, with some type of radiation installed along the outside walls of buildings. This radiation took many forms. Cast iron radiators were still in use; gravity and forced-flow convectors and baseboard radiators were the most modern answers to the problem.

Today, perimeter radiation is used in colder climates only as a supplemental heat source to offset cold wall and window effect. The main part of the heating load is carried by central station circulating air systems in which the air is heated by a hot water or steam *coil*. In warmer climates, such as in the southern half of the United States, perimeter radiation is not required, and the full heating load is carried by heating coils of some type.

8-2 SYSTEM COMPONENTS

The components of a hot water heating system consist of the following:

1 A hot water heating boiler in which water under pressure is heated. Even though this unit is called a boiler, the water in it does not boil at any time. It is called a boiler because, except for its controls, it is usually exactly like the boiler in a steam heating system in which the water does boil. In the hot water heating boiler, water is stored which is heated by the intense heat released from the combustion of fuel such as coal, gas, oil, wood, and refuse. The products of this combustion are carried out of the boiler, through a metal breeching (the smoke pipe) into some type of chimney which, by its vertical draft effect, discharges them into the atmosphere above the building (see fig. 8-1, and locate the boiler; see also fig. 8-8).

2 A fuel burner which charges fuel into the combustion chamber of the boiler and ignites the fuel. The burner may be designed to burn fossil fuels such as gas, oil, or coal; in an electric boiler an electric resistance heating element is substituted for the burner. Some boilers may be set up to burn a fossil fuel and also waste material such as wood, paper, and garbage when such material is available. Important fuel savings can result in many situations if the proper type of boiler is specified, and the proper type of burner is installed, so that waste products can be burned.

3 Heating devices of all types that can extract heat from the circulating hot water and deliver it to the spaces in the building that need heat. These devices take many forms, including radiators, baseboard radiators, wall radiators, gravity convectors, forced-flow convectors, unit heaters, radiant heating panels (see fig. 6-5), and the heating coils in central station air conditioning units.

4 A supply and return piping system by means of which hot supply water is delivered to the heating devices and cooler return water is returned to the boiler for reheating.

5 A circulating pump, or pumps, which cause the heated water to circulate from the boiler, or other source of heat, throughout the entire system.

6 A compression tank (sometimes called an expansion tank). This tank has one inlet connection and no outlet connection. It is open to the piping system at all times, and contains a trapped cushion of air which occupies about half the tank volume. The lower half of the tank contains water from the heating system.

When the temperature of the water in the heating system is increased, the water expands and increases its volume. However, the internal volume of all the parts of the system cannot expand; so the excess volume of water overflows into the compression tank and compresses the air contained therein. When the heating system cools, the water in it contracts and water then flows from the tank back into the system.

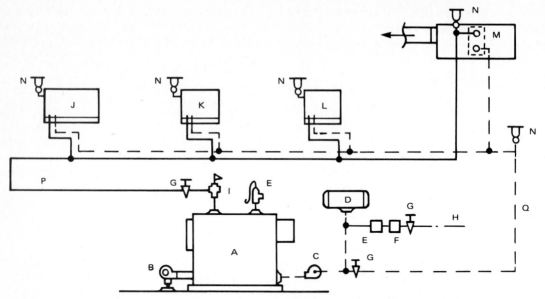

Figure 8-1 Schematic diagram of a typical hot water heating system. A, boiler; B, fuel burner; C, pump; D, compression tank; E, pressure relief valve; F, pressure reducing valve; G, hand shutoff valve; H, cold water makeup line; I, flow check valve; J, room heating and cooling unit; K, gravity covector; L, forced-flow heater; M, central station a/c unit heating coil; N, automatic air vent; P, hot water supply main; Q, reversed-return main.

7 One or more pressure relief valves. There are often two of these safety valves in the system as shown in fig. 8-1; one of these protects the boiler from excessive internal pressure, and one protects the piping system. These valves are very carefully designed, manufactured, tested, rated, and installed so as always to be capable of opening and releasing water from the boiler or the system when unsafe internal pressures develop.

8 A pressure-reducing valve. This valve is connected so as to permit cold water from the domestic water system of a building to flow into and pressurize the heating system to the proper pressure level. The pressure-reducing valve, then, reduces the water pressure from the 50 to 70 psig of the building water system down to a much lower pressure, usually 12 to 15 psig for one- or two-story buildings, but much higher for taller buildings.

9 Manual or automatic air vents. One strong enemy of hot water systems is entrained air. It enters the system whenever makeup water is added to the system, since air is absorbed in the cold makeup water. It separates from the water when the latter is heated; and it collects at all high points or trapped points in the system. It forms bubbles in pipelines which restrict or completely stop the flow of water, causing heating system failures.

To continuously purge the system of air, manual or automatic air vent devices are installed at all high points and elsewhere that air can collect.

8-3 GRAVITY HEATING SYSTEMS

Up until the year 1920 most hot water heating systems were of the gravity type, in which the heated water was circulated not by pumps, but by gravity action. Gravity circulation depends on a difference in weight of two interconnected columns of water, one of which is hotter than the other.

In fig. 8-2, the boiler provides a source of heat for the water, and the temperature of the water at the top of the boiler is higher than at

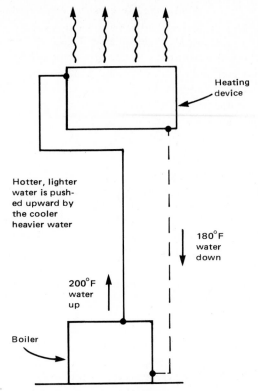

Figure 8-2   Gravity circulation in two columns of water.

the bottom of the boiler. This means that the left-hand column of water, which includes the boiler and the pipe up to the heating device (radiator, convector, etc.), is very slightly less dense and thus lighter in weight than the right-hand column of water, in the dashed return pipe.

This slight bit of weight difference causes a very slight circulation to begin. Soon the entire left-hand column is hot at, say 200°F. The heating device at the top removes heat from the water and delivers it into the space to be heated. In the process the circulating water is cooled in the heating device, so that the return line back to the boiler is somewhat cooler than the supply line. With this temperature difference established, a gravity circulation is established, which continues until the boiler stops heating and temperatures equalize.

This system would not circulate if the boiler were at the top of the loop. However, since most boilers are placed at the bottom as shown, gravity circulation does occur, even in pumped systems of the type shown in fig. 8-1 when the pump is turned off, and when circulation is not desired. Overheating in a pumped system will often occur when the pump is off unless specific steps are taken to prevent it.

8-4 FORCED CIRCULATION SYSTEMS

Forced circulation hot water heating systems do not depend on gravity action to provide water circulation; this is provided in a very efficient and positive manner by centrifugal pumps.

With forced circulation, flow rates are much higher, and as a result pipe sizes are greatly reduced. Pipe and pipe insulation costs are also much reduced. With forced circulation the entire system is much less expensive, and it operates in a much more responsive, accurate manner. Figure 8-1 typifies a very simple basic system of this type.

With forced circulation, long horizontal runs of piping, as needed in long, low buildings, present no problems of water circulation. Boilers may be located at any point in the system—high or low. With very large buildings, the building may be divided into zones with a pump and separate piping system for each zone. Many other advantages accrue to this type of system, so it is not strange that today the most modern sophisticated buildings utilize forced hot water as a means of distributing heat.

8-5 HIGH-TEMPERATURE-WATER SYSTEMS

Most hot water heating systems utilize supply water in a temperature range of 90 to 200°F. Also, most ordinary systems use a temperature difference, Δt, between supply water leaving the boiler and return water entering the boiler of 10 to 20°F.

This conventional practice has persisted through all the years since forced circulation became popular.

However, in the middle 1950s, heating engineers began to design heating systems that used water heated up to temperatures as high as 450°F with temperature drops, through the systems, as high as 100 to 150°F. The reader must remember here that the boiling point of water varies with the pressure to which the water is subjected.

We all know that water boils at a temperature of 212°F when it is subjected to an absolute pressure of about 14.7 psi (or 0 psi gauge pressure). That is, a pan of water sitting on the stove, with atmospheric pressure (14.7 psia) imposed on the water, near sea level, will boil at a temperature somewhere near 212°F. If the pan of water is carried up to the top of an 18,000-ft-high mountain, where atmospheric pressure is approximately half (7.3 psia) what it is at sea level, the boiling point is no longer 212°F. It will now boil at about 179°F. When the pressure imposed on water is lowered, the boiling point is lowered. When the pressure is raised, as it is in a high-temperature heating system boiler, the boiling point is raised. If the pressure is raised to 450 psia, the boiling point is now about 511°F; and we can heat that water to 450°F and it will not boil.

Now, if we again consider formula (1-4), we see that the amount of water that must be circulated, in gpm (gallons per minute), to deliver a given amount of heat is expressed as

$$\text{gpm} = \frac{\text{BH}}{500 \times \Delta t}$$

Here we see that if we use a Δt (in this case the water temperature drop through the system) of 120°F instead of the usual 20°F, the gpm is only one-sixth as much, and all the distribution piping becomes much, much smaller and less expensive. On the extensive campus of the U.S. Air Force Academy in Colorado, heat is distributed from a central boiler facility. With many miles of heated water supply and return piping involved, the cost

reduction through the use of a high-temperature-water (HTW) system was tremendous.

The use of HTW since the 1950s has not been nearly as extensive as was predicted in those days. However, in many situations, HTW or perhaps medium-temperature-water (MTW) systems will remain a viable alternative to conventional design, and should be considered by those in charge of design decision making.

8-6 PIPING SYSTEMS

Hot water heating systems are characterized by the arrangement of their distribution piping systems. To a very great extent, all such systems use the same boilers, pumps, controls, and accessories, but their piping systems are their distinguishing features. An understanding of the basic differences is necessary.

Piping systems, in general, fall into four categories, as follows:

1 One-pipe systems
2 Two-pipe systems with direct returns
3 Two-pipe systems with reversed returns
4 Series loop systems, sometimes called perimeter loop systems

8-7 ONE-PIPE SYSTEMS

In the schematic diagram of fig. 8-1 heated water from a boiler is circulated through a main supply pipe line to the room heating devices (radiators, convectors, etc.). After the water passes through the heating devices, it leaves those devices and returns to the boiler through a separate return piping system, shown dashed in fig. 8-1. This is a two-pipe system in which the hotter supply water is kept separate from the cooler return water.

In a one-pipe hot water heating system, there is no separation of supply and return water. As may be seen in fig. 8-3, after heated water passes through a heating device and gives up some of its heat, it returns to the same main pipeline from which the water was supplied to the heating de-

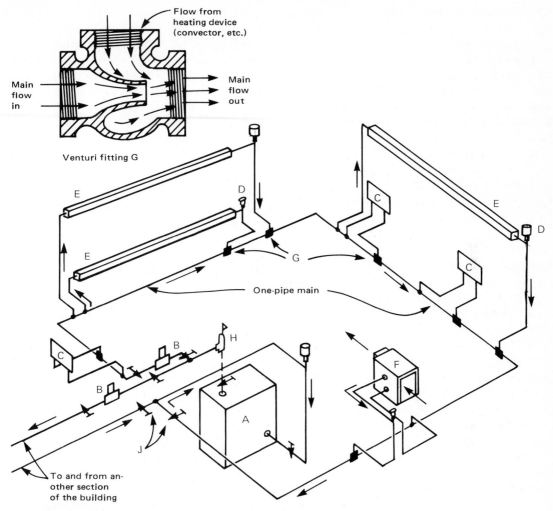

Figure 8-3 Schematic diagram of a one-pipe hot water heating system. Most of the required accessory equipment has been omitted from this diagram. A, boiler; B, circulating pumps; C, gravity or forced-flow convector or radiator; D, automatic air vents; E, wall radiator or baseboard radiator; F, air conditioning unit with heating coil; G, venturi-type flow fitting (see detail); H, flow control valve; J, gate valves.

vice. There is only one pipeline, which serves as both supply main and return main at the same time. This one pipe main is the same size from beginning to end, and usually circles or loops around the building, or a section of a building, as indicated in fig. 8-3.

The cooler water returning from the heating devices mixes with the hotter water in the main,

and reduces the main line temperature somewhat; and at the end of the loop near the last heating device, the main water temperature is 10 or 20°F cooler than at the beginning of the loop. Some designers take this fact into account and slightly oversize the heating devices in the latter half of the system.

As indicated also in fig. 8-3, a special fitting

is utilized where the branch return line from each heating device connects to the heating main. Without some such fitting there is not enough force to cause some of the water to leave the main and pass through the heating device. The fitting, shown in detail in fig. 8-3, incorporates a venturi which causes a reduction of pressure at the branch inlet, and positive flow of water through the heating device results.

In the venturi fitting a reduction in the diameter of the main water stream causes an appreciable increase in the velocity of the main stream. As a result its velocity pressure increases, and since the total pressure in the fitting cannot change, its static pressure must decrease. The reader will recall that total pressure is equal to the sum of the velocity pressure plus the static pressure, or $p_t = p_v + p_s$. The static pressure at the branch, or top, connection of the venturi fitting will actually be less than the static pressure at the inlet end of the heating device. Water flow through the heating device will result.

One-pipe heating systems are comparatively inexpensive and simple; they function well and positively when recognition is given to the limits of performance posed by the venturi fittings and the mixing of hot supply water with cooler return water.

When a large building is heated with this method, the piping system should be broken down into smaller individual loops each carrying a load of 300 to 500 MBH maximum. The one-pipe system will probably find its greatest use in future years in supplementary heating systems to provide perimeter heat needed to offset cold wall and window effect in colder climates.

In designing a one-pipe system the pumping capacity of its pumps may be calculated in gpm by the use of formula (1-4),

$$\text{gpm} = \frac{\text{BH}}{500 \times \Delta t} \qquad (1\text{-}4)$$

where BH is the total heating load on the system, and Δt, the temperature drop through the system, is selected to be 10 to 20°F.

The main loop piping should be sized so that water velocity through the venturi fittings is high enough to activate them properly. Design velocity in the main loop piping should be 2 feet per second (fps) or higher. The circulating pump must be able to develop enough static pressure to overcome the frictional resistance (pressure drop) of all the piping and fittings in the main loop, plus the resistance of the one heating device (and its piping) that has the greatest frictional resistance.

A study of the remainder of this chapter will advise the reader of many other design considerations applicable to one-pipe hot water heating systems.

8-8 TWO-PIPE SYSTEMS WITH DIRECT RETURNS

As described in art. 8-7, two-pipe hot water heating systems have heating devices, radiators, convectors, heating coils, and so on, which receive hot water from one pipe system, the supply main, and return their water to another pipe system, the return main.

The routing of the supply main is usually quite simple. It just runs by the shortest, most direct route to the vicinity of all the heating devices involved. However, the routing of the return main may be such that it runs by the most direct route back to the boiler, or it may take a more devious route, as shown later.

A direct return piping system is typified by fig. 8-4, in which the return connection from each heating device to the boiler is as direct as possible, involving the least possible number of feet of pipe. The low cost of the return piping in this system is an advantage, of course.

However, one big disadvantage of this system is that it is difficult to balance it so that each heating device receives its proper share of the circulating hot water. The natural tendency of this system is for heating device A to receive much more than its share of the water since it is closest to the boiler and the pump. The lineal feet of pipe in the circuit from the boiler up the supply piping to device A, and from there back the return piping to the

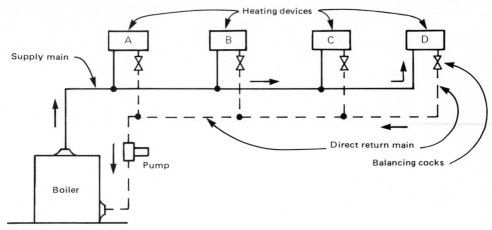

Figure 8-4   Schematic diagram of a two-pipe system with direct return.

boiler, is much less than the length of the circuit to any of the other devices. Therefore, most of the water would circulate through devices A and B; C and D would get very little water, and their rooms would be inadequately heated.

As shown in fig. 8-4, each heating device has a balancing cock (a valve) by means of which the flow to each device may be adjusted. In a system with only four devices as shown in fig. 8-4, this may be good enough; but in a large system with hundreds of heating devices, the balancing problem becomes almost insuperable. This is the primary disadvantage of a direct return system.

8-9   TWO-PIPE SYSTEMS WITH REVERSED RETURNS

In fig. 8-5 it may be seen that compared with the direct return system of fig. 8-4, the only differences are the elimination of the balancing cocks and the different routing of the return main. Notice that now the return main runs outward away from the boiler, and then doubles back and reverses its direction to return to the boiler. Now it may be seen that the lineal feet of pipe in the connection to each heating device, from the boiler to the device and back through the return main

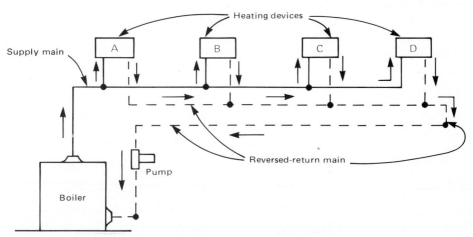

Figure 8-5   Schematic diagram of a two-pipe system with reversed return.

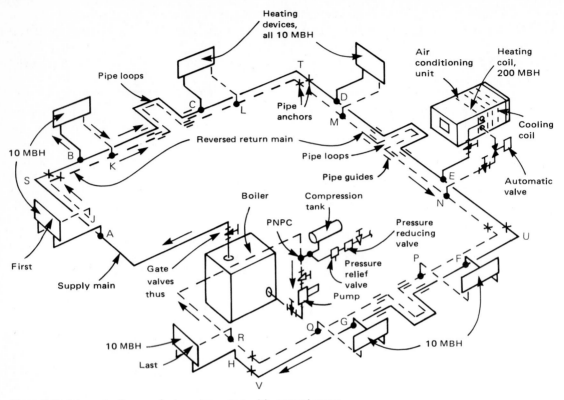

Figure 8-6 Schematic diagram of a two-pipe system with reversed return.

to the boiler, is exactly equal. The system is now essentially self-balancing, and balancing cocks are not needed. No matter how many heating devices the system may have, it will not be difficult to balance, so that each room in the building will receive about the right amount of heat.

It may seem, in examining fig. 8-5, that an inordinately large amount of return line piping is used, and that such a system would be inordinately expensive. However, this is not usually true, and fig. 8-6 demonstrates this fact.

In fig. 8-6, which is drawn for the same type of system, the supply and return mains have been made to loop around the perimeter of a building. This is usually a very efficient and economical method of routing the mains—around the perimeter. Notice that the return main begins at the *first* heating device, at reference point *J*, and runs *away* from the boiler, as reversed return mains do.

If this building had a *direct* return main, that return main would begin at the *last* heating device, loop the building perimeter in the same way, and return past the first heating device to the boiler. The lineal feet of return main would be almost identical with either the direct or the reversed return, with the latter having a very definite operational advantage.

In actual practice today, most hot water heating systems are of the two-pipe design, and have reversed returns.

8-10 SERIES LOOP SYSTEMS

In the series loop hot water heating system, the heating devices are all connected together in series so that all of the water being circulated flows from the first device to and through the second device, to the third and fourth, and so on, as shown in fig. 8-7. Each heating device carries the full flow of the system.

The heating devices usually take the form of a finned pipe wall radiator; which consists of a steel or copper pipe of 1 to 2 in. size with metal fins, perhaps 4 in. square with a hole in the center, slid on to the pipe, spaced 1/8 to 1/4 in. apart and tightly secured to the pipe. When concealed beneath a well-finished, perforated metal cover and mounted on an outside wall 4 in. or so above the floor, a very neat and effective heating device results.

For use in a series loop system, this type of *wall radiator* must have a pipe large enough to carry the entire flow of the system. Since 2 in. is the largest finned pipe wall radiator generally available, a series loop system is limited in size to the capacity of a 2-in. pipe. However, in a very large building, the system can be divided up into a large number of fairly small systems, and the series loop principle may be effectively utilized.

In this type system, Δt, the temperature drop through the system, must be kept small so that the last radiator in the loop receives adequately hot water to permit its size to be reasonable. A 20°F

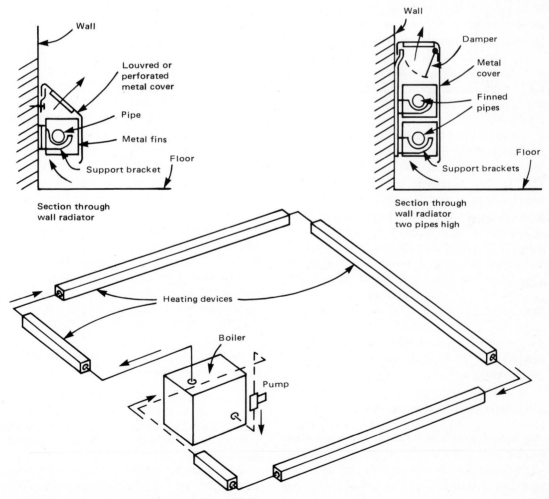

Figure 8-7 Schematic diagram of a series loop heating system.

Δt is satisfactory; but a $10°F$ Δt should be used for a basis of design, if possible.

The primary advantages of the series loop (also called perimeter loop) system is its simplicity and its low cost; and it should continue to find applications, mainly as a supplemental or perimeter source of heat to offset cold wall and window effect in colder climates.

There are also several disadvantages that must be recognized. Obviously, it is not possible to obtain automatic temperature control in a given room by throttling the volume of water, since that would affect all the other rooms on the loop. Individual room control can be effectuated to a limited degree through the use of dampers inside the perforated metal cover, as shown in fig. 8-7. However, such dampers do not give more than a 50% reduction in heat output, and it is awkward and impractical to position them automatically with a damper operator. So they are manual, and must be continually positioned by the room occupants.

Some degree of automatic temperature control may be achieved through the use of an outdoor thermostat which controls the burner on the boiler. This outdoor thermostat operates the burner in such a way as to provide an increasing water temperature as outdoor temperature falls, and vice versa. Such outdoor thermostatic control is used with all the various hot water heating systems, and the outdoor thermostat is often designed for a $1\,1/2 : 1$ ratio. This means that if outdoor temperature falls $1°F$, the circulating water temperature will be increased $1\,1/2°F$. Thus, if boiler water temperature is adjusted to be $90°F$ when outdoor temperature is $60°F$, boiler water temperature will rise $75°F$ (to $165°F$) when outdoor temperature falls $50°F$ (to $10°F$).

8-11 BOILER-BURNER UNITS

The boiler-burner unit is the heart of a hot water heating system in which some type of fuel or electricity is transformed into sensible heat and delivered into a moving body or stream of water, thus heating the water.

Boiler units are manufactured in many types and configurations by a very long list of manufacturers. Most people have very little concept of the extent to which boilers are used in the United States, or the extent to which their wintertime comfort depends on boilers.

Most manufacturers of boilers sell boilers alone (without burners), with the purchaser planning to install the burner and all necessary controls at the point of installation. However, these manufacturers also offer completely integrated boiler-burner units, which include the basic boiler, the fuel burner, all operating controls, all safety controls, a draft fan and motor (if required), boiler insulation, a metal jacket, and all electric wiring.

It is highly recommended that the integrated boiler-burner unit package be utilized at all times if at all possible. Many years ago the author, in his field practice, went 100% to this practice. Further, with units of larger size, the author's boiler unit specifications always include the requirement that a factory fire test, or operating test, be conducted and a notarized test report of this test be shipped with the unit. This procedure will eliminate much of the operational difficulty usually experienced when a large boiler unit is first set into operation.

One question that must be resolved early in the preliminary (schematics) stage of a building design is whether to use one large boiler unit or to use two or three smaller units. Almost always a single-unit installation will be less expensive—perhaps 25 to 35% less. In addition, less boiler room space will be required, perhaps 50 to 60% less. The temptation is thus great to use just one boiler unit.

However, there are many excellent reasons for using two or three boiler units; some of these are:

1 *Dependability*. With multiple units, a mechanical or localized electrical failure will not leave the building without heat. One or two units will probably be able to continue to keep the building usable.

2 *Efficiency*. During times of light load in mild or fairly mild weather, one large boiler having much more capacity than required at

that time will not provide high efficiency. With two or three smaller boilers, and with only one or two units in operation, capacity can be closely matched to heat requirements. Burner short-cycling can be minimized, as can heat loss up the chimney during off-cycles as air passing through the idle boiler carries away boiler heat.

However, it is also very true that one large boiler unit having a burner with a variable firing rate can, to a great extent, offset this efficiency disadvantage by nearly continuous firing at reduced rates when loads are light.

3 *Boiler room height.* A multiple-boiler installation will require more floor space, but a single-unit installation will usually require more boiler room ceiling height, since the single unit will be taller. This may very often work a hardship on the building design if the required ceiling height is greater than the planned ceiling height of the remainder of the floor on which the boiler unit is located.

4 *Future growth.* When future increases in building size are a good possibility, a twin boiler installation is a good idea, since a third boiler of similar design and equal size can be easily added. If one large boiler unit is originally installed, another unit of equal size and capacity would probably not be required for a building addition. So we would probably add a smaller boiler instead of one of equal size. When a small boiler is added alongside a much larger boiler problems do sometimes arise, especially if the boilers are steam boilers that have a water level in them that must be maintained. Steam boilers are often used in hot water heating systems when steam is required for other purposes. A steam convertor is then used to generate hot water with the heat of the steam. This will be discussed later in the chapter.

8-12 BOILER UNIT INSTALLATION

In either single- or multiple-boiler unit installations, one problem is that of providing space in the boiler room for pulling boiler tubes from the boilers for repair purposes. In many boilers, there are steel tubes approximately 3 in. in diameter through which either hot gas or water flows. These tubes frequently fail and need replacement. As shown in fig. 8-8, these tubes are often set hori-

zontally near the top of the boiler and must be cut loose at each end and pulled horizontally out of the front or rear of the boiler. The point of importance here is that uncluttered space must be provided for tube pulling, even though it may never be needed.

Sometimes it is possible to locate boiler room doors, or removable windows or louvers, in such a way that boiler tubes can be pulled out and replaced through these wall openings. Then the boiler room can be somewhat smaller. This problem exists wherever any type of tubular equipment, which includes such machines as water chillers, refrigerant condensors, and convertors, is to be installed.

The installation of boiler units, and any other type of fuel burning equipment, must very carefully involve provision for outside air for combustion. Fuel cannot be burned (oxidized) without oxygen, and surprisingly large quantities of air are required in large boiler installations.

The *1960 ASHRAE Guide* lists the following theoretical requirements for air in the process of burning the following fuels:

Anthracite coal	9.6 lb air/lb fuel
Semibituminous coal	11.2 lb air/lb fuel
Bituminous coal	10.3 lb air/lb fuel
Lignite	6.2 lb air/lb fuel
Coke	11.2 lb air/lb fuel
No. 1 fuel oil	102.6 lb air/gal
No. 2 fuel oil	105.5 lb air/gal
No. 5 fuel oil	112 lb air/gal
No. 6 fuel oil	114.2 lb air/gal
Natural gas	10.0 ft^3 air/ft^3 gas
Manufactured gas (530 to 570 Btu/ft^3 heat content)	4.7 ft^3 air/ft^3 gas
Propane	23.8 ft^3 air/ft^3 gas
Butane	31.0 ft^3 air/ft^3 gas

For practical combustion of fuel, it is mandatory that 25 to 50% excess air, beyond the theoretical requirements set forth above, be supplied into the combustion chamber. Other requirements for air supply into the boiler room must also be met. Therefore, it is recommended that the combustion air supply facility be sized for 200% of the theoretical air requirements. This

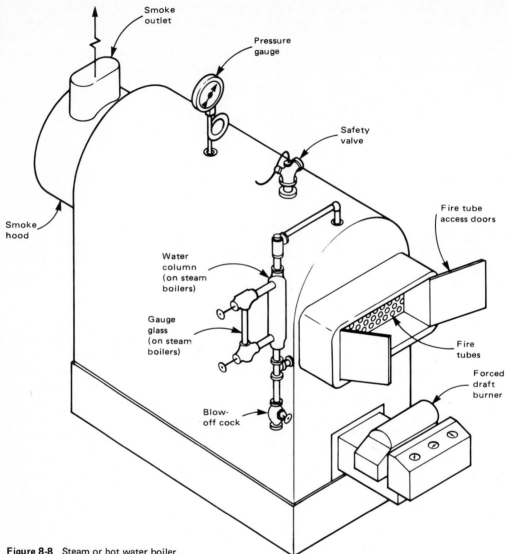

Figure 8-8   Steam or hot water boiler.

facility usually takes the form of a louvered opening in an outside wall of the boiler room, through which outside air can infiltrate at a low face velocity of 200 fpm.

Example 8-1 If two boilers each having a maximum firing rate of 30 gal/hr of No. 5 fuel oil are to be installed in a boiler room, the combustion air louver might be sized as follows:

30 gph $\times$ 2 boilers = 60 gph max. firing rate. 60 gph $\times$ 112 lb air/gal = 6720 lb air/hr (from the table above). Outdoor air at $20°F$ has a specific volume of 12.1 ft^3/lb.

6720 lb/hr $\times$ 12.1 = 81,312 ft^3 air/hr. 81,312 cfh $\div$ 60 = 1355 cfm to just meet the theoretical requirement. 200% of this amount for excess air, etc., means a total air quantity of 1355 cfm $\times$ 2 = 2710 cfm. If the outside air intake louver is then sized on a face velocity of 200 fpm, the gross louver area is then 2710 cfm ÷ 200 fpm = 13.55 ft^2. A louvered opening approximately 4 ft wide and 3.5 ft high would be adequate.

With larger fuel burners, some type of positive draft fan is usually incorporated with the burner—whether it is coal, oil, or gas fired. This fan has an appreciable ability to overcome some friction or resistance in the combustion air intake path, such as an air intake louver with an insect screen on it. However, some gravity-type atmospheric "gas" burners, sometimes used to fire boilers and furnaces, do not have positive draft fan equipment. With this type of burner, combustion air intake louvers must be sized on a face velocity of 100 fpm instead of 200 fpm. This will result in louvers that are twice as large as those required when positive fan draft burners are in use.

Whenever other fuel-burning devices, such as domestic water heaters, or incinerators, are located in the boiler room, their combustion air requirements must be included in any air intake facility calculations.

Boiler room ventilation is often required to keep room temperatures within reasonable limits. It should be easy to realize that an exhaust fan or a supply fan mounted in an outside wall can have considerable effect on the draft conditions in a boiler room. An exhaust fan can create a negative pressure that will actually pull air down a chimney and backward through a gravity draft boiler unit, causing a very dangerous firing condition in the boiler. Boiler room ventilation should be of the push-pull type, in which a supply fan and an exhaust fan are both installed and balanced to have equal capacity. An electrical interlock should prevent exhaust fan operation alone.

8-13   BOILER-BURNER UNIT CATEGORIES

Boiler-burner units are manufactured in a wide range of types which utilize different materials. They are made for widely varying operating conditions of pressure, type of load, different fuels, and different types of draft. There is also much overlapping in the types of units that are used for various operating conditions. In general, boiler units may be categorized as follows:

Low pressure	Induced draft type
High pressure	Forced draft type
Firebox type	Single fuel type
Scotch marine	Dual fuel type
Firetube type	Steel boilers
Water tube type	Cast iron boilers
Gravity draft type	

Low-pressure boilers are manufactured for working pressures of 160 psig maximum when heating water, and 15 psig maximum when generating steam. *High-pressure boilers,* then, are those suitable for working pressures in excess of these values of 160 psig with water and 15 psig with steam. Low-pressure boilers are further limited to 250°F working temperature. There is another unofficial category of working pressure, and that is an intermediate pressure of 30 psig for hot water boilers. By far the majority of hot water heating boilers through the years have been designed for use at working pressures of 30 psig or less. These are completely satisfactory in buildings of three stories or less where the height of highest points of the heating system is not more than about 40 ft above the boiler. This probably covers more than 90% of the buildings in the world.

The term *firebox boiler* is usually meant to indicate a boiler of steel construction which is of upright, fairly tall construction, in which the firebox where the fuel is burned is surrounded on all sides and above with water-backed steel. These are sometimes called "portable firebox" boilers, since they are usually shipped from the factory in one portable, welded assembly. The firebox boiler is contrasted in design to the Scotch marine boiler, which is built long and low to save headroom. The boiler sketched in fig. 8-8 is a firebox type.

One important parameter used in evaluating a boiler is its *heat release* rating. Heat release is

Figure 8-9 Modified Scotch marine boiler. (Photo provided by Cleaver Brooks Division, Aqua-Chem, Inc.)

determined by dividing the maximum firing rate, in BH or MBH, by the firebox, or effective combustion chamber, volume. Some Scotch marine boilers are fired with a heat release as high as 150,000 BH/ft^3. Other more conservative manufacturers may rate their firebox boilers as low as 55,000 BH/ft^3. It is recommended that all types of boilers be limited to a heat release of about 75,000 BH/ft^3.

Scotch marine boilers, as shown in fig. 8-9, are round in body and are long and low. They require much floor area but comparatively little ceiling height. They are all-steel and have long tubular construction; the flame and hot gases pass through these tubes and water surrounds the exterior of the tubes. Scotch marine boilers were originally designed for shipboard duty, and have been modified to be suitable for building heating and industrial power service.

Firetube boilers, as the name implies, are designed so that the flame and hot gases leaving the firebox or combustion chamber enter and pass through a bank of steel tubes which are surrounded by water. The fire tubes may be arranged in two, three, or four passes so that the hot gases serpentine back and forth from front to back, then back to front, and perhaps back again before leaving the boiler.

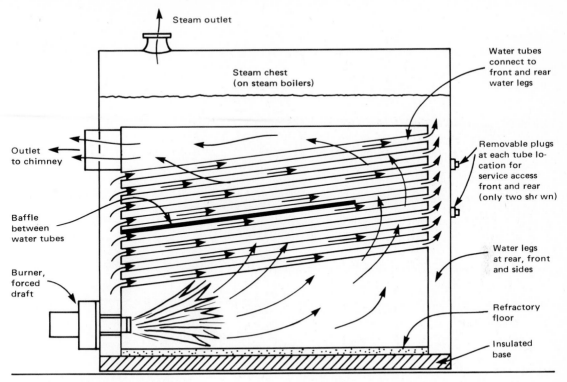

Figure 8-10   Section—water tube boiler.

Firetube boilers are less expensive than water tube boilers of equal capacity rating, and for that reason are found in more frequent use. Scotch marine boilers are of the firetube type.

Water tube boilers have water-filled tubes with the flame and hot gases surrounding the tubes. In smaller sizes, the water tubes are usually straight and run from a water passage at the front to a water passage at the rear, as shown in fig. 8-10. This type of boiler is made in capacities up to 25 million BH.

Larger water tube boilers usually have bent tubes which run from a lower water drum (tank) to an upper drum. Boiler walls, floor, and ceiling are lined with water tubes, and banks of tubes also occupy the center. Baffling causes the flame and hot gases to circulate back and forth over and through the tube banks; efficiency is very high. This type of boiler is available in standard sizes with capacities up to 50 million BH. In special designs, the capacities of this type of boiler are almost unlimited. A cutaway view of this type of boiler unit is shown in fig. 8-11.

Cast iron boilers are in strong competitive use today even though they were first made available well back into the nineteenth century. They are made in sections small enough to cast easily in sand molds and to handle easily after casting. The sections are bolted together either at the factory or in the field, and the capacity depends on the number of sections utilized.

One of the major advantages of cast iron is its comparative incorrodability and the very long life that results. Factory assembled, cast iron boiler packages complete with burners, all controls, boiler insulation, and well-finished metal jackets are available in sizes up to 8000 MBH gross output rating (see fig. 8-12).

Figure 8-11 Packaged, bent-tube, water tube steam boiler unit. (Courtesy of Babcock & Wilcox Company.)

8-14 CHIMNEY SIZING

As mentioned previously, air with its oxygen is required to support the combustion of any type of fuel, and very positive arrangements must be made for a continuous, dependable supply of air. In addition to an adequately sized outside air intake opening into the boiler room, equally positive arrangements must be made to assure a dependable flow of air through the boiler firebox whenever the burner is firing. The force that causes this air movement is called *draft*.

In a tall building, a chimney running up the full height of the building and extending 4 to 5 ft above the roof will usually provide plenty of draft. In lower buildings one or two stories in height, the natural or gravity draft provided by such a chimney might not be enough for the modern boiler unit of today. A mechanical draft fan of some type must then be provided.

In many boiler units a burner of some type is provided which has a centrifugal fan as part of the burner construction. Often this fan is not adequate to provide all the draft required, and is

Figure 8-12 Packaged cast iron boiler. (Photo by H. B. Smith Co., Inc.)

only designed to facilitate the mixing of the fuel with the combustion air in the firebox to promote clean combustion. The draft of a chimney is additionally required to process the products of combustion through the firebox, the boiler tubes, and the breeching into the chimney.

In this type of installation, if the designer can determine this draft loss through the boiler and breeching, he or she can determine whether a chimney could be provided to produce the necessary draft. If not, a draft fan will be required to cause the necessary flow of air and gases through the boiler unit.

The determination of proper chimney height and flue liner size is a difficult procedure if done accurately and in accordance with the latest theory. This procedure is detailed carefully in the latest issue of the *ASHRAE Equipment Handbook and Product Directory*, and the reader is referred thereto. For a simpler and perhaps more practical but less accurate procedure, the reader is referred to figs. 8-13 and 8-14, which have been reproduced from the *1960 ASHRAE Guide*. Figure 8-13 gives guidance in selecting the height of a smokestack

to provide a natural draft for automatically fired boilers. Figure 8-14 shows the minimum cross-sectional areas required for oil- and coal-stoker-fired boilers.

Example 8-2 An automatically fired, intermittently operated boiler must function under the following conditions:

Draft loss through the boiler	0.082
Draft required in the firebox	0.020
Total draft required at smoke outlet	0.102 in. water
Burner firing rate (oil), 11.3 gal/hr	
Gross stack temperature, 590°F	

Find the proper stack height and size.

Solution   From fig. 8-13, at the intersection of the horizontal 0.102 in. water line and the vertical 590°F stack temperature line, a 25-ft stack height may be read. Then, from fig. 8-14, for an oil-burning capacity of 11.3 gal/hr, we see that a 16 in. $\times$ 16 in. flue liner with a net inside dimension of 13 1/4 in. $\times$ 13 1/4 in. will suffice. Or a round flue liner with a 15-in. inside diameter will also suffice. If this boiler were stoker-fired with bituminous coal at the same heat input rate, the same percent of CO_2 in the flue gas, and the same stack temperature, the flue liner size should be increased about 40% in cross-sectional area. If the 13 1/4 in. $\times$ 13 1/4 in. flue liner area were increased 40%, it would be 13 1/4 in. $\times$ 13 1/4 in. $\times$ 1.4 = 246 in.^{2} in area, and the standard 20 in. $\times$ 20 in. flue liner would be required for coal firing. If the boiler were fired with natural gas under these same conditions, the flue liner area should be approximately 80% as large as that required for oil. It would, in this case be 13 1/4 in. $\times$ 13 1/4 in. $\times$ 0.8 = 140 in.^{2}, but the next size smaller flue liner, 12 in. $\times$ 16 in., having an area of only 128 in.^{2}, would be too small. The 16 in. $\times$ 16 in. flue would still be the proper size for natural gas firing. (The 1.4 multiplier for coal and the 0.8 multiplier for natural gas are estimated from data given in the *1975 ASHRAE Equipment Handbook and Product Directory*, fig. 3, p. 26.5.)

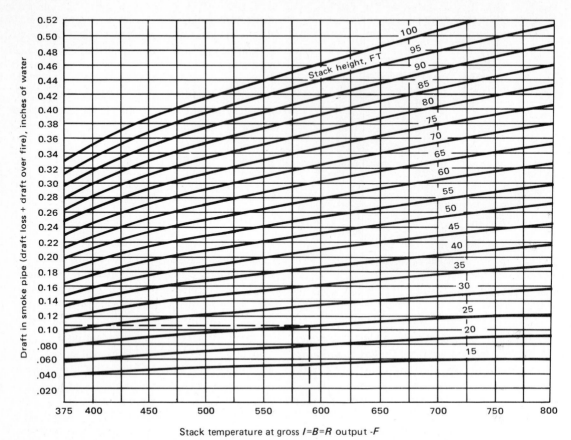

Figure 8-13 Height required, natural draft chimney for automatically fired boilers. (Reprinted from the 1960 ASHRAE Guide with the permission of ASHRAE.)

8-15 DRAFT FANS: FORCED AND INDUCED

Very often a boiler-burner unit will be equipped at the factory with a positive draft fan matched to the capacity of the burner and providing complete removal of the products of combustion. This positive action also provides the proper amount of air for combustion. When the boiler unit is so equipped, the sizing of the smokestack and breeching is much less critical, and the manufacturer's recommended flue size should be adequate no matter how short or tall the chimney may be.

These draft fans are of two types: *forced* and *induced*. Forced draft fans are mounted at the inlet to the boiler and are usually incorporated with the fuel burner into a common assembly; they force the combustion air into the boiler, and the firebox and boiler gas passages are pressurized above ambient barometric pressure.

Induced draft fans are mounted at the boiler smoke outlet, and pull the air and gases through the boiler by creating a negative pressure in the boiler in much the same manner as does a tall chimney. The induced draft fan then discharges into the breeching and through that into the chimney.

Figure 8-14 Minimum stack areas for oil and stoker-fired boilers. (Reprinted from the 1960 ASHRAE Guide with the permission of ASHRAE.)

Rectangular			Round	
(1) I = B = R burner capacity (not over)	**(2)** Nominal stack dimensions	**(3)** Inside dimensions of liner	**(4)** I = B = R burner capacity (not over)	**(5)** Inside diameter of liner
Gal.	In.	In.	Gal.	In.
2.1	8 × 8	6 3/4 × 6 3/4	1.3	6
3.5	8 × 12	6 1/2 × 10 1/2	1.8	7
5.3	12 × 12	9 3/4 × 9 3/4	2.5	8
7.7	12 × 16	9 1/2 × 13 1/2	4.5	10
11.5	16 × 16	13 1/4 × 13 1/4	5.6	11
15	16 × 20	13 × 17	7	12
21	20 × 20	16 3/4 × 16 3/4	12	15
26	20 × 24	16 1/2 × 20 1/2	19	18
33	24 × 24	20 1/4 × 20 1/4	28	21
41	24 × 28	20 1/4 × 24 1/4	40	24
52	28 × 28	24 1/4 × 24 1/4	53	27
59	30 × 30	25 1/2 × 25 1/2	69	30
76	30 × 36	25 1/2 × 31 1/2	88	33
100	36 × 36	31 1/2 × 31 1/2	109	36

Note: The inside dimensions or diameter of liner shown in columns 3 or 5 are for chimneys lined with a standard clay chimney tile and are the largest standard size that will fit within the dimensions specified for unlined chimney.

8-16 BOILER UNIT RATINGS

For many, many years there has been a confusing array of methods of rating and testing heating boilers, and the heating engineer has had to cut through and simplify these in order to establish a logical process for design. Fortunately, manufacturers' ratings, although still perpetuating the old confusing ratings, do now consistently include the one rating about which there can be little misunderstanding—boiler unit gross output in thousands of Btu/hr, or MBH.

Some of the ratings with which engineers have had to contend are:

SBI net. This is expressed in square feet of steam radiation, square feet hot water radiation or MBH net (not gross) output for steel boilers. "SBI" indicates the Steel Boiler Industry division of the Hydronics Institute. Net ratings are less than gross

ratings and reserve an allowance for *pickup* and *pipe tax.* The pickup allowance provides excess capacity to permit a steam or water heating system to heat a building from a cold start in a reasonable length of time. The pipe tax makes allowance for the thermal inertia of piping systems and heating devices (radiators, etc.), and also for heat loss from piping systems.

IBR net. This is essentially the same type of rating as SBI net, but for cast iron boilers; it is promulgated by the Hydronics Institute (formerly the Institute of Boiler and Radiator Manufacturers).

EDR ratings. EDR means *equivalent direct radiation* and is expressed in terms of "square feet" of radiation. Each square foot has a capacity of 240 BH on steam or 150 BH on hot water.

Boiler horsepower ratings. A boiler horsepower represents the ability of a boiler to boil 34.5 lb of water per hour from water at 212°F to steam at 212°F. Since the latent heat of vaporization of water at 212°F is 970.3 Btu, one boiler horse-power equals 33,475 BH (34.5 lb/hr × 970.3 Btu/lb = 33,475 BH). In using boiler horsepower ratings, the engineer had to know and remember and apply this conversion factor in order to find gross output in BH.

There have been other rating methods and variations of those listed above in use by boiler manufacturers; however, in the final analysis there is only one rating that the heating engineer needs, and that is gross output in BH or MBH. Fortunately, today most boiler manufacturers do include this rating.

There are other ratings, such as the MCAA net of the Mechanical Contractors of America, the AGA net and gross ratings of the American Gas Association, and the rating system of the Packaged Firetube Branch of the American Boiler and Affiliated Industries. When in doubt, the designer can usually cut through this welter of confusion and determine the approximate gross output of a boiler by multiplying the rated fuel firing rate by the heat content per unit of fuel and by an efficiency factor: 75 to 80% for oil and gas fuel and 65 to 70% for coal. For this procedure, the following rough estimates of fuel heat content may be used:

Anthracite coal	14,000 Btu/lb
Bituminous coal	12,000 Btu/lb
No. 2 fuel oil	135,000 Btu/gal
No. 6 fuel oil	150,000 Btu/gal
Manufactured gas	570 Btu/ft^3
Natural gas	1,040 Btu/ft^3

8-17 CONVERTORS: STEAM TO WATER

Often a hot water heating system of some type is required when the available source of heat is in the form of low- or high-pressure steam. This happens in many different situations—for example:

1 When an electric power generating plant is located in a city and uses steam to drive its generators, the waste steam leaving the turbines is distributed as low-pressure steam through underground piping to a large area of the city for heating purposes.

2 When an industrial plant needs steam for manufacturing processes, its boilers are then steam boilers and steam is available for building heating purposes.

3 In older hospital campuses or college campuses, steam has been the medium of heat distribution; steam is then the medium available for building heating also. In a modern campus situation, the medium for heat distribution would probably be high-temperature or medium-temperature water.

In all of the foregoing situations, hot water is heated with steam or high-temperature (300 to 450°F) water through the use of a heat exchanger, usually called a convertor.

A convertor is a vessel in which a bundle of tubes, made usually of copper or Admiralty metal, is enclosed inside a steel shell as shown in fig. 8-15. Water to be heated is pumped through the tubes, and the steam circulates around the exterior of the tubes inside the outer shell. In a convertor, a very great amount of heat exchange capacity can be packed into a very small unit. For example, a good-sized residence could be heated by a convertor 8 in. in diameter and 3 to 4 ft long.

8-18 INSTALLATION DETAILS

The piping connections around the boiler shown in fig. 8-16 are typical of what might be found in both small and large hot water heating systems. In very small buildings, only one water circulating pump might be found; it might be located at either the boiler inlet (return) connection or at the outlet (supply) connection.

In fig. 8-16, four circulating pumps are shown, indicating that the system is divided into four subsystem which supply heat to four different temperature control zones of the building. The four necessary supply branch mains and four branch return mains are also shown, to develop further the idea of zoning.

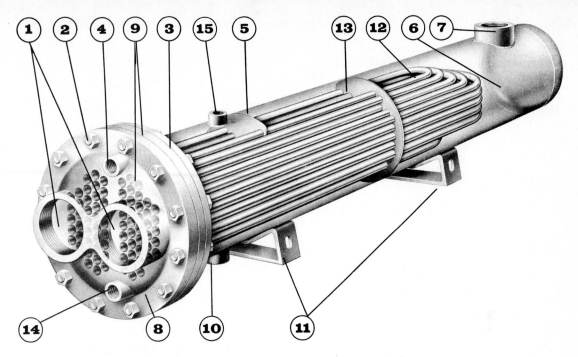

1 Water connections
2 Alloy steel bolts
3 Steel shell flange
4 Air vent
5 Steel shell
6 Steam inlet section

7 Steam inlet
8 Cast iron bonnet
9 Steel tubesheet
10 Condensate outlet
11 Cast iron cradles

12 ¾″o.d. seamless copper "U" tube removable bundle
13 Copper alloy support
14 Drain
15 Air valve connection

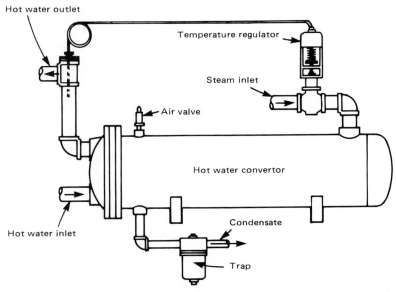

Figure 8-15 Hot water convertor details. (Courtesy of Patterson-Kelley Co., Division of Harsco Corp.)

As previously mentioned, the compression tank is a closed vessel which ideally is half full of water and half full of air. A gauge glass is often mounted on the tank to show the level of water in the tank. After a period of months of operation, or perhaps a year or two, the air originally contained in the tank will be carried away into the system and vented, by the automatic air vents, out into the atmosphere. When the compression tank has thus lost its air cushion and is full of water, whenever the fuel burner is turned on and the system water temperature rises and expands, the system pressure will rise until a pressure relief valve opens and releases the excess water volume.

Then, after the burner turns off, the water in the system cools and contracts and system pressure falls. However, there is a minimum below which the system pressure must not fall. A certain residual pressure is required to keep the piping system full to the top and always pressurized. When the falling pressure approaches this minimum, a valve, called a *pressure-reducing valve,* opens and admits makeup water from the building domestic water system into the system.

So without an air cushion in the compression tank, the foregoing sequence is repeated time after time on each firing cycle of the fuel burner. Much water is wasted, much heat is lost, and as raw water is charged into the system through the pressure reducing valve, dissolved air is also brought in. This air is carried throughout the system and causes trouble wherever it collects.

There is one concept of design that must be fully understood by all heating engineers of hot water heating systems. This concept is that at whatever point the compression tank is connected to the system, at that point the pressure will be essentially stabilized. In fig. 8-16, this point is at the top of the boiler and is labeled "point of no pressure change" (PNPC). The air cushion in the compression tank gives this stabilizing effect, forcing water out into the system when the PNPC pressure tends to fall, and accepting water from the system when the PNPC pressure tends to rise. There will, of course, be some slight pressure changes at the PNPC.

The cycling of the circulating pumps is one factor that causes pressure changes in a hot water heating (HWH) system. In fig. 8-16, if the pumps start running, they cause a considerable difference to exist between pump inlet pressure and pump outlet pressure. One of three actions will now result:

1 Pump inlet pressure will hold steady and outlet pressure will rise.
2 Outlet pressure will hold steady and pump inlet pressure will drop.
3 Pump outlet pressure will rise and inlet pressure will drop at the same time.

With the compression tank of fig. 8-16 connected as it is, we know that the inlet pressure at the pumps will hold essentially steady (it will vary a small amount) since the PNPC is at the top of the boiler. Of the three possible actions listed above, action 1 will result.

Further, notice that in fig. 8-16 the makeup water connection is tied in at a stabilized point near the compression tank. Since the pressure-reducing valve, with its balanced diaphragm type of control, is sensitive to pressure changes, this makes an ideal point of connection.

Also, it should be observed that a *flow-check valve* is installed by each circulating pump. These valves are weighted flapper valves or poppet-type valves which permit flow in only one direction. Further, they are weighted just enough that gravity circulation (see fig. 8-2) cannot open them. Their unidirectional character also prevents one pump which is running from drawing water backward through a pump that is idle.

Proprietary brand name equipment is available for facilitating the reestablishment of the compression tank air cushion when it is diminished or lost. However, the simple arrangement of gate valves to isolate the boiler, and the two valves to drain the tank and admit air into the tank, make any special equipment unnecessary.

In a large, important HWH system, it is often considered advisable to install a small, oil-less air compressor and a tank-mounted float valve to

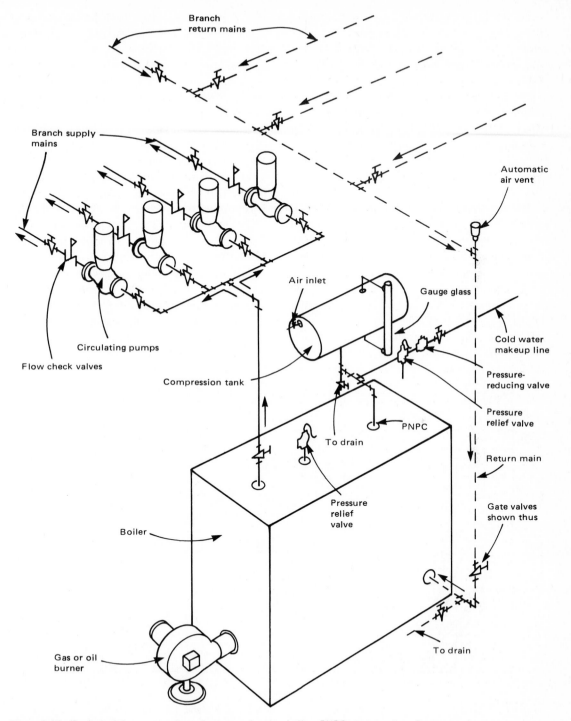

Figure 8-16 Typical piping connections—hot water heating boiler. PNPC means point of no pressure change.

Branch return mains

Branch supply mains

Automatic air vent

Air inlet

Gauge glass

Cold water makeup line

Circulating pumps

Flow check valves

Compression tank

Pressure-reducing valve

Pressure relief valve

To drain

PNPC

Return main

Pressure relief valve

Boiler

Gate valves shown thus

Gas or oil burner

To drain

restore the compression tank air cushion automatically when that becomes necessary.

Notice finally in fig. 8-16 the point where the water in the return main drops from overhead down to the boiler inlet connection. It is at points such as this, where the water drops, that air tends to collect and form an air bubble that can seriously impede water flow. It is advisable to install an automatic air vent at all such points.

8-19 CIRCULATING PUMPS

A very wide spectrum of circulating pumps is used in HWH systems. These range from the small fractional-horsepower in-line, pipe-mounted circulators required by a residence to the large base-mounted horizontally split case double suction pumps that would be used to circulate heated water all over a 500-acre or larger university campus.

There are many different basic types of pumps available: piston pumps, turbine pumps, centrifugal pumps, single-stage and multistage pumps, in-line and side inlet pumps, and pumps that are driven with all manner of prime movers (electric motors, turbines, etc.). In HWH systems, pumps are almost always of the centrifugal type. They are designed and constructed to be super quiet and free from vibration. They are designed for long-hour duty, and in fact, are sometimes applied to a HWH system in such a way that they never stop running from autumn until the following spring.

For HWH system use, centrifugal pumps are of two basic types: *steep curve* and *flat curve* pumps. This terminology refers to the curves or charts on which are plotted the performance of various types and sizes of pumps. Basically, these curves plot water delivery in gpm versus the pressure against which the pump must work expressed in feet of water. Remember that pressure can be expressed in terms of inches or feet of water; 2.31 ft of water equals 1.0 psi. Typical pump curves, both steep and flat, are shown in fig. 8-17. From these it may be seen that steep curve pumps are designed

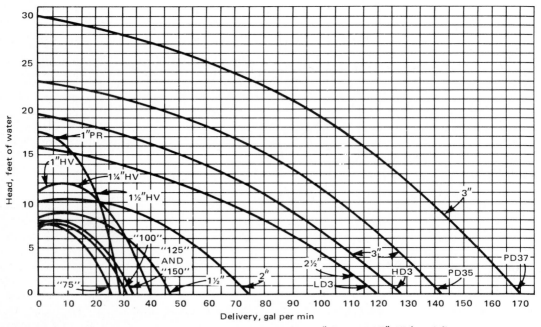

Figure 8-17 Centrifugal pump curves showing steep curves (e.g., 1″ PR and 1¼″ HV) and flat curves (e.g., LD₃). (Courtesy of ITT Fluid-Handling Division.)

to circulate a comparatively small volume of water against a high pressure. Pressure is often referred to as *head.*

With steep curve pumps, an increase in head, as when a number of automatic valves partially close, will result in only a modest reduction in gpm flow rate. With flat curve pumps, a small increase or decrease in head will result in a very great change in gpm. The designer can select the type of performance desired.

Most HWH systems need to be zoned for greatest accuracy of control. In year-around heating and cooling hydronic systems, it is often necessary to supply warm water to one or more zones of a large building while supplying chilled water for cooling in other zones. One easy way to zone a HWH system is to use a multiplicity of comparatively small circulators as shown in fig. 8-16. When these circulators can be small enough to be pipe mounted, installation costs can be reduced and floor space can remain uncluttered.

HWH system pumps should be designed to include rotary shaft seals whenever possible. A motor-driven pump has a pump shaft which extends out of the pump housing and is directly coupled to the motor. Where this shaft passes out through the pump housing, or casing, there is often water leakage. There is pressure inside the pump casing and there is the tendency for water to seep out along the shaft through whatever bearing supports the shaft.

This leakage can be wasteful of water and heat, it can keep the equipment room floor wet and messy, and the drippage from an overhead pump can be damaging to piping and equipment below it. In older-style pumps, a *packing gland* is used as a means of controlling this shaft leakage. In a packing gland, a graphite-impregnated rope-type jute or hemp packing material is wrapped around the shaft and compressed until it seals tightly around the shaft and against the pump casing.

This type of shaft seal is unsatisfactory and has largely been replaced with a newer device called a *rotary seal.* The rotary seal consists of two parts slid onto the pump shaft. One part is stationary

and seals tightly against the pump casing with a neoprene facing. The other part fits tightly around the shaft so as to seal against the shaft and rotates with the shaft. The two parts then are held together with a spring; and where they meet, the two matching faces are highly polished and smooth for a perfect fit. One face is made of compressed graphite or carbon which is self-lubricating, and the other face is stainless steel. When the two matching faces are properly made and installed, water cannot leak out between them. Rotary shaft seals are highly recommended on all HWH system pumps. Figures 8-18*a* and 8-18*b* are illustrations of typical in-line pipe-mounted circulating pumps; and figs. 8-19*a* and 8-19*b* show a typical base-mounted end suction pump made for floor mounting, and a close-coupled end suction pump made for mounting on a concrete pad.

8-20 HEATING DEVICES

Heating devices are the items of equipment in a HWH system which receive the hot water from the piping system, extract heat from the water, deliver that heat directly or indirectly into the spaces to be heated, and then return the water back to the piping system.

Heating devices come in many forms; some of these are:

1 *Radiators.* These are wall-hung or floor-mounted cast iron sectional devices, usually mounted at outside walls under windows. Cast iron radiators are bulky, rough, and poor in appearance; their manufacture has been largely discontinued.

2 *Convectors.* These devices have largely supplanted cast iron radiators in popular use because of their more modern appearance and reduced size. As shown in fig. 8-20, convectors consist of a finned tube heating element enclosed inside a well-finished furniture steel cabinet. They are usually mounted on outside walls beneath windows, or near doors in entries to buildings.

Convector heating elements are very different from those in the wall radiators shown in fig. 8-7

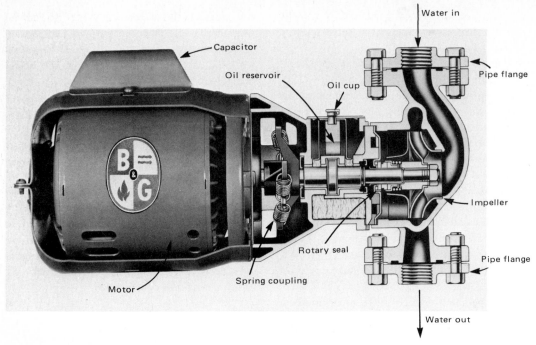

Figure 8-18 (*a*) Pipe-mounted, centrifugal, hot water circulating pump for vertical pipe. (Courtesy of ITT Fluid Handling Division.)

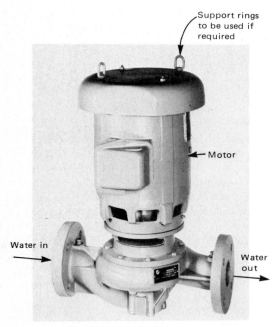

Figure 8-18 (*b*) Pipe-mounted, centrifugal, hot water circulating pump—for horizontal pipe.

and described below. They have a comparatively large amount of heating surface packed into a very small space. They consist of a group of straight, parallel copper tubes secured at each end into a cast brass or cast iron header or manifold. The tubes have very thin aluminum fins assembled tightly onto the tubes with a very close spacing of 8 to 14 fins per inch. Hot water (or steam in a steam heating system) is passed through the tubes from header to header. Supply and return pipes connect to each header as shown. An air vent is mounted on one of the headers since the heating element forms the top of an inverted loop where air can collect.

Convectors take many different forms to suit the needs of different applications. In most convectors the air circulates through the cabinet by gravity action, with the air entering the open bottom and leaving through a louvered or grilled opening at the top. When a great amount of capacity is required from a small package, electric-motor-driven centrifugal fans are added either above or below the heating element; these are called *forced flow convectors.*

Figure 8-19 (*a*) Base mounted, end suction centrifugal pump. (Courtesy of ITT Fluid Handling Division.)

Figure 8-19 (*b*) Close coupled, end suction centrifugal pump. (Courtesy of ITT Fluid Handling Division.)

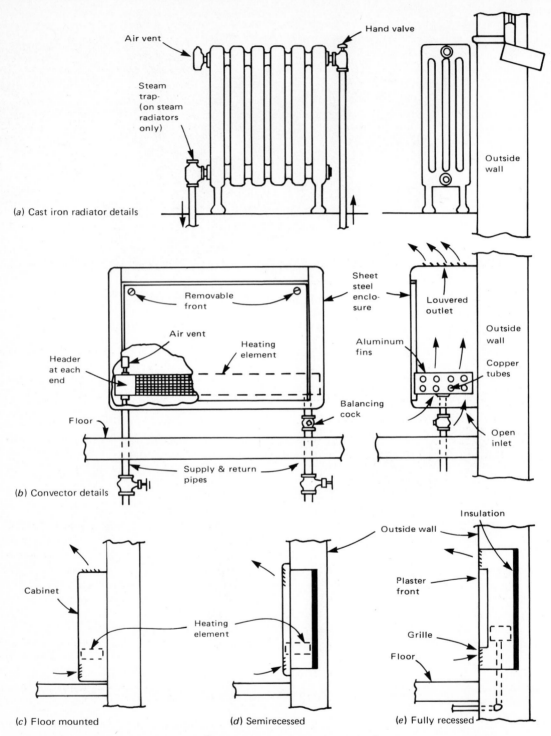

(a) Cast iron radiator details

Air vent

Hand valve

Steam trap- (on steam radiators only)

Outside wall

(b) Convector details

Removable front

Sheet steel enclosure

Louvered outlet

Outside wall

Air vent

Heating element

Header at each end

Aluminum fins

Copper tubes

Floor

Balancing cock

Supply & return pipes

Open inlet

Insulation

Outside wall

Cabinet

Heating element

Plaster front

Grille

Floor

(c) Floor mounted

(d) Semirecessed

(e) Fully recessed

Figure 8-20 Heating devices. (f, g, and h, © The Trane Co., used by permission.)

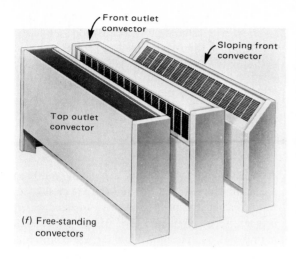

(f) Free-standing convectors

(g) Perimeter or wall radiators

(h) Fully recessed convector

Figure 8-20   *(Cont.)*

Convector cabinets may be wall hung as shown in fig. 8-20 or may be floor mounted. Floor-mounted units have cabinets that extend down to the floor and have a louvered or grilled inlet at the bottom as well as at the top. With this type, the connecting piping is fully concealed, whereas with wall-hung cabinets, two short sections of pipe are exposed to view.

One very popular convector cabinet is the semi-recessed type in which 2, 4, or 6 in. of an 8-in. cabinet (for example) are recessed into the wall behind the unit so that the projection of the cabinet into the room is minimal. Also, the cabinet may be fully recessed into the wall with louvered openings at top and bottom of the removable metal cabinet front. Convector cabinets may also be such that there is no cabinet front exposed to view. The front of the cabinet is made so that plaster or other wall finish material may be affixed to the cabinet front as shown in fig. 8-20h. In this case, only upper and lower grilles are exposed to view.

With semirecessed and fully recessed convectors the designer must be concerned about heat loss outward through the wall behind them. This will be considerable even with insulation installed as shown. An effort should be made to locate these types in other than exposed, outside walls.

In all types of convectors, manual control can be achieved through the use of metal dampers mounted near the air outlet opening and operated with a pull chain or a rotary knob on the cabinet front. When control is to be automatic, an automatic valve is located in the supply or return pipe below the floor. If there is a ceiling in the room below, an access panel must be installed in that ceiling to permit service access to the valve. If the convector to be controlled is a forced-flow type, automatic control may be easily accomplished by cycling the fan motor on and off. Of course, effective control may be achieved with all types by varying the supply water temperature in accordance with thermostat demands.

3 *Wall radiators.* As described in art. 8-10 and shown in fig. 8-7, wall radiators are essentially finned pipes exposed on a wall or concealed behind a perforated metal cover. They fit into the category of convectors, but in general terminology are kept distinct. Like all the heating devices described here, manufacturers' rating catalogs must be consulted for specific ratings and descriptions before selections can be made for installation.

4 *Unit heaters.* Unit heaters are small, compact heating devices which consist of a finned tube coil enclosed in a sheet metal housing, a single-speed or multispeed propeller-type fan, and directional-type louvers at the heater air outlet.

As shown in fig. 8-21, unit heaters are, in general, available in two patterns: horizontal discharge and vertical downward discharge. Unit heaters occupy a very special place in the HVAC picture, and they can perform one type of task which other types of heaters can perform only awkwardly and not as well.

Unit heaters do an excellent job of heating rough shop areas of a building where the appearance of the exposed piping and conduit is acceptable, where a somewhat drafty condition can be tolerated, where the high noise level of high-tip-speed fans will not be a matter of concern, and where minimum cost is necessary. Unit heaters of the type contemplated here and shown in fig. 8-21 should never be used in well-finished rooms with low ceilings where quiet conversations will be held and where gentle air movement is required.

Unit heaters should be mounted overhead in high bay areas, but with the capability of delivering their heated air downward so as to reach the floor. Horizontal discharge heaters should not be so installed that adjacent heaters discharge toward each other. The area of turbulence where their opposing air streams meet can be excessively drafty and uncomfortable. Instead, unit heaters

should be arranged in tandem all around a large room so as to cause a gentle circulation around the perimeter of the room. This can be accomplished even though each heater is angled somewhat toward the outside walls to offset the cold wall effect.

8-21 HWH SYSTEM DESIGN: PUMPING HEAD

After the total heat loss of a building and each zone and room within the building are calculated, the determination of the quantity of heated water, in gpm, to be circulated as a whole and to each part is not complicated. With the use of formula (1-4), in which

$$gpm = \frac{BH}{500 \times \Delta t}$$

these calculations are very simple after the arbitrary choice of the temperature drop through the HWH system, Δt, is made. This choice was discussed earlier in this chapter.

However, the selection of a circulating pump, or pumps, cannot be made until the pumping head is calculated. Pumping head is the total frictional resistance that the pump must overcome when it causes the heated water to circulate. Every foot of pipe, every pipe fitting, valve, and heating device, and the boiler or convertor all offer a certain amount of resistance to the flow of water. Each of these items, as a result of their frictional resistance, causes a certain amount of drop or loss in the pressure of the water. The circulator (pump) must be able to develop enough difference between the static pressures at its inlet connection and its outlet connection to equal exactly the sum of all such pressure losses. This assumes that there will be no appreciable difference in velocity or altitude between these connections.

Therefore, the HWH system designer is now faced with the problem of evaluating all these component pressure drops and totaling them. The

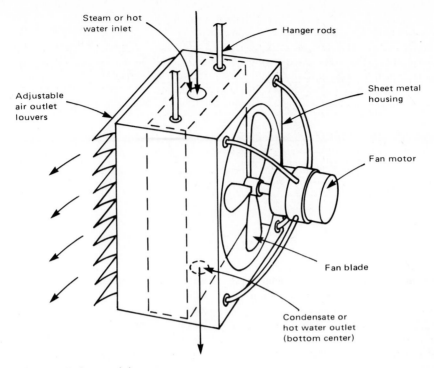

Steam or hot water inlet

Hanger rods

Adjustable air outlet louvers

Sheet metal housing

Fan motor

Fan blade

Condensate or hot water outlet (bottom center)

(a) Horizontal discharge unit heater

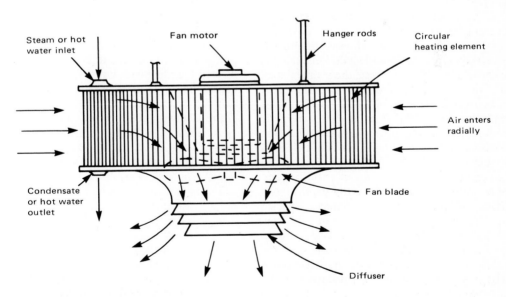

Steam or hot water inlet

Fan motor

Hanger rods

Circular heating element

Air enters radially

Condensate or hot water outlet

Fan blade

Diffuser

(b) Vertical discharge unit heater

Figure 8-21 Unit heaters.

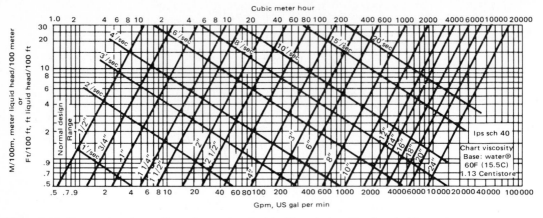

Figure 8-22 Pressure loss due to flow of water in schedule 40 steel pipe. (Reprinted with permission from the 1977 Fundamentals Volume, *ASHRAE Handbook and Products Directory.*)

system components with which the designer must now be concerned may be summarized as follows:

1 *Piping.* Pressure loss will depend on water velocity and the type of pipe and its condition. Figures 8-22 and 8-23 include charts by means of which pressure loss per lineal foot of commercial-grade steel and copper pipe may be determined when flow rate in gpm is known.

2 *Fittings, valves, boilers, and devices.* These offer considerable resistance to water flow, and their pressure loss is usually expressed in terms of their *straight pipe equivalent* length. For example, experience and laboratory tests show that a standard 2-in. 90° pipe elbow carrying water at a velocity of 3 feet per second will have the same pressure loss as will 5.4 ft of straight 2-in. pipe. Therefore, the straight pipe equivalent of a 2-in. 90° elbow at a velocity of 3 fps is 5.4 ft. This value may be found in fig. 8-24.

All types of fittings, valves, and so on, are empirically rated in accordance with their relative resistance in comparison with standard 90° elbows. For example, in fig. 8-24 it may be seen that an open iron pipe system gate valve is equivalent to half an elbow (0.5) of the same size. Figure 8-24 also shows the elbow equivalent value of pipe tees at various conditions of flow.

3 *Automatic control valves.* The resistance to flow of automatic valves is always changing as the valve opens and closes, but the designer is most

interested in its resistance in the wide-open position. It is assumed that under conditions of maximum load (coldest weather), all such valves will be open or nearly so; this is the time when proper pump delivery and distribution throughout the system is mandatory.

The allowable pressure drop through automatic temperature control valves is usually a value that is arbitrarily chosen by the designer. In most HWH systems, this should normally be approximately 2.0 to 3.0 psi. In the interest of minimizing pump horsepower and electric energy consumption, the pressure drop through automatic valves should be held to the minimum; however, control valves can control more accurately if higher pressure drops may be taken. The final choice must be a compromise between these two opposing factors.

4 *Heating coils.* The pressure drop through heating coils varies much too widely for it to be standardized and included in a table of pressure drops. The only reliable method of determining coil drop is to consult manufacturers' catalogs and make a selection of the coil to be used. The pressure drop may then be determined from that manufacturer's catalog data. Coil pressure drops vary widely with different types of coil construction and may be as low as 0.5 psi and as high as 5 to 7 psi.

Water system pressure drops for coils and other devices are, more often than not, expressed in terms of feet of water. The reader should guard

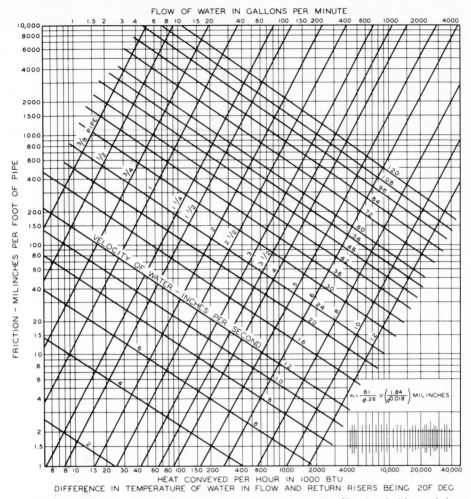

Figure 8-23 Pressure loss due to flow of water in type L copper piping. (Reprinted with permission from the 1977 Fundamentals Volume, *ASHRAE Handbook and Products Directory.*)

against confusion in this case and realize that this is a head or pressure rating the same as psi and remember that 1.0 psi = 2.31 ft of water. Sometimes a student confuses feet of water pressure with feet of pipe equivalent length, and a considerable error can result if this happens.

The reader will now begin to realize that the magnitude of work in accurately determining the total pressure loss of an HWH system is very considerable, and requires tremendous amounts of time. Each pipe fitting, valve, and heating de-

vice must be investigated and its pressure loss determined. As pipe sizes change throughout a system, the equivalent length of an elbow changes, and as a result, the equivalent length of all other components change since they are related to the resistance of an elbow, as shown in fig. 8-24.

This task is reduced if an electronic computer and suitable computer program are available. However, even then great care and much time is required to properly "input" the necessary data concerning a given piping system. Errors occur in

Figure 8-24 Equivalent lengths of iron and copper pipe for elbows, tees, and equipment. *Notes:* (1) The chart is based on straight lines, that is, branches A, B, and C are the same size. (2) Head loss in desired circuit is obtained by selecting proper curve according to illustrations, determining the flow at the circled branch, and multiplying the head loss for the same size elbow at the flow rate in the circled branch by the equivalent elbows indicated. (3) When the size of an outlet is reduced, the equivalent elbows shown in the chart do not apply. The maximum loss for any circuit for any flow will not exceed two elbow equivalents at the maximum flow (gpm) occurring in any branch of the tee. (4) The top curve of the chart is the average of four curves, one for each of the tee circuits illustrated. (Reprinted with permission from the 1977 Fundamentals Volume, *ASHRAE Handbook and Products Directory.*)

Equivalent length of pipe for 90° elbows

Velocity fps	Pipe size														
	1/2	3/4	1	1 1/4	1 1/2	2	2 1/2	3	3 1/2	4	5	6	8	10	12
1	1.2	1.7	2.2	3.0	3.5	4.5	5.4	6.7	7.7	8.6	10.5	12.2	15.4	18.7	22.2
2	1.4	1.9	2.5	3.3	3.9	5.1	6.0	7.5	8.6	9.5	11.7	13.7	17.3	20.8	24.8
3	1.5	2.0	2.7	3.6	4.2	5.4	6.4	8.0	9.2	10.2	12.5	14.6	18.4	22.3	26.5
4	1.5	2.1	2.8	3.7	4.4	5.6	6.7	8.3	9.6	10.6	13.1	15.2	19.2	23.2	27.6
5	1.6	2.2	2.9	3.9	4.5	5.9	7.0	8.7	10.0	11.1	13.6	15.8	19.8	24.2	28.8
6	1.7	2.3	3.0	4.0	4.7	6.0	7.2	8.9	10.3	11.4	14.0	16.3	20.5	24.9	29.6
7	1.7	2.3	3.0	4.1	4.8	6.2	7.4	9.1	10.5	11.7	14.3	16.7	21.0	25.5	30.3
8	1.7	2.4	3.1	4.2	4.9	6.3	7.5	9.3	10.8	11.9	14.6	17.1	21.5	26.1	31.0
9	1.8	2.4	3.2	4.3	5.0	6.4	7.7	9.5	11.0	12.2	14.9	17.4	21.9	26.6	31.6
10	1.8	2.5	3.2	4.3	5.1	6.5	7.8	9.7	11.2	12.4	15.2	17.7	22.2	27.0	32.0

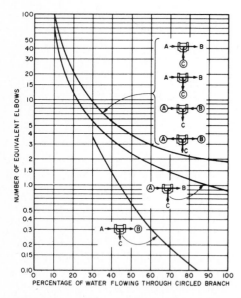

Iron and copper and elbow equivalents

Fitting	Iron pipe	Copper tubing
Elbow, 90-deg	1.0	1.0
Elbow, 45-deg	0.7	0.7
Elbow, 90-deg long turn	0.5	0.5
Elbow, welded, 90-deg	0.5	0.5
Reduced coupling	0.4	0.4
Open return bend	1.0	1.0
Angle radiator valve	2.0	3.0
Radiator or convector	3.0	4.0
Boiler or heater	3.0	4.0
Open gate valve	0.5	0.7
Open globe valve	12.0	17.0

this process with great frequency, and much time is required in checking and double checking input and in making computer reruns when errors are made and recognized.

Many designers take shortcuts in reducing the work of this laborious process. An experienced designer often, after studying the piping layout and measuring the "actual" developed length of the longest, most resistive circuit in the system, can intuitively ascribe a percentage to be added to the actual length to find the total equivalent length.

Other designers may design the HWH system layout and then size all piping. Then, with a few simple calculations, they can determine the mean (weighted average) pipe size, which falls somewhere near the midpoint of the range between the largest pipe size and the smallest. Using this mean pipe size and the mean water velocity similarly determined, a definite value can be resolved for the equivalent length of an elbow. All other fittings and system components can then be given a fixed value expressed in terms of feet of pipe equivalent length. Of course, the only really accurate method is the long, arduous method first described.

8-22 HWH SYSTEM DESIGN PROBLEM

To illustrate the foregoing concepts, the following HWH system design is detailed.

Example 8-3 Given:

1 The system is a two-pipe, reversed return system, as shown in fig. 8-6.
2 The heating devices consist of seven 10-MBH convectors on the first floor of a building and a year-around air conditioner on the second floor having a heating coil with a capacity of 200 MBH.
3 The highest point of the piping system, at the air conditioner, is 35 ft above the top of the boiler, which is also the elevation of the pressure-reducing valve and the PNPC near the boiler.
4 All piping is to be made of copper.
5 Boiler controls limit the supply water temperature to 225°F.
6 The design temperature drop through the system, Δt, is selected to be 30°F.
7 Piping is to be sized for a constant friction of 200 milinches of head loss per foot of pipe length. One milinch = 0.001 in. water; 200 milinches = 0.2 in. WG per foot of length.
8 The actual measured length of the pipe loop from the boiler along the supply main to the last heating device (convector) at point H is 370 ft. Also, the return main length from the first radi-

ator, point J, around the loop and back to the boiler is approximately the same length.
9 The pressure loss through the air conditioner coil is 4 ft of water head, and through its automatic valve is 6 ft of water head.

Solution

1 Calculate the hydrostatic pressure required in the system.

35 ft height of system ÷ 2.31 conversion factor = 15.15 psig required to fill the system to the top. Add ±5 psi to this for residual pressure at the top. Set the pressure reducing valve at the boiler for 15 psig + 5 psi = 20 psig.

2 Calculate the total heat load on the system and the required pump capacity in gpm.

Total load = 7 convectors × 10 MBH each = 70 MBH. Add a/c unit load of 200 MBH and total load = 270 MBH or 270,000 BH.

$$\text{Pump gpm} = \frac{270,000}{500 \times 30°F} = 18$$

3 Size all piping shown in fig. 8-6. Referring to fig. 8-23, the piping sizing chart for copper pipe, we find the horizontal 200-milinch line across the center of the chart. 200 milinches of water pressure drop per lineal foot of pipe = 0.2 in. WG = 0.01666 ft WG = 0.0072 psig (pressure drop per foot of pipe). The 200-milinch line has proven through the years to be a very practical basis for the design of HWH piping. Selections of pipe sizes have usually fallen in the range of 200 to 400 milinches of pressure loss per lineal foot of pipe, with the use today of 200 being a concession to the need to save energy through lower pumping cost. The table in fig. 8-25 shows a tabulation of the heat load on, and resulting GPM of water flow in, each section of the piping in the HWH system of fig. 8-6. For example, the section of supply main between reference letters D and E must carry enough hot water to supply the air conditioning unit and the last three convectors (heating devices) on the supply main. Their heat load totals

Figure 8-25 Pipe sizing table for piping in Fig. 8-6, example 8-3.

Pipe section	Heat load, BH	Water flow rate, gpm	Pipe size required, in.	Actual length, ft	Friction, mil inches/ft
Boiler to A	270,000	18	2	60	90
A to B	260,000	17 1/3	2	45	85
B to C	250,000	16 2/3	1 1/2*	40	240
C to D	240,000	16	1 1/2*	50	240
D to E	230,000	15 1/3	1 1/2*	50	220
E to F	30,000	2	3/4		
F to G	20,000	1 1/3	3/4		
G to H	10,000	2/3	1/2		
J to K	10,000	2/3	1/2		
K to L	20,000	1 1/3	3/4		
L to M	30,000	2	3/4		
M to N	40,000	2 2/3	1		
N to P	240,000	16	1 1/2*	55	240
P to Q	250,000	16 2/3	1 1/2*	30	250
Q to R	260,000	17 1/3	2	35	85
R to Boiler	270,000	18	2	55	100
Branch piping to convector	10,000	2/3	1/2		
Branch piping to air conditioner	200,000	13 1/3	1 1/2	30 ft X 2 = 60 ft	180

*Slightly undersized but the logical choice.

200, 10, 10, and 10 MBH, respectively = 230 MBH (or 230,000 BH).

This converts into 15.33 gpm as shown.

$$\text{gpm} = \frac{230,000 \text{ BH}}{500 \times 30°\text{F } \Delta t} = 15.33$$

On the chart of fig. 8-23, the point of the intersection of the vertical 15.33 gpm line and the horizontal 200 milinch line falls slightly to the right of the 1 1/2-in. pipe size line. This indicates that the 1 1/2-in. pipe size is slightly undersized, but so slightly that 1 1/2 in. is the logical choice. Remember that all the other pipe sizes selected in fig. 8-25 (except those marked with an asterisk) are larger than necessary, so that some slightly undersized piping is permissible.

4 Find the equivalent length of all the fittings, valves, and so on, in the system. In fig. 8-6 it is easy to see that the piping circuit with the greatest frictional resistance is the one from the boiler,

through the supply main to point E, through the air conditioning unit and back to the return main at point N, and then back to the boiler. This is true because the a/c unit and its control valve together have resistance of 4 ft + 6 ft = 10 ft of head loss. This 10 ft of head or pressure loss, in a system designed for 200 milinches per foot of pipe, is equal to the friction loss of head in 600 ft of straight pipe—(600 ft X 0.2 in./ft = 120 in. = 10.0 ft) (200 milinches per foot = 0.2 in./ft).

In fig. 8-25 it may be seen that all the piping in the above circuit is 1 1/2 in. and 2 in. in size. Also, in fig. 8-23, it may be seen that, at the flow rates in gpm shown in fig. 8-25, water velocities range between 24 and 30 in./sec. In fig. 8-24 it may be seen that the equivalent length of $1\frac{1}{2}$- and 2-in. elbows, with water velocities of 2 to 2.5 fps, averages about 4.5 ft.

In the pipe circuit through the a/c unit, the component equivalent lengths may be totaled as follows:

28 elbows at 4.5 ft	126.0
8 tees (with ± 84% flow straight through— lower curve of tee chart in fig. 8-24) × 0.1 × 4.5 ft (one tee = 0.1 elbow)	3.6
2 tees (with ±74% of flow in the side outlet) × 2.3 elbows/tee × 4.5 ft (see top curve of tee chart in fig. 8-24)	20.7
1 boiler at 4 elbows × 4.5 ft (see upper table in fig. 8-24)	18.0
5 gate valves open × 0.7 (fig. 8-24) × 4.5 ft (see upper table in fig. 8-24)	15.8
Total	184.1 ft

From fig. 8-25, the "actual" length of piping in the air conditioner circuit may be totaled at 480 ft (60 ft boiler to A + 45 ft A to B + 40 ft B to C + 50 ft C to D + 50 ft D to E + 60 ft branch piping to and from the air conditioner + 55 ft N to P + 30 ft P to Q + 35 ft Q to R + 55 ft R to boiler = 480 ft). Then the total equivalent length, including fittings, valves, etc. = 184.1 ft + 480 ft = 664.1 ft. This represents a pressure loss of 664.1 ft × 200 milinches/ft = 132.8 in. water. 132.8/12 = 11.07 ft water. Total pressure loss then = 11.07 ft + 6.0 ft loss in a/c unit automatic valve + 4.0 ft loss in a/c unit heating coil = 21.07 ft water.

The circulating pump, then, must be capable of circulating 18 gpm against a resistance of 21.07 ft water.

In the foregoing sample problem, a shortcut in the design procedure was taken by assuming an average pipe size in the most resistive circuit, and an average water velocity and friction loss per foot of pipe in this circuit. A more accurate, but much more laborious design process is sometimes used. This process involves evaluating each section of the pipe circuit, section by section, based on the actual length and the equivalent length of the fittings in each section. The author has solved this same sample HWH system design problem using the more detailed and laborious method. The total design pressure loss by this method was 20.54 ft water; this compares closely with the 21.07 ft water of the shorter method. The error here is less than 4%, and in the author's experience this error will always be small.

8-23 PIPE EXPANSION

The expansion and contraction of piping as it heats and cools can cause great difficulty if proper care and provision are not allowed for it. In a HWH system or steam heating system, piping systems are usually installed at outdoor temperatures, which may be as low as 20°F. When the heating system is later set into operation, its temperature may rise 200 or 300°F or more. Unless proper provision is made to allow for the resulting pipe expansion, tremendous forces can result, which can tear piping from its moorings or severely damage a building.

The easiest ways to solve the problems of pipe expansion are to build flexibility into piping systems with *pipe loops*, and, second, to use *expansion joints*. Both expansion loops and expansion joints are capable of absorbing the elongation of piping resulting from expansion, so that pipe stresses do not rise too high for safety.

Pipe loops are hairpin shaped or circular loops built into the piping at strategic locations. The piping system of fig. 8-6 includes hairpin loops located in a conventional fashion. It may be seen in fig. 8-6 that the loops are installed at the center of each long straight run of piping. It should also be noted that the piping is anchored at the ends of the long runs. At these anchor points (there are eight anchors indicated in fig. 8-6), the pipe is securely tied by means of welded flanges, brackets, and so on, to the rigid structure of the building, and providing points of "no movement" in the system. From these rigid points the pipe must expand toward the expansion loops, so that these flexible loops can accommodate the pipe movement.

With the piping expanding toward the loops, there is a tendency for the pipeline to "kick" off to one side, and most pipe support devices would not be strong enough to prevent this undesirable action. To hold the piping in proper alignment, it is provided with pipe *guides*, as shown near the loops in fig. 8-6. These guides, like the anchors, take many forms, but all of them are rigidly anchored to the building structure. They also loosely

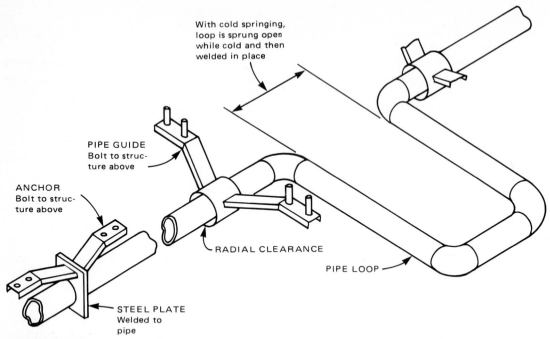

With cold springing,
loop is sprung open
while cold and then
welded in place

PIPE GUIDE
Bolt to struc-
ture above

ANCHOR
Bolt to struc-
ture above

RADIAL CLEARANCE

PIPE LOOP

STEEL PLATE
Welded to
pipe

Figure 8-26   Pipe loop, guide, and anchor details.

encircle the pipe in such a way that the pipe can expand and contract longitudinally, but cannot deflect laterally (see fig. 8-26).

Of course, when a pipe line is put into operation and becomes quite hot, its expansion does place a heavy stress in the fibers of the metal of the pipe, even if an expansion loop is used. This stress can be greatly reduced by a process of *cold springing* the loop outward before it is installed in a pipe line. After the loop is assembled, it is laid on the floor, and with a hydraulic jack, the loop is forced open a distance equal to about half the amount of the expected pipe expansion. A temporary prop is then tack welded in the loop to hold it open until it is assembled into its pipeline. Then the prop is removed. When the loop heats up during operation, the *cold stress* is first relieved and then a *hot stress* is applied, but this hot stress is much less than it would have been without cold springing.

In the foregoing process, the amount of the

expected pipe expansion must be determined. This may be done with the use of the formula

$$e = ab(\Delta t) \tag{8-1}$$

where e = pipe linear expansion, in.
a = coefficient of linear expansion, in./ft/$^\circ$ Δt
Δt = temperature change, $^\circ$F
b = length of the pipe run involved, ft

Values for a for various metals are:

Steel pipe: 0.000078 in./ft/$^\circ$ Δt
Wrought iron pipe: 0.0000816 in./ft/$^\circ$ Δt
Copper pipe: 0.0001116 in./ft/$^\circ$ Δt

as shown in the *1975 ASHRAE Handbook and Product Directory*.

Example 8-4   A 100-ft-long run of steel pipe which experiences a 100°F temperature increase will expand 0.78 in.

$$e = ab(\Delta t) = 0.000078 \times 100 \text{ ft}$$
$$\times 100° = 0.78 \text{ in.}$$

In designing a pipe loop, the centerline length L of the pipe in the loop, from the pipe main through the loop and back to the main but excluding fittings, may be found with the use of the formulas

For steel pipe: $L_s = 0.0544 \sqrt{d_o(\Delta t)b}$ (8-2)

For wrought iron:
$$L_w = 0.0556 \sqrt{d_o(\Delta t)b}   (8-3)$$

For copper: $L_c = 0.065 \sqrt{d_o(\Delta t)b}$ (8-4)

where L = pipe loop length exclusive of pipe fittings, ft

d_o = outside pipe diameter, in.

Δt = temperature change, °F

b = length of pipe run in which the loop is installed, ft

[Formulas (8-2), (8-3), and (8-4) are based on formula (4) in chap. 33 of the *1975 ASHRAE Equipment Handbook and Product Directory*.]

Example 8-5 In fig. 8-6 the length of the straight pipe run between points T and U is 120 ft, and the distance between the anchor points adjacent to points T and U is 110 ft. The mean pipe size in this run is 2 in. The pipeline is of steel; it was installed when ambient temperature was 40°F and will operate at a maximum temperature of 225°F. Find the required length of the pipe loop that will accommodate the expected pipe expansion, and limit fiber stresses to a tolerable value.

Using formula (8-2) for steel pipe, we obtain

$$L_s = 0.544 \sqrt{2.375(225°F - 40°F)110 \text{ ft}}$$
$$= 11.96 \text{ ft}   \text{(use 12 ft)}$$

where the outside diameter of 2.375 in. for 2-in. pipe was found in fig. 8-27. The amount of pipe expansion, sometimes called *traverse*, may be calculated using formula (8-1):

$$e = ab(\Delta t) = 0.000078 \times 110 \text{ ft}$$
$$(225°F - 40°F) = 1.59 \text{ in.}$$

A loop similar to the one shown in fig. 8-26 would be suitable in this case. The two straight sides between fittings could be 5 ft long, leaving a 2-ft straight length at the end of the loop; the total length exclusive of fittings (elbows) would then be 12 ft. The loop should be cold-sprung open before installation, an amount equal to half the expected traverse, approximately 0.8 in. (1.59 in. ÷ 2 = 0.795 in.).

8-24 EXPANSION JOINTS

In many installations of HWH and steam piping systems there is not adequate space in which to install pipe loops to absorb pipe expansion. Expansion loops do require a great amount of space, and when such is not available, a different type of expansion compensator called an *expansion joint* may be utilized.

As shown in fig. 8-28, expansion joints are flexible devices that may be mounted in a pipeline to absorb pipe expansion and to lengthen when pipe cools and contracts. There are many types of joints available, but in general they fall into two categories: the *packless* type and the *slip* type.

All those shown in fig. 8-28 are of the packless type. The slip type consists of two mating pieces, one of which can slide in and out of the other. It is installed in a pipeline with adjacent sections of pipe connected to the two halves of the joint. As the pipeline expands and contracts, this action results in relative movement within the joint. A packing material, either fibrous or semisolid, is tightly compacted into the annular space between the two mating halves to prevent leakage. This packing material does need repair and replacement, and because it does not require routine maintenance, the packless type is more popular.

In the packless type, the flexible bellows shown

Figure 8-27 Steel and copper pipe data. (Data from the 1975 *ASHRAE Handbook and Products Directory* with the permission of ASHRAE.)

Nominal pipe size† in.		Steel pipe data*					Copper pipe data			
	ASTM schedule‡	Outside diameter†	Inside diameter†	Volume, gal/ft	Weight per lin. foot, lb	Type	Outside diameter†	Inside diameter†	Volume, gal/ft	Weight per lin. foot, lb
1/4	40	0.540	0.364	0.00541	0.424	K	0.375	0.305	0.00379	0.145
	80	0.540	0.302	0.00372	0.535	L	0.375	0.315	0.00404	0.126
3/8	40	0.675	0.493	0.00992	0.567	K	0.500	0.402	0.00660	0.269
	80	0.675	0.423	0.00730	0.738	L	0.500	0.430	0.00753	0.198
1/2	40	0.840	0.622	0.0158	0.850	K	0.625	0.527	0.0113	0.344
	80	0.840	0.546	0.0122	1.09	L	0.625	0.545	0.0121	0.285
5/8						K	0.750	0.652	0.0174	0.418
						L	0.750	0.666	0.0181	0.362
3/4	40	1.050	0.824	0.0277	1.13	K	0.875	0.745	0.0227	0.641
	80	1.050	0.742	0.0225	1.47	L	0.875	0.785	0.0250	0.455
1	40	1.315	1.049	0.0449	1.68	K	1.125	0.995	0.0405	0.839
	80	1.315	0.957	0.0374	2.17	L	1.125	1.025	0.0442	0.655
1 1/4	40	1.660	1.380	0.0777	2.27	K	1.375	1.245	0.0634	1.04
	80	1.660	1.278	0.0666	3.00	L	1.375	1.265	0.0655	0.884
1 1/2	40	1.900	1.610	0.1058	2.72	K	1.625	1.481	0.0894	1.36
	80	1.900	1.500	0.0918	3.65	L	1.625	1.505	0.0925	1.14
2	40	2.375	2.067	0.174	3.65	K	2.125	1.959	0.157	2.06
	80	2.375	1.939	0.153	5.02	L	2.125	1.985	0.161	1.75
2 1/2	40	2.875	2.469	0.249	5.79	K	2.625	2.435	0.242	2.93
	80	2.875	2.323	0.220	7.66	L	2.625	2.465	0.247	2.48
3	40	3.500	3.068	0.384	7.57	K	3.125	2.907	0.345	4.00
	80	3.500	2.900	0.343	10.3	L	3.125	2.945	0.354	3.33
3 1/2	40	4.000	3.548	0.514	9.11	K	3.625	3.385	0.468	5.12
	80	4.000	3.364	0.462	12.5	L	3.625	3.425	0.478	4.29
4	40	4.500	4.026	0.661	10.8	K	4.125	3.857	0.607	6.51
	80	4.500	3.826	0.597	14.9	L	4.125	3.905	0.623	5.38
5	40	5.563	5.047	1.04	14.6	K	5.125	4.805	0.940	9.67
	80	5.563	4.813	0.945	20.8	L	5.125	4.875	0.971	7.61
6	40	6.625	6.065	1.50	18.0	K	6.225	5.741	1.35	13.9
	80	6.625	5.761	1.35	28.6	L	6.225	5.845	1.39	10.2
8	40	8.625	7.981	2.60	28.6	K	8.125	7.583	2.34	25.9
	80	8.625	7.625	2.37	43.4	L	8.125	7.725	2.43	19.3
10	30	10.750	10.130	4.19	34.2	K	10.125	9.449	3.65	40.3
	40	10.750	10.020	4.10	40.5	L	10.125	9.625	3.79	30.1
12	30	12.750	12.090	5.96	43.8	K	12.125	11.315	5.24	57.8
						L	12.125	11.565	5.45	40.4

*The data for wrought iron are approximately the same as for steel pipe except wall thicknesses are slightly heavier.

†Pipe sizes and diameters are in inches.

‡Schedule 40 is also known as standard weight and schedule 80 is extra heavy.

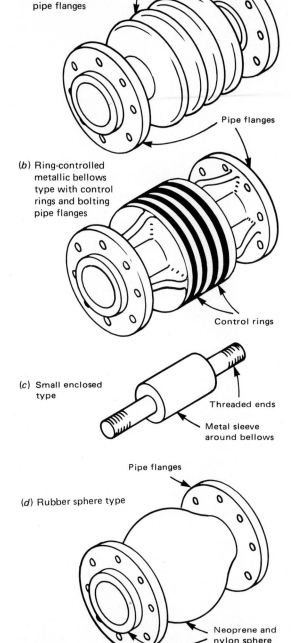

(a) Non controlled metallic bellows type with bolting pipe flanges

Flexible bellows

Pipe flanges

(b) Ring-controlled metallic bellows type with control rings and bolting pipe flanges

Control rings

(c) Small enclosed type

Threaded ends

Metal sleeve around bellows

Pipe flanges

(d) Rubber sphere type

Neoprene and nylon sphere

Figure 8-28 Expansion joints—packless type.

in fig. 8-28 is made of several different materials, such as stainless steel, copper, and nonmetallic materials such as neoprene. One type consists of a spherically shaped neoprene element reinforced with nylon.

The flexible bellows type is sometimes fitted with metallic control rings which fit into the convolutions of the bellows to prevent overstressing any one convolution to the point of material fatigue and failure.

Some expansion joints are externally fitted with a heavy metal sleeve to prevent centerline offset in the end connectors, and to prevent lateral buckling of the bellows. The small enclosed joint of fig. 8-28 is of this type; it is often installed in a long wall radiator of the type indicated in fig. 8-7. Here it is concealed behind the metal cover and relieves expansion stresses in the pipe of the wall radiator.

Expansion joints must be carefully and conservatively selected in accordance with the traverse ratings of their manufacturers. The small enclosed type of joint is generally available in pipe sizes from 3/4 to 3 in. The larger ring-controlled type is available in pipe sizes from 3 to 36 in. From the standpoint of cost, most mechanical contractors, if given a choice, will elect to install pipe loops in preference to expansion joints, where both are suitable.

8-25 PIPE INSULATION

Similar to ductwork, HVAC system piping is insulated for two purposes: to conserve energy and to prevent condensation. Energy is conserved when steam and hot water lines are insulated and kept hot, and when chilled water and cold refrigerant lines are insulated and kept cold. Condensation is prevented when cold pipelines are insulated to the extent that surface temperatures are raised to a point above the highest expected dew point temperature of the ambient air.

Many different types of materials are used for pipe insulating purposes; and there is no one material that is best for all insulating purposes. Some of these materials, together with their conductivities k at 40°F and 200°F (in that order) are:

Mineral wool (rock, slag, or glass)	0.22 and 0.27
Hair felt	0.27 at 40°F
Six-ply corrugated, laminated asbestos paper	0.59 at 200°F
Cellular glass	0.37 and 0.48
Cork	0.27 and 0.30
85% magnesia	0.42 at 200°F
Foamed plastic	0.26 at 40°F
Foamed rubber	0.23 at 40°F
Polyurethane	0.17 at 40°F
Polystyrene	0.25 at 40°F

In the incomplete list above, some materials are not suitable at both high and low temperatures and the conductivity at only one temperature is listed.

Space does not permit a full and exhaustive treatment of pipe coverings and a rational process of determining the most economical type and thickness to be used under varying conditions; the reader is referred to the *ASHRAE Handbook of Fundamentals* for this.

A rough approximation of the heat loss from a hot pipe or the heat gain into a cold pipe may be made by the following simple process:

1 Determine the heat flow resistance R of the insulation using formula (4-2), where

$$R = \frac{x}{k} = \frac{\text{insulation thickness}}{\text{insulation conductivity}}$$

and adding 0.68 for the still air film resistance.

2 Invert this total R to find the U coefficient.

3 Find surface area of the pipe insulation per lineal foot of pipe. The outside diameter of the pipe may be found in fig. 8-27; the OD of the insulation then is found by adding twice the insulation thickness to the pipe OD. The area of the covering per foot is then found by multiplying the diameter in feet by 3.1416.

4 The heat loss or gain is then found with formula (4-1): BH = $AU(\Delta t)$ after the Δt between

the air around the pipe and the fluid within the pipe is found.

Example 8-6 Find the heat loss from a 3 1/2-in. steel pipe carrying 270°F water in a 70°F room if the pipe is insulated with 2 in. of mineral wool insulation having $k = 0.27$.

Solution

$$\text{Insulation } R_T = \frac{2 \text{ in.}}{0.27} + 0.68 = 8.09$$

$$U = \frac{1}{8.09} = 0.124$$

Pipe OD = 4.0 in. from fig. 8-27

Covering OD = 4.0 in. + 2 in. + 2 in. = 8.0 in.

Covering area per linear foot
$$= 8 \text{ in.} \times 3.1416 \div 12 = 2.1 \text{ ft}^2$$

$\Delta t = 270°F - 70°F = 200°F$

Heat loss in BH per linear foot = $2.1 \times 0.124 \times 200°F = 52.1$. This 52.1 BH/ft loss is only a rough approximation, but is conservatively high.

One prevalent problem with pipe insulation is the cutting and damaging of the covering by the pipe hangers that support the pipe. Damaged pipe covering is a familiar sight to anyone who frequently visits boiler rooms and equipment rooms. Once the covering is cut, rapid deterioration of the covering seems to quickly follow.

Insulated pipelines that carry only hot fluids can be hung with a band iron pipe hanger fitting tightly around the pipe, and with the covering placed around and outside the hanger. The hanger rod that supports the band iron ring does perforate the covering at the top, but on heated lines this presents no problem. The hanger may be placed around the outside of the covering if it is not a soft, blanket-type material, and if a 16-gauge steel saddle, covering the bottom half of the insulation and about 4 pipe diameters long, is placed between the hanger and the covering. With a soft wool-type covering, a section of stronger covering material, such as cork or polyurethane, should be set in where each hanger occurs.

The latter procedure is mandatory for a pipeline that carries cold fluids. Such lines must have a vapor seal on the exterior of the covering and hangers must be on the outside of the sealed covering. If the covering is cut or damaged by pipe hangers, or if hanger rods perforate the covering, moisture will quickly enter the insulation and render it useless.

Cold pipe lines, like cold ducts, must have a type of insulation that is finished on the exterior with a high quality vapor barrier. Even if the surface temperature is above the dew point temperature of the surrounding air, without a vapor barrier, water vapor will pass through the covering and condense on the cold pipe. This water collects until the entire mass of the insulation is soaking wet and of no insulating value.

Moisture penetration can only be prevented by a high quality vapor barrier such as aluminum foil. All joints in the covering must be taped with a high quality tape. All pipe fittings must be fully surrounded by covering. All valves must be covered with only the operating handle or handwheel exposed. The vapor barrier on the entire cold pipe installation must be unbroken at any point.

8-26 ESTIMATING FUEL CONSUMPTION

A rough estimate of the fuel consumption for heating purposes in a building may be made with the use of the formula

$$F = \frac{BH(t_i - t_{ao})5088}{E(t_{id} - t_{od})H} \tag{8-5}$$

where F = units of fuel consumed per year
BH = calculated heat loss of building under design conditions, Btu/hr
t_i = indoor temperature maintained, °F

t_{ao} = average outdoor temperature during heating season, °F (see fig. 4-20 for guidance)
5088 = number of hours in heating season between October 1 and May 1 (if heating season is longer or shorter than this, substitute proper value)
E = overall fuel burning efficiency
t_{id} = indoor design temperature, °F
t_{od} = outdoor design temperature, °F (see fig. 4.20 for guidance)
H = heat content for each unit of fuel, Btu

In using formula (8-5) the units of F and H would usually be gallons when burning oil, pounds when burning coal, and cubic feet when burning gas. See the typical Btu content per unit of various fuels listed in art. 8-16.

Instantaneous fuel-burning efficiencies for gas and oil firing will, as mentioned previously, fall in the range 75 to 80%, and for coal, 65 to 70%. However, the overall combustion efficiencies over a heating season will not be this high, because of the low efficiency that prevails at the start of each burning cycle, because of radiation and convection losses from heating equipment to spaces that do not need heat, and because of draft losses of air passing through the boiler or furnace carrying heat up the chimney during burner off-cycles.

On the other hand, there are many things that help to heat buildings that do not require the consumption of fuel. These include the sun, lights, appliances, and people; these probably more than offset the reduced efficiencies mentioned and the standby losses. Therefore, the combustion efficiencies listed above are probably quite satisfactory for use in formula (8-5).

Example 8-7 A building in Montgomery, Alabama, has a calculated heat loss under design conditions of 650,000 BH. Its heating plant has a combustion efficiency of 75% and burns No. 2 fuel oil, which has a heat content of 135,000 Btu/gal. Indoor design temperature is 68°F, indoor maintained temperature is 71°F, and outdoor design temperature is 22°F. Find the estimated annual fuel consumption.

Solution Using formula (8-5) we see that all factors are given except t_{ao}, the average outdoor temperature. In the first page of the table of fig. 4-20, we see that for Montgomery, Alabama, t_{ao} is 55.4°F. Solving in formula (8-5) yields

$$F = \frac{650,000(71°F - 55.4°F)5088}{0.75(68°F - 22°F)135,000} = 11,077 \text{ gal}$$

PROBLEMS

8-1 An industrial building has a HTW heating system in it which has a heating capacity of 20,000,000 BH. If water is supplied to the system at 380°F and returned from the system at 250°F, what must be the pumping capacity, in gpm, of the circulating pumps?

8-2 What is the primary advantage of the reversed return in a reversed-return hot water heating system?

8-3 An outdoor thermostat controls boiler water temperature in a hot water heating system with a 2:1 ratio. If boiler water is 100°F when OA is 65°F, what will boiler water be when OA is 20°F?

8-4 A hot water heating system supply main is made of 3-in. schedule 40 steel pipe and is carrying hot water at a rate of 80 gpm. This main has an actual measured length of 140 ft and an equivalent length of 210 ft (allowing for fittings, valves, etc.). What is the pressure loss in this main in feet of water? Also, how much heat can this heating main supply, in MBH, if the system is designed for a temperature drop of 20°F?

8-5 In prob. 8-4, what is the water velocity in this main in fps, and what is the pressure drop that you calculated expressed in milinches of water. (Remember that 1 in. = 1000 milinches.)

8-6 Calculate the pumping resistance, in feet of head, of the one-pipe, main heating loop of fig. 8-3. The air conditioning unit and its venturi flow fitting have a total resistance of 5 ft of "head" and the convectors and radiators with their flow fittings have a resistance of 20 "ft of pipe." The flow control valve, *H*, has a flow resistance of 8 "ft of pipe." The size of the pipe main is 2 in. and it is of type L copper pipe with 30 gpm of water flowing in it. The actual length of 2-in. pipe in the main loop is 230 ft. The tee fitting near the air vent, *D*, in the return main near the boiler will have a resistance equivalent to two elbows.

8-7 Find the heat loss of 360 ft of 3-in. steel steam pipe covered with a 1-in. thickness of foamed plastic insulation. Steam temperature is 215°F, and ambient temperature is 65°F.

Chapter 9

Steam Heating Systems

9-1 GENERALITIES

For many generations, steam heating systems have been one of the most popular of all systems used to heat buildings, both residential and nonresidential. More often than not, steam heating systems consisted of cast iron radiators connected by piping to coal-fired steam-generating boilers.

Steam is still used to a very great extent to heat new buildings. However, the old cast iron radiator system has all but faded from the scene, and coal as a fuel is severely limited—although making somewhat of a resurgence because of the shortage of oil and gas today. Steam is used very extensively, although as an intermediary medium in the heating coils of year-round HVAC systems; and as such is providing the heat for a high percentage of today's new buildings.

In colder climates, perimeter steam radiation is still used extensively to offset cold wall and win-

dow effect, even though hot water is finding greater popularity for this purpose. There are some real disadvantages to the use of steam in perimeter systems, and other steam systems that require the installation of steam pipe lines throughout a building. Steam and accompanying condensate lines must usually be installed with a constant downward pitch, in the direction of flow, to permit drainage of water in the lines. This, as we shall see, involves many awkwardnesses and special equipment (lift pockets, lift traps, and pumps).

Steam systems require steam traps at many locations to drain condensed steam (water) from equipment and piping; hot water systems have nothing comparable. Steam traps are unsightly, often noisy, and require much maintenance—definite disadvantages. Also, steam distribution systems are very often noisy, especially during periods of startup, when a swiftly moving steam comes into contact with water of condensation in pipelines and radiators. This noise is called *water hammer;* it can be very loud and disturbing to building occupants.

Therefore, in today's new buildings we find steam limited to the task of heating the heating coils in HVAC units and outside air tempering coil installations and in unit heaters. However, at performing these tasks, steam does excel; no other heating medium can quite compare in these functions. Since more and more the heating loads of modern buildings are being carried by heating coils, we can expect steam systems to enjoy continued popularity through many years to come.

Of course, steam will continue to find great use in industry for industrial processes of many, many types. Where steam is thus available, we will continue to find steam utilized in *steam-to-water convertors* which will generate hot water for heating purposes.

9-2 CLASSIFICATION OF STEAM HEATING SYSTEMS

Steam heating systems are of many types and may be classified in many different ways. In broad categories, they may be classified as one-pipe systems or two-pipe systems, or as gravity return systems or pumped return systems. With regard to steam pressure they may also be classified as high-pressure, low-pressure, vapor, or vacuum systems. A more detailed listing of these follows:

1 Gravity return systems
2 One-pipe systems
3 Two-pipe high-pressure systems
4 Two-pipe low-pressure systems
5 Two-pipe vapor systems
6 Two-pipe vacuum systems

In general, *high pressure* means steam pressure in excess of 15 psig; however, in high-pressure systems, the supply steam pressure is usually in the range of 30 to 150 psig. *Low pressure* means steam supply pressures between 0 and 15 psig. The steam pressure in a *vapor* system will usually vary from

slightly above 0 psig to slightly below zero. *Vacuum* systems pressures will usually vary from slightly above zero to a vacuum as great as 5 to 25 in. of mercury (5 in. Hg vacuum = −2.45 psig or 12.25 psia).

9-3 GRAVITY RETURN SYSTEMS

When steam, generated in a boiler or other device, leaves the boiler and passes out into the piping system, an equal weight of condensate (condensed steam) must return to the boiler to maintain an adequate level of water in the boiler. A boiler can quickly overheat and suffer damage if some of the heated surfaces of the boiler are not backed up by, or in direct contact with water. Therefore, the prompt, positive return of condensate at a rate equal to the steam departure rate is mandatory. The method by which condensate is returned is important.

In gravity return systems, condensate returns by its own weight back into the boiler, as shown in fig. 9-1. There is no pump or other device to cause the condensate to return, only its own weight as the level of the condensate in the return line builds up above the level of the water in the boiler; and this is the critical design feature of a gravity return system.

The steam leaves the boiler at a pressure which in this type of system is usually quite low—less than 5 psig, but more often than not, at 1 or 2 psig. Of course, as the steam flows through its piping, heating devices, and so on, and as the condensate flows through its piping, traps, and so on, there is pressure drop. It is not possible to have flow without pressure drop. If, for example, boiler pressure is 2 psig, with normal line pressure loss (and with some small pressure regain as the condensate falls downward in the return piping) the pressure at the top of the water column in the return main may be 0.5 psig. This is 1.5 psi pressure less than is in the boiler.

For the condensate to return into the boiler against this pressure disadvantage, its level must build upward in the return main (see the enlarged

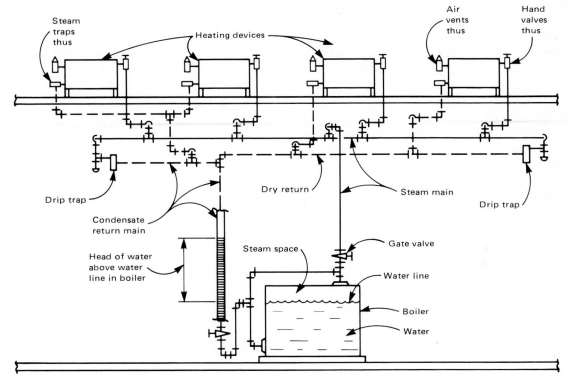

Figure 9-1 Gravity return system.

section of the return main in fig. 9-1) until its height above the boiler water line offsets and overcomes the pressure differential. In this example the height, or head, in feet must equal 2 - 0.5 psig = 1.5 psi. Since 2.31 ft of water equals 1.0 psi, the height above the water line must equal 1.5 psi × 2.31 = 3.47 ft.

The designer must calculate and anticipate what the height of this return line water column will be, and be certain that the building provides this amount of vertical space. It has happened too many times that the boiler room ceiling is too low, that the boiler is too tall, that the pressure drop through the system is too great (resulting from too small piping), and that, as a result, the top of the return line water column rises clear up into the heating devices (radiators, convectors, etc.), impairing their function. The system is then a failure.

9-4 ONE-PIPE SYSTEMS

As the name implies, one-pipe systems use only one pipe to carry the steam to the heating devices and to return the water to the boiler. Steam and condensate flow in opposite directions in the same pipe requiring steam velocities to be very low and pipe sizes accordingly great. The system diagrammed in fig. 9-1 is a two-pipe system with steam carried in one part of the system and separate piping provided for the return of condensate. The one-pipe system does not have this separation of piping.

One-pipe systems are rarely used today, and have not been installed to any appreciable extent in new buildings for many years. Further discussions on steam heating systems will be limited to two-pipe systems.

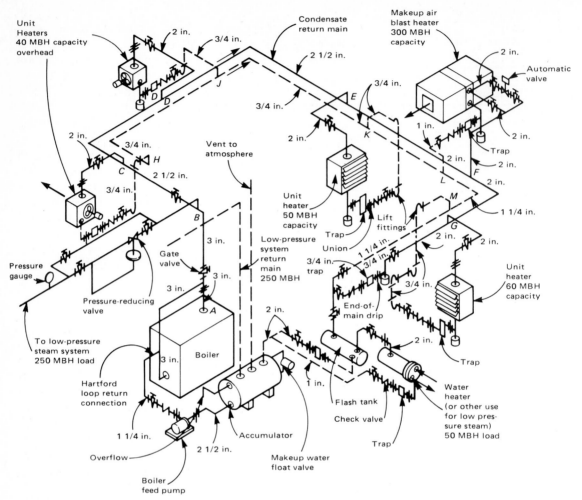

Figure 9-2 Typical high pressure steam system.

9-5 TWO-PIPE HIGH-PRESSURE SYSTEMS

High-pressure steam systems, characterized by steam pressures over 15 psig (usually in the range of 30 to 150 psig) are found mostly in industrial situations where high-pressure steam is required in manufacturing processes. In this case the high-pressure steam is also used directly for building heating purposes, usually in large, open manufacturing areas where noise levels, air movement levels, and temperature control requirements are not critical. However, it is more likely that the high-

pressure steam would be used for heating water for a hot water heating system, or it might be reduced in pressure for low-pressure steam heating.

Figure 9-2 is representative of a high-pressure steam system. Here it is not necessary for the condensate return main to be installed below the heating devices (unit heaters), but may be located overhead where it would be out of the way of manufacturing machines. There is usually an appreciable difference between the pressures of the steam main and the return main, so that it is practical to lift the condensate from the outlet of the heating devices upward and into the overhead return main.

If permissible, the return main may, however, be located below the heating devices. In this case, the *lift fittings* shown in fig. 9-2 would not be required. Lift fittings just provide dips in the pipeline, which facilitate the process of gathering the water of condensation together so that it may be pushed upward into the return main above. Notice that lift fittings are used at bottom and top of a vertical lift section of pipe.

The condensate in the return lines of a high-pressure system, while at a pressure appreciably lower than the steam pressure, will be much above atmospheric pressure, and at a temperature much above atmospheric pressure boiling point ($\pm 212°F$). It has been found practical to reduce its pressure and temperature before attempting to pump it back into the boiler. This reduces the possibility of the condensate *flashing* back into steam at the boiler feed pump inlet connection, which must not happen, and it facilitates the process of removing air from the condensate before returning it to the boiler.

As shown in fig. 9-2, the condensate return line is connected into a *flash tank,* which is maintained at lower pressure. Here the high-pressure condensate expands, a small part of it flashes into low-pressure steam, and the remainder is cooled in the process. The low-pressure steam may be delivered into a nearby low-pressure steam main, if such exists, or it may be used as shown to heat domestic water or for any other purpose that will conserve its heat energy.

The cooled condensate in the flash tank then flows by gravity into an accumulator tank which is vented to atmosphere. The accumulator will also usually receive other condensate from other steam systems in the building, as shown.

9-6 TWO-PIPE LOW-PRESSURE SYSTEMS WITH AND WITHOUT CONDENSATE PUMP

As set forth above, low-pressure steam systems are characterized by steam pressures at the boiler nozzle (outlet connection) in the range of 0 to 15

psig. A two-pipe system, of course, has separate steam supply and condensate return piping. Figure 9-1 is diagrammatically typical of a two-pipe low-pressure system with gravity return piping. Two-pipe low-pressure systems may have gravity returns, or may have pumped returns which utilize a condensate pump unit.

In the gravity return system of fig. 9-1, the boiler pressure must be kept quite low, perhaps 1.0 or 2.0 psig. If boiler pressure were higher, 14 psig, for example, and if the convention of designing the steam supply system to have a pressure drop 25 to 50% of the boiler pressure were followed, the system would be unworkable. At light load, the water column in the return main, necessary to overcome the boiler pressure and permit condensate to return, would need to be 20 to 30 ft high. The building would probably not accommodate this; therefore, a condensate return pump of some type would be required.

Condensate pumps, as shown in fig. 9-3, consist of a cast iron receiver (tank), maintained at atmospheric pressure, into which the condensate from the return piping system can easily flow. In the receiver, any entrained air separates from the water and vents out into the atmosphere. When the water level in the receiver rises to a certain height, an electric float switch starts the pump. The pump is a centrifugal type of pump which can return the condensate into the boiler even though boiler pressure may be comparatively high.

Condensate pumps are usually located in the boiler room near the boiler; however, that is not mandatory, and they may be located anywhere in the building where the condensate can be directed into them. In long, rambling buildings, condensate pumps may be located hundreds of feet from the boiler, and greatly facilitate the installation of the steam and return piping. In fact, in such extremely long buildings, the two-pipe low-pressure steam system would hardly be practical without some type of condensation pumps remotely located.

In the light of present-day heating practices, it would seem that the conventional steam heating system, which supplies steam to a great number of small heating devices (convectors, radiators, etc.)

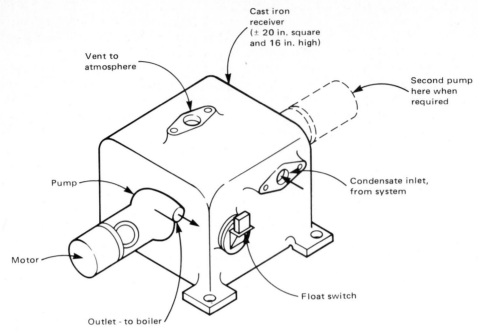

Figure 9-3 Condensate pump.

located around the perimeter of buildings and carrying the full heating load of the building, is a thing of the past, and will rarely be seen in buildings of the future. Certainly, supplementary perimeter radiation of many types, especially wall radiators (see fig. 8-7), will continue in use in colder climates to offset cold wall and window effect. In the main, however, these radiation systems will be supplied with hot water and not steam. The likelihood is great, though, that that water will be heated in a steam convertor similar to those shown in fig. 8-15.

In general, most of the heating load in nonresidential buildings of the future will be carried by central station air conditioning units which include steam and hot water heating coils. Steam will certainly perform its share of this work with mostly two-pipe low-pressure steam systems in use.

9-7 TWO-PIPE VAPOR SYSTEMS

Two-pipe vapor systems are gravity return systems as diagrammed in fig. 9-1, which are characterized by steam supply pressures that vary from a low positive pressure to a vacuum. The piping and all equipment and accessories are very carefully installed so as to be leakproof and able to maintain a vacuum when operating conditions require that.

In low-pressure steam heating systems, radiators and other heating devices are equipped with air vents by means of which air in the device may be purged or permitted to escape when steam enters and fills the device. These air vents are of two-way design, so that, when steam flow is stopped and the heating device cools and the steam in the device condenses, air returns through the vents and breaks the vacuum that otherwise would form. Therefore, the pressure throughout the system never falls below atmospheric pressure.

In vapor systems, the air vents that are installed on radiators and other heating devices, as well as elsewhere, are of one-way design. Air can escape through these vents to atmosphere, but a check valve in the air vent prevents air return as heating devices cool. Therefore, a vacuum will be developed throughout the system when outdoor weather moderates and the demand for steam diminishes, and the boiler firing rate is reduced.

One big advantage of this is that as system steam pressure falls into a vacuum, the boiling point of the water in the boiler falls, and the steam that circulates may be well below the atmospheric boiling point of 212°F. In fact, it may fall below 150°F. Heated spaces in the building can be much more easily controlled if steam temperatures are low when heat requirements are low.

9-8   TWO-PIPE VACUUM SYSTEMS

In the vacuum system, a vacuum heating pump is installed to maintain a subatmospheric pressure in all of the condensate return piping at all times. Pressure controls are mounted on the vacuum

pump to operate the pump in such a manner as to maintain a vacuum, or negative pressure, of about 5 to 6 in. of mercury (Hg) at all times (6 in. of Hg vacuum is equal to -2.95 psig or 11.75 psia) (see fig. 9-4).

In most vacuum heating systems, the steam supply piping is kept at a modest, positive pressure, slightly above atmospheric pressure, and only the return piping carries a vacuum. However, in some proprietary systems, both the supply and return piping systems operate under subatmospheric pressure when outdoor weather is mild. When positive steam pressures are maintained, temperature control is achieved by regulating the flow of steam into the heating devices or by the action of face-and-bypass dampers on heating coils. In the sub-atmospheric systems, the primary means of control

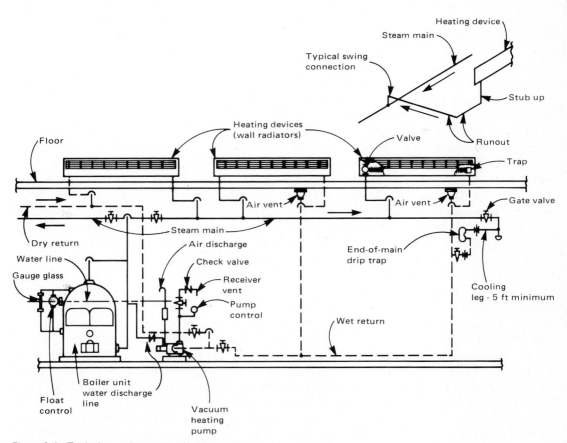

Figure 9-4   Typical two-pipe vacuum heating system.

is by regulating the boiler fuel burner action so as to proportion steam supply pressure to the severity of the winter weather. Secondary temperature control may then be achieved with modulating steam valves, face-and-bypass dampers, and so on. In some vacuum heating systems, the return line vacuum may greatly exceed the 5 to 6 in. Hg mentioned above; at times this may be as much as 25 in. Hg. The piping installations, under such operating conditions, must be exceedingly well installed and leakproof or the inward leakage of air will be a serious problem.

The vacuum heating pump unit looks very much like the condensate pump of fig. 9-3. It has a cast iron or steel receiver tank to which condensate, air, and noncondensible gases are returned. The pressure in this tank, of course, is maintained well below atmospheric pressure, and to rid the system of air and noncondensible gases, these must be pumped out against the ambient pressure. The motor-driven pump has this capability of pumping air and gases out to atmosphere while at the same time pumping the water of condensation back into the boiler. In the receiver, the water and gases separate so that they can be pumped separately.

In some vacuum heating pump units, the water pump is completely separate from the pump that ejects the gases, but in other units, one pump can handle both. In fig. 9-3, the condensate pump shown is a *simplex* unit; that is, it has only one pump. However, where great dependability is required, the unit will be fitted with two pumps, in which case it is a *duplex* unit. Vacuum heating pump units may also be either simplex or duplex. In duplex units, either of the two pumps can usually carry the heating load by itself. Therefore, if one pump suffers a mechanical or electrical failure, the remaining pump can continue on without heating system interruption.

More often than not, a duplex vacuum heating pump unit will be equipped with a mechanical or electrical *alternator*. The alternator will start alternate pumps on alternate pumping cycles so that the pumping load is carried equally by both pumps. However, some designers prefer to let one pump

carry the load while the remaining pump is left idle and used only enough to keep it in good operating condition. The second pump is then kept in like-new condition. The latter idea has much to recommend it; however, a majority of designers prefer the first method of control.

In vacuum heating systems, there is always an appreciable pressure difference between the steam supply mains and the return mains—made certain by the action of the vacuum pump. Thus it is possible, where desirable, to *lift* condensate out of a heating device and up into a return main located above the device. As indicated in fig. 9-2, where condensate is lifted upward, it is well to use lift fittings at the bottom and top of the lift leg. Lift fittings are merely U-shaped devices in which water can collect. Where the amount of lift is over 5 ft, two lift legs, or sections, should be utilized with a lift fitting at top and bottom of each leg. Lift legs should be separated by a horizontal section of pipe 18 to 24 in. long. Lift fittings may be satisfactorily fabricated in the field using standard pipe fittings. Of course, condensate lifts should be avoided if possible.

9-9 STEAM AND CONDENSATE PIPING

Most steam and condensate piping systems are fabricated out of schedule 40 black steel pipe; see the table in fig. 8-26. To a limited extent, type L copper, or type K if buried in the earth, is used. In condensate return lines, water and air are routinely carried and a more corrosive condition exists than in the steam supply lines. Often wrought iron pipe (presumably less corrodible than steel) and copper or brass pipe are used in return lines, especially if they are buried or somehow inaccessible for replacement.

In steel and wrought iron pipe lines, the necessary fittings (tees, elbows, etc.) are made of cast iron or malleable iron where fittings are threaded. In larger sizes of 6 in. and over, pipelines are usually welded to their fittings, which are of butt-weld type. When copper pipe is utilized, fittings are usually of the forged copper type soldered in place with silver solder or other high-fusing-temperature solder.

Horizontal pipelines carrying steam and condensate must always pitch downward in the direction that any condensate is flowing. In some cases, condensate must flow in steam lines in a direction opposite to the steam flow, and the pipe sizes must be increased until steam velocities are low enough to permit the condensate to pass. In most steam piping drawing layouts, arrows are drawn beside the pipelines; these arrows indicate condensate flow direction and not necessarily the direction of steam flow.

In straight runs of piping, most steam and condensate lines pitch downward at the rate of 1 in. in 40 ft. In branch connections from pipe mains to *stub-ups* and *risers,* any horizontal piping should pitch at the rate of 1/2 in./ft. Branch connections from steam and condensate mains usually consist of a *runout* and a stub-up to a heating device (see the small, separate detail in fig. 9-4) or a runout and a riser to an upper or lower floor(s).

The runout should include three or four 90° elbows to give an L or Z shape to the runout for flexibility (see fig. 9-4). The stub-up or the riser which the runout feeds is usually fixed in position in the building, while the mains are moving because of expansion and contraction. Branch connections must therefore provide flexibility, and the configuration shown for the runouts provides this. This type of branch connection is called a *swing connection.* With regard to expansion and contraction in steam and condensate piping, the same problems and their solutions pertain here as in hot water heating piping; the reader is referred to the discussion on this subject in chap. 8.

In steam mains, especially those that carry steam at somewhat higher pressures, the condensate that regularly forms flows along with the steam to the end of the main, and there it must be drained away. The facility at the end of the steam main is called an *end-of-main* (EOM) *drip.* As shown in figs. 9-4 and 9-2, this EOM drip consists of a vertical turn down at the end with a removable pipe cap for cleaning purposes. At the midpoint of

the turned-down end of the main, a horizontal pipe takes off and runs to a steam trap. This horizontal pipe is called the *cooling leg* and should be 5 ft or more in length to permit the condensate to cool somewhat before it passes through the trap. If it remains at the steam temperature, it may flash back into steam in the condensate return piping as its pressure is reduced. This is undesirable for many obvious reasons. Notice that the end-of-main drip is preceded and followed by gate valves which can be closed when the trap requires service or replacement.

In fig. 9-4 it may be seen that there are two return mains which return condensate to the vacuum heating pump; one of these is labeled *wet return* and the other is labeled *dry return.* As may be guessed, a wet return is one that runs its length below the water line of the boiler, while a dry return is mounted above the boiler water line. This nomenclature is more applicable to gravity return systems, as shown in fig. 9-1, but its use carries over to all types of steam systems. Wet returns run full of water and, as a result, have more capacity for a given pipe size than dry returns, which must carry both water and air (and other noncondensible gases). Branch return lines which drop down into a wet return main should be vented at the top, before they drop, with automatic air vents as shown in fig. 9-4.

As a steam main runs outward from the boiler area toward its end, the heating load is reduced as branch connections are made to various heating devices. As the load on the main is reduced, the size of the main is reduced also. These pipe size reductions may be made with a reducing tee at a branch connection or with a reducing coupling downstream from the branch connection. It is important that such pipe size reductions are made with *eccentric* fittings so installed that the bottom of the main continues in a straight line. Condensate in the line can then flow continuously downward in the sloping main with no water pockets formed.

Pipeline strainers should be used throughout steam piping systems just upstream from all equipment, such as automatic steam valves and steam humidifier nozzles, where foreign matter might collect in small openings, orifices, and valve seats and cause operational difficulties. Especially when such piping systems are new, there is a problem with foreign matter such as metal chips and pipe dope moving along with the steam and lodging in these small openings.

Strainers are cleanable and have a fine screen through which the steam must flow. Notice that in fig. 9-5, strainers are shown just ahead of the automatic steam valves included in that detail. Gate

valves are also shown ahead of and behind these automatic valves to facilitate their service and replacement when necessary; the strainers should also be located between these isolating gate valves. Many designers also locate pipe line strainers ahead of all steam traps; this practice has much to recommend it.

Sometimes in steam piping systems of considerable length and complexity, a problem is experienced in getting the proper amount of steam to flow to all parts of the system. The tendency is for

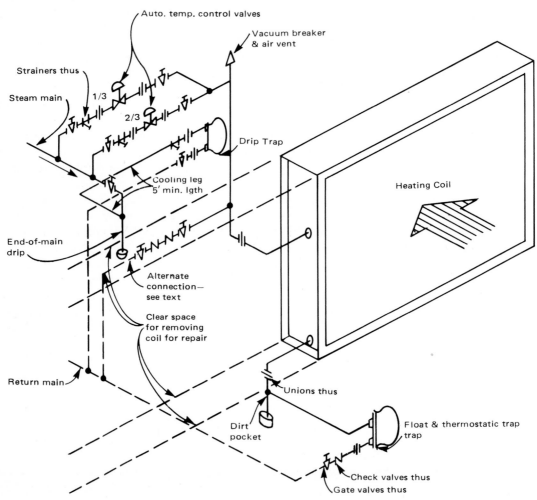

Figure 9-5 Typical heating coil installation details in low pressure steam systems.

heating devices nearest the boiler to receive more steam than required while more remote devices do not receive enough.

One solution to the foregoing problem in systems where the return line pressure can be fairly well stabilized (as with an automatically controlled vacuum heating pump) is to use graduated steam orifices at heating device inlets. The orifices are brass disks or cup-shaped pieces often fitted into the outlet connection of a radiator valve. The orifices have accurately sized holes in them that range in size from approximately 1/8 to 5/16 in. in diameter.

With each heating device fitted with the proper orifice, and with the return line pressure (or vacuum) automatically stabilized, the heating capacity of all heating devices can be closely regulated by accurately controlling steam supply pressure. With such a system, all heating devices can be expected to have adequate steam pressure at the orifice inlets, unless boiler capacity is inadequate. Where a steam distribution system is long and rambling in large buildings, with many long branch systems of unequal length, steam distribution can be materially improved with the installation of orifices in each branch main.

The specification and selection of steam orifices should be left to the manufacturers of these items, who are experts in such practices.

9-10 HEATING COIL CONNECTIONS

Heating coils in a/c (air conditioning) units will surely play a big part in our HVAC systems of the future. Their installation, as shown in fig. 9-5, is quite simple, and yet there are a few precautions that must be taken to assure successful performance. Heating coils will probably be found, in most cases, connected to two-pipe low-pressure systems, and fig. 9-5 is drawn with that type of system in mind. However, two-pipe high-pressure systems will surely be used often for this purpose also; fig. 9-5 is essentially correct for high-pressure steam except that steam traps would probably be of the high-pressure bucket type.

Notice that in fig. 9-5 there are two automatic temperature control valves to regulate the flow of steam into the coil. One large valve could be used here, but a large valve has great difficulty in accurately controlling steam flow at light load. With such a valve at light load the valve seat is so slightly open that even a very minute movement in the valve stem can cause a 50% increase in steam flow, which would surely be too much. Now, the valve must try to close a little and probably will close completely for a moment. The valve will thus continuously "hunt" open and shut and never find a stable position until demand for steam increases and the valve opens appreciably wider.

With a two-valve installation, as shown, one valve may be sized for one-third of the load and the other for two-thirds of the load. The larger valve closes first on falling demand leaving the smaller valve to carry the light load. This it can probably do in a fairly open position with little tendency to "hunt."

If only one valve is utilized, it should be installed with a *three-valve bypass.* Here a gate valve is installed at the inlet to the automatic valve and at the outlet also. A third valve is installed in a pipe bypass around the automatic valve. This three-valve configuration would allow the first two valves to be closed for service, removal, and replacement of the automatic valve while keeping the steam pressure up in the steam heating system. The third valve can then be manually operated to keep the heating coil in operation while the service to the automatic valve is being performed. With only one automatic valve the three-valve bypass is usually mandatory.

With the two-valve installation shown in fig. 9-5, either automatic valve may be removed for service with automatic operation continuing. The cost of this installation is little more than the cost of the large valve with the three-valve bypass.

Another problem that arises with a heating coil installation is that a heavy vacuum may be developed inside a coil when the steam flow stops and the airflow across the coil continues. In this case, the steam remaining in the coil quickly condenses when the automatic valves close and the vacuum develops. Any condensate remaining in the coil is held in the coil by the vacuum. If very cold air is passing over the coil, the condensate may freeze in the coil and rupture the coil tubes.

If water is thus held in a coil, and a steam valve opens quickly, a serious problem with water hammer in the coil can result. Again, the coil could be seriously damaged. The simple, inexpensive cure for these problems is the installation of a *vacuum breaker,* as shown in fig. 9-5. The vacuum breaker opens and admits air into the coil when a slight vacuum develops. The vacuum is then broken and the condensate can drain from the coil. When steam returns to the pipeline, the vacuum breaker closes.

Some designers are reluctant to permit air to enter the piping system as it does through a vacuum breaker. Air does promote corrosion in the system and may in some situations restrict the flow of steam and condensate. An alternative solution to the problem of water retention in a heating coil takes the form of a bypass connection between the top of the return main and the coil inlet piping; see the alternate connection in fig. 9-5.

Notice that this connection has two check valves in it; these permit flow only toward the coil. Because check valves are so prone to leak, two check valves should be used and these should be preceded and followed by gate valves for service and repair purposes.

When a vacuum builds within the coil, air and other gases will now flow from the return main to break that vacuum and the condensate held within the coil can drain away.

Although occurrences where a heating coil is damaged are rare, the possiblity of this should always be kept in mind. A clear space should always be maintained at one end or the other of a heating coil so that it can easily be disconnected and slid out of the a/c unit for repair or replacement. Of course, cooling coils require the same consideration. As shown in fig. 9-5, coil pipe connections must be such that pipe unions can be opened and the coil quickly freed. As shown, connecting piping must elbow out of the way to facilitate coil removal.

If a heating coil is to be exposed, even infrequently, to subfreezing temperatures, a new set of problems involved with coil freeze-up arises. If an ordinary heating coil is carrying subfreezing air, and the steam valves are only slightly open, as they often will be, there is not enough steam entering the coil to keep the entire coil hot. The reduced flow of steam may keep only one-fourth or one-third of the coil warm, the remainder of the coil may very likely be below freezing, and the condensate in that portion of the coil will freeze and damage the coil.

The use of *nonfreeze, steam distributing tube* coils will largely eliminate this problem. This type of coil is made with tubes that contain smaller perforated tubes within them. The steam enters through the inner tubes; in each tube it then passes through the open end and the perforations into the annular space between the two tubes. The steam then flows back the length of the outer tube, condensing as it goes, to the coil outlet. By this means, whatever steam is flowing is well distributed throughout the coil. It is well, in this situation, to install a contact thermostat on the condensate line at the coil outlet. This thermostat, set for about 40°F, would be connected either to stop the a/c unit fan or to open the steam valve if the return line temperature falls too low.

Another type of safety thermostat for use here is one that has a temperature sensitive bulb which is about 20 ft long. This 20-ft bulb is installed so as to be a few inches from the "leaving air" side of the coil, being bent so as to cover as much of the coil as possible. Whenever subfreezing air from the coil touches any part of this 20-ft-long sensitive bulb, the thermostat initiates some type of protective action.

Face-and-bypass dampers are also sometimes used with coils that are subject to freezing. Steam is permitted to enter such coils freely without the control of an automatic valve. Temperature control is achieved by the action of the face-and-bypass dampers, permitting only the correct amount of air to pass through the coil while the remainder is bypassed. In this case, the entire coil is hot at all times. One precaution must be observed here. If the dampers are not of high enough quality to achieve 98% tight shutoff, the leakage of air through the face dampers and through the hot coil may cause overheating. In this case a high limit thermostat controlling a steam valve may be required.

9-11 STEAM TRAPS

Steam traps perform the vitally important function of providing the points of separation between the steam piping system and the condensate return system. As the name implies, steam traps trap the steam and prevent it from passing. They do this, in general, utilizing two types of equipment: thermostatic devices and float-operated devices.

Thermostatic traps have flexible metallic elements such as copper or brass bellows with a charge of a volatile fluid sealed within. Another is the thermostatic disk, which again is metallic, approximately 1 1/2 in. diameter, 3/8 in. high, hollow, and filled with a sealed charge of volatile fluid. These metallic elements are mounted in a cast metal enclosure with the tops of the elements secured rigidly to the enclosure top and with the bottom free to move up and down (see fig. 9-6a and b). The bottom of the thermostatic disk is fitted with a tapered valve piece. When steam from the heating device enters the trap, it heats the disk and the volatile fluid inside the disk expands. The disk then also expands and the valve piece moves down into the valve seat closing the outlet opening. The steam in the trap then cools and condenses, the valve piece rises, the outlet opens, and the condensate in the trap flows out into the condensate return main.

The *float-operated trap* is a very simple piece of equipment in which a float ball in a float chamber is secured to a hinged float arm and a valve piece is secured to the arm. When the float rises as condensate fills the trap chamber, the valve piece is pushed away from its valve seat. The valve is thus opened and the condensate flows out into the return main. As the condensate level falls, the float lowers and the valve piece closes the seat. The valve seat is always submerged with water so that steam cannot escape into the condensate return piping (see fig. 9-6d).

One problem with the float trap is that air that enters the trap cannot escape, and the trap may become "air bound" so that condensate cannot escape. Many float traps are equipped with a thermostatic disk with valve piece and seat similar to that shown in fig. 9-6c. The disk, valve piece, and seat are mounted near the top of the float chamber, well above the water level. When steam contacts the disk, the valve closes; but when air enters the float chamber, the disk cools and the valve opens. The air is then pushed out through a short passage in the trap body to the trap outlet opening. This trap is logically called a *float and thermostatic trap* and is often referred to as an F & T trap. For general steam heating usage the F & T trap is used much more than any other type except on small heating devices such as radiators, convectors, and so on, where the thermostatic trap is the universal standard.

Another popular type of trap shown in fig. 9-6e is the open bucket type in which a small upright metal bucket floats on the condensate in the float chamber. When condensate rises high enough, it overflows into the bucket which then sinks and opens a valve. The valve is mounted in the bottom end of a metal tube which extends down to a point near the bottom of the open bucket, inside the bucket. When this valve opens, steam pressure pushes the condensate upward and out of the bucket until it floats upward on the surrounding condensate and closes the valve. Bucket traps are often used on high pressure steam systems. Figure 9-6f shows an inverted bucket trap with similar operating characteristics.

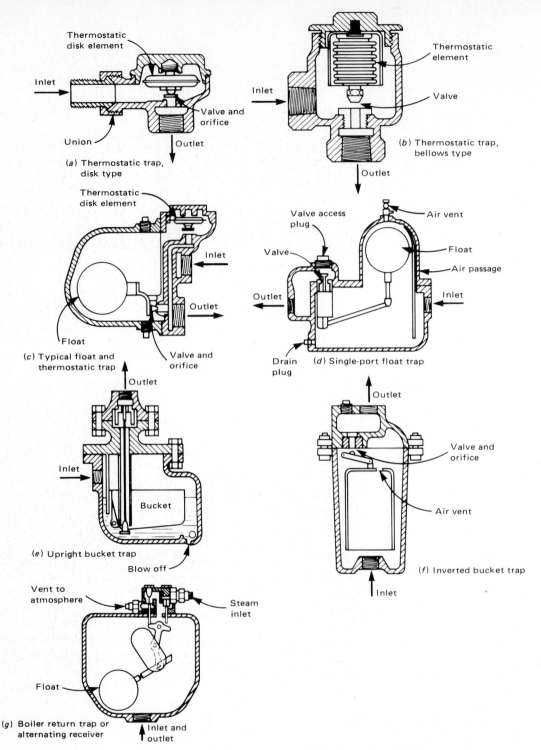

Figure 9-6 Steam traps of various types. (Reprinted with permission from the 1976 Systems Volume, ASHRAE Handbook and Products Directory.) (b, c, f, and g, © The Trane Co., used with permission.)

9-12   ALTERNATING RECEIVERS

An alternating receiver is a type of steam trap which is mounted at the end of the *dry returns* (near the boiler) in a gravity heating system of the general type shown in fig. 9-1. Its purpose is to return condensate to the boiler when it is not possible or practical to provide enough head above the boiler water line to return condensate by gravity against the pressure in the boiler.

This trap is mounted several feet above the boiler water line, and it is a float trap much like the type described in the preceding article. One difference, though, is that a small steam line is run from the boiler steam outlet and connected to a float valve at the top of the alternating receiver float chamber (see fig. 9-6g).

The float chamber is quite large and can hold several gallons of condensate. However, even with the chamber quite full, the condensate cannot flow back into the boiler against the higher pressure of the boiler. As condensate continues to flow into the receiver, any air in the receiver is pushed out through an air vent opening into the atmosphere. Then, when enough condensate collects and the float rises high enough, the air vent opening is closed and the steam valve is quickly opened. Now, with the same pressure in the receiver as is in the boiler, the condensate will flow by gravity into the boiler. When the float falls to a certain point, the steam valve closes, the air vent opens, and the cycle is repeated.

With the use of an alternating receiver, the need for a condensate pump is eliminated.

9-13   STEAM AND RETURN PIPE SIZING: GENERAL

The sizing of steam and condensate piping, with the help of tabular data provided by ASHRAE, is quite simple. After proceeding through one or two pipe sizing problems (complete system design), the beginning designer should be able to proceed into further design problems without any but occasional checking by an experienced designer.

The emphasis here will be placed on the piping design of two-pipe low- and high-pressure systems. However, the sizing charts included herein do give guidance in pipe sizing for one-pipe systems, vapor systems, and vacuum systems.

Before starting a steam piping system design, the designer must make a detailed room-by-room heat loss calculation and a block load calculation to determine the total heat loss of the building under design conditions. Chapter 4 deals with the subject of heat loss calculations in detail. For steam piping system design purposes, the block load heat loss total must be increased by a certain percentage to allow for a reasonably quick heat-up of a building from a cold start. With warm air heating systems, this percentage of surplus capacity is usually about 20% of the calculated heat loss. However, in steam and hot water heating systems, the mass to be heated from a cold start, including the water, the heavy boiler, and the extensive piping and heating devices, is much greater. The boiler and the piping system should be designed for a load 40 to 50% in excess of the calculated building heat loss. Room heating devices, including radiators, convectors, wall radiators, unit heaters, cabinet heaters, forced-flow convectors, and so on, must also be oversized to about 15 to 20% above individual room heat loss.

In view of the worldwide energy shortage today, much is being said about matching equipment capacity to the heating or cooling load without excess capacity being provided. This is especially true among nonpracticing individuals in government.

However, consider the case of the heating system that experiences equipment failure during peak winter weather, and the building becomes cold—perhaps as cold as 45°F. If the heating system capacity is matched closely to heating load, the building probably will not be restored to normal temperature (after the equipment failure is corrected) for several days or perhaps until the weather moderates.

To reheat this cold building in very cold weather in a reasonable time (perhaps 24 hr) requires excess capacity, and it must be provided.

This means that during normal operation the heating system steam or hot water boiler must operate at less than maximum capacity. With fixed-rate firing of a fuel-fired boiler, this will result in the fuel burner turning off and the boiler standing idle much of the time.

During such idle times, the standby losses of a large nonresidential boiler are considerable. Much heat is lost into the boiler room where it is not needed, and air passing through the boiler (as it often can) and up the chimney carries away great quantities of heat. Certainly, this is inefficient and wasteful.

However, this scenario does not, of necessity, take place; most of the time it does not. Usually, in a large nonresidential installation, one large boiler is not utilized. Two or three smaller ones are installed, and capacity can be closely matched to load by selective boiler operation.

Further, in larger boilers, on-off firing is not frequently used. The burners of larger boilers operate on modulating control cycles so that if only 60% of capacity is required, the burners run at 60% firing rate and run continuously. Standby time is minimal.

Also, as pointed out in a subsequent chapter on energy conservation, boiler breechings (smoke pipes) are now being fitted with automatic dampers which close when firing stops completely. Losses of heat up the chimney during standby periods are thus minimized.

Oversized boilers equipped as described above and operating at partial capacity will have appreciably lower stack temperatures. That is, the gases from the boiler passing up the chimney will be much cooler and less stack loss will occur. This is on the side of energy conservation.

In summation, we must conclude that equipment oversizing with proper control and operation is not wasteful; it is energy conservative. To a lesser degree this is also true of summer cooling equipment.

Steam heating equipment capacity and pipe sizing tables are often expressed in terms of "square feet of equivalent direct radiation,"

abbreviated EDR. This is just a unit of capacity rating that is equal to 240 BH in steam heating systems. Capacities and sizing tables are more often expressed in terms of "pounds of steam per hour" or in BH or MBH. It should be remembered that the latent heat of vaporization of water at 0 psig is about 970 Btu/lb. In other words, when a pound of steam condenses in a convector it yields about 970 Btu. If this happens at 5 psig, the yield is roughly 960 Btu, at 10 psig is 950, at 30 psig is 926, at 100 psig is 880, and at 150 psig is about 860 Btu. Therefore, we can say that roughly speaking 1.0 lb/hour of low-pressure steam condensing is equal to 4 ft^2 of EDR = 960 BH ÷ 240 BH = 4 (at low pressures).

When the choice of the type of heating devices to be used in a room has been made, and the room heating capacity required has been calculated, it is usually a very simple matter to select and locate the specific heating device(s) required. Manufacturers' catalogs dealing with such are very specific and precise in their information on appearance, dimensions, and heating output.

Manufacturers of heating coils and air conditioning units of all types which contain heating coils also give very good, clear information regarding heating capacity.

When all such equipment has been selected it should be located and drawn on the floor plan layouts of the various floors and sections of the building. A selection of the type of steam distribution system to be used must now be made, and a piping layout showing all steam mains, risers, branch mains, and connections to all heating devices must also now be drawn. The same is true for the condensate return system. When this layout is all complete, including the boiler and its location and its piping, the pipe sizing process may begin.

With regard to pipe sizing, a few general principles of conservative design must be carefully followed:

1 Minimum steam pipe size—2 in.
2 Minimum condensate return size—3/4 in.

3 Design pressure drops in low-pressure steam systems—the "pressure drop" through the entire system from the boiler outlet through the steam piping system, through the heating devices, and back through the condensate return piping to the boiler location shall be divided up as follows:
   a One-fourth to three-eighths of this pressure drop shall occur in the steam piping.
   b One-half shall occur in the heating devices and their control valves (if any) and their steam traps.
   c One eighth to one-fourth shall occur in the condensate return piping system.

4 Assume originally that the equivalent length of the steam piping system longest circuit is twice the actual measured length. After a preliminary design piping layout is completed, the validity of this assumption must be double checked. This is done by determining from fig. 9-9 the equivalent length (in feet) of each pipe fitting and valve that is included in the longest circuit of the piping layout as drawn. These equivalent lengths are totaled and added to the actual, measured length to determine the total equivalent length. If this total equivalent length is much different from the assumed length, some redesign may be necessary based on the information given by the new total equivalent length. Usually, this redesign will not be necessary.

5 Make the same assumption for condensate return system (as in principle 4) and double check its validity.

6 All runouts (see fig. 9-4) to heating devices and to upfeed steam risers shall pitch backward toward the steam main with a slope of 1/2 in. per foot if runout developed length is 8 ft or less. All such runouts 9 to 15 ft long shall be oversized one pipe size. Runouts longer than 15 ft shall pitch downward in the direction of steam flow and be dripped at the end (see end-of-main drip details in figs. 9-2, 9-4, and 9-5).

7 When condensate in steam lines flows in the same direction as the steam, piping should slope a minimum of 1 in. in 40 ft of run.

8 When steam mains are installed in the areas of buildings where noise of steam flow could be objectionable, steam velocities should be limited to 8000 fpm, or lower, if possible. Where noise is not a factor, velocities may be much higher if the attendant high pressure drop is permissible. When steam supply pressures are in excess of 30 psig, many HVAC engineers design more in consideration of velocities than pressure drop, and pressure drops in such steam mains would usually not exceed 15 to 25% of the supply pressure.

9 In high pressure systems, usual practice has been to design return piping for 0.5 psi drop per 100 ft in 30-psig systems and 1.0 psi drop in 150-psig systems.

10 In two-pipe vapor systems and low pressure systems, the design steam supply pressure will rarely exceed 2.0 or 3.0 psig, and design pressure drops in both steam and return piping will rarely exceed 1/8 psi per 100 ft.

11 In two-pipe vacuum systems, the total pressure drop in the steam supply or return piping will usually not exceed 1/4 psi in small systems nor more than 2.0 psi for large systems. Design steam supply pressures will not usually exceed 2.0 to 3.0 psig; and design pressure drops will rarely exceed 1/16 to 1/8 psi per 100 ft of equivalent length.

9-14 PIPE SIZING TABLES

A basic steam pipe sizing chart is shown in fig. 9-7. This chart may be used for sizing all steam mains, runouts, and downfeed risers where the steam and condensate are flowing in the same direction—in other words, where the steam line pitches downward in the direction of flow or is vertical with downward flow of steam.

Example 9-1 A 2 1/2-in. steam main has an equivalent length of 210 ft and must deliver 6700 lb/hr of 100 psig steam. Find steam line velocity and the pressure drop that will be experienced.

Solution Enter fig. 9-7 on the bottom horizontal scale at 6700 lb/hr (see heavy dashed line) and proceed upward to the horizontal 100-psig pressure line. Then proceed upward to the left as shown to the horizontal 0-psig pressure line. From

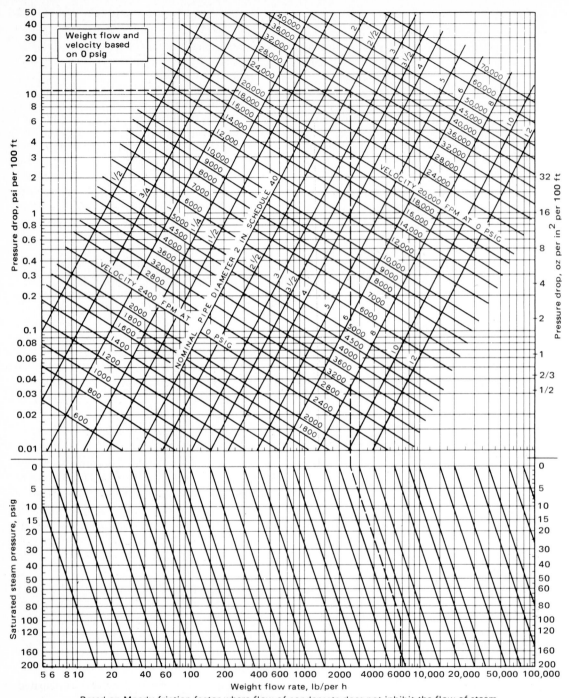

Based on Moody friction factor where flow of condensate does not inhibit the flow of steam.

Figure 9-7 Steam pipe sizing chart for schedule 40 steel pipe. (Reprinted with permission from the 1977 Fundamentals Volume, ASHRAE Handbook and Products Directory.)

this point proceed straight upward to the 2 1/2-in. pipe size sloping line. From this point the pressure drop of 11 psi per 100 ft of length may be read on the left-hand scale. Since the equivalent length is 210 ft, the total pressure drop will be 2.1 × 11 = 23.1 psi.

Also on fig. 9-7 may be read a preliminary velocity of 32,700 fpm. Now, if the chart of fig. 9-8 is entered on the left-hand scale at 32,700 fpm (see heavy dashed line), proceeding downward to the right as shown to the intersection with the vertical 100 psig line, and then horizontally to the right-hand scale, a reading of 13,000 fpm may be read. A judgment may now be made as to the suitability of this velocity from the standpoint of noise.

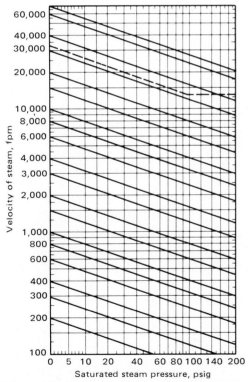

Figure 9-8 Velocity correction chart. (Reprinted with permission from the 1977 Fundamentals Volume, ASHRAE Handbook and Products Directory.)

In fig. 9-9 is included a table showing the equivalent lengths of various valves and pipe fittings. After a steam and return piping layout is drawn in detail and all piping sized, it is a simple matter to total the equivalent length of all valves and fittings with the use of fig 9-9, following the procedure set forth in art. 9-13 (see item 4 in the listing of eight design principles at the end of art. 9-13).

For the larger, nonresidential types of buildings with which this textbook is primarily concerned, it is highly recommended that only two-pipe systems be used, and that whenever possible, all steam piping be sloped so that any condensate in the steam piping flows along *with* the steam—not against it. This will result in small, economical pipe sizes and a minimum of noise resulting from water hammer.

However, there are many situations in which counterflow conditions are unavoidable. In upflow steam risers to upper floors, there will always be a certain amount of condensate descending against the rising steam. Such risers should always be "dripped" at their base, if possible, to remove this water. Also, most runouts from steam mains to upfeed risers and radiator stub-ups will have these counterflow conditions. Often, when runouts are unusually long, in excess of 15 ft, building conditions will prevent the installation of a condensate drip at the far end of the runout. Again, counterflow conditions will prevail in the runout.

In all such cases, pipe sizes may be selected from the table in fig. 9-10. Columns B and C in fig. 9-10 will be found to be most useful, whereas columns D, E, and F will be of use only in the unlikely event that a one-pipe steam system is being considered.

Condensate return piping should, as previously mentioned, be sized for the same rate of pressure drop that was used in sizing the steam supply piping. Allowable pressure drop in the steam supply and return piping must be based on the total pressure difference between anticipated boiler steam pressure and the pressure at the end

Figure 9.9 Equivalent lengths of steel pipe fittings and valves. (Reprinted with permission from the 1977 Fundamentals Volume, ASHRAE Handbook and Products Directory.)

	Length in feet of pipe to be added to actual length of run—owing to fittings— to obtain equivalent length				
	Length in feet to be added to run				
Size of pipe, in.	Standard elbow	Side outlet tee[a]	Gate valve[b]	Globe valve[b]	Angle valve[b]
1/2	1.3	3	0.3	14	7
3/4	1.8	4	0.4	18	10
1	2.2	5	0.5	23	12
1 1/4	3.0	6	0.6	29	15
1 1/2	3.5	7	0.8	34	18
2	4.3	8	1.0	46	22
2 1/2	5.0	11	1.1	54	27
3	6.5	13	1.4	66	34
3 1/2	8	15	1.6	80	40
4	9	18	1.9	92	45
5	11	22	2.2	112	56
6	13	27	2.8	136	67
8	17	35	3.7	180	92
10	21	45	4.6	230	112
12	27	53	5.5	270	132
14	30	63	6.4	310	152

[a]Valve in full open position.
[b]Values given apply only to a tee used to divert the flow in the main to the last riser.
Example of length in feet of pipe to be added to actual length of run:

```
Measured length = 132.0 ft
4 in. gate valve  =   1.9 ft
4–4 in. elbows    =  36.0 ft
2–4 in. tees      =  36.0 ft
                    ──────────
Equivalent        = 205.9 ft
```

of the condensate return piping near the boiler. If, for example, a vacuum heating system is planned in which boiler pressure will be 3.0 psig maximum, and the vacuum pump is to maintain 5.5 in. mercury vacuum in the pump receiver, the total pressure drop will be 3.0 psig + 5.5 in./2.04 = 5.7 psi (1.0 psi = 2.04 in. of mercury). The steam piping will usually be designed to cause one-fourth of this pressure drop, or 1.4 psi. The return piping system should then usually be designed to cause the same pressure drop of 1.4 psi. This will leave 2.8 psi allowable pressure drop in the radiation units (heating devices) and their control valves and steam traps. Normally, this would be adequate, but this must be carefully evaluated at this point in the design procedure. If the heating device were a fairly large heating coil with an automatic steam control valve, 2.8 psi might be inadequate. Manufacturers' catalog data would provide the necessary pressure drop information here.

In this example, if the 2.8-psi allowable pressure drop is inadequate, the design boiler steam pressure could be increased, or the design return line vacuum could be increased, or the design pressure drop in the steam and return piping could be reduced.

Figure 9-10 Low pressure steam pipe capacities for schedule 40 steel pipe with condensate flowing against the steam. (Reprinted with permission from the 1977 Fundamentals Volume, ASHRAE Handbook and Products Directory.)

Nominal pipe size, in.	Capacity, lb/hr				
	Two-pipe systems		One-pipe systems		
	Condensate flowing against steam		Supply risers upfeed	Radiator valves and vertical connections	Radiator and riser runouts
	Vertical	Horizontal			
A	B^a	C^b	D^c	E	F^b
3/4	8	7	6	. . .	7
1	14	14	11	7	7
1 1/4	31	27	20	16	16
1 1/2	48	42	38	23	16
2	97	93	72	42	23
2 1/2	159	132	116	. . .	42
3	282	200	200	. . .	63
3 1/2	387	288	286	. . .	119
4	511	425	380	. . .	186
5	1,050	788	. . .	. . .	278
6	1,800	1,400	. . .	. . .	545
8	3,750	3,000			
10	7,000	5,700			
12	11,500	9,500			
16	22,000	19,000			

(For use in one-pipe systems or two-pipe systems in which condensate flows against the steam flow.)

Note: Steam at an average pressure of 1 psig is used as a basis of calculating capacities.

^{a}Do not use column b for pressure drops of less than 1/16 psi per 100 ft of equivalent run.

^{b}Pitch of horizontal runouts to risers and radiators should be not less than 1/2 in. per ft. Where this pitch cannot be obtained, runouts over 8 ft in length should be one pipe size larger than called for in this table.

^{c}Do not use column D for pressure drops of less than 1/24 psi per 100 ft of equivalent run except on sizes 3 in. and over.

Figures 9-11, 9-12, and 9-13 include charts showing condensate return line capacities at three different steam design pressures, and at many different rates of pressure drop. Note that in fig. 9-11, different columns are provided for wet returns, dry returns, and vacuum system returns; the upper half of this table is concerned with horizontal return "mains," and the lower half with vertical, downfeed return "risers."

9-15 PIPE SIZING PROBLEM

Example 9-2 Size the piping in the high-pressure system of fig. 9-2.

Given:

1 Design boiler pressure: 30 psig.
2 Condensate return terminates at a flash tank carrying 1.0 psig pressure.

Figure 9-11 Condensate return main and riser capacities for low pressure systems (lb/hr) for schedule 40 steel pipe. (Reprinted with permission from the 1977 Fundamentals Volume, ASHRAE Handbook and Products Directory.)

Pipe size, in. (G)	1/32 psi or 1/2 oz drop per 100 ft			1/24 psi or 2/3 oz drop per 100 ft			1/16 psi or 1 oz drop per 100 ft			1/8 psi or 2 oz drop per 100 ft			1/4 psi or 4 oz drop per 100 ft			1/2 psi or 8 oz drop per 100 ft		
	Wet H	Dry I	Vac J	Wet K	Dry L	Vac M	Wet N	Dry O	Vac P	Wet Q	Dry R	Vac S	Wet T	Dry U	Vac V	Wet W	Dry X	Vac Y
Mains																		
3/4	...	...	...	...	...	42	...	...	100	...	...	142	...	...	200	...	...	283
1	125	62	...	145	71	143	175	80	175	250	103	249	350	115	350	...	...	494
1 1/4	213	130	...	248	149	244	300	168	300	425	217	426	600	241	600	...	...	848
1 1/2	338	206	...	393	236	388	475	265	475	675	340	674	950	378	950	...	...	1,340
2	700	470	...	810	535	815	1,000	575	1,000	1,400	740	1,420	2,000	825	2,000	...	...	2,830
2 1/2	1,180	760	...	1,580	868	1,360	1,680	950	1,680	2,350	1,230	2,380	3,350	1,360	3,350	...	...	4,730
3	1,880	1,460	...	2,130	1,560	2,180	2,680	1,750	2,680	3,750	2,250	3,800	5,350	2,500	5,350	...	...	7,560
3 1/2	2,750	1,970	...	3,300	2,200	3,250	4,000	2,500	4,000	5,500	3,230	5,680	8,000	3,580	8,000	...	...	11,300
4	3,880	2,930	...	4,580	3,350	4,500	5,500	3,750	5,500	7,750	4,830	7,810	11,000	5,380	11,000	...	...	15,500
5	...	...	...	...	...	7,880	...	...	9,680	...	...	13,700	...	...	19,400	...	...	27,300
6	...	...	...	...	...	12,600	...	...	15,500	...	...	22,000	...	...	31,000	...	...	43,800
Risers																		
3/4	...	48	...	...	48	143	...	48	175	...	48	249	...	48	350	...	...	494
1	...	113	...	...	113	244	...	113	300	...	113	426	...	113	600	...	...	848
1 1/4	...	248	...	...	248	388	...	248	475	...	248	674	...	248	950	...	...	1,340
1 1/2	...	375	...	...	375	815	...	375	1,000	...	375	1,420	...	375	2,000	...	...	2,830
2	...	750	...	...	750	1,360	...	750	1,680	...	750	2,380	...	750	3,350	...	...	4,730
2 1/2	...	...	...	...	...	2,180	...	...	2,680	...	...	3,800	...	...	5,350	...	...	7,560
3	...	...	...	...	...	3,250	...	...	4,000	...	...	5,680	...	...	8,000	...	...	11,300
3 1/2	...	...	...	...	...	4,480	...	...	5,500	...	...	7,810	...	...	11,000	...	...	15,500
4	...	...	...	...	...	7,880	...	...	9,680	...	...	13,700	...	...	19,400	...	...	27,300
5	...	...	...	...	...	12,600	...	...	15,500	...	...	22,000	...	...	31,000	...	...	43,800

Figure 9-12 Condensate return pipe capacities, 30-psig steam systems, schedule 40 steel pipe. (Reprinted with permission from the 1977 Fundamentals Volume, ASHRAE Handbook and Products Directory.)

Pipe size, in.	Drop in pressure—pounds per 100 ft in length				
	1/8	1/4	1/2	3/4	1
3/4	115	170	245	308	365
1	230	340	490	615	730
1 1/4	485	710	1,025	1,290	1,530
1 1/2	790	1,160	1,670	2,100	2,500
2	1,580	2,360	3,400	4,300	5,050
2 1/2	2,650	3,900	5,600	7,100	8,400
3	4,850	7,100	10,300	12,900	15,300
3 1/2	7,200	10,600	15,300	19,200	22,800
4	10,200	15,000	21,600	27,000	32,300
5	19,000	27,800	40,300	55,500	60,000
6	31,000	45,500	65,500	83,000	98,000

Note: Table is based on steam at pressures of 0 to 4 psig.

3 Flashed steam in the flash tank will be used to heat domestic hot water.

4 Pressure drop through the unit heater coils: 1/2 psi.

5 Pressure drop at the makeup air blast heater: heating coil, 2 psi; automatic valve, 1.5 psi; and steam trap, 0.25 psi.

6 Actual length of the steam main from point *A* (boiler) to point *G* is 220 ft.

7 Actual length of the condensate return main from point *H* to point *N* (flash tank) is 210 ft.

8 The steam main branch which connects at point *B* carries a heating load of 250 MBH. Its return main connects at point *P*. The length and pressure drop of this branch circuit is less than that of the circuit shown.

9 Actual steam main length from point *A* to point *F* (near makeup air heater) is 190 ft, and

Figure 9-13 Condensate return pipe capacities, 150-psig steam systems, schedule 40 steel pipe. (Reprinted with permission from the 1977 Fundamentals Volume, ASHRAE Handbook and Products Directory.)

Pipe size, in.	Drop in pressure—psi per 100 ft in length					
	1/8	1/4	1/2	3/4	1	2
3/4	156	232	360	465	560	890
1	313	462	690	910	1,120	1,780
1 1/4	650	960	1,500	1,950	2,330	3,700
1 1/2	1,070	1,580	2,460	3,160	3,800	6,100
2	2,160	3,300	4,950	6,400	7,700	12,300
2 1/2	3,600	5,350	8,200	10,700	12,800	20,400
3	6,500	9,600	15,000	19,500	23,300	37,200
3 1/2	9,600	14,400	22,300	28,700	34,500	55,000
4	13,700	20,500	31,600	40,500	49,200	78,500
5	25,600	38,100	58,500	76,000	91,500	146,000
6	42,000	62,500	96,000	125,000	150,000	238,000

Note: Table is based on steam at pressures of 1 to 20 psig.

from *F* to the automatic valve at the makeup air heater is 20 ft.

10 Actual pipe length from the makeup air heater to point *L* is 20 ft, and from *L* to point *N* is 60 ft.

11 Future planned expansion of load: none.

12 Water heater load is 50 MBH.

Solution

1 *Boiler capacity.* The boiler capacity equals connected load plus allowance for future growth plus 40 to 50% for pickup and pipe tax.

Connected load	MBH
1 unit heater at 40 MBH	40.0
1 unit heater at 40 MBH	40.0
1 unit heater at 50 MBH	50.0
1 makeup air heater	300.0
1 unit heater at 60 MBH	60.0
Branch main to other parts of the building	250.0
Water heater	50.0
Subtotal	790.0
Future expansion load	None
40% for pickup and pipe tax	316.0
Total boiler load	1106.0 MBH

2 *Allowable pipe pressure drop.* The element of the load with the greatest pressure drop is the makeup air heater; its pressure drop is:

Heating coil	2.0
Automatic valve	1.5
Steam trap	0.25
	3.75 psi

If this is arbitrarily chosen to be 50% of the total system pressure drop, then total pressure drop = 3.75 psi $\times$ 2 = 7.5 psi. Allowable pressure loss in the piping from point *A* to the makeup air heater and from it to point *N* at the flash tank then is also 3.75 psi.

3 *Allowable pipe loss per 100 ft.* As given, the steam main length from the boiler to the makeup air heater is 190 ft + 20 ft = 210 ft. If assumed to be double the actual length, the equivalent length is 210 ft $\times$ 2 = 420 ft. The actual return pipe length as given = 20 ft + 60 ft = 80 ft. Equivalent return length = 80 ft $\times$ 2 = 160 ft. Total equivalent length = 420 ft + 160 ft = 580 ft (or 5.8 lengths of 100 ft).

Allowable pressure drop = 3.75 psi/5.8 = 0.65 psi per 100 ft equivalent length in both the steam main and the return main and branch piping.

4 *Detail pipe sizing.* In the following tabulation the heat load on each section of pipe is multiplied by 1.4 to allow for pickup and pipe tax and divided by 0.926, the latent heat of vaporization of 1 lb/hr of 30 psig saturated steam, in MBH (or 926 BH/lb). Steam pipe sizes shown were taken from fig. 9-7, which shows that at 0.65 psi pressure drop per 100 ft and at 30 psig steam pressure a 2-in. pipe has a capacity of 590 lb of steam/hr, 2 1/2-in. pipe has a capacity of 950 lb/hr and 3-in. pipe has a capacity of 1700 lb/hr. These values were found in fig. 9-7 by entering the chart at 0.65 on the left-hand scale, moving horizontally to the right to the 2-in. (for example) sloping line, then projecting straight down to the bottom sloping lines, following these down to the right to the horizontal 30 psig line, and then straight down

Steam Piping

Pipe section	Load, MBH	Load, lb/hr = MBH $\times$ 1.4 $\div$ 0.926	Pipe size, in.
Makeup heater to point *F*	300	454	2
F to *E*	300 + 60 = 360	544	2
E to *D*	360 + 50 = 410	620	2 1/2
D to *C*	410 + 40 = 450	680	2 1/2
C to *B*	450 + 40 = 490	741	2 1/2
B to *A*	490 + 250 = 740	1119	3
F to *G*	60	91	2

to the bottom scale, where for the 2-in. size a value of 590 lb/hr may be read.

In the tabulation above the design load in MBH on each section of the steam supply main was totaled. For example, in pipe section F to E the steam main must have enough capacity to supply 300 MBH of steam to the makeup air heater and 60 MBH to the last heater on the steam main; total 360 MBH. This was converted to lb/hr during warm-up conditions by multiplying by 1.4 (adding 40%) and by dividing by 0.926 to equal 544 lb/hr. In pipe section E to D the load is 620 lb/hr of steam. Required pipe size is 2 1/2 in. since a 2-in. pipe has only 590 lb/hr capacity and a 2 1/2-in. pipe has a capacity of 950 lb/hr, as noted above, under the conditions of this problem. However, in pipe section F to E the 590 lb/hr capacity of a 2-in. pipe is adequate since the ultimate load is 544 lb/hr.

Condensate return pipe sizes were selected at 0.65 psi per 100 ft mainly from fig. 9-12 for 30 psig steam system return lines, and also from fig. 9-11 for the low pressure return lines from the water heater and the flash tank—all as "dry" returns. As with the steam lines, the load in MBH on the return lines has been converted to lb/hr and 40% added for extra capacity during startup conditions. The pipe size is then easily determined with the use of figs. 9-11 and 9-12.

The water heater load was given at 50 MBH. This was also converted to lb/hr, with allowance for startup extra load, to 75.6 lb/hr (50 × 1.4 ÷ 0.926 = 75.6). The flash tank would have only a very little pressure in it (1.0 to 2.0 psig), and the steam line to the water heater can easily be sized using fig. 9-7; however, the 2-in. minimum steam pipe size rule would prevail here. The water heater 1-in. dry return line was sized with use of fig. 9-11,

the very short length of pipe here permitting the use of a fairly high pressure drop rate such as 1/4 psi per 100 ft.

The condensate return line from the flash tank to the accumulator tank is a short, low-pressure return and may be sized with the use of fig. 9-11; however, the load is great since it handles all the condensate from the entire system except the water heater and the low-pressure system, 741 lb/hr. Again, as a dry return at 1/4 psi drop per 100 ft, the pipe size from fig. 9-11 is 2 in. The total load of 1119 lb/hr must be carried by the line from the accumulator tank to the boiler feed pump; this line should be 2 1/2 in. and kept as short and direct as possible with no appreciable pressure drop. Pressure drop here could cause the hot condensate to partially flash back into steam with resulting pumping problems. The pump discharge line back to the boiler may be much smaller and sized as a hot water heating line from a chart in chap. 8.

9-16 FLASH TANKS

Where a boiler supplies both a high-pressure and a low-pressure system, as in fig. 9-2, the condensate from the high-pressure system must be reduced down to low pressure so that all condensate can be returned by a common boiler feed pump. When high-pressure condensate is expanded down to low pressure, some of it will flash into steam since its temperature is higher than the boiling point of water at the lower pressure. The heat required to boil some of the condensate is taken from the condensate itself, so the condensate that remains liquid is cooled.

Condensate Return Piping

Pipe section	Load, MBH	Load, lb/hr = MBH × 1.4 ÷ 0.926	Pipe size, in.
H to J	40	60	3/4
J to K	80 (40 + 40)	121	3/4
K to L	130 (80 + 50)	197	3/4
L to M	430 (130 + 300)	650	1 1/4
M to N	490 (430 + 60)	741	1 1/4

The low-pressure steam that evolves in this process should be utilized, of course, and not wasted. Some secondary need for heat, such as heating domestic water as shown in fig. 9-2, can be met with such steam. Of course, it can be piped over into the low-pressure steam system.

A flash tank, as shown in fig. 9-2, is used to receive the high-pressure condensate and to provide volume enough for the flashing steam to separate itself from the remaining condensate. It is recommended that for this purpose the flash tank be horizontal, as shown in fig. 9-2, with the high-pressure condensate entering at the top near one end. The outlet for the steam, which forms when the high-pressure condensate is expanded to nearly 0 psig pressure, should be on the top of the tank at the opposite end. The remaining condensate should also leave at the opposite end from the bottom of the tank.

In sizing the tank, the diameter is critical and should be such that the velocity of condensate and flashed steam through the tank is 1 to 2 fps. This low velocity will permit the flashing steam and condensate to separate. Tank length is not as critical as diameter, but should be about four times the diameter. Minimum tank size should not be less than 8 in. in diameter and 32 in. in length.

Tank diameter in inches may be calculated with the use of the formula

$$d = \sqrt{\frac{0.0014\ WK}{V}} \qquad (9\text{-}1)$$

where d = tank diameter, in.

W = rate of condensate, lb/hr

K = a constant which varies with the pressure of the high-pressure condensate as follows:

at 150 psig, K = 158
at 100 psig, K = 129
at 30 psig, K = 67
at 15 psig, K = 38

Interpolation is permissible.

V = tank linear velocity, fps (V should be in the range 1.0 to 2.0 fps)

In example 9-2 the amount of condensate flowing in pipe section M to N is 741 lb/hr, including the 40% for pickup and pipe tax. The system is a 30 psig system. Using a design tank velocity of 1.0 fps, the tank diameter should be

$$d = \sqrt{\frac{0.0014 \times 741 \times 67}{1}} = 8.33 \text{ in.}$$

using formula (9-1) where K = 67.

9-17 BOILER WATER LINE MAINTENANCE

The water line of a steam boiler is the line below which is liquid water and above which is steam; it is the water level in a steam boiler. It is of the greatest importance that the water line be maintained at the correct level—not too high and, more important, not too low.

When metal parts of a boiler are in contact with liquid water, they will not overheat even though they are also in direct contact with the flame from a fuel burner. In a steam boiler, if the water line is kept at a level specified by its manufacturer, all metal parts that could be damaged by heat will be backed by water at all times. However, serious damage can result from firing a boiler when the water line falls too low.

It is mandatory, therefore, that steps be taken to ascertain that the boiler water line is properly maintained at all times. There are three frequently encountered operating conditions that cause the water line in a boiler to fall to an unsafe level:

1 Under heavy steaming conditions, if the steam supply piping system resistance is permanently or temporarily too high, boiler water is pushed backward out of the boiler into the return piping system.

2 During periods of very heavy load which is quickly applied (as when starting a system from a cold start or when increasing building temperature in the morning after a night of lower temperatures), the steam may leave the boiler faster than the condensate can return.

3 During faulty operation, when *foaming* or *priming* occurs.

The terms "foaming" and "priming" refer to a condition during heavy load when the evolving steam, rapidly leaving the water line in the boiler, carries boiler water along in great quantities until the water line falls—often very quickly and to a very low level. Foaming and priming occur when boiler water contains a high content of foreign matter, such as oil or pipe dope from threaded pipe connections.

One might think that backward flow of water out the condensate return connection (see condition 1 above) could be easily prevented with the installation of a check valve in the return main, which permits flow "into" the boiler only. However, check valves of all types are notorious for their failure to prevent backward flow. Foreign matter can easily settle in check valve seats and prevent their tight closing.

The one universal and dependable method of preventing backward flow involves the use of a *Hartford loop* type of return connection. This connection may be seen in figs. 9-1, 9-2, and 9-4 and involves connecting the return main to a vertical pipe that loops from the steam outlet pipe above the boiler down to the boiler return connection. The condensate return is connected to this loop at a point just below the water line. The water line can fall only a very few inches before steam enters the return line and equalizes the pressure that tends to push water from the boiler.

Even though it is difficult to see how boiler water can flow backward through a condensate pump or a vacuum heating pump, the Hartford loop connection should always be used, even when these pumps are utilized.

In comparatively small steam heating systems of 700 lb/hr and less, and where the heating load is fairly steady and continuously applied, the use of a float-type control is probably adequate for water line maintenance. Such a float control (see fig. 9-4) consists of a float ball and float chamber mounted beside the boiler at the level of the boiler water line. The float chamber is connected with piping to the boiler at points well above and below the water line. Thus, water stands in the float chamber at the same level as the water line, and the brass float ball floats at this water level.

The float chamber may be fitted with an electric switch or a water control valve, or both. If an electric switch is used, when the water level in the boiler and the float chamber falls, the float ball lowers and a float rod attached to the ball moves so as to open the switch. Thus, if the water level falls to an unsafe level, the switch is opened and the fuel burner is stopped to protect the boiler. The switch may have a second pair of electrical contacts which close, as the float falls, to energize an electric solenoid valve which opens to admit makeup water into the boiler. Or the closing contacts may start a pump which pumps water into the boiler. This makeup action would, of course, occur before the burner is turned off.

If the float rod is connected to a built-in water valve, lowering the float will cause the valve to open and water from the building water supply system will enter to restore the water level. This makeup water is usually raw, untreated water which carries dissolved minerals (hardness), air, and noncondensible gases with it. This is highly undesirable, and the addition of such water should be minimized as much as possible.

In a large steam heating system, it is frequently possible for a great amount of steam to be drawn from the boiler and temporarily retained in the system without an equal amount of condensate being returned. This, of course, causes the boiler water line to fall until makeup water is added to restore the water line to its proper level. Then, in time, the excess water in the system comes flooding back to the boiler until the water line is too high. This is undesirable too, and boiler water must now overflow into a float device which wastes the excess water to the sewer. When this sequence occurs frequently, a great amount of hardness, air, and other noncondensibles are brought into the system.

To overcome this disadvantage, large systems are usually equipped with an accumulator tank as shown in fig. 9-2. All condensate returns to this tank before it is pumped back into the boiler. A makeup water float valve is mounted on this tank to maintain a water level in the tank. However, this float valve is mounted and adjusted to open and admit water only when the tank level falls quite low—with the tank only about 20% full. The normal level in the accumulator tank will be above the midpoint, so that makeup water will rarely be added.

In this system, the boiler water line will be maintained by a boiler float switch, called a *pump controller,* which starts a "boiler feed" pump when water is required in the boiler.

With makeup water held to a minimum, hard-ness and noncondensibles are removed from the water and the water becomes of good quality. Usually in this case, chemical treatment of the makeup water is not necessary.

In all boiler installations, a low-water-level float switch, usually called a *low-water cutoff,* should be used to stop the fuel burner action when the water level falls too low. Any such switch should be approved by Underwriters Laboratory (UL) and so labeled. All boilers must also be fitted with a *pressure relief valve* which will open and relieve boiler pressure when that pressure rises to too high a value. All such valves should be tested and rated in full compliance with the American Society of Mechanical Engineers (ASME) Boiler Code and be so labeled. It is always wise to require the boiler manufacturer to supply the

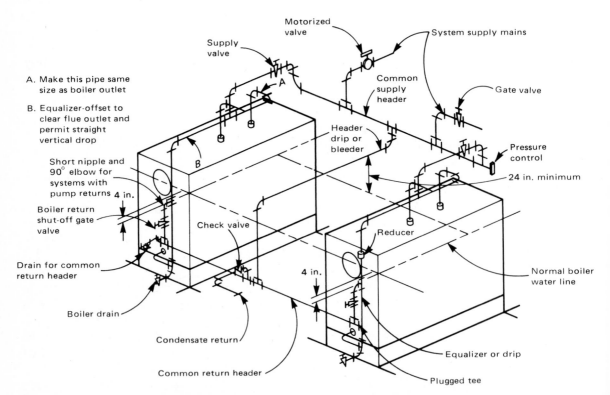

Figure 9-14 Twin boiler piping details. (Reprinted with permission from the 1976 Systems Volume, ASHRAE Handbook and Products Directory.)

pressure relief valve along with the boiler to ascertain that the valve is of the proper size and type.

Boilers should always be manufactured in full compliance with the ASME Boiler Code and should be so labeled with a permanent welded or stamped ASME label. When boiler-burner units are oil fired, they should be UL labeled as well as ASME labeled; and gas-fired units should have ASME and AGA (American Gas Association) labels.

As suggested in chap. 8, it is also highly recommended that all mechanically fired boiler units be purchased from one manufacturer complete with fuel burner, draft fan (if required), all safety controls, all operating controls, and pressure relief valves.

9-18 MULTIPLE-BOILER INSTALLATIONS

Multiple-boiler installations of two or three boiler units will, of course, permit the shutdown of one boiler for emergency repair or routine maintenance while the other boiler(s) continues in operation. If two boilers are used, each boiler will usually be sized to be able to carry 60% of the calculated load. If three boilers are used, they may all be sized for one-third of the load, since two of the three boilers can then provide two-thirds of maximum required capacity. These percentages may often be varied if the characteristics of the load are known and carefully analyzed.

Normally, all boilers should be of the same capacity, manufacture, and dimension, with installation made side by side with all water lines at exactly the same elevation. All boilers should have Hartford loop connections, and normally they will discharge into the top of a common steam header, which is dripped without a drip trap back into a common return header. See the typical twin boiler piping details in fig. 9-14.

Gate valves must be provided by means of which each boiler may be isolated from the system when it is shut down for repair or any other reason. Each boiler must have its own safety controls, operating controls, and relief valve. When an accumulator tank, as described in art. 9-17, is used, each boiler should have its own boiler feed pump and pump controller. However, it is possible to feed more than one boiler with a single feed pump if each boiler has its own pump controller which starts the pump and opens a solenoid valve in its own water inlet line. Other methods of returning water to multiple boiler installations have been used with varied success.

9-19 RADIATOR VALVES

Both manual and automatic control of steam into radiators, convectors, and so on, is achieved with valves such as those shown in figs. 9-15 and 9-16. The manual valve must be reset frequently as the need for heat in a room changes. The automatic valve does this without attention by room occupants.

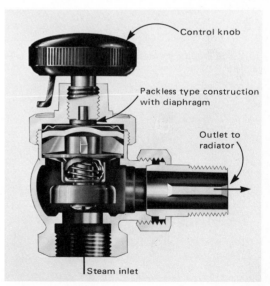

Figure 9-15 Manual radiator valve. (© The Trane Company, used by permission.)

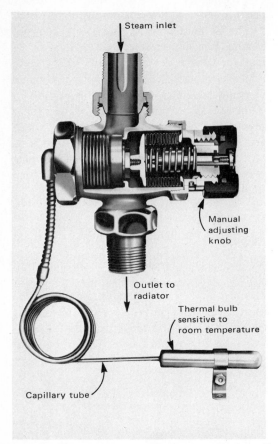

Figure 9-16 Automatic steam radiator control valve, self-actuated. (© The Trane Company, used by permission.)

PROBLEMS

9-1 What is the basic difference between a two-pipe vapor steam heating system and a two-pipe vacuum heating system?

9-2 Why is space necessary for the vertical column of water in the return main of fig. 9-1?

9-3 How do face-and-bypass dampers on a steam heating coil help to prevent coil freeze-up when subfreezing air is passing through the coil?

9-4 A steam supply main has an equivalent length of 120 ft and carries steam at 5.0 psig. If it carries 600 lb of steam per hour and the allowable pressure drop is 0.4 psi per 100 ft, what should the size of this main be if schedule 40 steel pipe is used? Also, what will the corrected steam velocity be?

9-5 A 3-in. steam main has an actual measured length of 40.5 ft. Fittings in this main include an angle valve (wide open), five standard elbows, and one tee at the last riser from the main. What is the total equivalent length of this main?

9-6 A steam supply runout from a 1.0-psig steam main to a large convector is 2 in. and is 20 ft long. What is the capacity of this runout in MBH? (1.0-psig steam yields 970 Btu/lb when condensed. Also note that steam and condensate flow in opposite directions in this runout.)

Chapter 10

Refrigeration

10-1 THE NEED FOR REFRIGERATION IN HVAC

The artificial cooling of modern buildings is no longer considered to be a luxury reserved for the rich or those engaged in competitive merchandising. In all but the lowest socioeconomic strata, summer cooling is considered to be a necessity—just as is winter heating. In many areas of larger buildings, artificial cooling is required all year around.

Summer cooling in almost all areas of the United States is accomplished with the use of some type of mechanical (including electrical and chemical) refrigeration system. Through the years we have, of course, utilized the natural cooling effect of cold groundwater or surface water, or cool or cold outside air when those are available. However, in the future we must do a much better job of this; there is a great deal of room for improvement.

Even so, mechanical refrigeration will certainly carry the bulk of our cooling loads in future years; and for a professional practitioner in the construction field, a basic understanding of refrigeration is exceedingly important.

In the spring and fall seasons, there are many times when both heating and cooling are required alternately or simultaneously. When they are required simultaneously, an opportunity is presented to use outside air for cooling. There is also a fine opportunity, when mechanical cooling is required, to use that mechanical system to collect heat where cooling is needed and to deposit the *same* heat in other parts of the building where heating is needed. The loop systems of refrigeration described in a subsequent chapter can do this; however, their study requires a basic understanding of the refrigeration cycles discussed in this chapter.

10-2 REFRIGERATION SYSTEMS IN GENERAL

There are five basic refrigeration systems in use today:

1 The compression cycle
2 The absorption cycle
3 The steam jet cycle
4 The air cycle
5 The thermoelectric cycle

Of those listed, the compression cycle is probably used in 98% or more of our mechanical cooling systems. For the remaining 2%, the absorption cycle is almost always used. In industrial, commercial, and residential process refrigeration systems, only rarely is a system other than the compression cycle utilized. The residential kitchen refrigerator is a good example of this. So the compression cycle is most important to us, and most of the chapter is devoted to it.

The primary function of any refrigeration system is to collect or absorb heat from a comparatively low temperature medium where there is too much heat, and somehow to increase the *intensity* of that heat until it represents a higher temperature. If the secondary temperature is high enough, it is then a simple matter to cause the heat to flow into a generally available medium (such as the outdoor air) where the heat may be acceptable or even needed. In other words, we are pumping heat uphill, figuratively speaking, from a low-temperature medium to a higher-temperature medium. To do this requires the application of power.

When there is an active need for the "transferred" heat in the higher-temperature medium, it is fortunate that most of the power required to make the process function is also converted to usable heat at the higher temperature level. The higher-temperature medium receives not only the heat transferred, but also the heat equivalent of most of the motive power utilized.

A good example of this is a large building that requires cooling in its inner unexposed areas, and at the same time requires heating in its perimeter, exposed areas. The refrigeration system that removes heat from the inner areas can be made to deliver that heat to the perimeter areas together with most of the heat equivalent of the power required to operate the refrigerating system. In this case, the heat delivered may be 20% greater in quantity than the heat removed from the inner areas.

In all refrigeration processes, heat is of necessity rejected from the system. In today's energy-scarce world, we must always make an assiduous effort to utilize that rejected heat whenever possible.

10-3 COEFFICIENTS OF PERFORMANCE

There are several units of performance in use in the refrigeration field that measure the efficacy of various types of systems. The term *coefficient of performance* (COP) is a measure of this efficacy and is applied in two situations.

In the first of these, the COP is applied to a refrigerating system, and expresses the amount of *refrigerating effect,* in BH (Btu/hr), for every BH of heat equivalent of the energy input into the motor or engine that drives the system. In other words,

$$\text{Refrigeration COP} = \frac{\text{refrigerating effect, BH}}{\text{power input, BH}}$$

Example 10-1 Many electric-motor-driven HVAC compression cycle refrigerating systems can deliver 1 ton of cooling for each horsepower of the motor that drives its compressor. If the motor efficiency were 70%, and remembering that the heat equivalent of a horsepower is 2544 BH, what is the refrigeration COP?

Solution

$$\text{Refrigeration COP} = \frac{12,000 \text{ BH/ton}}{2544 \div 0.7} = 3.30$$

for a 1.0-ton cooling system driven by a 1.0-hp motor which is 70% efficient.

The second COP is the *heat pump COP* and is applied when a refrigeration system is used as a heating device to extract heat from some available "heat source" and deliver that heat at higher temperature for heating purposes. Here the heat pump COP is the ratio of the heat delivered, in BH, to the BH equivalent of the power input of the driving mechanism.

$$\text{Heat pump COP} = \frac{\text{heat rejected, BH}}{\text{power input, BH}}$$

$$= \frac{\text{heat rejected, BH}}{(\text{motor horsepower} \times 2544)/\text{motor efficiency}}$$

Example 10-2 A heat pump extracts heat from outdoor air at 20°F and delivers that heat at 100°F to the interior of a building. If the heat rejected is 15,000 BH/ton of cooling effect, the driving motor horsepower is 1.9 hp/ton, and the motor efficiency is 60%, what is the heat pump COP?

Solution

$$\text{Heat pump COP} = \frac{15,000}{(1.9 \times 2544)/0.6} = 1.86$$

where "2544" is the heat equivalent of 1 hp in BH.

There is another performance ratio that is frequently utilized to express refrigerating efficiency; this is called *energy efficiency ratio* (EER) or *seasonal energy efficiency ratio* (SEER). It is applied as a rating for electric-motor-driven refrigerating systems, and is simply the ratio of the net refrigerating effect in BH to the watts of electrical energy input to the system.

$$\text{EER} = \frac{\text{refrigerating effect, BH}}{\text{watts, W}}$$

A fairly high EER for a summer cooling system might be of the order of 9.0 BH/W; older existing systems might have an EER as low as 4 or 5.

10-4 REFRIGERANTS AND PRESSURE-TEMPERATURE RELATIONSHIPS

Most refrigeration systems are in theory based on the important fundamental concept that the "boiling" point (temperature), the "condensing" point, and the "saturation" point (all three have the same numerical value) of a refrigerant vary in accordance with the changing pressure to which the refrigerant is subjected. Further, it is important to know that as the imposed pressure changes, these points change in a direct relationship. That is, a rise in imposed pressure on a refrigerant is accompanied by a rise in all three points: boiling, condensing, and saturation points. Similarly, a fall in the pressure to which a refrigerant is subjected results in a fall in these points.

It is widely stated that water boils at 212°F. This, of course, is true, but only when the water is subjected to a pressure of 14.696 psia (standard atmospheric pressure). If water is under a pressure of 15 psig (29.696 psia) as would sometimes be the case in a steam boiler, it will not boil until its temperature has been elevated to almost 250°F. If a mountain climber at 18,000 ft above sea level (where the atmospheric pressure is usually just half what it is at sea level) boils some water, he or she would find that it boils at 179°F—not 212°F.

So if the pressure on water, or any refrigerant, rises, its boiling point rises. If that pressure falls, the boiling point falls—this is a direct relationship. We can see, then, that if we wish to vary the temperature of a boiling refrigerant, we can do so by varying the pressure imposed on it.

For example, if we wish to cool a stream of air from 80°F to 60°F, we can do so by circulating that air over the surfaces of a cooling coil that has R-22 refrigerant inside the coil tubes at a pressure of 90 psia. We can see in fig. 10-1, the table of refrigerant-22 properties, that the saturation temperature (also the boiling point) at 90 psia is slightly over 44°F. With 80°F air entering this coil, an initial Δt of 36°F (80°F – 44°F = 36°F) will exist, and as a result, heat will flow from the air through the metal walls of the coil tubes into

Figure 10-1 Properties of monochlorodifluoromethane (CHClF$_2$) (ASHRAE designation: refrigerant 22). (Reprinted with permission from the 1960 ASHRAE Heating, Ventilating, Air Conditioning Guide.)

Saturation temperature, °F	Absolute pressure, lb/in.² (psia)	Volume, ft³/lb		Enthalpy, Btu/lb		Entropy		50° superheat		100° superheat	
									Enthalpy and entropy taken from −40°F		
		Liquid	Vapor	Liquid	Vapor	Liquid	Vapor	Enthalpy	Entropy	Enthalpy	Entropy
0	38.79	0.01192	1.373	10.63	105.02	0.0240	0.2293	112.35	0.2446	120.00	0.2590
2	40.43	0.01195	1.320	11.17	105.24	0.0251	0.2280	112.59	0.2442	120.26	0.2586
4	42.14	0.01198	1.270	11.70	105.45	0.0262	0.2285	112.83	0.2438	120.52	0.2581
5	43.02	0.01200	1.246	11.97	105.56	0.0268	0.2283	112.95	0.2436	120.65	0.2579
6	43.91	0.01201	1.221	12.23	105.66	0.0274	0.2280	113.07	0.2434	120.78	0.2577
8	45.74	0.01205	1.175	12.76	105.87	0.0285	0.2276	113.31	0.2430	121.04	0.2572
10	47.63	0.01208	1.130	13.29	106.08	0.0296	0.2272	113.55	0.2426	121.30	0.2568
12	49.58	0.01211	1.088	13.82	106.29	0.0307	0.2268	113.79	0.2422	121.56	0.2564
14	51.59	0.01215	1.048	14.36	106.50	0.0319	0.2264	114.02	0.2418	121.82	0.2560
16	53.66	0.01218	1.009	14.90	106.71	0.0330	0.2260	114.25	0.2414	122.08	0.2556
18	55.79	0.01222	0.9721	15.44	106.92	0.0341	0.2257	114.48	0.2410	122.33	0.2552
20	57.98	0.01225	0.9369	15.98	107.13	0.0352	0.2253	114.71	0.2406	122.59	0.2548
22	60.23	0.01229	0.9032	16.52	107.33	0.0364	0.2249	114.94	0.2402	122.84	0.2544
24	62.55	0.01232	0.8707	17.06	107.53	0.0375	0.2246	115.17	0.2398	123.10	0.2540
26	64.94	0.01236	0.8398	17.61	107.73	0.0379	0.2242	115.40	0.2395	123.35	0.2537
28	67.40	0.01239	0.8100	18.17	107.93	0.0398	0.2239	115.62	0.2391	123.60	0.2533
30	69.93	0.01243	0.7816	18.74	108.13	0.0409	0.2235	115.84	0.2387	123.85	0.2529
32	72.53	0.01247	0.7543	19.32	108.33	0.0421	0.2232	116.07	0.2383	124.10	0.2525
34	75.21	0.01250	0.7283	19.90	108.52	0.0433	0.2228	116.29	0.2380	124.35	0.2522
36	77.97	0.01254	0.7032	20.49	108.71	0.0445	0.2225	116.52	0.2376	124.59	0.2518
38	80.81	0.01258	0.6791	21.09	108.90	0.0457	0.2222	116.74	0.2373	124.84	0.2515
40	83.72	0.01262	0.6559	21.70	109.09	0.0469	0.2218	116.96	0.2369	125.08	0.2511
42	86.69	0.01266	0.6339	22.29	109.27	0.0481	0.2215	117.18	0.2366	125.32	0.2508
44	89.74	0.01270	0.6126	22.90	109.45	0.0493	0.2211	117.40	0.2363	125.56	0.2504
46	92.88	0.01274	0.5922	23.50	109.63	0.0505	0.2208	117.61	0.2359	125.80	0.2501
48	96.10	0.01278	0.5726	24.11	109.80	0.0516	0.2205	117.82	0.2356	126.04	0.2497
50	99.40	0.01282	0.5537	24.73	109.98	0.0528	0.2201	118.02	0.2353	126.27	0.2494
52	102.8	0.01286	0.5355	25.34	110.14	0.0540	0.2198	118.22	0.2350	126.50	0.2491
54	106.2	0.01290	0.5184	25.95	110.30	0.0552	0.2194	118.42	0.2347	126.73	0.2488
56	109.8	0.01294	0.5014	26.58	110.47	0.0564	0.2191	118.62	0.2343	126.96	0.2484
58	113.5	0.01299	0.4849	27.22	110.63	0.0576	0.2188	118.82	0.2340	127.19	0.2481
60	117.2	0.01303	0.4695	27.83	110.78	0.0588	0.2185	119.01	0.2337	127.42	0.2478
62	121.0	0.01307	0.4546	28.46	110.93	0.0600	0.2181	119.21	0.2334	127.65	0.2475
64	124.9	0.01312	0.4403	29.09	111.08	0.0612	0.2178	119.40	0.2331	127.87	0.2472
66	128.9	0.01316	0.4264	29.72	111.22	0.0624	0.2175	119.59	0.2327	128.10	0.2469
68	133.0	0.01320	0.4129	30.35	111.35	0.0636	0.2172	119.77	0.2324	128.32	0.2466
70	137.2	0.01325	0.4000	30.99	111.49	0.0648	0.2168	119.96	0.2321	128.54	0.2463
72	141.5	0.01330	0.3875	31.65	111.63	0.0661	0.2165	120.15	0.2318	128.76	0.2460
74	145.9	0.01334	0.3754	32.29	111.75	0.0673	0.2162	120.32	0.2315	128.97	0.2457
76	150.4	0.01339	0.3638	32.94	111.88	0.0684	0.2158	120.50	0.2312	129.19	0.2455
78	155.0	0.01344	0.3526	33.61	112.01	0.0696	0.2155	120.67	0.2309	129.40	0.2452

Figure 10-1 *(Cont.)*

Satura-tion temper-ature, °F	Absolute pressure, lb/in.² (psia)	Volume, ft³/lb		Enthalpy and entropy taken from −40°F							
				Enthalpy, Btu/lb		Entropy		50° superheat		100° superheat	
		Liquid	Vapor	Liquid	Vapor	Liquid	Vapor	Enthalpy	Entropy	Enthalpy	Entropy
80	159.7	0.01349	0.3417	34.27	112.13	0.0708	0.2151	120.85	0.2306	129.61	0.2449
82	164.5	0.01353	0.3313	34.92	112.24	0.0720	0.2148	121.02	0.2303	129.82	0.2446
84	169.4	0.01358	0.3212	35.60	112.36	0.0732	0.2144	121.18	0.2300	130.02	0.2443
86	174.5	0.01363	0.3113	36.28	112.47	0.0744	0.2140	121.34	0.2297	130.23	0.2441
88	179.6	0.01368	0.3019	36.94	112.57	0.0756	0.2137	121.50	0.2294	130.43	0.2438
90	184.8	0.01374	0.2928	37.61	112.67	0.0768	0.2133	121.66	0.2291	130.63	0.2435
92	190.1	0.01379	0.2841	38.28	112.76	0.0780	0.2130	121.82	0.2288	130.83	0.2432
94	195.6	0.01384	0.2755	38.97	112.85	0.0792	0.2126	121.97	0.2285	131.03	0.2429
96	201.2	0.01390	0.2672	39.65	112.93	0.0803	0.2122	122.12	0.2282	131.23	0.2427
98	206.8	0.01396	0.2594	40.32	113.00	0.0815	0.2119	122.26	0.2279	131.42	0.2424
100	212.6	0.01402	0.2517	40.98	113.06	0.0827	0.2115	122.40	0.2276	131.61	0.2421
102	218.5	0.01408	0.2443	41.65	113.12	0.0839	0.2111	122.53	0.2273	131.80	0.2418
104	224.6	0.01414	0.2370	42.32	113.16	0.0851	0.2107	122.66	0.2270	131.99	0.2416
106	230.7	0.01420	0.2301	42.98	113.20	0.0862	0.2104	122.79	0.2267	132.17	0.2413
108	237.0	0.01426	0.2233	43.66	113.24	0.0874	0.2100	122.92	0.2264	132.35	0.2411
110	243.4	0.01433	0.2167	44.35	113.29	0.0886	0.2096	123.04	0.2261	132.53	0.2408
112	249.9	0.01440	0.2104	45.04	113.34	0.0898	0.2093	123.16	0.2258	132.71	0.2405
114	256.6	0.01447	0.2043	45.74	113.38	0.0909	0.2089	123.28	0.2255	132.88	0.2403
116	263.4	0.01454	0.1983	46.44	113.42	0.0921	0.2085	123.40	0.2253	133.05	0.2400
118	270.3	0.01461	0.1926	47.14	113.46	0.0933	0.2081	123.51	0.2250	133.22	0.2398
120	277.3	0.01469	0.1871	47.85	113.52	0.0945	0.2078	123.62	0.2247	133.39	0.2395

the refrigerant. Since the air temperature is initially 36°F above the boiling point of the R-22, the R-22 will begin to boil, or expand, from a liquid to a vapor. Now, all we need to do is pump the vaporized R-22 out of the coil as fast as it evolves in order to hold the pressure at 90 psia. Of course, we will need to feed more liquid R-22 into the coil at the same rate as it is being pumped out; we now have a functioning refrigeration system, but not a complete system.

There is also another important concept or two concerning refrigerants that must be mastered before the study of a complete refrigeration system is begun. First, it must be realized that any refrigerant is at *saturation* when it is boiling and when both liquid refrigerant and refrigerant vapor are present in the same container. When R-22 is boiling (of course, both liquid and vapor are present when boiling) at a pressure of 90 psia, its

temperature will always be 44°F. It is possible to have liquid R-22 at 90 psia and 44°F and just ready to boil, but not yet quite boiling. The addition of the slightest amount of heat will cause some of the R-22 to change state from liquid to vapor (to evaporate or boil).

We may also have R-22 vapor at saturation (90 psia and 44°F temperature) with no liquid present. The slightest amount of cooling of this vapor will cause a small amount of it to condense back to a liquid at 90 psia and 44°F. So we can say that R-22 at 90 psia pressure has a boiling point of 44°F, a condensing point of 44°F, and, of course, a saturation temperature of 44°F. This type of relationship is true for all refrigerants. A brief study of the two left-hand columns in the tables in figs. 10-1, 10-2, and 10-3 show these pressure-temperature relationships for R-22, R-12, and water.

Figure 10-2 Properties of dichlorodifluoromethane (CCl_2F_2) (ASHRAE designation: refrigerant 12). (Reprinted with permission from the 1960 ASHRAE Heating, Ventilating, Air Conditioning Guide.)

								Enthalpy and entropy taken from $-10°F$				
Satura-tion temper-ature, °F	Absolute pressure, lb/in.^{2} (psia)	Volume, ft^3/lb		Enthalpy, Btu/lb		Entropy		25° superheat		50° superheat	
		Liquid	Vapor	Liquid	Vapor	Liquid	Vapor	Enthalpy	Entropy	Enthalpy	Entropy
0	23.87	0.0110	1.637	8.25	78.21	0.01869	0.17091	81.71	0.17829	85.26	0.18547
2	24.89	0.0110	1.574	8.67	78.44	0.01961	0.17075	81.94	0.17812	85.51	0.18529
4	25.96	0.0111	1.514	9.10	78.67	0.02052	0.17060	82.17	0.17795	85.76	0.18511
5	26.51	0.0111	1.485	9.32	78.79	0.02097	0.17052	82.29	0.17786	85.89	0.18502
6	27.05	0.0111	1.457	9.53	78.90	0.02143	0.17045	82.41	0.17778	86.01	0.18494
8	28.18	0.0111	1.403	9.96	79.13	0.02235	0.17030	82.66	0.17763	86.26	0.18477
10	29.35	0.0112	1.351	10.39	79.36	0.02328	0.17015	82.90	0.17747	86.51	0.18460
12	30.56	0.0112	1.301	10.82	79.59	0.02419	0.17001	83.14	0.17733	86.76	0.18444
14	31.80	0.0112	1.253	11.26	79.82	0.02510	0.16987	83.38	0.17720	87.01	0.18429
16	33.08	0.0112	1.207	11.70	80.05	0.02601	0.16974	83.61	0.17706	87.26	0.18413
18	34.40	0.0113	1.163	12.12	80.27	0.02692	0.16961	82.85	0.17693	87.51	0.18397
20	35.75	0.0113	1.121	12.55	80.49	0.02783	0.16949	84.09	0.17679	87.76	0.18382
22	37.15	0.0113	1.081	13.00	80.72	0.02873	0.16938	84.32	0.17666	88.00	0.18369
24	38.58	0.0113	1.043	13.44	80.95	0.02963	0.16926	84.55	0.17652	88.24	0.18355
26	40.07	0.0114	1.007	13.88	81.17	0.03053	0.16913	84.79	0.17639	88.49	0.18342
28	41.59	0.0114	0.973	14.32	81.39	0.03143	0.16900	85.02	0.17625	88.73	0.18328
30	43.16	0.0115	0.939	14.76	81.61	0.03233	0.16887	85.25	0.17612	88.97	0.18315
32	44.77	0.0115	0.908	15.21	81.83	0.03323	0.16876	85.48	0.17600	89.21	0.18303
34	46.42	0.0115	0.877	15.65	82.05	0.03413	0.16865	85.71	0.17589	89.45	0.18291
36	48.13	0.0116	0.848	16.10	82.27	0.03502	0.16854	85.95	0.17577	89.68	0.18280
38	49.88	0.0116	0.819	16.55	82.49	0.03591	0.16843	86.18	0.17566	89.92	0.18268
39	50.78	0.0116	0.806	16.77	82.60	0.03635	0.16838	86.29	0.17560	90.04	0.18262
40	51.68	0.0116	0.792	17.00	82.71	0.03680	0.16833	86.41	0.17554	90.16	0.18256
41	52.70	0.0116	0.779	17.23	82.82	0.03725	0.16828	86.52	0.17549	90.28	0.18251
42	53.51	0.0116	0.767	17.46	82.93	0.03770	0.16823	86.64	0.17544	90.40	0.18245
44	55.40	0.0117	0.742	17.91	83.15	0.03859	0.16813	86.86	0.17534	90.65	0.18235
46	57.35	0.0117	0.718	18.36	83.36	0.03948	0.16803	87.09	0.17525	90.89	0.18224
48	59.35	0.0117	0.695	18.82	83.57	0.04037	0.16794	87.31	0.17515	91.14	0.18214
50	61.39	0.0118	0.673	19.27	83.78	0.04126	0.16785	87.54	0.17505	91.38	0.18203
52	63.49	0.0118	0.652	19.72	83.99	0.04215	0.16776	87.76	0.17496	91.61	0.18193
54	65.53	0.0118	0.632	20.18	84.20	0.04304	0.16767	87.98	0.17486	91.83	0.18184
56	67.84	0.0119	0.612	20.64	84.41	0.04392	0.16758	88.20	0.17477	92.06	0.18174
58	70.10	0.0119	0.593	21.11	84.62	0.04480	0.16749	88.42	0.17467	92.28	0.18165
60	72.41	0.0119	0.575	21.57	84.82	0.04568	0.16741	88.64	0.17458	92.51	0.18155
62	74.77	0.0120	0.557	22.03	85.02	0.04657	0.16733	88.86	0.17450	92.74	0.18147
64	77.20	0.0120	0.540	22.49	85.22	0.04745	0.16725	89.07	0.17442	92.97	0.18139
66	79.67	0.0120	0.524	22.95	85.42	0.04833	0.16717	89.29	0.17433	93.20	0.18130

Figure 10-2 *(Cont.)*

Satura-tion temper-ature, °F	Absolute pressure, lb/in.² (psia)	Volume, ft³/lb		Enthalpy and entropy taken from –10°F							
				Enthalpy, Btu/lb		Entropy		25° superheat		50° superheat	
		Liquid	Vapor	Liquid	Vapor	Liquid	Vapor	Enthalpy	Entropy	Enthalpy	Entropy
68	82.24	0.0121	0.508	23.42	85.62	0.04921	0.16709	89.50	0.17425	93.43	0.18122
70	84.82	0.0121	0.493	23.90	85.82	0.05009	0.16701	89.72	0.17417	93.66	0.18114
72	87.50	0.0121	0.479	24.37	86.02	0.05097	0.16693	89.93	0.17409	93.99	0.18106
74	90.20	0.0122	0.464	24.84	86.22	0.05185	0.16685	90.14	0.17402	94.12	0.18098
76	93.00	0.0122	0.451	20.32	86.42	0.05272	0.16677	90.36	0.17394	94.34	0.18091
78	95.85	0.0123	0.438	25.80	86.61	0.05359	0.16669	90.57	0.17387	94.57	0.18083
80	98.76	0.0123	0.425	26.28	86.80	0.05446	0.16662	90.78	0.17379	94.80	0.18075
82	101.70	0.0123	0.413	26.76	86.99	0.05534	0.16655	90.98	0.17372	95.01	0.18068
84	104.8	0.0124	0.401	27.24	87.18	0.05621	0.16648	91.18	0.17365	95.22	0.18061
86	107.9	0.0124	0.389	27.72	87.37	0.05708	0.16640	91.37	0.17358	95.44	0.18054
88	111.1	0.0124	0.378	28.21	87.56	0.05795	0.16632	91.57	0.17351	95.65	0.18047
90	114.3	0.0125	0.368	28.70	87.74	0.05882	0.16624	91.77	0.17344	95.86	0.18040
92	117.7	0.0125	0.357	29.19	87.92	0.05969	0.16616	91.97	0.17337	96.07	0.18033
94	121.0	0.0126	0.347	29.68	88.10	0.06056	0.16608	92.16	0.17330	96.28	0.18026
96	124.5	0.0126	0.338	30.18	88.28	0.06143	0.16600	92.36	0.17322	96.50	0.18018
98	128.0	0.0126	0.328	30.67	88.45	0.06230	0.16592	92.55	0.17315	96.71	0.18011
100	131.6	0.0127	0.319	31.16	88.62	0.06316	0.16584	92.75	0.17308	96.92	0.18004
102	135.3	0.0127	0.310	31.65	88.79	0.06403	0.16576	92.93	0.17301	97.12	0.17998
104	139.0	0.0128	0.302	32.15	88.95	0.06490	0.16568	93.11	0.17294	97.32	0.17993
106	142.8	0.0128	0.293	32.65	89.11	0.06577	0.16560	93.30	0.17288	97.53	0.17987
108	146.8	0.0129	0.285	33.15	89.27	0.06663	0.16551	93.48	0.17281	97.73	0.17982
110	150.7	0.0129	0.277	33.65	89.43	0.06749	0.16542	93.66	0.17274	97.93	0.17976
112	154.8	0.0130	0.269	34.15	89.58	0.06836	0.16533	93.82	0.17266	98.11	0.17969
114	158.9	0.0130	0.262	34.65	89.73	0.06922	0.16524	93.98	0.17258	98.29	0.17961
116	163.1	0.0131	0.254	35.15	89.87	0.07008	0.16515	94.15	0.17249	98.48	0.17954
118	167.4	0.0131	0.247	35.65	90.01	0.07094	0.16505	94.31	0.17241	98.66	0.17946
120	171.8	0.0132	0.240	36.16	90.15	0.07180	0.16495	94.47	0.17233	98.84	0.17939
122	176.2	0.0132	0.233	36.66	90.28	0.07266	0.16484	94.63	0.17224	99.01	0.17931
124	180.8	0.0133	0.227	37.16	90.40	0.07352	0.16473	94.78	0.17215	99.18	0.17922
126	185.4	0.0133	0.220	37.67	90.52	0.07437	0.16462	94.94	0.17206	99.35	0.17914
128	190.1	0.0134	0.214	38.18	90.64	0.07522	0.16450	95.09	0.17196	99.53	0.17906
130	194.9	0.0134	0.208	38.69	90.76	0.07607	0.16438	95.25	0.17186	99.70	0.17897
132	199.8	0.0135	0.202	39.19	90.86	0.07691	0.16425	95.41	0.17176	99.87	0.17889
134	204.8	0.0135	0.196	39.70	90.96	0.07775	0.16411	95.56	0.17166	100.04	0.17881
136	209.9	0.0136	0.191	40.21	91.06	0.07858	0.16396	95.72	0.17156	100.22	0.17873
138	215.0	0.0137	0.185	40.72	91.15	0.07941	0.16380	95.87	0.17145	100.39	0.17864
140	220.2	0.0138	0.180	41.24	91.24	0.08024	0.16363	96.03	0.17134	100.56	0.17856

Figure 10-3 (a) Theremodynamic properties of water at saturation. (Reprinted with permission from the 1960 ASHRAE Heating, Ventilating, Air Conditioning Guide.)

Fahrenheit temperature t,°F (1)	Absolute pressure p_s		Specific volume, ft³/lb			Enthalpy, Btu/lb			Entropy, Btu/lb/°F		
	Lb/sq in. (2)	In. hg (3)	Saturated solid v_f (4)	Evaporation v_{fg} (5)	Saturated vapor v_g (6)	Saturated solid h_f (7)	Evaporation h_{fg} (8)	Saturated vapor h_g (9)	Saturated solid s_f (10)	Evaporation s_{fg} (11)	Saturated vapor s_g (12)
7	0.02653	0.05402	0.01743	10480	10480	-155.66	1219.84	1064.48	-0.3172	2.6088	2.2966
8	0.02791	0.05683	0.01743	9979	9979	-155.18	1219.80	1064.62	-0.3162	2.6081	2.2900
9	0.02936	0.05977	0.01744	9507	9507	-154.70	1219.76	1065.06	-0.3152	2.5025	2.2878
10	0.03087	0.06286	0.01744	9060	9060	-154.22	1219.72	1065.50	-0.3142	2.5969	2.2827
11	0.03246	0.06608	0.01744	8636	8636	-153.74	1219.68	1065.94	-0.3131	2.5912	2.2781
12	0.03412	0.06946	0.01744	8234	8234	-153.26	1219.64	1066.38	-0.3121	2.5857	2.2736
13	0.3585	0.07300	0.01744	7851	7851	-152.77	1219.59	1066.82	-0.3111	2.5801	2.2690
14	0.03767	0.07669	0.01744	7489	7489	-152.29	1219.55	1067.26	-0.3101	2.5746	2.2645
15	0.03957	0.08056	0.01744	7144	7144	-151.80	1219.50	1067.70	-0.3090	2.5690	2.2600
16	0.04156	0.08461	0.01745	6817	6817	-151.32	1219.46	1068.14	-0.3080	2.5635	2.2555
17	0.04363	0.08884	0.01745	6505	6505	-150.83	1219.41	1068.58	-0.3070	2.5581	2.511
18	0.04581	0.09326	0.01745	6210	6210	-150.34	1219.36	1069.02	-0.3060	2.5526	2.2466
19	0.04808	0.09789	0.01745	5929	5929	-149.85	1219.31	1069.46	-0.2049	2.5471	2.2422
20	0.05045	0.1027	0.01745	5662	5662	-149.36	1219.26	1069.90	-0.3039	2.5417	2.2378
21	0.05293	0.1078	0.01745	5408	5408	-148.87	1219.21	1070.34	-0.3029	2.5364	2.2335
22	0.05552	0.1130	0.01716	5166	5166	-148.38	1219.16	1070.78	-0.3019	2.5310	2.2291
23	0.05823	0.1186	0.01746	4936	4936	-147.88	1219.10	1071.22	-0.3008	2.5256	2.2248
24	0.06105	0.1243	0.01746	4717	4717	-147.39	1219.05	1071.66	-0.2998	2.5203	2.2205
25	0.06400	0.1303	0.01746	4509	4509	-146.89	1218.98	1072.09	-0.2988	2.5150	2.2162
26	0.06708	0.1366	0.01746	4311	4311	-146.40	1218.93	1072.53	-0.2978	2.5097	2.2119
27	0.07030	0.1431	0.01746	4122	4122	-145.90	1218.87	1072.97	-0.2968	2.5045	2.2077
28	0.07365	0.1500	0.01746	3943	3943	-145.40	1218.81	1073.41	-0.2957	2.4991	2.2034
29	0.07715	0.1571	0.01717	3771	3771	-144.90	1218.75	1073.85	-0.2947	2.4939	2.1992
30	0.08080	0.1645	0.01747	3608	3608	-144.40	1218.69	1074.29	-0.2937	2.4887	2.1950
31	0.08461	0.1723	0.01747	3453	3453	-143.90	1218.63	1074.73	-0.2927	2.4825	2.1908
32	0.08858	0.1803	0.01747	3305	3005	-143.40	1218.56	1075.16	-0.2916	2.4783	2.1867
32	0.088586	0.18036	0.01602	3304.6	3304.6	0.00	1075.16	1075.10	0.00000	2.1867	2.1867

#											
33	0.092227	0.18778	0.01602	3180.5	3180.5	1.01	1074.59	1075.60	0.00205	2.1811	2.1831
34	0.095999	0.19546	0.01602	3061.7	3061.7	2.01	1074.03	1076.04	0.00409	2.1755	2.1796
35	0.099908	0.20342	0.01602	2947.8	2947.8	3.02	1073.46	1076.48	0.00612	2.1700	**2.1761**
36	0.10396	0.21166	0.01602	2838.7	2838.7	4.02	1072.90	1076.92	0.00815	2.1644	2.1726
37	0.10815	0.22020	0.01602	2734.1	2734.1	5.03	1072.33	1077.36	0.01018	2.1589	2.1691
38	0.11249	0.22904	0.01602	2633.8	2633.8	6.03	1071.77	1077.80	0.01220	2.1535	2.1657
39	0.11699	0.23819	0.01602	2537.6	2537.6	7.04	1071.20	1078.24	0.01422	21480	2.1622
40	0.12164	0.24767	0.01602	2445.4	2445.4	8.04	1070.64	1078.68	0.01623	2.1426	2.1588
41	0.12646	0.25748	0.01602	2356.9	2356.9	9.05	1070.06	1079.11	**0.01824**	2.1372	2.4554
42	0.13145	0.26763	0.01602	2272.0	2272.0	10.05	1069.50	1079.55	0.02024	2.1318	2.1520
43	0.13660	0.27813	0.01602	2190.5	2190.5	11.05	1068.94	1079.99	0.02224	2.1265	2.1487
44	0.14194	0.28899	0.01602	2112.3	2112.3	12.06	1068.37	1080.43	0.02423	2.1211	2.1453
45	0.14746	0.30023	0.01602	2037.3	2037.3	13.06	1067.81	1080.87	0.02622	2.1158	2.1420
46	0.15317	0.31185	0.01602	1965.2	1965.2	14.06	1067.24	1081.30	0.02820	2.1105	2.1387
47	0.15907	0.32387	0.01602	1896.0	1896.0	15.06	1066.68	1081.74	0.03018	2.1052	2.1354
48	0.16517	0.33629	0.01602	1829.5	1829.5	16.07	1066.11	1082.18	0.03216	2.0999	2.1321
49	0.17148	0.34913	0.01602	1765.7	1765.7	17.07	1065.55	1082.62	0.03413	2.0947	2.1288
50	0.17799	0.36240	0.01602	1704.3	1704.3	18.07	1064.99	1083.06	0.03610	2.0895	2.1256
51	0.18473	0.37611	0.01602	1645.4	1645.4	19.07	1064.42	1083.49	0.03806	2.0842	2.1223
52	0.19169	0.39028	0.01602	1588.7	1588.7	20.07	1063.86	1083.93	0.04002	2.0791	2.1191
53	0.19888	0.40402	0.01603	1534.3	1534.3	21.07	1063.30	1084.37	0.04197	2.0739	2.1159
54	0.20630	0.42003	0.01603	1481.9	1481.9	22.08	1062.72	1084.80	0.04392	2.0688	2.1127
55	0.21397	0.43564	0.01603	1431.5	1431.5	23.08	1062.16	1085.24	**0.04587**	2.0637	2.1096
56	0.22188	0.45176	0.01603	1383.1	1383.1	24.08	1061.60	1085.68	0.04781	2.0586	2.1064
57	0.23006	0.46840	0.01603	1336.5	1336.5	25.08	1061.04	1086.12	0.04975	2.0535	2.1033
58	0.23849	0.48558	0.01603	1291.7	1291.7	26.08	1660.47	1086.55	0.05168	2.0485	2.1002
59	0.24720	0.50330	0.01603	1248.6	1248.6	27.08	1059.91	1086.99	0.05361	2.0434	2.0970
60	0.25618	0.52160	0.01603	1207.1	1207.1	**28.08**	1059.34	1087.42	0.05553	2.0385	2.0940
61	0.26545	0.54047	0.01604	1167.2	1167.2	29.08	1058.78	1087.86	**0.05746**	2.0334	2.0909
62	0.27502	0.55994	0.01604	1128.7	1128.7	30.08	1058.22	1088.30	0.05937	2.0284	2.0878
63	0.28488	**0.58002**	0.01604	1091.7	1091.7	31.08	1057.65	1088.73	0.06129	2.0235	2.0848
64	0.29505	0.60073	0.01604	1056.1	1056.1	32.08	1057.09	1089.17	0.06320	2.0186	2.0818
65	0.30554	0.62209	0.01604	1021.7	1021.7	33.08	1056.52	1089.60	0.06510	2.0136	2.0787
66	0.31636	0.64411	0.01604	988.65	988.63	34.07	1055.97	1090.04	0.06700	2.0087	2.0757
67	0.32750	0.66681	0.01605	956.78	956.76	35.07	1055.40	1090.47	0.06890	2.0039	2.0728

Figure 10-3 (a) (Cont.)

	Absolute pressure p_s		Specific volume, ft³/lb			Enthalpy, Btu/lb			Entropy/lb/°F		
Fahrenheit temperature t, °F (1)	Lb/sq in. (2)	In. hg (3)	Saturated liquid v_f (4)	Evaporation v_{fg} (5)	Saturated vapor v_g (6)	Saturated liquid h_f (7)	Evaporation h_{fg} (8)	Saturated vapor h_g (9)	Saturated liquid s_f (10)	Evaporation s_{fg} (11)	Saturated vapor s_g (12)
68	0.33900	0.69021	0.01605	926.06	926.08	36.07	1054.84	1090.91	0.07080	1.9990	2.0698
69	0.35084	0.71432	0.01605	896.47	896.49	37.07	1054.27	1091.34	0.07269	1.9941	2.0668
70	0.36304	0.73916	0.01605	867.95	867.97	38.07	1053.71	1091.78	0.07458	1.9893	2.0639
71	0.37561	0.76476	0.01605	840.45	840.47	39.07	1053.14	1092.21	0.07646	1.9845	2.0610
72	0.38856	0.79143	0.01606	813.95	813.97	40.07	1052.58	1092.65	0.07834	1.9797	2.0580
73	0.40190	0.81829	0.01606	788.38	788.40	41.07	1052.01	1093.08	0.08022	1.9749	2.0551
74	0.41564	0.84626	0.01606	763.73	763.75	42.06	1051.46	1093.52	0.08209	1.9701	2.0522
75	0.42979	0.87506	0.01606	739.95	739.97	43.06	1050.89	1093.95	0.08396	1.9654	2.0494
76	0.44435	0.90472	0.01606	717.01	717.03	44.06	1050.32	1094.38	0.08582	1.9607	2.0465
77	0.45935	0.93524	0.01607	694.88	694.90	45.06	1049.76	1094.82	0.08769	1.9560	2.0437
78	0.47478	0.96666	0.01607	673.52	673.54	46.06	1049.19	1095.25	0.08954	1.9513	2.0408
79	0.49066	0.99900	0.01607	652.91	652.93	47.06	1048.62	1095.68	0.09140	1.9466	2.0380
80	0.50701	1.0323	0.01607	633.01	633.03	48.05	1048.07	1096.12	0.09325	1.9419	2.0352
81	0.52382	1.0665	0.01608	613.80	613.82	49.05	1047.50	1096.55	0.09510	1.9373	2.0324
82	0.54112	1.1017	0.01608	595.25	595.27	50.05	1046.93	1096.98	0.09694	1.9328	2.0297
83	0.55892	1.1380	0.01608	577.34	577.36	51.05	1046.37	1097.42	0.09878	1.9281	2.0269
84	0.57722	1.1752	0.01608	560.04	560.06	52.05	1945.80	1097.85	0.10062	1.9236	2.0242
85	0.59604	1.2136	0.01609	543.33	543.35	53.05	1045.23	1098.28	0.10246	1.9189	2.0214
86	0.61540	1.2530	0.01609	527.19	527.21	54.04	1044.67	1098.71	0.10429	1.9144	2.0187
87	0.63530	1.2935	0.01609	511.60	511.62	55.04	1044.10	1099.14	0.10611	1.9099	2.0160
88	0.65575	1.3351	0.01610	496.52	496.54	56.04	1043.54	1099.58	0.10794	1.9054	2.0133
89	0.67678	1.3779	0.01610	481.96	481.98	57.04	1042.97	1100.01	0.10976	1.9008	2.0106
90	0.69838	1.4219	0.01610	467.88	467.90	58.04	1042.40	1100.44	0.11158	1.8963	2.0079
91	0.72059	1.4671	0.01610	454.26	454.28	59.03	1041.84	1100.87	0.11339	1.8919	2.0053
92	0.74340	1.5136	0.01611	441.10	441.12	60.03	1041.27	1101.30	0.11520	1.8874	2.0026
93	0.76684	1.5613	0.01611	428.38	428.40	61.03	1040.70	1101.73	0.11701	1.8830	2.0000
94	0.79091	1.6103	0.01611	416.07	416.09	62.03	1040.13	1102.16	0.11881	1.8786	1.9974
95	0.81564	1.6607	0.01612	404.17	404.19	63.03	1039.56	1102.59	0.12061	1.8741	1.9947
96	0.84103	1.7124	0.01612	392.65	392.67	64.02	1039.00	1103.02	0.12241	1.8698	1.9922
97	0.86711	1.7655	0.01612	381.51	381.53	65.02	1033.43	1103.45	0.12420	1.8654	1.9896

98	0.89388	1.8200	0.01612	370.73	370.75	66.02	1037.86	1103.88	0.12600	1.8610	1.9870
99	0.92137	1.8759	0.01613	360.30	360.32	67.02	1037.29	1104.31	0.12778	1.8566	1.9844
100	0.94959	1.9334	0.01613	350.20	350.22	68.02	1036.72	1104.74	0.12957	1.8523	1.9819
101	0.97854	1.9923	0.01614	340.42	340.44	69.01	1036.15	1105.17	0.13135	1.8480	1.9793
102	1.0083	2.0529	0.01614	330.96	330.98	70.01	1035.58	1105.59	0.13313	1.8437	1.9768
103	1.0388	2.1149	0.01614	321.80	321.82	71.01	1035.01	1106.02	0.13490	1.8394	1.9743
104	1.0700	2.1786	0.01614	312.93	312.95	72.01	1034.44	1106.45	0.13667	1.8351	1.9718
105	1.1021	2.2440	0.01615	304.34	304.36	73.01	1033.87	1106.88	0.13844	1.8309	1.9693
106	1.1351	2.3110	0.01615	296.02	296.04	74.01	1033.29	1107.30	0.14021	1.8266	1.9668
107	1.1688	2.3798	0.01616	287.96	287.98	75.00	1032.73	1107.73	0.14197	1.8224	1.9644
108	1.2035	2.4503	0.01616	280.14	280.16	76.00	1032.16	1108.16	0.14373	1.8182	1.9619
109	1.2390	2.5226	0.01616	272.58	272.60	77.00	1031.58	1108.58	0.14549	1.8140	1.9595
110	1.2754	2.5968	0.01617	265.24	265.26	78.00	1031.01	1109.01	0.14724	1.8098	1.9570
111	1.3128	2.6728	0.01617	248.14	258.16	79.00	1030.44	1109.44	0.14899	1.8056	1.9546
112	1.3510	2.7507	0.01617	251.25	251.27	80.00	1029.86	1109.86	0.15074	1.8015	1.9522
113	1.3902	2.8306	0.01618	244.57	244.59	80.99	1029.30	1110.29	0.15248	1.7973	1.9498
114	1.4305	2.9125	0.01618	238.10	233.12	81.99	1028.72	1110.71	0.15423	1.7932	1.9474
115	1.4717	2.9963	0.01618	231.82	231.84	82.99	1028.15	1111.14	0.15596	1.7890	1.9450
116	1.5139	3.0823	0.01619	225.73	225.75	83.99	1027.57	1111.56	0.15770	1.7849	1.9426
117	1.5571	3.1703	0.01619	219.83	219.85	84.99	1026.99	1111.98	0.15943	1.7809	1.9403
118	1.6014	3.2606	0.01620	214.10	214.12	85.99	1026.42	1112.41	0.16116	1.7767	1.9379
119	1.6468	3.3530	0.01620	208.54	208.56	86.98	1025.85	1112.83	0.16289	1.7727	1.9356
120	1.6933	3.4477	0.01620	203.16	203.18	87.98	1025.28	1113.26	0.16461	1.7687	1.9333
121	1.7409	3.5446	0.01621	197.93	197.95	88.98	1024.70	1113.68	0.16634	1.7647	1.9310
122	1.7897	3.6439	0.01621	192.85	192.87	89.98	1024.12	1114.10	0.16805	1.7606	1.9286
123	1.8396	3.7455	0.01622	187.93	187.95	90.98	1023.54	1114.52	0.16977	1.7566	1.9264
124	1.8907	3.8496	0.01622	183.15	183.17	91.98	1022.96	1114.94	0.17148	1.7526	1.9241
125	1.9430	3.9561	0.01622	178.51	178.53	92.98	1022.39	1115.37	0.17319	1.7486	1.9218
126	1.9966	4.0651	0.01623	174.00	174.02	93.98	1021.81	1115.79	0.17490	1.7446	1.9195
127	2.0514	4.1768	0.01623	169.63	169.65	94.97	1021.24	1116.21	0.17660	1.7407	1.9173
128	2.1075	4.2910	0.01624	165.38	165.40	95.97	1020.66	1116.63	0.17830	1.7367	1.9150
129	2.1649	4.4078	0.01624	161.26	161.28	96.97	1020.08	1117.05	0.18000	1.7238	1.9128
130	2.2237	4.5274	0.01625	157.25	157.27	97.97	1019.50	1117.47	0.18170	1.7289	1.9106
131	2.2838	4.6498	0.01625	153.36	153.38	98.97	1018.92	1117.89	0.18339	1.7250	1.9084
132	2.3452	4.7750	0.01626	149.58	149.60	99.97	1018.34	1118.31	0.18508	1.7211	1.9062
133	2.4081	4.9030	0.01626	145.91	145.93	100.97	1017.76	1118.73	0.18676	1.7172	1.9040
134	2.4725	5.0340	0.01626	142.34	142.36	101.97	1017.18	1119.15	0.18845	1.7134	1.9018
135	2.5382	5.1679	0.01627	138.87	138.89	102.97	1016.59	1119.56	0.19013	1.7095	1.8996

Figure 10-3 (a) (Cont.)

Fahrenheit temperature t, °F (1)	Absolute pressure p_s		Specific volume, ft³/lb			Enthalpy, Btu/lb			Entropy/lb/°F		
	Lb/sq in. (2)	In. hg (3)	Saturated liquid v_f (4)	Evaporation v_{fg} (5)	Saturated vapor v_g (6)	Saturated liquid h_f (7)	Evaporation h_{fg} (8)	Saturated vapor h_g (9)	Saturated liquid s_f (10)	Evaporation s_{fg} (11)	Saturated vapor s_g (12)
136	2.6005	5.3049	0.01627	135.50	135.52	103.97	1016.01	1119.98	0.19181	1.7056	1.8974
137	2.6743	5.4450	0.01628	132.22	132.24	104.97	1015.43	1120.40	0.19348	1.7018	1.8953
138	2.7446	5.5881	0.01628	129.04	129.06	105.97	1014.85	1120.82	0.19516	1.6979	1.8931
139	2.8165	5.7345	0.01629	125.94	125.96	106.97	1014.26	1121.23	0.19683	1.6942	1.8910
140	2.8900	5.8842	0.01629	122.94	122.96	107.96	1013.69	1121.65	0.19850	1.6903	1.8888
141	2.9651	6.0371	0.01630	120.01	120.03	108.96	1013.11	1122.07	0.20016	1.6865	1.8867
142	3.0419	6.1934	0.01630	117.16	117.18	109.96	1012.52	1122.48	0.20182	1.6828	1.8846
143	3.1204	6.3532	0.01631	114.40	114.42	110.96	1011.94	1122.90	0.20348	1.6790	1.8825
144	3.2006	6.5164	0.01631	111.70	111.72	111.96	1011.35	1123.31	0.20514	1.6753	1.8804
145	3.2825	6.6832	0.01632	109.09	109.11	112.96	1010.77	1123.73	0.20679	1.6715	1.8783
146	3.3662	6.8536	0.01632	106.54	106.56	113.96	1010.18	1124.14	0.20845	1.6678	1.8753
147	3.4517	7.0277	0.01633	104.06	104.08	114.96	1009.59	1124.55	0.21010	1.6641	1.8742
148	3.5390	7.2056	0.01633	101.65	101.67	115.96	1009.01	1124.97	0.21174	1.6604	1.8721
149	3.6282	7.3872	0.01634	99.306	99.322	116.96	1008.42	1125.38	0.21339	1.6567	1.8701
150	3.7194	7.5727	0.01634	97.022	97.038	117.96	1007.33	1125.79	0.21503	1.6530	1.8680
151	3.8124	7.7622	0.01635	94.799	94.815	118.96	1007.24	1126.20	0.21667	1.6493	1.8660
152	3.9074	7.9556	0.01635	92.635	92.651	119.96	1006.66	1126.62	0.21830	1.6457	1.8640
153	4.0044	8.1532	0.01636	90.528	90.544	120.97	1006.06	1127.03	0.21994	1.6421	1.8620
154	4.1035	8.3548	0.01636	88.477	88.493	121.97	1005.47	1127.44	0.22157	1.6384	1.8600
155	4.2046	8.5607	0.01637	86.480	86.496	122.97	1004.88	1127.85	0.22320	1.6348	1.8580
156	4.3078	8.7708	0.01637	84.536	84.552	123.97	1004.29	1128.26	0.22482	1.6312	1.8560
157	4.4132	8.9853	0.01638	82.642	82.658	124.97	1003.70	1128.67	0.22645	1.6276	1.8540
158	4.5207	9.2042	0.01638	80.798	80.814	125.97	1003.11	1129.08	0.22807	1.6239	1.8520
159	4.6304	9.4276	0.01639	79.001	79.017	126.97	1002.51	1129.48	0.22969	1.6204	1.8501
160	4.7424	9.6556	0.01639	77.251	77.267	127.97	1001.92	1129.89	0.23130	1.6168	1.8481
161	4.8566	9.8882	0.01640	75.546	75.562	128.97	1001.33	1130.30	0.23292	1.6133	1.8462
162	4.9732	10.126	0.01640	73.885	73.901	129.97	1000.74	1130.71	0.23453	1.6097	1.8442
163	5.0921	10.368	0.01641	72.267	72.283	130.98	1000.13	1131.11	0.23614	1.6062	1.8423

164	5.2134	10.615	0.01642	70.690	70.706	131.98	999.54	1131.52	0.23774	1.6027	1.8404
165	5.3372	10.867	0.01642	69.153	69.169	132.98	998.94	1131.92	0.23935	1.5990	1.8384
166	5.4634	11.124	0.01643	67.654	67.670	133.98	998.35	1132.33	0.24095	1.5956	1.8365
167	5.5921	11.386	0.01653	66.194	66.210	134.98	997.75	1132.73	0.24255	1.5920	1.8346
168	5.7233	11.653	0.01644	64.770	64.786	135.98	997.16	1133.14	0.21414	1.5887	1.8328
169	5.8572	11.925	0.01644	63.382	63.398	136.99	996.55	1133.54	0.24574	1.5852	1.8309
170	5.9936	12.203	0.01645	62.029	62.045	137.99	995.95	1133.94	0.24733	1.5817	1.8290
171	6.1328	12.487	0.01645	60.710	60.726	138.99	995.36	1134.35	0.24892	1.5782	1.8271
172	6.2746	12.775	0.01646	59.423	59.439	139.99	994.76	1134.75	0.25051	1.5748	1.8253
173	6.4192	13.070	0.01647	58.168	58.184	141.00	994.15	1135.15	0.25209	1.5713	1.8234
174	6.5666	13.370	0.01647	56.944	56.960	142.00	993.55	1135.55	0.25367	1.5679	1.8216
175	6.7168	13.676	0.01648	55.750	55.766	143.00	992.95	1135.95	0.25525	1.5644	1.8197
176	6.8699	13.987	0.01648	54.586	54.602	144.00	992.35	1136.35	0.25683	1.5611	1.8179
177	7.0259	14.305	0.01649	53.450	53.466	145.00	991.75	1136.75	0.25841	1.5577	1.8161
178	7.1849	14.629	0.01650	52.341	52.357	146.01	991.14	1137.15	0.25998	1.5543	1.8143
179	7.3469	14.959	0.01650	51.260	51.276	147.01	990.54	1137.55	0.26155	1.5508	1.8124
180	7.5119	15.295	0.01651	50.203	50.220	148.01	989.93	1137.94	0.26312	1.5475	1.8106
181	7.6801	15.637	0.01651	49.173	49.190	149.02	989.32	1138.34	0.26468	1.5442	1.8089
182	7.8514	15.986	0.01652	48.168	48.185	150.02	988.72	1138.74	0.26625	1.5408	1.8071
183	8.0258	16.341	0.01652	47.187	47.204	151.02	988.12	1139.14	0.26781	1.5375	1.8053
184	8.2035	16.703	0.01653	46.229	46.246	152.03	987.50	1139.53	0.26937	1.5341	1.8035
185	8.3845	17.071	0.01654	45.294	45.311	153.03	986.89	1139.92	0.27093	1.5308	1.8017
186	8.5688	17.446	0.01654	44.381	44.398	154.04	986.28	1140.32	0.27248	1.5275	1.8000
187	8.7565	17.829	0.01655	43.489	43.506	155.04	985.67	1140.71	0.27404	1.5242	1.7982
188	8.9476	18.218	0.01656	42.619	42.636	156.04	985.07	1141.11	0.27559	1.5209	1.7965
189	9.1422	18.614	0.01656	41.769	41.786	157.05	984.45	1141.50	0.27713	1.5176	1.7947
190	9.3403	19.017	0.01657	40.939	40.956	158.05	983.84	1141.89	0.27868	1.5143	1.7930
191	9.5420	19.428	0.01658	40.128	40.145	159.06	983.22	1142.28	0.28022	1.5111	1.7913
192	9.7473	19.846	0.01658	39.337	39.354	160.06	982.61	1142.67	0.28176	1.5078	1.7896
193	9.9563	20.271	0.01659	38.563	38.580	161.06	982.00	1143.06	0.28330	1.5045	1.7878
194	10.169	20.704	0.01659	37.807	37.824	162.07	981.38	1143.45	0.28484	1.5013	1.7861
195	10.386	21.145	0.01660	37.069	37.086	163.08	980.76	1143.84	0.28638	1.4980	1.7844
196	10.606	21.594	0.01661	36.348	36.365	164.08	980.15	1144.23	0.28791	1.4949	1.7828
197	10.830	22.050	0.01661	35.643	35.660	165.08	979.54	1144.62	0.28944	1.4917	1.7811

Figure 10-3 (a) (Cont.)

Fahrenheit temperature t, °F (1)	Absolute pressure p_s Lb/sq in. (2)	Absolute pressure p_s In. hg (3)	Specific volume, ft³/lb Saturated liquid v_f (4)	Specific volume, ft³/lb Evaporation v_{fg} (5)	Specific volume, ft³/lb Saturated vapor v_g (6)	Enthalpy, Btu/lb Saturated liquid h_f (7)	Enthalpy, Btu/lb Evaporation h_{fg} (8)	Enthalpy, Btu/lb Saturated vapor h_g (9)	Entropy/lb/°F Saturated liquid s_f (10)	Entropy/lb/°F Evaporation s_{fg} (11)	Entropy/lb/°F Saturated vapor s_g (12)
198	11.058	22.515	0.01662	34.954	34.971	166.09	978.91	1145.00	0.29097	1.4884	1.7794
199	11.290	23.987	0.01663	34.281	34.298	167.10	978.29	1145.39	0.29250	1.4852	1.7777
200	11.526	23.468	0.01663	33.623	33.640	168.10	977.68	1145.78	0.29402	1.4820	1.7760
201	11.767	23.957	0.01664	32.980	32.997	169.11	977.05	1146.16	0.29554	1.4789	1.7744
202	12.011	24.455	0.01665	32.351	32.368	170.11	976.43	1146.54	0.29706	1.4756	1.7727
203	12.260	24.961	0.01665	31.737	31.754	171.12	975.81	1146.93	0.29858	1.4725	1.7711
204	12.513	25.476	0.01666	31.136	31.153	172.12	975.19	1147.31	0.30010	1.4693	1.7694
205	12.770	26.000	0.01667	30.549	30.566	173.13	974.56	1147.69	0.30161	1.4662	1.7678
206	13.031	26.532	0.01667	29.974	29.991	174.14	973.94	1148.08	0.30312	1.4631	1.7662
207	13.297	27.074	0.01668	29.413	29.430	175.14	973.32	1148.46	0.30463	1.4600	1.7646
208	13.568	27.625	0.01669	28.863	28.880	176.15	972.69	1148.84	0.30614	1.4568	1.7629
209	13.843	28.185	0.01669	28.326	28.343	177.16	972.06	1149.22	0.30765	1.4536	1.7613
210	14.123	28.754	0.01670	27.801	27.818	178.17	971.43	1149.60	0.30915	1.4506	1.7597
211	14.407	29.333	0.01671	27.287	27.304	179.17	970.81	1149.98	0.31065	1.4474	1.7581
212	14.696	29.921	0.01671	26.784	26.801	180.18	970.17	1150.35	0.31215	1.4444	1.7565

Figure 10-3 (*b*)

Absolute pressure p, lb/in.^{2}	Tempera-ture t, °F	Specific volume		Enthalpy			Entropy		
		Saturated liquid v_f	Saturated vapor v_g	Saturated liquid h_f	Evapo-ration h_{fg}	Saturated vapor h_g	Saturated liquid s_f	Evapo-ration s_{fg}	Saturated vapor s_g
14.696	212.00	0.01672	26.80	180.07	970.3	1150.4	0.3120	1.4446	1.7566
16	216.32	0.01674	24.75	184.42	967.6	1152.0	0.3184	1.4313	1.7497
18	222.41	0.01679	22.17	190.56	963.6	1154.2	0.3275	1.4128	1.7403
20	227.96	0.01683	20.080	196.16	960.1	1156.3	0.3356	1.3962	1.7319
22	233.07	0.01687	18.375	201.33	956.8	1158;1	0.3431	1.3811	1.7242
24	237.82	0.01691	16.938	206.14	953.7	1159.8	0.3500	1.3672	1.7172
26	242.25	0.01694	15.715	210.62	950.7	1161.3	0.3564	1.3544	1.7108
28	246.41	0.01698	14.663	214.83	947.9	1162.7	0.3623	1.3425	1.7048
30	250.33	0.01701	13.746	218.82	945.3	1164.1	0.3680	1.3313	1.6993
32	254.05	0.01704	12.940	222.59	942.8	1165.4	0.3733	1.3209	1.6941
34	257.58	0.01707	12.226	226.18	940.3	1166.5	0.3783	1.3110	1.6893
36	260.95	0.01709	11.588	229.60	938.0	1167.6	0.3831	1.3017	1.6848
38	264.16	0.01812	11.015	232.89	935.8	1168.7	0.3876	1.2929	1.6805
40	267.25	0.01715	10.498	236.03	933.7	1169.7	0.3919	1.2844	1.6763
42	270.21	0.01717	10.029	239.04	931.6	1170.7	0.3960	1.2764	1.6724
44	273.05	0.01720	9.601	241.95	929.6	1171.6	0.4000	1.2687	1.6687
46	275.80	0.01722	9.209	244.75	927.7	1172.4	0.4038	1.2613	1.6652
48	278.45	0.01725	8.848	247.47	925.8	1173.3	0.4075	1.2542	1.6617
50	281.01	0.01727	8.515	250.09	924.0	1174.1	0.4110	1.2474	1.6585
52	283.49	0.01729	8.208	252.63	922.2	1174.8	0.4144	1.2409	1.6553
54	285.90	0.01731	7.922	255.09	920.5	1175.6	0.4177	1.2346	1.6523
56	288.23	0.01733	7.656	257.50	918.8	1176.3	0.4209	1.2285	1.6494
58	290.50	0.01736	7.407	259.82	917.1	1176.9	0.4240	1.2226	1.6466
60	292.71	0.01738	7.175	262.09	915.5	1177.6	0.4270	1.2168	1.6438
62	294.85	0.01740	6.957	264.30	913.9	1178.2	0.4300	1.2112	1.6412
64	296.94	0.01742	6.752	266.45	912.3	1178.8	0.4328	1.2059	1.6387
66	298.99	0.01744	6.560	268.55	910.8	1179.4	0.4356	1.2006	1.6362
68	300.98	0.01746	6.378	270.60	909.4	1180.0	0.4383	1.1955	1.6338
70	302.92	0.01748	6.206	272.61	907.9	1180.6	0.4409	1.1906	1.6315
72	304.83	0.01750	6.044	274.57	906.5	1181.1	0.4435	1.1857	1.6292
74	306.68	0.10752	5.890	276.49	905.1	1181.6	0.4460	1.1810	1.6270
76	308.50	0.01754	5.743	278.37	903.7	1182.1	0.4484	1.1764	1.6248
78	310.29	0.01755	5.604	280.21	902.4	1182.6	0.4508	1.1720	1.6228
80	312.03	0.01757	5.472	282.02	901.1	1183.1	0.4531	1.1676	1.6207
82	313.74	0.01759	5.346	283.79	899.7	1183.5	0.4554	1.1633	1.6187
84	315.42	0.01761	5.226	285.53	898.5	1184.0	0.4576	1.1592	1.6168
86	317.07	0.01762	5.111	287.24	897.2	1184.4	0.4598	1.1551	1.6149
88	318.68	0.01764	5.001	288.91	895.9	1184.8	0.4620	1.1510	1.6130
90	320.27	0.01766	4.896	290.56	894.7	1185.3	0.4641	1.1471	1.6112
92	321.83	0.01768	4.796	292.18	893.5	1185.7	0.4661	1.1433	1.6094
94	323.36	0.01769	4.699	293.78	892.3	1186.1	0.4682	1.1394	1.6076
96	324.87	0.01771	4.606	295.34	891.1	1186.4	0.4702	1.1358	1.6060
98	326.35	0.01772	4.517	296.89	889.9	1186.8	0.4721	1.1322	1.6043
100	327.81	0.01774	4.432	298.40	888.8	1187.2	0.4740	1.1286	1.6026
150	358.42	0.01809	3.015	330.51	863.6	1194.1	0.5138	1.0556	1.5694
200	381.79	0.01839	2.288	355.36	843.0	1198.4	0.5435	1.0018	1.5453
300	417.33	0.01890	1.5433	393.84	809.0	1202.8	0.5879	0.9225	1.5104
400	444.59	0.0193	1.1613	424.0	780.5	1204.5	0.6214	0.8630	1.4844
500	467.01	0.0197	0.9278	449.4	755.0	1204.4	0.6487	0.8147	1.4634

Figure 10-3 (c)

Tempera-ture t, °F	Absolute pressure p, lb/in.²	Specific volume		Enthalpy			Entropy		
		Saturated liquid v_f	Saturated vapor v_g	Saturated liquid h_f	Evapo-ration h_{fg}	Saturated vapor h_g	Saturated liquid s_f	Evapo-ration s_{fg}	Saturated vapor s_g
212	14.696	0.01672	26.80	180.07	970.3	1150.4	0.3120	1.4446	1.7566
214	15.289	0.01673	25.83	182.08	969.0	1151.1	0.3149	1.4385	1.7534
216	15.001	0.01674	24.90	184.10	967.8	1151.9	0.3179	1.4323	1.7502
218	16.533	0.01676	24.01	186.11	966.5	1152.6	0.3209	1.4262	1.7471
220	17.186	0.01677	23.15	188.13	965.2	1153.4	0.3239	1.4201	1.7440
222	17.861	0.01679	22.33	190.15	963.9	1154.1	0.3268	1.4141	1.7409
224	18.557	0.01680	21.55	192.17	962.6	1154.8	0.3298	1.4080	1.7378
226	19.275	0.01682	20.79	194.18	961.3	1155.5	0.3328	1.4020	1.7348
228	20.016	0.01683	20.07	196.20	960.1	1156.3	0.3357	1.3961	1.7318
230	20.780	0.01684	19.382	198.23	958.8	1157.0	0.3387	1.3901	1.7288
232	21.567	0.01686	18.720	200.25	957.4	1157.7	0.3416	1.3842	1.7258
234	23.379	0.01688	18.084	202.27	956.1	1158.4	0.3444	1.3784	1.7228
236	23.217	0.01689	17.473	204.29	954.8	1159.1	0.3473	1.3725	1.7199
238	24.080	0.01691	16.886	206.32	953.5	1159.8	0.3502	1.3667	1.7169
240	24.969	0.01692	16.323	208.34	952.2	1160.5	0.3531	1.3609	1.7140
242	25.884	0.01694	15.782	210.37	950.8	1161.2	0.3560	1.3551	1.7111
244	26.827	0.01696	15.262	212.39	949.5	1161.9	0.3589	1.3494	1.7083
246	27.798	0.01697	14.762	214.42	948.2	1162.6	0.3618	1.3436	1.7054
248	28.797	0.01699	14.282	216.45	946.8	1163.3	0.3647	1.3379	1.7026
250	29.825	0.01700	13.821	218.48	945.5	1164.0	0.3675	1.3323	1.6998
252	30.884	0.01702	13.377	220.51	944.2	1164.7	0.3704	1.3266	1.6970
254	31.973	0.01704	12.950	222.54	942.8	1165.3	0.3732	1.3210	1.6942
256	33.093	0.01705	12.539	224.58	941.4	1166.0	0.3761	1.3154	1.6915
258	34.245	0.01707	12.144	226.61	940.1	1166.7	0.3789	1.3099	1.6888
260	35.429	0.01709	11.763	228.64	938.7	1167.3	0.3817	1.3043	1.6860
262	36.646	0.01710	11.396	230.68	937.3	1168.0	0.3845	1.2988	1.6833
264	37.897	0.01712	11.043	232.72	936.0	1168.7	0.3874	1.2933	1.6807
266	39.182	0.01714	10.704	234.76	934.5	1169.3	0.3902	1.2878	1.6780
268	40.502	0.01715	10.376	236.80	933.2	1170.0	0.3930	1.2824	1.6753
270	41.858	0.01717	10.061	238.84	931.8	1170.6	0.3958	1.2769	1.6727
272	43.252	0.01719	9.756	240.88	930.3	1171.2	0.3986	1.2715	1.6701
274	44.682	0.01721	9.463	242.92	929.0	1171.9	0.4014	1.2661	1.6675
276	46.150	0.01722	9.181	244.96	927.5	1172.5	0.4041	1.2608	1.6649
278	47.657	0.01724	8.908	247.01	926.1	1173.1	0.4069	1.2554	1.6623
280	49.203	0.01726	8.645	249.06	924.7	1173.8	0.4096	1.2501	1.6597
282	50.790	0.01728	8.391	251.10	923.3	1174.4	0.4124	1.2448	1.6572
284	52.418	0.01730	8.146	253.15	921.8	1175.0	0.4152	1.2395	1.6547
286	54.088	0.01732	7.910	255.20	920.4	1175.6	0.4179	1.2343	1.6522
288	55.800	0.01733	7.682	257.26	918.9	1176.2	0.4207	1.2290	1.6497
290	57.556	0.01735	7.461	259.31	917.5	1176.8	0.4334	1.2238	1.6472
292	59.356	0.01737	7.248	261.36	916.0	1177.4	0.4261	1.2186	1.6447
294	61.201	0.01739	7.043	263.42	914.6	1178.0	0.4288	1.2134	1.6422
296	63.091	0.01741	6.844	265.48	913.1	1178.6	0.4315	1.2083	1.6398
298	65.028	0.01743	6.652	267.53	911.6	1179.1	0.4343	1.2031	1.6374
300	67.013	0.01745	6.466	269.59	910.1	1179.7	0.4369	1.1980	1.6350

Figure 10-3(c) (Cont.)

Tempera-ture t, °F	Absolute pressure p, lb/in.^{2}	Specific volume		Enthalpy			Entropy		
		Saturated liquid v_f	Saturated vapor h_g	Saturated liquid h_f	Evapo-ration h_{fg}	Saturated vapor h_g	Saturated liquid s_f	Evapo-ration s_{fg}	Saturated vapor s_g
310	77.68	0.01755	5.626	279.92	902.6	1182.5	0.4504	1.1727	1.6231
320	89.66	0.01765	4.914	290.28	894.9	1185.2	0.4637	1.1478	1.6115
330	103.06	0.01776	4.307	300.68	887.0	1187.7	0.4769	1.1233	1.6002
340	118.01	0.01787	3.788	311.13	879.0	1190.1	0.4900	1.0992	1.5891
350	134.63	0.01799	3.342	321.63	870.7	1192.3	0.5029	1.0754	1.5783
360	153.04	0.10811	2.957	332.18	862.2	1194.4	0.5158	1.0519	1.5677
370	173.37	0.10823	2.625	342.79	853.5	1196.3	0.5286	1.0287	1.5573
380	195.77	0.01836	2.335	353.45	844.6	1198.1	0.5413	1.0059	1.5471
390	220.37	0.01850	2.0836	364.17	835.4	1199.6	0.5539	0.9832	1.5371
400	247.31	0.01864	1.8633	374.97	826.0	1201.0	0.5664	0.9608	1.5272
410	276.75	0.01878	1.6700	385.83	816.3	1202.1	0.5788	0.9386	1.5174
420	308.83	0.01894	1.5000	396.77	806.3	1203.1	0.5912	0.9166	1.5078
430	343.72	0.01910	1.3499	407.79	796.0	1203.8	0.6035	0.8947	1.4982
440	381.59	0.01926	1.2171	418.90	785.4	1204.3	0.6158	0.8730	1.4887
450	422.6	0.0194	1.0993	430.1	774.5	1204.6	0.6280	0.8513	1.4793
460	466.9	0.0196	0.9944	441.4	763.2	1204.6	0.6402	0.8298	1.4700
470	514.7	0.0198	0.9009	452.8	751.5	1204.3	0.6523	0.8083	1.4606
480	566.1	0.0200	0.8172	464.4	739.4	1203.7	0.6645	0.7868	1.4513
490	621.4	0.0202	0.7423	476.0	726.8	1202.8	0.6766	0.7653	1.4419
500	680.8	0.0204	0.6749	487.8	713.9	1201.7	0.6887	0.7438	1.4325

Suppose, now, that we isolate the above-mentioned R-22 "vapor," still at 90 psia and 44°F temperature, and add heat to it. Since there is no liquid R-22 present to evaporate, the temperature of the vapor must now rise above 44°F. If we heat it until its temperature rises to 54°F (pressure still 90 psia), we say that the vapor is now *superheated* and has 10°F (54°F – 44°F = 10°F) of *superheat*. Therefore, we may say that superheat is the heat that is added to a "vapor" which increases its temperature, and the amount of superheat equals the actual temperature minus the saturation temperature for the pressure to which it is subjected.

Further, if we now isolate the above-mentioned R-22 liquid, still at 90 psia pressure and 44°F temperature, and remove heat from it, its temperature must fall. If we cool it to 34°F while its pressure remains unchanged, we say that the liquid is *subcooled*. In this case, it is subcooled 10°F.

With this introduction to refrigerants and their operating characteristics, we should now examine some of the desirable traits that a successful refrigerant should have. Some of these may be listed as follows:

1 For the desired evaporator temperature, the saturation pressure should be appreciably above atmospheric pressure. Any leakage will then be outward to atmosphere. At subatmospheric pressures, any leakage would be inward, permitting air and moisture to enter the system. This inward leakage would be extremely disadvantageous to the system. In HVAC systems, the desired evaporator (cooling coil, for example) refrigerant temperature is usually in the range of 35 to 45°F.

2 Condensing pressures should not be so high as to require special piping, valves, and equipment.

3 The specific volume of the refrigerant vapor at desired evaporator temperature should be low,

so that the volumetric capacity of the compressor that must pump the vapor can be reasonably low.

4 The latent heat of vaporization of the refrigerant at evaporator conditions should be comparatively high, so that for a given rate of heat flow (refrigerating capacity) the refrigerant flow rate, in lb/hr, may be low.

5 Obviously, for air conditioning purposes, a refrigerant must be nontoxic, noncorrosive, and nonflammable. Some of the refrigerants of the past, such as ammonia and sulfur dioxide, are highly toxic; and methyl chloride is highly combustible.

They are not generally used for HVAC purposes.

6 Production cost must be low so that a refrigerant may be commercially distributed at a reasonable price.

There is fortunately a family of refrigerants which very admirably qualifies and meets all these requirements. It is a family of halogenated hydrocarbons. All of these refrigerants contain carbon in chemical combination with one or more of the halogen group, which includes bromine, chlorine, fluorine, and iodine.

A listing of some of the more popular refriger-

Figure 10-4 Comparative refrigerant performance at 40°F evaporating temperature and 100°F condensing temperature. (Reprinted with permission from the 1965 and 1966 Fundamentals and Equipment Volume, ASHRAE Guide and Data Book.)

Refrigerant number	Refrigerant name	Chemical formula	Evaporation pressure psig	Condensing pressure psig	Net refrigerating effect Btu/lb	Refrigerant flow lb/min per ton	Specific volume vapor ft³/lb	Compressor displacement cfm/ton	Compression ratio	Horsepower per ton
11	Trichloro-monofluoro-methane	CCl_3F	−7.66	8.9	68.6	2.92	5.45	15.89	3.4	0.62
12	Dichloro-difluoro-methane	CCl_2F_2	37.0	117.2	50.3	3.97	0.77	3.07	2.6	0.66
21	Dichloro-monofluoro-methane	$CHCl_2F$	−2.36	25.3	90.0	2.22	4.13	9.17	3.2	0.63
22	Monochloro-difluoro-methane	$CHClF_2$	68.5	195.9	68.9	2.90	0.66	1.91	2.5	0.68
113	Trichloro-trifluoro-ethane	$C_2Cl_3F_3$	−12.03	−4.22	55.7	3.59	10.85	38.95	4.0	0.65
114	Dichloro-tetrafluoro-ethane	$CClF_2CClF_2$	0.52	31.7	44.7	4.48	2.04	9.15	3.0	—
500	Refrig.12—73.8% and difluoro-ethane—26.2%	CCl_2F_2 and CH_3CHF_2	46.2	141.9	61.4	3.26	0.80	2.61	2.6	0.67
717	Ammonia	NH_3	58.6	197.2	467.8	0.43	3.97	1.70	2.9	0.65
718	Water	H_2O	−14.59	−13.75	1010.7	0.20	2445.0	483.8	7.8	—

ants together with other pertinent data is shown in fig. 10-4. This table includes, for comparative purposes, ammonia and water; the remainder are of the halogenated hydrocarbon family. Ammonia, because of its high degree of toxicity, is not suitable for direct use in HVAC equipment. Water is not suitable as a refrigerant in the ordinary compression cycle, because, as shown in fig. 10-4, its evaporator pressure is so exceedingly low (-14.59 psig, nearly a perfect vacuum) and because the volume of vapor that must be compressed is so exceedingly high (483.8 cfm per ton of refrigeration).

One other characteristic of refrigerants must be examined in the general study of refrigeration. This characteristic is *absorptivity*—the affinity of one refrigerant for another. An example of this is the strong affinity of cool anhydrous (dry) liquid ammonia for water vapor.

If a closed vessel of anhydrous ammonia is connected by a pipe to a second closed vessel containing water, at the same pressure, in time water vapor from the water vessel will pass over into the ammonia vessel. The great affinity of ammonia for water vapor will cause the water vapor to be chemically absorbed in the ammonia. This process will continue until the ammonia, now aqueous ammonia, becomes diluted and the action stops.

In this process, heat is required, of course, to boil some of the water from a liquid into a vapor. Some of this heat may be drawn from the surroundings; however, some or all of this heat will be taken from the water itself. When this happens, the temperature of the water will, of necessity, drop. A refrigeration process has taken place; the water has been chilled. If we can somehow continuously replace the diluted ammonia with new cool anhydrous ammonia, and at the same time replace the water that has boiled away, we can have a continuous refrigeration process. This is the basis of the absorption cycle of refrigeration, which will be discussed more extensively herein later. Although ammonia was used in early absorption systems, it has been largely supplanted by a liquid solution of lithium bromide.

10-5 COMPRESSION CYCLE

In the compression cycle of refrigeration, a compressor of some type is utilized in the process of condensing the refrigerant vapor to a liquid after it has boiled (evaporated) from a liquid to a vapor in the cooling process. If we had an inexhaustible supply of liquid refrigerant such as R-12 or R-22, we would need nothing in our refrigeration system except an evaporator. As the liquid refrigerant was fed into the evaporator (cooling coil, freezer shelf, etc.), it would be released from its pressure and would turn very cold. As it then absorbed heat from its cooling load, it would boil away into a vapor and could be discarded.

However, we cannot, of course, waste the expensive refrigerant; it must be captured and somehow condensed back into a liquid so that it can be used again and again. One way to condense it is to compress it until its temperature is, for example, 100°F. Now we can cool it with 90°F air, 85°F water from a cooling tower, 60°F well water, and so on. As we remove heat from the high-pressure high-temperature vapor, it condenses into a high-pressure high-temperature liquid. It can then be fed back through a pressure-reducing valve (expansion valve) into the evaporator, and the cycle can then be repeated. See fig. 10-5 for a schematic diagram of the system just described.

The system detailed in fig. 10-5 is based on the cooling system that might be found in a small to medium-sized commercial establishment. It would consist of a cooling coil type of evaporator located in a forced air central station air conditioning unit located inside the building. It would also include an air-cooled *condensing unit* located outdoors exposed to the weather.

The term "condensing unit" is usually used to designate a factory-assembled unit complete with a compressor, compressor motor, condenser coil, condenser fan that circulates large quantities of outside air through the condenser coil, a receiver to provide storage of extra refrigerant, and a louvered steel cabinet to enclose and protect all

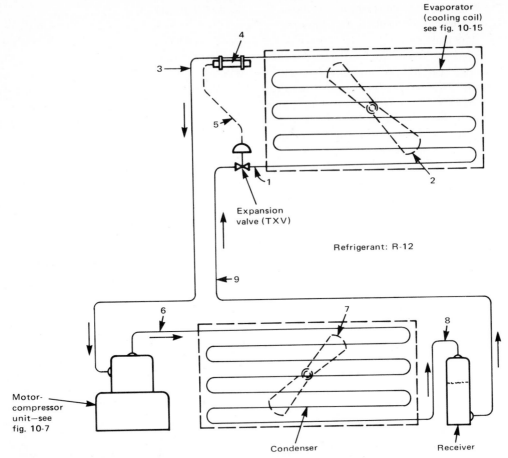

Figure 10-5 Schematic diagram—compression cycle of refrigeration. 1, liquid entering evaporator ±35°F, 47.2 psia, includes a small amount of vapor; 2, evaporator fan—circulates room air through evaporator; 3, suction line—±40°F, 46 psia—superheated vapor; 4, thermal bulb—clamped to suction line—refrigerant filled. 5, capillary tube—connects thermal bulb to expansion valve; 6, hot gas discharge line to condenser—superheated vapor—172.8 psia, 170°F; 7, condenser fan—circulates outside air through condenser; 8, high pressure, high temperature liquid into receiver, 171.8 psia, 120°F, saturated (may be subcooled below 120°F, perhaps 10°F); 9, liquid line to expansion valve —171.8 psia, 110°F.

these components. In some condensing units the condenser is water cooled, using cooling tower water or other source water. In this case, there is no condenser fan, and the unit is usually located indoors for freeze-up protection.

As noted in fig. 10-5, the refrigerant in use is R-12, dichlorodifluoromethane; see fig. 10-2 for the operating characteristics of R-12. The legend

of fig. 10-5 includes typical operating conditions for such a system that might be cooling indoor air from 80°F to about 55°F when the outdoor air temperature is 95°F. The condenser coil of fig. 10-5, like the evaporator cooling coil, consists of several rows of finned copper tubes serpentined back and forth as shown and enclosed in a galvanized steel or aluminum frame. The 95°F outdoor air is blown over the surfaces of the condenser—between the tubes and the fins that are secured to the tubes.

Let us begin a study of fig. 10-5 at reference point 9, at the liquid line where the saturated liquid refrigerant, at a pressure of 171.8 psia and a temperature of 110°F, is being delivered to the expansion valve at the evaporator inlet. The expansion valve is an automatic restrictor or a pressure-reducing valve. The orifice or opening in this valve [sometimes called a *thermostatic expansion valve* (TXV)] is an exceedingly fine orifice; and the pressure drop through the TXV is necessarily very great. The TXV is sized to permit an adequate amount of liquid refrigerant to pass only when the pressure drop through the valve is, in this case, about 125 psi.

At reference point 1, the refrigerant is now reduced down to a pressure of about 47.2 psia, at which pressure its boiling point (saturation point) is ±35°F. However, its temperature is actually ±120°F, so a small percentage of the liquid will boil, and most of the heat required for boiling will come from the liquid refrigerant itself. In giving up this heat, the liquid will be cooled, and its temperature will very quickly drop down to the saturation temperature at the lower pressure of 47.2 psia; this temperature is about 35°F.

In this condition, the refrigerant enters the evaporator coil; but the tubes of this coil through which the refrigerant is passing have 80°F air blowing over and around them. Obviously, with a 45° Δt (80°F – 35°F) existing across the tube walls, a lot of heat is going to pass into the refrigerant. As it does, the refrigerant boils as it progresses toward the coil outlet. If the correct amount of R-12 is passing through the TXV, it will all be boiled away from a liquid to a vapor shortly *before* it reaches the coil outlet. If this happens, the R-12 will continue to receive heat from the coil after it is all turned to vapor, and as it leaves the coil and enters the suction line near reference point 3, it will be superheated; that is, it will be heated to a temperature somewhat above its saturation temperature.

At point 3, the pressure will probably be about 46 psia. This is 1.2 psi less than the 47.2 psia listed for point 1; the 1.2-lb pressure drop is just the result of friction in the coil tubes. From fig. 10-2 we can see that the saturation temperature for 46 psia pressure is about 33.5°F. However, the vapor in the suction line at point 3 is at 40°F. This is 6.5°F above the saturation temperature. Therefore, at point 3 the vapor is superheated 6.5°F.

It is mandatory that the vapor entering the compressor be superheated; this is the only way that we can know that it does not contain any unvaporized liquid. Most compressors of the reciprocating piston type (which a very great majority of refrigeration compressors are) cannot tolerate any liquid refrigerant coming into them. For high efficiency, the clearance between the piston and the cylinder head at top-dead-center is only a few thousandths of an inch. A small "slug" of liquid caught in this tight squeeze can blow the head right out of a compressor. Having 6 to 8°F of superheat in the suction vapor is assurance that all liquid is evaporated. As explained later in this chapter, the TXV, working with its thermal bulb (reference number 4) through the capillary tube 5, controls the refrigerant flow so that the suction vapor always has the necessary superheat to assure the absence of liquid.

Responding to the pull or drawing effect of the compressor the R-12 vapor flows into it and is compressed to the condition shown for point 6 of fig. 10-5. Here the vapor has been compressed until its saturation temperature is 15 to 25°F warmer than whatever medium is to be used to cool the condenser—in this case the 95°F outdoor air mentioned above. At the 172.8 psia pressure shown for point 6, the R-12 saturation temperature is slightly over 120°F. This is 25°F warmer than the 95°F OA. The 95°F OA blowing over the condenser coil surfaces does cool the 120°F refrigerant in the tubes of the condenser coil and the R-12 condenses and returns to the receiver for reuse.

However, notice that at point 6 the R-12 temperature is 170°F; the compressor discharge vapor has 50°F (170°F – 120°F) of superheat in it. This results from the work done on the vapor by the compressor and by the heat of the friction as the piston moves in its cylinder. Before the condenser can remove the latent heat of vaporization in the R-12 vapor so as to condense it, the superheat must first be removed. This the condenser is designed to do.

Very often the condenser is designed to have enough capacity that it cannot only condense the R-12 vapor to a liquid at its saturation temperature, but can also subcool the liquid somewhat below the saturation temperature. Therefore, the liquid R-12 is shown to be at 110°F, which is about 10°F below the saturation temperature for the pressure shown. Thus, the R-12 liquid is subcooled 10°F at point 9.

10-6 PRESSURE-ENTHALPY DIAGRAM

A convenient method of visualizing and understanding the compression cycle described in art. 10-5 and in fig. 10-5 is through the use of the pressure-enthalpy (P-E) diagram such as that shown in fig 10-6. In fig. 10-6 the compression cycle is outlined showing the same operating conditions encountered in the sample system of art. 10-5.

Of the P-E chart of fig. 10-6, the ordinate (vertical scale) lists refrigerant pressure in psia; and the abscissa lists enthalpy in Btu per pound of R-12 refrigerant. The primary feature of the P-E chart is the saturation curve. This saturation curve really consists of two curves—the saturated liquid line (or curve) on the left, and the saturated vapor

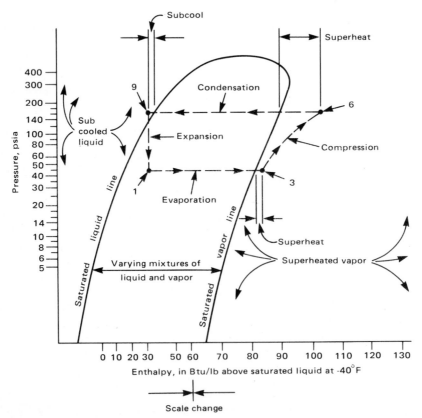

Figure 10-6 Pressure-enthalpy diagram for the compression cycle described in Fig. 10-5 and in art. 10.5, using refrigerant R-12. (Reprinted with permission with data excerpted from the 1960 ASHRAE Heating, Ventilating, Air Conditioning Guide, p. 560.)

line on the right. These two curves merge at the top of the dome, but the area at the top represents extremely erratic operating conditions and does not represent anything of practical interest here.

In the P-E chart any point on the liquid line represents R-12 liquid at its boiling point, but still liquid. The addition of the slightest amount of heat will cause some of it to boil. Also any point on the saturated vapor line represents R-12 vapor at its condensing point, but still vapor. The removal of the slightest amount of heat will cause some of the vapor to condense.

The area between the liquid and vapor lines represents mixtures of saturated liquid and saturated vapor. A point between these lines but close to the liquid line (such as point 1) represents a mixture of R-12 liquid and vapor that is predominantly liquid, with very little vapor. A point between the lines that is close to the vapor line represents a mixture that has very little liquid in it; we say it has high *quality*. The mixture at point 1 has low quality by comparison. Quality is expressed as a percentage to indicate the percentage by weight of vapor in the mixture. A point on the liquid line represents 0% quality, and a point on the vapor line represents 100% quality.

In fig. 10-6 the area of the chart to the left of the saturated liquid line indicates R-12 liquid which is at a temperature below the saturation temperature for a given pressure, and thus is subcooled. Similarly, any point in the area to the right of the saturated vapor line represents superheated vapor that is at a temperature higher than its saturation temperature.

Superimposed on the P-E chart in fig. 10-6 are the lines that describe the functions that take place in the typical compression cycle. The line segment between point 9 and point 1 shows the expansion that takes place as the R-12 enters the TXV as a subcooled, high-pressure, high-temperature liquid and expands in the TXV to a low-pressure low-temperature mixture of low quality.

The line segment between points 1 and 3 represents the evaporation or boiling that takes place in the evaporator (in this case an air cooling coil).

Notice that before the R-12 leaves the evaporator, it passes through the saturated vapor curve, where all the liquid has evaporated, and on into the superheat area to point 3. Here we may be certain that the R-12 contains no liquid—only superheated vapor.

The line segment between points 3 and 6 represents compression in the compressor to a much higher pressure and, as a result, to a much higher temperature. At the elevated temperature of point 6, we may now cool the R-12 with outdoor air even though that OA is quite hot (95°F or hotter). The line segment between points 6 and 9 represents the condensation of the R-12 as it passes through the tubes of a condenser coil with 95°F OA passing over the condenser coil surfaces. This completes the cycle.

10-7   REFRIGERATION COMPRESSORS

The compressor may be thought of as the heart of the compression cycle refrigeration system. By its pumping action the refrigerant is caused to circulate as necessary. By its "pulling" action, the pressure in the evaporator is pulled down until the refrigerant boils at a suitably low temperature. By its "pushing" action, the refrigerant is compressed until its temperature is suitably higher than the temperature of an available condenser cooling medium.

General Types

Refrigeration compressors used in the compression cycle of refrigeration may be divided into three broad categories:

1 Positive displacement type. This includes reciprocating piston type (by far the most popular and numerous), rotary vane type, rotary screw type, and rolling piston type.
2 Centrifugal type.
3 Steam jet type.

Reciprocating Piston Compressors This type of compressor utilizes one, or as many as 16 pistons driven by a crankshaft or an eccentric cam and

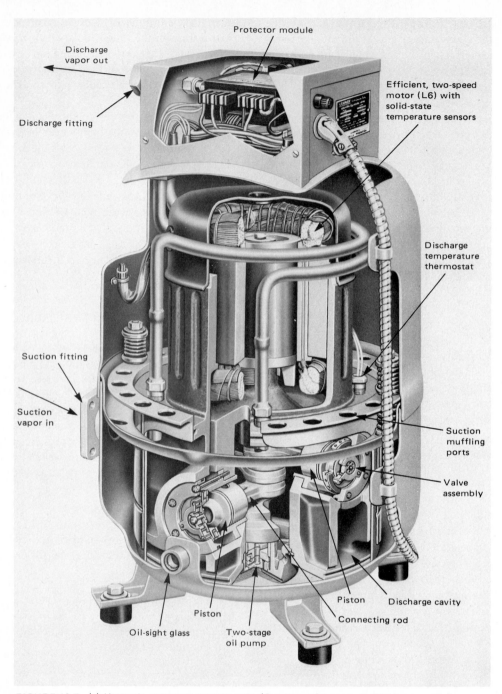

Protector module

Discharge
vapor out

Discharge fitting

Efficient, two-speed
motor (L6) with
solid-state
temperature sensors

Discharge
temperature
thermostat

Suction fitting

Suction
vapor in

Suction
muffling
ports

Valve
assembly

Piston

Discharge cavity

Connecting rod

Oil-sight glass

Piston

Two-stage
oil pump

FIGURE 10-7 (a) Hermetic motor-compressor unit. (Courtesy of Lennox Industries, Inc., Dallas, Texas.)

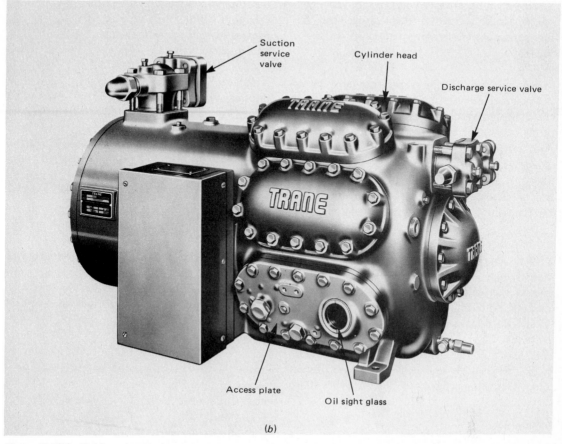

Figure 10-7(b)   Field serviceable hermetic motor-compressor unit. (© The Trane Company, used by permission.)

sliding in cylinders. Many other types of machines utilize the same piston-cylinder arrangement because of its efficiency in pumping comparatively small quantities of liquid or gas against a comparatively high discharge pressure. These other machines include air compressors, water pumps, and internal combustion engines such as those used in automobiles and trucks.

The general trend in refrigeration compressor design through the years has been to the use of higher rotative speeds—from the old lumbering monsters running at 50 rpm to current speeds of 1750 and 3500 rpm. Other trends have been toward the use of "over-square" machines in which piston diameters are relatively greater and

piston strokes are shorter until diameters are now greater than the length of the stroke.

Higher compressor speeds have long ago necessitated a departure from the heavy cam-operated or poppet-type compressor valves to the lightweight Swedish steel "feather" valves, which respond lightly and quickly to pressure changes in the cylinder.

Another trend in reciprocating compressor design is to the hermetically sealed unit in which the electric motor that drives the compressor is directly connected thereto (on the same steel shaft), and all sealed in the same gastight, leakproof chamber (see fig. 10-7). The use of separate motors driving through belt drives or direct flexible coupling drives is on the wane. This trend, which started in tiny household refrigerators, has now spread upward to units of hundreds of tons of capacity.

Rotary Vane Compressors Another type of positive displacement refrigeration compressor is the sliding vane rotary type schematically detailed in fig. 10-8. This compressor is suitable for use with refrigerants having comparatively high discharge pressures such as R-12 and R-22 (see fig. 10-4). It is most suitable with refrigerants that generate a low volume of suction gas per ton; this translates into low cylinder displacement per ton.

The rotary vane type of compressor has been used mostly in very small refrigeration systems such as domestic refrigerators and small air conditioners under 3 tons capacity. This rotary compressor is essentially a vibrationless, well-balanced machine with only the sliding of the vanes to disturb the balance.

It may be seen in fig. 10-8 that, as the rotor spins inside its housing, the vanes maintain contact with the inside of the housing. The refrigerant vapor that is trapped between the two vanes above

the rotor is compressed as the rotor turns, and the volume is continuously reduced until the vapor is released at high pressure out past the thin flexible steel discharge valve.

Rotary Screw Compressors Rotary screw compressors are comparatively new to the refrigeration scene, having developed a following and regular manufacture during the last 10 years or so. They are positive displacement compressors which can operate against high discharge pressure, and utilize refrigerants that require minimum volumetric capacity.

As shown in fig. 10-9, screw compressors utilize two closely fitting worm gears, one male and one female. As they turn, one being driven by the other, refrigerant, such as R-22, is permitted to enter axially at one end of the mating screw assembly, and the turning action squeezes the refrigerant through and out at the other end at high pressure.

Screw compressors run at high speed and are usually directly driven by two-pole electric motors; hence they rotate at a speed of 3500 rpm. Efficiency is quite high in general; and since there are no reciprocating parts, they operate with very little vibration.

Compressor and condensing units utilizing rotary screw compressors are commercially available in capacities of 25 to 1000 tons. The screw compressor does not lend itself readily to use in small sizes (residential, etc.), but in larger sizes gives efficiency equal to or better than other types of compressors. This, coupled with compact size and vibrationless operation, forecasts much favor and acceptance in future years.

One important feature of the rotary screw compressor is the ease with which its capacity may be efficiently reduced for light loads. To reduce capacity at constant speed a *slide valve* controller operates to create an opening in the wall of the housing that encloses the rotors. When this escape port in the housing opens, refrigerant which has been only very slightly compressed escapes back to the inlet and thus is not delivered to the condenser.

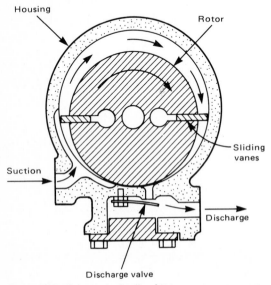

Figure 10-8 Schematic details of rotary vane compressor.

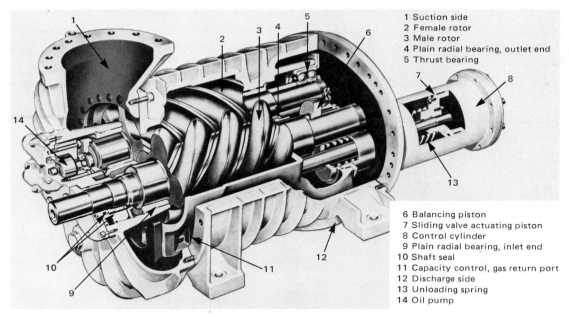

1 Suction side
2 Female rotor
3 Male rotor
4 Plain radial bearing, outlet end
5 Thrust bearing

6 Balancing piston
7 Sliding valve actuating piston
8 Control cylinder
9 Plain radial bearing, inlet end
10 Shaft seal
11 Capacity control, gas return port
12 Discharge side
13 Unloading spring
14 Oil pump

Figure 10-9 Rotary screw compressor. (Courtesy of Vilter Manufacturing Corp., Milwaukee, Wis. —manufacturer of industrial refrigeration and heat transfer equipment.)

By this method, capacity may be smoothly and continuously reduced in infinite stages down to as low as 10% of maximum capacity. It would be fortunate indeed if the electrical power input to a motor driving this type of compressor would reduce in proportion to the reduction in the load placed on it. Unfortunately, this is far from true. As the load on an induction motor is reduced, there is initially a reduction in power consumption; but as load is further reduced, a point is fairly quickly reached where power demand levels off and reduces very little as load is further reduced. It would be better to reduce motor and compressor speed to reduce capacity.

Figure 10-10 is an illustration of a packaged water chilling unit which includes a rotary screw compressor. This unit is such that might be used for the summer cooling of a large building. Notations in fig. 10-14 indicate where the chilled water, at about 45°F, would leave the unit to be delivered through piping to the various air conditioning units in the building, and where the returned chilled wa-

ter at 53 to 60°F would enter the chiller unit. Also noted are inlet and outlet connections where condenser water, probably from a cooling tower, would enter and leave the condenser. Here, the entering water might be 85°F on a hot day, and leaving temperature might be 95°F.

Rolling Piston Compressors The rolling piston compressor (see fig. 10-11) is very similar in principle, appearance, performance, noise and general application to the rotary vane compressor. In the rolling piston type there is only one vane, and it slides in and out of a slot in the stationary housing. The rolling piston revolves on an eccentric shaft and rolls around the inside of the housing, pushing the refrigerant vapor ahead of it as it rolls.

A flexible Swedish steel feather valve operates at the vapor outlet, and opens when the pressure inside the housing exceeds that of the discharge line. A spring exerts a force on the sliding vane to keep it in contact with the rolling piston. In this compressor there is considerably more weight

Figure 10-10 Water chiller unit with rotary screw compressor. (Photo courtesy of Dunham-Bush Inc.)

being moved eccentrically than in the rotating vane compressor; as a result there is more tendency toward vibration.

One disadvantage of both the rotating vane and the rolling piston compressors is the difficulty of maintaining a tight seal at each end of the cylindrical housing. With differential expansion and contraction among the various component parts, achieving and maintaining a near perfect fit between the end walls of the cylindrical housings and the ends of the vanes, the rolling piston, and the rotors has been the major problem and source of service difficulties.

Service Life: Reciprocating Compressors One disadvantage to the reciprocating piston, positive displacement line of refrigeration compressors has been the comparatively short life of certain types of units in most popular use. The life expectancy of the motor-compressor unit of the type that is enclosed in a hermetically sealed steel shell and used for summer cooling purposes has been limited, on an average, to about 7 to 10 years. This includes units that range in size from 1 hp up to 25 hp.

Where such units are used for winter heating (in heat pumps) as well as summer cooling, the life in years may be appreciably less. However, when we

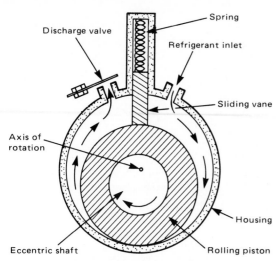

Figure 10-11 Schematic detail of rolling piston compressor.

realize that, for summer cooling only, a unit may operate 12,000 hr in 8 years, perhaps we have no right to expect more than this. Compare that with the average automobile engine, which may operate only 300 hr per year.

On the other hand, we know that where motor-compressor units are conservatively designed, and constructed so that routine service operations can be performed on them, their service life can be made almost unlimited. Such units would optimally be of the field-serviceable hermetic type, in which the driving electric motor is connected directly to the compressor shaft and sealed in a bolted cast iron, leakproof chamber. In this type of unit all parts of the compressor are accessible for repair and replacement as necessary.

In the welded hermetic unit of the type shown in fig. 10-7, should a compressor part, such as a simple discharge valve, fail, the entire unit is usually discarded and replaced—a very expensive procedure. The cost of returning the motor-compressor unit to its manufacturer, where it could be cut open, repaired, reassembled in a new hermetic shell, and returned to its owner would be prohibitive. Also, the weeks of time required for

this repair would, in hot, summer weather when the unit is sorely needed for cooling, be totally unacceptable.

In any application where for business or health reasons a service shutdown would work serious hardship, a field-serviceable refrigeration compressor unit should be given first consideration. In this case, a small supply of the parts most likely to fail should be kept in the owner's storage.

A detail of a field-serviceable hermetic condensing unit is shown in fig. 10-12. In this detail it may be seen that the entire unit is bolted together, and may be unbolted for service at the point of installation.

Centrifugal Compressors Centrifugal compressors have played an exceedingly important role in the HVAC business in larger installations. They operate on the principle of refrigerant vapor being drawn axially into the center of a rapidly spinning impeller or wheel; the vapor is then thrown radially out from the impeller at extremely high velocity (see fig. 10-13). This high-velocity vapor is then guided efficiently to a chamber, where the velocity is reduced to a low value. As the velocity and the resulting velocity pressure are reduced, the velocity pressure is converted to static pressure. This static pressure is high enough that the corresponding saturation temperature is higher than the available cooling and condensing medium—outdoor air, cooling tower water, and so on. This high-pressure refrigerant may now be conducted into a condenser and condensed for reuse.

Centrifugal compressors are very limited as to the discharge pressure that they can develop. Fortunately, there are a number of suitable refrigerants which can be condensed at a comparatively low discharge pressure. This may be seen in the table of fig. 10-4; here the evaporator pressure and the condensing pressure (for the conditions shown) for R-11 is listed at -7.66 and 8.9 psig, respectively, and for R-113 they are -12.03 and -4.22 psig. The operating range for R-11 is 16.56 psi (7.66 + 8.9) and for R-113 is 7.81 psi

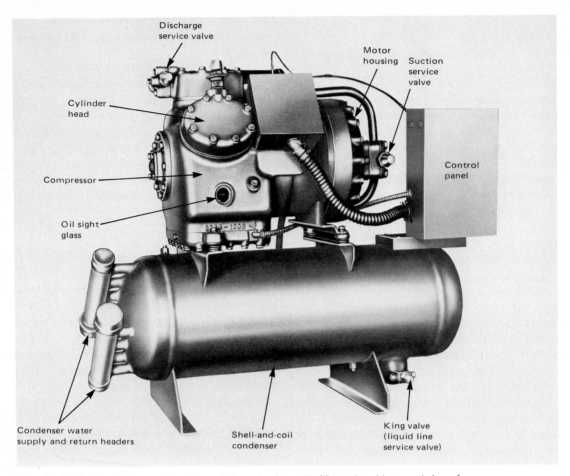

Figure 10-12 Serviceable hermetic water cooled condensing unit. (Reproduced by permission of Carrier Corp., © 1980 Carrier Corp.)

[−4.22 − (−12.03)]. These pressure ranges are eminently suitable for centrifugal compressors and R-11 and R-113 are commonly used in them.

Figure 10-4 also shows that the required compressor displacement, or volumetric capacity, for the conditions shown is 15.89 cfm/ton for R-11 and 38.95 cfm/ton for R-113. These volumes are much too high to be practical for a piston-type compressor, but the centrifugal compressor can handle these large volumes easily if the pressure range is low enough.

Centrifugal compressors have no reciprocating or eccentric action since their only moving part,

the wheel (also called the impeller), is perfectly balanced. As a result, these compressors operate comparatively quietly and without vibration. The only parts that are subject to wear are the motor and compressor shaft bearings. Some centrifugal compressors do have a gear drive by means of which the impeller may be driven at any optimum speed while the driving motor runs at a standard synchronous speed. With a gear drive, there are a few more moving parts which detract only a little from the extreme simplicity of the compressor. The effective life of a centrifugal compressor is practically unlimited.

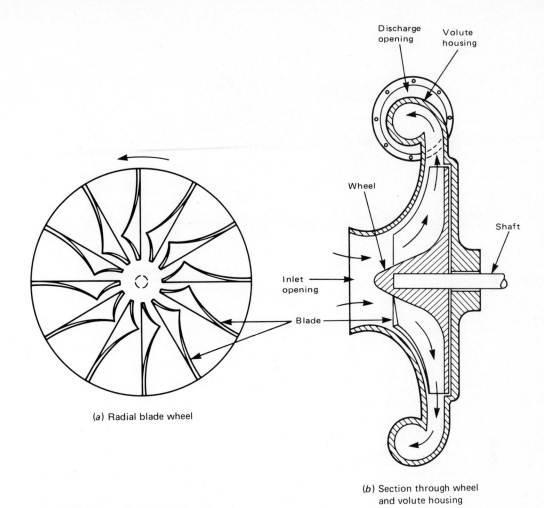

(a) Radial blade wheel

(b) Section through wheel
and volute housing

Figure 10-13 Centrifugal compressor details.

The capacity of a centrifugal compressor may be very effectively regulated from 100% of full capacity smoothly and continuously down to about 10% of full capacity. This is accomplished through the use of inlet guide vanes mounted at the compressor inlet. These guide vanes can be automatically opened and closed to provide necessary compressor capacity. Better capacity control is now being accomplished with great power savings through the use of frequency inverters to vary motor and compressor speeds.

Figure 10-14 shows exterior views of typical water chilling units with a centrifugal refrigeration system; fig. 10-14a also includes a schematic section through such a chiller unit that shows water and refrigerant flow patterns. The schematic section is not drawn to be representative, as to arrangement, of the chiller unit shown in fig. 10-14a and b.

Compressor Control

One ever-present fact of life in the HVAC business is that the loads on heating and cooling systems are continually changing; they are never static. In

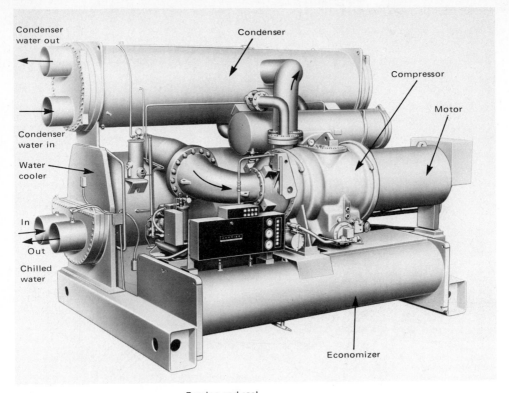

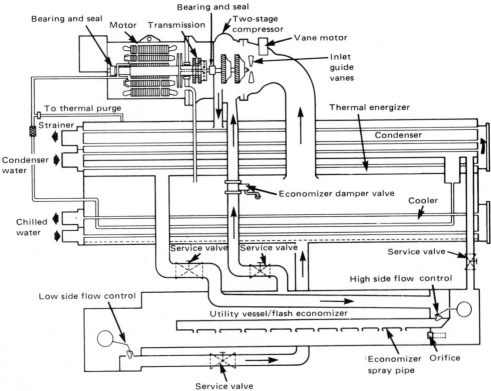

Figure 10-14(a) Centrifugal water chiller details. (Reproduced by permission of Carrier Corp., © 1980 Carrier Corp.)

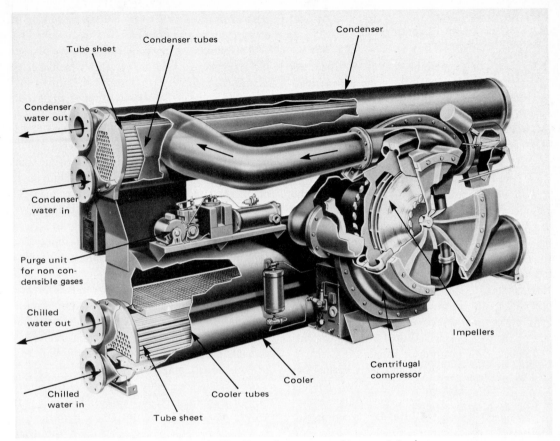

Figure 10-14(b) Centrifugal water chiller. (© The Trane Company, used by permission.)

summer, the position of the sun is always changing, cloud patterns are always changing and varying the effect of the sun, occupancy patterns in buildings have a transitory character, and lights are frequently being turned on and off. This means, of course, that the capacity of our cooling systems must be accurately variable so as to match cooling capacity with cooling load.

With some types of cooling systems, control of capacity is not difficult. In the centrifugal compressor described above and shown in fig. 10-14, inlet guide vanes can be automatically positioned to vary compressor capacity smoothly through an infinite number of steps of capacity from 100%

down to 10%, and compressor speeds can be varied. In the absorption cycle of refrigeration, described later, capacity can again be smoothly controlled by modulating the flow of steam or hot water into the generator.

However, in the great majority of our HVAC systems a reciprocating piston type of compressor is utilized; modulating the capacity of such compressors is far from a simple matter. Some of the methods of doing this may be listed as follows:

1 On-off control
2 Multiple compressor control
3 Cylinder unloading

4   Hot gas bypass
5   Compressor speed control

There are other methods that have been used through the years; these include the use of clearance pockets which automatically increase the volume of the cylinder at piston top-dead-center position, and also the use of cylinder side wall openings, which permit some of the partially compressed gas to escape back to the suction line. These have been used very little.

With *on-off control,* as the term implies, the motor-compressor unit is stopped when cooling is not required. Most residential and small commercial units are controlled this way. Although undesirable, this method is accepted in such use since the cost of any other system would be unacceptable.

When on-off control is used in larger systems, some precautions should be taken for the protection of the compressor and its starting and driving equipment. The compressor should, first of all, operate on a *pump-down* cycle. This means that when cooling is not needed, the flow of liquid refrigerant is stopped, usually by closing an electrically operated solenoid valve. As the compressor continues to run without a supply of refrigerant, the evaporator is cleared of refrigerant and suction pressure falls. Also, refrigerant that is absorbed in the compressor crankcase lubricating oil begins to leave the oil and pass through the cylinders to the condenser.

When the suction pressure falls to a predetermined low value a low-pressure limit control interrupts power to the driving motor and the compressor stops. Under the usual conditions, the suction pressure will quickly rise again as the refrigerant remaining in the evaporator and compressor crankcase continues to evaporate. The low-pressure control starts the compressor again, often in a fraction of a minute. Thus the compressor can short-cycle on low-pressure control; and with intermittent calls for cooling (solenoid valve openings), the result is that the compressor may seri-

ously short-cycle, with very adverse effects on the compressor and its drive and starting equipment.

The answer to this problem is the use of a simple, inexpensive time delay relay which will not permit the compressor to restart for 5 min or so. If larger compressors are simply stopped while under load, without a pump-down action, very heavy starting loads will result on the next running cycle. The suction pressure will be very high, and the possibility of drawing foaming oil out of the crankcase and into the cylinder (as refrigerant in the crankcase rapidly boils) is dangerously high. The answer, then, is the use of the pump-down cycle and the time-delay restart relay.

With *multiple compressor control,* reduction in capacity can result from cycling on and off one or more of a group of motor-compressor units. With two equal units, it is possible to run at 50% capacity with one unit running, and at 100% capacity with both units running. With only two units, short cycling is still a problem, although not nearly as bad a problem as with only one unit. With three or four equal compressor units, the problems of short cycling are greatly reduced. See the illustration of a four-compressor water chiller unit in fig. 10-15. Also, notice in fig. 10-15 that there are two separate condensers, and the water cooler vessel on top is divided into two halves with two liquid inlet connections and two suction line connections. This chiller really consists of two separate water cooling systems, each having two motor-compressor units, one condenser, and one evaporator. This chiller unit can operate, of course, with capacity steps of 25%, 50%, 75%, and 100%.

One of the most popular capacity control systems for recriprocating compressors is the *cylinder unloading* system. This is applied to multiple cylinder compressors, and is most effective with compressors having four or more cylinders. Capacity modulation is achieved by causing one or more cylinders to stop pumping refrigerant. This is achieved through the use of an *unloader mechanism,* which usually consists of actuating fingers in the cylinder head which, when activated, hold

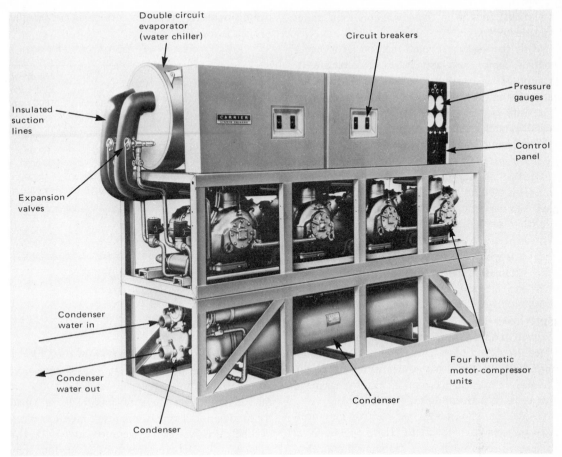

Figure 10-15 Multiple-compressor water chiller. (Reproduced by permission of Carrier Corp. ©
1980 Carrier Corp.)

open the suction valve for a given cylinder. In this
case, the suction refrigerant vapor is drawn in as
the piston descends, but the vapor is pushed back
through the open suction valve as the piston rises
on the compression stroke. Thus, no refrigerant is
pumped.

Cylinder unloaders can be integrally controlled
by a built-in pressure sensor which causes cylinders
to unload automatically as suction pressure falls.
For a given compressor capacity, suction pressure
always falls as cooling load is reduced, and vice
versa.

Unloaders may also be controlled by a direct
space controller such as a room thermostat. As
temperature falls in a room, the compressor capacity is reduced by unloading cylinders under thermostat control. In this case, the last step of capacity
would be curtailed, if necessary, by the thermostat closing a liquid line refrigerant solenoid valve.
With the refrigerant flow stopped, the compressor
would pump down and be turned off by the low-
pressure controller previously described.

With cylinder unloading there is some inefficiency of operation since all pistons continue mov-

ing against friction in their cylinders even under unloaded operation.

With the *hot gas bypass* method of capacity control, compressed vapor leaving the compressor is rerouted back to the compressor inlet for a net reduction in the amount of refrigerant pumped. It is easy to see the great inefficiency of such a system; it is rarely used.

The last method of compressor capacity control discussed here (there are others that might be discussed) is one that involves *compressor speed control*. This method has been little used in the past, but does have some appreciable benefits, and will probably see greater utilization in future years. With an ac electric motor drive, which has been the usual prime mover, speed regulation has been difficult. Alternating current motors always run near their synchronous speeds of 1800 rpm with a four-pole motor or 3600 rpm with a two-pole motor.

Even though direct current motors give good speed regulation, dc power is not generally available; and the high cost of rectifying ac to dc, coupled with the high cost of dc motors, has made this alternative much too expensive.

Diesel, gasoline, and gas engine drives have been used to a very limited extent. These engines have, in general, been much more economical than electric motors as far as power cost is concerned. However, initial costs, maintenance costs, space costs, and noise have placed severe limitations on their use, even though they can provide good speed regulation.

Where low-cost steam is available, steam turbines and steam engines have been used to drive com-

However, again, initial costs, space costs, and maintenance costs have placed a limit on their use.

With ac electric motor drive, some motor-compressor units, both hermetically sealed and open, have been driven by combination two-pole/four-pole two-speed 3600 rpm/1800 rpm motors. The results of this arrangement have been particularly favorable. One manufacturer (Lennox Corporation), publishes the following information, which

demonstrates the efficiency advantages (in percent) of such two-speed operation:

	Cylinder unloading unit	Two-speed 3600 rpm/ 1800 rpm unit
Full load capacity*	100%	100%
Partial load capacity*	50%	58.8%
Power input, full load	100%	100%
Power input, partial load	—†	38.8%
EER,‡ full load	9.18	9.18
EER,‡ partial load (58.8%)	—§	13.3
Mechanical friction at full load	100%	100%
Mechanical friction, partial load	100%	50%
Fluid friction, full load	100%	100%
Fluid friction, partial load	50–75%	25%

*Air-cooled condensing at 85°F DB outdoor air.
†Data not given, but probably ±60%.
‡Energy efficiency ratio, BH/W-hr.
§ Data not given.

This tabulation demonstrates how the EER can improve during partial load, half-speed operation. As mentioned above, capacity steps of 100% and 50% may not give adequate smoothness of capacity modulation and may still result in serious short cycling. However, a refrigeration unit with two such two-speed compressor units, giving four steps of capacity, and the extra efficiency of half-speed operation, would seem to have many advantages.

Another facility that offers much hope for the future, in the way of capacity control through speed regulation, involves the use of *variable frequency drives* for standard induction-type three-phase motors. Since the rotative speed of an ac electric motor depends on the cycle frequency of its power supply, power supply *inverters* which can receive standard three-phase 60-cycle power and deliver to a standard three-phase 60-cycle motor that power with its frequency varied can then vary the rotative speed of that motor (see fig. 10-16).

In the HVAC industry, frequency inverters are now beginning to find use in automatically varying the rotative speeds of VAV fans, pumps, and so

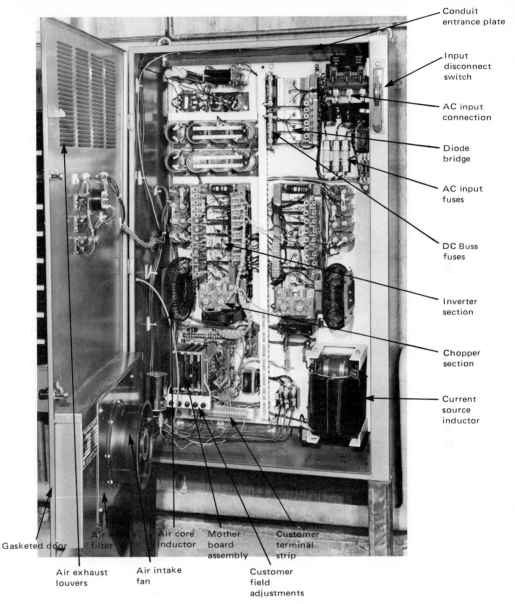

Conduit
entrance plate

Input
disconnect
switch

AC input
connection

Diode
bridge

AC input
fuses

DC Buss
fuses

Inverter
section

Chopper
section

Current
source
inductor

Gasketed door

Air intake
filter

Air core
inductor

Mother
board
assembly

Customer
terminal
strip

Air exhaust
louvers

Air intake
fan

Customer
field
adjustments

Figure 10-16   Frequency inverter motor speed control panel. (Courtesy Graham Co., Milwaukee, Wis.)

on, and these should deliver many benefits when applied to compressor motors. The efficiency of three-phase motors controlled in this manner is not only maintained very high at reduced speeds, but the power factor is actually improved to as high as 95%. These benefits, coupled with the benefits tabulated above for reduced speed operation at partial load conditions, should make possible the real reductions in electrical power use that the worldwide energy shortage of today demands.

10-8　EVAPORATORS

For air conditioning purposes, evaporators are essentially limited to two types: *water chillers* and *cooling coils*. As set forth in chap. 6, cooling coils are fairly simple devices made up of assemblies of tubes, usually copper, and fins pressed onto the tubes, usually aluminum, all assembled into a compact bundle and housed in a galvanized steel or aluminum frame.

Cooling coils are of two types: *chilled water* and *direct expansion*. Of course, chilled water coils are not evaporators since no refrigerant is evaporated within them. However, direct expansion (DE or DX) coils are evaporators, because refrigerant is expanded from the liquid phase to the vapor phase within the coil tubes (see fig. 10-17).

Water chillers, as evaporators, are usually of two types: *direct expansion* and *flooded*. In the DE type, as in a DE cooling coil, the refrigerant is metered into a group of parallel copper tubes which are enclosed in a steel shell with the tubes secured to a tube sheet (flat steel end plate) at each end of the vessel. Cast iron or steel manifolds are bolted to each end of the vessel to direct the refrigerant through the proper tubes (see fig. 10-18). The water to be chilled passes through the shell over and around the exterior of the tubes. Baffling is usually installed in the shell to require the water to serpentine up and down, or back and forth, on its way through the shell from inlet to outlet.

In a flooded water chiller, the refrigerant would be contained in the shell of a vessel similar to that in fig. 10-18, and would be maintained at a certain

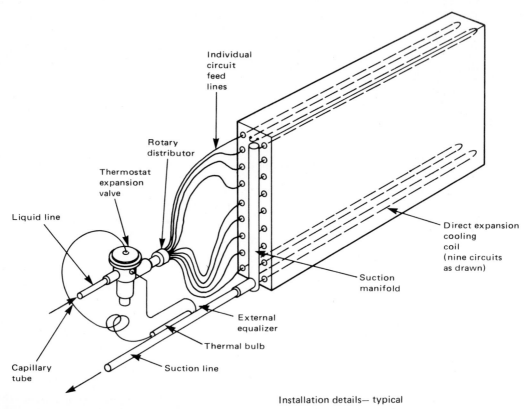

Installation details— typical

Figure 10-17　Direct expansion cooling coils. (© The Trane Co., used by permission.)

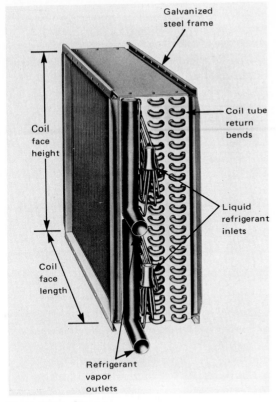

Galvanized
steel frame

Coil tube
return
bends

Coil
face
height

Liquid
refrigerant
inlets

Coil
face
length

Refrigerant
vapor
outlets

Figure 10-17 *(Cont.)*

level within the shell by an externally mounted float chamber and float valve. The refrigerant would enter the bottom connection of the shell as a liquid, and would evaporate within the shell and leave as a vapor out the top connection. In this case, the float valve is the dividing line between the low- and high-pressure parts of the system.

Another type of vessel used for both DE and flooded operation is similar to that shown in fig. 10-18 except that only one tube sheet is used; all tubes are U-shaped, with each end secured to the same tube sheet. The end of the shell opposite the tube sheet is welded shut with a steel plate.

In fig. 10-14 both the condenser and the water cooler are of the shell-and-tube type. This is the usual configuration.

10-9 CONDENSERS

Condensers in the compression cycle of refrigeration usually fall into one of the following three categories:

1 Air cooled
2 Water cooled
3 Evaporative cooled

The *air-cooled condenser* is of the finned coil configuration and looks, in general, just like a cooling coil. It consists of finned copper tubes arranged in serpentined rows, two, three, or four rows in depth, similar to the cooling coil of fig. 10-17 (without the expansion valve and circuit feed lines).

Air-cooled condensers are mounted outdoors so that they have completely free access to the outdoor air. A fan, or fans, usually of the propeller type, draws outdoor air through the coil and discharges it back into the atmosphere. Much more often than not, the condenser is an integral part of a condensing unit, which by definition includes a motor-compressor unit and an enclosing louvered housing. However, very often it is connected to a remotely located compressor unit with refrigerant piping.

For HVAC summer use, the air-cooled condenser must reject to the outdoor atmosphere all the heat removed from a building by its cooling system plus the heat of compression and friction generated in the compressor. These, on average, amount to about 15,000 BH/ton of cooling. This heat rejection must be done when the outdoor air is at its hottest, perhaps 95°F. To cool the condenser and the hot vapor within it with 95°F air means that the hot vapor must have a saturation temperature of 115° or 120°F or so—20° or 25°F hotter than the outdoor air (OA). This requires a comparatively high condensing pressure, which causes high power consumption and is something of a disadvantage for air-cooled condensers.

However, in most areas of the United States there are many times during hot summer weather

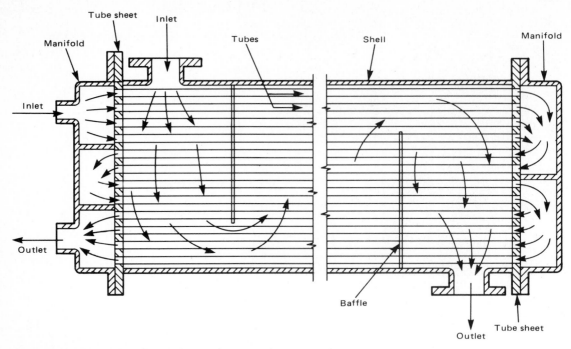

Figure 10-18 Typical shell-and-tube heat exchange vessel.

when the OA is favorably low in temperature—during mornings, evenings, and at night, and on unseasonably cool days—and the condensing pressure is lower than it would be with some types of water-cooled condensers. The history is that with an air-cooled condenser, the overall power consumption for a season will be no more than with a water-cooled condenser, even though there is a disadvantage on the very hot days.

Installations with air-cooled condensers are usually less expensive and less complicated, and much less maintenance is required. Therefore, there has long been a gradual swing toward air-cooled condensing in preference to water-cooled or evaporative cooled condensing.

Water-cooled condensing involves the use of a shell-and-tube vessel almost exactly like the evaporator of that type shown in fig. 10-18. Here, the high-pressure high-temperature refrigerant enters the top of the shell as a vapor. As it condenses on contact with the exterior of the tubes, through

which water is circulating, the refrigerant falls to the bottom and flows out the bottom opening. Often, the shell is designed with extra volume so that liquid refrigerant can be stored in the bottom; no separate receiver is then required.

The water that is pumped through the tubes of a shell-and-tube condenser is usually water that has been cooled in a cooling tower or spray pond. Or it could be water drawn from a nearby lake or stream and carefully filtered before it is pumped through the condenser tubes. See fig. 10-19 for details of a typical cooling tower.

In the cooling tower shown, water is pumped into the water boxes atop the tower, from which the water trickles downward through the layers of corrugated fill while the outside air is drawn rapidly through the fill material. In the resulting air-water contact the water is cooled down to within about 7°F of the wet bulb temperature of the OA. Most efficient cooling towers can achieve a 7°F "approach" under usual operating conditions.

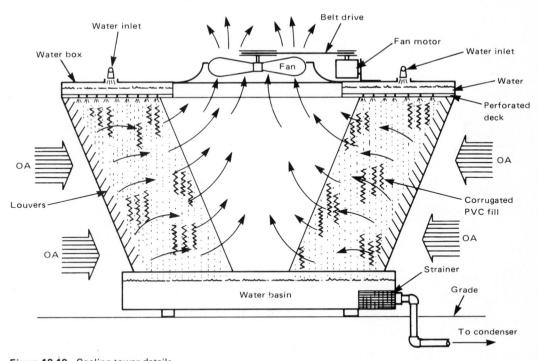

Figure 10-19 Cooling tower details.

Under usual mid-America operating conditions, water might leave the condenser and enter the tower at 95°F; and when the OA wet bulb temperature is 78°F, water might leave the tower and enter the condenser at 85°F. The usual saturated condensing temperature in the condenser would be about 105°F, 20°F above the entering water temperature. This compares favorably with the 115° to 120°F condensing temperature that might result with air-cooled condensing at peak load conditions.

Evaporative-cooled condensers are devices which include most of the components of a cooling tower and a condenser combined. They are usually an assembly which includes a fan or fans that draw or push outdoor air through a water spray chamber in which a bare pipe coil or finned pipe coil is installed (see fig. 10-20). In this illustration it may be seen that below the water spray nozzles the cabinet is filled with water spray. As the outdoor air is circulated up through this water, the water is cooled to within 7°F or so of the OA wet bulb temperature. Some of the water is evaporated, and the remaining water is thereby cooled. This water circulating over the condenser coil surfaces removes

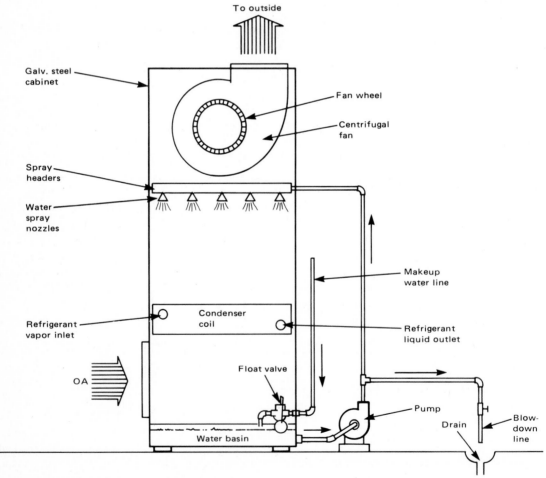

Figure 10-20   Evaporative-cooled condenser.

heat from the coil and the hot refrigerant vapor within the coil tubes. The refrigerant then condenses and leaves the coil as a high-pressure high-temperature liquid.

Since some of the water is evaporated, and since some of the liquid water will be carried away as fine spray, a continuous flow of makeup water must be supplied into the unit. This makeup water must be carefully treated to prevent excessive buildup of algae and solids in the water. To help dissipate the concentrations of solids in the water resulting from continuous evaporation of spray water, a certain amount of water, called *blow-down,* is wasted to the sewer. This further increases the requirements for makeup water. As is true in cooling towers as well, the makeup water quantity, in gpm, usually amounts to about 5% of the water being circulated by the pump. Makeup water is often added through a float valve installed to maintain a certain level of water in the water basin.

To help reduce the amount of liquid spray water carried away by the moving stream of air, a set of moisture eliminators is often installed between the spray headers and the fan housing. This eliminator usually consists of closely spaced, parallel metal blades formed into a zigzag configuration.

Evaporative-cooled condensers are often mounted outdoors exposed to the weather; this gives the easiest access to the outside air that is required in great quantities. However, such condensers are also often installed inside a building to improve building appearance and weather protection, and to shorten refrigerant piping connections. When this is done, of course, the outside air required must be brought in to the condenser and back outdoors through ductwork.

10-10 ACCESSORY EQUIPMENT

Refrigeration systems require a very wide range of accessory equipment to make systems most efficient and trouble free. The list of such equipment is too long to exhaustively cover in a text of this type. However, some of the more important items require mention and a brief description. Expansion valves and solenoid valves were discussed earlier in this chapter.

Dryers

One of the greatest enemies of any refrigeration system is water in any form, and in any installation great care must be taken to exclude it. When all precautions possible have been taken to ensure a completely dry system, one last step should always be taken—the installation of a dryer. This is usually a device mounted in the liquid line between the condenser and the expansion valve, and all refrigerant that circulates must pass through it. It usually contains a moisture adsorbent material such as silica gel or activated alumina. Dryers are sometimes built together with a filter and installed as a filter-dryer unit. Such a unit can correct many of the sins of a faulty or careless installation.

Liquid Indicator

A liquid indicator, sometimes called a *bulls-eye,* is a device that is mounted in the liquid line near the inlet to the liquid line solenoid valve or the expansion valve to indicate whether or not the system is charged with enough refrigerant. The indicator is usually a small cast brass device with inlet and outlet pipe connections arranged for straight-through refrigerant flow, and with two openings on the sides which are sealed shut with thick glass disks. These glass disks permit a view into the inside of the indicator.

When a refrigeration system is charged with an adequate refrigerant charge, the liquid line leading to the expansion valve will contain nothing but liquid. This liquid is clear, like water, and a look into the liquid indicator shows nothing at all. However, if the refrigerant charge is inadequate, the liquid line, during operation, will carry a mixture of liquid and vapor which sighted through the glass of the indicator appears milky or foamy. As refrigerant is added to the system while it operates, the foam will be seen to lighten and finally disappear.

Oil Separators

All refrigeration compressors, except centrifugal compressors, are involved with closely machined parts such as a piston in a cylinder moving in such a way as to require lubrication. The refrigerant that circulates through such compressors is miscible with such oil, and as refrigerant passes through, oil is carried along with it. This oil does become something of a problem when it is delivered out into the refrigeration system. It insulates, to a certain extent, all the tubing of an evaporator, for example, and slows down the heat transfer, which is desired. If enough oil is removed from the compressor and delivered out into the system, the compressor, in effect, may run low on oil and suffer the problem of inadequate lubrication as a result. The solution to this problem is the installation of an oil separator located in the hot gas discharge line leading from the compressor. The oil is collected in the oil separator and is usually returned by high pressure back to the compressor crankcase through a float valve arrangement.

Heat Exchangers

The heat exchanger is a device mounted in the piping between a condensing unit and an evaporator through which both the liquid from the condenser and the suction gas from the evaporator pass. As they pass through this heat exchanger, they interchange heat from one to the other. In this case, the liquid passing through the liquid line is hot and needs to be cooled, while the suction gas from the evaporator is cold and needs to be heated. Therefore, by bringing these two fluids into close communication with each other, heat exchange does occur, and both fluids benefit from the process.

Heat exchangers are usually shell-and-coil devices in which a spiral coil, for example, is located within a metal shell. One of the fluids passes through the interior of the coil while the other fluid passes through the interior of the shell around the outer surfaces of the coil. An appreciable improvement in the overall efficiency of the system can result from the use of a heat exchanger.

10-11 HEAT PUMPS

A heat pump is nothing more than a compression cycle refrigeration system which has the ability to reverse its action. Like all refrigeration systems, one part of the heat pump system is cold, as in a cooling coil, and the other part is hot, as in a condenser coil. By virtue of its ability to maintain two different temperatures, the heat pump is able to extract heat from one medium, called the *heat source,* and to deliver that heat at higher temperature to another medium, called the *heat sink.*

In a typical residential heat pump system, during the heating cycle the heat pump system refrigerates the outdoor air, extracts heat from the outdoor air, and delivers that heat at higher temperature to an indoor coil which is able to heat the indoor air of the building. That same heat pump system is able to reverse its action, and in the summertime refrigerate the indoor air and deliver its heat at high temperature into the outdoor air.

Heat pumps are used for many purposes, but always to remove heat from the heat source, which is at a low temperature, pump the heat up into a higher temperature, and deliver the heat into the heat sink. The heat source may be many things containing heat, such as outdoor air in wintertime or well water; or it may be able to extract heat from any source of waste heat that may be coming from a building.

If we remove heat from a water source and deliver the heat to an air-type sink, we call this a water-to-air heat pump. Or if we remove heat from an air source and pump it up to a higher temperature and deliver it into an air-type sink, this is an air-to-air heat pump. Of course, we can also have an air-to-water heat pump.

One type of heat pump application that has come into play frequently in the last 5 to 10 years is the installation where the heat pump removes heat from one part of a building where cooling is required and transfers that heat into another part of the same building where heat may be required. In this process, then, we utilize the heat from the parts of the building where there is excess heat and, instead of throwing it away from that part of the building, we reuse the heat in another part where heat is required. This is a highly conservative action.

In fig. 10-21 we see two diagrams, one of an air-to-air heat pump, the other of a water-to-air heat pump, which, of course, may reverse itself

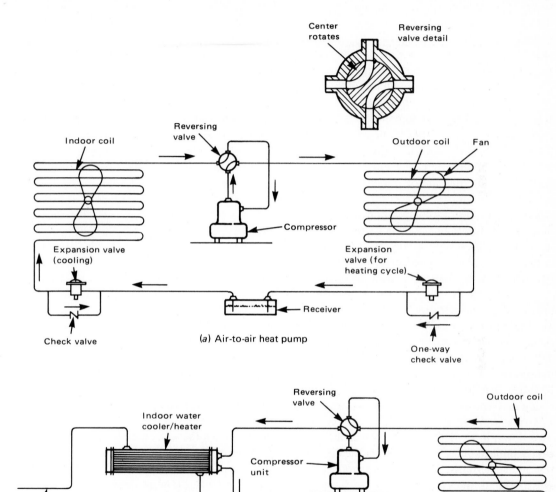

(a) Air-to-air heat pump

(b) Air-to-water/water-to-air heat pump

Figure 10-21 Schematic heat pump diagrams.

and be an air-to-water heat pump. Both of these diagrams represent heat pump systems that can reverse their action by the use of a reversing valve, which is detailed in fig. 10-21. This valve is able to reverse the direction of refrigerant flow through the system so that at one moment the indoor coil becomes a cooling coil and after reversal, the indoor coil becomes a heating coil. By the same token, the outdoor coil during the heating cycle is a cooling coil and refrigerates the outdoor air, and then upon reversal, the outdoor coil becomes a heating coil which delivers heat into the outdoor air—as would be the case in summer operation.

In fig. 10-21*a*, the reversing valve is in the position representing the cooling action, as would be the case in summer. Here, the refrigerant that is discharged from the motor compressor unit is delivered by the reversing valve into the outdoor coil, where the heat of compression and the heat that is removed from the building is dissipated into the outdoor atmosphere through the action of the fan which circulates outdoor air through and over the outdoor coil. Also, one may see that the left-hand expansion valve, of the two shown, is now in action and refrigerant is flowing through it into the bottom of the indoor coil, which is now an evaporator or cooling coil. So here in fig. 10-21*a*, the heat pump is pumping heat from the indoor coil and thus cooling the building, and delivering that heat to the outdoor coil and releasing the heat into the outdoor atmosphere.

As may be seen in the detail of the reversing valve shown in fig. 10-21, the center of this valve rotates through 90° so that in effect the direction of flow in the refrigeration system is reversed. In fig. 10-21*a*, if the reversing valve is changed in position, the compressor now delivers its hot gas into the indoor coil, and the indoor air is heated. In the indoor coil, of course, the refrigerant is now condensed; and it flows as a liquid through the receiver shown, through the right-hand expansion valve and into the outdoor coil. It is now acting as an evaporator, and refrigerates the outdoor air, and thus collects heat from the outdoor air.

In fig. 10-21*b*, the outdoor coil is shown again

as a finned tube coil with a fan circulating outdoor air over the coil. Indoors is shown a shell-and-tube type vessel which can either heat or chill water, depending on the position of the reversing valve. The reversing valve is shown in a position such that the compressor unit delivers its hot gas into the shell-and-tube vessel. The refrigerant passes through the tubes of this vessel and is condensed. It leaves the vessel as a high-pressure high-temperature liquid and flows into the receiver. At the same time, water is being circulated through the shell of the shell-and-tube vessel and thus is being heated. That heated water can be delivered to an air conditioning unit, where it gives up its heat to the heating coil in that unit. The condensed refrigerant then passes on over through the right-hand expansion valve and, as a low-pressure low-temperature refrigerant, into the outdoor coil. The outdoor coil refrigerates the outdoor air and collects heat from it.

When the reversing valve in fig. 10-21*b* is reversed, the compressor unit now delivers its hot gas into the outdoor coil, which now serves as a condenser. The refrigerant is then condensed in the outdoor coil, and it flows as a high-pressure high-temperature liquid into the receiver, through the receiver, through the left-hand expansion valve, and on into the shell-and-tube vessel. In the shell-and-tube vessel, the water that is being circulated through it is now refrigerated, and it leaves the vessel as chilled water and is thus capable of providing cooling action in the air conditioning unit to which the water is circulating.

Another popular use of the heat pump involves the installation of a water chilling unit, which serves as a water-to-water heat pump. In this case, water such as well water or from a nearby lake or stream is pumped into one of the vessels of the water chiller unit, either gives up heat to the unit or removes heat from the unit, and the heat pump action delivers the heat from one vessel to the other. In this case, the refrigerant circulating in the system does not reverse direction. The only reversal is in the direction that the outdoor water flows. First, it may flow through the condenser of the water chilling unit, and thus give condensing action. When reversed, the outdoor supply of water is circulated through the evaporator of the water chilling unit and gives up its heat to the evaporator.

It is expected that in future years, the heat pump will play a great part in the development of HVAC systems. The great versatility of the heat pump has only recently been utilized to the fullest, and great expectations may be had for the heat pump in the future.

As mentioned earlier, the efficiency of performance or efficacy of a heat pump is expressed in terms of its coefficient of performance (COP). COP is expressed in terms of the Btu delivered to the heat sink for each Btu that is purchased in the form of electricity to drive the heat pump.

An air-to-air heat pump, such as might be used to heat a building in wintertime, using outdoor air as a heat source might very well develop a COP of 2.0. In this case, the heat pump is delivering 2 Btu into the building for every Btu that is purchased in the form of electricity. If the heat source is at a higher temperature, such as 50°F well water, the COP might very well be much higher—on the order of 4.5.

One use for the heat pump which in the past has been largely ignored is the recovery of heat from the wastewater of large buildings. It has long been known that large buildings, especially manufacturing facilities, discharge great quantities of waste water at fairly high temperatures of 60°F and up. The application of the heat pump in this case could very well extract heat from this wastewater, and at a coefficient of performance of 6 to 7, deliver great quantities of heat back into the building.

Another application for the heat pump, which may pay great dividends in the future, is in the use of supplementing solar collectors. In this case, the solar collector, of course, collects the sun's heat and stores it in some kind of a storage mechanism. Instead of becoming comparatively inoperative when the temperature of the storage mechanism falls below 100°F, with heat pump application the

temperature of the storage mechanism could be carried on down to 40°F or even 30°F and great amounts of heat recovered which otherwise would not be usable. All in all, it is certainly expected that the heat pump will make a great contribution to our quest for energy conservation.

10-12 ABSORPTION CYCLE REFRIGERATION

The absorption cycle of refrigeration is used where any form of inexpensive heat, such as steam or gas or solar heat, is generally available. The absorption cycle uses water as a refrigerant and a material such as ammonia or lithium bromide as an absorbent. The function of the absorbent in this cycle is to create an area of very low water vapor pressure above a body of water, so that by virtue of the heat in the water some of the water will vaporize. The action of vaporizing, of course, requires the application of heat. That heat is drawn from the body of water itself, and the temperature of that body of water consequently is greatly reduced. The absorbent, for example lithium bromide, has a high affinity for water vapor, and a body of anhydrous lithium bromide will absorb a great amount of the water vapor that may be in the space above the lithium bromide. Of course, as the lithium bromide absorbs water vapor which is drawn from the body of water, the lithium bromide becomes more and more dilute. The action will stop when the lithium bromide becomes completely diluted.

Consider fig. 10-22a. Here there are two vessels, one containing water and one containing anhydrous, or dry, lithium bromide. There is an interconnecting pipe between these two vessels with a gate valve in the pipe. When the gate valve is closed so that no interchange is possible between the two vessels, if the space above the water is evacuated to an almost perfect vacuum, the water will in time assume the same temperature as the ambient space around the water vessel, which in this case is an evaporator. The space in the evaporator above the water level will be filled with

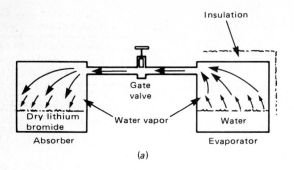

(a)

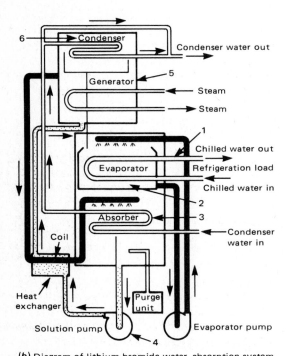

(b) Diagram of lithium bromide water absorption system

Figure 10-22 Absorption refrigeration system schematic details. (Reprinted with permission from the 1977 Fundamentals Volume, ASHRAE Handbook and Products Directory.)

water vapor, and the pressure of that water vapor will correspond to the temperature of the water. If the space above the lithium bromide in the absorber is also evacuated of air and all other gases, the water vapor pressure in the space above the lithium bromide will be essentially zero. When the

gate valve is opened, there will be a very substantial difference in water vapor pressure between the evaporator and the absorber. As a result, there will be a rapid flow of water vapor from the evaporator into the absorber. Because of its affinity for water vapor, the absorbent liquid, lithium bromide, will absorb as much of the water vapor that comes from the evaporator as possible. By this means a continuous process will be carried on until either all of the water is evaporated, or the lithium bromide becomes completely diluted with water.

If the evaporator is fairly well insulated on its exterior, as water evaporates in the evaporator, the latent heat of the evaporation will be drawn from the water and its temperature will fall. This water could now be pumped from the evaporator through a cooling coil, where the cooling effect would be used to cool the air passing over the cooling coil.

Water could thus be circulated from the evaporator to the cooling coil, and a cooling process could continue.

If the lithium bromide in the absorber were likewise pumped continuously from the absorber and put through some kind of a heating device in which the water is evaporated and driven from the lithium bromide, the lithium bromide, now in concentrated form, could be returned to the absorber, where it could absorb more water vapor. Thus the process could continue until all the water was evaporated. Of course, liquid water could be added to the evaporator as needed so that the process would be continuous.

Now let us apply the principles enumerated above to the schematic diagram shown in fig. 10-22*b*. In this diagram we see the evaporator (reference 2) and the absorber (reference 3), which were shown above, and in addition we have two other major vessels, a generator (reference 5), and a condenser (reference 6). Also used in accessory fashion to these four major vessels, we see a heat exchanger, a purge unit, a solution pump (reference 4), and an evaporator pump. In part *b* it is assumed that a supply of steam is available, and that a supply of condenser water, probably from a cooling tower, is also available. Further, it may be seen that there are external connections where chilled water may be drawn from the evaporator, delivered to some point in the building where cooling is needed, and then returned to the evaporator.

In fig. 10-21*b* it may now be seen that the water which is being sprayed into the evaporator is exposed to the absorbing influence of the concentrated lithium bromide in the absorber. Water vapor will be drawn from the evaporator; the water in the evaporator will thus be chilled, and the chilled water coil in the evaporator likewise. As the water vapor is absorbed in the absorber, the

lithium bromide becomes more dilute; it is then pumped by the solution pump (reference 4) up into the generator, where the lithium bromide is now heated. As the lithium bromide is heated, water is driven from it in the form of water vapor and this water vapor rises up to and comes in contact with the condenser coil in the condenser chamber. Here the water vapor is cooled, and it condenses and returns through the pipe connection shown back to the evaporator and the process is continuous.

In the heat exchanger shown, it may be seen that the lithium bromide which is being pumped

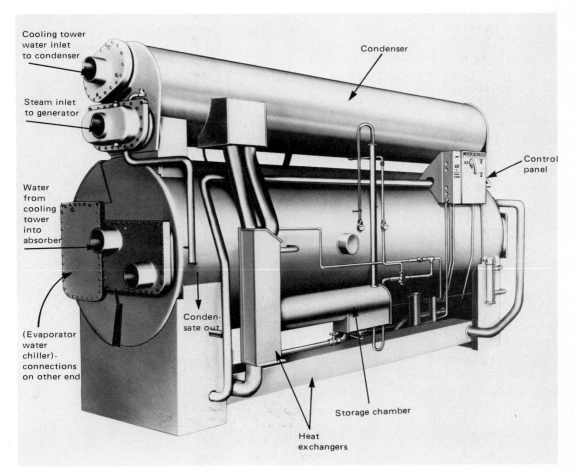

Figure 10-23 Typical absorption type water chiller—steam-operated. (Reproduced by permission of Carrier Corp. © 1980 Carrier Corp.)

from the absorber needs to be heated and is at a comparatively low temperature; and the concentrated lithium bromide returning from the generator is hot and needs to be cooled. Bringing these two streams of fluid together in the heat exchanger causes a heat interchange, and efficiency is improved thereby.

The purge unit shown is a device that continuously withdraws a certain amount of fluid from the absorber so that any noncondensible gases in the system can be removed by one means or another. Notice that the water in the evaporator is

being constantly recirculated by the evaporator pump. Efficiency is improved if this water is sprayed on the evaporator coil. The same principle is applied when the concentrated lithium bromide is returned to the absorber; efficiency is improved if it can be sprayed on the condenser coil in the absorber.

Notice also that condenser water coming from a cooling tower first enters through the coil in the absorber and then passes on up to the cooling coil in the condenser. This water would pick up a great deal of heat in the process and would now be re-

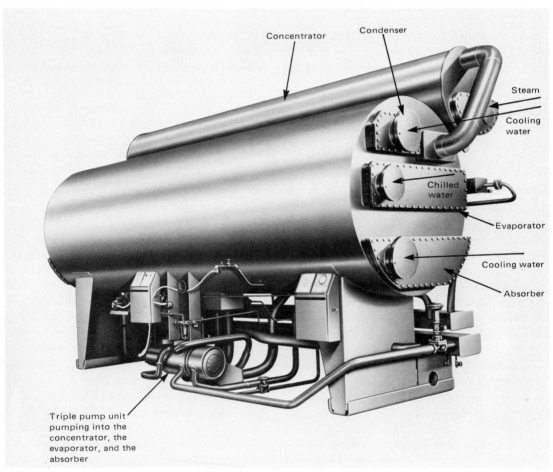

Figure 10-24 Two-stage absorption type water chiller. (© The Trane Company, used by permission.)

turned to a cooling tower, where that heat will be removed and delivered into the atmosphere surrounding the cooling tower.

Two typical manufactured absorption-type water chillers are illustrated in figs. 10-23 and 10-24, which show the components listed in fig. 10-22 as well as other components of interest. The efficiency of an absorption water chiller depends on the cost of the heat that is required for regeneration purposes. Ordinarily, the cost of operation of an absorption water chiller is very competitive with the cost of an electric-motor-driven compression cycle water chiller.

PROBLEMS

10-1   A residential kitchen refrigerator cooling system can remove 640 BH from its refrigerator cabinet and is powered by a 1/6-hp electric motor which has an efficiency of 60%. What is the refrigeration COP of this system?

10-2   A certain existing summer cooling system has a maximum capacity of 42 tons and at full load draws electric power at the rate of 53,000 W. What is the EER of this system? Is it likely that it could be improved with newer, more modern equipment?

10-3   Refrigerant 22 in a closed vessel is subjected to a pressure of 41.0 psig. What is the boiling point of this refrigerant? What is its saturation temperature? What is its condensing temperature?

10-4   Refrigerant 12 in a storage drum is stored in a storage room having a temperature of $70°F$. What is the pressure inside the drum, in psia?

10-5   Water at standard atmospheric pressure is at a temperature of $70°F$. Is this water subcooled water? If so, how many $°F$ is it subcooled?

10-6   Is the refrigerant at reference point 1 in fig. 10-5 at saturation, or is it subcooled or superheated? Explain.

10-7   Describe the functions of the compressor of fig. 10-5.

Chapter 11

Central Station and Unitary HVAC Systems

11-1 GENERALITIES

In the study of HVAC systems we are now ready to apply all the principals, basic concepts, and information that has been presented in all the preceding chapters. In other words, we are going to apply such principles as the requirements for comfort, for temperature control, for system flexibility, for energy conservation, for noise control, and so on. This chapter will be concerned with central station and unitary HVAC systems of many types, and it will be important for us to be able to differentiate between these various types and their applicability to various types of situations.

In general, central station HVAC systems fall into two categories. The first category is the variable air volume system, which is almost universally abbreviated as VAV; and the other category includes constant volume systems. In VAV systems the temperature of the air that is supplied is fairly steady, and the volume of the air is constantly varied in accordance with the requirements of the building being conditioned. In constant volume (CV) HVAC systems, the temperature is constantly being varied while the volume of the air being circulated is, as the name implies, constant.

Let us first examine some of the characteristics of CV types of systems. CV systems are, in general, of two types: single-zone and multizone. The single-zone constant volume system utilizes both blow-through and draw-through types of air conditioning units. These are centrally located in the building and supply conditioned air through ductwork to all the various spaces that are being conditioned.

A single-zone HVAC system can supply air in only one condition, and thus can supply air only to spaces that have similar load characteristics. In other words, it can only supply warm air to spaces that all need heating at the same time; and when one needs cooling, they should all need cooling. Single-zone HVAC systems have in the past often been applied many times to multizone buildings; and, of course, in this case a great amount of trouble can arise. If a single-zone system is applied to a building that really constitutes two or more temperature control zones, the single-zone air conditioning unit simply cannot supply air at a condition that will satisfy the needs of all these various kinds of spaces. In the early days of air conditioning, probably one of the greatest sources of operational trouble arose as a direct result of attempts to use single-zone air conditioning units in spaces and buildings which really constitute two or more zones.

The single-zone HVAC system enjoys the advantage of being low in first cost, and where it can do the job satisfactorily, enjoys a low operating cost. Usually, single-zone systems are applied to buildings and zones in buildings of comparatively small extent, and since these buildings are comparatively small, no return air fan is required. A good example of a single-zone type of air conditioning unit is the roof-top unit, which is seen in such extensive application in shopping centers and commercial applications of that type.

A single-zone air conditioning unit may have one coil or it may have two coils. If it has one coil, this coil will usually be supplied with warm water in wintertime, for heating purposes, and with chilled water in summertime for cooling purposes. The thermostat which provides temperature control for such a single-zone air conditioning unit usually sends a signal which positions one or two automatic control valves that regulate the flow of warm water or chilled water into the one or two coils.

In winter the thermostat that controls this single-zone air conditioning unit must position the water regulating valve that permits warm water to enter the single coil in the single-coil unit; and when that thermostat experiences a rise in temperature in the controlled space, it reacts to close that valve either fully or partially. In other words,

with a rise in temperature on the heating cycle, the valve is closed. However, in the summer cycle when a rise in temperature is experienced by the thermostat, it must not close the valve; it must open the valve and permit a greater flow of chilled water into that coil in the single-coil unit. Thus it may be seen that with a single-coil unit, the thermostat must be of a type that can reverse its action with the changing seasons.

In a two-coil type of single-zone HVAC unit, this is not the case. Again, in this type of unit one coil is for heating and the other coil is for cooling. And a water-regulating control valve regulates the flow of warm water into the heating coil, and another regulating valve controls the flow of chilled water into the cooling coil. Now when the thermostat in the controlled space experiences a temperature rise in wintertime, it must close or partially close the heating coil valve. In the summer cycle when a temperature rise is experienced, all the thermostat must do is to open the control valve on the cooling coil. Thus there is no need for the thermostat to be of a reversing type. In other words, the thermostat closes the heating coil valve on a rise in temperature, winter or summer, and opens the valve on the cooling coil, winter or summer. There is no change in the action of the thermostat.

In a single-zone HVAC unit of this type, when there are two coils—one for heating and one for cooling—these two coils are arranged for series flow. In other words, the air passes through one coil and the same air then passes on through the other coil, so that it is important in controlling these coils that one coil be completely turned off before the other coil is brought into play. In other words, the thermostat must be sure that the heating coil control valve is completely closed, on a rise in temperature, before it begins to open the control valve on the cooling coil.

Sometimes a single-zone type of HVAC unit that has only one coil is not controlled by valves at all, but is controlled by face-and-bypass dampers. These dampers, as the name implies, are so arranged that a group of opposed blade dampers covering the face or entering air area of the coil is matched by a damper or dampers, installed in a bypass around the coil, so that through the action of the face-and-bypass dampers the air may be either permitted to flow through the coil or to be caused to bypass around the coil either fully or partially.

With this type of arrangement, very often the warm water in winter or chilled water in summer is permitted to flow at full volume through the coil at all times, and the control that is achieved is, of course, through the operation of the face-and-bypass dampers. In this case, the thermostat located in controlled space must again be of the reversing type; for example, in winter when a rise in space temperature is experienced, the thermostat must close the face dampers and open the bypass dampers, thus causing more air to bypass around the coil and pick up less heat from the coil. However, in summertime operation when a rise in space temperature is experienced, the thermostat

must now open the face dampers and close the bypass dampers, thus causing all or nearly all of the circulating air to pass through the coil, which is now a cooling coil.

Figure 11-1 shows a typical installation of a single-zone HVAC unit in a small area of building. This illustration shows a floor-mounted vertical pattern air conditioning unit (reference 1), which supplies air through supply duct work to various types of supply air outlets: a supply grille located in a sidewall of the first room, a square or round ceiling diffuser in the ceiling of that same room, and a linear diffuser located in the ceiling of the second room. The air is returned through a very short return duct and return air grille (reference 14) to the HVAC unit. This return air meets with and mixes with outside air which is drawn in through an outside intake louver (reference 15). The outside air and the return air then, as mentioned, mix in the bottom of the air conditioning unit, pass upward through the air filter, then

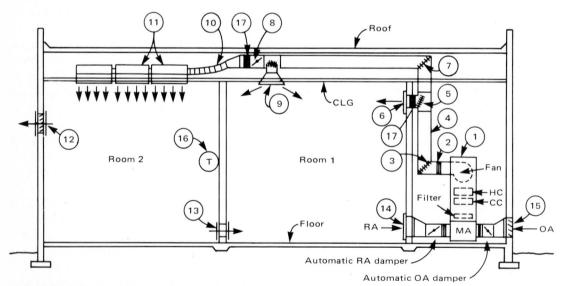

Figure 11-1 Section through building showing small single-zone HVAC system—typical for a/c system number 1. 1, air conditioning unit; 2, flexible connection; 3, turning vane elbow; 4, supply duct; 5, extractor; 6, supply grille; 7, turning vane elbow; 8, volume damper; 9, ceiling diffuser—round or square; 10, flexible supply duct; 11, linear diffusers; 12, air relief opening—barometric; 13, double-faced grille; 14, return air grille; 15, outside air intake louver; 16, thermostat; 17, heating coils—system number 4 only.

through the cooling coil, then through a heating coil, and then into and through the supply fan which causes the air circulation in the system.

Figure 11-1 could be representative of a constant volume system or a VAV system. The components illustrated are properly displayed for either one of those two types of systems.

Part of the ductwork shown in fig. 11-1 is made of sheet metal and includes at the outlet of the air conditioning unit a flexible connection to eliminate the vibration of the unit followed by a square turning vane type of elbow. Above that, at reference 5, we see an *extractor*, which is an adjustable turning vane type of device installed to extract air from the main supply duct and divert it into the supply grille (reference 6). In this illustration, note also that reference 8 shows a volume damper which would be installed to control the volume at the last air supply device shown in the system. And also notice (reference 10) a flexible supply duct which leads to and carries air into the linear diffuser (reference 11). This linear diffuser would be so installed that it could supply air outward in both directions along the ceiling and cause a circular pattern of air distribution throughout the room. Reference 12 shows an air relief opening which is of the barometric type. This means that there is a damper installed in this air relief opening which responds to air pressure inside the building whenever building air pressure rises to the point above the outdoor air pressure. This barometric damper would open and allow air to flow out of the building to the outdoors and thus relieve any internal pressure. The damper in this air relief opening is also designed so that air may not return from the outdoors back into the indoor space.

Whenever air is permitted to enter from the outdoors through the outdoor air intake opening (reference 15) into the air conditioning unit and from it into the building, an equal amount of air must leave the building and the air relief opening (reference 12) will permit this to happen. In our consideration of single-zone systems as above, it should be mentioned here that single-zone systems

may be of the VAV type. However, VAV as such gives its greatest benefits when multizone systems are considered.

In the VAV single-zone system, the equipment shown in fig. 11-1 would be fairly applicable. However, some type of volume control device would need to be attached to each of the three air supply devices (references 6, 9, and 11). This volume control device in each case would take the form of some kind of dampering equipment installed in the supply duct leading to the air supply device.

It may be seen in fig. 11-1 that with such volume control devices, which would be automatically positioned, as they all began to close, the pressure in the supply duct system would begin to build to inordinately high values, so in a VAV system of this kind the fan must be equipped with some type of device to regulate its output volume, and reduce that volume as the static pressure in the supply duct begins to rise.

In single-zone VAV systems the temperature control system would be quite different from those described above. In the case of VAV, what the thermostat does primarily is to regulate the quantity of air supplied through each of the air supply devices, so that the function of the thermostat is to position these dampers automatically so as to deliver the right amount of air and, as a result, the right amount of heating or cooling effect into each room.

VAV systems will be discussed at much greater length in a later article in this chapter.

Most nonresidential buildings of even modest size do have a requirement for two or more temperature-control zones, and in most cases, these nonresidential buildings do have many temperature control zones necessarily required. Each of these zones has its own requirements for heating and cooling and for ventilation, and each zone would have its own primary zone thermostat which is in control of equipment that can provide the necessary supply air to make proper control possible.

Multizone buildings are usually fitted with one

or more multizone air conditioning units. Some multizone units have the capability of mixing warm air and cool air, or warm air and neutral air, or neutral air and cool air in varying proportions as necessary to supply the required temperature air to be delivered to each of the various zones. One such multizone air conditioning unit thus would do its own internal mixing and would be fitted with a large number of individual supply ducts, each extending from the air conditioning unit to the building zone it controls (see figs. 11-9 and 11-10). Other multizone systems will be equipped with a multizone air conditioning unit which supplies air under two conditions or three conditions. Usually from this type of HVAC unit, two supply ducts are run throughout the building. One of these supply ducts would be warm and the other cool, or in certain seasons of the year one of the two ducts might be a neutral temperature duct. So that according to season and according to need, warm air could be mixed with cool air by extracting a small sample of air from each duct and mixing them at the location of the zone. Also, at other seasons of the year, in order to meet the requirements of each zone, warm air could be mixed with neutral air in the same fashion; and yet at other seasons, neutral air could be mixed with cool air. This, in general, is called a double-duct multizone system (see fig. 11-11).

In both of these two types of multizone systems, the individual-duct multizone system and a double-duct multizone system, the function of the primary room thermostat is to operate mixing dampers which mix air at two conditions, as mentioned, to cause the proper temperature of air to be delivered into the zone space.

All the HVAC systems described above may be designed to circulate air at high, medium, or low velocities and, as mentioned in another chapter, there is a great difference in the design characteristics of each of these three types. As mentioned also, it is this author's general recommendation that low-velocity duct work be used wherever possible on the premise that this will provide systems of lowest initial cost and lowest operating cost.

11-2 METHOD FOR HVAC SYSTEM SELECTION

Very often the selection of the type of HVAC system to be used in a given building is a difficult decision. Many types of systems are available, of course, and to evaluate each one in the light of the requirements of a given building and to place all these values into proper perspective is a difficult process; unfortunately, this is a process which is often made without adequate investigation. Figure 11-2 is presented here as a possible method of giving guidance to the persons involved in the selection of the type of HVAC system to be used. In fig. 11-2, three separate hypothetical HVAC systems are being considered. These are listed in the right-hand columns as system A, system B, and system C. No particular types of HVAC systems are considered here.

In the left-hand column we see a list of parameters by means of which various HVAC systems can be evaluated. These are arranged alphabetically and are not in any order of general importance. The first item in this list of parameters is appearance, and is almost always a very important consideration. For example, in a unitary type of HVAC system, the air conditioning units, which are usually quite small, are located directly in the occupied space. Of course, this detracts from the general appearance of that space. Also, very often HVAC systems are characterized by many supply grilles or registers or diffusers, and often these air supply devices have a great deleterious effect on general room appearance.

Going to the extreme, a ventilating ceiling could be used through which air is supplied into the room and in which there is absolutely no visual indication that an HVAC system exists.

The second item in the list of parameters is dependability, and it is difficult to see how this item could ever be an inferior item of consideration. Dependability is of primary importance.

Third in the list of parameters is energy conservation, and of course today a great effort is being made to conserve energy.

Figure 11-2 Sample comparative system rating study.

Parameter	Relative* impor- tance	System A Rating[†]	Score	System B Rating[†]	Score	System C Rating[†]	Score
Appearance	4	9	36	9	36	2	8
Dependability	9	8	72	4	36	5	45
Energy conservation	7	3	21	9	63	2	14
Flexibility and controllability	5	6	30	9	45	6	30
Initial cost	2	5	10	8	16	10	20
Life-cycle cost	10	4	40	8	80	4	40
Maintenance	3	3	9	4	12	4	12
Noise	8	9	72	3	24	8	64
Operating cost	6	6	36	8	48	3	18
Space requirement	1	5	5	5	5	10	10
Total comparative rating[‡]			331		365		261

*Relative importance ratings (from 1 to 10) vary for each project and should reflect the building owner's and building user's opinions. The higher the rating, the better it is.

[†]System ratings ascribed by HVAC designer.

[‡]Total of the "scores" for each system. Each score = importance rating X system rating.

The next item, flexibility and controllability, usually involves the temperature control system and the equipment it controls. Such control systems can involve great expense if a great amount of importance is placed on flexibility and controllability. Many systems have very minimum expense applied in this direction, and of course the accuracy of control suffers. Then there are three items of cost: initial cost, life cycle cost and operating cost. In almost every case these are items of great concern to the prospective building owners. The item of maintenance involves cost too, of course, and the extent to which a system is made to be of low maintenance will depend on whether the owner and operator of the building have an adequate maintenance department. If maintenance will not be readily available for a given system, the design of the system will be influenced extensively, because such a system must in effect operate almost without maintenance attention.

Noise is always an item of great concern except in such applications as industrial buildings, where the ambient noise level may be exceedingly high and where the HVAC system as a result need not

be designed for low noise operation. Space requirements sometimes would not be of great concern. Perhaps the HVAC system is to be placed on the roof exposed to the weather. In this case, whether it occupies a lot of space or a little space, is usually not of great concern. If the HVAC system in its entirety is to be enclosed within the building, the item of space becomes a matter of great concern. Every square foot of building devoted to the HVAC system equipment must be charged as an expense to that system.

In the second column of fig. 11-2, a relative importance rating is given to each of these parameters. The values shown in fig. 11-2 are not suggested as absolute values which will be used in every case. The magnitude of each of these values would depend on the relative importance the building owner places on each parameter.

In this case there are 10 items listed, so the parameters are weighted from 1 to 10, with 10 being best or of highest quality. Therefore, it may be seen for each of the three nonspecific, hypothetical systems—A, B, and C— listed, a rating from 1 to 10 is given for each system and for each parameter. For example, in system A for initial cost, a value of 5 is shown, indicating that for system A a midrange value of initial cost would result. In system B for initial cost, a value of 8 is shown, indicating that the initial cost of system B is somewhat less, and thus better than for system A, and it is even better yet for system C, which has for initial cost a rating value of 10. A score value is given in fig. 11-2 for each of the three systems and for each parameter. This score is merely the product of the relative importance times the rating given. For example, under Appearance, where the owner has expressed a relative importance of 4, a rating of 9 is shown for system A, which, when multiplied by the relative importance 4, gives a score of 36. So a score thus may be developed for each system and for each parameter. These scores for each system are then totaled at the bottom, and it may be seen in fig. 11-2 that system A has a total score, which is a comparative rating, of 331, compared to 365 for system B and 261 for system C. This clearly indicates that system B is the best choice of an HVAC system for this particular building and for this particular building owner.

It is suggested that in the use of this method of HVAC system determination, the relative importance values given in the second column be ascribed by the HVAC system designer but in complete consideration of the importance placed on these parameters by the owner. Similarly, the rating values which are shown for each of the three systems A, B, and C should probably be ascribed by the HVAC system designer only.

11-3   AIR QUANTITY DETERMINATION

One of the most important considerations in the design of a central station air conditioning system is the proper establishment of the quantity of air to be circulated. So often in this type of air conditioning system, the air quantity is not correct and as a result the rooms that are conditioned are drafty and overaired or conversely are underaired and stuffy.

According to the peak load characteristics in a given room or group of rooms, there is one air quantity that is correct and no other air quantity can do the work exactly the way it should be done. At peak load conditions, the air quantity must be correct so as to carry the proper proportions of sensible heat and latent heat. In addition, the temperature and the relative humidity of the supply air as it enters conditioned rooms must be exactly right.

A large number of the existing HVAC systems in this country are completely unsatisfactory because proper recognition has not been given to the need of establishing the correct air quantity and the correct supply air conditions. In the very early days of the air conditioning industry in the United States, Willis Carrier, who is considered to be the Father of Air Conditioning as it is known today, enunciated a system of calculating the proper air quantity. This system is called the *apparatus dew point method of calculating air quantity*.

Figure 11-5 shows a tabulation form on the basis of which an apparatus dew point calculation may be made. Before considering that form, however, a few basic principles must be established. For that purpose let us consider fig. 11-3. In fig. 11-3, we see the outline of a psychrometric chart on which are superimposed the lines and curves that represent a mixed-air cooling cycle. These lines include the point OA, representing the outdoor air condition; the point RA, representing the room air condition; and the point MA, which represents the mixed-air condition of the air entering the cooling coil of the air conditioning unit. So the MA point is also the EA point representing the entering air condition. The dashed curved line shown there running from the MA/EA point to the LA/SA point represents the course that the air would follow as it passes through the cooling coil from the entering side to the leaving side.

Willis Carrier stated that to properly establish the air quantity we must first establish an *apparatus dew point*, which is the ADP point on the psychrometric chart of fig. 11-3. To establish the ADP point we first calculate the sensible heat ratio of

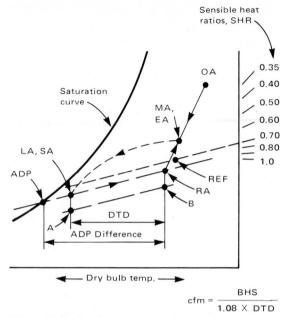

$$cfm = \frac{BHS}{1.08 \times DTD}$$

Figure 11-3 Plotting apparatus dewpoint temperature; ADP, apparatus dewpoint; DTD diffusion temperature difference = RA – SA; EA, entering air; LA, leaving air; MA, mixed air; OA, outside air; RA, room air or return air; REF, Reference point; SA, supply air.

the room load. The sensible heat ratio, remember, is simply the calculated room sensible heat divided by the room total heat. On fig. 11-3 the right-hand scale of the psychrometric chart shows a scale of sensible heat ratios, and they range from 0.35 at the top of the scale to 1.0 at the bottom of the scale. To determine the ADP point, a line is first drawn from the proper point on the sensible heat ratio scale through the reference dot, which is usually a point established at 80°F dry bulb temperature and 50% relative humidity.

This reference point is usually shown on psychrometric charts, although it is not always at the same 80°F dry bulb and 50% relative humidity point.

After the line is drawn as shown in fig. 11-3 from the sensible heat ratio value through the reference dot, a second line is drawn parallel to the first line through the RA (room air) condition. This line is extended to the left until it crosses

the saturation curve as shown. At the point where the second line crosses the saturation curve, we may read the apparatus dew point temperature.

The two lines that have been drawn on the psychrometric chart of fig. 11-3 have a very definite slope which is peculiar to load conditions in the space considered. In other words, the slope of these lines will vary from project to project. An air conditioning load which is almost all sensible heat with very little latent heat would have almost horizontal lines on the chart. Conversely, a load such as might be experienced in an auditorium or a theater where the sensible heat is comparatively low and the latent heat is comparatively high, the slope of these two lines would be much more nearly vertical. So it is important to realize that in the case shown, the slope of the lines is indicative of the characteristics of the load to be encountered in the space. The ADP temperature, shown on the psychrometric chart (fig. 11-3) represents the condition at which air would leave a cooling coil if that coil had zero bypass effect.

It may be remembered from art. 3-11 that in almost any cooling coil, some of the air which passes through it is not conditioned. Some of the molecules, in other words, pass right through the coil and never contact any part of the coil—neither a cold tube nor a cold fin. This air is called bypass air and shortly downstream from the cooling coil the bypassed air mixes with the air which does contact the coil and presents a uniform condition.

In fig. 11-4 we see a table that presents typical bypass factors for various types of coils under various operating conditions. In the left-hand column of fig. 11-4, we see the rows of tubes that a cooling coil might have—four rows, six rows, or eight rows. In the second column from the left, we see the fins per inch that a cooling coil might have: eight fins per inch, 12 fins per inch, or 14 fins per inch. The other three columns in fig. 11-4 show bypass factors at face velocities of 400, 500, and 600 fpm. For example, a four-row coil having eight fins per inch with air passing through it at a velocity of 500 fpm would have a bypass factor

Figure 11-4 Cooling coil bypass factors.

Rows of tubes	Fins per inch	400-fpm face velocity	500-fpm face velocity	600-fpm face velocity
4	8	0.18	0.22	0.25
4	12	0.10	0.11	0.14
4	14	0.07	0.08	0.11
6	8	0.08	0.11	0.13
6	12	0.05	0.06	0.07
6	14	0.03	0.035	0.04
8	8	0.035	0.05	0.07
8	14	0.01	0.01	0.02

Note: Factors are for coils wet with condensation.

of 0.22. This means that of the air passing through that coil, 22% passes through without contacting the coil in any way. It also means that 78% of the air passing through (100% - 22% = 78%) does contact the cooling coil effectively, and this 78% of the air quantity is cooled approximately down to the apparatus dew point temperature. It may also be seen from fig. 11-4 that the faster the air moves through the coil, the higher the bypass factor will be.

In addition, it may be seen that the greater number of rows of tubes in the coil, the lower the bypass factor will be. Also, the greater the number of fins on the tubes of the coil, the lower the bypass factor will be.

Suppose, again, that a cooling coil has four rows or tubes eight fins per inch and face velocity is 500 fpm, the bypass factor is 0.22, as mentioned above. Referring to fig. 11-3, we can see that point LA or SA in this figure represents air leaving the coil and entering the conditioned spaces at a condition which is somewhat warmer than the apparatus dew point temperature condition. In other words, the air entering the rooms will not be quite as cold as the apparatus dew point temperature would indicate. If we have a bypass factor of 0.22 and 22% of the air does bypass through the coil without contacting the coil, it may be seen that the points LA and SA will be located 22% of the distance from the ADP point to the RA point, so that point LA or SA is established by the characteristics of the coil. In

other words, in fig. 11-3, the distance indicated as DTD (diffusion temperature difference) would be exactly equal to 78% of the distance indicated as ADP difference. For example, suppose that the room air (RA) condition is 78°F dry bulb and the LA/SA condition is 55°F; the DTD is then equal to 23°F. It is now a simple matter to determine the required air quantity in cfm because as is shown on fig. 11-3, the cfm is equal to the sensible Btu/hr (BHS) of the room load divided by the constant 1.08 and by the DTD—in this case, 23°F. We have now established an air quantity which is exactly correct for the load characteristics of the conditioned spaces and for the operational characteristics of the cooling coil.

We are now ready to proceed to the air quantity determination form shown in detail in fig. 11-5. As may be seen in this figure, the form is divided into two sections—the upper section represents internal load and the lower section, lines 17 through 20, is involved with external load. The very top line in this form sets forth the design conditions under which the cooling load is to be carried. All the spaces in this form of fig. 11-5 have been filled in with exemplary figures to show how the form would be utilized. In this case, our design conditions outdoors are 95°F dry bulb and 76°F wet bulb. Indoor design conditions are 78°F dry bulb and 63.5°F wet bulb. In lines 1 through 10 of fig. 11-5, the internal load is entered and totaled. It may be seen on examination that the amount of air to be circulated is concerned only with the internal load. In other words, the air must enter the conditioned spaces at a low enough dry bulb temperature and a low enough specific humidity that as the quantity of air determined passes through the conditioned spaces, it will just pick up the amount of sensible heat and the amount of latent heat which is generated within the space. The air quantity which is to be determined is not at all concerned with external load, such as outdoor air load.

In the exemplary figures listed in fig. 11-5, on line 1 is entered the internal room sensible and internal room latent heat which would be totaled

Figure 11-5 Air quantity determination form.

Design conditions:
Outdoors ___95°___ DB, ___76°___ WB, indoors ___78°___ DB, ___63.5°___ WB

Internal load:	Sensible	Latent
1. Calculated zone heat gain—BHS & BHL	60,000	20,000
2. Duct heat gain (1%–10% of line 1)	1,200	
3. Duct air loss (2–5% of line 1)	1,800	600
4. Fan motor horsepower ___1.0___ X 2545 when air conditioning unit is "draw-through" type	2,545	
5. Other internal load	—	—
6. Bypassed outside air. Sensible cfm OA ___400___ X 1.08 (t_o – t_i = ___17°___) BPF ___0.22___	1,616	
7. Bypassed outside air, latent cfm OA ___400___ X ΔG ___41___ X 0.68 X BPF ___0.22___		2,453
8. Subtotal internal load (lines 1-7)	67,161	23,053
9. Safety factor—2 to 10% of line 8	3,358	1,153
10. Internal load total lines 1–9	70,519	24,206

11. Internal "total heat" from line 10 = sens. ___70,519___ + lat. ___24,206___ = ___94,725___ BHT

12. Sens. heat ratio = $\dfrac{\text{BHS } \underline{70,519} \text{ line 10}}{\text{BHT } \underline{94,725} \text{ line 11}}$ = ___0.74___

13. Coil "contract factor" = (1 – BPF ___0.22___) = ___0.78___ "CF"

14. "ADP"—apparatus dew point temp.—from psych. chart ___47°F___

15. Req'd air quantity = $\dfrac{\text{BHS } \underline{70,519} \text{ line 10}}{\text{CF } \underline{0.78} (t_i \underline{78} - \text{ADP } \underline{47}) 1.08}$ = ___2,700___ cfm

16. $\dfrac{\text{Room BHS}}{\text{Multiplier}}$ = $\dfrac{\text{CFM } \underline{2,700} \text{ line 15}}{\text{BHS } \underline{60,000} \text{ line 1}}$ = ___0.045___ cfm/bh

External load:		
17. OA sens. = $\dfrac{(1 - \text{BPF } \underline{0.22})}{\text{BPF } \underline{0.22}}$ X BHS ___1,616___ line 6	5,729	
18. OA lat = $\dfrac{(1 - \text{BPF } \underline{0.22})}{\text{BPF } \underline{0.22}}$ X BHL ___2,453___ line 7		8,697
19. Fan hp _____ X 2544 (blow-through type)	—	
20. Total external (add lines 17, 18 & 19)	5,729	8,697
21. Total load (add lines 10 & 20)	76,248	32,903
22. Grand total load, BHT ___109,151___ (BHS + BHL line 21)		

as a result of a room-by-room calculation. The totals shown on line 1 would be for one room or for one zone, which might consist of several or many rooms. The figures, then, that are entered on line 1 are those which would be totaled in a separate room heat gain calculation. In this case these figures are 60,000 Btu/hr sensible and 20,000 Btu/hr latent. On line 2 would be entered any heat that would be gained by the supply duct running from the air conditioning unit to the conditioned spaces such as might be incurred when a conditioned air duct runs through an unconditioned space. Presumably, such an unconditioned space in summer would be at a higher temperature and there would be a sensible heat gain into the air inside the duct. However, there would not be any latent heat gain in this case. The amount entered on line 2 was taken to be 2% of line 1. The amount of this duct heat gain, as the form indicates, usually ranges from 1% to 10% of line 1. The percent to be used on line 2 would need to be estimated by the designer when he knows what the ductwork layout is like, and how many lineal feet of supply duct would be exposed to unconditioned spaces.

On line 3 is entered an allowance for duct air loss. The air that is being supplied through the supply ductwork to the conditioned spaces is, in the summer, at a low temperature and a comparatively low relative humidity. If, as is usually the case, air leaks out of that supply duct into unconditioned spaces that may surround the duct; this is a loss to the system, and it is both sensible and latent. So on line 3, values have been entered in both the sensible heat column and the latent heat column, and in this case an estimated value of 3% of line 1 was used in each column.

On line 4 is entered the value of the horsepower of the motor which drives the fan that circulates the air in this HVAC system. In this case it was assumed that a 1-hp motor would be required, so on line 4 this "one" for 1 hp is multiplied by 2545, which is the heat equivalent of 1 hp, so on line 4 in the sensible heat column only is entered the value 2545.

On line 5 would be entered any other internal load which might prevail in any circumstance. No values were entered in this particular exemplary case.

On line 6 is entered the sensible heat value of the outside air which bypasses through the cooling coil. At this point on this air quantity determination form, the designer must make an estimate of the type of cooling coil which would be required, and also make an estimate of the face velocity that might be expected of such a coil. In this case, the author has assumed that a four-row coil with eight fins per inch and with a 500-fpm face velocity would be suitable for this application. Such an estimate is the result of experience on the part of the designer, and most designers would not have great difficulty in making an estimate here which is reasonably close.

With a four-row, eight-fin coil, and a face velocity of 500 fpm, the bypass factor from fig. 11-4 is 0.22. As was mentioned before, this means that 22% of the air that passes through the coil is not conditioned by the coil at all. In this case, if we have outdoor air mixed with return air passing through this coil, it may be assumed that some of the air which bypasses through this coil will be outdoor air.

For this particular example, it was assumed that 400 cfm of outdoor air would be required in this building for ventilation purposes. So as a result, 22% of this 400 cfm of outdoor air would bypass through the cooling coil and thus appear downstream from the cooling coil and as such must be considered to be internal load. In this case, on line 6, then, the quantity of outdoor air (400 cfm) is multiplied by the constant 1.08 and by the temperature difference between outdoor air and room air, which in this case is 17°F, and finally multiplied by the bypass factor 0.22; the result of this calculation is the entry of 1,616 BH in the sensible heat gain column.

By the same line of reasoning, it may be assumed on line 7 that outdoor air bypassing through the coil will also contribute latent heat load. Again, 400 cfm is used as the outdoor air quantity, and the 22% of this will bypass through the coil unconditioned. Using the latent heat gain formula found elsewhere in this text, we next must multiply the cfm by ΔG, which is the difference in specific humidity in grains per pound between outdoor air condition and room condition. In this case, the specific humidity of the outdoor air is 105 grains/lb, and the specific humidity of the indoor air is 64 grains/lb. The difference, ΔG, in this case is 41 grains/lb, which is entered on line 7. Therefore, the multiplication on line 7 is 400 cfm $\times$ 41 grains/lb, ΔG, $\times$ the constant 0.68 $\times$ the bypass factor 0.22, which results in an entry on line 7 in the latent heat column of 2453 BH.

Line 8 is just a summation of lines 1 through 7, and is a subtotal amount entered on line 8. These totals equal 67,161 BH sensible heat and 23,053 BH latent heat.

To these subtotals is added a safety factor, as shown on line 9. The safety factor will normally range between 2 and 10% of line 8, depending on how accurate the engineer felt the information he had been given to work with might be. If he felt that there was a lot of inaccuracy in the values he was given, he might use a higher safety factor. In this case, the author has used a 5% value, so that on line 9, 5% of the values on line 8 have been entered. These are then 3358 BH sensible heat and 1153 BH latent heat.

On line 10, then, there is a summation of lines 1 through 9, which results in 70,519 BH sensible heat and 24,206 BH latent heat.

On line 11, the sensible heat total and the latent heat total from line 10 have been added to obtain the total heat quantity of 94,725 BH total heat.

On line 12 of this air quantity determination form, the sensible heat ratio has been calculated. Sensible heat ratio is sometimes also referred to as sensible heat factor. These terms are synonymous. By definition, sensible heat ratio means the ratio of the internal sensible heat gain, in this case, 70,519 BH from line 10, divided by the total internal heat gain 94,725 BH from line 11. This ratio works out to be 0.74. The meaning of this expres-

sion is that of the total internal heat gain, 74% is sensible.

On line 13 is calculated the cooling coil *contact factor*. The contact factor is merely 1 minus the bypass factor. In other words, if 22%, in this case, of the air bypasses through the cooling coil without being conditioned, then 78% is fully conditioned as it passes through the cooling coil, so that 78% of the air that passes through the coil does contact the coil. This is called the contact factor and abbreviated CF.

On line 14 is entered the apparatus dew point temperature, in this case, 47°F. This apparatus dew point temperature was plotted on the psychrometric chart in the same manner as was described for fig. 11-3.

On line 15, then, we finally reach the point where the required air quantity may be determined. As shown in fig. 11-5, this required air quantity is equal to the total internal sensible heat load from line 10, in this case 70,519, divided by the values that appear in the denominator of the fraction on line 15, namely, the 0.78 contact factor and the 78°F inside design temperature minus the apparatus dew point temperature of 47°F all multiplied by the constant 1.08. The result of this calculation is 2700 cfm:

$$\text{cfm} = \frac{70{,}519}{0.78(78°F - 47°F)1.08} = 2700$$

At this point the designer must now stop and determine whether the estimates made on lines 6 and 7 were correct. He will now calculate the coil entering temperature, and knowing the amount of the sensible and latent heat load, he can calculate the coil leaving air conditions. By consulting manufacturers' coil rating catalogs, he can determine whether in this case the four-row, eight-fin cooling coil with a face velocity of 500 fpm will perform the required amount of cooling. In this particular case, the coil described will very easily perform the cooling function required when the 2700 cfm of air is passing through, when the coil is a four-row coil having eight fins per inch, and when the face velocity is approximately 500 fpm. In other words, the assumptions made in this particular case are valid. If the designer finds that the required results cannot be achieved with the cooling coil that he or she assumed would be used, it will be necessary to go back to line 6, make a new assumption, and start over.

Usually, an experienced designer will have little trouble in making an accurate estimate of the type of coil that will be used on either the first or the second attempt.

On line 16 of fig. 11-5 is calculated a convenience factor by means of which the designer can easily determine the amount of air to be supplied into each of the rooms that constitute the zone for which the values on line 1 were calculated. On line 16, the cfm determined on line 15, in this case 2700 cfm, is divided by the sensible heat gain of 60,000 Btu/hr entered on line 1. The result is the value 0.045 cfm/BH. This convenience factor of 0.045 may now be applied to the sensible heat gain for each room. For example, if one of the rooms in the zone represented here had a heat gain of 10,000 BH sensible, that value multiplied by 0.045 would show that that particular room would require an airflow rate of 450 cfm (10,000 × 0.045 = 450).

We may now proceed to line 17 and those that follow and determine the external load, which when added to the internal load will develop the total load of this particular HVAC system. On line 17 is entered the amount of sensible heat in the remainder of the outdoor air load. Remember that on line 6, 22% of the outdoor air load was introduced so that the remaining 78% must now be entered on line 17. This value is 5729 Btu/hr sensible.

On line 18 a similar value for latent heat is entered, and the value of 8697 Btu/hr latent heat results.

On line 19 would be entered the heat of the fan that circulates the air, if the unit were of a blow-through type. The author was contemplating a draw-through type, so that fan motor horsepower was entered on line 4 and therefore must not be entered on line 19. Therefore, line 19 is blank. Had the unit under consideration been a blow-through type, a value would be entered on line 19 and not on line 4.

On line 20 we may now total the external load represented by lines 17, 18, and 19; and these amounts are 5729 Btu/hr sensible heat and 8697 Btu/hr latent heat.

We may now add to this external load the amount of the internal load shown on line 10, so line 21 shows the total of these two amounts, the internal load and the external load; this amounts to 76,248 Btu/hr sensible heat and 32,903 Btu/hr latent heat. These two values are added together and entered on line 22 to show the grand total heat of this system: 76,248 BH sensible + 32,903 BH latent = 109,151 BH total heat.

From the calculations shown in fig. 11-5, then, it may be determined that the required air quantity is 2700 cfm, and the total cooling load of this particular zone is 109,151 Btu/hr total heat, or approximately 9.1 tons.

11-4   RETURN AIR FANS AND DUCTS

In most central station HVAC systems there is only one fan that causes the air to be supplied into the controlled spaces and also returned from the controlled spaces back to the air conditioning unit. This fan is, of course, usually located inside the air conditioning unit. However, in some very large HVAC systems, two fans are required—one supply fan and one return air fan. Whether a return air fan is required depends on the acceptable static pressure which may be carried in the controlled spaces. In fig. 11-6 we see a cross section through a building that has a very simple HVAC system installed. This system has an air conditioning unit (reference 1) and a supply duct system (reference 2). It also has a return air duct system (reference 7) which represents a comparatively lengthy or extensive return air duct. The system in fig. 11-6 also includes an outside air intake (reference 10), an outside air intake damper (reference 11), a return air damper (reference 12),

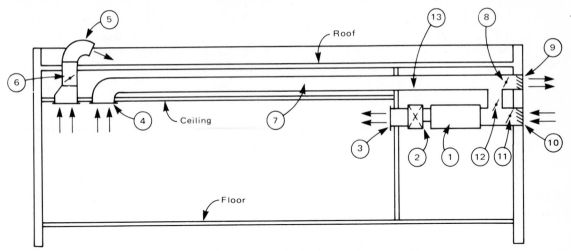

Figure 11-6 Building section showing outside air intake and relief system. 1, air conditioning unit; 2, supply ductwork; 3, supply grilles; 4, return air grille; 5, alternate air relief opening; 6, barometric damper; 7, return duct; 8, automatic air relief damper; 9, air relief opening louver, 10, outside air intake opening; 11, automatic OA damper; 12, automatic return air damper; 13, possible RA fan location.

and a relief damper (reference 8). During normal operation, outside air is drawn in through the outside air damper, where that outside air is mixed with return air passing through the return air damper (reference 12). This creates a mixed-air condition which enters the air conditioning unit. In most nonresidential buildings there is a definite requirement for the continuous introduction of outdoor air for ventilation. The problem that results from this is that of relieving an equal amount of air from the building so as to maintain a fairly neutral static pressure inside the building. If air is to be relieved from the building through the relief damper and the outside air relief louver (reference 9), there must be a slight pressure in the duct at the relief damper in excess of atmospheric pressure. This must be so or air will not flow from the return air duct to the outdoors. The amount of static pressure required in the return duct at the relief damper must be equal to the frictional resistance of the relief damper and the louver in the relief opening. Normally, a relief damper of this type would have a static pressure loss of 0.07 in. WG. Also, the relief louver would normally have a

static pressure loss of 0.05 in. WG, so that the total static pressure loss through the relief damper and louver would normally be in the range of 0.12 in. WG. Therefore, there must be a static pressure equal to that in the return duct in order to have a flow of air from the duct to the exterior.

If the return air duct from controlled space has a static pressure loss, as it must have, of, for example, 0.15 in. WG, and if the return air grille (reference 4) has a static pressure loss of 0.05 in. WG, there is then a static pressure loss of 0.20 in. WG between the air in the room and the relief damper (reference 8). Adding to this the 0.12 in. static pressure loss that would be incurred in the relief damper and the air relief louver, we find that a total static pressure of more than 0.32 in. WG must exist in controlled space in order to have enough pressure to push air from the controlled space through the return air duct and to the exterior of the building. This 0.32 in. WG of static pressure in the building is equivalent to 0.0115 psi of pressure. This pressure multiplied by 144, the number of square inches in a square foot, gives us a static pressure inside the building of 1.66 lb/ft^2.

If we have a 3 ft × 7 ft door leading to the exterior of the building, there would then be 1.66 times 21 ft² equal to 34.8 lb of force on this door holding it shut if the door swings in, or trying to push it open if the door swings out. Of the 34.8 lb of force on the door, the hinges would carry one-half or 17.4 lb of force, and the lock side of the door would carry the remaining 17.4 lb of force. If a person is to open this door, the person must then overcome the 17.4 lb of force on the lock side. If an automatic door closer is installed to keep the door closed, this door closer must develop a force of approximately 20 lb to hold an outswinging door closed. One problem with this situation is that when a person leaving the building opens this door outward, the force of the air inside the building prevents the closer from closing the door fully, and thus security is lost. If this door swings in and has an automatic door closer to close it, when it is closed there is the force of the static pressure in the building holding the door closed. In addition, the door closer itself will exert an extra pressure so that a person opening this inswinging door must provide an effort equal to about 25 lb of force. This is too much; in fact, the 20 lb of force on the outswinging door is also too great. An older person holding lots of packages just cannot manage this much effort. One solution to this problem is the installation of a direct relief opening such as that shown in references 5 and 6. In this case, the air may be relieved directly from controlled space to the exterior without the frictional resistance of a long return air duct. By this means, the required static pressure inside the building could easily be reduced to about 0.1 in. WG as opposed to the 0.32 in. WG mentioned above. In such a relief opening there must be some type of damper, such as the barometric damper of reference 6. This is a pressure-sensitive damper which opens when a certain amount of pressure develops within the building, and closes when less than that pressure exists. This type of damper would also prevent wind pressure outside the building from forcing air inward through the air relief opening.

When such an alternative air relief opening is utilized, the air relief opening indicated at references 9 and 8 would not be used.

Another solution to the problem of excessive static pressure in a building can be solved through the use of the return air fan. In this case, a centrifugal return air fan would be installed where shown at reference point 13 in fig. 11-6. The return air fan provides the necessary motive power to overcome the frictional resistance of the long return air duct and also to provide a slight positive pressure at the relief damper (8). This works very well except that there is a serious problem when VAV (variable air volume) systems are utilized. With VAV the fan in the air conditioning unit is able to modulate its capacity and reduce the airflow down to approximately 20% of its design or maximum airflow. When the supply fan in the air conditioning unit does modulate its capacity, a return air fan in the return air duct would be required to reduce its capacity in exactly the same ratio. This presents a serious control problem, one that has never really been completely solved by the temperature control industry.

If the two fans are not exactly matched in capacity, some very strange occurrences are encountered. Many different temperature control systems have been utilized in order to properly modulate the capacity of the return air fan. These include the installation of a static pressure regulator in controlled space to modulate the return air fan capacity in accordance with the static pressure encountered there. Also, efforts have been made to modulate return air fan capacity by the same controller that modulates the capacity of the supply fan. This leaves much to be desired from an operational standpoint.

In addition, efforts have been made to install "sail" switches in both the supply duct system and the return duct system to measure the velocity of air movement in those ducts and to control the two fans so that these velocities are properly regulated. This has not been a successful system either. By far the best solution to the problem of excessive static pressure within the controlled space is merely to keep the length of the return air duct system to an absolute minimum. This can be done by utilizing corridors for return air, or by utilizing ceiling furred spaces for return air purposes. It has also been found necessary in some cases (to minimize the return air duct length) to return air from one space through another controlled space in order to eliminate the return duct from the first space. Many HVAC designers frown on this technique. However, in many cases it has proven to be completely satisfactory, if there is no problem of air pollution from one space to the other and if the total air movement through the second space does not exceed 20 air changes per hour.

11-5 VARIABLE AIR VOLUME SYSTEMS

Variable air volume (VAV) systems have come onto the HVAC market in great numbers during the last 10 years as a means of temperature control alternative to that which has been conventionally utilized. Through the years our primary methods of temperature control have consisted of varying the temperature, as necessary, of a constant volume of air. It may be seen that the same effect can be achieved through the use of a varying air supply volume with the temperature held essentially constant.

In new, larger nonresidential HVAC systems today VAV is probably used more than constant volume systems. Variable air volume is achieved in many different ways, and may consist of varying the quantity of the main air supply or may consist of varying the quantity of the individual zone air supply; or both may be utilized.

In a minority of the VAV systems, while the volume of air supplied is varying, the temperature of the air may also be varied.

In conventional constant volume HVAC systems, the air quantity supplied by the main supply air fan must equal the total required air volume of each zone at its greatest load peak, even though the maximum peak loads in all zones never occur concurrently. In other words, a south zone in a building must be supplied with enough air quantity to handle its peak load even though its peak load occurs only at one limited time during each day.

With VAV, the total air quantity to be circulated is not the total of the peak air quantities of all the zones in a building, but would consist of the peak air quantity of the zones that are experiencing maximum load plus the reduced air quantity of those zones not experiencing maximum load. Therefore, the total air requirements in a VAV system are always less than the total air requirements in a CV (constant volume) system. This itself achieves a considerable reduction in power consumption of the supply fan.

With VAV systems, the total air supply quantity is reduced as the several zones experience a reduction in load, and usually the air supply required into a given zone is reduced through the throttling effect of dampers in the supply duct to each zone. During periods of overall light load on a building, it may be seen that most of the zones would experience a throttling effect, and as a result, the static pressure in the supply duct at the supply fan outlet will tend to rise. In many VAV systems as a rise in static pressure is experienced, the air supply capacity of the supply fan is automatically reduced. This supply fan capacity reduction is accomplished in many different ways. Some of these methods are listed as follows:

1 A fan bypass duct with an automatic damper causes supply air to bypass from the supply duct around the fan and back to the fan inlet. The automatic damper in this bypass duct may be automatically positioned by a damper motor or it may be a pressure-sensitive damper operating like a barometric damper in response to increasing supply duct pressure.

2 Supply fan inlet vanes may be utilized which throttle the amount of air that is permitted to enter the inlet opening of the supply fan. The inlet vanes which accomplish this throttling effect would normally be automatically positioned by a damper motor that operates in response to a pressure-sensitive controller measuring the static pressure in the supply ducts.

3 The speed of the supply fan may be automatically reduced as the requirements for air are reduced. This is accomplished through the use of a frequency inverter, or variable speed mechanical drive.

Of the three methods listed above, there is a great difference in the efficiency with which the air supply volume reduction is accomplished. With method 1, utilizing a bypass duct, there is very little reduction in fan motor horsepower as the requirements for air are reduced. This, of course, defeats one of the primary purposes of the variable air volume system, which is to conserve energy through fan power reduction. With a fan inlet vane control, method 2, as the air quantity is reduced, there is a true power reduction accomplished. If the air quantity is reduced to 50% of its maximum rating, the power requirement would usually be reduced to approximately 50% of maximum power demand. However, with method 3, the use of fan speed control through the use of frequency inverters or variable mechanical drives, an even greater power reduction is accomplished; and when air quantity supply is reduced to 50% of maximum, the power requirement may be between 25 and 30% of maximum power requirement. Thus, with system 3, a much greater saving in energy is accomplished.

In fig. 11-7 are presented two separate charts which outline the performance characteristics of VAV systems. The chart in fig. 11-7a shows first that the power requirement of a centrifugal fan falls off rapidly as the air quantity requirement is reduced. This curve shows that at 60% of rated cfm, only approximately 20% of full rated horsepower is required. None of the methods of driving such a fan, however, are able to quite duplicate this performance. As may be seen, the power demanded by the motor that drives the fan is, in some cases, greatly in excess of the power required by the fan itself. When a throttling damper control is used in a VAV system, the top curve in fig. 11-7a shows that as the dampers, either at the fan outlet or farther out in the system, are throttled,

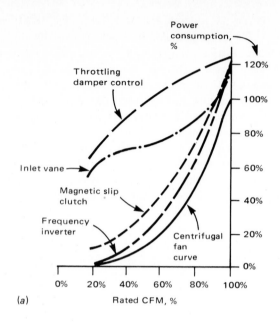

(a)

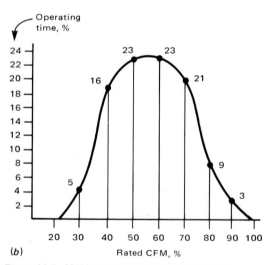

(b)

Figure 11-7   VAV systems operating characteristics.

the air quantity is reduced but the power consumption of the fan motor reduces very little. The chart of fig. 11-7a also shows the curve for inlet vane control. In this case, the inlet vanes are located at the inlet of the fan and throttle the air quantity on the suction side of the fan. In this case, better performance is achieved than with throttling damper control. However, the power requirements of the fan motor do not fall off at all in proportion to the reduction in air quantity of the fan.

One of the curves in the chart of fig. 11-7a also shows the power demand curve for a frequency inverter type of fan motor control. In this case it may be seen that the fan motor power requirement is very little more than the theoretical fan requirement. Also, it should be noted in this chart that with almost all types of fan motor control, the power requirement of the fan motor at 100% rated fan capacity is appreciably in excess of the theoretical power requirement of the fan. This is equally true when frequency inverter control is utilized. However, since the full capacity of an HVAC supply fan is rarely required in a VAV system, the power savings resulting from the use of a control such as a frequency inverter greatly offsets any disadvantage that may be incurred at 100% fan capacity.

The chart of fig. 11-7b gives an idea for the average HVAC system as to what percentage of fan capacity is required. This chart shows that 100% fan capacity in a VAV system is almost never required, and that 50 to 60% of total fan capacity is only required about 23% of the time. This lower chart then shows graphically the importance of achieving fan motor power reduction when air quantity reductions occur.

In fig. 11-8 is presented a photograph of a frequency inverter such as one might find in typical manufacture today. This assembly represents an enclosed panel which usually runs approximately 20 in. wide by 30 in. high and extends out from the wall to which it is secured approximately 9 in. Even though it is obviously true that great complexity is involved in a panel such as is shown in fig. 11-8, the operating history of such devices has proven to be very good from a service standpoint. Initial costs of inverters today are very high but should moderate appreciably in the next few years.

A frequency inverter operates on alternating current power and rectifies that alternating current power to direct current power, and then converts that power back to alternating current again at whatever frequency may be required. Of course, the fan motor rotative speed is in direct proportion to the frequency of the alternating current power.

There are some special problems attendant on the use of VAV type systems. One of these problems is associated with the use of the supply diffusers by means of which air is introduced into controlled spaces. Diffusers that are utilized with VAV must be of a special design, and must be tested to demonstrate the fact that as air quantity falls off to as low as 20% of maximum quantity, the airflow performance patterns of the diffuser will still be maintained. Unless proper diffusers are utilized, the air will have a tendency to dump into the controlled space without any proper distribution pattern maintained.

Many manufacturers have faced this problem and have solved it, so that many supply diffusers are available that can introduce air into the controlled spaces and maintain a good supply airflow pattern even though the total air quantity is greatly reduced.

Another problem attendant to the use of VAV systems is in connection with the maintenance of a satisfactory relative humidity in controlled spaces during summertime operation. It should be realized that the cooling load in most buildings is of such a nature that as outdoor summertime conditions moderate, the sensible cooling load will be reduced. However, in most situations the latent cooling does not reduce at all, or very little. If the air supply quantity is modulated in proportion to the diminished sensible heat load, the latent heat load may not be properly handled. Therefore, great care should be used in utilizing VAV in buildings where the latent heat load is inordinately high in comparison to the total load. This would include all buildings of assembly where large numbers of people gather, as in an auditorium or even as in a restaurant. In these cases, as the outdoor conditions moderate, the sensible load may fall off appreciably, whereas the latent heat internal load

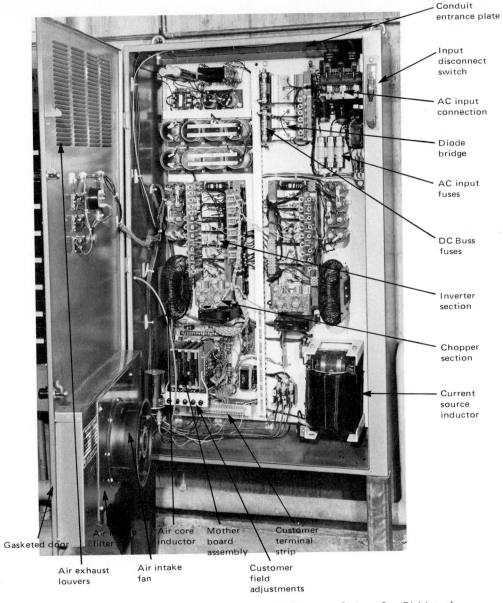

Figure 11-8 Frequency inverter motor speed control panel. (Courtesy Graham Co., Division of Stowell Industries.)

will not diminish at all. Therefore, if the air supply quantity is greatly reduced, the latent heat load may not be properly cared for. This problem may be partially offset by the use of a temperature control system which will permit the cooling coil in

the HVAC unit to reduce its temperature as the load is reduced. This reduced cooling coil temperature will give greater dehumidification to the air that does pass through the coil, and it may be that the latent heat load will be satisfactorily carried.

Face-and-bypass damper type of control can give the necessary reduced coil temperatures.

One appreciable advantage of VAV is its lower initial cost. The lower initial cost of the VAV systems is mainly the result of less complicated and less extensive supply and return duct systems, and as a result of smaller and less expensive HVAC units. The supply duct system can be substantially smaller and simpler than would be required of a multizone individual duct system, or a multizone double-duct system. Ordinarily, the VAV supply duct system is a single-duct system, and zoning is usually accomplished by the variable air quantity supply equipment that is located at the end of each duct run.

The overall air supply quantity is less with the VAV system than with a constant volume system. The air supply quantity is in proportion to the block load of the building; this lower air supply quantity, of course, does result in smaller supply ducts, smaller return ducts, and in a smaller and less expensive air conditioning unit.

The major benefit in the cost of VAV, however, is in connection with operating cost, as mentioned previously. The air supply quantity may be greatly reduced in a VAV system, and if proper fan motor control is utilized, the power demand of such a system may be only a small fraction of the power demand of a constant volume system. This results in a great reduction in power cost.

As was shown in fig. 11-7, the air quantity being supplied is usually about 50% of the total air quantity that might otherwise be required in a constant volume system.

One other problem that does arise through the use of VAV systems results from reduced air quantity, which, of course, will result in less air circulation rate in controlled spaces. This may be in conflict with applicable ventilating codes. It may also be difficult in VAV systems, when the main air supply quantity is greatly reduced, to introduce enough outside air to ventilate the building properly. These are problems which should be thoroughly investigated, and it may be necessary in some cases to put a lower limit on the amount

of air that may be circulated in order to meet ventilating code requirements.

In the next 14 articles of this chapter, arts. 11-6 through 11-19, we will closely examine various types of HVAC systems which constitute nearly all the systems in general use today. The first of these will be constant volume systems. These will be followed by a number of VAV systems, followed by unitary systems, utilizing small air conditioning units located generally within the conditioned spaces.

11-6   SYSTEM 1: CENTRAL STATION SINGLE-ZONE CONSTANT VOLUME HVAC SYSTEMS

As previously described, system 1 is the simplest of all the central station types of HVAC systems and consists of a single-zone central station air conditioning unit located in a space remote to the spaces that are being conditioned. This single-zone unit is designed so that it is able to produce air at one condition only. Unlike multizone units, it cannot produce different streams of air at different conditions. Therefore, the air may be supplied at a given moment at one temperature and one relative humidity only. It is important to realize that system 1 is therefore not applicable to a building or an area of a building that constitutes more than one temperature control zone. One danger with system 1 is the attempt that has frequently been made in the past to utilize a system 1 type on a multizone type of building.

System 1 is characterized by fig. 11-1, which shows the central station air conditioning unit discharging its conditioned air into the supply duct system, which includes the supply grilles, registers, and diffusers. Figure 11-1 also shows a return duct and an outside air intake duct showing how outside air and return are mixed before they enter the air conditioning unit. Figure 11-1 shows an air relief opening (reference 12) by means of which any excess pressure in the building may be relieved to the exterior. This, of course, is necessary whenever outside air is brought into a building for ventilation purposes.

Temperature control in system 1 is usually accomplished by a room thermostat which positions an automatic valve that controls the flow of hot water or chilled water through a common heating-cooling coil. Often system 1 will have an air conditioning unit with two separate coils, one for heating and one for cooling, in which case there will be two temperature control valves under the control of the room thermostat. System 1 also very often includes a central station air conditioning unit which is fitted with face-and-bypass dampers in which case bypass control is accomplished by the room thermostat positioning these dampers. Number 1 HVAC systems are usually quite simple, uncomplicated, and comparatively inexpensive. When bypass control is utilized, this system may do a good job of controlling not only temperature but relative humidity. System 1 air conditioning units may be of almost any size from the very smallest to the very largest. When the air conditioning unit is equipped with a two-speed fan motor, year-round operation is benefited, when the fan is caused to run on high-speed in the summer and on low speed in the winter. It is usually true that much more air quantity is required for the cooling function than is required for the heating function. The two-speed fan therefore accommodates itself very well to this principle and does operate to save electrical energy in wintertime operation. System 1 may be designed for either a high-velocity supply duct system or a low-velocity duct system. One advantage of system 1 is that there are no operating parts out in the duct system and all operating parts that probably would need service are located in the equipment room where the air conditioning unit is located.

One disadvantage of system 1 is that in a multizone building (and most nonresidential buildings are of this type), a large number of system 1 units may be required, one for each temperature control zone in the building. This may work to a cost disadvantage of the HVAC equipment in the entire building. Another disadvantage of system 1 is that it is a constant volume system in which the same amount of air is circulated at all times, and the power to run the fan motor is greater than in other systems currently in use.

11-7   SYSTEM 2: CENTRAL STATION MULTI-ZONE CONSTANT VOLUME INDIVIDUAL-DUCT HVAC SYSTEM

As may be seen in fig. 11-9, system 2 consists of a centrally located multizone type of air conditioning unit from which a large number of individual supply ducts run and extend to the various temperature control zones of a building. The multizone type of air conditioning unit which is utilized, as has been pointed out previously, is capable of supplying air under many different conditions. Each of the many individual supply ducts, which extend to the various parts of the building, can handle air at different conditions according to the needs of the zones that the unit supplies. The air conditioning unit may be a double-deck unit, such as that shown in fig. 6-14, or it may be a triple-deck unit, as shown in figs. 11-9 and 11-10. The triple-deck unit shown in fig. 11-9 has the advantage of being able to supply either heated air or cooled air or a neutral air which is neither heated nor cooled. By this means it can supply air to a zone that needs neither heating nor cooling, without utilizing either heated or cooled air, but utilizing neutral bypass air.

System 2 may utilize high-velocity supply duct work or low-velocity supply duct work. Either is suitable to this system. Air relief should be provided, as shown in fig. 11-6, either by a separate air relief opening (see references 5 and 6) or by a relief opening which is tied into the duct system (see references 8 and 9 of fig. 11-6).

System 2 is basically a constant volume–variable temperature type of system, and does not enjoy any of the economic advantages of a VAV system. The usual temperature controls consist of a room thermostat which positions the mixing dampers to deliver to each zone the air under the condition required. This is a very simple, inexpensive type of temperature control system and is able to provide

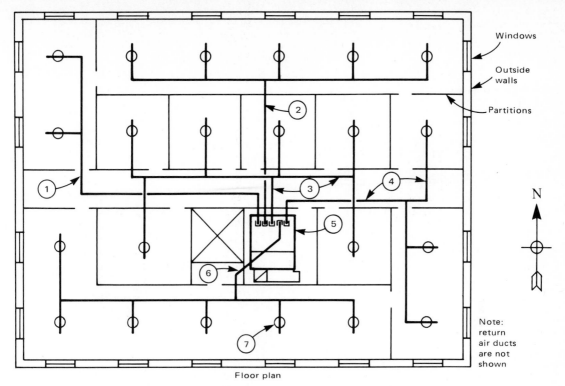

Floor plan

(a) Typical duct layout

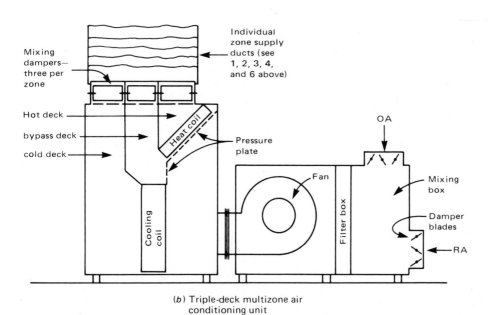

(b) Triple-deck multizone air conditioning unit

Figure 11-9 Details of HVAC system number 2. (1) West zone duct; (2) north zone duct; (3) interior zone duct; (4) east zone duct; (5) air conditioning unit (see detail below and fig. 11-10); (6) south zone duct; (7) typical ceiling diffusers.

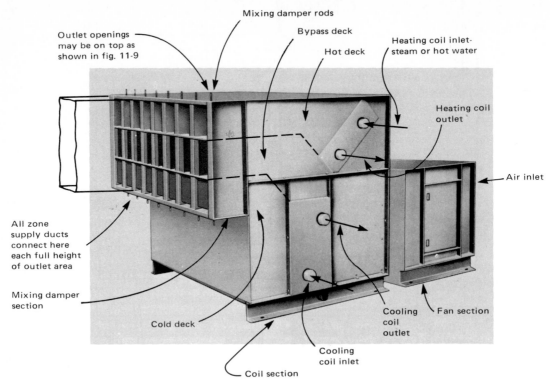

Figure 11-10   Triple-deck multizone air conditioning unit. (Courtesy Aladdin Heating Corp., San Leandro, Calif.)

very accurate and trouble-free temperature control. There is no need in system 2 for a thermostat to be able to reverse its action—in other words, it provides the same action year-round without any complications. It should be pointed out that the multizone unit utilized in system 2, either double deck or triple deck, does provide face-and-bypass damper control, so that this system is very suitable for use with either high sensible heat ratio projects or comparatively low sensible heat projects. In other words, this system will be able to keep good control of the relative humidity in controlled spaces at all times, even when the sensible heat load is quite low and the latent heat load is quite high.

It would be helpful if in system 2 a two-speed fan motor were utilized whenever possible. With this type of fan motor, high-speed operation may

be utilized in summertime when maximum air quantity is required, and low-speed operation would be utilized in wintertime when less air quantity is required. The low-speed fan operation, of course, would save power whenever the fan runs at low speed. It would also be helpful if in system 2 the temperature control system would automatically cycle the fan motor on and off at all times when the building is unoccupied. This would further save fan motor power consumption.

The supply duct system utilized in HVAC system 2 is inherently comparatively expensive, since a great number of supply ducts are utilized instead of, for example, one supply duct as used in HVAC system 1. In other words, it is less expensive to supply a given amount of air through one large duct rather than many small ducts. For this reason, it is advantageous in system 2 for the air conditioning unit to be located centrally in the building, as shown in fig. 11-9, rather than at one end of the building. Further, it is advantageous if system 2 is applied to a building which is comparatively compact and square rather than to a long, slender, rambling building.

If a double-deck air conditioning unit is utilized in system 2, some energy will be wasted during the spring and fall, as heated air is mixed with cooled air when an intermediate temperature air is required. This disadvantage usually disappears in the middle of the summer and the middle of the winter, because in summer the heating coil is shut down and is inactive, and in the middle of the winter the cooling coil is inactive. Very often in wintertime operation when some cooling is required, that may be achieved through the use of outdoor air, and energy will then be saved when a refrigeration unit is not operating. System 2 may utilize any types of grilles, registers, and diffusers or may utilize ventilating ceilings of the type described previously. In fig. 11-9, round ceiling diffusers are indicated. However, these are not necessarily required.

In system 2, it is important that the multizone unit utilized be very carefully manufactured to be certain that all of the mixing dampers are carefully fabricated with resilient edges, for example, so that almost 100% complete shutoff can be achieved. It should be evident that considerable energy will be wasted in this system if the zone mixing dampers controlling the heated air and the mechanically cooled air do not close tightly and securely. System 2 has been utilized for many years and is able to give very satisfactory operation, especially when a triple-deck unit is utilized to eliminate the one disadvantage to the operation of this system.

It is highly recommended at all times to use factory-assembled and manufactured units, with a manufacturer to stand behind the maintenance and satisfactory operation of each unit. Some dissatisfaction has arisen through the use of system 2, which utilizes field-assembled air conditioning units.

System 2 is best utilized in a building where the temperature control zones are comparatively large, as in a general office in an office building, and where the number of temperature control zones is comparatively small. System 2 is at a disadvantage in an office building or other type of building where a large number of very small temperature control zones, such as private offices, must be supplied from a central station unit. In this case, the great number of individual supply ducts that would be required would place system 2 at a cost disadvantage.

Recapping then, system 2 may be best utilized in a building which is comparatively compact, where the air conditioning unit may be centrally located, where the temperature control zones are comparatively large, and where the number of temperature control zones is comparatively small.

11-8 SYSTEM 3: CENTRAL STATION MULTIZONE CONSTANT VOLUME DOUBLE-DUCT SYSTEMS

System 3 is laid out and detailed as shown in fig. 11-11. System 3 is very much like system 2 except that system 3 can use only a double-deck constant volume multizone air conditioning unit (see reference 1 in fig. 11-11). It should be remembered that system 2 can use a double-deck unit or a triple-deck unit as well. System 3 is limited to the use of a double-deck air conditioning unit.

The air conditioning unit in system 3 is basically a multizone, blow-through type of air conditioning unit, but with the mixing dampers eliminated. Figure 6-14 shows a unit of this type with the mixing dampers in place. In system 3, as mentioned, these mixing dampers would be eliminated. System 3 has a warm air supply duct which is warm at all times of the year and is shown by reference 4 in fig. 11-11. This warm air supply duct connects to the warm air plenum, or deck, in the air conditioning unit and extends from that unit throughout the building. System 3 also has a cool air supply duct, shown by reference 5. This cool air duct connects to the cool air plenum, or deck, of the air conditioning unit and extends

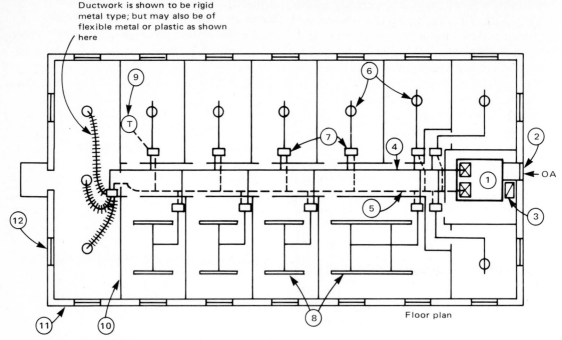

Ductwork is shown to be rigid
metal type; but may also be of
flexible metal or plastic as shown
here

Floor plan

Figure 11-11 Typical duct layout—system number 3. Central station, multizone, double duct CV system. 1, double deck air-conditioning unit; 2, OA intake louver; 3, RA duct; 4, warm air supply main duct; 5, cool air supply main duct; 6, round ceiling diffusers; 7, mixing boxes; 8, ceiling diffusers—slot type; 9, room thermostats—one for each mixing box (or zone); 10, room partition; 11, outside wall; 12, window. Note: all ducts and mixing boxes are above ceilings.

from that unit throughout the building, running adjacent to and parallel to the warm air supply duct.

Both of these ducts—the warm air supply and the cool air supply ducts—would be extended throughout the building to all points where air conditioning is required. Notice also in fig. 11-11 that in all temperature control zones there is a mixing box shown by reference 7. These mixing boxes have a duct connection to each of the two main supply warm and cool air ducts. In each of the mixing boxes there is a pair of dampers which control the flow of warm or cool air into the mixing box. These boxes may also take some of each of the warm air and the cool air from the two main supply ducts. The mixing dampers in each mixing box are controlled by a room thermostat in each temperature control zone, in such a way as to

mix warm air and cool air to achieve exactly the proper temperature of air to be supplied into the temperature control zone. Each mixing box also has an outlet opening connected to a supply duct which extends from the mixing boxes to one or more supply outlets. These supply outlets may be grilles, registers, or diffusers; in fig. 11-11 these are shown as round ceiling diffusers (reference 6) or slot-type ceiling diffusers (reference 8). The supply duct systems extending from the air conditioning unit to the mixing boxes throughout the building may be of either high-velocity or low-velocity design. In all cases, the supply ducts that extend from the mixing boxes to the grills, registers, and diffusers would be low-velocity low-pressure duct work.

As mentioned, the basic temperature control would consist of room thermostats, located in each temperature control zone, which position the mixing dampers in the mixing boxes in order to supply into each zone air of exactly the correct temperature condition.

Control of temperature in the hot and cool decks of the air conditioning unit is usually achieved through the use of insertion-type remote bulb thermostats. These thermostats usually control automatic control valves in the warm water supply to the heating coil and in the chilled water supply to the cooling coil. Temperature control would be also set up with an outdoor thermostat such that as outdoor temperature falls in winter, the temperature of the hot deck would be increased. It would be helpful in system 3 if the air conditioning unit were equipped with a two-speed fan motor such that the fan could run at high speed in summer, when maximum air quantity is required, and could be manually set to run at low speed in the winter, when appreciably less air supply quantity is required. Such two-speed motor control would make possible the saving of considerable electrical energy to drive the fan motor in winter.

It would also be possible to effectuate energy conservation through the use of a nighttime thermostat located at a central point in the area that the air conditioning unit serves to cycle the fan motor on and off during the periods when the building is not occupied. This would result in considerable time during nighttime and other unoccupied periods when the fan motor would not run at all; and electrical energy could be conserved.

With system 3, it is not necessary that the building be nearly square and compact as is the case with system 2. With system 3 the building may be long and rambling or of complicated shape, such as L-shaped, X-shaped, or perhaps Y-shaped. With system 3 it is quite convenient and economical to extend the two warm and cool supply main ducts to all parts of such a building.

In most air conditioning systems it would always be advantageous to locate the air conditioning unit at a central point in the building with the supply duct work extending in all directions from that unit. However, with system 3 it is economically

feasible to locate the air conditioning unit at one end of a building, as shown in fig. 11-11.

System 3 should be equipped with outside air, return air, and relief air automatic dampers connected and installed as shown in fig. 11-6. It should be realized that with system 3 during the spring and fall seasons there will be some inefficiency as a result of mixing warm air with mechanically cooled air to achieve exactly the proper temperature of the supply air going to each temperature control zone. However, during the middle of the summer and during the middle of the winter, this possibility is greatly minimized. In summer the heating coil would be completely shut down, so that there is no heat in the hot deck of the air conditioning unit. Similarly, in the middle of the winter the cooling coil might very well be shut down, so that the temperature of the cold deck is not maintained by mechanical cooling.

This energy waste during the spring and fall seasons is one of the major disadvantages of system 3. This disadvantage does not apply to system 2 when a triple-deck air conditioning unit is utilized. As is the case in system 2, with system 3 an economizer temperature control cycle may be utilized. In this economizer cycle maximum use of outdoor air for cooling purposes is made whenever the outdoor temperature is below approximately 60°F. In the economizer cycle, outside air dampers would automatically open to maintain a low temperature in the cool air deck, and this would be possible whenever outdoor air temperatures are low enough.

Since in system 3 there are two main supply ducts, one warm and one cool, each capable of carrying the entire air supply load, it is evident that the supply duct system of system 3 is not as economical as would be the supply ducts of a type 1 system. However, in long and rambling or complicated buildings the supply ducts of system 3 would be less costly than would be the supply ducts of system 2. As is true in system 2, system 3 does give bypass control, which makes system 3 suitable for use in buildings where the sensible heat ratio is comparatively low or, in other words, where the latent heat ratio is comparatively high.

A high latent heat ratio is usually found in buildings where large numbers of people gather, such as in a theater, auditorium, or restaurant.

One of the major advantages of system 3 is in the use of a building that has a large number of comparatively small temperature control zones. This type of building is typified by an office building in which there are a large number of small individual offices, each having its own thermostat, making each individual office a temperature control zone.

System 3 adapts itself very well and very economically to this type of a building. In system 2 the cost of the supply duct work for such a building would be prohibitively high.

11-9   SYSTEM 4: CENTRAL STATION MULTIZONE CONSTANT VOLUME REHEAT SYSTEM

HVAC system 4 consists primarily of a single-zone air conditioning unit and a large common supply duct which extends to all zones of a large or small building. System 4 is so designed as to accommodate any number of temperature control zones, whether large or small. The supply duct which extends from the air conditioning unit throughout the building carries the air for the entire building at one temperature. Branch connections are made from this main supply duct in such a way that each branch duct extends to a certain temperature control zone, and does not supply air into any other temperature control zone. In each of these branch ducts from the main supply duct, a heating coil of some type is installed so that air may be heated after it leaves the main supply duct and before it reaches the area of the temperature control zone being served.

In fig. 11-1 is shown a small, limited HVAC system which is drawn to represent a type 1 system. However, as is shown in fig. 11-1, with the addition of two heating coils (reference 17) system 1 is converted to system 4. A study of fig. 11-1 will show that as air leaves the air conditioning unit and extends out to the two rooms of that

figure, the air is in effect being supplied to two temperature control zones. As shown in fig. 11-1, a thermostat is installed in room 2. To complete the conversion to system 4, a thermostat would also need to be located in room 1, thus making a two-zone HVAC system. The two thermostats then shown in rooms 1 and 2 would control the two heating coils (reference 17) which are shown in fig. 11-1.

The automatic temperature control system used with system 4 is such that, whenever any thermostat in any temperature control zone calls for cooling, the air conditioning unit supplies cool air into the main supply duct so that all zones in the building are supplied with cool air. Of course, all zones in a building are not apt to need cool air at all times when any one zone requires cool air, so that as a result, one or more of the temperature control zones will be overcooled. To prevent overcooling, the thermostat in each zone then brings its heating coil into play, and the cooled air is reheated before it is supplied into the zone so that overcooling does not occur.

It is obvious that an HVAC system such as system 4, which cools all the air supplied to all the zones, whether cooling is required or not, and then reheats some of the air to many of the zones which do not require cooling, is very wasteful of energy. It is to the discredit of the HVAC industry that many thousands of HVAC systems incorporating the principles of system 4 have been designed and installed and that the procedure is still going on. In the interest of energy conservation, such systems must not be used in the future.

The air conditioning unit shown in fig. 11-1 has a heating coil and a cooling coil installed in it. The cooling coil is required, of course, to provide the cooling already described. The heating coil would be utilized to temper the mixed air which enters in winter at a temperature below 55°F. This coil is then used to bring the temperature of the supply air in winter up to 55°F, at which temperature it would be delivered into the main supply duct system. It is, of course, true that the mixed air entering the air conditioning unit may be well above

55°F if no outside air is being utilized or very little outside air is being utilized for ventilation purposes. In that eventuality the heating coil in the air conditioning unit has nothing to do. At whatever temperature the supply air enters the main supply duct system, the individual zone heating coils will elevate this temperature as required by the zone that coil serves.

There is one expedient that may be utilized in connection with system 4 which will minimize its excessive wastefulness. Whenever the mechanical refrigeration system is running to provide cooling as described above, there is, of course, heat being rejected from the condenser of that refrigerating machine. It is entirely possible and practical to capture this wasted or rejected heat and deliver it to the zone reheating coils. In effect, then, the reheating will be performed with heat which would otherwise be wasted. Even if this principle is fully utilized, this system is inordinately wasteful of energy and should not be contemplated.

When condenser waste heat is utilized, it probably is most convenient to capture that heat in the form of condenser water which would be circulated through a water-cooled condenser. This water, when heated by the condenser, can then be directed to the zone reheat coils before being delivered to the cooling tower, if a tower is utilized for further cooling. The heating coil in the air conditioning unit probably would be heated with hot water generated in a hot water heating boiler.

As an example of the operation of system 4, suppose that the thermostat (reference 16 in fig. 11-1) which controls conditions in room 2 calls for cooling and further assume that at the same time room 1 does not need cooling but perhaps needs heating. The room thermostat in room 1 will at this time activate the heating coil that is adjacent to the supply grille (reference 6). This heating coil would then supply enough heat into room 1 to prevent overcooling by the cool air that is being circulated. The same sequence could take place if room 1 became overheated and needed cooling and the thermostat added to room 1 calls for cooling. The air conditioning unit then supplies cool air and there is a danger that room 2 would be overcooled. When this condition occurs, the thermostat in room 2 will activate its heating coil and prevent overcooling.

11-10 SYSTEM 5: CENTRAL STATION VAV SYSTEM WITH CONSTANT VOLUME PERIMETER SYSTEM

System 5 is an all-air type with two air conditioning units serving all building areas involved. When system 5 is in use, the building is divided into two separate areas; one area consists of the perimeter or "skin" areas extending completely around the perimeter of the building and extending into the interior approximately 12 in. Thus this perimeter area is merely an envelope extending completely around the outside of the building and extending only 12 in. into the building. The other area of the building involved consists of all interior rooms and spaces, and includes the areas of all outside rooms to within 12 in. of the outside walls. These two areas are served by two separate air conditioning units. The interior areas are served by a variable air volume unit, and the perimeter or skin areas are served by a constant volume air conditioning unit.

It should be realized that if the interior areas of the building are separated from the perimeter or skin areas, these interior areas have a need for cooling all year round. Theoretically, they never need heating. It may be true that some of the interior areas are on the top floor of a multiple-story building or have an exposed roof; in that case, there will be a certain heat loss from the building through the roof in winter. However, in today's modern buildings, the ceilings and roofs of all buildings must be so well insulated that the heat loss upward would be very small indeed. In effect, the statement just made—that the interior areas never need heating but always need cooling—can be permitted to stand. The constant volume air conditioning unit that serves the perimeter areas of the building carries a very heavy heating load in winter and a very heavy cooling load in summer.

In areas of the United States where the winters are comparatively mild, this constant volume unit may supply its air entirely through ceiling diffusers of some type. In this case, the load of the perimeter is carried by air being supplied from overhead, which extends over and down across the outside windows and walls. However, in areas where the winter weather is severe, this may not be adequate. In this case, the perimeter supply air may need to be supplied from the floor or beneath the windows. The constant volume perimeter unit circulates only returned air and does not supply any outside air for ventilation purposes. However, the VAV unit is connected to supply outside air for ventilation, and, of necessity, has a heating coil for tempering outside air in winter. One advantage of system 5 is that the VAV unit which carries the load of almost all the building may be shut down during nighttime, or other unoccupied periods, and a great amount of energy saved.

In fig. 11-12 the VAV unit is indicated by reference 1, and the constant volume perimeter unit is indicated by reference 2. Figure 11-12 also shows a typical layout such as might be utilized with HVAC system 5. In fig. 11-12, a large number of VAV control units (reference 10) are utilized for the purposes of controlling the volume of air that is being circulated. As shown in the detail included in fig. 11-12, the VAV control unit consists of a sheet metal box with outlet connections as required to permit connection of supply ducts to the various ceiling diffusers, and with an inlet connection by means of which air is permitted to enter the box.

The air that enters the VAV control unit box does so under the control of an automatic valve. This valve is thermostatically positioned so that the air quantity that enters the box does so under the indirect control of a room thermostat. It should be stressed that the quality of the valve that controls this air inlet quantity is very critical. This valve should not be some type of device that is fabricated at the job site by the sheet metal contractor. Rather, it should be a carefully manufactured unit designed for this specific purpose. Usually, these valves will be so installed as to close

and reduce the air supply quantity as cooling load in the interior spaces reduces. However, usually this valve will not close completely, but will close only down to a preset minimum. Such valves should be carefully tested by their manufacturer to determine that linear performance is provided. In other words, it should be such that as the damper in the control valve assembly closes to a 50% position, the air supply quantity is reduced to 50% of full volume.

During periods of light load in the interior spaces of the building, it will often be true that a considerable number of these air volume control valves will throttle down the air quantity, and as a result the air pressure in the main air supply duct (reference 11 of fig. 11-12) will tend to rise. As this air supply pressure rises, the supply fan in the air conditioning unit (reference 1) must be so designed as to reduce its air supply quantity. By this means, as the air valves in the VAV control units close, the quantity of air supplied by the supply fan in the air conditioning unit will, indirectly, be proportionately reduced. Appreciable amounts of electric energy to drive the fan will thus be saved.

In general, the perimeter system air conditioning unit will be controlled by an outdoor air thermostat which is shielded from the sun. This thermostat will be so connected as to cause the perimeter unit to supply warm air in winter and cool air in summer. Control may also be such that during nighttime or unoccupied periods, the perimeter unit may be controlled by a return air thermostat set for approximately 60°F in winter and 83°F in summer. This return air thermostat may be so connected as to be able to cycle the supply fan in the perimeter unit off and on as necessary to carry the load properly. This type of on-off cycling control during unoccupied periods can give further energy savings.

The VAV air conditioning unit (reference 1) is a single-zone unit which must be able to heat outside air for ventilation purposes in winter and cool return air, or mixtures of return air and outside air, in summer. Both air conditioning units may be

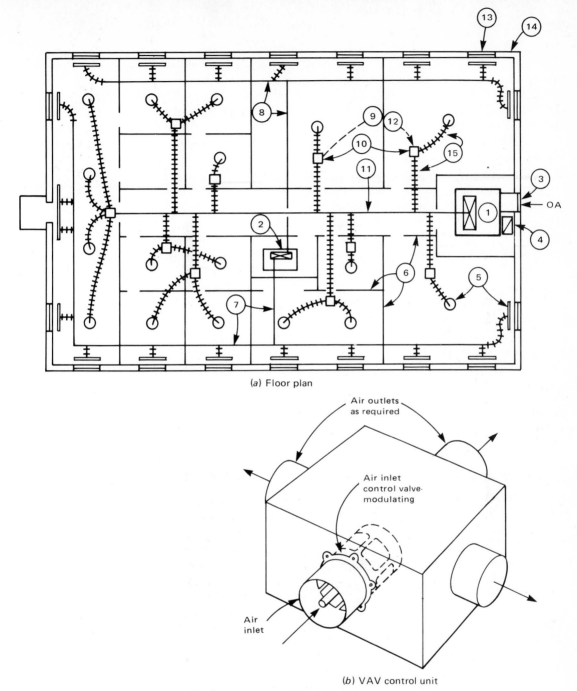

(a) Floor plan

(b) VAV control unit

Figure 11-12 Typical system number 5. Central station VAV system with constant volume perimeter system. 1, VAV air conditioning unit; 2, CV air conditioning unit; 3, OA intake louver, 4, RA duct connection; 5, ceiling diffusers, round and linear types; 6, building partitions; 7, perimeter or "skin" area supply duct—south and west walls; 8, perimeter supply duct—north wall; 9, room thermostat; 10, VAV control units; 11, VAV main supply duct; 12, room thermostat; 13, window; 14, outside wall; 15, flexible duct (round). Notes: All ducts shown as flexible may be rigid if preferred. Each control unit requires thermostat control. All ducts and control units above ceiling. Return air ducts (not shown) may be of any type.

377

of the type that has one coil with both hot water and chilled water supply connections so that the coil can either heat or cool. Alternatively, the units may be equipped with two coils which have separate hot water and chilled water supplies.

If accurate control of relative humidity in the building is important, a humidistat may be installed to operate in connection with the VAV unit. This humidistat would be so connected as to reduce the air supply temperature of the VAV unit in summer. This would permit the cooling coil to operate at a lower temperature, which would give more latent heat removal. This humidistat could then also be connected to operate some type of humidifier to provide humidity as necessary in winter.

As mentioned above, the VAV unit must have some means of efficiently reducing the air supply quantity during periods of reduced load. As previously described in this chapter, there are many ways of doing this, and some of these ways provide great reduction in energy consumption, whereas other methods do not. Of course, it is highly desirable that one of the more efficient methods be utilized.

The supply ducts in system 5 may be of either high-velocity design or low-velocity design. In fig. 11-12 it may be seen that the main supply air duct (reference 11) is drawn as a solid duct, while all the branch connections to that main duct are shown to be flexible ducting. Much of this branch duct work could, of course, be rigid metal duct.

It should be observed that with HVAC system 5, the building may be of any type. It need not be square and compact as in system 2, but may be long and rambling and complicated or of any configuration. It is also true that the temperature control zones may be large or small, and the location of the air conditioning unit is not in any way critical. Therefore, it may be seen that the cost of the duct system for system 5 is minimal, as is the cost of the air conditioning units and temperature controls required since they are simple and inexpensive.

As is true of the other HVAC systems discussed, system 5 should be equipped with an OA and an RA and relief dampers as shown in fig. 11-6. With system 5 it is entirely practical to use outside air for cooling when outdoor temperature is suitable for that. Most types of grilles, registers, and diffusers may be used in system 5. However, they must all be carefully selected to be able to provide good airflow patterns in a room even when the air quantity is greatly reduced.

With system 5, whenever mechanical cooling is required by the interior zones of the building, and at the same time heating is required by the perimeter zones of the building, rejected heat from the mechanical refrigeration unit condenser should always be utilized. In summation, it may be seen that system 5 is an excellent system in many respects. The initial cost is very low compared to some of the other systems available and in use today. Also, the operating cost may be very greatly reduced from the operating cost of those other systems. The accuracy of temperature control is not impaired in the least by the characteristics of design. In almost all respects, it may be seen that HVAC system 5 is an excellent one.

11-11   SYSTEM 6: CENTRAL STATION VAV BYPASS SYSTEM

System 6 is an all-air VAV system similar in many respects to HVAC system 5. It includes a central station VAV air conditioning unit similar to the reference 1 unit in fig. 11-12 and supplies air, as does that unit, through a main duct system from which extend the various branch ducts leading to VAV control units. In system 6 the control units are of different design than are those in system 5. The VAV control units in system 6 are so designed that as the load reduces in a given space, instead of reducing the airflow quantity into the VAV control unit, the same amount of air enters at all times, but some of the air that enters is bypassed from the VAV control unit out into the space that surrounds it. The remainder of the air that enters the VAV control unit is delivered through the ductwork to the ceiling diffusers. The air that is bypassed from the control units is often permitted to dump into the ceiling furred space which surrounds the control unit and from that into the return air duct system wherever that may be. Alternatively, the air that is bypassed from the control units may be delivered directly into duct work which connects to the return air duct system. Therefore, it may be seen that the central station air conditioning unit which supplies air to all the VAV control units supplies essentially the same quantity of air at all times. Therefore, system 6 does not enjoy the energy conservation benefits that go along with reduced air quantity. This is the major disadvantage of system 6. It does give VAV control, but it does not enjoy the benefits of re- duced power consumption resulting from reduced airflow quantity.

In an HVAC system where for some reason it is not possible to modulate the supply capacity of the air supply fan, system 6 may be appropriate. As is the case in most modern HVAC systems, the refrigeration capacity of system 6 is calculated to meet the block load requirements; however, the total air quantity being circulated, like all constant volume systems, is based on the cumulative peak load. With system 6 there is some advantage over constant volume systems in that the supply duct system is simpler and less expensive. For example, in systems 2 and 3, the cost of the supply duct work is excessive since there is duplication of sup- ply ducts. This is not the case with system 6. The supply ducts for system 6 would be essentially the same as those shown in fig. 11-12 for HVAC system 5.

11-12   SYSTEM 7: CENTRAL STATION VAV WITH PERIMETER RADIATION

As is true with system 5, system 7 is a very popular energy-conservative system. It is very similar to system 5 (see fig. 11-12) except that the constant volume perimeter air system is replaced with some type of perimeter radiation—wall radiators, base- board radiation, convectors, and so on. This pe- rimeter radiation is usually installed under the windows in the outside walls or adjacent to out- side doors, in such a way as to be capable of off- setting the cold wall and window effect in winter. This perimeter radiation may be heated with hot

water, steam, or electricity. However, because of the wasteful nature of electric heat, this use is discouraged.

The central VAV air system, which is almost identical to that central system in HVAC system 5, carries the entire summer cooling load. Remember that in system 5 the central VAV system carries all of the summer cooling load except the perimeter cooling load, which is carried by the perimeter HVAC system.

In system 7 this is not the case; all the summer cooling load, including the perimeter cooling load, must be carried by this one system. Therefore, it does have, for a given building, a greater capacity. HVAC system 7 is most applicable in the northern states of the United States, where winter weather is more severe and where low-level perimeter radia- tion is considered to be a necessity. However, this system is certainly applicable in the southern states, where the appearance of the perimeter radiation and the space that it requires is not objectionable.

The initial cost of system 7 would compare favorably with system 5; this is another reason why it might very well be found in use in the southern states. Both HVAC systems 5 and 7 are probably optimally equipped with a hot water type of heating boiler located somewhere in the building, to supply heated water to the cooling coils for heat when that is necessary. If this is the case, it certainly makes good sense to use hot water perimeter radiation in system 7 when the boiler capable of providing the hot water is already installed. Where hot water is utilized to heat the perimeter radiation, the temperature of this hot water would usually be modulated under the con- trol of an outdoor thermostat.

11-13   SYSTEM 8: CENTRAL STATION VAV SEASON-ZONED HEATING AND COOLING SYSTEM

System 8 consists of one or more single-zone VAV air conditioning units located in and serving build- ing zones whose boundaries are drawn according to weather and sun exposure. In this case, the building is divided into zones in which the various rooms of the zone are all likely to need heating at the same time, or to need cooling at the same time. In other words, the zoning of the building is such that all the rooms in a given zone would require changeover from heating to cooling or back from cooling to heating at approximately the same time.

As shown in fig. 11-13, each air conditioning unit has its own independent duct system. The air distribution duct system is so installed that each room is equipped with an automatically controlled VAV control unit. Each control unit is of the type shown in detail in fig. 11-13, and each unit is under the control of a room thermostat. The room thermostat positions automatically an air valve at the inlet to the control unit. It would be possible, very

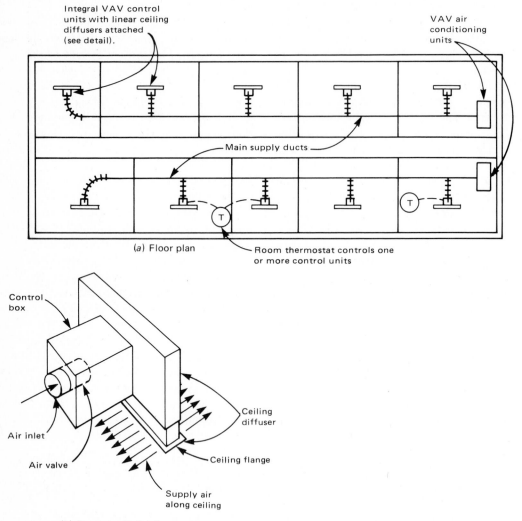

(a) Floor plan

(b) Control unit detail

Figure 11-13 Typical HVAC system number 8. Central station VAV season-zoned heating and cooling system. Notes: This plan shows only one of many possible ceiling diffuser types and arrangements. Ducts and control units located above ceilings.

often, for the entire system and the area served by that system to be controlled by a single room thermostat strategically located. However, the usual case is for each room to have its own thermostat, controlling its own automatic control unit.

In fig. 11-13 linear ceiling diffusers are shown to be connected directly to the control boxes. However, any type of ceiling diffuser may be utilized, and they may or may not be in direct contact with the control box.

As shown in fig. 11-13, all the air is supplied from the ceiling. However, in very cold climates, this may not be satisfactory, and some type of under-the-window supply grille or diffuser may be required. In system 8 the seasonal changeover from winter to summer operation, or vice versa, may be accomplished automatically with the help of an outdoor air thermostat, or it may be accomplished manually. As mentioned elsewhere in this text, automatic changeover from heating to cooling, or from cooling to heating, is often very unsatisfactory, and many designers rely only upon manual changeover.

The air conditioning units utilized in system 8 are of a VAV type, having an efficient method of reducing air supply quantity when that is necessary, and are also equipped with heating and cooling coils. These air conditioning units may bring in outdoor air for ventilation, and ideally may utilize the economizer cycle, to use outdoor air for cooling as much as possible when cooling is required. If the economizer cycle is utilized, the introduction of outdoor air in great quantities should be under the control of an *enthalpy* type of outdoor air controller. This will prevent the introduction of great quantitites of outdoor air which may be at the proper dry bulb temperature but which may have too high a wet bulb temperature for suitable ventilation.

With system 8 both the total air supply quantity and the cooling capacity are determined on the basis of block load calculations; in other words, it is assumed that all spaces in the building will not require maximum air quantity and maximum cooling load at the same time, and that some diversity

factor may be applied which will reduce the total air supply quantity and the total cooling capacity.

In system 8 the supply duct system may be of either high-velocity design or low-velocity design. The building may be of any type: square and compact or long, rambling, and complicated. As opposed to some other systems that may be used, the temperature control zones may be either large or small without limitation. The location of the air conditioning units is not at all critical. The cost of the duct system in system 8 is minimal and the air conditioning units and their controllers are simple and comparatively inexpensive. Each air conditioning unit in system 8 should be equipped with an outdoor air intake opening, a return air connection, and a relief air opening, with duct work and dampers as shown in detail in fig. 11-6.

All types of grilles, registers, and diffusers may be utilized as long as they are capable of maintaining a good flow pattern of air within each room at low airflow quantities.

11-14   SYSTEM 9: CENTRAL STATION VAV REHEAT SYSTEM

As shown in fig. 11-14*a* and *b,* system 9 consists of a single-zone VAV type of air conditioning unit and a single supply duct system which delivers air to all spaces within the building. Airflow is controlled by VAV control units as shown and as detailed in fig. 11-14*a* and *b.* The control units consist of a sheet metal box with an automatic air control valve located at its inlet and with a heating coil contained within the enclosure of the control unit. This heating coil (see fig. 11-14*b*) may utilize hot water or steam or may be an electrically heated coil. The control unit would include one or more outlet connections. The control valve in each control unit would be regulated by a room thermostat to reduce supply air volume as load is reduced to a preset minimum. As the temperature in the space continues to fall and the cooling load continues to reduce, instead of further reducing the air supply quantity, the heating coil in the control unit is

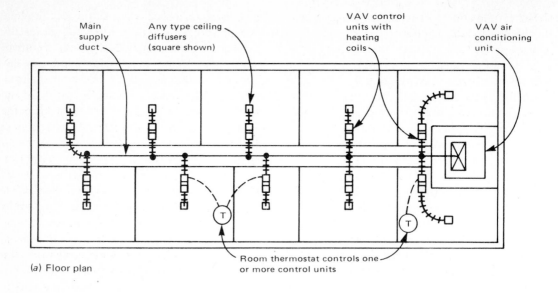

Main supply duct

Any type ceiling diffusers (square shown)

VAV control units with heating coils

VAV air conditioning unit

(a) Floor plan

Room thermostat controls one or more control units

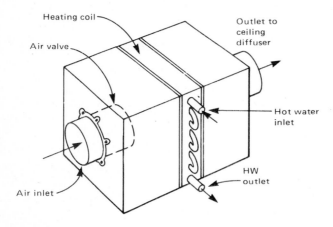

Heating coil

Air valve

Outlet to ceiling diffuser

Hot water inlet

HW outlet

Air inlet

(b) Control unit detail

Figure 11-14 (a) Typical HVAC system number 9. Central station VAV reheat system. All ducts and control units are above ceiling. (b) Control unit with heating coil, one-row.

activated. Through this action a further fall in room temperature is prevented.

Usually, the air supplied in system 9 is at a temperature of approximately 55 to 60°F, for cooling purposes, and reheated by the heating coils in the control units as necessary. There may be many times in the operation of system 9 that the air being supplied to a given room is mechanically cooled and energy has been spent in that process. Then the air is reheated to prevent over cooling and more energy is spent in that process. It is easy to see that a great amount of energy may be wasted in this overall process. The supply ducts shown in fig. 11-14a and b and the control units contained therein are all located above the furred ceilings of the building; and ceiling diffusers are shown. This may not be satisfactory in cold climates and some type of under-the-window supply grilles or diffusers may be necessary.

In the detail of the control unit in fig. 11-14b, the air valve is shown at the inlet to the control box; this valve may take many forms other than the round one shown. However, it should be emphasized that this air valve must be of excellent design. It must be further tested in both the laboratory and in the field to determine that very accurate control may be achieved from it.

The heating coil drawn in the control unit detail is shown as a hot water heating coil. This would usually be the case; however, as mentioned, this heating coil may be operated on steam or electricity. But these media are more difficult to control, and in this case even and smooth automatic control is quite important. In the event that rejected heat, from the condenser of the refrigerating machine in use, is to be recirculated to these heating coils for heating purposes, the use of hot water is most advantageous. Of course, the use of the rejected heat from the condenser should be considered for every system and should be utilized to the greatest extent possible. If the condenser of the refrigerating machine that provides building cooling is of the water-cooled type, it is a fairly simple process to recirculate some of the hot water leaving the condenser to these heating coils for reheating purposes. However, if the condenser of the refrigerat-

ing machine is air cooled, this process becomes appreciably more difficult.

The duct work in system 9 may be of either high-velocity design or low-velocity design. The shape of the building is not at all critical, and it may be either square and compact or long and rambling. It should be apparent that with system 9 seasonal changeover from heating to cooling, and from cooling to heating, is not necessary. The central station air conditioning unit essentially provides cool air at all times of the year; when heating is required, this is done by the reheat coils located in the control unit. This is an appreciable advantage.

The air conditioning unit in system 9 is, as mentioned, a **VAV** type and must have some efficient method of reducing air supply quantity and power consumption in proportion thereto. This air conditioning unit would have a cooling coil cooled either by chilled water or by direct expansion of refrigerant, and it would also have a heating coil. This air conditioning unit would normally also be supplied and equipped with outdoor air, return air, and relief air duct connections, as shown in detail in fig. 11-6.

The economizer cycle for the control of outdoor air, and the use of outdoor air for cooling purposes, to the extent possible, would probably be utilized in system 9. In a large building using system 9 the equipment of that system would probably include a central water chiller for cooling purposes, and a fossil-fueled boiler of some type to provide hot water for heating. When the building to be conditioned is located with a group of other buildings, such as on a college campus, it is entirely possible that the supply of chilled water and hot water would come from a central location on the campus and that a local water chiller and boiler would not be necessary. The installed cost of a system 9 is fairly midrange. Temperature control is simple and comparatively inexpensive. The cost of the heating coil in each of the control units, and the piping necessary to supply steam or hot water to it, do make the cost of this system somewhat higher than that of the minimum cost system.

In fig. 11-14a and b, the duct system shown

includes square ceiling diffusers. However, any type of diffuser may be utilized that is properly designed for VAV use and that is capable of giving good airflow patterns within a room at reduced air supply quantities. When system 9 is in use, the airflow quantity is never reduced below the preset minimum mentioned above. In some spaces in some buildings, it is necessary that a minimum amount of outside air be supplied at all times and that a minimum amount of total air movement be supplied. This preset minimum must be balanced against ventilating code requirements. The advantages of system 9 are that there is no need for seasonal changeover, which is so often awkward and difficult to accomplish, and also that interior spaces needing cooling can usually be served by the same supply system which is supplying air to spaces needing heating. It should also be observed that with system 9 in some interior spaces of the building where heating is never required, the heating coil may be omitted from the control unit. The big disadvantage of system 9 is that it is very often wasteful of heat when air is precooled and supplied to a given room and then reheated to the temperature required in the room.

11-15 SYSTEM 10: CENTRAL STATION VAV WITH INDUCTION CONTROL UNITS

HVAC system 10 is very similar to HVAC system 9 as drawn in fig. 11-14a and b. The layout of the duct work and the central station air conditioning unit and the control units would be approximately the same. However, in system 10 the control units are of a greatly differing type and are called induction control units. This is true because they are designed to have the ability of inducing a secondary airflow from the ceiling furred space that surrounds each control unit.

In system 10 the control units are located above the ceiling and are supplied with primary air from the main supply duct system. This flow of primary air is regulated by internal primary air dampers. Details of this induction control unit are shown in fig. 11-15. This illustration includes an exterior view of the induction unit complete with duct connections and shows the induced air inlet and dampers. A small detail in fig. 11-15 also shows some of the interior construction of the control unit and does show the primary air dampers as well as the induced air dampers. In the use of the induction control units, air is drawn from the usually warm air that surrounds the control unit. Since this is true, a return air grille opening of some type must be provided in the ceiling below the control unit so that room air can be returned into the ceiling plenum or furred space.

With the use of the control units in system 10, during the cooling cycle when room temperature is approximately at the control point and the room thermostat is satisfied, the primary air dampers are throttled so as to reduce the primary quantity. However, when the primary air dampers are throttled, the air that does enter through these primary air dampers enters the control unit at a greatly increased velocity. This means that the velocity pressure of this entering air is increased. However, the total pressure of this air is not increased, so as the velocity pressure is increased, the static pressure downstream of the primary air dampers is appreciably reduced. As this static pressure is reduced, induced air will be drawn into the control unit whenever the induced air dampers are open. It is usually true that the air in the ceiling furred space surrounding the control units is warm and this represents a source of heat which is often wasted in other systems. System 10 is designed to make use of this waste heat.

Usually, the temperature controls in system 10 are installed such that the induced air damper on a given control unit does not open until the primary air dampers have closed to some preset minimum airflow quantity. System 10 is a reheat type of system in which the primary air is always cool, perhaps 55 to 60°F, whenever any one of the many temperature control zones in a building calls for cooling. Therefore, when any one zone calls for cooling, all zones receive cool air. To circumvent the possibility of many of the spaces of the building being overcooled by this process, it

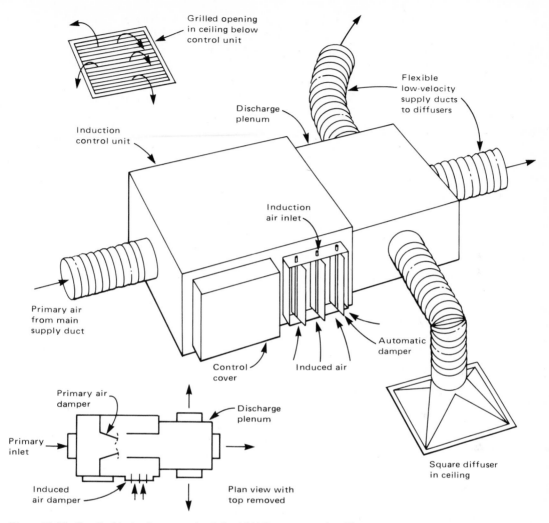

Figure 11-15 Detail of induction control unit for HVAC system number 10.

is necessary that reheat be used. It is quite economical in this case to utilize waste heat which exists in the ceiling furred space surrounding the control units. However, it will not always be true that the heat available from the ceiling furred space is adequate to provide enough reheat, and in some cases reheat coils utilizing hot water or steam or electricity will need to be installed in the discharge plenum downstream of the control unit. It is usually most economical to heat these reheat coils with hot water.

During periods of light cooling load the total primary air quantity supplied by the central station air conditioning unit is greatly reduced. When this air quantity reduction occurs, the air conditioning unit must be able to reduce its air quantity in proportion to the air requirements at the control units. Therefore, the central station air conditioning unit must be equipped with some type of capacity reduction device. It is most advantageous, of course, if as shown in fig. 11-7, this capacity reduction device is of the type that reduces the power demand of the fan motor in proportion to the reduced need for air quantity.

The primary air supply duct work leading from the air conditioning unit to the several control units may be either of high-velocity design or low-velocity design. However, all duct work downstream from the control units will usually of necessity be of low-velocity design. It is very necessary that all the ductwork and grilles; registers, and diffusers located downstream from the control units be of low-velocity design and have very low frictional resistance. It is hoped that the static pressure loss in the discharge plenum and all ductwork at the downstream side of the control units will be 1/4 in. WG or less.

One advantage of system 10 is that the air quantity being supplied to the grille, registers, and diffusers is essentially constant at all times. As the primary air quantity is reduced, the induced air quantity is increased so that the total airflow to the air supply outlets is not appreciably diminished at any time. This is of benefit since then any type of outlet may be utilized. It is not necessary to limit one's specifications to the type of air supply outlet that will satisfactorily utilize reduced air quantities.

With some types of grilles, registers and diffusers, as the air supply quantity is appreciably reduced, there is a tendency for the air to "dump" into the room without maintaining a satisfactory airflow pattern within the room. When the primary air distribution duct system is of high-velocity design, it is mandatory that the control units be acoustically treated so that the high level of noise resulting from the high-velocity movement of air is thoroughly trapped out in the control unit and not permitted to pass on through into the occupied spaces.

System 10, like systems 4 and 9, is a reheat type of system that is inherently wasteful of energy. These reheat types of systems are wasteful even when the reheating which is often necessary is done with waste heat. It is still true that when any zone calls for cooling, all zones in the building receive mechanically cooled air during the warmer seasons of the year. Thus, it is apparent that many zones which do not need cooling must receive mechanically cooled air and then must be reheated by some means. Obviously, such a process is wasteful of energy.

With the use of system 10, one of its major advantages is the flexibility that may be achieved with its temperature control system. Independent temperature control of each of many small rooms in a building is easily arranged. Also, it is easily possible to arrange the building for a small number of very large temperature control zones which would consist of many rooms.

Induction-type control units as used in system 10 are available in a wide range of sizes from 100 cfm to approximately 3000 cfm. This makes it possible to handle zones that are exceedingly small and zones that are quite large. Of course, it is possible in a very large temperature control zone to use a multiplicity of control units, all under the control of one thermostat if that is necessary.

System 10 as described here contemplates ceiling supply only. However, it may be necessary in the colder climates to supply heat under the windows in order to properly curtail the cold wall and window effect that would exist. With system 10 it probably would be most advantageous to use some type of perimeter wall radiation, perhaps utilizing hot water as the source of heat. It is not impossible, of course, with system 10 to supply some of its air through floor registers or low-level air diffusers located beneath windows at outside walls.

If heating coils are used for reheat as may be necessary in some situations, it is highly recommended that the source of heat be hot water, which lends itself most readily to the use of condenser waste heat rejected from the refrigerating unit which is providing the cooling effect. In system 10 seasonal changeover of the temperature control system is not necessary, and this is considered to be an advantage.

The central station air conditioning unit that supplies primary air to the several control units throughout the building may be of almost any single-zone type and may be located almost anywhere in the building. It would be equipped with a heating coil and a cooling coil and the duct system associated with this air conditioning unit should include outside air, return air, and relief air connections as shown in fig. 11-6. It is probably most advantageous with this type of air conditioning unit to utilize the economizer cycle for the introduction of outside air for cooling purposes. As mentioned previously, when the economizer cycle is utilized, some type of enthalpy controller should be installed and utilized.

The general cost of system 10 is midrange and the temperature control system is comparatively simple and inexpensive. If it is advantageous to do so, the induction control units of this system may be arranged to reduce the primary air supply to zero as cooling load is greatly reduced, and in this case the induced air supply is also reduced to zero. This should not be done in the type of building where ventilating codes require a minimum of outside air to be supplied and a minimum amount of room air circulation is required. In general, HVAC system 10 could be classified as a very advantageous one. Although its energy consumption characteristics are not quite as good as some other VAV types of systems, its energy consumption would certainly be less than that of most constant volume HVAC systems.

11-16   SYSTEM 11: CENTRAL STATION MULTIZONE VAV INDIVIDUAL-DUCT SYSTEM

HVAC system 11 is very much like the individual-duct constant volume system 2 shown in fig. 11-9, except that system 11 is designed for VAV and not constant volume. HVAC system 11 utilizes a double-deck multizone air conditioning unit similar to that shown in fig. 6-14. However, the zone dampers of that type of unit are controlled much differently in system 11. It should be remembered that in HVAC system 2 the double-deck air conditioning unit utilized therein has two damper blades operated by one damper motor and mounted on a common damper shaft. These two damper blades control the airflow into each individual zone duct. One of the damper blades controls the amount of cool air that enters the duct, and the other damper blade controls the amount of warm air that enters the duct. It is possible, of course, for these two dampers to be positioned in such a way that they mix both warm air and cool air in proper proportions in order to achieve the mixed air temperature required for the temperature control zone.

In system 11 the cool air and warm air dampers of each zone are operated independently of each other. For example, during the cooling cycle when the system is operating under a fairly heavy cooling load, the cool deck damper in a given zone duct is open wide to the cool deck and the warm deck damper is fully closed. As the cooling load on this zone decreases, the cool deck damper modulates slowly closed as cooling load is reduced until that cool deck damper is 70% closed. In this position the cfm from the cool deck entering the individual zone duct is only 30% of its maximum rate of flow. When the cool deck damper closes to this point, the warm deck damper then begins to modulate open and the cool deck damper continues to modulate closed. When the warm deck damper is 30% open, the cool deck damper will be fully closed and the airflow quantity will still be approximately 30% of maximum zone rated air quantity. On a further increase in the need for heat in the temperature control zone, the warm deck damper will then continue to modulate open until it reaches the wide-open position and full rated flow will occur through the warm deck. Thus, it may be seen that most of the time the cool deck damper will circulate air when the warm deck damper is fully closed. At many other times, the warm deck damper will operate in the open position when the cool deck damper is fully closed. There will be some times when both dampers are open a certain amount, in which case the total rated airflow will not exceed 30% of maximum. When the cold deck damper and the warm deck damper are both partially open, there will, of course, be mixing of the cool air and the warm air. This is wasteful. Whenever air that has been cooled mechanically is mixed with air that has been mechanically heated, there will be a waste of energy.

In system 11 the amount of time when warm air and cool air are being mixed is much reduced below the amount of time when this would happen in a system such as HVAC system 2. There is little likelihood that warm air will be mixed with cool air during the middle of the heating season or during the middle of the cooling season. Warm air and cool air will usually be mixed during the in-between seasons of fall and spring.

The temperature of the warm deck in the air conditioning unit should be controlled in accordance with the dictates of an outdoor air thermostat, so that when outdoor temperature is quite low, the warm deck temperature will be quite high. When outdoor air temperature is quite mild as it would be in spring and fall, the warm deck temperature would be quite low, perhaps on the order of 80°F. Therefore, if there is mixing of some warm deck air with cool air from the cool deck, the waste is not as great as it would be if the warm deck temperature were very high.

Since HVAC system 11 is a VAV system, it is true that when the warm air deck damper and the cold deck damper are both in a nearly closed position, the air quantity flow to a given zone will be greatly reduced. As mentioned above, it may be as low as 30% of the rated air quantity. When many of the zones served by this air conditioning unit are modulated down to a low air quantity, the total air quantity flow of the unit will likewise be greatly reduced. It is necessary then that this unit be equipped with a fan control of the type that will reduce the fan capacity in proportion to the needs for air.

In system 11, the supply ducts may be of high-velocity design or may be of low-velocity design; as discussed in the description of HVAC system 2, the air conditioning unit should be centrally located so as to minimize the length of the supply duct runs from the air conditioning unit to the various zones of the building. It is also true that with system 11 it is advantageous to have the tem-

perature control zones large in area so that there are a small number of such zones. It will also be advantageous in the use of system 11 if the building is fairly square or compact and is not a long, rambling, and complicated structure.

11-17 SYSTEM 12: FAN-COIL UNITARY SYSTEM

System 12 departs from the basic idea discussed thus far of having centrally located air conditioning units which supply air to the various conditioned spaces through supply duct work. In general, with system 12 there is no ductwork involved unless it is found necessary to supply outside air for ventilation in a small separate duct system. Since the duct system is eliminated in system 12, or nearly so, there is a very substantial cost saving in that direction. However, a very extensive piping system would be required to supply chilled water and hot water or steam to each of the various fan-coil units utilized. As shown in figs. 11-16 and 11-17, these fan-coil units consist

Figure 11-16 Fan-coil unit with two-pipe piping connections. (© The Trane Company. Used by permission.)

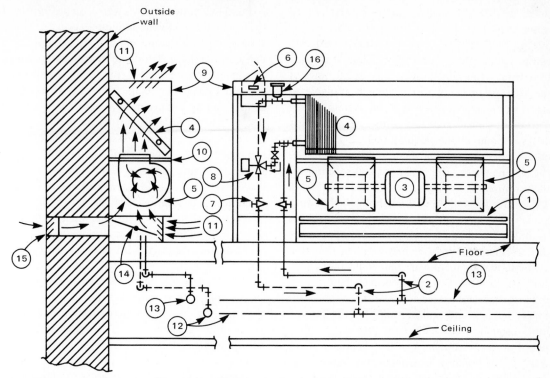

Figure 11-17 Fan-coil unit installation details showing two-pipe piping connections. 1, air filter; 2, branch pipe connections; 3, fan motor; 4, heating and cooling coil; 5, fan; 6, fan speed control knob; 7, gate valves; 8, automatic temperature control valve; 9, enclosing cabinet; 10, condensate drain pan; 11, supply and return grilles; 12, hot/chilled water return; 13, hot/chilled water supply; 14, outside air and return air damper; 15, outside air intake louver; 16, air vent—manual to automatic.

of a heating-cooling coil, a fan and fan motor, a filter, a drain pan, and an outside air damper, all enclosed in a well-finished furniture steel cabinet. In most cases, the fan-coil units are located at the outside walls of a building underneath the windows and usually standing on the floor. However, fan-coil units are made for mounting in many other positions, including at the ceiling, and may also be concealed above false work at the ceiling. The fan motor that drives the fan in this type of unit is usually a three-speed motor which may be controlled manually by a three-speed selector switch, such as that shown in reference 6 of fig. 11-17.

Fan-coil units may include two coils: one for heating and one for cooling. However, usually there is only one coil, and hot water is directed

through that coil in winter and chilled water directed through it in summer. Sometimes the cooling coil is arranged for the use of direct expansion of refrigerant, in which case a heating coil must be separate. Very often, it is an electrically heated coil but most economically should be heated with hot water or steam.

In selecting a system 12 for use in a given building, the HVAC designer must first make a choice of whether to use a two-pipe system or a four-pipe system. In a two-pipe system, there is one supply pipe which carries hot water in winter and one return pipe which carries the return water in winter. These two pipes, of course, also carry chilled water in summer. In a four-pipe system there are two supply mains and two return mains. One of the two supply pipes will carry hot water at all times and the other supply pipe will carry chilled water at all times. One of the return pipes carries hot water at all times, and the other return pipe carries chilled water at all times. Thus, it may be seen with a four-pipe system that at all times of the year either cooling or heating is available to any unit connected with a four-pipe system.

It is of course necessary with system 12 that at some point in the building there is a boiler or other device for heating water and a water chiller for chilling water. The piping, of course, connects these sources of hot water and chilled water to all the various fan-coil units throughout the building. Since each room in the building that requires heating and cooling is supplied with one or more of these fan-coil units, it may be seen that it is a simple matter to provide individual room temperature control through the installation of a room thermostat in each room to control the supply of hot and chilled water to the fan-coil units in that room. This does provide excellent temperature control and makes it possible for any room in the building to maintain the temperature required by the occupants of that room.

In fig. 11-17 are shown the piping details of the connections to a fan-coil unit when a two-pipe system is utilized. Here, as shown, there are one supply main and one return main. In this illustration it is assumed that this piping is installed below the floor on which the fan-coil unit is mounted and is concealed above the ceiling of the room below. In this two-pipe system, the piping installation is very simple and as shown, a three-way valve is installed to control the flow of either hot water or chilled water through the heating-cooling coil. A three-way valve is shown because in some systems it is important to maintain a certain amount of flow to each unit at all times.

This three-way valve might be replaced with a two-way valve, in which case when no heating or cooling is required, there would be no flow at all to the fan-coil unit. At certain times of the year, it is probable that all fan-coil units throughout a building require neither heating nor cooling and all valves in all units would be closed; the pump that

is pumping either chilled water or hot water at that moment would be pumping against a piping system which is completely closed. There is some danger in this installation in that a pump which continues to run but does not circulate any water can build dangerous temperatures inside its pump casing, and an explosion or serious damage could result. It is not difficult in this case to make provisions for some relief of pressure when all valves in a system of this type would close, but that is necessary. Some designers would prefer to have three-way valves installed at their fan-coil units so that there is circulation through and to the piping to each fan-coil unit. This maintains a flow of water in the piping system at all times.

Also, it is true that with two-way valves when only a few of the valves installed at fan-coil units are open, a very substantial increase in the pressure of the supply water results and makes control of that water flow into each of the units requiring water quite difficult. With a two-pipe system, as shown in fig. 11-17, the supply main (reference 13) supplies hot water in winter and chilled water in summer, and there is some point or perhaps several points in time during the year when changeover from heating to cooling is required. This may be done automatically, but, as mentioned previously, automatic changeover leaves much to be desired, and many designers prefer to rely on manual changeover.

With a two-pipe system, when the piping throughout a given building consists of only one large piping system, all piping throughout the building carries hot water, and all zones and areas of the building must utilize hot water. However, at many times of the year, both heating and cooling will be required in a given building at the same time. Therefore, it is necessary to divide the piping in a two-pipe system such that it is possible to supply chilled water to one area of a building and hot water to another area of the building. If this is carefully and accurately done, the disadvantage of the two-pipe system and its requirement for summer-winter changeover will be greatly minimized. With a four-pipe system, there is no problem. With a four-pipe system, of course, hot water and chilled water are supplied to every unit at all times. Therefore, any unit may provide heating if that is what is required, or it may provide cooling if that is what is required in a given space. However, it is obvious that the cost of a four-pipe system is greatly in excess of the cost of a two-pipe system; this is its biggest disadvantage.

Whether to use a two-pipe system or a four-pipe system in a building involves serious consideration by the HVAC designer, and he or she is wise to involve the prospective owner of the building in this decision. In most cases, if a very good study is made of the needs for hot water and chilled water throughout the building, a two-pipe system can function very satisfactorily. However, the owner of the building must realize that if he benefits from the reduced cost of a two-pipe system, he will suffer some operational difficulties. That is, it may not always be possible in his building to provide exactly the proper conditions in all spaces at all times.

Figure 11-18 shows piping details of a four-pipe supply and return system. In fig. 11-18a it may be seen that there are three automatic temperature control valves installed. One of these valves is merely a changeover valve which is either wide open to the chilled water return main or wide open to the hot water return main. This valve does not take any intermediate positions. The other two valves in fig. 11-18a are two-way valves—one controlling the supply of hot water into the coil and the other controlling the supply of chilled water into the coil. These two valves must operate in sequence; that is, one must fully close before the other can open. The usual arrangement here is that when the space in which the fan-coil unit is installed requires heating, the hot water valve will be wide open and the chilled water valve will be completely closed. As the temperature rises in that space, the hot water valve will modulate toward a closed position, and when the temperature is satisfactory, that valve will be completely closed. Also, at that moment, the chilled water supply valve will also be completely closed. If the temperature in

the space then continues to rise to the point that cooling is required, the chilled water valve will begin to modulate open; and when it does begin to open, the changeover valve will change its position so that the flow may be through the coil and back to the chilled water return main. In this way there is never any mixing of hot water with chilled water; and the waste that results from that action never occurs. In this particular piping detail when neither heating nor cooling is required, both of the two-way control valves will be closed; and the disadvantage mentioned earlier in this article will accrue when there is no flow at all through the unit.

In fig. 11-18b the same type of control performance is achieved. However, now, instead of having a three-way valve and 2 two-way valves, we have 3 three-way valves installed. One of these as noted is a changeover valve and operates as mentioned previously. The other 2 three-way valves control the flow of hot water and chilled water. These other three-way valves, of course, operate sequentially as previously mentioned, controlling either the flow of chilled water into the coil or hot water into the coil, according to the needs of the space in which the fan-coil unit is installed. When neither heating nor cooling is required, there will continue to be flow of water into the piping chamber of the unit and back so that there is circulation at all times throughout the piping system.

In both of the details in fig. 11-18, an air vent is shown, which is very important to the successful operation of any water-heated or water-cooled device. One of the enemies of a hydronic system is air, and the fact that it can be trapped at high points throughout the system. Therefore, whenever possible at all high points, as shown in fig. 11-18, an air vent should be installed. The question must be resolved as to whether to use automatic air vents or manual air vents. With manual air vents it will become necessary from time to time for maintenance personnel to operate the manual air vent of each fan-coil unit to be certain that no air has collected in the piping at the high point shown. An automatic vent will do this

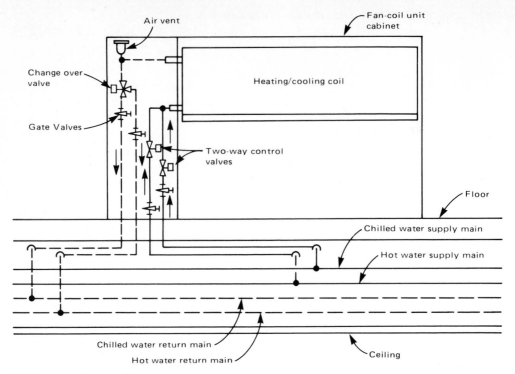

(a) Two-way valve control

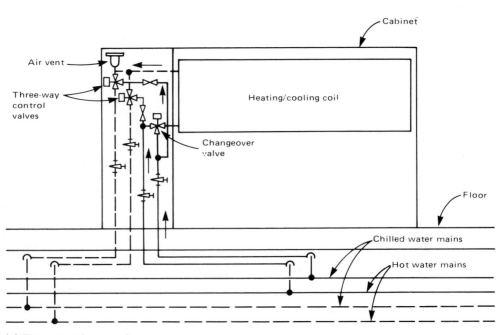

(b) Three-way valve control

Figure 11-18 Four-pipe details—fan-coil units.

automatically and continuously. However, one problem in the use of automatic vents is that they sometimes will vent water as well as air, and the release of water at this point may cause damage. Therefore, it is necessary with an automatic air vent to have some type of drain line connected to it, such that when a small amount of water is passed through the air vent, it will not cause damage but will be carried away to the drainage piping. Whenever the cooling function is performed by a unit of this type, water of condensation will collect on the coil, which will drain away if a drain pipe facility is provided. Therefore, in addition to the piping shown, there must be a drain line of some type connected to the drain pan so that any water of condensation is disposed of properly. The drain line from an automatic air vent may, of course, run to and terminate just above the drain pan in the unit so that no damage will result.

In fig. 11-16, the photograph of a fan-coil unit shows a four-pipe connection and shows each of these four pipes extending off to one side, as would be the case when a column enclosure is installed in a building. Sometimes the column enclosure that encloses a structural building column may be made somewhat larger than necessary and enclose the vertical pipe mains which run from floor to floor in a tall building.

In fig. 11-16 only two automatic valves are shown. This would be possible if the fan-coil unit were equipped with two separate coils—one for heating and one for cooling. In that case, all that is necessary is an automatic control valve controlling the flow of chilled water to the cooling coil and another valve controlling the flow of hot water to the heating coil.

In fig. 11-17 one of the details is a section through a fan-coil unit and the outside wall behind it. It may be seen in this section that provisions have been made for the introduction of outdoor air for ventilation when that is considered to be necessary. In this case, a small louver is installed in the outside wall, which does show on the exterior of the building. Air may be drawn in through this outside air louver and controlled by a damper

as shown in reference 14 of fig. 11-17. This damper would normally be manually adjusted, and once it is positioned in a satisfactory position, it remains that way at all times. However, it is also possible to install a small damper motor to position this damper for varying amounts of outdoor air. Usually, this complication is not involved in the installation of a fan-coil unit.

This method of bringing outdoor air into a building has some very unsatisfactory operating characteristics. For example, when a strong wind is blowing directly on the outside face of the wall behind the fan-coil unit, a great amount of outdoor air may be forced into and through the outside air intake louver (reference 15 in fig. 11-17). A great deal more outside air may be forced into the space than is required; on a cold winter day, overcooling, and perhaps even freeze-up of the fan-coil unit, may result. With many installations of this type, when wind pressure is felt on the outside of the building, enough outside air may rush in that it cannot pass up and through the heating coil of the unit, and it may flow backward through the return air grille (reference 11) and on into the room. In winter, a blast of cold air of this type sweeping across the floor of an occupied space can be very uncomfortable for the occupants.

Some manufacturers of fan-coil units have made an effort to solve this problem by making dampers that close when this flow of outside air at high velocity is experienced. However, it is this author's opinion that this is a very unsatisfactory method of ventilating a building and that whenever possible, a central supply system of ventilation should be installed. This involves installing at some point in the building a small ventilating unit which can bring in the necessary quantity of outside air required for ventilation, either heat it or cool it as necessary, and supply that outside air through ductwork to all points of the building where ventilation is required.

Thus, the ventilation system in the building is completely distinct and separate from the heating and cooling system of the building. Such a central system of ventilation does involve extra cost, and this may preclude its use. However, when this cost can be borne, much better operating characteristics of the ventilating system will result. One of the advantages of this central ventilating system is that when the building is not occupied, the central ventilating system may be shut down and no money is spent in heating or cooling outside air when ventilation is not required. Another advantage of such a central ventilating system is that during the winter the air may be supplied into the building at approximately 60°F and during summertime operation this supply air may be approximately 82°F. It may be seen that in winter with 60°F air being supplied, a small amount of cooling will result when the occupied spaces are maintained at a temperature between 65 and 70°F. This may be a big advantage in spaces that get lots of sunshine in winter, which causes them to tend to overheat. A small amount of 60°F air can do enough cooling perhaps to keep the room from overheating. This is particularly important when a two-pipe system is utilized, because at that time during winter, the system is probably being supplied with hot water, and cooling from the water system is not available. This small amount of cooling from the ventilation air may thus be of great advantage.

The same benefit accrues during summertime operation when chilled water is being circulated in a two-pipe system. Here the 82°F air supplied through the ventilation system can provide a small amount of heating if that should be necessary in a given space which is sheltered from the sunshine. Thus it may be seen that the central ventilating system can participate in the overall temperature control of a building, as well as providing ventilation.

In general, fan-coil units as those in system 12 should not be installed when the load is of a high-latent-heat nature. In other words, system 12 is not satisfactory in a building where many people congregate, as in an auditorium, assembly hall, or restaurant. The fan-coil units are not able to provide dehumidification when sensible cooling is not required. As has been discussed previously, the problem of the control of high-latent-heat loads is best solved through the use of face-and-bypass damper control of an air conditioning unit. Most manufacturers do not make fan-coil type units with face-and-bypass damper control. Therefore, the use of system 12 should not be attempted in buildings where the load is high in latent heat. Also, the use of system 12 is not satisfactory in buildings that are characterized by large rooms.

Fan-coil units of the type used in system 12 are not capable of establishing good circulation throughout a large room. And when such is attempted, usually only circulation is established in the area near the outside walls where the fan-coil units are installed. However, good results may be achieved through the use of fan-coil units of this type in conjunction with a central station circulating air system of some type. In this case, the central station system maintains circulation throughout the areas of large spaces, with the fan-coil units limiting their effect to the areas near the outside walls. It is possible, of course, to use fan-coil units which are mounted at or near the ceiling and located away from the outside walls in a room. Then they may achieve reasonably good circulation throughout a fairly large space.

One of the problems attendant on the use of system 12 is the noise that results from the operation of the fan in these fan-coil units. Very few of the manufacturers of these units have adequately solved the problem of noise; and when the fan in such a unit is running at high speed, the noise of such operation is very noticeable. The room or space in which a fan-coil unit is installed has considerable influence on the overall sound level in the room. *Room effect* adjusts the sound power level in accordance with the room construction and the furnishings of that room. When analyzing the sound power data presented in the catalogs of the various manufacturers, these room effects must be subtracted out to arrive at the resulting sound pressure level of the unit.

Room effect may be calculated, and a procedure for this is outlined in the *ASHRAE Handbook of Fundamentals*. In this author's experience, the only satisfactory way of determining the loudness or quietness of a fan-coil unit is to procure a manufacturer's sample of the type contemplated for use and connect it to operate in a room where the sound level is very low. It is possible, of course, to procure several manufacturers' samples, and connect them all in the same room so that an accurate comparative analysis can be made. This may seem to add an inordinate amount of difficulty to the selection process, but the dissatisfaction that results from the use of fan-coil units which are too noisy justifies any trouble that may be involved.

In general, the cost of system 12 may be considered to be comparatively low when a two-pipe system is utilized, and may be considered to be midrange when a four-pipe system is installed. However, when fan-coil units are installed at the outside walls, standing on the floor, it is necessary to ascribe a certain cost to the floor area that the fan-coil unit occupies. In other words, if a fan-coil unit extends 9 in. out from the outside wall and is 5 ft long, probably the area effectively occupied by that unit is approximately 7 to 10 ft^2 of floor. If the cost of this much floor space, at perhaps $40 to $50 per square foot, is added to the cost of system 12, its overall cost may be considered to be in high range. On the other hand, with the use of system 12 with little or no duct space above ceilings required it may be possible to reduce the floor-to floor-heights of a multistory building, thus attributing a great saving in the cost of the building to the use of system 12. It is clear, therefore, that there are many factors which should be included in an overall installed cost analysis.

11-18 SYSTEM 13: HIGH-VELOCITY INDUCTION UNIT SYSTEM

Like HVAC system 12, system 13 is of unitary type with one or more small individual units located in each room of a building. System 13 does have a central station air conditioning unit, but it is comparatively small and is only for the purpose of conditioning and supplying the outside air required by the building. The individual room units used in system 13 are not fan-coil units of the type utilized in system 12, but, as shown in fig. 11-19, consist of an induction arrangement by means of which room air is induced through a cooling coil by the action of high-velocity nozzles. In fig. 11-19 it may be seen that the unit includes a high-pressure air plenum in which primary air is supplied at static pressures of 3/4 to 3 in. WG, and this high-pressure plenum is equipped with many rows of high-pressure nozzles.

These nozzles are so arranged that as high-pressure air from the high-pressure plenum passes through them, the static pressure surrounding them is reduced so that room air is caused to flow through the cooling and heating coil into that area surrounding the nozzles. This room air, having passed through the coil, is entrained with the primary air leaving the nozzles, and the entire air mass rises and leaves the air conditioning unit at the top outlet opening. Because of their special design, the induction nozzles shown in fig. 11-19 have a very high aspiration ratio, of the order of 4:1. In other words, if 100 cfm of primary air enters the unit through the nozzles, 400 cfm of room air would be induced through the cooling coil and mixed with the primary air so that 500 cfm leaves the air conditioning unit at its outlet opening.

The coil shown as a part of the unit in fig. 11-19 may be supplied with hot water for heating or chilled water for cooling, so that this unit can either heat or cool, as required. There is a filter at the inlet to the heating/cooling coil so that the room air which is induced does have filtration. The flow of heated or chilled water into the coil would be controlled by an automatic valve under the control of a room thermostat.

The high-pressure plenum shown in fig. 11-19 is very carefully acoustically lined and acoustically treated so that the high level of noise carried along in the high-velocity primary airstream is effectively trapped out. By this means this type of air conditioning unit is made to be very satisfactorily quiet.

Usually, the primary air that is supplied to each of the induction units is 100% outside air, so that it serves two purposes. First, it provides ventilation

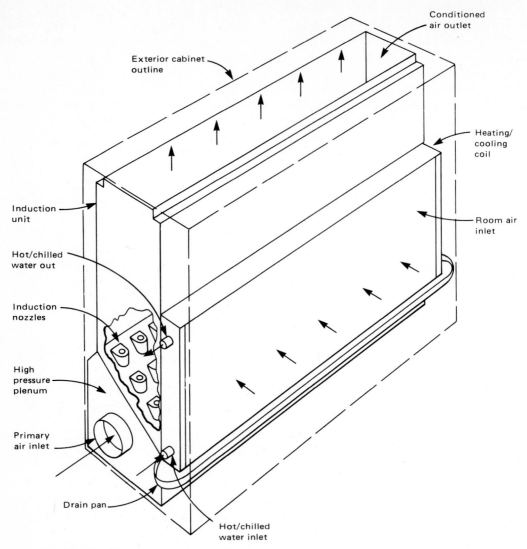

Figure 11-19   Typical high velocity induction unit.

with outdoor air; second, it provides the aspirating effect that causes the room air to flow through the coil and be heated or cooled. In summer the primary air is very thoroughly dehumidified so that the primary air can usually carry any latent heat load. If this is true, the heating-cooling coil, when in the cooling cycle, does not need to carry anything but sensible load. In that case, there is no condensation of moisture on the cooling coil, and there is no problem of disposal of the moisture of

condensation. However, one cannot always depend on the cooling coil not condensing any moisture, and a drain pan, as shown in fig. 11-19, is provided.

Figure 11-20 shows a schematic diagram of a complete high-velocity induction system, and does include all the various components that such a system would require. Shown in fig. 11-20 is a hot water heating boiler to provide heat in winter. There is also a water chiller unit which consists primarily of a condenser (reference 1) and a water

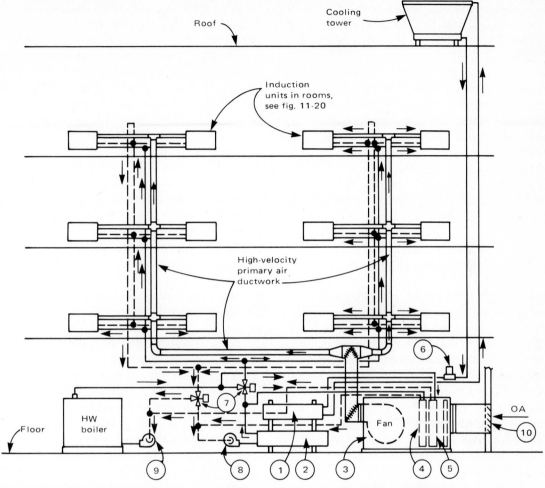

Figure 11-20 HVAC system number 13. High velocity induction system installations details. 1, condenser—water chiller unit; 2, cooler (evaporator)–water chiller unit; 3, primary air conditioner; 4, cooling coil; 5, heating coil; 6, cooling tower pump; 7, three-way changeover valves; 8, chilled water pump; 9, hot water heating pump; 10, OA intake louver.

cooler (reference 2). The water chiller unit would also, of course, include the necessary refrigeration compressor and piping. Also shown in fig. 11-20 is a primary air unit (reference 3), which includes a fan for circulation, a cooling coil (reference 4), a heating coil (reference 5), air filters, and provisions for outdoor air intake.

Figure 11-20 also includes a chilled water pump (reference 8) and a hot water heating pump (reference 9). Of course, these two pumps are for the

purpose of circulating hot water and chilled water to the primary air conditioning unit and to each of the induction units shown.

Leading from the primary air conditioner (reference 3) may be seen a supply air duct which is a high-pressure high-velocity duct system carrying primary air to all the various induction units throughout the building. Whenever possible, this primary air ductwork should be round, for least cost. Also included in fig. 11-20 is a cooling tower mounted in this case on the roof and a cooling tower pump (reference 6) to circulate cooling tower water through the condenser of the water chilling unit.

The piping shown in fig. 11-20 is of conventional design and routing, with the hot water heating boiler supplying hot water to all the various induction units, and to the primary air unit for heating purposes. When the use of HVAC system 13 is contemplated, consideration should always be given to the possibility of directing the hot water that leaves the water chilling unit condenser directly to the heating coil and to the induction units so that heating may be accomplished with the use of waste heat rather than drawing heat from the hot water heating boiler.

Also included in fig. 11-20 are two three-way changeover valves (reference 7). These valves are, of course, for the purpose of changing over from winter operation to summer operation, and vice versa. With these two valves in one position, chilled water may be circulated through the piping and to the coils in the various induction units. When the three-way valves occupy their alternate position, only hot water may be circulated through the piping to the system. It may be seen then that a building utilizing this HVAC system must be zoned in such a way that either hot water or chilled water may be circulated to each zone according to the needs of that zone.

It is not possible with the piping diagram shown, to supply either hot water or chilled water to any particular unit at all times. However, it is possible that the building could have a four-pipe supply and return system rather than the two-pipe design shown. In this case, with a four-pipe system, any individual induction unit could heat while all the other units are cooling, and vice versa, so that at any time, according to the dictates of a room thermostat, any room could have either heating or cooling as desired. As has been previously mentioned, a four-pipe hot and chilled water distribution system is exceedingly expensive compared with a two-pipe system.

One advantageous use of HVAC system 13 is

during the heating cycle when the building is not occupied. At this time, the primary air unit may be shut down with the hot water circulating pump (reference 9), running and circulating hot water to all induction units throughout the building. Even though those units are not supplied with primary air and there is no induction action of the unit, there is still appreciable heating capacity resulting from gravity circulation of air through the air conditioning unit. Very often the gravity heating capacity of the induction units, when the primary air is not circulating, is adequate to maintain a reasonable room temperature during winter.

In summertime operation, when the building is not occupied, the primary air must continue to circulate if an appreciable amount of cooling is required from the various induction units. When the primary air is stopped, there is no appreciable cooling effect from the induction units, even though chilled water may continue to circulate. It is possible, in the use of system 13, for enough air to be "recirculated" from the building through the primary air unit during unoccupied periods to cause the induction action in the induction units to take place so that cooling can result.

Usually, the initial installed cost of system 13 is quite high. Also, the operating costs, with high outside air intake required, are appreciably higher than would be the operating costs with one of the other systems, especially those which provide variable air volume operation. With system 13 there is very little duct space required since all the primary air ducts are comparatively small, operating at high velocity and carrying only 20% or so of the air that otherwise would be circulated.

Floor space in the occupied rooms is a matter of concern and should be taken into consideration in any type of comparative cost analysis.

11-19 SYSTEM 14: SELF-CONTAINED UNIT SYSTEM

System 14, like systems 12 and 13, is of unitary type utilizing small individual room-type air conditioning units. Each room in a given building would have one or more of these types of air conditioning units installed in it. These units are complete with a cooling coil, a condenser, a motor-compressor unit, an evaporator fan and motor, a condenser fan and motor, a drain pan, a filter, and all necessary piping and controls, all enclosed in a well-finished furniture steel cabinet. See fig. 11-21 for details of this type of unit.

As shown in fig. 11-21, the self-contained air conditioning unit is mounted in an outside wall in such a way that it has full access to outdoor air. The refrigeration system in such an air condition-

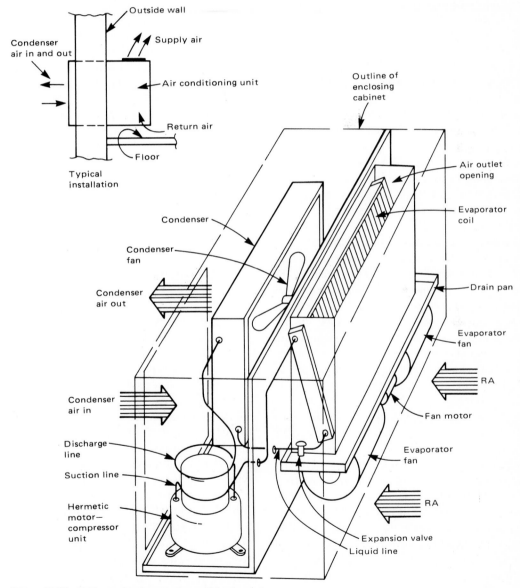

Figure 11-21 Self-contained room air conditioning unit.

ing unit has an air-cooled condenser which requires large quantities of outdoor air drawn into the unit and blown out through a condenser coil. For best appearance, such a unit should be installed with the extension of the unit to the outdoors held to a minimum. If the extension of the air conditioning unit past the outside face of the outside wall is held to 1 or 2 in., of necessity there will be a very considerable extension of the unit into the interior room. When this type of unit is mounted in a 13-in.-thick masonry wall, the extension into the room would be approximately 8 in. Many times this type of unit is installed in a comparatively thin window wall, in which case, the extension into the interior may be as much as 18 in. The installation of such a unit is quite simple. An opening is cut in the outside wall and a steel frame is installed in this opening. The air conditioning unit is then slid into this mounting frame. When the unit is used for cooling only, the only requirement for connection is the electrical connection for electrical supply to the unit and a drain line connection for carrying away the water of condensation.

When such a unit is used for heating, as well as cooling, a heating coil is installed adjacent to the cooling coil. When a heating coil is installed in this type of unit, it is usually supplied with hot water from a central hot water heating system. In this way the air conditioning unit is made to serve both the heating and cooling needs of the room in which it is installed. Very often in this type of unit an electric heating coil is installed because it is inexpensive and requires very little space. However, the exceedingly high operating cost of such a heating coil should preclude its use in most cases.

Very often this type of air conditioning unit is so equipped at the factory that it is able to reverse its action and thus become a heat pump, so that it can pump heat from the building to the exterior in the summer and reverse its action so that in winter it pumps heat out of outdoor air and into the interior of the building. When such a unit is utilized year-round for both heating and cooling, the motor compressor unit must operate almost continuously; thus its life expectancy is greatly reduced.

As with any type of heating and air conditioning system, system 14 has both advantages and disadvantages. Unfortunately, the disadvantages greatly outweigh the advantages, and it is not likely that system 14 will find much application in new buildings of the nonresidential type in the future.

Of the advantages of system 14 we may say that it enjoys a very low initial cost. Its low cost might very well make it possible for an owner to build a building that he or she otherwise could not afford. The difference in initial cost of system 14 and one of the other more expensive types is appreciable. Another advantage of system 14 is that it does give, without any penalty, individual room control, so that any room in which these units are installed may be considered to be a separate temperature control zone.

Of the disadvantages we may say, first, that system 14 consists of units which are very noisy in operation. With a fan that circulates the room air in operation, and with the fan that circulates the outdoor air in and out in operation, and with the motor compressor unit in operation, there is a lot of noise generated. Manufacturers have made strenuous efforts to reduce this noise to a suitable level. However, as yet they have not succeeded to an extensive degree.

A second disadvantage is the general appearance of the units used in system 14. Although manufacturers do a good job of streamlining the cabinet that encloses these units and providing them with an excellent finish, they still do not make a good appearance in a room. As it is usually not practical to conceal them, their appearance must be considered a disadvantage.

A third disadvantage is that in most cases, this type of unit will occupy considerable floor space in a building. Usually, 7 to 10 ft^2 of floor will either be occupied or made otherwise inaccessible for use; if these 7 to 10 ft^2 are charged to the cost of system 14 at the rate of \$40 to \$50 per square foot of floor, the initial cost is no longer low but very high.

Fourth, the operating cost is much greater with

this type of unit than with most other types of heating and cooling units. With equipment of this type, it is just not possible to achieve the high efficiency that is achievable with a central station unit.

A fifth disadvantage of the units used in system 14 is the extremely short life of the motor-compressor unit incorporated in such equipment. Operating as a cooling-only unit, such equipment is usually assumed to have a life of 7 to 10 years. However, when this type of unit is utilized as a heat pump unit and is operated both winter and summer, its life is appreciably reduced. When the motor-compressor unit fails, it is usually not practical to repair it; the entire motor-compressor unit must be removed and replaced. This replacement cost is excessive.

Because of the short life of the motor-compressor unit, another disadvantage of this type of equipment is that it is not field serviceable. When a motor-compressor unit fails, it must be removed and sent back to the factory for repair, or replaced with a unit of similar size and capacity: the life-cycle cost of system 14 is excessive.

A final disadvantage of this type of equipment is that it is not suitable for application in any but quite small rooms. As is true with all unitary equipment, such as that described in systems 12, 13, and 14, it is not possible for a small unit located under a window to establish and maintain a good overall room circulation pattern when the room is quite large.

11-20   SYSTEM 15: HEAT PUMP LOOP SYSTEM

HVAC system 15 is a very special energy-conservative method of using small to medium-sized heat pumps to provide heating and cooling in a medium-sized or large building. System 15 uses water-to-air heat pumps and a two-pipe circulating water system. Connections are made from this circulating water system to each heat pump in such a way that the heat pumps may either pump heat from a circulating stream of water, or pump heat into the same circulating stream of water. The two-pipe circulating water system shown in fig. 11-22 is equipped with an evaporative water cooler so connected as to be able to remove heat from a circulating stream of water and discharge that heat into the outdoor atmosphere. The system is also equipped with a hot water heating boiler so connected that it can add heat to the circulating water stream whenever that becomes necessary.

In summertime operation, in general, the heat pumps will be extracting heat from the air of the building and will pump that heat into the circulating stream of water. In winter the reverse action takes place; heat is pumped from the stream of water into the air of the building. In summer, of course, the circulating water will have an excess of heat, and the evaporative cooler will remove this heat and discharge it to the atmosphere. In winter, the circulating water will need to have heat added; the boiler shown in fig. 11-22 will do this. The overall temperature control of the system will be such as to maintain the water in the supply piping in the range of 60 to 90°F.

At 90°F the water in the circulating piping is not too hot to serve as a heat sink when the heat pumps are mainly on the cooling cycle and are extracting heat from the room air and delivering it into the water. At a temperature of 60°F, the circulating water in the supply piping is not too cold to serve as a very satisfactory heat source on the heating cycle when heat is being extracted from the water and delivered into the building air.

The heat pumps utilized in system 15 are very much like those detailed in fig. 10-21b. As shown in that schematic diagram, each heat pump would include a heating/cooling coil and also a shell-and-tube heat exchanger. The water from the circulating water piping passes through the shell-and-tube heat exchanger and either gives up heat to the refrigerant, which also passes through the heat exchanger, or removes heat from that refrigerant in the heat exchanger. The coil shown in fig. 10-21b has refrigerant passing through the tubes of the coil and has room air passing over the exterior surfaces of the coil; it serves both as a heating coil in winter and as a cooling coil in summer.

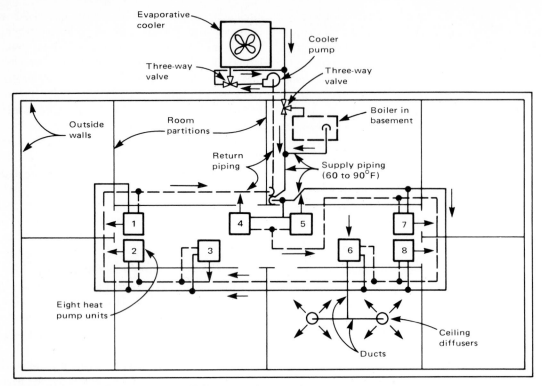

Figure 11-22   HVAC system number 15. Heat pump loop system.

In the heating cycle, the shell-and-tube heat exchanger acts as an evaporator and refrigerates the water passing through it. The heat thus extracted is pumped by the compressor over to the coil, which is now acting as a condenser. The heat of condensation is then removed by the circulating airstream and delivered into the spaces to be heated. In the cooling cycle, the coil acts as an evaporator, and because it is cold, it removes heat from the circulating room air; the compressor pumps that heat over to the shell-and-tube heat exchanger, where the heat is picked up by the circulating stream of water. Therefore, in the heating cycle, the circulating water is a heat source and in the cooling cycle the circulating water is a heat sink. The reader may wish to refer to the discussion in chap. 10 on the subject of heat pumps and the theory of their operation.

The evaporative cooler shown in fig. 11-22 is exactly the same as a cooling tower and has a spray of water that is maintained by a circulating pump and spray nozzles; it also has a fan by means of which outdoor air is drawn through the tower to cool the water. To make it an evaporative cooler, an extra coil is added to the cooling tower. This coil is subjected to the spray of water which is maintained in the tower, and the circulating water from the building system is pumped through this coil to be cooled by the water in the evaporative cooler. Figure 10-19 shows the details of a cooling tower; this tower could be converted to an evaporative cooler by the addition of a heat exchanger coil in the manner just described.

The heat pumps utilized in HVAC system 15 are usually of 7 1/2 tons capacity and smaller. However, they may be larger and often are, but they must be limited to one building temperature control zone. In other words, each building exposure must have its own heat pump unit—one or more. The heat pumps utilized in HVAC system

15 may be of constant volume design or of VAV design. The ductwork connected to them and running from them to the various conditioned spaces may be of high-velocity design or of low-velocity design. The supply grilles, registers, and diffusers may also be of any type design appropriate to the basic air distribution system in use. The return air duct system utilized in system 15 may also be of any type suitable to the building and to the type of HVAC units in use.

The most important characteristic of HVAC system 15 is its ability to extract heat from one part of the building, where cooling is required, and transfer that heat to another area of the building, where heat is required. It should be realized that this may be done without fuel of any type being burned. Therefore, HVAC system 15 is a highly conservative system in its use of energy. In most conventional HVAC systems, when a building needs both heating and cooling at the same time, energy is required to provide the cooling, and the consumption of fuel is also required to provide the necessary heating. In HVAC system 15 this is minimized to a great extent. However, there are times when fuel must be burned during cold winter weather.

The heat pump loop system detailed in fig. 11-22 may be improved through the addition of a large storage tank to be used in conjunction with the evaporative cooler to store hot water as it is delivered from the building during the cooling cycle. This heated water, perhaps as high as 90°F, would then be stored to the extent possible before the evaporative cooler is turned on to discharge heat to the atmosphere. In this case the storage tank would be maintained essentially full of hot water, which would be available at any time when heating is required. This type of installation would also minimize the use of the boiler and the consumption of fuel in that boiler. Figure 11-22 shows two three-way valves installed in the piping in such a way as to divert only enough water through the boiler to maintain its temperature above 60°F or to divert enough water through the evaporative cooler to maintain the water temperature at 90°F or below.

Of the heat pumps shown in fig. 11-22, only heat pump 6 is shown to be connected with ductwork and ceiling diffusers. However, all eight heat pumps shown would need to be connected with supply and return ducts and with necessary grilles, registers, and diffusers. In many cases where HVAC system 15 is utilized, the heat pump units are small enough that they may be mounted above suspended ceilings serving comparatively small zones nearby. However, these heat pump units are quite noisy and have a considerable amount of vibration. They may very well be objectionable from this standpoint; an additional disadvantage is the difficulty of servicing such heat pump units when they are concealed above building ceilings.

With this type of system, when the heat pump units are suspended above ceilings, there is very little requirement in the building for equipment rooms and fan rooms such as might be required with other types of HVAC systems. However, there is the requirement of space for the boiler, which is shown in fig. 11-22 as being in a basement area. This may not always be possible. There is also a problem in the location of the evaporative cooler. Since it is circulating water, it is subject to freezing; and if mounted outdoors in cold climates, freeze protection may be a considerable problem. Very often the evaporative cooler is mounted inside the building in such a way that great quantities of air may easily be drawn in from the outdoors, passed through the evaporative cooler, and then discharged back to the outdoors. In this case, the problem of freeze-up is greatly minimized.

The system detailed in fig. 11-22 does not make any provision for the use of outdoor air for ventilation in the building. Almost all nonresidential buildings require ventilation, and this system would benefit from the use of an outdoor air ventilating unit which circulates 100% outside air and delivers that air, filtered and tempered, to the various spaces of the building requiring ventilation. One benefit of this type of installation is that during unoccupied periods, this separate ventilating unit may be shut down and no energy wasted in heating or cooling outdoor air. It would be possible for each of the heat pump units shown to be connected with an outdoor air intake supply. However, in system 15 when the individual heat pump units are scattered, as they normally would be, throughout a large building, it is quite difficult and expensive to extend outside air intake ducts to each one. Therefore, it is recommended that a single unit of some type be used for introducing outside air into the building for ventilation.

Since the motor-compressor units in the heat pump units shown in HVAC system 15 are required to run all year round, both during the heating season and during the cooling season, their life in terms of years is usually quite limited. This is especially true when the motor-compressor units are not of heavy-duty design, and are not field serviceable. When larger heat pump units are utilized, it is entirely possible that the motor-compressor units may be of heavy-duty design, and may be field serviceable, so that their life may be extended well beyond that of the lighter-duty type. Light-duty heat pumps probably would have a service life of 7 years or less. If a heavier-duty design can be utilized, the service life may be extended considerably.

The major disadvantage to HVAC system 15 is probably that very often a multiplicity of comparatively small heat pump units are used, and the noise and vibration that result are excessive. Also, with a great number of units, the service problem is increased, especially when the units are suspended above building ceilings and thus made comparatively inaccessible. The major advantage of the heat pump loop system is its energy-conservative nature. It can transfer heat from a part of the building where it is not required to a part of the building where it is required, and do this without burning any fuel.

11-21 CENTRAL CHILLER LOOP SYSTEM

The central chiller loop system is not a numbered system that can take its place in the lineup of the numbered systems described above. Rather, it is a method by which most of those systems could be applied to a building. In other words, most of the numbered systems described above can be applied in a building in such a way as to take advantage of the warm water and chilled water loops shown in fig. 11-23. The loop system shown is designed to provide additional energy savings by dividing the building into areas according to exposure, and like system 15, can transfer heat from an area of the building where heat is in excess to an area of the building where there may be a deficiency. Unlike the heat pump loop system of HVAC system 15, where small individual self-contained heat pump units are utilized, here only one refrigerating water chiller unit would be installed—at a central utility point in the building. Of course, there might be two centrally located water chillers installed at the same point in the building for dependability.

The air conditioning units shown in fig. 11-23 merely indicate air conditioning units of most any type, single-zone or multizone, located in the building according to the exposure to which various parts of the building are subjected. The remainder of the system shown in fig. 11-23 consists of a hot water heating boiler, an evaporative cooler mounted so as to utilize outdoor air, a chilled water pump for circulating chilled water, a hot water heating pump, and two pipe loops which circulate throughout almost all of the building. One of these pipe loops is maintained at temperatures in the range of 80 to 100°F. The other loop is a cooled water loop maintained in the range of 45° to 60°F. Most of the numbered HVAC systems described above could be applied in this case except the self-contained unit system 14, and of course the heat pump loop, system 15.

In fig. 11-23 it may be seen that an effort has been made to reduce pipe costs throughout the building by utilizing only two mains—one warm and one cool—both serving as supply and return mains at the same time. Of course, the pipe loops could be a four-pipe system, with one chilled water supply, one chilled water return, one warm water supply, and one warm water return. However, in this case, the piping loops would be much more expensive. In the two-pipe loops shown,

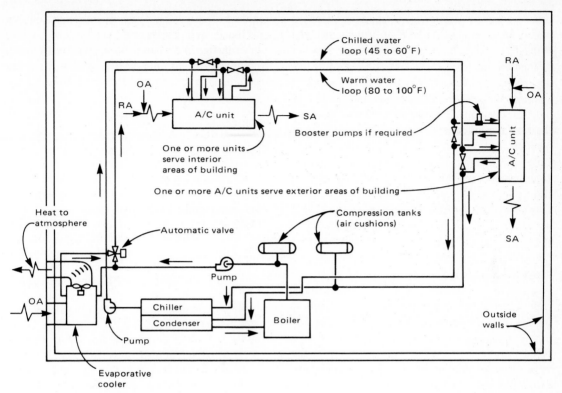

Figure 11-23 Central chiller loop system.

several methods may be utilized to divert the water from the warm water and chilled water mains into the various air conditioning units as required. As shown in fig. 11-23, balancing cocks may be installed in the mains to introduce enough resistance to the flow of water in the mains that this resistance is greater than the resistance would be if the water were diverted from one pipe loop through a heating or cooling coil and back to the loop. In this case, whenever an automatic control valve in the air conditioning unit opens, the water is inclined to flow from the main through the coil and back to the main downstream of the balancing cock shown. It would be possible, of course, to utilize venturi-type pipe tees of the type utilized in a one-pipe hot water heating system. In some cases it may be necessary to utilize booster pumps to cause the water to flow from one of the mains

through a heating or cooling coil and back to the main as required.

The central chiller loop system shown is similar to the heat pump loop system in that when the water chiller runs and extracts heat from the chilled water loop, the rejected heat is delivered into the warm water loop. If the temperature of the warm water loop rises to too high a valve, the three-way valve shown will divert some of the warm water into the coil of the evaporative cooler, which will run and remove the heat and discharge it into the exterior.

Also, if the temperature of the warm water loop tends to fall to too low a value, the hot water heating boiler will come into action and deliver heat into the warm water loop as necessary. The connections to the hot water heating boiler may be of many types. One type that might be considered is a three-way setup as shown in fig. 11-22, to divert an adequate amount of water into and through the boiler to pick up the necessary amount of heat. Normally, the air conditioning units utilized, shown in fig. 11-23, would have separate heating and cooling coils installed; and these coils might be controlled by automatic valves controlling the flow of chilled water or warm water, or might be controlled by the face-and-bypass damper principle. It is possible that the air conditioning units could utilize one common coil with the four-pipe connections made thereto as shown in fig. 11-18. It is necessary that the warm water and the chilled water loops always be completely separated, and the automatic valving would need to ascertain that this separation is maintained.

As was mentioned in the description of HVAC system 15, it is possible that a large storage tank could be utilized to store warm water and hold it instead of rejecting its heat to the exterior, so that heat is available later for heating purposes, should that become necessary. It is also possible that the water chilling unit or units utilized could have *double-bundle condensers* with the evaporative cooler connected to one of the circuits in the double-bundle condenser and the other bundle in the condenser connected as shown in fig. 11-23. Of course, in a central chiller loop system, a basic purpose is to make it possible to transfer heat from one area of the building, which may encompass several or many temperature control zones, to another area of the building where heat may be required. This process is energy conservative and must be considered wherever possible.

If the interior areas of the building are large compared to the exterior or perimeter areas of the building, the excess heat generated in those interior areas may often be adequate to provide all the heat required by the exterior areas of the building. In this case, much of the time during the heating season, no fuel may be required. In the colder climates such a building may have to be equipped with perimeter hot water radiation of some type. In this case, the warm water loop of fig. 11-23 could easily be made to supply the warm water

required for such radiation. It must certainly be concluded that the central chiller loop system shown in fig. 11-23 can make a great contribution to our efforts to save energy, and it is highly recommended for consideration in all cases.

PROBLEMS

11-1 What is the basic difference in the temperature control action between a CV type of HVAC system and a VAV system?

11-2 What is the function of the air relief damper (reference 12) in fig. 11-1?

11-3 In a given air conditioned room the calculated sensible heat gain is 20,000 BH, and the calculated latent heat gain is 5000 BH. If the desired room air condition, RA, is 76°F DB and 50% RH, find the sensible heat ratio (SHR) and the apparatus dew point temperature (ADP). Use the psychrometric chart in fig. 1-9.

11-4 A cooling coil has a face area, through which air enters the coil, which is 4 ft wide and 2 ft high. This coil is four rows of tubes deep (in the direction of airflow) and the coil tubes have metal fins which are spaced 12 to the inch. What percent of the air passing through this coil does not come in contact with the tubes or fins when the quantity of air passing through the coil is 3200 cfm? Find the same value for 4000 cfm.

11-5 In a given HVAC situation, RA is 78°F DB, ADP is 52°F, the bypass factor is 0.2, and the room internal total sensible heat load, BHS, is 120,000 BH. Find the DTD, the temperature of the air leaving the coil (LA), and the proper cfm of airflow required.

11-6 If in a VAV air conditioning system, the requirement for supply air is reduced at a given time to 60% of full rated volume, what percent of full rated fan power is required when a frequency inverter is used, when throttling damper control is used, and when fan inlet vane control is used?

11-7 If HVAC system 2 detailed in fig. 11-9 is installed on the second floor of a three-story building, is it likely that in winter the interior zone duct (reference 3) would supply cool air most of the time? Could this HVAC system 2 do this?

11-8 Is the triple-deck a/c unit of fig. 11-9 a blow-through or a draw-through unit? Can it provide face-and-bypass damper control?

11-9 What is the basic difference between the a/c units in systems 2 and 3?

11-10 HVAC system 4, the terminal reheat system, is very wasteful of heat energy. There is one measure that can be taken to make system 4 less wasteful. What is that?

11-11 The heat pump loop system (system 15) is very effective at conserving energy. Basically, how does it conserve energy?

Chapter 12

Heat Conservation and Recovery Systems

12-1 GENERALITIES

As almost every citizen of almost every nation is painfully aware, there is an energy shortage of monumental proportions today. In an industrial nation such as the United States, the economic and political ramifications of this shortage, and the upheaval and hardship that can result from an unsatisfactory solution to the problems looming on the horizon, make every person responsible for contributing to a solution of these problems. We in the construction industry bear a particularly heavy responsibility since it is in buildings that most of our energy is utilized.

The Federal Power Commission reports that residential, commercial, and institutional buildings demand 52% of the electrical energy generated. Industry draws 43%, and of this a very substantial portion can be attributed to the needs of these industrial buildings for heating, cooling, lighting, and so on.

Therefore, we in the construction industry have a great opportunity to contribute by influencing the design and construction of new buildings, the remodeling and rehabilitation of existing buildings, and the operating and control of all buildings. This is a challenge that we do not dare to refuse.

The problems that arise can, in general, be placed into either of two broad categories:

1 *Conservation:* preventing the expenditure of energy to the greatest extent possible
2 *Recovery:* the recovery of waste heat, for useful purpose, from energy-consuming processes that are mandatory and that cannot be eliminated

Both categories offer tremendous opportunity for improvement. This chapter does not include an exhaustive and detailed study of the conservation and recovery processes that the construction industry should investigate, but provides merely an incomplete checklist of many of the steps that may be taken. Illustrative material and explanatory comments are included for some of these steps.

12-2 CONSERVATION MEASURES: HVAC SYSTEMS

There is great opportunity for energy conservation in the design of new HVAC systems and the remodeling of existing systems. The criticism that, in the past, HVAC system designers have been highly remiss in the performance of their design activities is certainly justified. To conserve energy has not been a primary goal. One example of this is the great frequency with which reheat-type HVAC systems (system 4 of chap. 11) have been utilized. Reheat systems cool all the air being supplied to all zones of a building even though most zones may need warm air. To prevent overcooling these zones, the air is reheated. Energy is required to cool the air, and then more energy is required to reheat—a very wasteful process.

Following are listed some conservation measures for HVAC systems.

1 *Use VAV (variable air volume) systems.* Their use has been proven to be very effective in reducing operating costs, especially when frequency inverters have been utilized as a means of reducing air conditioning unit fan speeds. All VAV systems are not outstanding in this respect. Study of the various HVAC systems in chap. 11 will give guidance in this respect.

2 *Reheat systems—Do not use.* As mentioned earlier, reheat systems, even VAV reheat systems, are wasteful of energy. Their use should be avoided.

3 *Loop systems.* The heat pump and central chiller loop systems described in chap. 11 are capable of heating one zone or one area of a build-

ing with heat transferred from another portion of the building where cooling is required. This is a highly conservative practice, especially when the central chiller loop system incorporates some of the more conservative VAV systems.

4 *Electric resistance heating—Do not use.* The installed cost of resistance electric heaters is often comparatively low. As a result, many HVAC system designers have yielded to the temptation to use them even though they know that operating costs will be painfully high.

However, the worst aspect of this is the horrible waste of fuel energy attendant to the use of resistance electric heating. Considering that the overall efficiency of electric power generating and distribution processes is perhaps 20%, we can hardly justify the use of electricity for heating if any other type is available. The fact that 80% of the heat content of the fossil fuels used in commercial power generation is lost into the atmosphere, into our rivers, and so on, seems to be lost on many designers.

When electric power is generated from nuclear energy or water power, the problem disappears, but when oil, gas, or coal is used, the waste of energy is a disgrace. It has been said that "our reserves of coal are adequate to serve our needs for 400 to 600 years; so let's use coal without restraint." However, 70 years or so ago, we could see no end to our supplies of oil and gas.

Fossil fuels can be burned in heating boilers and furnaces with an instantaneous efficiency of 75 to 80% and an overall efficiency of perhaps 65%. How then can we justify the use of electricity for heating when the overall efficiency may be as low as 20% or less?

5 *Utilize condenser heat.* When any refrigerating machine is operated, heat is removed from one location and discharged at its condenser at another location. Historically, in HVAC practices our only thought has been to discard this condenser heat as expeditiously as possible. Very little thought has been given to its reuse.

That is now changing. HVAC equipment manufacturers have begun to produce equipment which facilitates the recovery of condenser heat. A good example of this is the double-bundle type of condenser available on some water chilling units and other refrigerating machines. Here a normal flow of condenser water (from a cooling tower, perhaps) is possible through one bundle of tubes in the condenser shell. Also, a secondary flow of water, or other fluid, through a second bundle of condenser tubes, with priority over the first bundle, can capture most of the condenser heat and convey it to some point of usage. However, even with standard condensers, the 95°F leaving water or 105°F leaving condenser air may be used effectively for many purposes.

6 *Reduce outside air required for ventilation.* It is possible to substantially reduce outside air quantities through the use of banks of activated charcoal. With this method, banks of canisters containing cocoanut shell charcoal are installed in the mixed airstreams entering central station air conditioning units.

Charcoal has a strong capability to adsorb odors and other vapors from the airstream, thus rehabilitating the air until it is suitable for reuse. A small amount of outside air is still required to maintain a minimum oxygen count and to reduce concentrations of CO_2 and CO. Of course, the great reduction in outside air makes possible a very substantial reduction in energy consumption.

This process of outside air reduction has been available for decades, but has never been popular from an economic standpoint and because until recently the need to save energy was not pressing. There is quite a lot of trouble involved in the process of maintaining fresh charcoal canisters in use at all times, and in regenerating other canisters for reuse. It would seem that the need to save energy is now great enough that building operators may be willing to suffer the cost and inconvenience involved; the benefits from such are considerable.

7 *Reduce outside air quantities through filtration.* There are many industrial processes in which air carrying dust and other particulate matter is discharged into the atmosphere. When such matter is filterable, filtration equipment can probably often be economically justified if this permits the air to be reused and not wasted into the atmosphere.

8 *Reduce temperature stratification with overhead fans.* In rooms with high ceilings, it is often found that the temperature gradient from floor to ceiling in winter is as much as 10 to 15°F.

This results in unnecessarily high temperatures in the upper parts of the room volume, and increased heat loss through roofs and upper walls.

At Greenfield Community College in Greenfield, Massachusetts, high-ceiling auditoriums and lecture halls were found to have a temperature gradient of as much as 19°F from floor to ceiling. Experimental ceiling fan installations were found to reduce this gradient to 2°F. While breathing-level temperatures were held essentially constant, upper-level temperatures were reduced 10 to 15°F. Heat loss reductions were, of course, appreciable. This idea was felt to be so effective that 15 more fan installations are planned for one library building. To date, this and many other methods of conservation have resulted in a 45% reduction in annual energy consumption at Greenfield. With regard to the fan installations mentioned, the heat loss reductions were accompanied by a substantial improvement in human comfort.

9 *Use small air conditioning units on small special loads.* In nonresidential structures there are often small, localized areas involving small but critical cooling or heating loads. Sometimes these loads, as in a computer room, persist for comparatively long periods and exist when other loads in the building are at a minimum. A conference room utilized by many people at odd hours of the day presents load of the type considered here.

If loads of this type are carried by a large central HVAC system, it may be necessary to operate the entire system, including a large water chiller unit, just to handle these small loads. Great inefficiency can result from this.

It is obviously much better to carry such loads on small, localized HVAC systems which serve only the areas of special interest. In this case, the initial, overall cost may be slightly higher but the extra cost will soon be recovered in terms of reduced and perhaps more satisfactory operating characteristics.

This item illustrates the principle, with which we will all become more and more familiar, that to save energy we must often invest more capital initially. However, the payback period is usually short, and the overall benefits are great.

10 *Insist on higher EERs.* We must all continuously concentrate on the acquisition and use of HVAC equipment of highest EER (energy effi-

ciency ratio) or SEER (seasonal energy efficiency rating).

Manufacturers are able to make equipment of high rating but are reluctant to do so because it makes their products more expensive and thus less competitive. For example, a refrigeration system can be made more efficient by including a condenser of greater surface area; this will result in lower condensing pressures and less power demand by the compressor motor.

Similarly, the evaporator surface area may, at greater cost, be increased. This will raise compressor suction pressures, more refrigerant vapor will be pumped per piston stroke, and power demand per ton of refrigeration will be reduced.

Again, we can see that to save energy (and operating cost) we are very often (but not always) required to invest more capital at the outset. The EER is the ratio of the heat delivered, by a refrigerating machine, air conditioner, or heat pump, to the power required to run the machine. The EER for an air conditioner may be as high as 10 or more. In other words, it can deliver 10 BH of cooling effect for each watt of electricity consumed, or 10 BH/W.

11 *Automatic breeching dampers.* Heating boilers and furnaces may lose great quantities of heat out through their breechings (smoke pipes) and up their chimney flues during off-periods when their burners are not operating. In many cases there is nothing to prevent the rapid flow of building air into and through such units carrying residual heat away and out into the atmosphere.

This can be a very substantial loss if boilers and furaces are oversized (as is often the case), and burners operate on an on-off cycle. In this situation, burners will be idle a great percentage of the time and residual losses will be high.

The National Aviation and Space Agency (NASA) has conducted investigations that indicate that overall fuel utilization in many types of buildings is such as to indicate an overall seasonal fuel-burning efficiency of less than 50%. This NASA found to be true even when firing tests indicated an instantaneous efficiency of 80%. If these figures are correct, the difference would be explained largely by standby losses.

However, it is suggested that a value as low as 50% be considerably upgraded in the light of ac-

tual field experience. For example, one fuel oil supplier in Indianapolis has found that for conditions in that city a multiplier of 0.02 should be applied to the calculated hourly maximum heat loss to determine annual consumption of No. 2 fuel oil.

If an Indianapolis residence had a calculated heat loss, under design conditions of 70°F indoor temperature and (-10°F) outdoor temperature, of 100,000 BH, its expected annual fuel consumption would be 100,000 × 0.02 = 2000 gal per year. This multiplier was developed over several years of observation of typical fuel requirements.

Annual fuel-burning efficiency where fuel is used for space heating only may be calculated with the use of the formula

$$E = \frac{HL \times 5088 \times \Delta t_a}{F \times FC \times \Delta t_d} \qquad (12\text{-}1)$$

where
    E = overall annual fuel-burning efficiency
    HL = hourly heat loss under design conditions, BH
    F = annual fuel consumption in the fuel units used (gallons of oil, etc.)
    FC = heat content of one unit of the fuel used (Btu/gal of oil, etc.)
    5088 = hours in a heating season, October 1 to May 1 (212 days)
    Δt_a = average temperature difference (actual room temperature minus average OA temperature in winter)
    Δt_d = design temperature difference (design room temperature minus design OA temperature)

In Indianapolis, the average winter outdoor temperature is 39.6°F, and the outdoor design temperature recommended by ASHRAE was -10°F. If No. 2 fuel oil were used, if its heat content were 140,000 Btu/gal, if 2000 gal were burned per season, and if indoor temperature were maintained at 70°F,

$$E = \frac{100,000 \times 5088(70°F - 39.6°F)}{2000 \times 140,000[70°F - (-10°F)]} = 0.69$$

Thus the efficiency would be 69%.

Had it been possible to maintain an overall efficiency of 80%, fuel consumption would have been 1726 gal per year—or 274 gal less. The loss of 274 gal would be mainly standby loss.

A large percentage of standby losses can be eliminated through the use of automatic dampers mounted in the breeching between the boiler or furnace outlet and the chimney. Such dampers close whenever the oil or gas burner stops firing. Residual heat in the boiler or furnace is thus trapped and prevented from escaping up the chimney.

The American National Standards Institute (ANSI) and Underwriters Laboratory (UL) have both drawn up specifications and criteria for making breeching damper installations. Since there is an element of safety involved, these criteria should be closely followed in planning damper installations.

12 *Waste-burning boilers and furnaces.* In many nonresidential buildings a great amount of combustible waste is generated. Historically, these waste products have been largely discarded even though cost has been incurred in the process of doing so.

Boilers and furnaces are available which can receive and burn such waste materials even though they are designed primarily to burn a fossil fuel of one or more types. When coal is the fuel, waste materials can usually be consumed with little or no modification required.

When gas or oil is the primary fuel, modifications to the firebox and combustion chamber will be required, or a separate combustion chamber, mounted alongside the boiler or furnace, may be necessary.

When provisions are made to burn waste materials, the opportunity to burn firewood, a renewable source of energy, is thus presented. By these means, our nonrenewable sources of energy, coal, gas, and oil may be conserved.

13 *Use cold outside air for refrigeration.* The use of outside air for cooling in HVAC systems has been standard practice for decades, and in the interests of energy conservation, this practice must continue. However, with respect to commercial refrigeration practices, the use of indirect outside air in very cold winter weather has never become popular, and to a great extent has not even been attempted.

This nation is loaded with refrigerated spaces

maintained at 34 to 45°F for food storage and many other purposes. The majority of such spaces (reach-in coolers, walk-in coolers, food processing rooms, etc.) are located in the areas of the world where winter temperatures routinely stay between 20 and 30°F or below for weeks and months at a time. Just as routinely in these areas, refrigerating effect is achieved through the use of mechanical refrigeration systems which consume great quantities of energy.

This ridiculous situation should be corrected through the use of outside air coils with large-diameter tubes (1 1/4 to 2 in.) through which frigid outside air could be circulated. These coils with fans and controls could be located in the refrigerated spaces alongside the regular refrigerating equipment that is needed when outside air temperatures are too high for cooling without mechanical refrigeration.

The initial cost of equipment is, of course, appreciably higher, but consider the energy savings during those hundreds of hours each winter when outside air temperatures are low. Surely the energy cost savings would, in a short time, repay the extra cost of equipment; and all the while energy is being conserved.

It is certainly possible that with our best air filtration and purification systems in use, outside air could be cleaned and circulated directly into and through the refrigerated spaces. Local public health authorities might object to this, but they could certainly find no fault with the process when a coil is used.

14 *Solar energy.* The capture and use of solar energy for heating and cooling processes has been so thoroughly documented so repetitively that further discussion seems pointless. It is mentioned here primarily for thoroughness in our checklist of energy conservative measures. However, the reader is strongly urged, in all HVAC design projects with which he or she may be concerned, to consider the possibility of utilizing equipment to capture the sun's energy in new and imaginative ways. Remember that solar collecting, storing, and utilizing equipment, like insulation, in the long run does not cost—it pays.

15 *Night setback.* HVAC engineers have for many decades debated the question of the advisability of reducing space temperatures during nighttime hours and unoccupied hours. In residences, there is a question as to whether night setback (from 10:00 P.M. to 6:00 A.M.) is worthwhile. In an elementary school building where night setback runs from 2:00 P.M. until the following 6:00 A.M. (16 hours) there can be no question of the value of night setback.

Clock thermostats and programmed computer control systems can very easily provide the necessary operation. Room thermostats are available equipped with an override button so that night setback for a given room or zone may be manually circumvented for an evening meeting or other purpose.

The possibility of night setback should be considered thoroughly for every building project. The U.S. Department of Energy in its Bulletin DOE/OPA-0022 (2-78) suggests that overall heating costs may be reduced by the percentages shown in fig. 12-1 for the listed cities when setback is 5 or 10°F.

16 *Combined hot water heating and domestic water heating systems.* In large buildings where both hot water for space heating and domestic hot water (for the plumbing system) are widely distributed throughout a building, an opportunity for cost savings and energy reductions exists.

By drawing 140°F or cooler water for heating purposes from the domestic hot water piping, an appreciable reduction in the lineal feet of insulated hot water piping can result. Water at 140°F or even much less can be easily utilized for space-heating purposes.

The reduced length of pipe, even though somewhat larger than needed for domestic hot water only, can effectuate great reduction in pipe heat loss. In some cases, heat lost from such piping does help to heat the building and overall energy reduction may not be great.

If the building is mechanically cooled and heated simultaneously, an appreciable reduction may result.

17 *Proper automatic temperature controls.* In many older buildings and some not so old, existing temperature control instruments, and the systems of which they are a part, are defective, out of adjustment or just plain misapplied. It is surprising how much improvement in operation and energy conservation can result from an open-minded, imaginative survey by a highly qualified temperature control engineer.

Such a survey can ascertain that controls in use are properly applied and that they are functioning properly. Even if tune-up and adjustment is all that is done, the benefits can exceed any cost involved many times over. Two routine checks that should always be made at this time are:

a Check and balance air supply quantities at all supply grilles, registers, and diffusers.

Figure 12-1 Heating costs saved with nighttime setback.

City	Approximate percentage saved with 8-hour nighttime setback of—	
	5°F	10°F
Atlanta, GA	11	15
Boston, MA	7	11
Buffalo, NY	6	10
Chicago, IL	7	11
Cincinnati, OH	8	12
Cleveland, OH	8	12
Columbus, OH	7	11
Dallas, TX	11	15
Denver, CO	7	11
Des Moines, IA	7	11
Detroit, MI	7	11
Kansas City, MO	8	12
Los Angeles, CA	12	16
Louisville, KY	9	13
Madison, WI	5	9
Miami, FL	12	18
Milwaukee, WI	6	10
Minneapolis, MN	5	9
New York, NY	8	12
Omaha, NE	7	11
Philadelphia, PA	8	12
Pittsburgh, PA	7	11
Portland, OR	9	13
Salt Lake City, UT	7	11
San Francisco, CA	10	14
Seattle, WA	8	12
St. Louis, MO	8	12
Syracuse, NY	7	11
Washington, DC	9	13

From U.S. Department of Energy bulletin DOE/OPA-0022 (2-78).

b Check and adjust building static pressure as compared to outdoor atmospheric pressure.

A negative pressure inside a building means that whenever a door or window is opened, a rush of outdoor air will enter. An effort should be made to moderate the cause, whatever it may be, of the negative pressure (exhaust fans, chimney effect, etc.).

If building static pressure is excessively high, more than 0.05 to 0.08 in. WG above atmospheric pressure, the cause should be sought. Excessive pressure is usually the result of too much outdoor air being pumped into the building by its HVAC systems. Too much outside air represents high operating costs in either cold or hot weather.

18 *Existing HVAC equipment.* Building owners rarely raise the question of the quality and efficiency of their existing HVAC equipment—boilers, fuel burners, refrigerating machines, water chillers, air conditioners, and so on. However, the question should be raised, because new equipment, designed and manufactured with regard to our attempts to conserve energy, may be appreciably more efficient.

What building owner would not be happy to exchange old equipment for new if the new will pay for itself in terms of energy cost reductions in a period of 5 to 7 years? The immediate benefit is, of course, a reduced drain on our energy reserves.

At the very least, in the process of comparing the feasibility of new equipment, the old equipment will probably be checked, adjusted, and tested for peak operating efficiency. This process alone should result in energy savings.

19 *Eliminate gas pilot lights.* For many, many years efforts have been made to contrive an electric igniter for gas heating and cooking equipment which would make possible the elimination of the continuous gas pilot. Such pilots have been standard equipment on most gas cooking equipment and on almost all heating furnaces and boilers of 3000 MBH or less gross output capacity.

The waste involved in using continuous pilots has been tremendous; one authority estimates that in some installations more than half the gas consumed is burned in the continuous pilot. Of this pilot consumption a very high percentage represents waste.

It seems that electric pilot problems have been solved; dependable electric pilots to light the gas are now available. One manufacturer (Controlyne, Inc., 16 Church Street, Montclair, NJ 07042) uses a silicon carbide igniter with a life expectancy of 250,000 ignitions.

20 *Engine drives.* Whenever feasible, the use of gas engines or diesel engines to drive HVAC equipment instead of electric motors should be seriously considered. The cost of required operating energy is usually much less with natural gas, for example, than with electricity—often only half as much. Even considering the greater maintenance costs with an engine, the overall cost can be appreciably less.

However, the point to be considered is that energy is conserved. The same general thought may apply to the use of steam turbine drives when steam is available.

It is true that the HVAC industry is not properly geared to the use of engines instead of electric motors; and the opportunities to use engines are comparatively rare. However, there are many engines in use in this country today driving refrigeration compressors, pumps, and fans.

21 *Building automation systems.* Until recently, computerized building automation systems, described elsewhere in this text, were applicable only to the largest buildings. This is no longer true; systems are now available that are very practical and feasible for buildings as small as 30,000 ft^2 of floor space.

These automation systems can provide very superior control of all the functions of a building, including HVAC control, with definite energy savings. This new generation of microprocessor-based systems should certainly be considered for buildings of 30,000 or more square feet.

22 *Run HVAC fans at slow speed in winter.* Much more often than not, the HVAC system fans that supply air for cooling in summer also circulate the air needed in winter for heating purposes. However, usually much less air is required for heating than is required for cooling—often 50% less.

With constant volume (CV) systems (which constitute a large majority of existing HVAC systems today) there is a very substantial waste of energy in circulating an unnecessarily large amount of air in winter. The fans should somehow be slowed down in winter.

This may be accomplished with two-speed fan motors (usually 1800 rpm/900 rpm), with frequency inverters, or other devices, as described elsewhere in this text.

23 *Ventilate hot attics and similar spaces.* Spaces such as attics and some furred spaces above ceilings reach temperatures as high as 130°F on hot summer days. The heat flow through the ceilings below these spaces is then 2.5 times as great as it would be if such spaces were ventilated with outside air. It would be even better if waste building air could be used for this purpose.

12-3 CONSERVATION MEASURES: PLUMBING SYSTEMS

The plumbing systems of today's modern building do not consume the great quantities of energy that HVAC systems and lighting systems do, so the opportunities for energy use reductions are more limited. These opportunities are involved in two general ways: use of less hot water and use of less cold water.

Hot Water Energy Reduction Possibilities

1 *Reduce circulating hot water (HW) temperatures.* Where hot water piping must be kept hot during all occupied hours, it is usually possible to reduce HW temperatures from the standard 140°F to around 110°F. This will minimize heat loss from the HW piping. The 110°F temperature is adequate for handwashing and showering and many other uses.

2 *Eliminate HW systems.* In many buildings, such as schools, offices, and public rest rooms, only cold water is required. Little hardship is suffered if only cold water is made available. In many existing buildings of this type, the HW system can be deactivated.

3 *Use small localized water heaters.* Where a long length of HW piping and recirculating piping must extend to a remote point of HW use, it may be more efficient and less costly to install a small, well-insulated heater at the point of usage than to use a central HW system.

Also, small localized HW boosters may be effectively used to boost HW temperatures from 110°F or 140°F when higher temperatures are required for dishwashing, clothes washing, and so on.

4 *Use better insulation.* Historically, the type and amount of insulation used on water heaters and HW piping have left much to be desired. Typically, the maintenance of pipe insulation has been very poor. Why should a high-temperature vessel such as a water heater or hot water storage tank use only 2 or 3 in. of insulation? Surely 5 or 6 in. of covering with a conductivity k of 0.25 or better can be easily justified today.

5 *Limit use of electricity for water heating.* The use of electricity for resistance heating of water and other media must continually be questioned. When fossil fuels, including coal, are used in the electric power generating process, and when 80% of the heat energy in those fuels is wasted in the generation and distribution process (the usual case), the decision to use electricity for resistance water heating should always be given close scrutiny. Fossil-fuel-fired water heaters waste only 20 to 25% of fuel energy.

6 *Use small HW storage tanks.* In designing a water heating and circulating system, the designer must sometimes make an arbitrary decision, choosing between a small water heater with a large hot water storage tank, or a large water heater (high recovery rate) with a small HW storage tank. Either system can provide adequate hot water.

It is highly recommended here that the latter choice be made in most cases. There are many reasons why a larger heater with a smaller tank is the better choice—including lower first cost and a lower space requirement. It also has the advantage of energy efficiency resulting from less heat loss from the tank and interconnecting piping.

When a smaller tank is used, the selection of a well-insulated factory-made, assembled, and tested water heater unit complete with tank is possible; this has many advantages. The use of hot water storage tanks mounted separate from their heaters is expensive and energy wasteful.

7 *Use flue dampers.* With fossil-fuel-fired water heaters, the use of automatic flue dampers installed in the breeching between a water heater and its chimney is highly recommended for its ability to limit off-cycle heat loss up the chimney—as mentioned elsewhere in this chapter. Such damper installations must be carefully made to comply with all safety requirements.

8 *Use hot water flow limiters.* On such devices as showers (for bathing) flow-limiting devices should always be utilized. Many fancy, expensive shower heads with normal water pressure supplied will throw a shower of 4 to 7 gpm. This is wasteful and unnecessary. There are many good shower heads available that will supply a perfectly adequate shower pattern with 1.5 to 2 gpm flowing. This can save great quantities of both cold and hot water in schools with gymnasiums etc.

A simple flow limiter fitting installed just ahead of the shower head will guarantee that the shower water flow rate will not exceed the 1.5 or 2.0 gpm flow rate desired—no matter how the shower control valve is set, or how high the water supply pressure may rise. Hot water usage can thus be substantially reduced.

Reduce Cold Water Usage

The reduction in energy use is not as dramatic when cold water use reduction is achieved as when hot water is conserved; however, considerable amounts of energy are expended in the process and treatment of cold water. The greatest expenditure is in pumping the water—several times, but much energy is also required in the processes of filtration, flocculation, chlorination, fluoridation, and so on.

The most productive steps in energy conservation for the water consumer to take are:

1 *Consume less water*
2 Reuse water as much as possible

Reductions in water use may be achieved through such measures as:

1 Using "water-saver" water closets. These may use 3 gal per flush instead of the usual 5 gal per flush.
2 Use shower limiters as mentioned above.
3 Use special water-saver lavatory faucets in nonresidential buildings. (*Note:* Some "self-closing" faucets waste more water than they save.

Examine a manufacturer's use test results before making a selection.)

4 Do not use "automatic flushing" of plumbing fixtures (mainly urinals) during unoccupied hours. It is probably impossible to justify automatic flushing at any time.

The reuse of building waste water has much promise for water conservation as well as energy savings. In a reuse system, the drainage from "soil"-type plumbing fixtures such as water closets and urinals is kept separate from the effluent from other fixtures. The soil drainage and kitchen drainage is wasted directly to the sanitary sewer. All other drainage, including some storm drainage, is directed to a large storage tank. This water is often termed *gray water*, while soil drainage is called *black water*.

From the storage tank the gray water is pumped through a filter, a chlorinator, and then through supply piping leading to water closets and urinals throughout the building. If the water level in the tank falls too low, fresh potable water is automatically added to the tank. When the tank overflows, the excess drains away to the sewer.

12-4 CONSERVATION MEASURES: ELECTRICAL SYSTEMS

A great opportunity exists for reduction in power consumption in building electrical systems.

Reduce Lighting Levels

For many decades, the recommended levels of illumination offered by various lighting authorities have climbed steadily and inexorably. All the while our rate of power usage followed the same curve steeply upward.

The energy shortage finally brought us to our senses and the illumination-level curve is now bending downward without appreciable detriment to our visual performance.

The use of *task-ambient* lighting systems is one useful technique for reducing overall power for lighting. Here the general level of illumination is greatly reduced, with emphasis lighting used to produce high levels of light where visual tasks are being performed.

One very effective method of reducing illumination levels when these have gotten out of hand, and when preheat or rapid-start series-sequenced fluorescent lamps are in use, is to install a nonluminous substitute device. These substitute devices are similar in configuration to a standard lamp with the same bi-pin socket arrangement, but they produce no light.

Simply removing one lamp of a pair may have a deleterious effect on the accompanying ballast. The use of the substitute device will provide ballast protection while permitting lighting-level reductions and proportionate power consumption reductions. If the resulting level of illumination is inadequate for difficult seeing tasks, task lighting assistance may be added with a substantial net reduction in power still remaining.

Reducing lighting levels also requires the imaginative use of less light for advertising purposes. Some efforts have been made nationwide to reduce the amount of promotional display lighting, but these efforts have not been effective. Legislation may be required to achieve this.

Use More Efficient Sources of Light

As has been shown previously and discussed again in chap. 20 the amount of light produced per watt of power consumed varies widely. The more efficient sources of light can produce many times more lumens per watt than can less efficient sources, such as incandescent lamps. Lighting designs of necessity must abandon use of inefficient sources of light even though their initial cost is less and their aesthetic appeal may be greater.

Also, it must be realized that with a given efficient light source, efficacy is lost through the use of poorly designed luminaires (light fixtures) with low coefficients of utilization (CU). Many luminaires in use today, and in continuous manufacture, can deliver only 25 to 35% of the light produced

to the work plane where light is required. Consider the difference in power consumption if the CU is higher and 55 to 65% is delivered to the work plane.

Use Photocell Control of Night Lights

There are many types of outside lights and some inside lights that need to be switched on at dusk and off the following morning. Quite often a time clock, working through a magnetic contactor, switches large banks of lamps or as few as one individual lamp. These may be floodlights, spotlights, area lights, street lights, and so on.

These time clocks have a frequent need to be reset for on and off patterns. The ever-changing incidence of sun-up and sundown, together with semiannual changes from standard time to daylight-saving time, necessitate these frequent changes. More often than not, it seems, these adjustments are not made when required, and powerful lamps are left burning when they are not required—a heavy waste of electrical energy.

Very often a *photosensitive switch* may be used, to give accurate control of light patterns, which are not dependent on human memory for successful operation. Of course, when a *building automation system* is in use, a very superior pattern of lighting events can be accurately programmed on an annual basis.

Provide Illumination Control in Perimeter Areas

In almost every case, buildings must be adequately illuminated at night and on dark, gloomy days as well as on bright, sunny days. However, in many buildings, many areas are adequately lit by natural light on sunny days; these are usually the perimeter areas. Other areas, including portions of the perimeter rooms, need artificial light even on sunny days.

This means that in the future we must do a much better job of designing flexibility into our lighting control systems so that luminaires, or certain lamps in multilamp luminaires, may be switched off as much as possible. It is certainly feasible to have automatic light sensors vary light use patterns as natural light varies. Dashpot relays or other time-delay relays would be needed to prevent too-rapid cycling of lights as natural light patterns change with changing cloud patterns.

Provide Power Factor Correction

In today's modern nonresidential buildings, the use of inductive electrical power load is an ever-increasing phenomenon. Loads such as electric motors, transformers, magnetic starters and contactors, fluorescent lights, and HID (high-intensity discharge) lamps are all inductive in nature. These throw electric current out of phase with voltage, causing the current to lag the voltage timewise, and, in effect, requiring appreciably increased amperage flow to provide a given amount of electrical power.

It is probably not possible to revise our electrical loads until they are less inductive in nature. Fortunately, it is not necessary to do so, since the cure for this intolerable situation is quite simple and comparatively inexpensive. The cure involves the installation of capacitors to raise building power factor to 85 to 90% or higher.

As explained in chap. 18, the use of capacitors provides a tendency for electrical current, amperage, to *lead* its voltage. This offsets the tendency of current to *lag* voltage when inductive load is present. The result of this is to reduce the amount of lag of the building power systems. The power factor is improved, and less current is required to carry a given amount of electrical load.

Provide Individual Metering Where Possible

It is a well-established fact that where multiple tenancy exists in a given building, such as an apartment building, power consumption will be drastically reduced if each tenant pays directly for the electrical energy used.

This fact should be evident to anyone planning the electrical systems of a building, yet how frequently this obvious fact is ignored! This must not be so in the future.

12-5 BUILD BETTER BUILDINGS

The construction industry has no choice but to admit, ashamedly, that nonresidential buildings, through the decades, have been and still are being designed and constructed in a slipshod, irresponsible manner with reference to energy conservation. Until recently, it has been practically impossible to convince a design architect that the flat roof of a building should have more than a 1.5-in. thickness of insulation.

This has resulted in nearly all of our nonresidential buildings having a roof total heat flow resistance R_T of 5 to 7, not including furred ceilings, or an R_T of 8 to 10 with 3/4-in. acoustical ceilings below. These resistances should be, and through the years should have been, 30 or more. Thousands of office buildings have been built that have walls that are nearly 100% glass, with an R_T of less than 1.2.

There are many steps that may be taken to improve future building designs, and these steps must be considered for every future construction project. Some of the possible steps that may be taken are listed below.

1 Equal or exceed the recommendations of ASHRAE Standard 90-75. One recommendation of Standard 90-75 is to provide building walls, including windows and doors, that have an *overall heat transfer coefficient, U_o* that is better than a certain allowable maximum. The U_o is merely a weighted average of all the various component U coefficients of all the exposed surfaces that make up the building exterior walls.

If large areas of glass are to be used, and this must be the architect's decision, the remaining opaque wall areas must be exceedingly well insulated. If walls are not to be well insulated, windows and doors must indeed be limited in area and U coefficient.

Figure 12-2 presents a table listing suitable U_o coefficients for walls, roofs, and floors in various situations. Adherence to these values as maxima will result in energy conservative buildings in the future. All persons of influence should work for

Figure 12-2 Overall heat transfer coefficients, U_o, for walls, roofs, and floors. (Extracted and reprinted from ASHRAE Standard 90-75, with the permission of ASHRAE.)

Types of Exposure	Annual Fahrenheit Degree Days (65°F base), thousands						
	1	2	4	6	8	10	12
Walls—detached one- and two-family dwellings	0.29	0.28	0.25	0.22	0.19	0.16	0.16
Walls—all other residential buildings not more than three stories in height	0.37	0.35	0.31	0.28	0.24	0.20	0.20
Walls—nonresidential three stories high or less	0.37	0.35	0.31	0.28	0.24	0.20	0.20
Walls—nonresidential in excess of three stories high	0.46	0.43	0.38	0.33	0.28	0.28	0.28
Roofs and ceilings	0.10	0.10*	0.092	0.076	0.06	0.06	0.06
Floors over unheated spaces	0.32	0.25	0.11†	0.08	0.08	0.08	0.08

*For 3000° days (roofs and ceilings) U_o = 0.10.

†For 5000° days (floors) U_o = 0.08.

Note: Straight-line interpolation is permissible except as noted with * and †.

the inclusion of ASHRAE 90-75 requirements in their state HVAC construction codes.

Compliance with ASHRAE 90-75 recommendations will, in general, result in smaller glass areas in buildings, better-quality windows of double- and triple-pane arrangements, and more and better insulation in walls, roofs, and floors.

2 Reduce infiltration. The losses resulting from unwanted infiltration of outdoor air into a building in both winter and summer are much greater than is generally realized. It is not at all unusual for infiltration losses in winter for a given building to equal 30% or more of the total heat loss.

Much can be done about this situation, and fortunately the payback of any funds expended in this effort is quickly accomplished in terms of energy cost reduction. Some steps that may be taken to reduce infiltration are listed below.

a *Improve window quality.* Chapter 4 gives information on outdoor air infiltration rates for various types of windows. Some of these are very good and permit almost no infiltration, even when the air pressure difference between OA and RA is comparatively high. The building owner whose windows permit as much as 100 cfh of infiltration per foot of operating window crack is really paying for new and better windows over and over without getting them.

Sometimes weatherstripping and gasketing can be applied with great benefit at very little cost. However, this is not always possible or practical.

Storm windows applied outside poor-quality, leaky windows can achieve a substantial reduction in infiltration—perhaps 50% in the usual installation. However, a really good, carefully gasketed storm window can reduce infiltration to almost zero. At the same time the U coefficient may be reduced from 1.13 to 0.57 or less. Storm sash applied over the best-quality windows, of course, reduces infiltration very little.

Before purchasing windows for a new building, or for replacement in an older building, manufacturers' performance data should be carefully compared. The initial cost of windows, although important, should be of secondary consideration compared to infiltration performance.

Of course, it is vitally important that all windows fit tightly in their wall openings, that perimeter caulking is in excellent condition, and that caulking is properly maintained.

b *Improve outside door quality.* In many commercial establishments that cater to the general public, building owners and operators feel that doors should be easy to operate. An older person loaded with packages must still be able to get in and out through doors. Properly weatherstripped doors are undoubtedly more difficult to open and close.

Gasketing with resilient stripping secured to the door stops (surfaces against which doors close) on the lock side and top of a door are very effective and need not offer much resistance to door operation. The same material may be applied effectively to the edge of the door on the hinge side. However, a problem arises at the threshold, and the most effective treatment here is the resilient strip set into the threshold or secured to the door bottom; this does increase operating resistance.

A problem also arises in commercial establishments where double doors are used. Often, in this case, the fixed vertical door stile between the two doors is intentionally omitted, resulting in a very substantial vertical crack between the doors. This crack is often as wide as 1/8 to 1/4 in. and great quantities of outdoor air (OA) can enter. This is an intolerable situation and represents a practice that must be eliminated in the future. The vertical stile should be installed, and its door stop surfaces should be gasketed (see fig. 4-16).

c *Reduce atmospheric pressure differential between OA and RA.* Of course, infiltration will always be in direct proportion to the difference between total pressure outdoors and static pressure indoors. The building designer has considerable control over this differential.

In tall buildings of three stories or more, the wintertime chimney effect is considerable. It creates a negative pressure in the lower half of the building which greatly increases infiltration rates. Chimney effect can be appreciably reduced by sealing all openings in each floor of the building, by using elevator lobbies on each floor, and so on, as discussed in art. 5-8.

Building pressure differential can also be controlled through a balanced use of air exhaust from a building and air supply into the building. It is possible in most good-quality buildings to charge tempered outside air into the building until it has a positive static pressure related to atmospheric pressure.

This may require great quantities of OA, and to heat or cool these quantities may consume as much energy as is required to condition infiltration air. However, when outside air is all brought in at one point, some possibilities are presented. The outside air may be heated in cold weather with waste heat rejected from refrigeration machine condensers. Or it may be tempered by the heat in air that is being exhausted. A heat pump could extract heat from building wastewater and pump it into the outside airstream.

By one or two established processes, heat can be extracted from the lighting fixtures of a building, and utilized for tempering outside air.

d *Supply outside air directly to points of heavy air exhaust.* Outside air may be tempered, as described above, and supplied under very slight pressure to areas of a building where air is being removed or exhausted. These areas include kitchens, toilet rooms, locker rooms, natatoriums, fireplaces, and so on (see fig. 12-5). In many such places, the outside air supply may not need cooling in summer, as in commercial kitchens, or heating in winter. Energy savings are possible, then, and building infiltration will be minimized.

3 *Install automatic shutters on windows.* The use of automatically positioned, intelligently controlled, tightly fitting louvers or shutters on building windows has great potential for conserving energy in buildings during both winter and summer.

Many types have been utilized, ranging from heavy masonry or simulated masonry slabs to light metal slats which can be manually or automatically positioned. These may be mounted indoors or outdoors and may be mounted on horizontal or vertical axes of rotation. It is more usual for exterior mounting on horizontal axes to be utilized.

A shutter of the roll-down type is shown in fig. 12-3. As may be seen, this shutter, manufactured by Pease Company of New Castle, Indiana, is neat and close fitting and is able to provide very tight closure. Shutters of this type when fully closed can provide window insulation, a bar against wind infiltration, and a complete blockage against direct solar transmission. They can aid

Figure 12-3 Roll-down-type window shutter. (Photo by courtesy of Pease Company of Indiana, Ever-Strait Division-Rolling Shutters, New Castle, Ind.)

materially in holding summer heat out and winter heat in.

They can be fully closed during unoccupied hours (more than half the time) and partially open during occupied hours. They can be positioned to intercept the sun's rays, while admitting light, in summer, and can admit all of the sun's rays in winter.

In large buildings with computerized control, louver and shutter positioning may be programmed on an annual basis so that maximum benefit may be achieved at all times with no human supervision required. In smaller buildings a programmable clock control system may be provided at small cost.

Three big problems involved with louver and shutter use are appearance, maintenance, and initial cost. The cost problem is only a temporary one that is self-eliminating. The savings in energy, if properly maximized by optimum operation, can return the initial cost in only a few years.

Appearance is a highly subjective consideration and presents an interesting challenge to building designers to incorporate louvers and shutters with all their many benefits while presenting a facade that is acceptable. It certainly is possible that after sufficient exposure and conditioning, people may fully accept and even prefer the appearance that louver and shutters present. Many people prefer the appearance of the old-fashioned wooden shutter on homes even though they perform no function at all.

Louvers and shutters will always require a certain amount of maintenance, but the cost of this will be very small compared to the energy cost saving they can provide. As to initial cost, it is entirely possible that louvers and shutters properly controlled can reduce the cost of HVAC systems enough to offset all or most of the initial cost of their installations.

4 *Use louver screen on windows.* Louver or shade screen is a form of insect screen that may be used on windows. It is constructed of very fine metal slats spaced closely enough together to provide a screen against insects. The metal slats, which are about 0.05 in. wide and 0.005 in. thick, are set horizontally and are sloped downward at their outer edge—much like a venetian blind that is partially open (see fig. 5-16).

There are approximately 17 to 20 slats per inch, and the screen is mounted outside the window glass, like an insect screen. The sun angling down from above cannot pass directly through the screen, although visibility outward through the screen is good.

This shade screen can reject about 80% of the sun's direct radiation. Unfortunately, it does this in winter as well as summer. However, the advantage in summer greatly outweighs the wintertime disadvantage from the standpoint of energy consumption.

5 *Install better vapor barriers.* In chap. 4 the need for vapor barriers in buildings, especially in walls, ceilings, and floors, was discussed. The construction industry has done a miserable job of meeting this need, and there is much room for improvement in the future.

Building elements need to be very well insulated throughout. However, without adequate vapor barrier protection, insulation can be soaked with water resulting from vapor condensation in the insulation. Wet insulation can be worse than no insulation, and can cause much secondary damage to a building.

We must start thinking of continuous vapor barrier coverage of walls, ceilings, and floors. If we do a good job of vapor sealing buildings, a great secondary benefit will result. We will see an important reduction in the infiltration of outdoor air which comes right through exterior walls, especially around window and door openings, at sill plates in frame construction, and around duplex electrical receptacles in outside walls.

6 *Use sunscreen films on windows.* The use of an aluminized polyester film on the interior of exterior glass areas can result in considerable reduction in energy consumption in a building with year-round conditioning. It does this by reducing solar transmission through windows as much as 75%; it also reduces glare from a sunlit exterior by 82% and screens out 98% of the sun's ultraviolet rays (according to one manufacturer).

Unfortunately, it reduces solar transmission in winter when such heat is needed. However, its promoters state that sunscreen reduces radiant heat transfer outward in winter, and that this benefit is greater than the loss of solar input from the exterior in winter. This may or may not be,

but there is no doubt that the overall, year-round benefit is very substantial, and sunscreen returns its cost very quickly in terms of reduced operating power consumption. A secondary benefit is that with sunscreen applied, the window U coefficient for single glass may be reduced from 1.13 to as low as 0.68 in winter.

12-6 IMPROVE BUILDING OPERATION

The most intelligent planning and careful construction of a building can be offset by unintelligent operation of the building by its owner or occupants. The following is a listing of some of the practices that should be utilized in keeping energy consumption to a minimum.

1 Turn off lights when not in use. During lunch periods, before starting time in the morning, after quitting time in the evening, and at all possible times lights should be off. Frequent switching of lights, especially fluorescent lights, may result in shorter lamp life and greater lamp cost; however, power will be saved, and more important, energy will be conserved.

2 Turn off outside air supply systems during unoccupied periods. This is obvious and needs no discussion.

3 Turn off exhaust fans during unoccupied periods; this will save fan operating cost, and under many conditions will reduce the energy required to heat or cool the outside air that enters when building air is exhausted. During periods of light occupancy, fans such as toilet exhaust fans can be controlled to operate intermittently—such as for 5 min or more every half hour. Or such fans may be wired to operate 5 min or so whenever a toilet room door is opened.

4 Precool buildings in summer, when outside air conditions are proper, by circulating large quantities of cool night air. Such a ventilating system would need to be under the supervisory control of an "enthalpy" controller to be certain that the "total heat" of the outside air is low enough. Overall operation should probably be manual.

5 Turn off water heaters and hot water recirculating pumps during unoccupied periods.

6 Manually turn off lights in perimeter areas whenever natural light is adequate. Natural light with localized "task" lighting may be adequate to permit switching off systems of general illumination.

7 In winter, close off all inactive chimneys and other gravity stack devices serving no useful purpose.

8 Minimize elevator operations by requesting that all personnel walk down stairways when descending one or two stories in tall buildings. Consideration should be given to permitting elevator cars to remain where they stop until called for—instead of always returning to the top or bottom of their shafts.

9 Have a computerized energy use survey conducted periodically by experts especially trained and equipped for studying possibilities of energy use reductions.

10 Revise ventilating codes. Building owners and operators, as well as anyone else who is in position to bring any pressure to bear, should work with state officials and members of state legislatures to seek revisions to state ventilating codes. Most state ventilating codes were drawn decades ago when energy was cheap and thought to be plentiful.

These codes are often archaic, unrealistic, and obsolete; they place requirements and constraints on HVAC designers which can only result in tremendous waste of energy. Preceding chapters have sought to demonstrate how great is the heating and cooling load resulting from the introduction of outside air for ventilation.

It is very difficult to know how much outside air is really required in various building situations. Those well-meaning but perhaps untrained persons who have written most of our state and local ventilating codes have apparently prescribed greater quantities of outside air than necessary in order to be certain that enough ventilation is provided, and because to do so did not bear the importance and adverse effect that is felt in our energy-short situation today.

It is surely true that many ventilating codes require much more outside air than is really necessary. For example, in Massachusetts the minimum outside air quantity required in most cases is 25% of total circulated air volume. Also, the HVAC

industry itself has been remiss in this regard. One very popular system is the high-velocity induction system described in chap. 11. This system operates at all times with about 20% outside air.

Of appreciable help in this problem is the guidance offered by ASHRAE Standard 62-73, which is discussed more extensively in chap. 13. This standard gives detailed minimum and recommended requirements for ventilation for various specific types of building spaces. It is this author's recommendation that the "minimum" quantities set forth in ASHRAE Standard 62-73 be the basis for writing new ventilating codes and rewriting existing codes.

In the final analysis, the use of outside air by building operators will be predicated on two considerations: the need to control odors in a building, and the quality of available outdoor air. Only the building operator is able to judge his need for ventilation. As long as some conservative minimum is met, the remainder of the problem should be left in the hands of the operator. Ventilating codes should be written on this basis.

12-7 HEAT RECOVERY METHODS AND EQUIPMENT

There is very little new in the business of recovering waste heat from building mechanical and electrical systems and processes. In years past, the techniques have been known, but the incentives to utilize them have apparently been inadequate. Now, the incentives are surely present and results should be meaningful in the future. The U.S. federal government is offering substantial tax concessions for those who purchase and install recovery systems. The energy shortage and the ever-escalating cost of energy also provide real incentives toward recovery systems.

A checklist of some of the many types of energy recovery equipment follows:

1 Heat pipes
2 Thermal wheels
3 Runaround coils
4 Plate heat exchangers
5 Tubular heat exchangers

6 Radiation or annular heat exchangers
7 Gas-to-liquid heat exchangers
   a Waste heat boilers
   b Gas turbine exhaust exchangers
   c Reciprocating engine exhaust exchangers
   d Incinerator discharge exchangers
8 Heat pumps
   a On building wastewater
   b On solar heat storage systems (when below 85°F)
   c On heat from lights and appliances

Space limitations permit discussion of only a few of the systems listed above.

12-8 HEAT PIPES

A heat pipe is a heat exchange device which consists of a sealed metal pipe, with a porous wick type of lining, into which a measured amount of a volatile fluid is charged. Assemblies of heat pipe, as shown in fig. 12-4, may be utilized to exchange sensible heat from a stream of comparatively high temperature gas, such as air, to a second stream of lower-temperature gas. Heat pipes may also be used to exchange heat from and to many different media, including liquid to gas, gas to liquid, and liquid to liquid.

The lining of a heat pipe may be selected from a wide range of materials from porous ceramics, to fiber wicking, to wire screen wicking, and may even in some cases be omitted completely. To a great extent the heat exchange capacity depends on the porosity of the wicking and its capillarity. The velocity with which the heat exchange liquid flows through the wicking depends greatly on the position of the pipe. The vertical position with the evaporation end at the bottom gives greatest capacity since gravity aids the liquid flow through the wicking.

In operation, the high-temperature medium, carrying waste heat, passes over and in contact with the evaporation end of the pipe. The fluid at this end is vaporized by the heat, and the vapor flows through the center of the pipe to the con-

densation end. Here the comparatively lower temperature of the pipe and the flowing medium around it cause the vapor to condense on the inner surfaces of the pipe and its wicking. The condensed liquid then flows through the wicking back to the evaporation end.

The fluid inside the pipe may be any noncorrosive fluid having reasonable pressure-temperature relationships. Many fluids, including water, have been successfully utilized, but the halogenated hydrocarbons (fluorocarbons) have found greatest use.

Capacity may be increased through the use of pipes with external fins to give extended surface area. In fig. 12-4, the pipes have plain surfaces and are mounted in a nearly horizontal position. Greater capacity could be delivered if the assembly shown were rotated to a more vertical position. In some installations, provision is made to permit rotation of the pipe bundle inside the enclosure to deliver maximum capacity.

The divider sheet shown in fig. 12-4 provides support for the pipes at their midpoint, but more important, it provides separation of the two moving streams of gas and does permit some direct heat transfer.

The heat pipe can exchange only sensible heat from one gas to the other. In some buildings it is important to maintain a comparatively high level of relative humidity; when this is true, it is advantageous to exchange both sensible and latent heat from building exhaust air to incoming outside ventilation air. In this case, the heat pipe type of exchanger will not be the best choice. Other types of heat exchangers can transfer both sensible and latent heat.

Figure 12-5 shows details of a factory-made heat pipe type of heat recovery unit. It also shows how such a unit might be installed in the exhaust air and supply airstreams from and to a range hood in a commercial kitchen. So often in a restaurant kitchen, the exhaust air with its heat is thrown away into the outside atmosphere. This is bad, but to make matters worse, the cold outside air that

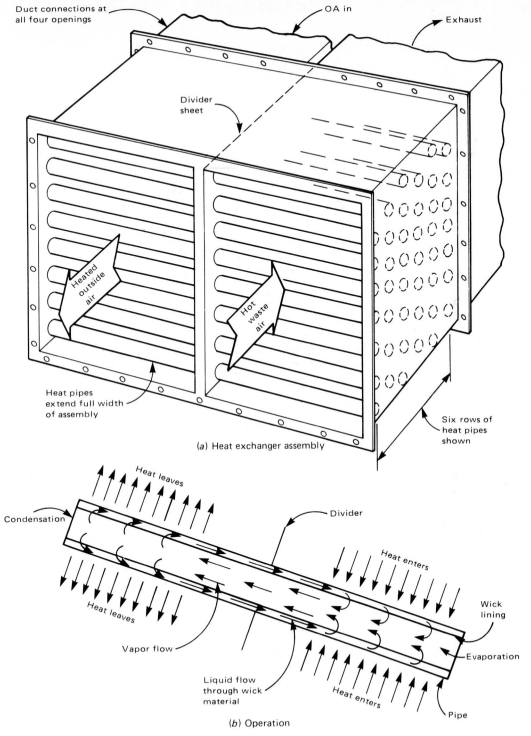

Duct connections at all four openings

OA in

Exhaust

Divider sheet

Heated outside air

Hot waste air

Heat pipes extend full width of assembly

Six rows of heat pipes shown

(a) Heat exchanger assembly

Heat leaves

Condensation

Divider

Heat enters

Heat leaves

Wick lining

Vapor flow

Evaporation

Liquid flow through wick material

Heat enters

Pipe

(b) Operation

Figure 12-4 Heat pipe details.

enters in winter to replace that which is exhausted comes in wherever it can—usually, through the front door of the restaurant, through the dining area, and then into the kitchen.

Great discomfort as well as high energy cost can result from such an unfortunate situation. Of course, the problem is equally bad in summer.

12-9 THERMAL WHEELS

A thermal wheel is a rotary wheel device used to exchange heat between two moving streams of gas, one of which contains an appreciably higher level of heat than does the other. Thermal wheels are given many names, including rotary exchangers,

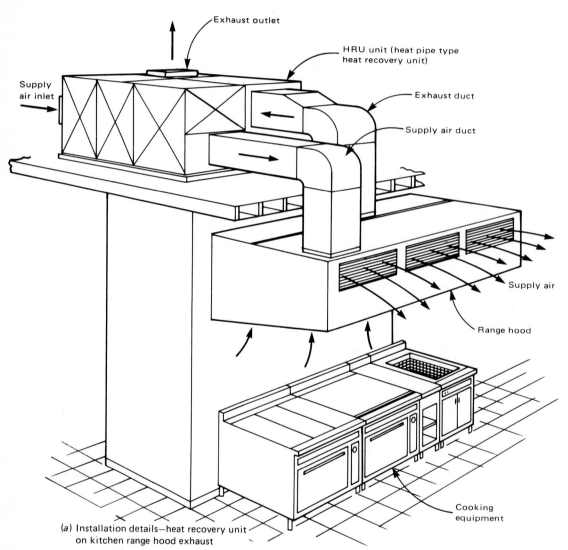

(a) Installation details—heat recovery unit on kitchen range hood exhaust

Figure 12-5 Heat pipe heat recovery unit details. (Courtesy Gaylord Industries, Inc., Wilsonville, Or.)

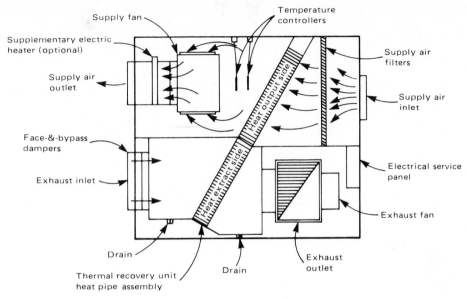

(*b*) Plan view—typical heat pipe heat recovery unit

Figure 12-5

rotating regenerators, heat wheels, and energy recovery wheels.

Thermal wheels consist of a round wheel made of a heat transfer medium encased in a supporting wheel-shaped frame. The wheel is contained in a square, sheet metal housing which supports the wheel, its electric motor, and its drive, and which provides four flanged openings for duct connections.

As shown in fig. 12-6, the wheel enclosure, or housing, provides for duct connections of building exhaust air into the wheel and out, and for outdoor air supply into the wheel and on into the building. The wheel rotates in its housing at varying speeds of 5 to 20 rpm. Sometimes the rotative speed is constant, and sometimes it is automatically varied.

It may be seen that as the air that is exhausted from a building in winter at approximately 70°F passes through the penetrable medium of one-half of the wheel, that part of the wheel achieves a temperature approaching 70°F. If outside air enters through the other half of the wheel at some lower temperature such as 20°F, the outside air will receive heat from the rotating medium which has just been warmed by the 70°F exhaust air. Most of the heat, above 20°F, in the exhaust air will be transferred to the incoming outside air which may be heated up to 60°F or so. Thus a dramatic reduction results in the heat required to temper the incoming outside air properly. Summer operation is also very effective in saving energy.

In the case just cited, the heat exchanged is all sensible heat, and some wheels are designed to do only that. However, other wheels are designed to transfer both sensible and latent heat. It all depends on the type of heat transfer medium that is carried in the wheel. There are many other types of heat recovery equipment today, such as the heat pipe. However, the thermal wheel is the only such device that can exchange both sensible and latent heat.

The thermal wheel has some complications and

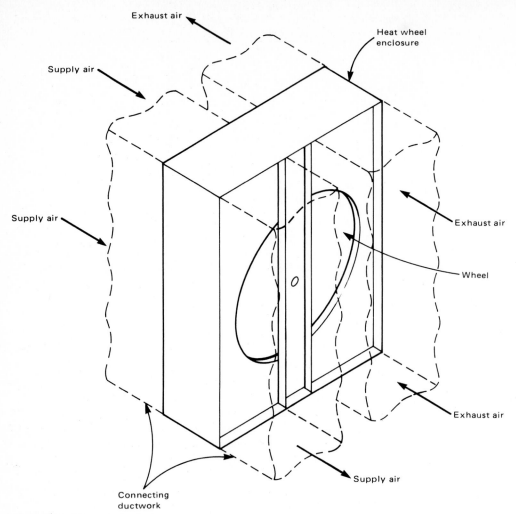

Figure 12-6 Thermal wheel.

adverse characteristics. It has a motor and drive, requires automatic controls, and so on. These can require maintenance and cause service shutdowns which do not occur with other heat exchangers. However, thermal wheels continue to lead in popularity because of their capability to exchange both sensible and latent heat.

The heat transfer medium in a thermal wheel may be made of several different materials. For simple sensible heat transfer, the medium may be of spun aluminum or stainless steel wire. This medium gives good efficiency at low cost; however, the static pressure loss through this medium is comparatively high and may be as much as 1 to 1.5 in. WG. Most manufacturers have also developed a channelized, honeycomb medium in which the gases pass through very small passageways whose length is perpendicular to the face of the wheel. This type of medium permits much lower static pressure loss and a resulting reduction in the power required to force the gases through.

In wheels designed to transfer total heat, or

enthalpy (both sensible and latent), a different medium is required. This *hygroscopic wheel* has in the past used a honeycombed asbestos material into which a hygroscopic material such as lithium chloride is impregnated. Because of its supposed carcinogenic qualities, asbestos has lost favor. A newer medium uses honeycombed metal the internal surfaces of which are coated with an hygroscopic aluminum oxide material. For very high temperature exchange, ceramic materials have been used in the heat exchange medium, but these are not required in the typical HVAC outside air tempering application.

In some thermal wheel applications the problem of cross-contamination between the exhaust and the supply airstreams is of much concern. Most wheels can limit this to 6% of the exhaust quantity. When special provision is made to minimize cross-contamination, this percentage can be reduced to 0.04%. This is accomplished primarily by minimizing the static pressure difference between the exhaust gas and the supply gas (air) but always maintaining the supply stream at a slightly higher static pressure. A *purge* section is also built into such wheels that permits the extra pressure of the supply stream to blow back into the exhaust stream any contamination that is carried over from the exhaust stream. In most HVAC applications some cross-contamination is not of much concern.

Since in summer the heat of the outside air that is introduced for ventilation is usually more than 60% latent, the importance of using an hygroscopic wheel is obvious. These wheels may be one-third more expensive than "sensible"-type wheels, but the payback of this extra cost can often be accomplished very quickly.

With hygroscopic wheels the moisture exchange is accomplished in the vapor phase without involving the liquid water phase, so no drain line for water is required. In some cases, in colder weather the outside air supply may be well below the dew point temperature of the exhaust air, and condensation or icing of the wheel may result. A drain line is then required, and a preheat coil in the entering outside airstream may also be required.

Where the entering outside airstream is possibly contaminated with tree leaves, dust, and other particulate matter, an outside air prefilter may be necessary.

Thermal wheels are available in a range of sizes from 3 to 10 ft square, with air flow rates from 600 cfm to perhaps 70,000 cfm. Heat exchange efficiencies usually fall in the range 65 to 80%. It is sometimes desirable to vary the heat exchange capacity of the wheel, and this may be done by varying the rotative speed of the wheel. This may be accurately done with the use of a frequency inverter responding to a remote control signal.

One of the biggest obstacles to the use of thermal wheels is the problem of bringing the exhaust airstream and the supply airstream together so that they can pass through the wheel. Cost considerations may require the use of one large wheel (or a few smaller wheels), and much ductwork may be required to collect and deliver large quantities of exhaust air to the wheel. Space in which to run such large ducts may not be available or may be expensive to acquire.

The cost payback time period may be excessive, in terms of energy saved. However, perhaps a longer than usual payback period can be tolerated when it is remembered that the primary goal is energy conservation, and that conservation begins immediately after installation is complete.

12-10 RUNAROUND COILS

For HVAC purposes, the runaround coil installation consists merely of two extended surface, finned coils, interconnecting piping, a circulating pump, a circulating heat transfer liquid, and necessary temperature controls. As shown in fig. 12-7, the two coils are housed in the ducts that convey exhaust air from the building and fresh outdoor air into the building for ventilation purposes.

The heat transfer liquid may be water where the danger of freeze-up is not present, although this is rare. Usually, the liquid will need to be an antifreeze solution such as glycol/water, silicone

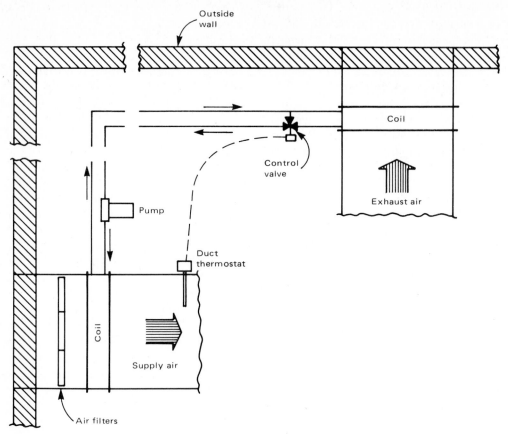

Figure 12-7 Runaround coil installation.

fluid, or a heat transfer oil. The circulating liquid receives heat in the coil that is passing the warmest air, and delivers that heat through the other coil into the lower-temperature airstream.

Thus in winter, heat will be transferred from the building exhaust air into the outside air supply. In summer, the reverse is true. In both cases, waste heat is recovered and energy is conserved.

One major advantage of the runaround system is that the two coils may be located at any convenient points in the building and may be widely separated. This can greatly minimize the cost of ductwork; the piping that, in effect, substitutes for the ductwork can be run at much less expense. This is especially true where a runaround system is installed in an existing building.

Of course, there is no way that the circulating

fluid can transfer latent heat in the form of water vapor from one airstream to the other, so this system is essentially a sensible heat transfer system. However, when one coil is operating below the dew point temperature of its airstream, the circulating liquid does pick up the latent heat of vaporization of the water that is condensed, and this heat is transferred to the other coil.

Most runaround systems will be able to transfer more than 50% of the excess heat of one airstream above the other. This efficiency may rise as high as 70% as a maximum. Of course, there is no possiblity of cross-contamination from one airstream to the other, although in HVAC practices this advantage is small.

It is possible to generalize by stating that the cost of a runaround system of equal capacity will be less than the costs of a heat pipe or thermal wheel system. However, there may be many exceptions to this. One cost benefit of the runaround system results from the use of standard products, such as finned coils, pumps, and controls, which are manufactured in great quantity for other purposes.

Automatic control may be quite simple and inexpensive. As shown in fig. 12-7, a three-way bypass valve may be installed to reduce the amount of liquid passing through the exhaust air coil. With this three-way valve positioned by an insertion type of thermostat, sensing the temperature of the air leaving the supply air coil, the supply air temperature may be controlled. The temperature of the supply may be prevented from rising too high or too low. When the danger exists of ice collecting on the exhaust air coil in winter, liquid may be made to partially bypass that coil. When the condition of the outside air supply stream is such that the building cannot benefit from the heating or cooling effect of the system, the circulating pump may be made to stop operating.

12-11 PLATE-TYPE HEAT EXCHANGERS

Plate-type heat exchangers consist of a series of square metal or glass plates assembled closely together in a mounting frame. The spaces between adjacent plates is sealed on two edges in an alternating fashion in such a manner that airflows through adjacent spaces move at an angle of 90° to each other (see fig. 12-8).

With only a thin sheet of metal between adjacent streams of moving air, heat will readily flow from one stream to the other if a temperature difference exists. In winter, when the supply air from outdoors is quite cold, moisture may condense from the exhaust airstream and provision for draining such condensation away is made. If the supply air is cold enough, ice or frost will form which may plug the space between plates. It may be necessary to preheat the supply air to prevent this.

Cross-contamination between exhaust air and supply air cannot happen in this type of exchanger. Plates are coated as necessary to provide protec-

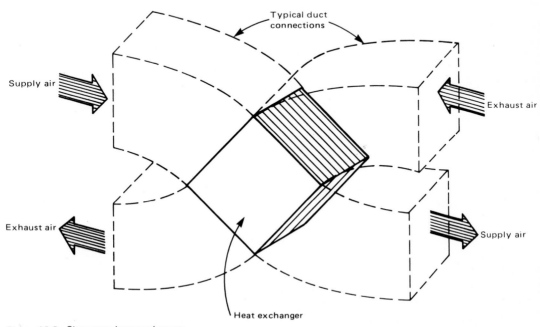

Figure 12-8 Plate-type heat exchanger.

tion against corrosion. Like the heat pipe exchanger, only sensible heat can be transferred.

The efficiency of this type of heat recuperator is slightly less than that of the thermal wheel, and its cost is also slightly less. This type of recuperator, of course, shares with the wheel and the heat pipe the costly disadvantage of requiring the two streams of air to be brought together through ductwork.

12-12 OTHER TYPES OF HEAT EXCHANGERS

As mentioned in art. 12-7, there are many other types of heat exchangers that deserve consideration. Many of these, such as the tubular and the annular exchangers, function in the same fashion as does the plate type but, of course, have greatly differing configurations.

For HVAC purposes, the exchangers already discussed in detail have the greatest possibility of suitable application.

12-13 HEAT PUMPS

As a heat recovery unit, the heat pump has tremendous potential. Most buildings, especially industrial buildings, reject great amounts of heat to the atmosphere, to sewers, and to nearby streams and bodies of water.

To recover this heat, which is often rejected at comparatively high temperatures (60 to 120°F), heat pumps are being applied in ever-increasing numbers.

To serve this type of duty, high-temperature heat pumps must be specially designed to operate at inordinately high evaporator pressures and condensing pressures. Several manufacturers have

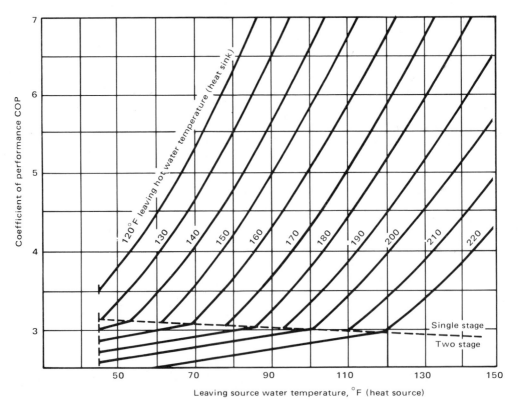

Figure 12-9 Typical performance curves—high-temperature heat pumps. (Courtesy Westinghouse Electric Corporation.)

Delivery water in   Delivery water out   Control center   Heat source water in   Heat source water out

Condenser
Evaporator

Figure 12-10 Typical high-temperature heat pump installation. (Courtesy Westinghouse Electric Corporation.)

succeeded in solving this problem effectively. A real benefit to our effort to conserve energy is the result.

Figure 12-9 shows typical performance curves under varying conditions of heat source temperature and heat delivery (heat sink) temperature. These curves show heat delivery temperatures as high as 220°F. These curves also show, for example, that rejected waste heat at 85°F could be "pumped" up to a temperature of approximately 128°F (at which it would be eminently suitable for a hot water heating system) with a coefficient of

performance (COP) of 6. For every Btu purchased in the form of electricity to drive the heat pump, 6 Btu could be delivered for useful purpose. What a wonderful way this is to save energy!

Figure 12-10 shows an installation of a high-temperature heat pump at a major eastern U.S. university, where it recovers the heat rejected from the cooling system of a computer complex. It boosts the temperature to 150°F, at which it is utilized for space heating and domestic water heating. The owner of this equipment estimates an annual fuel oil saving of 40,000 gal.

Chapter 13

Ventilation

13-1 GENERALITIES

To many health authorities in this world, the letter "V" in HVAC is by far the most important. Their concern about proper ventilation is great, and the need for setting and enforcing acceptable standards of ventilation claims a great percentage of their time. It is, of course, true that the health and safety of the public occupying public and private buildings of all types depends to a great extent on adequate ventilation.

In industrial buildings, a tremendous array of ventilation problems involved with industrial processes presents itself to the ventilating engineer. Although this author has spent many, many years wrestling with industrial types of problems, their discussion can play no part in this text. We will, of necessity, limit our discussions here to general building ventilation.

There are many reasons why buildings need ventilation, and there are differing ways in which those needs can be serviced. Some of the needs may be listed as follows:

1 To maintain suitable oxygen levels
2 To reduce CO_2 count
3 To minimize carbon monoxide levels to safe values
4 To provide adequate air movement
5 To reduce levels of airborne particulate matter (dust, etc.)
6 To minimize levels of contamination by chemicals such as sulfur oxides, hydrocarbons, photochemical oxidants, nitrous oxides, etc.
7 To provide some degree of temperature control under extreme conditions
8 To control odors

As a reason for ventilating a building, item 8 easily outweighs all the others. Control of odors in a commercial building is our biggest problem, claiming more of our time and money than perhaps all the others combined. There are many sources of odors in buildings that ideally should be met at their source for proper processing. Unfortunately, our HVAC systems are themselves at times a source of objectionable odor. Some of the other sources of odors are:

1 Cooking (onions, garlic, cabbage, etc.)
2 Toilet activities
3 Shower and locker rooms
4 Body odor (perspiration, etc.)
5 Special rooms such as natatoriums, chemistry laboratories, etc.
6 Inordinately high humidities—penetrating carpeting, furniture, etc.
7 Cleaning agents
8 Insect sprays
9 Tobacco smoking

Basically, our methods of combating odors are to dilute them with supplies of outdoor air and to remove them with exhaust ventilation processes. No building can be properly ventilated without the judicious use of both supply and exhaust ventilation. In many spaces of a building such as kitchens and toilets, it is mandatory that a slight negative pressure, compared to adjacent spaces, be maintained. A toilet room should always experience an inflow of air from its adjacent corridor whenever the corridor door is opened. For this reason, many designers hesitate to direct a supply of air into a toilet room lest that supply should, for some reason, exceed the exhaust flow from the room.

In that case, the toilet room would be pressurized, and airflow out into the corridor would occur with each door opening. Toilet exhaust fans do sometimes fail, or are switched off (perhaps to save energy).

Almost all buildings experience the unwanted infiltration of some outdoor air. We struggle to minimize this, but in too many public and private buildings this is the only ventilation system. Of course, it is much, much better to curtail infiltra-tion and to introduce the proper amounts of outside air through HVAC supply systems. In this way the outside air can be filtered, heated, cooled, humidified, or dehumidified as necessary before it is allowed to enter the building.

Ideally, enough outside air is supplied to meet ventilation requirements, both supply and exhaust, and to provide enough excess to maintain a very slightly positive pressure in the building relative to outdoor atmospheric pressure. This will help to discourage outside air infiltration.

As has been mentioned elsewhere in this text, the processing of outdoor air in both summer and winter is an expensive operation. Great quantities of energy are required. However, it must be fully realized that just as much energy is required to heat and cool outside air when it infiltrates through door and window cracks as when it is properly introduced through the HVAC system. In the latter case, we may be able to reduce the energy requirement greatly though the use of waste heat— as in a thermal wheel (see chap. 12).

Since our greatest need for building ventilation is involved with odor control, the possibility exists that outside air quantities may be reduced if odors can be controlled by means other than with outside air. This raises the subject of odor control with activated charcoal. This material has a high capability of adsorbing the airborne vapors that constitute many odors.

In this process, the odor-laden air is circulated through banks of charcoal canisters, and the odor-free air is returned to the building. Much less outside air is then required. Before planning the use of activated charcoal adsorbers, it must be determined that the chemical composition of the odor contaminants is such that the charcoal can adsorb them. *ASHRAE Handbooks* give complete information on this.

It must be realized also that in the more heavily industrialized metropolitan areas of the world, the outside air is not always fresh air and is not always suitable for ventilation purposes. ASHRAE Standard 62-73 establishes the maximum allowable concentrations of the various types of contami-

Figure 13-1 Maximum allowable contaminant concentrations for ventilation air (Reprinted from ASHRAE Standard 62-73, with the permission of ASHRAE.)

Contaminant	Annual average (arithmetic mean) $\mu g/m^3$ [†]	Short-term level (not to be exceeded more than once a year) $\mu g/m^3$ [†]	Averaging period (hr)
Particulates	60[a]	150	24
Sulfur oxides	80	400	24
Carbon monoxide	20,000	30,000	8
Photochemical oxidant	100	500	1
Hydrocarbons (not including methane)	1,800	4,000	3
Nitrogen oxides	200	500	24
Odor		Essentially unobjectionable[b]	

[a] Federal criteria for the United States by 1975.

[b] Judged unobjectionable by 60 percent of a panel of 10 untrained subjects.
The levels listed are met by ambient outdoor air in many major cities, or will be met by such outdoor air when passed through minimal air treatment systems (containing suitable combinations of heaters, coolers, humidifiers, etc., and including roughing particulate filters).
[†] Micrograms/m^3 ÷ 35.314 = micrograms/ft^3.

nant most often found in outdoor air. These criteria are presented in fig. 13-1.

Finally, it must be realized that many spaces in a building may be very satisfactorily ventilated without the use of outside air. Much energy may be saved by ventilating such spaces as toilets, shower rooms, locker rooms, and cloakrooms with air drawn from other parts of the building. This assumes that the remainder of the building is reasonably well served with outside air.

In other words, we can require the outside air to perform double duty—to ventilate the main occupied areas of a building and secondarily, to ventilate the ancillary spaces as the air is on its way out of the building.

13-2 REQUIREMENTS FOR SUPPLY VENTILATION

For general building ventilation, the amount and makeup of the supply air is calculated on two bases:

1 The amount of total air movement required
2 The amount of outside air required

The total air supply consists of the air that has been recirculated from the building, through return air ducts and so on, plus the outside air that is added to the recirculated air; it is the sum of the return air plus outside air. Total air movement is usually based on a certain cfm per person occupying a space and on the rate of air change in the space. Both requirements must be met, with the larger of these resulting air quantities controlling.

The required amount of outside air is almost always based on the number of people occupying a space—cfm of OA per person. In some cases a ventilating code will further stipulate that outside air quantities be adequate to provide a certain amount of thermal control from the standpoint of cooling.

Figure 13-2 shows recommended rates of ventilation for two different types or classes of occupied spaces in buildings. One class includes the types of

Figure 13-2 Supply air ventilation rates for two classes of rooms.

The following listed building rooms and spaces need "total" air movement at the rate of 30 cfm per occupant or 8 room air changes per hour whichever is greater. They also need outside air, as part of the total air, at the rate of 10 cfm per person. Outside air should constitute at least 7% of the total circulated air volume.

Type of room or usage	Minimum occupancy per 1000 ft^2 of floor	Type of room or usage	Minimum occupancy per 1000 ft^2 of floor
Arenas, field houses	150	School, drawing room	40
Assembly halls	150	School, kindergarten	30
Conference rooms	60	School, laboratories	30
Gymnasium, seating area	200	School, lecture hall	80
Gymnasium, playing floor	50	School, music rehearse	60
Lecture halls	150	Shopping malls	40
Library reading room	40	Theater lobby	150
Music, group rehearsal	70	Vocational instr. art	35
Residences, liv. rm. and bed rm.	5	Vocational, home ec.	25
Retail sales, basement	50	Vocational, lab's	25
Retail sales, main floor	35	Vocational, shop	20
Retail sales, upper floors	20	Waiting room, dentist,	
School auditoriums	150	doctor, employ.	
School classrooms	50	agency	40

The following listed building rooms and spaces need "total" air movement at the rate of 20 cfm per occupant or 4 air changes per hour, whichever is greater. They also need outside air, as part of the total air, at the rate of 7.5 cfm per person. Outside air should constitute at least 5% of the total circulated air volume.

Banquet halls	70	Lodge halls	120
Churches	160	Recreation rooms	70
Ballrooms	80	Residences, l.r. and b.r.	4
Dining rooms	70	Restaurants	70
Dormitories	25	School cafeterias	100
Drafting rooms and		Storage rooms	4
comm'l art studios	20	Taverns	70
General offices	15	Theater auditorium	160
Hospital bedrooms	15	Vocational school	
Hospital wardrooms	20	playrooms	70

rooms or spaces that need greater amounts of ventilation than do those rooms in the other class. For both classes of rooms two different criteria are offered: "total" air circulation and outside air supply.

For reasonable ventilation, not only must proper quantities of outside air be supplied, but a minimum rate of room air turnover must be provided. In the upper class of rooms (upper half, fig. 13-2)

a total air movement of 30 cfm per occupant or eight air changes per hour is required. Total air is merely the sum of the return air (air returned from the rooms to the HVAC unit) and the outside air. Total air = RA + OA.

One *air change* is the total removal of all air in a room and the replacement of same with other air. If this happens eight times in an hour, we have eight changes per hour—or a 7.5-min air change (one air change in 7.5 min). For example, if a room contains 7500 ft^3 volume and is ventilated with 1000 cfm of total air, it will experience eight air changes per hour:

$$\frac{1000 \text{ cfm} \times 60 \text{ min/hr}}{7500 \text{ ft}^3} = 8$$

The two separate requirements listed above will usually result in two required total air quantities. The larger of these two should be utilized. Of this total air quantity, the outside air should represent 10 cfm per room occupant. However, outside air should never be less than 7% of the total air. Usually, it will be appreciably more than 7%.

The lower class of rooms in fig. 13-2 (lower half of fig. 13-2) presents a lesser requirement for ventilation, both as to total air movement and as to outside air supply. These general requirements are for 20 cfm per person total air and 7.5 cfm per person is to be OA. As listed in fig 13-2, outside air should never be less than 5% of the total air.

For both classes of rooms, upper and lower, fig. 13-2 offers a basis for establishing the number of people in a given room for whom ventilation should be supplied. Even if the anticipated room occupancy in actual use is less than is indicated by the numerical values in fig. 13-2, the lower occupancy rate should not be used. In other words, the occupancy indicated by fig. 13-2 should be considered to be a minimum basis for design.

Example 13-1 In a school classroom:

Floor area is 25 ft $\times$ 40 ft = 1000 ft^2
Ceiling height is 10 ft

Occupancy from fig. 13-2 will be 50 students
　　　　　　　(50 people/1000 ft^2 of floor)

OA required = 50 students $\times$ 10 cfm/person
　　　　　= 500 cfm

Total air = 30 cfm/person = 50 $\times$ 30
　　　　= 1500 cfm

or

Total air = 8 air changes /hr
$$= \frac{25 \text{ ft} \times 40 \text{ ft} \times 10 \text{ ft} \times 8}{60 \text{ min/hr}}$$
= 1333.33 cfm

Use the greater total air quantity of 1500 cfm, of which 500 cfm must be OA.

Example 13-2 In a theater auditorium, floor area is 70 ft wide $\times$ 120 ft long and ceiling height is 20 ft.

occupancy (see fig. 13-2) = $\dfrac{70 \text{ ft} \times 120 \text{ ft} \times 160}{1000 \text{ ft}^2}$

= 1344 people (at 160
people/1000 ft^2
of floor)

OA required = 1344 $\times$ 7.5 cfm/
person (see fig. 13-2) = 10,080 cfm
Total air = 1344 people $\times$ 20
cfm each = 26,880 cfm

or

Total air = 4 air changes/hr
$$\frac{70 \text{ ft} \times 120 \text{ ft} \times 20 \text{ ft} \times 4 \text{ air changes/hr}}{60 \text{ min./hr}}$$
= 11,200 cfm

Use the greater total air quantity of 26,880 cfm of which 10,080 cfm must be OA.

13-3 REQUIREMENTS FOR EXHAUST VENTILATION

Any space in a building will need exhaust ventilation if within that space there is the continuous or intermittent production of gases, odors, vapors, excessive heat, or airborne particulate matter which are unpleasant or a hazard to the health of the occupants of the building. Included in these types of spaces are bathrooms, shower rooms, kitchens, laboratories, laundries, locker rooms, motion picture booths, natatoriums, wood- and metalworking shops, welding booths, wardrobes, clothes lockers, cloakrooms, toilet rooms, and any space which encloses such equipment as furnaces, forges, chemical vats and tanks, or machines.

It is important that in all such spaces a slight negative pressure is maintained relative to surrounding building areas. In most of the spaces mentioned, air will be supplied by some type of HVAC system. The exhaust system must have an air removal capacity greater than the greatest possible air supply capacity.

In most cases the HVAC designer will design for air exhaust quantities that will provide adequate room air turnover. He will then ascertain by some means that air supply quantities can never exceed this amount. Further, the designer must ascertain that it is not easily possible to switch "off" the exhaust fan while the air supply into a space continues. This, of course, could cause noxious air to spill out into adjacent spaces. Often used are electrical interlocks which automatically start an exhaust fan, if it is not already operating, whenever the HVAC supply fan is started.

In general, the amount of exhaust ventilation required in specific applications depends on the rate of production of contaminants; this can vary greatly. The following criteria will give some guidance in the establishment of exhaust air quantities:

	Cfm/ft^2 of floor	Exhaust air changes per hour
Bathrooms	2	6
Garages, repair	1	—
Garages, storage	3/4	—
Kitchens	3	—
Locker rooms	2	6
Swimming rooms	2	6
Shower rooms	2	6
Toilets	2	6
Wardrobes and cloakrooms	2	6

In this table, where both cfm/ft^2 floor and air changes per hour are listed, the *smaller* of the two resulting air quantities may govern.

Exhaust fan and duct systems that serve toilets, bathrooms, shower rooms, and swimming rooms must be kept separate from any other exhaust system in a building. Exhaust ducts of this type should be extended upward through the building roof, if possible, and should discharge into the atmosphere above the building. The point of discharge should at least be 20 ft (much more if possible) away from any outside air intake or operative window of any building.

In any exhaust ventilation system, the location of exhaust registers or grilles should be carefully selected. These should be located at points in a room farthest from points of air entrance so that, to the extent possible, the moving air sweeps across all areas of the room.

In general, exhaust registers should be located in or near the ceiling, especially when air enters the room through a low-level door louver (the usual case). In toilet rooms, however, it is good practice to locate exhaust registers at both high and low levels in a given room.

Exhaust registers should be of the *lock-louver* type, in which a louver-type shutter damper may be adjusted for proper air quantity and then locked.

Adequate provision for air entrance into an exhaust ventilated room must always be made. Toilet, shower, locker room, cloakroom, and swimming room doors must be louvered or undercut so that air can enter easily. Door louvers should be sized for 200-fpm face velocity based on total exhaust quantity. When doors are undercut, a velocity of 500 fpm under the door is satisfactory.

In nonresidential kitchens, air should not be drawn from adjacent dining rooms or any other building space. Usually, the exhaust air quantity required for kitchen range hoods, dishwasher hoods, and so on, is much too great to be satisfactorily drawn from anywhere except the outdoor atmosphere.

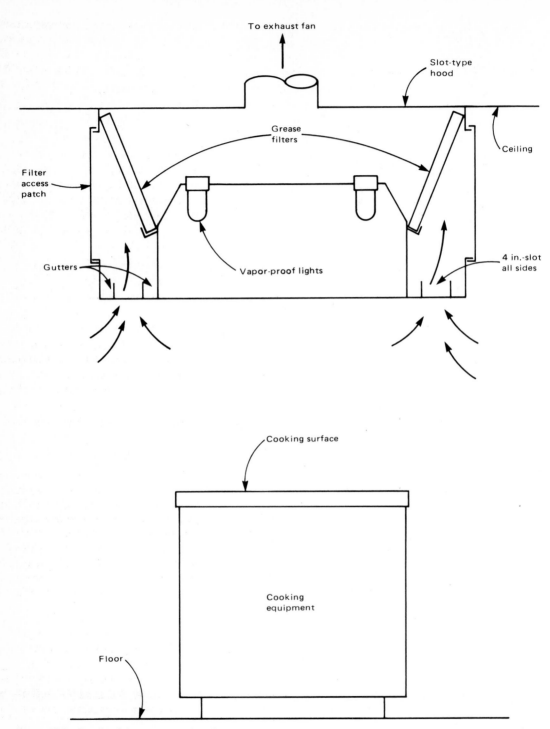

Figure 13-3 Details of slot-type range hood.

Of course, in this case the outside air will be very cold in winter and hot and humid in summer; a 100% outside air ventilating unit must be provided to filter and temper properly this great quantity of outside air. Figure 12-5 gives some details of such a ventilating unit, which, incidentally, uses heat pipes.

Most range hoods used for kitchen exhaust ventilation are of two types: *open type* and *slot type*. The open type, as the name implies, is completely open on its underside. It is usually hung directly above heavy cooking equipment (ranges, fry-tops, ovens, deep-fat fryers, steamers, and kettles), which is grouped closely together in a heavy cooking center. Any such range hood should extend at least 12 in. in all directions beyond the outer parts of all such cooking equipment.

Installed in such a fashion, range hoods become quite extensive in length and width, and the open underside of even a modestly sized (8 ft × 10 ft, for example) hood could be of 80-ft² area. To provide adequate capture of evolving smoke and vapors, a minimum face velocity with an open hood of 100 fpm must be maintained. In the case of the 80-ft² hood, the exhaust quantity is 8000 cfm (80 ft² × 100 fpm = 8000 cfm).

In winter, when the outside air is at 10°F, for example, to heat 8000 cfm to 65°F requires a tremendous amount of heat per hour:

$$BH = 8000 \times 1.08(65°F - 10°F) = 475,200$$

This heat load can be greatly reduced with the use of a "recovery" unit such as that shown in fig. 12-5. If the hot humid air leaving through the range hood is at 85°F, and the heat exchange efficiency of the recovery unit is 65%, the heat demand can be greatly reduced. The heat demand at 10°F outside air will now be

$$BH = 8000 \text{ cfm} \times 1.08(65°F - 58.75°F)$$
$$= 54,000$$

Here the air leaving the recovery unit will be 58.75°F since it can recover 65% of the temperature difference between the exhaust air (85°F) and the outside air at 10°F. (85°F – 10°F) × 0.65 = 48.75°F rise above the 10°F OA. (10°F + 48.75°F = 58.75°F.)

This heat load can be even reduced further by the use of a slot-type range hood. In this type, the entire center portion of the open bottom of the hood is blanked off with sheet metal, except that a 4-in.-wide open slot is left around the entire perimeter (see fig. 13-3).

For satisfactory capture of evolving smoke, heat, and vapor from the cooking equipment, air velocity through the 4-in. peripheral slot must be 250 fpm. If the hood is 8 ft wide and 10 ft long, as mentioned in the open hood example above, the total area of the slot opening is 11.11 ft². At a 250-fpm slot velocity, the exhaust air volume is 11.11 × 250 = 2777.5 cfm. It is obvious that reducing the exhaust volume from 8000 cfm to 2777.5 cfm will permit a great reduction in the requirement for heat to temper the makeup air. Slot-type hoods are very effective and are highly recommended. Their extra cost can be very quickly recovered in terms of energy conservation.

PROBLEMS

13-1 A lecture hall is 40 ft wide, 70 ft long, and has a 10-ft ceiling height. For how many occupants of this room should ventilation be provided? How much outside air must the HVAC system circulate? How much total air must the HVAC system circulate to meet the cfm per occupant requirement as well as the room air change requirement?

13-2 A large general office in an office building is 40 ft wide, 70 ft long, and has a 10-ft ceiling height. Find the number of occupants requiring ventilation, the amount of OA required in cfm, and the amount of total air circulation needed.

13-3 A toilet room in a nonresidential building is 20 ft wide, 30 ft long, and has a ceiling height of 9 ft. Find the exhaust air volume needed to provide the required cfm/ft² of floor and the required air changes per hour. Which of these two quantities would govern?

Chapter 14

Building Water Supply Systems

14-1 GENERALITIES

In this chapter we are concerned with the network of piping, valves, fittings, and accessories in a building that supplies water to all plumbing fixtures and water-consuming appliances. The water that is distributed through this network is called *domestic water,* which is admittedly somewhat of a misnomer.

The domestic water, both hot and cold, must be pure and suitable for human consumption. If it is suitable, it is said to be *potable.* What constitutes potability is a question receiving great attention today. Vociferous opponents of the use of fluorine in public water supplies are countered by equally vociferous proponents. Each side presents what seems to be irrefutable evidence to support its claims.

The U.S. Environmental Protection Agency has set up standards of quality which it expects each public water supply entity in the nation to meet. However, there are probably more municipal water supply utilities that cannot meet these standards than can meet them.

One problem that is found repeatedly all over the United States is an excessive level of trihalomethanes. These are carcinogenic compounds of chlorine and other chemicals. The EPA has set a standard limiting trihalomethane levels to 100 parts per billion, but in 1975 there were many major cities, including Louisville, Kentucky, Charleston, South Carolina, Columbus, Ohio, Houston, Texas, Montgomery, Alabama, and Tampa, Florida, that failed to pass this test.

The sales of pure bottled water are booming at prices which are thousands of times more expensive than "city" water. The sight of the bottled water dispenser, with its inverted glass jug, is becoming ever more common in offices and other places of business. At the residential level, the use of domestic water filters and "stills" is also becoming more common. Many writers make a strong case for the health benefits of distilled water.

There is only a little that the designers of building systems can do in the solution of this problem. Chlorinators may be added, but the methods of adding chlorine to potable water can be exactly wrong, and the advice of an expert must be sought. Electric and steam stills may be installed, and the problems involved therein are minimal.

Sometimes the plumbing piping itself contributes to the problem. If the supply water is extremely soft and perhaps acidic, this water passing through lead, copper, zinc, and asbestos piping can erode the fibers of which the pipe is made, and deliver those fibers into drinking water. One psychiatrist found an excess of copper in the tissues of schizophrenic patients at a mental hospital and traced the source to the drinking water.

Water supply facilities for buildings are of two types: public and private. Most nonresidential buildings are, of course, supplied with water from municipal water utility companies. Their water is procured from lakes, reservoirs, rivers and streams, springs, and wells. Most water utilities use lakes, reservoirs, and rivers—all surface water sources. Rarely are springs and well fields adequate to the task of supplying water to a metropolitan community. Surface water is most likely to be polluted with commercial and industrial chemicals.

Municipal water supply systems usually utilize underground water piping and overhead elevated water tanks (see fig. 14-1) and standpipes. The buried water supply piping is usually made of flanged cast iron pipe. Cast iron is comparatively incorrodible, and when laid with flexible joints or ductile cast iron material (to permit accommodation to earth settlement) may last for hundreds of years.

Most municipal water utility companies are ready and willing to extend their piping network to any point in their area of responsibility where the cost of their piping can be recovered. If this

Figure 14-1 1,000,000-gal elevated municipal water storage tank.

possibility does not exist, the water utility may require a prospective building owner to pay for the extension of a water main to the building location.

Further, it is possible that a water main may run directly in front of a proposed building site, but be overloaded and unavailable to the new building. The main may also have been installed by the water utility but at the expense of another customer near the end of the main. In this event, the new building owner may procure water rights by paying the original water customer for a share of the cost of the main.

The primary point here is that the existence of a water main near a building site does not guarantee free and unencumbered access to the main. Before recommending a building site to a prospective building owner, the professional designer must check many aspects of the site. Certainly, the possibility of an adequate, potable water supply is one of the most important considerations.

One aspect that must not be overlooked is the capacity of the public water supply network.

Capacity may be more than adequate to meet the building needs for water consumption, but be totally inadequate to provide enough water at high enough pressure for firefighting purposes. If this is the case, the fire insurance premiums may be inordinately high.

The presence of one or more fire hydrants, for fire department use, is also a matter of real concern. Fire hydrants can always be added, but these are expensive, and their cost will probably be a responsibility of the building owner. This cost should be recognized early.

The firefighting capacity of a water main can be determined with certainty only by a *flow test*. The fire underwriter may require this, and its cost should be anticipated during the site evaluation process. If water main capacity is inadequate, a problem arises, the best solution of which may be the installation of a *fire pump*.

A fire pump is usually quite an expensive item of equipment. Its volumetric capacity must be very high, and its pressure building characteristics must be very good. This pump is most often connected to pump water from the water main (thus increasing the main's capacity) into the fire standpipes, fire hose cabinets, and sprinkler systems of buildings. This problem is somewhat eased if a body of water, such as a lake, reservoir, or river, is nearby and accessible to the fire pump. Privately owned elevated water storage tanks are sometimes used to assist in the solution of an emergency water supply problem.

An elevated water storage tank, of perhaps a million gallons, used for municipal water supply will normally not freeze in winter—even in very cold climates. In a municipality there is always enough flow of water well above freezing to bring in adequate heat to maintain above-freezing temperatures. With a private elevated tank this will not be true, and freeze-up may be a very definite hazard.

Sometimes the tank can be located in an enclosure extending up from the building roof, with enough heat in the enclosure to maintain above-freezing temperatures. Sometimes heat can be added directly to the water to keep it at 35°F

or more. All such problems in connection with water supply must be anticipated and cost evaluated by the professional designer before site procurement.

14-2 WATER SERVICE

The water service of a building is that part of the water piping system that extends from the water main (usually buried under or beside the street or roadway in front of the building) to and into the subject building. It usually includes a curb cock, a shutoff valve, located on private property but near the street curb. It is also usually considered to include the building water meter, whether located inside the building or outside.

The water service is almost always buried in the earth at a depth that is below the frost line. In colder, northern climates this may require depths of 3.5 ft or more. In southern latitudes, of 30° north latitude or so, the frost line depth may be less than 12 in. In this case a minimum depth of 18 in. to the top of the service pipe should be maintained for protection.

The service pipe may be made of many different materials; however, accepted practice usually results in the use of type K copper for smaller water services of 3/4 to 2 in. and cast iron water pipe, A.S.A. Specification A21.1, for larger water services. With copper piping, joints are soldered and are easily made leakproof. Solder joints may be made with 50-50 (lead-tin) soft solder or 95-5 soft solder. However, these solders on copper pipe and fittings require great care in preparation before soldering. Both the pipe exterior and the interior of the "socket"-type fittings must be thoroughly burnished and fluxed (with an acid flux) before heat is applied. Many failures of this type of joint have been experienced.

It is better to use one of the many high-fusing-point solders with a melting point of over 1100°F. These "hard" solders have much greater strength, and some of the phosphorus-copper solders are much less critical in their need for joint preparation. Some do not require burnishing or the use of acid flux and result in consistently perfect joints if adequate heat (from an acetylene torch) is applied.

In cast iron water service lines both *bell-and-spigot joints* and *mechanical joints* are used (see fig. 14-2). In larger service lines, 6 in. and over, flanged and gasketed joints are frequently utilized. However, flanged joint cast iron pipe assembles into a rigid, inflexible joint which suffers the threat of joint or pipe breakage if a buried pipeline ex-

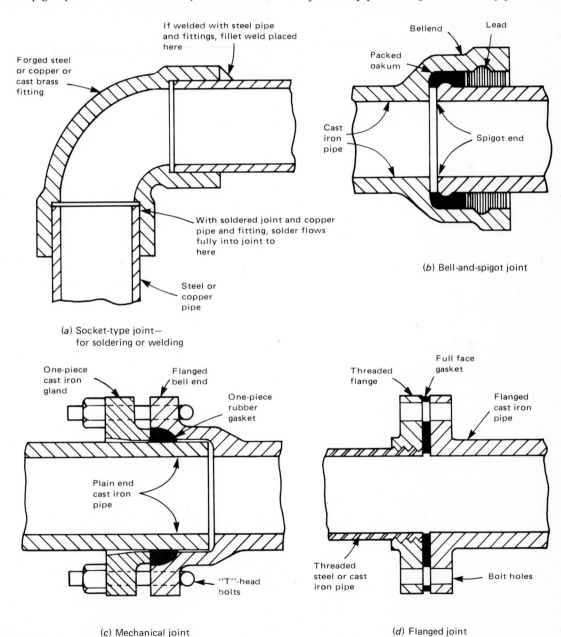

(a) Socket-type joint— for soldering or welding

(b) Bell-and-spigot joint

(c) Mechanical joint

(d) Flanged joint

Figure 14-2 Typical pipe joints.

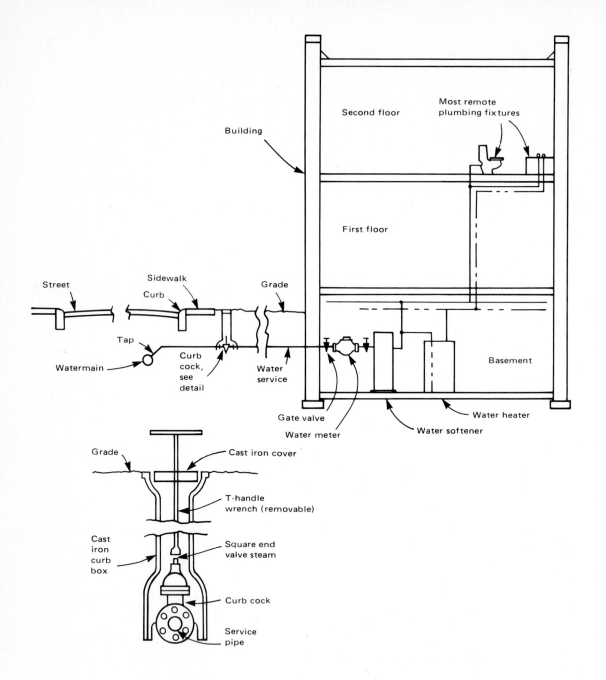

Figure 14-3 Water service details.

periences earth movement or settlement. The use of *ductile* cast iron, which can bend and is exceedingly tough, makes flanged joints quite satisfactory.

Cast iron pipe is also manufactured in standard iron or steel pipe sizes, so that standard threaded fittings may be utilized when the pipe is threaded with a screw thread. Steel pipe-size cast iron pipe is mainly useful in smaller sizes. It is available in sizes of 1 1/4 in. or 1 1/2 to 6 in.

Cast iron pipe is, in general, comparatively inexpensive, and since it is also comparatively incorrodible it makes an excellent choice for buried water service lines. Its major disadvantage is its brittleness, but this disadvantage is overcome in ductile cast iron pipe.

One problem with bell-and-spigot joints, and to a lesser extent with mechanical joints, is that when water is carried at a pressure of 50 to 70 psig (usual pressures), there is the tendency for the joints to blow apart. To counter this tendency, concrete bumper or restrainer blocks are poured around the pipe at intervals and at elbows where a change in direction occurs. These blocks are large enough to present adequate area to the surrounding earth so that the earth can bear the forces exerted. Such a pipeline if unrestrained will blow apart if it can lengthen in the earth or if it can buckle upward out of the trench in which it is buried. Soldered, welded, or threaded joints, of course, do not suffer this disadvantage.

As shown in fig. 14-3, curb cocks, located near the street curb, are installed. These permit turning the water service on and off as necessary. The curb cock is a valve located down below grade at the level of the water service pipe. It is enclosed and protected by a cast iron *curb box.* This box straddles the service pipe and encloses the valve. The valve (curb cock) has a square end on the valve stem at the top; and the valve is operated by a T-handle socket wrench which engages the square end of the valve stem. The wrench is removed when not in use, and a round cast iron cover closes the upper end of the valve box flush with the earth surface. Sometimes the upper end of the valve box is surrounded by a small, 18-in. square concrete pad flush with the earth surface.

14-3 WATER SUPPLY DEMAND

The amount of potable water a building requires is referred to as its water *demand.* Buildings experience two types of demand: *daily demand* and *maximum momentary demand.* The daily demand is, of course, the total amount of water that a building requires during a busy 24-hr period.

Figure 14-4 presents a table of daily sewage flow rates for many different types of buildings and occupancies. Since the sewage flow rates correspond very closely to the water supply demand of a building, fig. 14-4 may be used for both purposes—daily water demand as well as daily sewage flow rates. It should be noticed that in fig. 14-4, the flow rate is in gallons per day per person; however, there are many exceptions to this basis, as noted. For example, motels (without kitchen) are rated at 50 gpd per bed space.

It is often necessary for a plumbing system designer to know the amount of daily water demand and daily sewage flow rate. If a private water supply system is to be installed, obviously the daily demand placed on that system must be known. If a water softener is to be installed to soften the incoming supply of water, and if the softener is to be regenerated every 3 days, the designer must know the water demand in 3 days and the amount of hardness that must be removed. Knowing daily water demand in gpd, and the hardness in grains per gallon, will solve this problem.

Similarly, if a private sewage disposal system is to be used, daily demand must be known to size a septic tank and absorption field.

Maximum momentary (maxmo) demand in gpm must also be determined for the process of sizing water piping. The sizes of the water service pipe and other water piping throughout a building are not in any way involved with the daily water demand. Pipe sizes must be adequate to permit water to flow at its maximum rate with reasonable pressure drop.

For example, a 200-room hotel would probably experience a daily water demand of 20,000 gal. This represents an average flow rate of 833 gal/hr or 13.89 gal/min. However, available criteria

Figure 14-4 Sewage flows according to type of establishment. [From the National Standard Plumbing Code, ASA–A40.8–1955. Note: This is an out-of-date document. Both ANSI and ASME have withdrawn their approval of it as a valid document (taken as a whole). But data in this figure coincide well with data from other current sources of information.]

Type of Establishment	Gallons per day per person (Except as noted otherwise)
Schools (toilet and lavatories only)	15
Schools (with above plus cafeteria)	25
Schools (with above plus cafeteria and showers)	35
Day workers at schools and offices	15
Day camps	25
Trailer parks or tourist camps (with built-in bath)	50
Trailer parks or tourist camps (with central bathhouse)	35
Work or construction camps	50
Public picnic parks (toilet wastes only)	5
Public picnic parks (bathhouse, showers, and flush toilets)	10
Swimming pools and beaches	10
Country clubs	25 gal per locker
Luxury residences and estates	150
Rooming houses	40
Boarding houses	50
Hotels (with connecting baths)	50
Hotels (with private baths—two persons per room)	100
Boarding schools	100
Factories (gallons per person per shift—exclusive of industrial wastes)	25
Nursing homes	75
General hospitals	150
Public institutions (other than hospitals)	100
Restaurants (toilet and kitchen wastes per unit of serving capacity)	25
Kitchen wastes from hotels, camps, boarding houses, etc. serving three meals per day	10
Motels	50 gal per bed space
Motels with bath, toilet, and kitchen wastes	60 gal per bed space
Drive-in theaters	5 gal per car space
Stores	400 gal per toilet room
Service stations	10 gal per vehicle served
Airports	3 - 5 gal per passenger
Assembly halls	2 gal per seat
Bowling alleys	75 gal per lane
Churches (small)	3 - 5 gal per sanctuary seat
Churches (large with kitchens)	5 - 7 gal per sanctuary seat
Dance halls	2
Laundries (coin operated)	400 gal per machine
Service stations	1000 gal (first bay)
	500 gal (each add. bay)
Subdivisions or individual homes	75
Marinas—flush toilets	36 gal per fixture per hour
urinals	10 gal per fixture per hour
wash basins	15 gal per fixture per hour
showers	150 gal per fixture per hour

indicate that a maximum flow rate of 330 gpm will be experienced, and the size of the water service piping must be based on the latter value. So for pipe sizing purposes, the maxmo demand must be determined at all points throughout a building water piping system.

This may seem to be a formidable task, but as will be seen, this is not the case because of the work done by the late Roy B. Hunter of the National Bureau of Standards many years ago. Hunter's tests and his application of the theory of probability resulted in the formation of curves which translate directly into maxmo gpm from the totalization of units called *fixture units*.

Fixture units are parameters by means of which the relative demand weights of various types of plumbing fixtures may be indicated. In the beginning, one fixture unit (abbreviated herein as FU) was meant to indicate the maximum flow rate of 7.5 gpm; however, this relationship does not apply directly and may not be meaningfully utilized.

Figure 14-5 includes a table listing many types of plumbing fixtures, and the demand weight, or load value, of each type of plumbing fixture is expressed in fixture units. The reader must be specifically warned that another table of fixtures and fixture unit values is presented in chap. 15. The FU values in that table and in fig. 14-5 *are not the same.* Figure 14-5 deals with *water supply* FUs, while the table in chap. 15 presents *drainage* FUs; they are different, and an appreciable error may be made by using the wrong table.

It should be noted in fig. 14-5 that many of the fixtures listed have three ratings: one for "cold" water, one for "hot" water, and one for "total" water. These fixtures are, of course, only those which do use both hot and cold water. A fixture such as a water closet, which uses only cold water, has only a total water FU rating and a cold water FU rating, which are the same.

In totaling the FUs on a branch main in a supply water system, attention must be given to whether the branch main supplies hot or cold water. Suppose, for example, that a hot water supply main delivers hot water to 20 public lavatories. The hot

Figure 14-5 Load values assigned to fixtures. [From the National Standard Plumbing Code (ASA–A40.8–1955) Appendix b, Table B.5.2. Note: This is an out-of-date document. Both ANSI and ASME have withdrawn their approval of it as a valid document (taken as a whole). But data in this figure coincide well with data from other current sources of information.]

Fixture	Occupancy	Type of supply control	Load values, in water-supply fixture units		
			Cold	Hot	Total
Water closet	Public	Flush valve	10.0	—	10.0
Water closet	Public	Flush tank	5.0	—	5.0
Urinal	Public	1-in. flush valve	10.0	—	10.0
Urinal	Public	3/4-in. flush valve	5.0	—	5.0
Urinal	Public	Flush tank	3.0	—	3.0
Lavatory	Public	Faucet	1.5	1.5	2.0
Bathtub	Public	Faucet	3.0	3.0	4.0
Shower head	Public	Mixing valve	3.0	3.0	4.0
Service sink	Offices, etc.	Faucet	2.25	2.25	3.0
Kitchen sink	Hotel, restaurant	Faucet	3.0	3.0	4.0
Drinking fountain	Offices, etc.	3/8-in. valve	0.25	—	0.25
Water closet	Private	Flush valve	6.0	—	6.0
Water closet	Private	Flush tank	3.0	—	3.0
Lavatory	Private	Faucet	0.75	0.75	1.0
Bathtub	Private	Faucet	1.5	1.5	2.0
Shower stall	Private	Mixing valve	1.5	1.5	2.0
Kitchen sink	Private	Faucet	1.5	1.5	2.0
Laundry trays (1 to 3)	Private	Faucet	2.25	2.25	3.0
Combination fixture	Private	Faucet	2.25	2.25	3.0
Dishwashing machine	Private	Automatic		1.0	1.0
Laundry machine (8 lb)	Private	Automatic	1.5	1.5	2.0
Laundry machine (8 lb)	Public or general	Automatic	2.25	2.25	3.0
Laundry machine (16 lb)	Public or general	Automatic	3.0	3.0	4.0

Note: For fixtures not listed, loads should be assumed by comparing the fixture to one listed using water in similar quantities and at similar rates. The assigned loads for fixtures with both hot and cold water supplies are given for separate hot and cold water loads and for total load, the separate hot and cold water loads being three-fourths the total load for the fixture in each case.

water FU rating of a public lavatory is shown in fig. 14-5 to be 1.5 FU, not 2 FU. Therefore, the total water supply load on this hot water main is 20 × 1.5 FU = 30 FU.

Suppose also that a cold water supply branch main delivers cold water only, to 10 public flush valve water closets and 20 public lavatories.

10 water closets × 10 FU/closet	100
20 lavatories × 1.5 FU/lavatory	30
	130 FU

The total FU load is 130 FU on a pipe which supplies only separate cold water loads and no hot water load.

Now suppose the main cold water service line which carries water from a city water main into a public building supplies a load of 30 flush valve water closets (WCs) and 50 lavatories. This service pipe is supplying water some of which will be heated into hot water while some will stay cold. This service pipe is meeting "total" water demand. Its load will be:

30 WC × 10 FU/WC	300
50 Lavs × 2 FU/Lav	100
Total	400 FU

Notice here that the lavatories were not counted at 1.5 FU each, but rather at 2 FU each, because the service pipe is meeting both the hot and cold water needs of the 50 lavatories.

From the preceding example it is evident that for the water supply system of a building, or for a branch or portion of that system, the FUs of all fixtures are totaled. However, to be meaningful these totals must be translated into a useful value such as gpm. This translation is accomplished by means of figs. 14-6, 14-7 and 14-8. These three charts embody the probability values resulting from Hunter's investigations, and show what the flow rate of water will be in gpm when the FU total is known.

In figs. 14-6 and 14-7 a gpm difference is shown between systems that are predominantly flush valve (for water closets and urinals) and those that

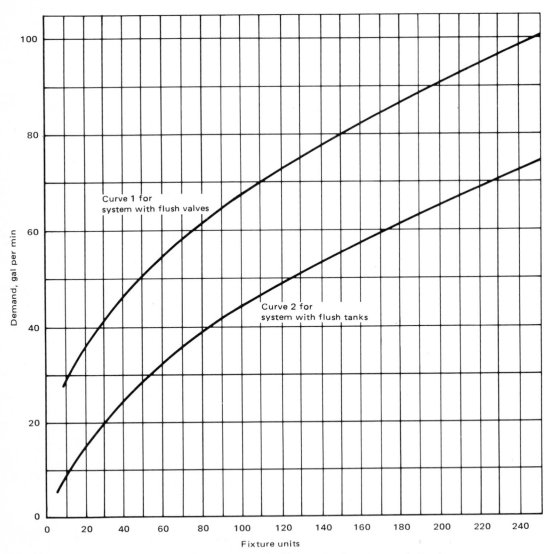

Figure 14-6 Hunter curves (up to 250 fixture units). (From U.S. Department of the Army Engineering Manual, March 1946, part V, Chap. 4.)

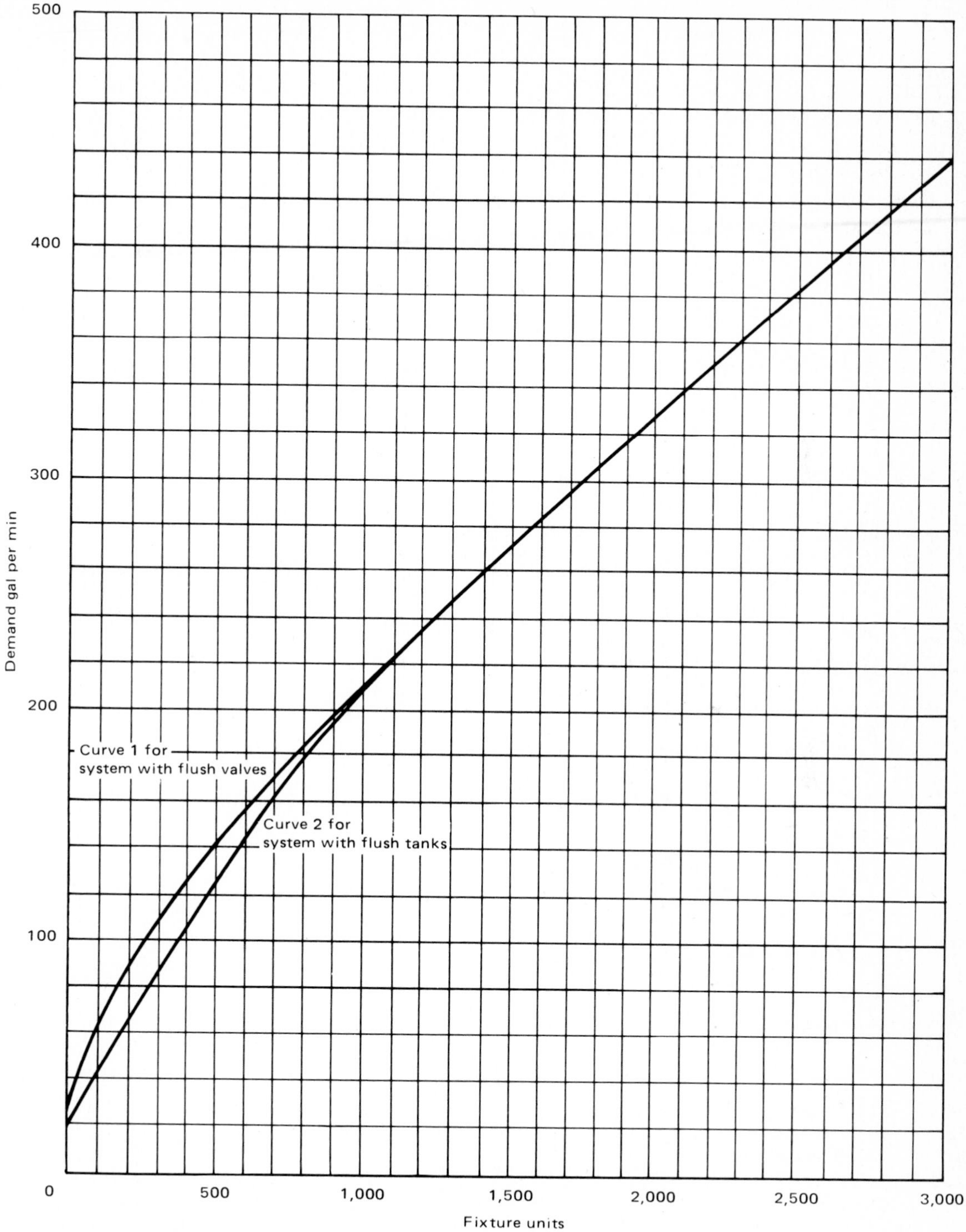
500
400
300
200
100
0
Demand gal per min
Curve 1 for
system with flush valves
Curve 2 for
system with flush tanks
500
1,000
1,500
2,000
2,500
3,000
Fixture units

Figure 14-7 Hunter curves (up to 3000 fixture units). (From U.S. Department of the Army Engineering Manual, 1 March 1946, part V, chap. 4.)

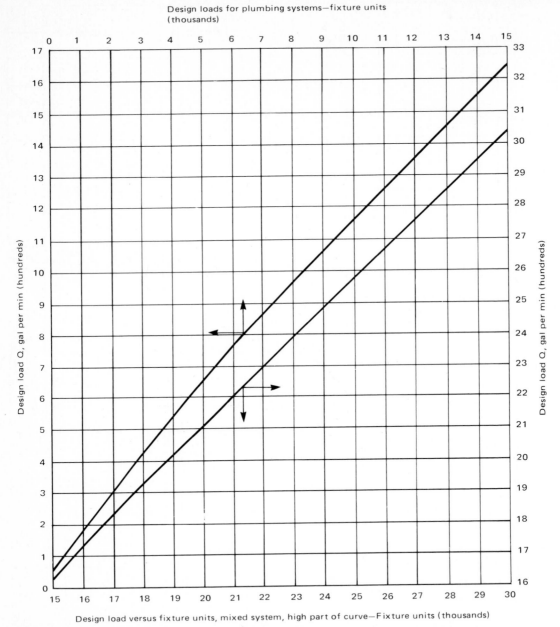

Figure 14-8 Expanded Hunter curves (up to 30,000 fixture units). (From Vincent T. Manas, *National Plumbing Code Handbook*, Copyright © 1957 by McGraw-Hill, Inc. Used with permission of McGraw-Hill Book Company.)

are predominantly flush tank. Most residential water closets are of the flush tank type; that is, there is a vitreous china water storage tank that is about 20 in. wide and 14 in. high mounted at the rear of the water closet assembly. The flush valve type of closet does not have a flush tank; it is flushed by a special, lever-operated valve which is large enough, along with its 1 1/4 in. water supply pipe, to flush the water closet with a vigorous scouring action so as to keep the water closet clean.

In fig. 14-6 and in part of fig. 14-7 there are two curves: a No. 1 curve for water supply piping systems that are predominantly flush valve type, and a No. 2 curve for systems that are predominantly flush tank type. Since there are no flush valves on fixtures that use hot water, the No. 2 curve is *always* used in sizing piping that supplies hot water.

In the example above where 20 public lavatories are supplied by a hot water main, the FU total is 30 FU (20 × 1.5). In fig. 14-6, using curve 2, we see that the 30 FU translate into 20 gpm maxmo demand.

14-4 HOT AND COLD WATER PIPE SIZING

In sizing hot and cold water piping there are two factors that must be given consideration. When good data are known about these two factors, the selection of the necessary pipe size is very easy; it may be selected directly from pipe sizing charts such as those shown in figs. 14-9 and 14-10.

The two factors are:

1 Maximum momentary (maxmo) demand in gpm as determined in art. 14-3
2 Allowable pressure loss due to pipe friction

The first of these factors has been discussed, but the second factor needs explanation. Whenever flow of a fluid in a conduit occurs, there must be a drop in the fluid pressure. Flow cannot occur unless the static pressure at one point in the conduit is greater than that at another point. If a pressure differential exists, flow in a low-viscosity fluid

must result. If the pressure differential is low, the resulting rate of flow will be low. If the rate of flow is inadequate, it can be increased by increasing the pressure differential. The differential can be increased by increasing the upstream pressure or lowering the downstream pressure—or both. The rate of flow in the conduit can also be increased by holding both pressures steady and increasing the size of the conduit.

In hot and cold water piping distribution systems, the initial or upstream pressure is usually fixed by the pressure which the water supply utility company maintains in the city water main. Similarly, the terminal or downstream pressure in buildings is fixed by the *residual* pressure that must be maintained to make a plumbing fixture function. A tank-type water closet, for example, when flushed must refill quickly with water so that it can be flushed again, if necessary. Pressure is required to fill the tank quickly, usually about 15 psig at the tank inlet connection. This is the residual, or minimum, working pressure for satisfactory operation.

The question now is—how much pressure drop (or differential) is available for forcing water from the city main into the building, throughout the building piping system, to the farthest and highest point of water usage. If city water main pressure is 60 psig and the residual that must be maintained at the fixtures is 15 psig, is the 45-psig differential (60 – 15 = 45 psig) available for overcoming pipe friction?

No; only a portion of the 45 psig is available. Some of the 45 psig must be used for overcoming the frictional resistance of the water meter, the water softener (if one is in use), the valves, filters, and other accessories through which the water flows; and some of the 45 psig must be used to lift water vertically from the level of the water main (which is usually quite low) to the level of the highest plumbing fixture (or other water user) in the building. The reader may wish to review art. 1-18 and fig. 1-4, which deals with the relationship between altitude and hydrostatic pressure. Article 1-18 advises that 1.0 psig is equal to 2.31 ft of

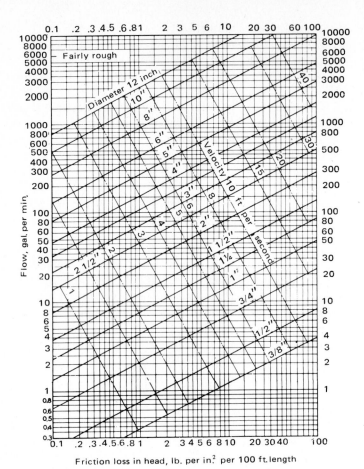

Figure 14-9 Pipe sizing chart for fairly rough pipe. (From Vincent T. Manas, *National Plumbing Code Handbook*. Copyright © 1957 by McGraw-Hill, Inc. Used with permission of McGraw-Hill Book Company.)

vertical water column. If the highest fixture is 23.1 ft higher in elevation than the city water main, 10 psig of the pressure in the main is lost to that elevation and is not available to do the work of causing water to flow in the building water piping.

Example 14-1 In fig. 14-3, find the size of the water service pipe if the following conditions exist:

1. City water main pressure   55 psig
2. Length of fairly rough straight pipe from the water main to the meter   180 ft
3. Pressure drop through the meter   3 psig
4. Pressure drop through the water softener   5 psig

5. Plumbing fixtures in the building include 1 flush tank water closet, 4 flush valve water closets, 1 bathtub with shower, 4 lavatories, 1 kitchen sink, 1 dishwasher, 1 clothes washer, 1 two-compartment laundry tray, and 2 sill cocks for connecting garden hoses
6. The vertical height between the water main and the highest plumbing fixture   18 ft
7. The actual measured, developed length of the fairly rough piping between the water meter and the most remote plumbing fixture   120 ft
8. Sill cocks draw 5 gpm while they are sprinkling the lawn, etc.
9. The building is limited to private use and is not available to the public

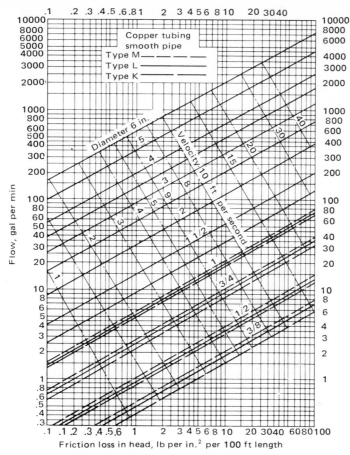

Figure 14-10 Pipe sizing chart for smooth pipe.

Solution

1 *Determine the maxmo demand in gpm.*

Total the FU count using fig. 14-5:

1 flush tank water closet	3
4 flush valve water closets at 6 FU each	24
1 bathtub (the shower does not count)	2
4 lavatories at 1 FU each	4
1 kitchen sink	2
1 dishwashing machine	1
1 clothes washer (laundry machine)	2
1 laundry tray	3
Total FU	41

From fig. 14-6 determine that the maximum demand of the fixtures listed above is 47 gpm for 41 FU using curve 1 (the system is predominantly flush valve). However, this is not the total demand; there are two sill cocks, and it must be assumed that they will be in use. At 5 gpm each they demand 10 gpm, which added to the 47 gpm indicated above gives a total maximum momentary demand of 57 gpm. The designer must always be alert for water users not listed in the schedule of fixtures in fig. 14-5.

2 *Determine the allowable pressure drop in the water piping.* This equals the city water main pressure (55 psig) minus the pressure loss in everything in the system except piping.

Loss due to elevation = 18 ft ÷ 2.31	7.79
(18 ft given—highest fixture above the water main)	
Water meter pressure loss	3.00
Water softener pressure loss	5.00
Residual pressure required	15.00
Total	30.79 psi

The total loss for everything in the water supply system except piping, valves, and fittings is 30.79 psi.

The allowable pressure loss in the piping system, then, is 55 psig (pressure in the water main) minus 30.79 psi = 24.21 psi.

3 *Determine the total equivalent length of the piping from the water main to the most remote fixture.* As discussed in arts. 8-21 and 8-22 and Example 8-3 (which see), the equivalent length is the actual installed length in feet, of a pipe run, plus an extra number of feet which is judged to be equal in frictional resistance to the valves, fittings, and so on. In water piping systems, the total equivalent length is usually 150 to 200% of the actual length.

An experienced designer can study a piping layout and intuitively judge what this percentage should be. Or, the designer may follow the procedure outlined in chap. 8 and total the resistance of each valve and fitting to find the equivalent length. In our example, since we have no piping layout to follow, let us assume that the equivalent length of the longest pipe run (to the fixtures shown in fig. 14-3) is 175% of the actual length. In item 7 above, it is noted that the piping developed actual length from the meter to the most remote fixtures is 120 ft. Increasing this to 175%, we find that the equivalent length is 120 ft × 1.75 = 210 ft.

Since the water service line into the meter runs straight, without fittings and only one valve, we can add its actual length in without modification. The total equivalent length may now be found to be the 180-ft service pipe plus the 210 ft calculated above = 390 ft.

Notice in fig. 14-9, the pipe sizing chart for fairly rough pipe, that the horizontal scale, the abscissa, is denominated in terms of pressure loss in psi per 100 ft of length. In our example we have 3.9 100-ft lengths (390 ft).

4 *Find the allowable pressure drop in pounds per 100 ft of equivalent length.* The allowable pressure loss in the piping was found in step 2 above to be 24.21 psi. This 24.21 ÷ 3.9 from step 3 = 6.21 psi allowable pressure drop per 100 ft of equivalent length.

5 *Select the size of the water service pipe from the chart of fig. 14-9.* The maxmo demand from step 1 is 57 gpm. The allowable pressure drop per

100 ft of equivalent length of pipe is 6.21 psi. If we make a dot on the chart of fig. 14-9 at the intersection of the imaginary 6.21 vertical line (just to the right of the 6.0 line shown) and the horizontal imaginary 57-gpm line (just below the 60-gpm line shown), we see that this dot lies between the 1 1/2-in. pipe size line and the 2-in. pipe size line and that it is somewhat closer to the 2-in. line.

Obviously, the demand is too great for a 1 1/2-in. service pipe, and the next larger size, 2 in., must be used. From the chart of fig. 14-9, we see that 57 gpm flowing in a 2-in. fairly rough pipe will experience a pressure drop of about 5 psi per 100 ft. So our actual pressure drop in this system will be 5 psi/100 ft × 3.9 = 19.5 psi and the residual pressure at the most remote plumbing fixtures will be 55 psig − 7.79 psi (elevation loss) − 3.0 psi (meter loss) − 5.0 psi (water softener loss) − 19.5 psi (piping loss) = 19.71 psig. This residual pressure is somewhat more than the minimum required; and that is good—within reasonable limits.

In the piping downstream from the water softener, branch connections would be taken from the 2-in. main running to a water heater and to fixtures in all parts of the building. As branch connections are made, the 2-in. main will be reduced in size in accordance with the load still connected to it. By the time it reaches the most remote plumbing fixtures, its size will probably be reduced to 3/4 or 1/2 in.

When the plumbing designer has laid out all the fixtures and other load on the water piping layout drawing, he or she can note on each section of the piping the number of fixture units (FU) of load. These can then be translated into gpms by use of figs. 14-6, 14-7, or 14-8. Using the allowable pressure drop per 100 ft that has been calculated (in our example this is 5 psi per 100 ft), the designer can size each section of pipe in the entire system using the chart in fig. 14-9 for fairly rough piping (such as cast iron pipe or galvanized steel or wrought iron). If the designer is using smooth piping, such as copper, the chart in fig. 14-10 may be used. Throughout the entire system, however, the *allowable pressure drop* in psi per 100 ft that has been calculated for the route to the most remote fixtures can be used to select pipe sizes.

Using this same value of psi per 100 ft for piping circuits that are shorter than the longest run does cause some oversizing of the shorter circuits. If the designer feels that this is too wasteful of material, he or she can, of course, calculate each circuit allowable pressure drop based on its total equivalent length. Usually, this would only be done on very large buildings.

One difficulty that the plumbing designer will experience is that of determining the water demand rate of appliances and other equipment not listed in a fixture unit table such as fig. 14-5. Heavy-duty laundry machines, automatic car washers, gang showers, and so on, are typical. The designer must then carefully research such items so that the values selected do not represent guesswork. Manufacturers of such equipment can usually give much information, but the designer must go to the trouble of soliciting their assistance.

When demand values of "unlisted" equipment are determined, the designer must then apply his or her own diversity factor to the total of such demand. The resulting gpm value may then be added to the gpm determined from the FU total. The available literature gives little help in ascribing a suitable diversity factor, and this is left to the designer.

Some machines that use water draw their maximum amount continuously for appreciable lengths of time (15 min or more); on such machines the diversity factor must be 1.0. Other machines draw water on a cycling or intermittent basis with cycles of only a few minutes or less duration. Diversity factors as low as 0.2 may sometimes be used in this case.

Another problem that may arise results from paying inadequate attention to the question of the pressure drop experienced in water meters, and the *tap* made to the city water main. This tap, the point where the water service line connects to the city water main, is not usually a streamlined connection designed to minimize

Figure 14-11 Minimum size water main tap for 1.0 psi or less pressure drop.

Estimated maximum (maxmo) flow rate in gpm through service tap	Minimum tap size, in inches, for 1.0–psi pressure drop in the tap
10	3/4
20	1
30	1 1/4
50	1 1/2
90	2
140	2 1/2
200	3
270	3 1/2
350	4

pressure loss—and the only safe procedure is to be certain that the tap is large enough. Otherwise, a pressure drop at this point can be surprisingly high.

Many water utility companies have only a few sizes of tapping machines. These are special machines which can drill and tap a water main and connect a service pipe without turning off the water pressure. Frequently, a utility will have taps for only 3/4-, 1-, 2-, and 4-in. sizes. If a building has a maxmo demand of 300 gpm and a 2-in. tap is made, the pressure loss will be in excess of 10 psig in this tap. This is intolerable.

It is recommended that the tap pressure loss be limited to 1.0 psi. Figure 14-11 lists the sizes that taps should be for various flow rates to meet this limitation.

Similarly, the pressure drop through a water meter should not exceed 3.0 psi. Figure 14-12 shows the size, according to most meter manu-

Figure 14-12 Water meter size to limit pressure drop to 3.0 psig.

Estimated maximum (maxmo) flow rate in gpm through service tap	Meter size for 3.0–psi pressure drop
10	1"
20	1 1/2 "
35	2 "
75	3 "
120	4 "
210	6 "

facturers, that a meter should be, to meet this 3.0 psi limitation.

14-5 WATER PIPING ISOMETRIC DIAGRAMS

In presenting the details of the plumbing system in a building, the plumbing designer will provide a floor plan of each floor of the building with all plumbing fixtures superimposed thereon. In addition, as much of the plumbing system piping as possible will be shown connecting to the fixtures.

However, on the small-scale (1/8 in. = 1 ft) drawings usually utilized, it is impossible to show all the water and drain and vent piping. In order to supplement and clarify the floor plan drawings, isometric three-dimensional drawings are provided. These isometric drawings do show all the piping, fittings, and equipment that constitute the plumbing system.

In large buildings, where the fixtures are widely separated and scattered over large areas, isometric details are prepared for localized groups of fixtures. However, often no effort is made to show one large, overall, encompassing drawing that includes all the fixtures in the building. When the building is small and the fixtures are fairly closely grouped, as shown in the building of figs. 14-13 and 14-14, one overall isometric detail may be prepared. The diagram of fig. 14-15 is typical.

There are many benefits of the isometric diagram. It enables the designer to better visualize and streamline a design. It permits plumbing inspectors and code-enforcing authorities to ascertain that proper piping connections will be made. It provides a basis on which all pipe sizes may be properly established and shown. It also provides an accurate format on the basis of which the plumbing contractor may accurately estimate the cost of the system.

Some plumbing code enforcement authorities will refuse to accept a set of plumbing plans, which has been submitted for approval, if the isometric details are not shown. This is especially true of the drain and vent piping, but sometimes the hot and cold water isometrics may be omitted if the water piping system is not too complicated.

14-6 PIPE SIZING METHODS

Figure 14-13 shows, for illustrative purposes, the first-floor plan of a three-story building. The plan arrangement of the second and third floors would probably vary, but it is assumed that the toilet room and plumbing fixture layout is identical— except for the two sill cocks which would be required on the first floor only.

As further illustration of the methods used in designing and sizing the H & CW (hot and cold water) piping system in a building, the piping system of the building, shown in fig. 14-13, has been fully detailed. In following through this design, the reader should first understand the interrelationship between figs. 14-13 through 14-16—all deal with the same problem.

Figure 14-13 shows only the building, the plumbing fixtures, the water heater, the water meter, the water service entrance location, and the location of the two sill cocks (for connecting garden hoses)—one on the north wall and one on the south wall. Figure 14-14 shows only a portion of the first-floor plan, but at a somewhat larger drawing scale. As much of the water piping as can be made meaningful has been shown in fig. 14-14. Also, a few of the water pipe sizes have been shown.

Figure 14-14 also establishes the practice of designating the various segments or sections of the piping system by ascribing single- or double-letter designators at each end of each pipe segment. For example, that segment of the piping running from a point near the water meter to the first branch connection (to the water heater) is designated C-B or B-C. The reader must be careful not to confuse the double-letter piping designators with the double-letter designators of the plumbing fixtures—such as SK for sinks, CL for water closets, and UR for urinals.

However, in fig. 14-14 many of the water piping details are not and cannot be shown. The vertical pipe risers that extend up to the second

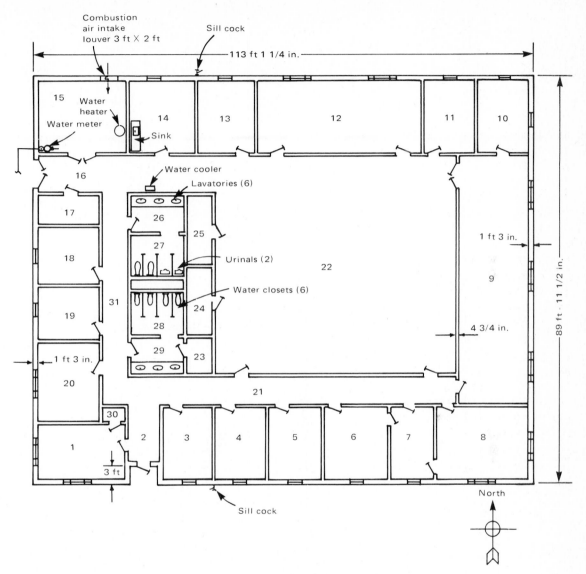

Figure 14.13 First-floor plan—three-story office building. Scale: 1/16″ = 1′0″. All ceiling heights, 9′0″. Room schedule and sizes: 1, display room, 20′ × 12′; 2, entry, 7′-4″ × 12′; 3, receptionist, 11′-4″ × 16′; 4, office, 11′-4″ × 16′; 5, office, 11′-4″ × 16′; 6, office, 14′-8″ × 16′; 7, office, 10′ × 16′; 8, office 20′-8″ × 16′; 9, office, 16′ × 54′-8″; 10, office, 12′ × 16′; 11, office, 11′-4″ × 16′; 12, accounting, 37′-4″ × 16′; 13, office, 12′-8″ × 16′; 14, snack room, 15′-4″ × 16′; 15, equipment room, 20′ × 16′; 16, rear entry, 40′-8″ × 8′; 17, storage, 14′ × 6′-8″; 18, office, 14′ × 12′-8″; 19, office, 14′ × 12′; 20, office, 14′ × 18′; 21, corridor, 74′-6″ × 6′; 22, general office, 54′-8″ × 48′-8″; 23, restroom, 6′-8″ × 7′-4″; 24, storage, 6′-8″ × 14′-6″; 25, storage, 6′-8″ × 14′-6″; 26, men's lavatory, 12′ × 8′; 27, men's toilet, 12′ × 9′-4″; 28, women's toilet, 12′ × 9′-4″; 29, women's lavatory, 12′ × 8′; 30, closet, 5′-4″ × 3′; 31, corridor, 6′ × 47′-4″.

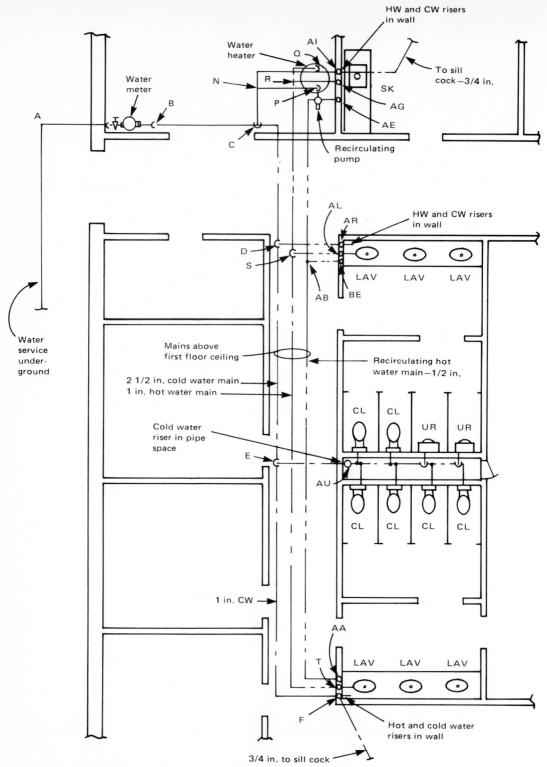

Figure 14-14 Partial first-floor plan—three-story office building. Scale: 1/8″ = 1′-0″.

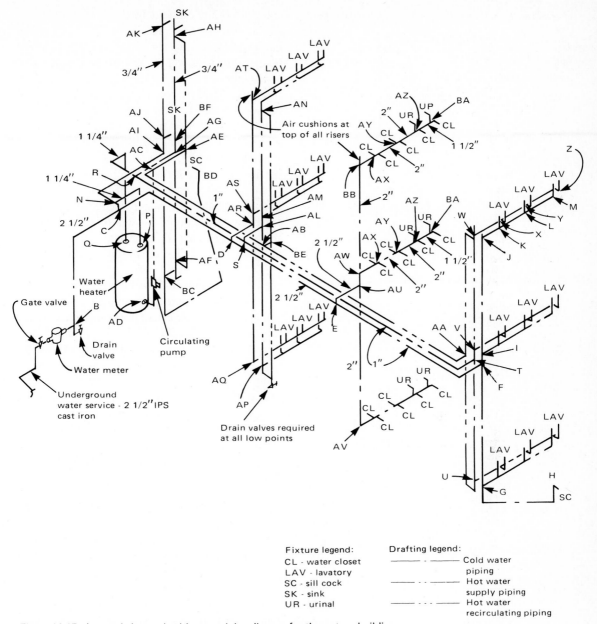

Figure 14-15 Isometric hot and cold water piping diagram for three-story building.

Fixture legend:
CL - water closet
LAV - lavatory
SC - sill cock
SK - sink
UR - urinal

Drafting legend:
——— · ——— Cold water piping
——— ·· ——— Hot water supply piping
——— ··· ——— Hot water recirculating piping

Figure 14-16 Pipe sizing table for the piping diagram of fig. 14-15.

Pipeline segment	Load fixt. units	Gpm	Curve no. from fig. 14-6	Pipe size
M-L	1.5	2	2	1/2″
L-K	3	3	2	3/4″
K-J	4.5	5	2	3/4″
J-I	4.5	5	2	3/4″
I-F	9	8	2	1″
H-G	1	5	—	3/4″
G-F	5.5	10	2	1″
F-E	14.5	12	2	1″
BA-AZ	15	32	1	1 1/2″
AZ-AY	30	42	1	2″
AY-AX	50	55	1	2″
AX-BB	70	58	1	2″
BB-AW	70	58	1	2″
AW-AU	140	77	1	*2″
AV-AU	70	58	1	2″
AU-E	210	93	1	2 1/2″
E-D	224.5	96	1	2 1/2″
AR-D	13.5	12	2	1″
D-C	239	98	1	2 1/2″
AK-AJ	3	3	2	3/4″
AJ-AI	6	6	2	*3/4″
BD-BC	1	5	—	3/4″
BC-AI	4	8	2	1″
AI-N	10	9	2	1″
Z-Y	1.5	2	2	1/2″
Y-X	3	3	2	3/4″
X-W	4.5	5	2	3/4″
W-V	4.5	5	2	3/4″
V-T	9	8	2	1″
U-T	4.5	5	2	3/4″
T-S	13.5	12	2	1″
AL-S	13.5	12	2	1″
S-R	27	18	2	1 1/4″
AH-BF	3	3	2	3/4″
BF-AG	6	6	2	*3/4″
AF-AG	3	3	2	3/4″
AG-R	9	8	2	1″
R-Q	36	23	2	*1 1/2″
P-N	36	23	2	*1 1/2″
N-C	46	27	2	1 1/2″
C-B	258	103	1	2 1/2″
B-A	258	103	1	2 1/2″

*Slightly undersized intentionally.

and third floors can only be shown as small circles —as at points AA, T, and F. Notice, though, that in the isometric fig. 14-15, every foot of every pipe is shown as well as all fittings, fixtures, and accessories.

Figure 14-15 is too tightly packed and compressed in order to fit it onto a page in this book, but if it were three times larger, as it would be in a set of plumbing plans, it would be easily readable. However, even at its present size, the details can be read if the reader will persevere.

In fig. 14-15, three types of piping are shown: hot, cold, and hot water recirculating piping. Different delineation is used to indicate these three systems; see the drafting legend included in fig. 14-15, as well as the fixture legend.

The hot and cold water piping, of course, supplies hot and cold water wherever required. The hot water recirculating piping, however, together with the circulating pump shown, exists for the purpose of keeping the hot water piping hot. The circulating pump is usually quite small, with just enough capacity to maintain a slight flow of water from the water heater out through the HW piping and back the return piping. Only enough flow is required to provide adequate heat to offset the loss of heat from the HW supply piping.

In a small system, such as the one pictured, no exhaustive design process is followed. The piping is of the smallest size usually used for distribution piping (in this case 1/2 or 3/4 in.), and the pump is a small, pipe-mounted, in-line, all-bronze, 1/3- to 1/2-hp pump.

However, when the building HW piping system is hundreds of feet long, an accurate determination of size and capacity must be made. First, the total heat loss of the entire hot water piping system, from the water heater to the most remote points, must be made. This may be done easily by the use of fig. 14-17, which gives heat loss in BH per linear foot when piping is insulated with 1 or 1 1/2 in. of insulation with a conductivity k of 0.33. A proportionate correction may be made if the conductivity planned for use is higher or lower than 0.33.

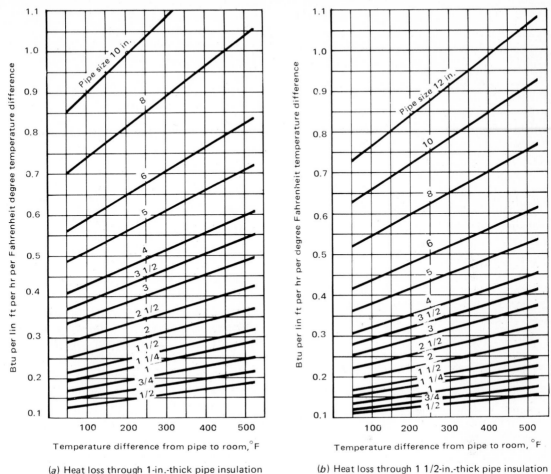

(a) Heat loss through 1-in.-thick pipe insulation

(b) Heat loss through 1 1/2-in.-thick pipe insulation

Figure 14-17 Heat loss from insulated pipes with 1 or 1 1/2 in. of insulation ($k = 0.33$) (BH/lin ft/° temperature difference). (Reprinted with permission from the 1960 Guide Volume, ASHRAE Handbook and Products Directory.)

Knowing the total heat lost, the designer may then calculate the pump capacity with an assumed temperature drop of 20°F and with formula (1-2). In this formula, BH = gpm × 500 × Δt, we must solve for gpm. With the gpm known, and the sizes of all HW piping known, the pressure drop per 100 ft of equivalent length may be estimated. This will usually be very low; and the total pressure drop through the entire system will also be quite low, since it may be assumed that no other flow in the piping system except that

caused by the pump is occurring. The pipe velocity will be much lower than usual design velocities.

Having calculated the required gpm and the total piping system pressure drop, a circulating pump may be selected. This pump is usually controlled by a "strap-on" or immersion-type thermostat sensing the temperature of the HW piping at the most remote point. A thermostat, sensing pipe temperature in the recirculating line at the pump inlet, may also be used if it is adjusted for a temperature 10°F below the desired HW supply line temperature to allow for recirculating line temperature drop.

The step-by-step method of sizing H & CW "supply" piping is shown in fig. 14-16. In this tabulation the "line segment" designators are used to isolate one specific section of the piping shown in fig. 14-15. The process was begun at the most remote point of the CW piping; this is point M at the third-floor lavatories at the right-hand side of fig. 14-15.

The pipe section between points M and L (line segment M-L) serves only one lavatory. As shown in fig. 14-16, the load on M-L is 1.5 FU, which translates into 2 gpm on curve 2 of fig. 14-6. With the use of the pipe sizing chart of fig. 14-9, a pipe size of 1/2 in. was selected for pipe segment M-L. An allowable pressure drop of 7.0 psi per 100 ft of equivalent length was used; this was calculated as follows on the basis of the information listed below.

Given:

1. Actual pipe length of city water main to the meter — 150 ft
2. Vertical height of the highest plumbing fixture above the water main — 30 ft
3. Water meter pressure drop at maximum flow — 3 psi
4. Residual pressure required at the highest water closet — 15 psig
   Note: Water closets require more residual than do lavatories, and this must be taken into consideration
5. Actual developed length—meter to the farthest fixture (lavatories) — 94 ft
6. Actual developed length—meter to farthest water closet — 75 ft
   Note: Here it may be seen that a water closet requiring 15 psig residual and 75 ft away is a more rigorous requirement than a lavatory 94 ft away, which requires only a 5 to 8 psig residual.
7. Equivalent length—meter to farthest water closet = 75 ft actual length × 1.6 = — 120 ft
   Here the 1.6 multiplier represents the designer's estimate based on the general complexity of the piping system. It will be seen later that a more accurate procedure is usually not required here.
8. Pressure in the water service pipe near the city water main — 50 psig

9. All piping is cast iron or galvanized steel which are rated as "fairly rough."
10. Water closets and urinals are "flush valve" operated.

The allowable pressure drop in the H & CW piping may be determined, as in the example problem previously included earlier in this chapter, as follows: Loss of pressure to the vertical height of the highest fixtures above the water main of 30 ft is equal to 30 ft ÷ 2.31 ft/psi = 12.98 psi. This 12.98 psi added to the meter loss of 3 psi and the required residual of 15 psi = ± 31 psi. The water main pressure of 50 psi minus this 31 psi leaves 19 psi that may be lost in the piping.

Since the pipeline from the water main to the meter is very simple and uncomplicated with only one elbow and two wide open gate valves the actual service length of 150 ft is increased 10% to an equivalent length of 165 ft. This, added to the equivalent length of 120 ft for building piping calculated above, equals a total equivalent length of 165 ft + 120 ft = 285 ft (or 2.85 100-ft lengths).

The allowable pipe loss of 19 psi ÷ 2.85 = 6.67 psi allowable loss per 100 ft of equivalent length; use 7 psi per 100 ft for design purposes. Entering the pipe sizing chart of fig. 14-9 on the vertical 7 psi per 100 ft line we find the gpm capacities of the various sizes of pipes to be as follows:

1/2-in. pipe 2 gpm
3/4-in. pipe 5 1/2 gpm
1-in. pipe 12 gpm
1 1/4-in. pipe 21 gpm
1 1/2-in. pipe 33 gpm
2-in. pipe 70 gpm
2 1/2-in. pipe 130 gpm

In fig. 14-16, for each pipeline segment listed, the loads in fixture units and the resulting gpm, taken from the proper curve in fig. 14-6, are listed. With the above listed pipe capacities established, it is a simple matter to select a pipe size for each pipeline segment. These are listed in fig. 14-16.

It should be observed by the reader that, in figs. 14-16 and 14-6, the curve 1 of fig. 14-6 (for flush valve systems) was not used in branches of the sys-

Figure 14-18 Allowance in equivalent length of pipe for friction loss in valves and threaded fittings. (Reprinted with permission from the 1972 Fundamentals Volume, ASHRAE Handbook and Products Directory.)

	Equivalent length of pipe for various fittings						
Diameter of fitting, inches	90-deg stand-ard ell, feet	45-deg stand-ard ell, feet	90-deg side tee, feet	Coupling or straight run of tee, feet	Gate valve, feet	Globe valve, feet	Angle valve, feet
3/8	1	0.6	1.5	0.3	0.2	8	4
1/2	2	1.2	3	0.6	0.4	15	8
3/4	2.5	1.5	4	0.8	0.5	20	12
1	3	1.8	5	0.9	0.6	25	15
1 1/4	4	2.4	6	1.2	0.8	35	18
1 1/2	5	3	7	1.5	1.0	45	22
2	7	4	10	2	1.3	55	28
2 1/2	8	5	12	2.5	1.6	65	34
3	10	6	15	3	2	80	40
3 1/2	12	7	18	3.6	2.4	100	50
4	14	8	21	4.0	2.7	125	55
5	17	10	25	5	3.3	140	70
6	20	12	30	6	4	165	80

tem having no flush valve water closets or urinals. Similarly, the curve 1 was not used in portions of the cold water main beyond the last branch that serves such flush valve fixtures. Of course, all hot water piping was sized with the use of curve 2.

In fig. 14-16 it may also be seen that some pipeline segments are intentionally undersized (noted by an asterisk) when the required gpm demand is only slightly greater than the listed capacity. However, notice that in the majority of the pipeline segments the required demand is appreciably less than the pipe capacity listed. This means that in most cases the pipeline pressure drop will be appreciably less than 7.0 psi per 100 ft, and the total pressure drop of the entire system will be much less than the 19 psi calculated as being allowable.

Thus it may be seen that the entire process is only an approximation, and the procedure of roughly estimating equivalent lengths in the manner described previously is entirely appropriate. Some designers feel that the oversizing of piping that results from the procedure shown above is justifiable on the basis that piping installations are often

poorly made (piping not properly reamed or cleaned, etc.) and that with use some pipelines do "lime" up and lose capacity.

However, for those who feel unable to adequately estimate equivalent lengths by increasing actual lengths with a certain percentage, fig. 14-18 will give assistance. This table lists the equivalent lengths in feet that may be added to the actual pipe length for various types and sizes of valves and pipe fittings. Adding these individual equivalent lengths will then develop the overall equivalent length of the longest circuits.

14-7 WATER SUPPLY IN TALL BUILDINGS

As mentioned previously, a pressure of 1.0 psi in a horizontal pipe such as a buried water main will lift water in a vertical branch line 2.31 ft. A 20-psi pressure would push water upward 46.2 ft in a vertical branch line, and if that vertical branch were 50 ft high, water would not overflow at the upper end even though it is wide open to the atmosphere.

With the pressure in most municipal water system distribution mains ranging from 50 to 70 psig, there is a limit to the height of a multistory building that receives water distributed in the building by city main pressure only. Four or five stories in building height is usually the limit. This can vary quite a lot, of course, depending on available pressure, extent of the water piping system and its pressure drop, and the distribution of plumbing fixtures.

If water is to be distributed throughout taller buildings, it must be lifted by some type of pumps. The types of pumps and the types of distribution systems to receive the pumped water have varied

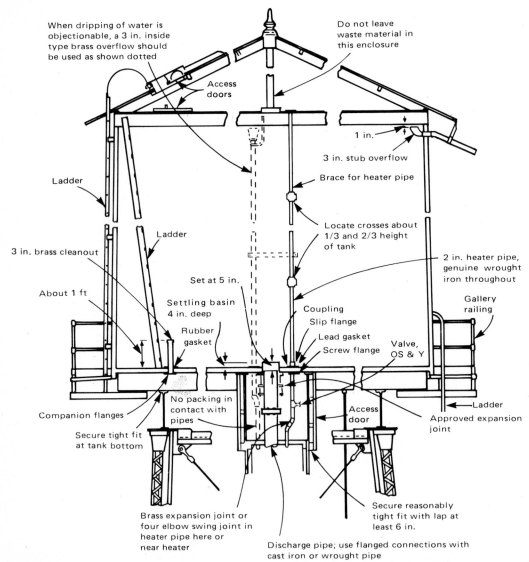

Figure 14-19 Elevated water storage tank, older type, wood construction. (From Babbitt, *Plumbing*, McGraw-Hill, New York, 1950, p. 144.)

greatly. Prior to the decade of the 1950s, an elevated storage tank on the building roof, exposed or in a penthouse, was usually utilized.

14-8 WATER STORAGE TANKS

The elevated tank has much to recommend it in certain situations. When the private or municipal water supply is undependable and subject to frequent interruption, a storage cushion of 7000 gal or more may permit continued building operation when otherwise it would need to stop. Variations in supply pressure are smoothed out completely; and, of course, the stored water may be of inestimable value for fire extinguishing purposes. Figure 14-19 shows details of an older-type wooden tank, and fig. 14-20 a more modern steel tank.

However, there are pros and cons with respect to elevated water storage tanks. Such tanks are very costly and the maintenance cost of them is also appreciable. The cost of the piping system in a building with such a tank is much greater than

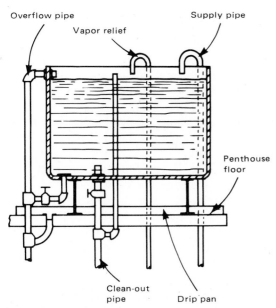

Figure 14-20 Elevated water storage tank, steel construction, for interior mounting. (From Babbitt, *Plumbing*, McGraw-Hill, New York, 1950, p. 145.)

with other available systems. The cost of providing heat to prevent tank freezing is great both in initial cost as well as in operating and maintenance costs. If the tank is to have a heated enclosure to prevent freezing and to improve appearance, these costs are again very high. The cost increase in the building structure to carry the extra 40,000 to 100,000 lb of concentrated weight is also appreciable.

One problem in the use of elevated tanks is that unless the tank is mounted appreciably higher than the building roof, the downward feeding pressure on the top floors of the building is inadequate. However, if the tank is mounted too high, the downward pressure on the lower floors of the building is excessive, and pressure reducing valve stations, a maintenance problem, must be installed.

Of course, if all building supply water, except that used on a few lower floors, is pumped to the elevated tank (higher than necessary for most stories of the building), energy is wasted. This waste is no longer conscionable and must be avoided even if greater initial system cost is incurred in doing so.

If a tall building is on fire, and the structural integrity of the building is being threatened by that fire, the great weight of an elevated water tank and its contents becomes a very real hazard. If it falls, its great weight crashing down through the weakened building is a serious threat to those who have not managed to escape from the building, and to those attempting to fight the fire.

Perhaps the case presented here against elevated water storage tanks is somewhat overstated. Such tanks are being installed in tall buildings and probably will continue to be in the future. It is difficult to place a weighted value on each advantage and each disadvantage in order to reach a balanced decision in the design of an individual building. However, this must be done, and the architect and prospective owner of that building must require that their engineering consultants provide the written results of such a study.

In all probability, most water supply systems in tall buildings of the future will be of the "tankless" type, using neither atmospheric vented tanks at the tops of buildings nor hydropneumatic pressure tanks at low or intermediate heights.

Hydropneumatic tanks have been used extensively in water supply systems, with the building pumps charging water into these pressurized tanks. The pressure carried must be high enough to boost water from the tank to the highest point in the plumbing with an adequate residual pressure remaining at that point. In a tall building, this tank must be of ASME-approved design for these high pressures; as such it will be very costly.

Such a tank will need to be two to three times larger than an elevated storage tank, since most of the tank is occupied by air. An air compressor system must be provided to help maintain the tank air cushion required. The controls for such a tank system are complicated and costly—to maintain the water at the proper level and at the same time maintaining proper pressure.

In a hydropneumatic tank the air must be free of oil and other contamination. Great quantities of air will be absorbed in the water as a result of the pressures carried; this air can be a problem as it leaves the water when pressure is reduced. These tanks are subject to considerable corrosion, as is the piping system, and tank maintenance costs are high. Because of their great size and required accessory equipment, much floor space in the building must be charged, as a cost, to the tank-type system. The future of hydropneumatic tanks in tall buildings is definitely limited.

When a building is located in an area where the municipal water supply system is undependable or where the water supply is limited, it may be wise to use a suction tank at the point of service water entrance into the building. Such tanks provide a reserve supply of water and permit building operation during periods of no water supply. Suction tanks also provide a reserve for firefighting.

Suction tanks may be either open to atmosphere or may be closed and pressurized. When open, they, like elevated tanks, provide opportunity for contamination from dust and vermin, and much maintenance to control rust, dirt, and so on, is required. One disadvantage of open tanks is that the entering water pressure is lost; this represents a loss of energy. Closed suction tanks provide the necessary storage cushion without suffering the open tank's disadvantages. However, the closed tank must carry hydrostatic pressure, and therefore it is more expensive.

Any type of storage tank represents a maintenance problem, and periodic shutdown of the system to permit this maintenance is necessary. In some buildings a nighttime shutdown for maintenance is no hardship; in others, such as a hotel, a shutdown may be intolerable.

14-9 TANKLESS WATER SYSTEMS

Tankless water systems consist merely of a multipump pumping system which accepts potable water from the municipal water supply main through the building water service, and delivers that water at proper pressure to all points of the building. There is no tank of any type included in this system. Usually, two, three, or perhaps four pumps are utilized with at least one pump running at all times.

With a tankless system the peak demand of the building is applied directly to the city water main with no cushioning effect such as might be provided by a storage tank. Therefore, this system should not be used unless the water supply utility engineers can give assurance that these peak demands can be satisfactorily carried. Most of the time this will be the case.

Usually two or three pumps of unequal sizes are used; and these are sometimes assembled at the factory on a common steel base with all interconnecting piping and some of the necessary wiring completed. Figure 14-21 shows typical installation details. Both horizontally split case multistage pumps and vertical multistage diffuser-type turbine pumps are frequently utilized.

The choice of the basic design of the pumps is not one to be made lightly. Of course, high discharge pressures are necessary, and pumps that boost water 800 to 900 ft upward are sometimes

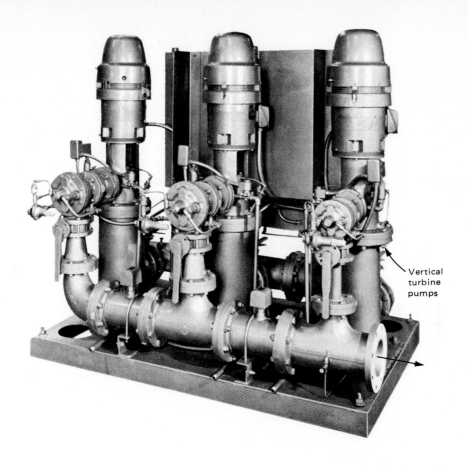

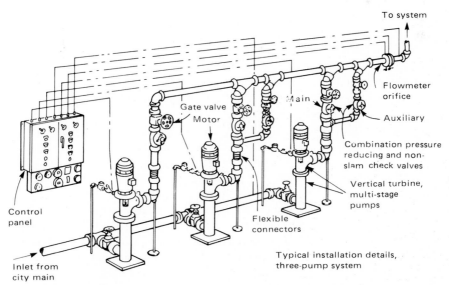

Figure 14-21 Tankless water systems using three pumps. (Photo courtesy of Peerless Pump, an Indian Head Company.)

required. Nine hundred feet of static hydraulic pressure is equal to 390 psig pressure, and the piping, valves, and accessories that are required to sustain such a pressure must be carefully selected. Of course, this burden can be eased with the use of pumping stations located on intermediate floors of a tall building, with the lowest pumps delivering water only one-third or one-half of the building height.

Pumps must also be carefully selected in the light of the water demand characteristics of a given building. Of necessity, the water demand on occasion will be very low—almost zero. A pump designed to provide, as is important, a relatively flat pressure curve (one in which discharge pressure remains high as gpm delivery falls off) will involve great hydraulic turbulence at very low delivery rates. This can not only be damaging to the pump but also very noisy and disturbing to building occupants.

Further, such a pump operating at very high delivery rates when discharge pressures are comparatively low can experience destructive cavitation, resulting in complete pump failure. Therefore, pump performance characteristics are exceedingly important, and pump selections should be made only by those who are fully familiar with the special problem involved and the pumps contemplated.

Since operational noise is a critical factor in most tall buildings, it is recommended that pumps always be selected with an impeller that is at least 15% smaller in diameter than the maximum size that will fit into a given casing. An impeller that fits too tightly in its casing with very little clearance between the impeller and the casing cutoff at the casing outlet will transmit a waterborne noise throughout the piping system.

Of course, pump vibration causes a mechanical noise through the pump base and into the building structure, and also through the piping as well. Best-quality pumps will be essentially free from vibration, but it is still cost justifiable to use vibration eliminator pump mountings and flexible, rubber pipe connections at pump inlets and outlets.

In a pumping system such as that pictured in fig. 14-21, the three pumps all run at constant speed, probably 3500 rpm in a very tall building, but they are of different capacities, and much of the time only one pump will be running. One popular arrangement is with a No. 1 pump (which starts first) having 25% of estimated required total capacity. Each of the other two pumps would be sized for 55% of total required capacity. This provides flexibility, and each of the two larger pumps serves as a standby for the other. It also provides excess capcity to allow for future growth in load.

Because the pressure in the city water main may be subjected to considerable variation, the pump inlet pressure will vary, and corresponding pressure variations will be experienced in pump discharge pressure and piping system pressures. Where this is objectionable (and it may not be), pressure reducing valves may be installed in the pump discharge piping. One manufacturer integrates its pressure-reducing valves and its nonslam check valves into one device. These are often installed in unequal pairs—one small and one large. The large valve opens only on high flow rates when two pumps are operating.

It is helpful in any system if a flow meter orifice is installed in the primary supply main to the building. An indicating meter head may then be mounted in the control panel to show at all times, with the pressure gauges required, what is happening in the system.

With vertical turbine type pumps in use, comparatively little floor space will be required. This, with the elimination of water storage tanks and the floor space and structure cost reductions involved, can make the tankless water system very favorable in initial overall cost. Operating characteristics are also quite favorable. It may be easily seen, then, why the tank-type systems are losing popularity in tall buildings.

With tankless systems one old familiar problem that has not previously caused too much concern now takes on new dimensions. The problem is one of estimating the maxmo or peak rate of water demand on the basis of which a system could be sized and selected. With the older tank systems, the result of oversizing a system was an extra initial outlay of money, and this was unfortunate; but there were no permanent operational penalties to be suffered.

With a tankless system, it is important that system sizing be accurate, because at stake are both initial cost and operating cost characteristics. An oversize pump, or system of pumps, operating 24 hr a day, often at only a small fraction of peak load, can involve great inefficiency as well as severe maintenance problems. Called to attention, then, is the fact that many designers have expressed the opinion that the Hunter curves, such as figs. 14-6 and 14-7, do give flow rates that are appreciably too high. Further research is badly needed to corroborate or negate this opinion.

James Braxton, C. E., reporting in *Consulting Engineer,* May 1965, indicates that actual flow tests, on a large number of housing projects owned by the Chicago Housing Authority, showed peak flow rates of about 60% (44 to 68% range) of the flow rates (in gpm) projected by the Hunter curves. These housing projects included nearly 2000 apartments for elderly people. Approximately the same results (44 to 65%) appeared in flow tests on housing projects in Chicago for low-income families (not elderly).

In sizing tankless pumping systems, it may be satisfactory to discount the Hunter curves down to 60% of their indicated values, if total pumping capacity of the selected system has some intentional excess capacity. In the three-pump system discussed above, total capacity is 135% (25% + 55% + 55%) of anticipated peak flow rate. Here the intentional excess is 35%.

14-10 DOMESTIC HOT WATER SYSTEMS

The design of domestic hot water systems does not usually pose any serious problems for the building designer. The sizing of the hot water piping is quite conventional, and the Hunter curves and fixture unit tables may be used as set forth earlier in this chapter. The only diffculty usually experienced is in selecting the maximum *hourly* demand for hot water and the size of a water heater and hot water storage tank to meet that demand. Notice

that this is not maximum *daily* demand, nor is it maximum momentary (in gpm) demand.

On rare occasions, an "instantaneous" water heater may be selected for use. Such a heater has no storage tank and must be capable of heating water as fast as it is drawn. In this case, the maxmo demand is all important. However, in larger nonresidential buildings the use of hot water storage tanks is really necessary to meet good design requirements. In the problem of determining maximum hourly hot water demand, the Edison Electric Institute has performed a very valuable service. During the decade of the 1960s, EEI conducted a very extensive investigation into the usage of domestic hot water in many types of buildings. Actual metered flow tests have shed much light where great darkness previously existed; for this we are deeply indebted to the EEI.

The information advanced by the Edison Electric Institute takes the form of a table and eight charts. The table reproduced in fig. 14-22 shows demands for hot water for many types of establishments expressed in terms of gallons per hour (gph) and gallons per day (gpd) for a maximum use day and an average-use day. The eight charts, figs. 14-23 through 14-30, show required hot water recovery (heating) rates in relation to the size of hot water storage tanks to be used.

The water heating capacity of a heater in gph is usually referred to as its *recovery rate*. Recovery rate is usually based on some cold water inlet temperature, such as 40 to 60°F, and a final temperature which is almost always 140°F. The EEI data also assume, appropriately, that for a given load, the larger the recovery capacity of a water heater may be, the smaller the size of a hot water storage tank may be, and vice versa.

In the table of fig. 14-22 the maximum hour demand shown was experienced during the maximum day, which is also listed. Further, these maximum hour values seem to indicate, and the eight charts confirm, the recovery capacities that water heaters would need if no storage tank (zero storage) is utilized. As mentioned, these would be called *instantaneous heaters.*

The Edison Electric Institute report indicates,

Figure 14-22   Hot water demands and use for various types of buildings. (Excerpted with permission from Edison Electric Institute Publication 9C–203.)

Type of Building	Maximum Hour	Maximum Day	Average Day
Men's dormitories	3.8 gal/student	22.0 gal/student	13.1 gal/student
Women's dormitories	5.0 gal/student	26.5 gal/student	12.3 gal/student
Motels: No. of units			
20 or less	6.0 gal/unit	35.0 gal/unit	20.0 gal/unit
60	5.0 gal/unit	25.0 gal/unit	14.0 gal/unit
100 or more	4.0 gal/unit	15.0 gal/unit	10.0 gal/unit
Nursing homes	4.5 gal/bed	30.0 gal/bed	18.4 gal/bed
Office buildings	0.4 gal/person	2.0 gal/person	1.0 gal/person
Food service establishments			
Type A-full meal restaurants and cafeterias	1.5 gal/maximum meals/hour	11.0 gal/maximum meals/hour	2.4 gal/average* meals/day
Type B-drive-ins, grilles, luncheonettes, sandwich and snack shops	0.7 gal/maximum meals/hour	6.0 gal/maximum meals/hour	0.7 gal/average* meals/day
Apartment houses: No. of apartments			
20 or less	12.0 gal/apartment	80.0 gal/apartment	42.0 gal/apartment
50	10.0 gal/apartment	73.0 gal/apartment	40.0 gal/apartment
75	8.5 gal/apartment	66.0 gal/apartment	38.0 gal/apartment
100	7.0 gal/apartment	60.0 gal/apartment	37.0 gal/apartment
over 130	5.0 gal/apartment	50.0 gal/apartment	35.0 gal/apartment
Elementary schools	0.6 gal/student	1.5 gal/student	0.6 gal/student*
Junior and senior high schools	1.0 gal/student	3.6 gal/student	1.8 gal/student*

*Per day of operation.

however, that it is not safe to assume that an instantaneous heater may be sized in the light of the data presented. Before this could be done, a definition of a suitable time frame that could be called instantaneous and that would be universally ac-

cepted would need to be made. This has not been attempted, and no reliable and accepted information is available for sizing instantaneous heaters.

In each of the eight charts of figs. 14-23 to 14-30, the left-hand vertical line, for zero storage

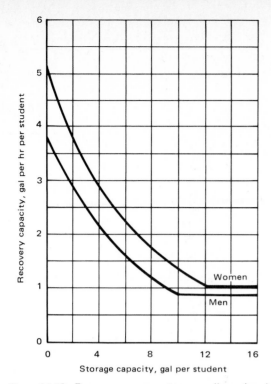

Figure 14-23 Recovery versus storage—college dormitories. (Excerpted with permission from Edison Electric Institute Publication 9C–203.)

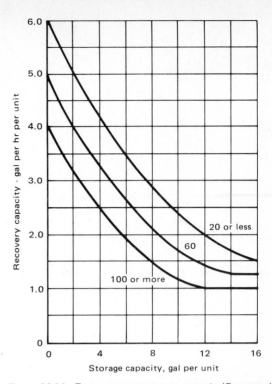

Figure 14-24 Recovery versus storage—motels. (Excerpted with permission from Edison Electric Institute Publication 9C–203.)

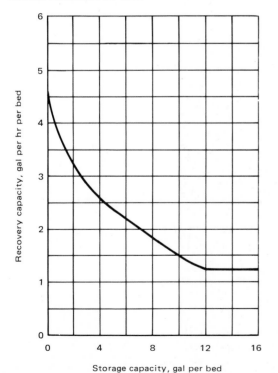

Figure 14-25 Recovery versus storage—nursing homes. (Excerpted with permission from Edison Electric Institute Publication 9C–203.)

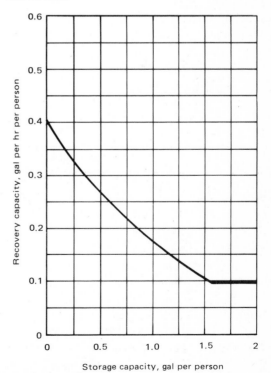

Figure 14-26 Recovery versus storage—office buildings. (Excerpted with permission from Edison Electric Institute Publication 9C–203.)

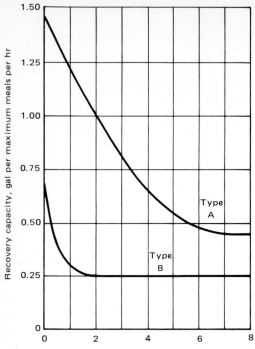

Figure 14-27 Recovery versus storage—food service. (Excerpted with permission from Edison Electric Institute Publication 9C-203.)

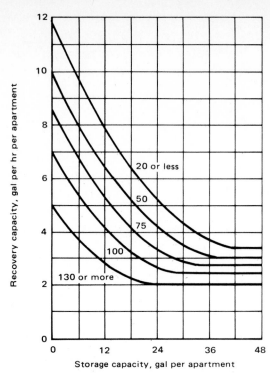

Figure 14-28 Recovery versus storage—apartments. (Excerpted with permission from Edison Electric Institute Publication 9C-203.)

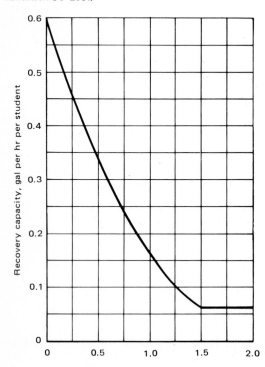

Figure 14-29 Recovery versus storage—elementary schools. (Excerpted with permission from Edison Electric Institute Publication 9C-203.)

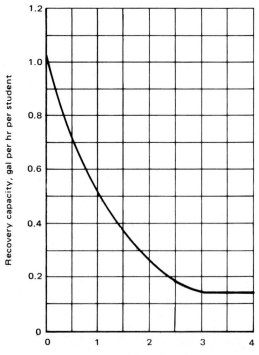

Figure 14-30 Recovery versus storage—high schools. (Excerpted with permission from Edison Electric Institute Publication 9C-203.)

capacity, indicates the maximum hour demand at points where the chart curves intersect this vertical zero line. For example, in a 60-room motel, the maximum hour demand from the table in fig. 14-22 is 5.0 gph per motel room or unit. In fig. 14-24, the chart for motels, the intersection of the "60" curve with the vertical zero line indicates the same value, 5.0 gph per unit. Notice that in every curve of every one of the eight charts, as the storage capacity is increased the recovery capacity decreases—but only to a certain minimum value.

The storage capacities shown in the eight charts are available capacities and not gross storage tank volumes. There is an appreciable difference. Suppose, for example, that a 500-gal hot water storage tank is full of 140°F hot water from bottom to top. If a heavy demand is placed on this tank with cold water entering at the bottom and hot water leaving at the top, the temperature of the leaving water will fall below 140°F long before 500 gal has been drawn off. By the time that 500 gal has been drawn, the temperature may be well below 100°F or even 80°F, if 60°F water is entering and the recovery capacity is only a fraction of 500 gph—as it normally would be. It is usually assumed that only 70% of the volume of a storage tank is "available" as fully heated water; in this example, 70% of 500 = 350 gal is available.

14-11 WATER HEATERS

In using the EEI capacity charts, the designer must make a decision as to whether to use a water heating installation with high recovery capacity and low storage capacity, low recovery and high storage, or something in between. Several factors bear on this decision:

1 The rate of availability of heat in the form of electricity, fossil fuel, steam, high-temperature water, and so on. With fossil fuels there is usually no limitation; with the others there may be.

2 Building space available. A large storage tank requires a great volume of space, but a high-capacity heater may require only a very little more space than a low-capacity heater.

3 Is a combination heater and storage unit to be used or will the heater and the tank be procured and mounted separately? Storage tank sizes are very definitely limited in combined heater and tank units.

4 The type of tank lining (for corrosion protection) to be required. If a glass lining is to be used, the tank size is limited; if a cementitious field-applied lining is required, the tank must not be too small because a worker must crawl inside to apply the lining (300-gal minimum).

It is recommended here that, in general, heater capacities be very large and that storage capacities be proportionately small. It is also strongly recommended that whenever possible, an integrated, factory-assembled heater and tank unit be utilized. In this case, all controls, necessary piping and wiring, insulation, and metal jacket will be factory applied, and the need for expensive field labor will be minimized. It is further recommended that heater-tank units be fabricated in a vertical pattern, rather than horizontal, to reduce floor space requirements.

The old-style installation in which a separate, horizontal storage tank hung at the equipment room ceiling, or mounted on tall legs, and served by a separate heater with lots of interconnecting piping should be considered obsolete and unnecessarily wasteful of material, energy, installation labor, and building space. Factory-integrated heater-tank units are available in recovery capacities ranging up to 4,000,000 BH. When arranged in duplex or triplex there is little probability of need for a capacity greater than this.

Figure 14-31 shows illustrations of typical factory-assembled vertical pattern water heaters which use steam and electricity as a source of heat. Figure 14-31a shows a heater having both an electric heating element and a steam heating element. Such heaters are for use where steam from a steam heating system is used in winter and where the electric element is used in summer when the steam heating system is inoperative. Figure 14-32 illustrates a vertical pattern, factory-assembled, fossil-fuel-fired water heater complete with burner and all controls, and a vertical, glass-lined storage tank.

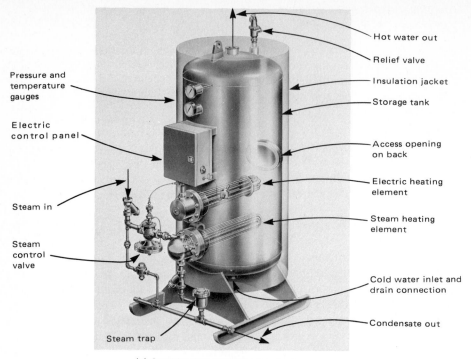

Hot water out

Relief valve

Insulation jacket

Storage tank

Access opening
on back

Electric heating
element

Steam heating
element

Cold water inlet and
drain connection

Condensate out

Pressure and
temperature
gauges

Electric
control panel

Steam in

Steam
control
valve

Steam trap

(*a*) Combination steam-electric heater

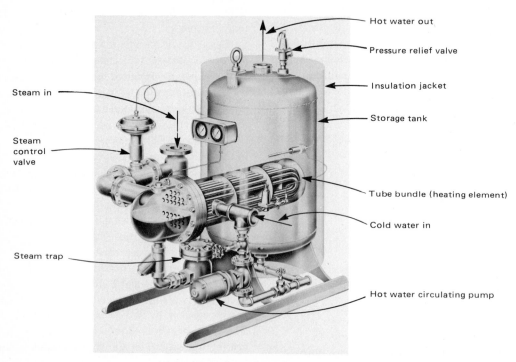

Hot water out

Pressure relief valve

Insulation jacket

Storage tank

Tube bundle (heating element)

Cold water in

Hot water circulating pump

Steam in

Steam
control
valve

Steam trap

(*b*) Steam type water heater

Figure 14-31 Storage water heaters, steam and electrically operated. (Courtesy of Patterson-Kelley Co., Division of Harsco Corp.)

Insulated
metal jacket

Typical specifications:
Diameter: 28 in.
Height. 73 in.
Recovery capacity
at 100°F rise: 420 gph
Tank size: 69 gal.
Glasslined tank
AGA. labeled
ASME labeled

s valve

Figure 14-32 Typical gas-fired water heater unit. (Courtesy of A. O. Smith Corp., Kankakee, Il., 60901.)

Water heater units must be equipped with storage tanks that are properly protected from corrosion, electrolytic action, and chemical attack from almost all types of water. Unless quite small, 200 gal or less, tanks should not be made of galvanized steel. With any type of galvanized steel tank, a sacrificial magnesium anode should be installed in such a way as to suffer the attack of any electrolytic action that may occur. Of course, such sacrificial anodes will need replacement frequently.

However, if a restrictive budget prevents the use of a properly lined tank, it is better to use an extra-thick black steel tank than to use a galvanized tank. Tanks with a fused glass lining are now available in larger and larger sizes—up to 3500 gal. Glass-lined tanks offer excellent protection, and some manufacturers of such tanks provide 5- to 10-year warranties on them.

Other satisfactory tank linings are also available. Copper linings weighing 3 to 4 lb/ft², if properly secured and extended outward through all tank openings, can provide adequate protection. Of

course, copper linings are exceedingly expensive. Another suitable tank lining is a cementitious material such as Formula G-8 Pre Krete (a registered proprietary trade name). This material is chemically inert to most waters, such as soft water, acidic water, steam condensate, and demineralized water. This aluminous cement material is nonporous and cures to high hardness and durability.

Some manufacturers provide tank linings which consist of a four-coat phenolic epoxy resin. Each coat is baked at a temperature of 400°F, and when properly applied can withstand the attack of highly corrosive water containing salts, acids, and alkalies. Considering the high cost of such water heating packages, the elimination of a good tank lining to save cost is certainly false economy.

All such water heaters must be manufactured in strict compliance with established codes. All tanks should be constructed and labeled in accordance with ASME Code Section I, III, IV, or VIII. Electrically operated or oil-fired heaters should be UL (Underwriters Laboratory) labeled, and all gas-fired units should be AGA (American Gas Association) labeled. Whenever possible the pressure relief valve, or the pressure-temperature relief valve, should be selected by the manufacturer and mounted on the heater unit at the factory. Such valves must be ASME (American Society of Mechanical Engineers) labeled and guaranteed to satisfy all local installation code requirements.

In some cases the operator of a building may require water at two temperatures, one of which may be 170 or 180°F for dishwashing, cooking, pot scrubbing, and so on. It is possible to set the heater thermostat to maintain 180°F water in the heater at all times. This water is used directly for such high-temperature purposes. The lower-temperature needs are met through the use of thermostatic blender or mixing valves.

These thermostatic valves automatically draw 180°F water from the heater and cold water from the domestic cold water system and mix these to deliver hot water at whatever temperature is desired. In the author's experience, it is much better to maintain the primary water heater at a lower temperature and use localized booster heaters at points where extra-high-temperature water is required.

14-12　WATER HEATER SIZING EXAMPLES

Examples are needed here to illustrate the use of the table and charts shown in figs. 14-22 through 14-30. In using these charts, the designer must first develop a philosophy of the design of water heating systems. It is suggested here that this philosophy should embrace the following few principles:

1　Storage tanks should always be used and dependence never placed on instantaneous heaters.

2　Water heaters should be comparatively large in capacity.

3　As a result of item 2, storage tanks should be comparatively small, but not smaller than 50 gal in volume except in very small projects.

4　Hot water tanks should be integrated into a common factory-assembled package, including the heater and all controls, piping, and wiring.

5　Water heater packages should be of essentially a vertical pattern to conserve floor space.

Example 14-2　A motel is to include 100 room units. An 80% heater capacity is to be used. Find the heater recovery capacity in gph and the storage volume in gallons of the required storage tank.

Solution　The term "80% heater" is used to indicate a heater having 80% of the capacity required of a "zero storage" unit; this means 80% of the maximum hourly demand shown in fig. 14-22. In fig. 14-22 the maximum hourly demand of a 100-unit motel is 4 gph per unit—or 4 × 100 units = 400 gph. An 80% heater would then need recovery capacity of 80% of 400 gph = 320 gph.

In fig. 14-24, the 100-motel-unit curve indicates that for a recovery capacity of 3.2 gph per unit (320 gph ÷ 100 = 3.2 gph per unit) a storage capacity of 2 gal per unit is required. Therefore, a tank is required that can *deliver* 2 × 100, or 200 gal of hot water. However, this is not tank size; it is delivery capacity, which is only 70% of tank size

—as previously explained. Therefore, tank volume must be 200 ÷ 0.7 = 286 gal (286 × 0.7 = 200).

Example 14-3　Determine proper water heater recovery capacity and storage tank size for a 300-student women's dormitory which has a cafeteria that must serve 300 meals per hour (maximum rate) and is a full service, three meals per day facility. The water heater is to be an 85% heater.

Solution　Figure 14-23 shows that for a women's dormitory a 100% heater would need a capacity of 5 gph recovery rate per student. An 85% heater would then require a recovery capacity of 5 × 0.85 = 4.25 gph per student. Figure 14-23 then shows a storage tank delivery capacity of about 1.1 gal per student. For the dormitory, then, a recovery capacity of 4.25 gph × 300 students = 1275 gph is required; and a tank delivery capacity of 1.1 × 300 = 330 gal is also required.

In addition, fig. 14-27 shows that for a full service (type A) food service facility a 100% heater would need a recovery capacity of 1.5 gph per meal served during the time of maximum service. An 85% heater would then need recovery capacity for the cafeteria of 0.85 × 1.5 × 300 meals per hour = 382.5 gph.

Figure 14-27 also shows that for a recovery rate of 1.275 gph per meal (85% of 1.5), the storage tank delivery capacity = 0.8 gal per meal. 0.8 gal × 300 meals = 240 gal delivery capacity.

The dormitory and cafeteria needs may now be added to find the total requirements:

Recovery capacity—dorm	1275
Recovery capacity—cafeteria	382.5
Total recovery	1657.5 gph
Storage tank delivery	
Capacity—for dormitory	330
Capacity—for cafeteria	240
Total delivery	570 gal

To achieve a tank delivery of 570 gal, the storage tank size must be 570 gal ÷ 0.7 = 814 gal. Therefore, this building needs a heater with a recovery rate of 1657.5 gph and an 814-gal hot water storage tank.

PROBLEMS

14-1 A hotel has 400 guest rooms with connecting baths, and each room has one double bed. On special occasions all rooms are occupied with either one or two persons. The average occupancy rate on those occasions is 1.8 persons per room. Find the probable total daily demand for potable water in gpd.

14-2 A motel has 150 motel rooms each of which has one flush tank water closet, one bathtub, and one lavatory. Find the number of total water supply fixture units (for maxmo demand) of load on the cold water service pipe that supplies water to this motel. Motel rooms are considered to be private and not public rooms.

14-3 Find the FU load on the hot water supply main that delivers hot water only to the bathtubs and lavatories in the 150-unit motel of prob. 14-2.

14-4 Find the FU load on the cold water supply main that delivers cold water only to the water closets, bathtubs, and lavatories in the 150-unit motel of prob. 14-2.

14-5 Find the maxmo water demands in gpm for the fixture unit totals calculated in probs. 14-2, 14-3, and 14-4.

14-6 If the allowable pressure drop in fairly rough water piping is 8 psi per 100 ft of equivalent length, what would be the pipe sizes of the supply mains in probs. 14-2, 14-3, and 14-4?

14-7 An office building has a regular occupancy of 1200 people. If the domestic water heater is to be a 90% heater, what would be the required recovery rate in gph, and what would be the actual tank size of the required hot water storage tank?

Chapter 15

Sanitary Drainage and Venting

15-1 GENERALITIES

The modern building as we know it today would be impossible without the high-quality plumbing systems that are now in mandatory use. It is difficult to understand how a populace could remain healthy under the unsanitary conditions that prevailed during times as recent as the year 1900.

The famous cartoon which shows the upstairs chambermaid getting rid of the contents of the vitreous china commode by tossing the contents out an upstairs window into the street gutter below was based on fact and not fantasy. It is not strange that Thomas Crapper (his real name) was given a royal commission from King Edward VII in about 1885 to install his invention in the king's new country home at Sandringham, England, after perfecting his "waste water preventer"—the first practical water-flushed water closet that began the

era of effective inside plumbing as we know it today.

The primary purpose and function of building plumbing systems, of course, is to provide the transportation and proper disposal of animal and human wastes. These wastes are highly offensive and dangerous to human health, and their prompt and efficient disposal is all important to public well-being. The science of this disposal is a study to which hundreds have devoted their lives, and thousands upon thousands of people are fully dedicated to the application, in a practical way, of the principles which that science has developed.

Many diverse codes for plumbing system design and installation have been written and voted into law. Nearly every incorporated municipality, county, and state in the United States has its official plumbing code. There are many differences in these codes, but slowly the similarities are overtaking and engulfing the differences. There will always be justifiable differences based on local special needs and conditions; but someday, we hope, we will have a nearly universal, uniform national plumbing code. This will be of great value to the construction industry and will contribute extensively to public health.

Basically, sanitary plumbing systems consist of plumbing fixtures which when supplied with adequate quantities of suitable water can receive waste products and deliver them into a well-designed drainage and sewerage system. (A "sewerage" system is a network of "sewers" that carries "sewage.") Of course, the picture is incomplete until we add the very necessary sewage treatment facilities that can render the dangerous sewage products innocuous and environmentally acceptable.

The design and operation of plumbing systems has evolved during the last 100 years from a very imprecise and greatly misunderstood science to a well-developed discipline which is based on a well-defined and extensively accepted set of *Principles.* These principles form the foundation of our uniform National Plumbing Code, which provides much of the information set forth in this text. These principles must be studied and fully understood by any student of construction.

Principle 1 All premises intended for human habitation, occupancy, or use shall be provided with a supply of pure and wholesome water, neither connected with unsafe water supplies nor subject to the hazards of backflow or back siphonage.

Principle 2 Plumbing fixtures, devices, and appurtenances shall be supplied with water in sufficient volume and at pressures adequate to enable them to function satisfactorily and without undue noise under all normal conditions of use.

Principle 3 Plumbing shall be designed and adjusted to use the minimum quantity of water consistent with proper performance and cleaning.

Principle 4 Devices for heating and storing water shall be so designed and installed as to prevent dangers from explosion through overheating.

Principle 5 Every building having plumbing fixtures installed and intended for human habitation, occupancy, or use on premises abutting on a street, alley, or easement in which there is a public sewer shall have a connection with the sewer.

Principle 6 Each family dwelling unit on premises abutting on a sewer or with a private sewage-disposal system shall have at least one water closet and one kitchen-type sink. It is further recommended that a lavatory and bathtub or shower shall be installed to meet the basic requirements of sanitation and personal hygiene.

All other structures for human occupancy or use on premises abutting on a sewer or with a private sewage-disposal system shall have adequate sanitary facilities, but in no case less than one water closet and one other fixture for cleaning purposes.

Principle 7 Plumbing fixtures shall be made of smooth nonabsorbent material, shall be free of concealed fouling surfaces, and shall be located in ventilated enclosures.

Principle 8 The drainage system shall be designed, constructed, and maintained so as to guard against fouling, deposit of solids, and clogging, and with adequate cleanouts so arranged that the pipes may be readily cleaned.

Principle 9 The piping of the plumbing system shall be of durable material, free of defective workmanship, and so designed and constructed as to give satisfactory service for its reasonable expected life.

Principle 10 Each fixture directly connected to the drainage system shall be equipped with a water-seal trap.

Principle 11 The drainage system shall be designed to provide an adequate circulation of air in all pipes with no danger of siphonage, aspiration, or forcing of trap seals under conditions of ordinary use.

Principle 12 Each vent terminal shall extend to the outer air and be so installed as to minimize the possibilities of clogging and the return of foul air to the building.

Principle 13 The plumbing system shall be

subjected to such tests as will effectively disclose all leaks and defects in the work.

Principle 14 No substance that will clog the pipes, produce explosive mixtures, destroy the pipes or their joints, or interfere unduly with the sewage-disposal process shall be allowed to enter the building drainage system.

Principle 15 Proper protection shall be provided to prevent contamination of food, water, sterile goods, and similar materials by backflow of sewage. When necessary, the fixture, device, or appliance shall be connected indirectly with the building drainage system.

Principle 16 No water closet shall be located in a room or compartment which is not properly lighted and ventilated.

Principle 17 If water closets or other plumbing fixtures are installed in buildings where there is no sewer within a reasonable distance, suitable provision shall be made for disposing of the building sewage by some accepted method of sewage treatment and disposal.

Principle 18 Where a plumbing drainage system may be subjected to backflow of sewage, suitable provision shall be made to prevent its overflow in the building.

Principle 19 Plumbing systems shall be maintained in a sanitary and serviceable condition. See definition "Plumbing."

Principle 20 All plumbing fixtures shall be so installed with regard to spacing as to be reasonably accessible for their intended use.

Principle 21 Plumbing shall be installed with due regard to preservation of the strength of structural members and prevention of damage to walls and other surfaces through fixture usage.

Principle 22 Sewage or other waste from a plumbing system which may be deleterious to surface or subsurface waters shall not be discharged into the ground or into any waterway unless it has first been rendered innocuous through subjection to some acceptable form of treatment.

It is also imperative, of course, that we clearly define all terms that are peculiar to plumbing prac-

tices, since there are many of those that are not self-explanatory. The necessary definitions follow, arranged alphabetically.

Air gap An air gap in a water-supply system is the unobstructed vertical distance through the free atmosphere between the lowest opening from any pipe or faucet supplying water to a tank, plumbing fixture, or other device and the flood-level rim of the receptacle.

Area drain An area drain is a receptacle designed to collect surface or rainwater from an open area.

Backflow Backflow is the flow of water or other liquids, mixtures, or substances into the distributing pipes of a potable supply of water from any source or sources other than its intended source. (*See also* Back siphonage.)

Backflow connection Backflow connection or condition is any arrangement whereby backflow can occur.

Backflow preventer A backflow preventer is a device or means to prevent backflow into the potable-water system.

Back siphonage Back siphonage is the flowing back of used, contaminated, or polluted water from a plumbing fixture or vessel into a water-supply pipe due to a negative pressure in such pipe. (*See also* Backflow.)

Battery of fixtures A battery of fixtures is any group of two or more similar adjacent fixtures which discharge into a common horizontal waste or soil branch.

Boiler blowoff A boiler blowoff is an outlet on a boiler to permit emptying or discharge of sediment. This also applies to the hot discharge from a water-storage tank or any other equipment which may discharge hot water over 140°F or steam.

Branch A branch is any part of the piping system other than a main, riser, or stack.

Branch interval A branch interval is a length of soil or waste stack corresponding in general to a story height, but in no case less than 8 ft, within which the horizontal branches from one floor or story of a building are connected to the stack.

Branch vent A branch vent is a vent connecting one or more individual vents with a vent stack or stack vent.

Building drain The building (house) drain is that part of the lowest piping of a drainage system which receives the discharge from soil, waste, and other drainage pipes inside the walls of the building and conveys it to the building (house) sewer, beginning 3 ft outside the building wall.

Building sewer The building (house) sewer is that part of the horizontal piping of a drainage system which extends from the end of the building drain and which receives the discharge of the building drain and conveys it to a public sewer, private sewer, individual sewage-disposal system, or other point of disposal.

Building storm drain A building (house) storm drain is a building drain used for conveying rainwater, surface water, groundwater, subsurface water, condensate, cooling water, or other similar discharge to a building storm sewer or a combined building sewer, extending to a point not less than 3 ft outside the building wall.

Building storm sewer A building (house) storm sewer is the extension from the building storm drain to the public storm sewer, combined sewer, or other point of disposal.

Building subdrain A building (house) subdrain is that portion of a drainage system which cannot drain by gravity into the building sewer.

Building trap A building (house) trap is a device, fitting, or assembly of fittings installed in the building drain to prevent circulation of air between the drainage system of the building and the building sewer.

Cesspool A cesspool is a lined excavation in the ground which receives the discharge of a drainage system or part thereof, so designed as to retain the organic matter and solids discharging therein, but permitting the liquids to seep through the bottom and sides.

Circuit vent A circuit vent is a branch vent that serves two or more traps and extends from in front of the last fixture connection of a horizontal branch to the vent stack.

Code The word "code" when used alone shall mean the regulations, subsequent amendments thereto, or any emergency rule or regulation which the administrative authority having jurisdiction may lawfully adopt.

Combination fixture A combination fixture is a fixture combining one sink and tray or a two- or three-compartment sink or tray in one unit.

Combination waste and vent system A combination waste and vent system is a specially designed system of waste piping embodying the horizontal wet venting of one or more sinks or floor drains by means of a common waste and vent pipe adequately sized to provide free movement of air above the flow line of the drain.

Combined building sewer A combined building sewer receives storm water and sewage.

Common vent A common vent is a vent connecting at the junction of two fixture drains and serving as a vent for both fixtures.

Continuous vent A continuous vent is a vertical vent that is a continuation of the drain to which it connects.

Continuous waste A continuous waste is a drain from a combination fixture or two or three fixtures in combination connected to a single trap.

Cross connection A cross connection is any physical connection or arrangement between two otherwise separate piping systems, one of which contains potable water and the other water of unknown or questionable safety, whereby water may flow from one system to the other, the direction of flow depending on the pressure differential between the two systems.

Dead end A dead end is a branch leading from a soil, waste, or vent pipe, building drain, or building sewer, which is terminated at a developed distance of 2 ft or more by means of a plug or other closed fitting.

Developed length The developed length of a pipe is its length along the centerline of the pipe and fittings.

Diameter Unless specifically stated, the term "diameter" is the nominal diameter as designated commercially.

Diversity The diversity is the degree of variation from 100% full or continuous usage.

Drain A drain is any pipe which carries wastewater or waterborne wastes in a building drainage system.

Drain arm A drain arm is that portion of the drain line of an individual plumbing fixture from the crown or downstream side of its trap to the point where it is vented or where it connects to another drain line.

Drainage system A drainage system (drainage piping) includes all the piping within public or private premises, which conveys sewage, rainwater, or other liquid wastes to a legal point of disposal, but does not include the mains of a public sewer system or a private or public sewage-treatment or disposal plant.

Durham system Durham system is a term used to describe soil or waste systems where all piping is of threaded pipe, tubing, or other such rigid construction, using recessed drainage fittings to correspond to the types of piping.

Effective opening The effective opening is the minimum cross-sectional area at the point of water-supply discharge, measured or expressed in terms of (1) the diameter of a circle; (2) if the opening is not circular, the diameter of a circle or equivalent cross-sectional area.

Effluent Effluent means that which comes out of or emerges from—for example, a plumbing fixture or a building drain, etc.—usually applied to sewage effluent.

Fixture branch A fixture branch is a horizontal sanitary drain line to which several or many fixture drains connect.

Fixture drain A fixture drain is the drain from the trap of a fixture to the junction of that drain with any other drain pipe.

Fixture supply A fixture supply is a water-supply pipe connecting the fixture branch.

Fixture unit A fixture unit is a quantity in terms of which the load-producing effects on the plumbing system of different kinds of plumbing fixtures are expressed on some arbitrarily chosen scale.

Fixture-unit flow rate Fixture-unit flow rate is the total discharge flow in gallons per minute of a single fixture divided by 7.5 which provides the flow rate of that particular plumbing fixture as a unit of flow. Fixtures are rated as multiples of this unit of flow.

Flood-level rim The flood-level rim is the top edge of the receptacle from which water overflows.

Floor drain A floor drain is a drainage fixture set flush in a floor to drain away any liquid which may be on or fall on that floor; it is integrally or separately trapped and has a round or square grating which is in or slightly below the floor finished surface.

Flow line (sewer) A flow line (sewer) is the surface of a liquid flowing in a horizontal pipe which is running less than 100% full.

Flush valve A flush valve is a valve which controls the flow of water that flushes a water closet or urinal. It may be located in the bottom of a water closet flush tank or may be a separate, exposed pipe mounted valve (*see* Flushometer valve).

Flushometer valve A flushometer valve is a device which discharges a predetermined quantity of water to fixtures for flushing purposes and is actuated by direct water pressure.

Frostproof closet A frostproof closet is a hopper that has no water in the bowl and has the trap and the control valve for its water supply installed below the frost line.

Grade Grade is the slope or fall of a line of pipe in reference to a horizontal plane. In drainage it it is usually expressed as the fall in a fraction of an inch per foot length of pipe.

Grease trap A grease trap is a plumbing trap (*see* Trap) designed to separate grease and oil from the water effluent of a sink or similar device (*see* Interceptor).

Horizontal branch A horizontal branch is a drain pipe extending laterally from a soil or waste stack or building drain, with or without vertical sections or branches, which receives the discharge from one or more fixture drains and conducts it to the soil or waste stack or to the building (house) drain.

Horizontal pipe A horizontal pipe is any pipe or fitting which is installed in a horizontal position or which makes an angle of less than 45° with the vertical.

Indirect waste pipe An indirect waste pipe is a pipe that does not connect directly with the drainage system but conveys liquid wastes by discharging into a plumbing fixture or receptable which is directly connected to the drainage system.

Individual vent An individual vent is a pipe installed to vent a fixture trap and which connects with the vent system above the fixture served or terminates in the open air.

Industrial wastes Industrial wastes are liquid wastes resulting from the processes employed in industrial establishments and are free of fecal matter.

Influent Influent is that which flows into—a plumbing fixture, a tank, sewage disposal field, etc.

Insanitary Contrary to sanitary principles—injurious to health.

Interceptor An interceptor is a device designed and installed so as to separate and retain deleterious, hazardous, or undesirable matter from normal wastes and permit normal sewage or liquid wastes to discharge into the disposal terminal by gravity.

Invert An invert is the bottom of the inside of a horizontal drain line at a sewer manhole or other specific point. The elevation, with vertical reference to a bench mark, of the sewer inside bottom is its "invert elevation."

Labeled Labeled means equipment or materials bearing a label of a listing agency.

Leader A leader (downspout) is the water conductor from the roof to the building storm drain, combined building sewer, or other means of disposal.

Liquid waste Liquid waste is the discharge from any fixture, appliance, or appurtenance in connection with a plumbing system which does not receive fecal matter.

Load factor Load factor is the percentage of the total connected fixture-unit flow rate which is likely to occur at any point in the drainage system. It varies with the type of occupancy, the total flow unit above this point being considered, and with the probability factor of simultaneous use.

Loop vent A loop vent is the same as a circuit vent except that it loops back and connects with a stack vent instead of a vent stack.

Main The main of any system of continuous piping is the principal artery of the system, to which branches may be connected.

Main sewer *See* Public sewer.

Main vent The main vent is the principal artery of the venting system, to which vent branches may be connected.

Manhole A manhole is a structure built from the earth surface downward to give human access to a sewer line, water line, steam line, electric power line, and so on, usually made of masonry or concrete.

Nuisance The word "nuisance" embraces public nuisance as known at common law or in equity jurisprudence. Whatever is dangerous to human life or detrimental to health; whatever building, structure, or premises is not sufficiently ventilated, sewered, drained, cleaned, or lighted, in reference to its intended or actual use; and whatever renders the air or human food or drink or water-supply unwholesome are considered nuisances.

Offset An offset in a line of piping is a combination of elbows or bends which brings one section of the pipe out of line but into a line parallel with the other section.

Pitch *See* Grade.

Plumbing Plumbing includes the practice, materials, and fixtures used in the installation, maintenance, extension, and alteration of all piping, fixtures, appliances, and appurtenances in connection with any of the following: sanitary-drainage or storm-drainage facilities, the venting system and the public or private water-supply systems, within or adjacent to any building, structure, or conveyance; also the practice and materials used in the installation, maintenance, extension, or alteration of the storm-water, liquid-waste, or sewerage, and water-supply systems of any premises to their connection with any point of public disposal or other acceptable terminal.

Plumbing fixtures Plumbing fixtures are installed receptacles, devices, or appliances which are supplied with water or which receive or discharge liquids or liquid-borne wastes, with or without discharge into the drainage system with which they may be directly or indirectly connected.

Plumbing system The plumbing system includes the water-supply and distribution pipes; plumbing fixtures and traps; soil, waste, and vent pipes; building drains and building sewers, including their respective connections, devices, and appurtenances within the property lines of the premises; and water-treating or water-using equipment.

Potable water Potable water is water which is satisfactory for drinking, culinary, and domestic purposes and meets the requirements of the health authority having jurisdiction.

Private or private use In the classification of plumbing fixtures, "private" applies to fixtures in residences and apartments and to fixtures in private bathrooms of hotels and similar installations where the fixtures are intended for the use of a family or an individual.

Private sewage disposal system Private sewage disposal system is a septic tank with the effluent discharging into a subsurface disposal field, into one or more seepage pits or into a combination of subsurface disposal field and seepage pit, or of such other facilities as may be permitted under the procedures set forth elsewhere in this Code.

Private sewer A private sewer is a sewer privately owned and not directly controlled by public authority.

Public or public use In the classification of plumbing fixtures, public applies to fixtures in general toilet rooms of schools, gymnasiums, hotels, railroad stations, public buildings, bars, public comfort stations, or places to which the public is invited or which are frequented by the public without special permission or special invitation, and other installations (whether pay or free) where a number of fixtures are installed so that their use is similarly unrestricted.

Public sewer A public sewer is a common sewer directly controlled by public authority.

Relief vent A relief vent is a vent the primary function of which is to provide circulation of air between drainage and vent systems.

Riser A riser is a water-supply pipe which extends vertically one full story or more to convey water to branches or fixtures.

Roof drain A roof drain is a drain installed to receive water collecting on the surface of a roof and to discharge it into the leader (downspout).

Roughing-in Roughing-in is the installation of all parts of the plumbing system which can be completed prior to the installation of fixtures. This includes drainage, water-supply and vent piping, and the necessary fixture supports.

Sand interceptor *See* Interceptor.

Sanitary sewer A sanitary sewer is a pipe which carries sewage and excludes storm, surface, and ground water.

Septic tank A septic tank is a watertight receptacle which receives the discharge of a drainage system or part thereof and is designed and constructed so as to separate solids from the liquid, digest organic matter through a period of detention, and allow the liquids to discharge into the soil outside of the tank through a system of open-joint or perforated piping or disposal pit.

Service A service is the facility by means of which water, electric power, gas, or telephone is delivered into a building (water service, gas service, etc.).

Sewage Sewage is any liquid waste containing animal or vegetable matter in suspension or solution and may include liquids containing chemicals in solution.

Sewer A sloping drainage pipe carrying liquid wastes.

Slope *See* Grade.

Soil Soil is the liquid effluent from fixtures such as water closets and urinals which contain human or animal wastes.

Soil pipe A soil pipe is any pipe which conveys the discharge of water closets, urinals, or fixtures having similar functions, with or without the discharge from other fixtures, to the building drain or building sewer.

Soil stack A soil stack is a vertical drain pipe into which the effluent from soil producing fixtures, perhaps mixed with the effluent from non-soil producing fixtures, is discharged.

Stack A stack is the vertical main of a system of soil, waste, or vent piping.

Stack vent A stack vent (sometimes called a waste vent or soil vent) is the extension of a soil or waste stack above the highest horizontal drain connected to the stack.

Storm drain *See* Building storm drain.

Storm sewer A storm sewer is a sewer used for conveying rainwater, surface water, condensate, cooling water, or similar liquid wastes, exclusive of sewage and industrial waste.

Subsoil drain A subsoil drain is a drain which receives only subsurface or seepage water and conveys it to a place of disposal. It is generally an open-joint or perforated drain which is installed around the exterior of the building to collect underground water. A subsoil drain conveys this water into a sump or to a point of disposal so that it will not enter the basement of a building.

Sump A sump is a tank or pit which receives sewage or liquid waste, located below the normal grade of the gravity system, and which must be emptied by mechanical means.

Tap A tap is the connection of a branch pipe to a main pipe (such as a water main) made after the main pipe is already in place.

Trap A trap is a fitting or device so designed and constructed as to provide, when properly vented, a liquid seal which will prevent the back passage of air without materially affecting the flow of sewage or waste water through it.

Trap arm A trap arm is the same as a "drain arm."

Trap seal The trap seal is the maximum vertical depth of liquid that a trap will retain, measured between the crown weir and the top of the dip of the trap.

Vacuum breaker A vacuum breaker is a valve mounted on a pipeline, tank, or water supply faucet which opens to admit air into its device whenever internal pressure falls, or tends to fall, below surrounding atmospheric pressure and into a vacuum.

Vent pipe *See* Vent system.

Vent stack A vent stack is a vertical vent pipe installed primarily for the purpose of providing circulation of air to and from any part of the drainage system.

Vent system A vent system is a pipe or pipes installed to provide a flow of air to or from a drainage system or to provide a circulation of air within such system to protect trap seals from siphonage and back pressure.

Vertical pipe A vertical pipe is any pipe or fitting which is installed in a vertical position or which makes an angle of not more than 45° with the vertical.

Waste Waste is the effluent from plumbing fixtures that do not produce "soil" (*see* Soil).

Waste pipe A waste pipe is a pipe which conveys only liquid waste free of fecal matter, or urine.

Waste stack A waste stack is a vertical drain pipe which carries liquid waste products that do not contain "soil" (*see* Soil).

Water main The water (street) main is a water-supply pipe for public or community use.

Water-service pipe The water-service pipe is the pipe from the water main or other source of water supply to the building served.

Water-supply system The water-supply system of a building or premises consists of the water-service pipe, the water-distributing pipes, and the necessary connecting pipes, fittings, control valves, and all appurtenances in or adjacent to the building or premises.

Wet vent A wet vent is a vent which receives the discharge from wastes other than water closets.

Yoke vent A yoke vent is a pipe connecting upward from a soil or waste stack to a vent stack for the purpose of preventing pressure changes in the stacks. A yoke vent is also called a relief vent.

15-2 BASIC CONCEPTS

For a full understanding of the drain and vent systems of buildings, there are a few basic concepts which must be understood.

Gravity Drainage

The water and sewage waste products that flow out of plumbing fixtures and into horizontal drain lines do not flow as a result of pressure or pressure differential as does water in a supply main. It flows because the pipe that carries it is sloped; the pipe is not installed dead level. Therefore, the sewage flows only because it is running downhill under the pull of gravity.

Drain lines usually slope in the range of 1/16 in./ft minimum to 1/2 in./ft maximum. Such drain lines do not run full but only partially so—perhaps 50% at the most. Figure 15-1 presents a table which lists the approximate flow velocities in various sizes of drain lines at four different downward slopes in inches of fall per foot of horizontal run.

Good design indicates that for good scouring of drain lines, the velocity should be 2 fps or more, at which velocity food particles (from waste disposers) and sewage products will be waterborne

Figure 15-1 Approximate flow velocity of sewage for given slopes and pipe diameters. (From Vincent T. Manas, National Plumbing Code Handbook. Copyright © 1957 by McGraw-Hill, Inc. Used with permission of McGraw-Hill Book Company.)

Diam of pipe (in.)	Flow velocity (fps)			
	1/16-in. fall/ft	1/8-in. fall/ft	1/4-in. fall/ft	1/2-in. fall/ft
1 1/4	. . .	. . .	1.61	2.28
1 1/2	. . .	1.24	1.76	2.45
2	1.02	1.44	2.03	2.88
2 1/2	1.14	1.61	2.28	3.23
3	1.24	1.76	2.49	3.53
4	1.44	2.03	2.88	4.07
5	1.61	2.28	4.23	4.56
6	1.76	2.49	3.53	5.00
8	2.03	2.88	4.07	5.75
10	2.28	3.23	4.56	6.41

and will not settle out and clog the pipe. The slope of 1/8 in./ft seems to be a favorite of plumbing designers, and is used much more often than any other for drain lines inside buildings. Figure 15-1 shows that horizontal drain lines of sizes 3 in. and smaller must slope more than 1/8 in./ft to maintain velocities of 2 fps or more.

However, plumbing designers do not always have complete freedom in the selection of drain line slopes. These slopes, and the resulting downward drop of drain lines must be carefully correlated with the need to reach a public sewer (or manhole or other point of termination) at a level somewhat higher than the flow line of the liquid in that public sewer. If the public sewer is not laid deeply enough in the earth, a real problem in this respect may arise. Too often the solution of this problem is to run building drains and sewers with inadequate slope. This, of course, can result in clogged drain lines, and the excessive maintenance resulting therefrom.

Drainage Fittings

In order that the sewage flowing in building drain lines be carried efficiently and expeditiously from the building, the course that such sewage must

follow should be as smooth as possible with any turns in the flow line made gently and with as little interruptive turbulence as possible. For example, a branch drain is never connected into a main drain with a square, 90° connection as would be a water supply line in a 90° tee fitting. The branch drain line must always make an angling connection to the main drain, usually at a 45° angle.

Figure 15-2 shows details of many types of drainage fittings both for bell-and-spigot connection as well as for threaded pipe connection. Notice that in the "bell" connection there is space in the bell to receive the spigot end of the adjacent section of pipe such that the inside surfaces, of both the pipe and the fitting, line up with very little break between them. This promotes smooth, nonturbulent flow.

Notice also that in the Y-branch and combination Y and 1/8 bend fittings, the branch connection is made at a 45° angle; thus the fluid in the branch is turned and directed downstream in the direction of the flow in the main line. Reducing fittings, in which the branch connection is smaller than the main, are also available.

The sanitary tee fitting shown illustrates that the amount of turning effect in the branch connection is less than in a Y fitting. Sanitary tee fittings should be used only in vertical stacks so that gravity assists in causing the liquid in the branch to change its course and join the flow in the main line.

Traps

The drainage system of a building carries waste products, including human wastes, which are malodorous and which bear disease-producing bacteria and other harmful agents. It is extremely important that these waste products, and the noxious gases that form as they decompose, be kept out of all the occupied areas of the building. To accomplish this, a trap is installed in the drain line at each plumbing fixture, floor drain, open sight drain, and so on.

The trap is essentially a dip in the drain line which fills with water and seals the line against the

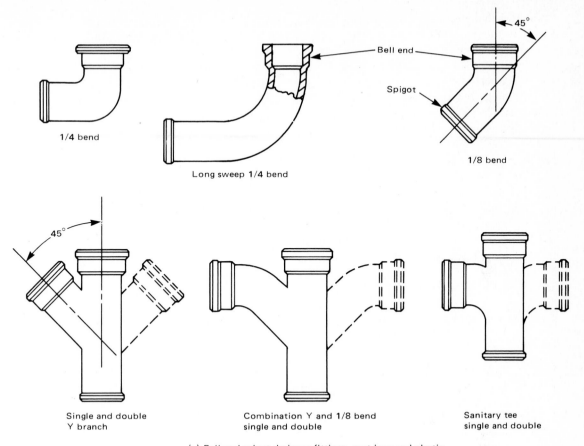

1/4 bend

Long sweep 1/4 bend

Bell end

Spigot

45°

1/8 bend

45°

Single and double
Y branch

Combination Y and 1/8 bend
single and double

Sanitary tee
single and double

(a) Bell and spigot drainage fittings—cast iron and plastic

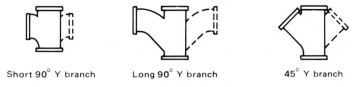

Short 90° Y branch

Long 90° Y branch

45° Y branch

(b) Threaded cast iron drainage fittings—
single and double

Figure 15-2 Drainage fittings.

passage of sewer gas from the drainage system through the plumbing fixture and into the rooms of the building. The main building drain connects through a building sewer to the public sewer that serves large areas of a municipality. The pub-

lic sewers are, of course, full of sewer gas, which in most systems is free to flow backward through building sewers and into the drainage systems of buildings that connect to the public sewer.

Sewer gas from the public sewer is not only a

threat to public health, but is combustible, being mostly methane, and presents a fire hazard. Current thought among plumbing and health authorities is that considerable benefit results from providing avenues of escape for public sewer gases (through building drainage systems) into the upper atmosphere above adjacent buildings. This is much better than permitting those sewer gases to escape at street level through manhole cover perforations near where people are passing.

There are several basic types of traps such as P traps, S traps, drum traps, running traps, grease traps, and plaster traps; all operate on the basic idea of trapping and holding an amount of water which seals and prevents the passage of harmful and unpleasant gases. Any trap, if left inoperative for long periods of time (weeks or months) will dry out and lose its seal and permit the entry of those gases. This frequently happens to the traps that are part of floor drains. Floor drains are quite often so situated that no water enters them for long time periods, and they do dry out. This situation may be helped by filling the trap with a thin oil such as kerosene which does not readily evaporate.

Figure 15-3 shows sketches of various types of traps. Of these, the P trap is used much more than all the others combined; it is presumably in the shape of a letter "P" laid horizontal. In fig. 15-3c the P trap installation detail shows one necessary component—that a vent pipe be connected before or at the point where the drain line turns downward. If the drainage tee shown were replaced with an elbow and the vent omitted, an S trap installation would result; in most plumbing codes this would be illegal.

The S trap shown in fig. 15-3b is illegal and for good reason. In any type of fixture such as a lavatory or sink where a full basin of water can be collected with the waste opening closed, when the waste opening is opened a heavy flood of water at high velocity down the drain and through the trap results. If an S trap is utilized and the trap and drain line below the trap run full of water at high velocity, the trap will experience self-siphonage

which may empty the trap so that the seal is lost. Then noxious gases can enter the room through the unsealed trap.

Drum traps have been used in the past in connection with bathtub drains. They have been installed in such a way that the flat, removable top is flush with the finished floor beside the tub. Very often, instead of the square lug shown in fig. 15-3 for wrench application during removal of the top, a recessed square socket is provided so that a perfectly flat top surface results.

The running trap shown in fig. 15-3e may be used anywhere that a trap is required in a horizontal drain line. It is wise always to use at least one cleanout opening, and perhaps two, on a running trap as shown. Running traps are often used in a main building drain just before the point where such drain passes outward through the building foundation to the exterior.

Many building codes prevent the use of running traps in this manner, and such use will probably disappear completely in the future. Such a trap does prevent the venting of gases from a public sewer through the branch connections to that sewer—a process now considered to be desirable. However, area drains, window well drains, and some types of floor drains can benefit from the use of running traps.

Figure 15-3h also shows a detail of a grease trap, sometimes called a *grease interceptor*. These should be used in almost all nonresidential heavy-duty food service facilities to intercept the large quantities of grease generated in such establishments. Such a trap may be installed at the drain outlet of a pot sink, in which case it replaces the trap otherwise required. Or a grease trap may be installed to receive all the wastewater flow from the kitchen—including that from the dishwasher, salad preparation sink, cook's table sink, and so on—as well as the pot sink.

Grease traps may be mounted on the kitchen floor or recessed with the top flush with the floor. In any case, it must be accessible for cleaning; and this unpleasant task can be made doubly unpleasant if the trap is awkwardly located. So that cleaning

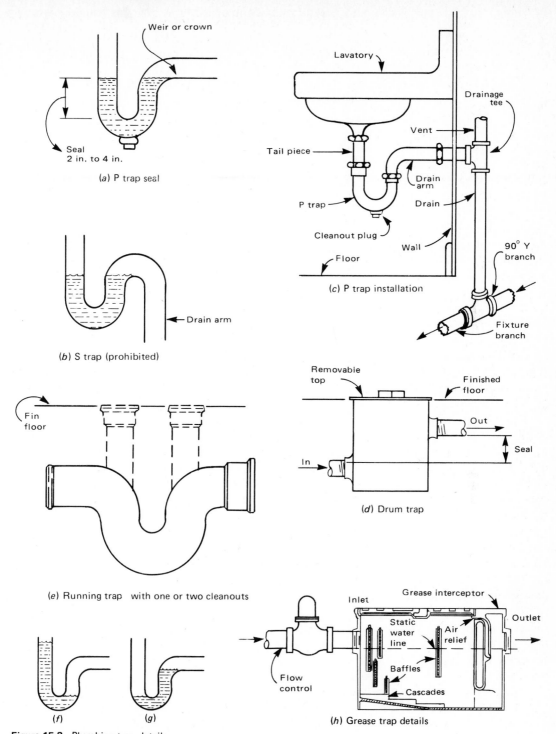

(a) P trap seal

(b) S trap (prohibited)

(c) P trap installation

(d) Drum trap

(e) Running trap with one or two cleanouts

(f)

(g)

(h) Grease trap details

Figure 15-3 Plumbing trap details.

can be made easy and not neglected, the trap should be located in an open area with easy access.

As shown in fig. 15-3, a flow control device in the entering water drain line is often used. This device slows the flow when necessary and provides a smooth, even flow into the grease trap so that turbulence can be minimized, and effective separation of water and grease accomplished.

There are also many other special-purpose traps available such as plaster traps to intercept plaster of paris residue in art studios and hospitals, hair interceptors in barber and beauty parlors, glass interceptors in bottling plants, and the like.

All traps involve the one primary principle of incorporating a water seal to prevent passage of gas. It is then evident that the protection of this water seal is mandatory. As described above, the action in an S trap can be self-siphoning. It is also possible to a lesser extent for this to happen with a P trap. The water that seals a trap is constantly subjected to changing pressures on the downstream side of the trap with these pressures ranging from negative to positive.

A positive pressure tends to push the downstream leg of the trap seal down until gases can push through the water at the bottom of the trap dip (see fig. 15-3*f*) and gurgle upward through the water on the left side of the trap. Similarly, a negative pressure in the drain arm (downstream from the trap) can, as shown in fig. 15-3*g*, cause the water level to fall in the left side, with some water leaving the trap and draining away. This reduces the amount of water seal in the trap dip and makes the trap more susceptible to gas passage when a downstream pressure exists.

Also, it is possible for enough negative pressure to exist downstream to pull water out of the trap until not enough water remains to seal the trap. Especially when the trap size is reduced by grease, soap, hair, and other deposits, the room air gurgling through the trap water can carry water downstream, with resulting loss of seal.

In fig. 15-3*c*, the horizontal *fixture branch* to which the lavatory drain connects is shown (isometrically). If a heavy surge of water, as from a flushing water closet, is approaching the lavatory drain connection, a pressure is developed in the 90° Y branch fitting shown. While the heavy surge of water is passing through this fitting, a negative pressure is drawn in the lavatory drain—if it is not properly vented.

As drawn in part *c,* a vent pipe connection is included. The pressure generated by the "approaching" water in the fixture branch can be relieved by the vent pipe. Also, the vacuum developed by the "passing" water in the 90° Y branch fitting can also be broken by air entering through the vent. However, the effectiveness of the vent in performing these two functions depends on the size of the vent pipe and its length.

The vent pipe shown in part *c* would probably be connected to a nearby branch vent line, which would in turn connect to a vent stack, or stack vent which extends through the building roof and is open to atmosphere. This construction may be seen in fig. 15-4.

Important here is the frictional resistance to the flow of air between the plumbing fixture location and outdoor atmosphere through the vent pipe system. Remember that for a fluid to flow in any type of conduit, other than by force of gravity, a pressure differential must exist. If air is to enter through a vent pipe and travel through the vent system to a fixture location to break the vacuum that can cause siphonage and "pulling" of a trap, the pressure drop through the vent system must not exceed about 1 in. of water (1 in. WG).

If this pressure drop were 4 in. WG, for example, it would be easier for air to enter through the fixture and the 2 to 3 in. of water in the trap than for the air to enter through the vent system; the water seal in the trap might very well be lost in this process. So the path for air movement from the fixture and trap location to or from atmosphere must be perfectly free and open; and the vent pipe size, in relation to its length, is critical. Not only must the vent piping be adequate for a given plumbing fixture, but also for all other fixtures connected to that particular branch of the system that are simultaneously requiring ventilation. The tables presented in this chapter give good guidance, based on many decades of actual field experience

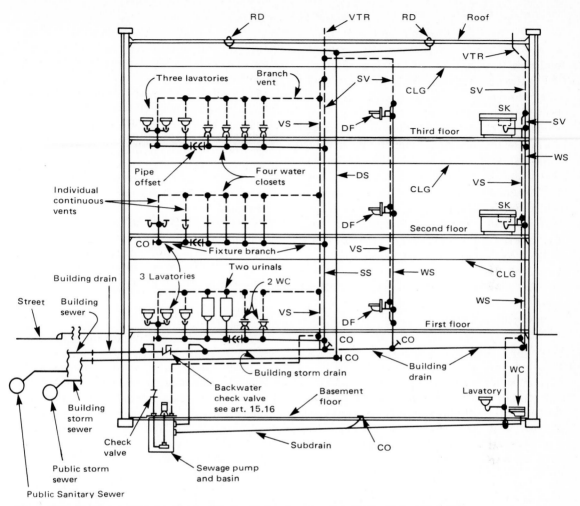

Figure 15-4 Building section showing typical plumbing system elevation details. CLG, ceiling; CO, cleanout; DF, drinking fountain; DS, downspout; RD, roof drain; SK, sink; SS, soil stack; SV, stack vent; VS, vent stack; VTR, vent through roof; WC, water closet; WS, waste stack.

by many people in the sizing of drains and vent piping of all types.

15-3 PLUMBING SYSTEM COMPONENTS AND CONNECTIONS

Figure 15-4 is presented to give graphic representation of some of the more common components of a drain and vent system. It also shows some of the drafting techniques used to portray drain and vent systems. Notice that the fixtures and their locations on the second and third floors are identical, but that part of those on the second floor are indicated by cryptic notation. The reader must become familiar with this method of portrayal since it is so extensively used in the plumbing business.

The components shown in fig. 15-4 and their usual notational abbreviations (see the legend) should be compared with the definition of the same listed at the beginning of this chapter. All fixtures in this figure, except the basement lavatory are individually vented with continuous vents;

each fixture has its own individual independent vent, including those pairs of lavatories which connect to the same vertical waste and "common" vent pipe. The basement lavatory is connected to the "wet vent" of the adjacent water closet. In this case, the water closet vent is wetted by the effluent from the lavatory.

Only light-duty, nonsoil types of fixtures may drain into the vent of another fixture, and that vent must not be more than 50% loaded. None of the fixtures in fig. 15-4 are vented with a "loop" or "circuit" vent. This is good, since individually vented fixtures function better than those loop or circuit vented. However, loop and circuit vents cost less and for this reason are often used. It is highly recommended here that, whenever possible, individual venting should be utilized. Circuit and loop vents are discussed later in the chapter. Other brief observations regarding fig. 15-4 should be made as follows:

1 The public sanitary sewer is at too high an elevation for the basement fixtures, and these must drain into a sewage lift pump. Such a pump operates in a cast iron basin recessed into the floor; this basin has a sealed, gasketed, cast iron cover and must be properly vented as shown.

2 The storm drainage (roof drainage) piping must not connect to the sanitary drainage system at any point within the building. However, if the public sewer is a *combination sewer* which carries both storm and sanitary effluent, the *building sewer* and the *building storm sewer* may connect together outside the building before extending out to the public sewer. If possible, both sewers should extend to the public sewer separately to facilitate future connection to "separate" public sewers. The vertical storm drain, which in fig. 15-4 is labeled "DS" for downspout, is also called the storm *leader*.

3 Cleanouts are points of access to the interior of a drainage system for cleaning purposes. They usually consist of a threaded, brass plug which may be unscrewed and removed. The plugs are made of lightweight metal so that if efforts to unscrew them are unsuccessful, they may be broken and cut out with a hammer and chisel.

Cleanouts should be provided at the base of all

soil stacks and waste stacks, and on horizontal drain lines should be installed no more than 50 ft apart. Although not shown in fig. 15-4, a cleanout would be needed in the floor beside the basement water closet.

4 Drainage fittings, as previously described herein, would be required throughout the system shown in fig. 15-4. In a small-scale drawing efforts at drawing drainage fittings where needed are largely ineffectual. Such fittings would be required at all points where soil and waste stacks connect to the building drain, where fixture branches connect to stacks, and where fixtures connect to fixture branches and stacks.

5 Building sewers are, in most plumbing codes, considered to begin (and the building drains to end) at a point 3 ft outside the building foundation. The building drain is always required to be of some durable, permanent material such as cast iron or DWV-type copper. Very often it is buried beneath a concrete floor, and is comparatively inaccessible.

From the 3 ft point, outside the building, onward to the public sewer (or other terminus), a less expensive material such as vitrified tile may be used where only an earth cover exists. Unless buried very deeply (10 ft deep or more) the buried sewer is quite accessible for repair, and the less costly but more friable material is satisfactory. Where such building sewers pass under driveways, roadways, or parking areas, either paved or unpaved, a return to cast iron is probably wise.

Where a brittle material such as vitrified tile is laid where trucks, automobiles, and so on, are apt to pass, the depth of bury should be at least 3 ft. However, such material should not be buried too deep, where earth pressure is great. In general, vitrified tile [often referred to as VCP (vitrified clay pipe)] may be buried 9 ft deep. For greater depths of bury, a stronger pipe, such as cast iron, standard weight or extra heavy, or reinforced concrete must be used.

Unreinforced concrete pipe is very little stronger than VCP and may not be buried at depths greater than 9 or 10 ft, and since VCP has a much smoother interior finish, and is more resistant to acid attack, it is a better choice at shallower depths. For depths of 10 to 20 ft, reinforced concrete pipe, RCP, class IV or V, is suitable. However, RCP is not generally available in sizes smaller than 12 in., and for smaller sizes at 10 to 20 ft depth of bury, cast iron pipe or cement-asbestos pipe, class 3300 or heavier, may be used.

6 In fig. 15-4, both the sanitary sewer and the storm sewer connect directly to the public sewers. It is important that the branch sewers connect, as shown, to the upper half of the public sewers. The 45° angling connection shown is ideal when it is made so that the inflowing sewage flows smoothly down the side of the public sewer—rather than dropping in from the top and splashing on the bottom. This splashing may cause solid material to splatter and adhere to the sides of the public sewer, and cause blockage.

It is also important that branch sewer connections not be made to the lower half of the public sewer. Such connections permit solids to flood backward into the branch sewer and cause partial or total blockage. In many locations, plumbing authorities and their codes will not permit a direct connection to a public sewer as shown in fig. 15-4, but require a sewer manhole to be installed if one is not already available.

7 Figure 15-5 shows details of both a brick, custom-made manhole and a precast concrete manhole, factory-made in standard sections. Both are mounted on a poured-in-place concrete base. The elevation of this base (below a surveyor's benchmark) must be very carefully established since the *invert* (inside bottom) of the main sewer line may fall within its thickness. In an alternative fashion, the main sewer may be run through the manhole above the concrete base, and concrete fill poured around it up to the sewer centerline as shown in fig. 15-5*b*. The upper half of the sewer is then cut away.

In fig. 15-5*a,* two branch sewer connections are shown. One enters the manhole at the bottom just above the concrete base and the influent liquid will flow smoothly across the base to the main sewer. The other branch sewer enters the manhole several feet above the concrete base; if the influent sewage were permitted to drop and splash, unsatisfactory operation would result. The solid wastes in the sewage would splatter and foul the inside of the manhole.

With the "drop"-type connection shown, the sewage can enter smoothly and the solids can be conveyed into the main sewer line and be properly disposed of. There is considerable opinion among plumbing system designers that a sewer line should not slope downward too much, and that the velocity of the liquid in the sewer should not be too great. With excessive velocity, the solids in the sewage are sometimes left behind in the pipe, especially at elbows and other changes in direction. If this were not a problem, the drop-type connection would never be needed; the branch sewer could just be sloped at whatever slope is required to bring it into the manhole at optimum elevation. Of course, holding the branch sewer high, with a gentler yet adequate slope, does reduce the cost of excavating the trench for the branch sewer.

15-4 CIRCUIT AND LOOP VENTS

As described above, the vent piping of a plumbing system performs the function of preventing siphonage of fixture traps by supplying air into the system to prevent the formation of a vacuum, and performs the function of preventing the forcing of gases through a trap by relieving any pressure that may occur. The vent system also performs a third important function of venting to the upper atmosphere any noxious gases that may be generated within the drain and vent piping.

The most efficient method of performing these necessary ventilation functions is with the use of individual, or continuous, vents. However, plumbing codes do permit the use of circuit and loop vent systems which do not provide individual vents for each plumbing fixture.

Circuit and loop vents are essentially the same except for the connection of them into the main vent stack or stack vent. Circuit vents connect into a vent stack, while loop vents connect only to a stack vent. Both, of course, are branch vents which serve a fixture branch. Circuit vents would be used on an intermediate floor of a multistory building. Loop vents may be used only in a single-story building or on the top floor of a multistory building, since, by definition, they connect to a stack vent which would not be available on, for example, the third floor of a six-story building.

As shown in fig. 15-6, when circuit and loop vents are used, individual fixture vents are not used. Therefore, only certain types of fixtures may

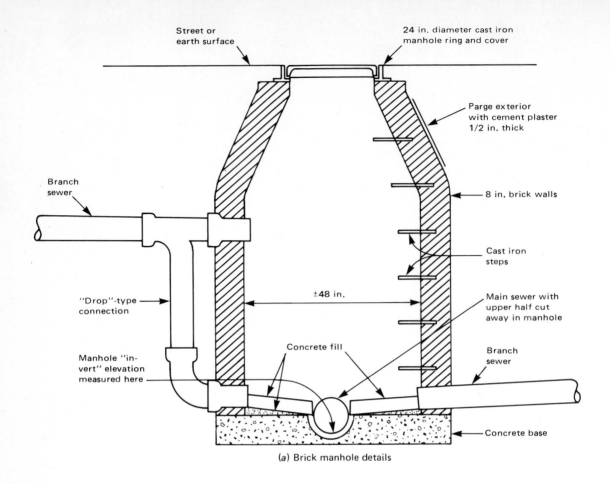

(a) Brick manhole details

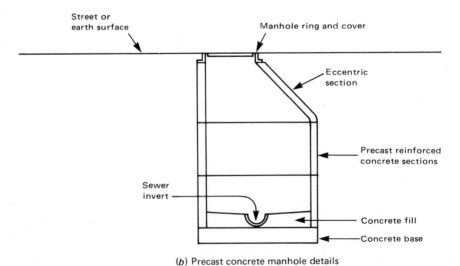

(b) Precast concrete manhole details

Figure 15-5 Sewer manhole details.

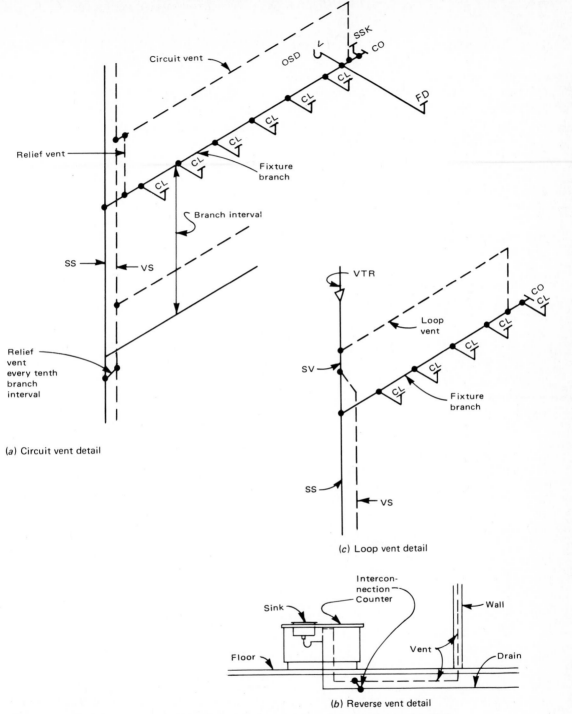

(a) Circuit vent detail

(c) Loop vent detail

(b) Reverse vent detail

Figure 15-6 Circuit, loop, and reverse vent details. CL, water closet (may also be listed as WC); CO, cleanout; FD, floor drain; OSD, open sight drain; SS, soil stack; SSK, service sink; SV, stack vent; VS, vent stack; VTR, vent through roof.

be connected when circuit and loop vents are used. These include water closets, floor urinals, pedestal urinals, trap standard-mounted sinks with outlets that turn down toward the floor, floor drains, shower drains, and such fixtures.

For sinks, lavatories, drinking fountains, and other fixtures whose drain arms are installed well above the floor, the fixture branch may not be connected to a circuit or loop vented fixture branch. Were they to be so connected their drains would of necessity turn down to reach the fixture branch; this turn down near the end of a P trap would constitute an S trap, which, of course, is forbidden by most plumbing codes.

Sinks, lavatories, and so on, may be connected to a circuit or loop vented branch, but they must have individual vents. Blowout-type water closets and wall-hung urinals must always be individually vented. Notice in fig. 15-6 that both loop and circuit vents are connected to the fixture branch at a point between the last two fixtures connected to the branch.

There are some other limits to the use of circuit and loop vents and fixture branches that are so vented. These limitations are:

1 On a 3 in. fixture branch, not more than 20 FU (fixture units) should be connected, and of these fixtures not more than two water closets should be included. See the definition of "fixture units" given in the definitions at the beginning of this chapter.

2 On a 4 in. or larger fixture branch, not more than 48 FU should be circuit or loop vented.

3 Circuit and loop vented fixture branches on other than the top floors of multistory buildings that serve more than three water closets should have a relief vent connected in front of the first fixture connection as shown in fig. 15-6. This will relieve pressure generated in the soil stack by liquids descending in the soil stack from upper floors of the building. Such pressure, if not relieved, would tend to restrict the flow of sewage from the fixture branch.

Circuit and loop vents rely on the air space at the top of fixture branch pipes to deliver air to, or remove air from, the individual fixture connections.

Therefore, the fixture branch must always be generously and conservatively sized.

15-5 RELIEF VENTS

As mentioned above, heavy sudden flows of liquid descending in a soil or waste stack can impose a pressure on the gases in the lower part of the stack. These pressurized gases tend to flow outward from the soil or waste stack into the fixture branches that connect thereto. The pressure tends to impede liquid flow in the fixture branches, and tends, of course, to work backward through the seals of the traps of connected fixtures. To prevent this, an interconnection between the soil or waste stack and its accompanying vent stack is made for direct relief of this pressure. Most codes require a relief vent to be provided at every tenth *branch interval* in tall buildings. This is just a pipe set at 45° as shown in fig. 15-6; it should be of the same size as the vent stack. The term "branch interval" is explained in the circuit vent detail of fig. 15-6.

15-6 FLOOR DRAIN VENTING

A floor drain, or a group of floor drains connected to a common drain line, can always benefit from being vented. Such a vent should, if possible, connect to the top of the floor drain's drain line, or at least connect to the side with a 45° upward angle.

Floor drains may be connected to soil or waste stacks, or fixture branches or building drains without being vented, but the point of connection should not be more than 4 ft below the floor in which the floor drains are installed. Also, floor drains should not be connected unvented to a building drain within 10 ft downstream of the base of any soil or waste stack that connects to the building drain.

Unvented floor drains are susceptible to trap siphonage, with resulting loss of seal if connected to a fixture branch which experiences frequent heavy liquid flows, as from water closets located upstream from the point of connection. This is especially true if the length of the drain arm from the floor drain to the fixture branch is short. Protection for the floor drain is given if it is located 15 ft or more from the fixture branch. In this case, a large volume of air must be evacuated from the drain arm before the drain arm pressure will drop to the point that the floor drain's trap will be "pulled."

The floor drain shown in fig. 15-6 is well protected by the circuit vent which connects nearby. Also, the floor drain is in a safer position than it would be if connected closer to the soil stack and downstream from some of the water closets shown.

15-7   OPEN SIGHT DRAINS

Open sight drains are also called "indirect" drains or wastes, or "funnel" drains or "air gap" drains; they are usually noted as "OSD" on plumbing drawings. They usually include a funnel-shaped, open fitting near the floor but above the floor, from which a drain line runs downward to a P trap located below the floor. From the trap a drain runs to the nearest fixture branch or other drain line.

An OSD is used to receive water waste from some device, such as an air conditioner or refrigerator, which generates water of condensation or other water waste. A tightly piped connection from the device to the building sanitary drainage system would involve the hazard of noxious gases flowing backward into the device should the trap dry out or be "pulled." To avoid this possibility, an air gap of 3 in. or more is provided in this drain connection. The drain from the refrigerator, or other such device, terminates at the top of this air gap and the open funnel fitting is located directly below to catch any drainage that occurs.

Should the trap dry out and foul gases emanate therefrom, it is not likely that they could travel across the gap and up the drain line into the protected device.

15-8   REVERSE VENT CONNECTIONS

Sometimes the vent from a plumbing fixture cannot extend upward from the fixture as it should do. The sink in a cook's table out in the center of a large commercial kitchen is a good example of this; see the reverse vent detail in fig. 15-6. Here the sink is not near a wall which would permit the vent to run straight up. To proceed straight up in the normal manner, the vent would be exposed in midair. This would almost always be objectionable, and it is necessary for the vent to be reversed and turned downward instead.

As shown in the detail in fig. 15-6, the vent runs upward from the fixture drain arm connection as high as it can beneath the countertop and then it reverses and turns downward. It drops down beneath the floor and runs horizontally to any point where it can rise and ultimately connect to the building vent system. This is fine except that the portion of this vent below the floor will in time fill with water (condensed water vapor from the sink) and become inoperative.

To prevent this, a piping interconnection is made between the vent and the drain line below it as shown; any water in the vent will then drain away. Of course, if this sink is on an intermediate floor of the building, and there is vent piping below that floor, the sink vent may connect to it. The sink vent line in that case must grade downward until it reaches such other vent piping.

15-9   VENTS THROUGH ROOFS

In all but the warmest climates where freezing temperatures rarely occur, a plumbing vent passing upward through a roof should not be too small in size. The recommended minimum size is 4 in. In colder climates, the water vapor which regularly emanates from such vents will condense and freeze and form a heavy ring of frost around the outlet opening. If the vent is too small, the opening may frost nearly shut and impair the function of the vent.

A 2-in. vent stack, for example, should be increased with an increasing coupling just below the roof deck. Usually, a lead sleeve with a 12- to 15-in. square flat base is slid down over the portion of the vent that extends above the roof. The flat base rests on the roof deck and is flexible enough that it can be formed to the roof contour if it slopes.

The roofing membrane, or shingles, is then laid over the lead base and sealed in place with hot asphalt or roofing cement. The upper end of the lead sleeve, which surrounds the vent pipe, is cut off at a point 2 in. or so above the top of the vent pipe. The end of the sleeve is then turned inward and forced downward inside the end of the vent 1 1/2 in. to make a weathertight seal. Of course, the lead sleeve inside the vent pipe reduces its inside diameter and increases the possibility of frosting shut.

Soil, waste, and vent stacks should be terminated 6 in. above the roof surface. However, if the roof is to be used for some purpose such as sun bathing, weather observations, and so on, such stacks should be extended so as to terminate above the area of activity. If more than 4 ft above the roof, they should be properly braced or guyed.

If possible, vents should not terminate above a low roof of a building which has a higher roof. All vents should be carried through the highest roof if possible. Vents that must terminate at a low-level roof must be as far as possible from windows, air intakes, and so on, in the taller section of the building or adjacent buildings. Many plumbing codes specify a horizontal clearance from such openings of 12 to 20 ft and a vertical clearance above them of 3 ft. Both horizontal and vertical clearance should be much more if possible; a gentle breeze can carry vent stack odors much more than 20 ft with little dilution.

15-10 MAIN VENTS

A main vent is a vertical stack into which horizontal branch vents connect, or it may be a horizontal vent header into which two or more vertical vent stacks connect. It must be sized to have a fixture unit (FU) capacity equal to the total of all the FU loads of the branch vents and vent stacks that connect to it.

All soil and waste stacks with fixtures on two or more floors must have a main vent. It may extend upward and through the building roof into outdoor atmosphere, or it may connect at its upper end to a stack vent of equal or greater size which extends through the roof. At its bottom end it must connect either to the soil or waste stack that it serves, below the point of lowest fixture or fixture branch connection, or to the building drain into which its soil or waste stack empties. Both of these options are illustrated in the vent stacks of fig. 15-4.

The size of the main vent is based, as mentioned, on total FU load, and also on the size of the soil or waste stack it serves and its developed length in feet from atmosphere to its bottom end. The established size should remain unchanged throughout its total length, and it should be as large or larger than any of the branch vents or vent stacks that connect to it.

15-11 SUPPLEMENTAL RULES AND RECOMMENDATIONS

The following rules and recommendations are involved with obtaining good plumbing design. Some are required in most plumbing codes, whereas others are not.

1 No drain may be smaller than 1 1/4 in.

2 No vent may be smaller than 1 1/4 in.

3 The maximum load on a 1 1/4-in. drain or vent line is one fixture unit.

4 An individual fixture vent should be no smaller than half the fixture drain size.

5 An individual fixture vent should be no larger than the fixture drain.

6 Loop and circuit vents are legal but not recommended in best practice.

7 Water closets with 3-in. drain line connections are legal according to plumbing codes, but a 4-in. minimum connection size is highly recommended and in nonresidential construction is almost always used.

15-12 FIXTURE UNITS

As stated in the definitions near the beginning of this chapter, a "fixture unit" is a quantity on the basis of which, and in multiples thereof, plumbing fixtures may be given a comparative yet finite or absolute rating. The rating of plumbing fixtures, in these arbitrarily chosen units, gives a positive value which may be used in totaling the load on groups of fixtures and determining piping requirements for those groups.

The reader should remember that in chap. 14 various types of plumbing fixtures were given FU ratings as to their water supply demand characteristics. It must always be remembered that the "water supply (FU) fixture unit" ratings for fixtures are not the same as the "drainage FU" ratings given in this chapter, and they may not be used interchangeably. To confuse these two sets of FU ratings can result in appreciable error in the design of plumbing systems.

The drainage fixture unit values of many different types of plumbing fixtures are listed in fig. 15-7. Notice that in fig. 15-7 a flush-valve-operated water closet has a drainage FU valve of 6; we can remember that the water supply FU value of such a fixture is 10—an appreciable difference.

15-13 DRAIN AND VENT ISOMETRIC DIAGRAMS

As mentioned in chap. 14, the chapter dealing with water supply piping systems, the three-dimensional isometric drawing plays an important part in the design and portrayal of plumbing systems. It is very important where water supply systems are concerned, but even more important in showing all the details of a drain and vent system. Water supply isometrics might occasionally be omitted from the plans of a larger, nonresidential building, but not the drain and vent isometrics.

The student of construction must, of course, be fully capable of reading and understanding plumbing isometrics, and the best method of learning to read them is to learn to draw them. As described in chap. 14, a plumbing isometric is begun by laying off on the drawing paper two light construction lines, one sloping upward to the right 30° above horizontal and beginning near the center of the drawing detail area, and another starting at the center and sloping 30° upward to the left. All pipe lines of the isometric detail are then drawn either vertical or parallel to one of these two lines.

As mentioned previously, drainage fittings must be used throughout to provide a long-radius, gentle turn wherever one pipe intersects and joins another, and also to provide a gentle slope for horizontal pipe lines. However, attempting to show the drainage fittings, and the 45° angle they usually incorporate, in such a drawing detail becomes messy and often confusing. It is better just to show the point of intersection with a dot, and with perhaps a general note that drainage fittings are to be used throughout.

It is important for the reader to be able to study a floor plan drawing, and to visualize and then draw isometrically what is showing in the plumbing floor plan. This process takes considerable practice in graphic presentation before a neat, readable isometric diagram can be drawn. Of course, a considerable amount of knowledge of plumbing practices must be acquired first.

There is a large group of plumbing fixtures that are connected in much the same fashion as is the lavatory in fig. 15-3c. This group includes lavatories, almost all types of sinks, laundry trays, dishwashers, wall-hung urinals, and drinking fountains. All of these are characterized by a mounting fairly high above the floor, a P trap below the fixture, a drain arm that runs horizontally backward into the wall, or plumbing space behind the fixture, where connection is made to a vertical pipe. This vertical pipe provides drainage downward, from the point of connection, and a vent upward.

There is also a second group of fixtures in which the drainage outlet is at or very near the floor, and not up on the wall. This group of fixtures includes water closets, stall urinals, bathtubs, floor drains, shower drains, and bidets. These fixtures connect directly or indirectly to a drain line or fixture branch located below the floor or just above the floor. So often, the fixture vent originates at the point of connection to the fixture branch if individual vents are used—as is recommended. Sometimes the vent connects to the fixture drain arm before it reaches its drain.

Figure 15-7 Drainage fixture unit values for various plumbing fixtures. [From the National Standard Plumbing Code, ASA-A40.8–1955. Note: This is an out-of-date document. Both ANSI and ASME have withdrawn their approval of it as a valid document (taken as a whole). But data in this figure coincide well with data from other current sources of information.]

Type of fixture or group of fixtures	Drainage fixture unit value (d.f.u.)	Usual drain arm size
Automatic clothes washer (2-in. standpipe)	3	
Bathroom group consisting of a water closet, lavatory, and bathtub or shower stall:		
Flushometer valve closet	8	
Tank type closet	6	
Bathtub[a] (with or without overhead shower)	2	1 1/2
Bidet	1	2
Clinic Sink	6	
Combination sink-and-tray with food waste grinder	4	1 1/2 (2)
Combination sink-and-tray with one 1 1/2-in. trap	2	1 1/2
Combination sink-and-tray with separate 1 1/2-in. traps	3	1 1/2
Dental unit or cuspidor	1	1 1/4
Dental lavatory	1	1 1/4
Drinking fountain	1/2	1 1/4
Dishwasher, domestic	2	1 1/2
Floor drains with 2-in. waste	1	2
Kitchen sink, domestic, with one 1 1/2-in. trap	2	1 1/2
Kitchen sink, domestic, with food waste grinder	2	1 1/2
Kitchen sink, domestic, with food waste grinder and dishwasher 2-in. trap	3	2
Kitchen sink, domestic, with dishwasher 1 1/2-in. trap	3	1 1/2
Lavatory with 1 1/4-in. waste	1	1 1/4
Laundry tray (1 or 2 compartments)	2	1 1/2
Shower stall, domestic	2	2
Showers (group) per head	2	
Sinks		
Surgeon's	3	1 1/2
Flushing rim (with valve)	6	3
Service (trap standard)	3	3
Service (P trap)	2	2
Pot, scullery, etc.	4	1 1/2
Urinal, pedestal, siphon jet blowout	6	3
Urinal, wall lip	4	1 1/2
Urinal, stall, washout	4	2
Urinal trough (each 6-ft section)	2	1 1/2
Wash sink (circular or multiple) each set of faucets	2	1 1/2
Water closet, tank-operated	4	4
Water closet, valve-operated	6	4
Fixtures not listed above:		
Trap size 1 1/4 in. or less	1	
Trap size 1 1/2 in.	2	
Trap size 2 in.	3	
Trap size 2 1/2 in.	4	
Trap size 3 in.	5	
Trap size 4 in.	6	

[a]A shower head over a bathtub does not increase the fixture unit value.

The variety of types of fixture connections to both drain and vent pipes is endless; they cannot all be described here. However, this is not necessary as long as it is understood that all fixtures must be trapped and connected as directly as possible to a fixture branch or other drain facility while being properly vented. Some fixtures have built-in, concealed, integral traps; these include water closets, urinals, and drinking fountains. Other fixtures are supplied without traps, and these must be added separately; lavatories and sinks fall into this category.

In the isometric drain and vent diagram of fig. 15-8, it may be seen that some of the fixtures, the lavatories, service sink, and floor drains are drawn with a dip in the line to indicate that a trap must be added (floor drains are available both with and without traps). Other fixtures, the water closets, and urinals have integral traps which are not drawn separately. Drain lines are shown with solid lines and vent piping is dashed.

In fig. 15-8, a partial floor plan of a building showing two public toilet rooms and a janitor's closet is drawn. On this plan, all plumbing fixtures are shown and much of the drain and vent piping is also shown. However, all such piping is not shown, because it is not possible to show it. Also some license has been taken in drawing the piping that is shown. For example, in the pipe space that separates the women's and men's toilet rooms, the branch vent (dashed line) is shown offset from the fixture branch (the solid line), but this is not accurate presentation. The branch vent is directly above the fixture branch, and when drawn in plan (top view) the two lines are coincident. They are offset and shown to be separate for clarity.

The reader should now study the isometric drain and vent diagram to see that it is a three-dimensional representation of the piping required for the fixtures shown in the floor plan. Notice that 100% of the drain and vent piping is shown and in proper relationship. All pipe sizes are thus easily noted.

The note below the isometric diagram advises that all water closets and urinals are wall hung,

and that they are flush-valve-operated (not flush-tank-operated—see the later discussion of plumbing fixtures). This is the most satisfactory choice for the modern, nonresidential buildings with which we are primarily concerned. With wall-hung water closets, the drainage outlet is at the rear of the fixtures, not at the bottom as in floor-mounted closets; and the drainage flow is outward to the rear and not downward through the floor. In this case, the fixture branch to which the water closets connect is located above the structural floor and not below it. See fig. 15-9 for details of back-to-back wall-hung water closets with a common pipe space between.

In fig. 15-9, notice that the horizontal fixture branch is above the floor, and that the wall-hung water closets are also high enough above the finished floor to permit easy cleaning of the floor—a sanitary feature. The same type of installation is also possible with fixtures on only one side of the pipe space. The cast iron closet fitting then has only one closet connection, and the fitting is somewhat narrower. In this case, the inside width of the pipe space then becomes about 12 in. minimum.

Also in fig. 15-9, a "crow's-foot" support is shown under each closet to provide stability and resist the overturning force, which is considerable when the closet is in use. Appreciable stress is applied to the walls of the pipe space, and these must have considerable strength. Sometimes the same general configuration is used except with a vertical stack in place of the horizontal fixture branch. This vertical stack may connect into a horizontal drain line or fixture branch located just below the floor, or it may continue on down, as well as up, to adjacent floors.

Figure 15-10 gives some of the details of the installation of a floor-mounted water closet. Here, of course, the fixture branch to which the closet connects must be below the floor. Connection at the water closet is usually made with a closet bend, as shown; this has a floor flange to which the closet is bolted. The closet has a male protuberance on the bottom of it called a *horn.* The horn engages the closet bend with a thick, formable

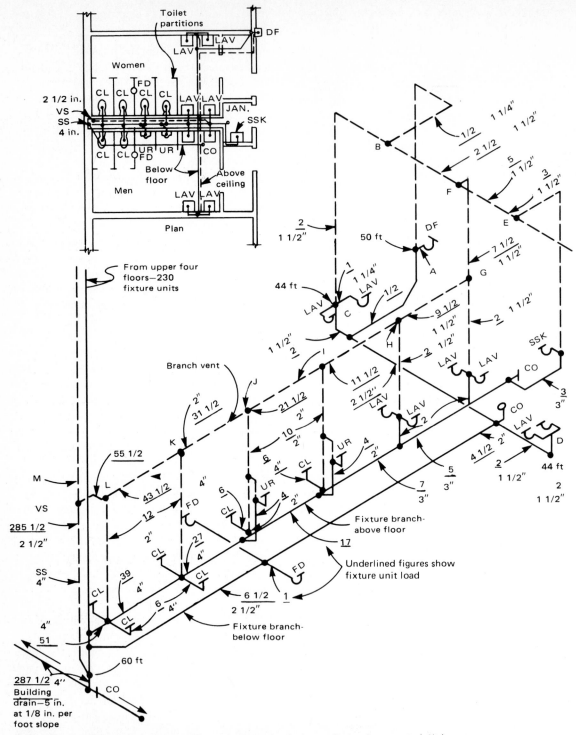

Figure 15-8 Drain and vent diagram. Water closets and urinals are flush-valve-operated and are wall hung. CL, water closet; CO, cleanout; DF, drinking fountain; FD, floor drain; LAV, lavatory; SS, soil stack; SSK, service sink; VS, vent stack; UR, urinal.

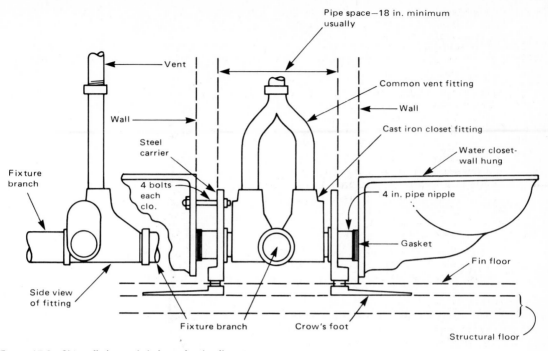

Figure 15-9 Closet fitting and chair carrier details.

Labels on figure: Pipe space—18 in. minimum usually; Vent; Common vent fitting; Wall; Cast iron closet fitting; Water closet-wall hung; Steel carrier; 4 bolts each clo.; 4 in. pipe nipple; Fixture branch; Gasket; Side view of fitting; Fixture branch; Crow's foot; Fin floor; Structural floor

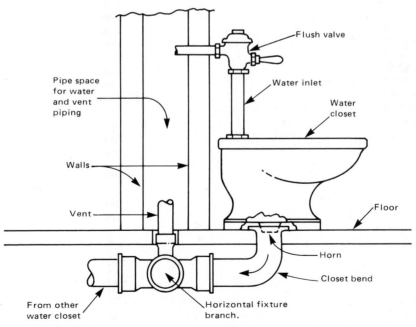

Figure 15-10 Floor-mounted water closet connections.

Labels on figure: Flush valve; Pipe space for water and vent piping; Water inlet; Water closet; Walls; Vent; Floor; Horn; Closet bend; From other water closet; Horizontal fixture branch.

gasket making a tight seal around the horn. The closet bend makes connection to the fixture branch below the floor at a drainage-type fitting which may or may not include a vent connection.

If the water closet is one of a battery or group of closets, a circuit or loop vent might be used, and each closet would not have an individual vent. However, individual vents are strongly recommended even though piping costs may be somewhat higher. Figure 15-10 shows a vent in use and the closet bends and the vent shown are connected to a drainage-type fitting, which, as drawn, is a "double combination Y and eighth bend with top inlet vent" (see fig. 15-2).

In fig. 15-8, the drain and vent diagram contemplates the use of the water closet connections shown in fig. 15-9. At two points in fig. 15-8, a water closet is back to back with a wall-hung urinal. Here the centerline of the urinal drain outlet is about 22 in. above the floor while that of the water closet is about 4 1/2 in. above the floor. The drain from the urinal might be connected into the vertical vent from the water closet, in which case the closet would be "wet vented." However, many designers feel that the effluent from a urinal carries too much solid matter (cigarette butts, etc.) and other contaminants to drain into the vent of another fixture. The connection shown in fig. 15-8 is then necessary, but there is nothing peculiar about a urinal that makes mandatory, in all cases, the type of connection shown. If two urinals were to be installed back to back, they would simply connect straight back and into a vertical pipe as are the back-to-back lavatories shown adjacent to the urinals.

15-14 DRAIN AND VENT PIPE SIZING

The sizing of drain and vent piping is very simple and can be learned quickly and easily. Drain pipe sizes are selected directly from a table in accordance with the load in fixture units (FU) carried by the drain. Vent pipes are also sized according to FU loads, but, in addition, the length of a vent from its *source of air* must also be considered.

The source of air for a vent stack is the outdoor atmosphere, and the distance that air must travel from this outdoor source to the base of the vent stack is important in determining vent stack size. The source of air for a branch vent, or an individual fixture vent, or a loop vent, or a circuit vent is the vent stack to which it directly or indirectly connects.

Of course, of real importance to any individual fixture and its vent, and any other point in the vent system, is the distance from that point to its vent stack *plus* the additional distance, from the point of connection to the vent stack, and up the vent stack to atmosphere. This actual, developed length from atmosphere down the vent stack to a branch vent, and along the branch vent to any point needing venting, is the distance that air must be drawn for that point. The frictional resistance, or in other words, the pressure drop, resulting from airflow for that distance must not exceed about 1 in. of water. Remember that 1.0 psi pressure drop is equal to 27.7 in. of water, so 1 in. of water is equal to 0.036 psi—an exceedingly small amount of pressure.

However, branch and individual vent pipe sizing tables are not based on the total distance to atmosphere, but rather on the distance to the vent stack. Only the vent stack is concerned with distance to atmosphere.

In calculating pipe sizes, and in preparing the pipe sizing tables available to us, plumbing researchers have assumed a condition in which drain piping is running half full of water and the upper half full of air. Further, it has been assumed that the air is carried along with the water, and that the volumes of moving water and moving air are equal. Knowing the volume of water that is typically drained tells us how much air must be delivered through the vent system. The overall picture of air movement throughout the plumbing system, after these two very simple assumptions, becomes quite confused and complicated; but a study of this is not necessary to an understanding of the methods used in plumbing design. The empirical data presented in our pipe sizing tables give good, dependable results.

Let us now consider the tables presented in figs. 15-7, and 15-11 through 15-14. Figure 15-7 gives us a list of the plumbing fixtures normally utilized, together with the drainage FU value of each and the usual size of its trap and drain arm. Figure 15-11 lists the capacity, in FU values, of various sizes of horizontal fixture branches, individual fixture drains, and soil and waste stacks.

Figure 15-12 shows capacities of the various sizes of building drains and building sewers when they are installed at the slopes of 1/16, 1/8, 1/4, and 1/2 in./ft. It is recommended here that, as much as possible, the use of 1/16- and 1/2-in./ft slopes should be avoided.

Figure 15-13 gives information for the sizing of vent stacks based on the size of the soil or waste stack which the vent stack serves, the total FU load carried by the soil or waste stack, and the developed length of the vent stack from its lowest point up through the building to atmosphere. Some plumbing texts use this same table for sizing branch vents and individual vents as well as vent stacks, but this is awkward and imprecise and does not face the situation of the single-story building in which there is no soil or waste stack.

Information for sizing branch vents, individual vents, and loop and circuit vents is presented in fig. 15-14. This table is from the Minnesota plumbing code and is based on FU load and the length of a branch vent measured from its vent stack. The size of a branch vent, unlike a vent stack, is not held constant for its full length. Each section of it is sized in accordance with the FU load connected between the beginning of that particular section and the end of the branch vent farthest from the vent stack. This should be made more clear in the sizing of the diagram of fig. 15-8, which will be discussed here. Vent "stacks" are

Figure 15-11 Horizontal fixture branches and stacks (soil and waste). [From the National Standard Plumbing Code, ASA-A40.8–1955. Note: This is an out-of-date document. Both ANSI and ASME have withdrawn their approval of it as a valid document (taken as a whole). But data in this figure coincide well with data from other current sources of information.]

	Maximum number of fixture units that may be connected to:			
			Stack sizing for more than 3 stories in height	
Diameter of pipe, inches	Any horizontal fixture branch[a]	Stack sizing for 3 stories in height or 3 intervals	Total for stack	Total at 1 story or 1 branch interval
1 1/2	3	4	8	2
2	6	10	24	6
2 1/2	12	20	42	9
3	20[b]	48[b]	72[b]	20[b]
4	160	240	500	90
5	360	540	1,100	200
6	620	960	1,900	350
8	1,400	2,200	3,600	600
10	2,500	3,800	5,600	1,000
12	3,900	6,000	8,400	1,500
15	7,000			

[a]Does not include branches of the building drain.

[b]Not more than two water closets or bathroom groups within each branch interval nor more than six water closets or bathroom groups on the stack.

Stacks shall be sized according to the total accumulated connected load at each story or branch interval; and may be reduced in size, as this load decreases, to a minimum diameter of 1/2 of the largest size required, but not less than 4 in. when water closets are connected.

Figure 15-12 Building drains and sewers. [From the National Standard Plumbing Code, ASA-A40. 8–1955. Note: This is an out-of-date document. Both ANSI and ASME have withdrawn their approval of it as a valid document (taken as a whole). But data in this figure coincide well with data from other current sources of information.]

| Diameter of pipe, inches | Maximum number of fixture units that may be connected to any portion of the building drain or the building sewer including branches of the building drain | | | |
| | Fall per foot | | | |
	1/16 in.	1/8 in.	1/4 in.	1/2 in.
2			21	26
2 1/2			24	31
3		36[b]	42[b]	50[b]
4		180	216	250
5		390	480	575
6		700	840	1,000
8	1,400	1,600	1,920	2,300
10	2,500	2,900	3,500	4,200
12	2,900	4,600	5,600	6,700
15	7,000	8,300	10,000	12,000

[a]On-site sewers that serve more than one building may be sized according to the current standards and specifications of the Administrative Authority for public sewers.

[b]Not over two water closets or two bathroom groups.

sized according to the total FU load connected thereto; this one size is maintained from its base all the way to its top.

The isometric diagram of fig. 15-8 may be used to illustrate the process of sizing the piping in a plumbing system. This diagram should be carefully studied and fully understood as well as its relationship to the floor plan of fig. 15-8. Then the sizing of the drain piping should be started. First, the FU value of each fixture involved should be determined from the table in fig. 15-7. Here we see that lavatories are 1 FU, drinking fountains are 1/2 FU, service sinks of the trap standard type are 3 FU,

urinals of the stall washout type are 4 FU, floor drains are 1 FU, and water closets of the valve-operated type are 6 FU.

Next, we start at the end of the fixture branch farthest from the soil stack and ascribe FU totals for each section of the fixture branch, adding fixture load and accumulating the total as we move toward the soil stack. Let us begin at the two lavatories in the upper, center portion of the diagram (at reference letter "c"), and progress toward the soil stack. The FU loads on each section of the drain line will be noted and underlined as shown. This summation would be as follows:

Type of fixture	Number of fixtures	FU each	FU running total	Fixture pipe size, in.	Fixture branch size, in.
Lav	2	1	2	1 1/4 and 1 1/2	1 1/2
DF	1	1/2	2 1/2	1 1/4	1 1/2
Lav	2	1	4 1/2	1 1/4 and 1 1/2	2
FD	2	1	6 1/2	2 and 2	2 1/2
		(fig. 15-7)		(fig. 15-11)	(fig. 15-11)

Figure 15-13 Size and length of vent stacks. [From the National Standard Plumbing Code, ASA-A40.8–1955. Note: This is an out-of-date document. Both ANSI and ASME have withdrawn their approval of it as a valid document (taken as a whole). But data in this figure coincide well with data from other current sources of information.]

Size of soil or waste stack	Fixture units con-nected	Diameter of vent stack required (inches)								
		1 1/4	1 1/2	2	2 1/2	3	4	5	6	8
		Maximum length of vent (feet)								
Inches										
1 1/2	8	50	150							
1 1/2	10	30	100							
2	12	20	75	200						
2	20	26	50	150						
2 1/2	42		30	100	300					
3	10		30	100	100	600				
3	30			60	200	500				
3	60			50	80	400				
4	100			35	100	260	1000			
4	200			30	90	250	900			
4	500			20	70	180	700			
5	200				35	80	350	1000		
5	500				30	70	300	900		
5	1100				20	50	200	700		
6	350				25	50	200	400	1300	
6	620				15	30	125	300	1100	
6	960					24	100	250	1000	
6	1900					20	70	200	700	
8	600						50	150	500	1300
8	1400						40	100	400	1200
8	2200						30	80	350	1100
8	3600						25	60	250	800
10	1000							75	125	1000
10	2500							50	100	500
10	3800							30	80	350
10	5600							25	60	250

Figure 15-14 Individual and branch vent capacity. (From the Minnesota Plumbing Code.)

Fixture units connected (dfu)	Diameter of vent (in.)							
	1 1/4	1 1/2*	2	2 1/2	3	4	5	6
	Minimum developed length of vent (ft)							
2	50	ul						
4	40	200	ul					
8	np	150	250					
10		100	200	ul				
24		50	150	400	ul			
42		30	100	300	500			
72		np	50	80	400			
240			np	50	200	ul		
500				np	180	700	ul	
1100					50	200	700	

ul-unlimited length   np-not permitted

*Except 6-FU fixtures.

In this tabulation, the FU for each fixture (third column) was taken from fig. 15-7. The first figure in the pipe sizes (fifth column) was also taken from fig. 15-7; this is the drain size for a single fixture. The second pipe size (if any) in the fifth column was found in the second column of fig. 15-11; this is the drain size for the number of fixtures (two) being added at this point. The pipe size in the sixth column was found in the second column of fig. 15-11 also, and was based on the running total of FU found in the fourth column of the foregoing table.

This table also shows that on the fixture branch that runs below the floor there are seven fixtures (four lavatories, one drinking fountain, and two floor drains), a total of 6 1/2 FU. Each lavatory has a 1 1/4-in. drain and two lavatories require a 1 1/2-in. drain. Four lavatories and one drinking fountain total 4 1/2 FU and require a 2-in. drain; and the total load of 6 1/2 FU requires a 2 1/2-in. drain. This 2 1/2-in. drain then connects to the soil stack as shown in the diagram.

The fixture branch above the floor is sized in exactly the same way by starting at the service sink and progressing to the soil stack. This summation would be as shown below.

From both of these tabulations the figures in the third, fifth, and sixth columns were transferred to the drain and vent diagram of fig. 15-8 to show FU loads (underlined) and drain pipe sizes.

The sizing of the vent piping follows very much the same procedure, except that now we must also consider the length of the vent piping measured from the vent stack to the most remote point in the diagram. This most remote point of the particular branch vent is at the drinking fountain. The developed length to this point from the vent stack is 50 ft, as noted.

As before, the FU values for all fixtures are noted for individual vents, and the running total for each section of the branch vent is also computed and added to the drain and vent diagram. As before, these fixture unit totals are underlined, and when the proper pipe size is determined, it is noted immediately adjacent to its underlined FU value.

To aid in vent pipe section designation, each juncture in the isometric diagram has been given a letter designator. In the following branch vent sizing tabulation, we will start at the most remote point, the drinking fountain, which is labeled point *A*.

The first section of the branch vent to be sized, then, is section *A-B*. Remember that the distance to this most remote point is 50 ft; this value is used in sizing each section of the branch vent. As before, the FU values are totaled as we progress toward the vent stack. This summation would be as shown in the table on page 511.

The remainder of the vent piping (including individual vents) in fig. 15-8, except the vent stack, may be sized directly with the use of fig. 15-14,

Type of fixture	Number of fixtures	FU each	FU running total	Fixture pipe size, in.	Fixture branch size, in.
SSk	1	3	3	3	3
Lav	2	1	5	1 1/4 and 1 1/2	3
Lav	2	1	7	1 1/4 and 1 1/2	3
1 Clo and 1 UR	2	6 and 4	17	4 and 2	4
1 Clo and 1 UR	2	6 and 4	27	4 and 2	4
Clo	2	6	39	4	4
Clo	2	6	51	4	4
		(fig. 15-7)		(fig. 15-11)	(fig. 15-11)

Branch vent section	FU running total	Branch vent size, in.
A-B	1/2	1 1/4
C-B	2	1 1/2*
B-F	2 1/2	1 1/2
D-E	2	1 1/2
E-F	5	1 1/2
F-G	7 1/2	1 1/2
G-H	9 1/2	1 1/2
H-I	11 1/2	1 1/2
I-J	21 1/2	2 †
J-K	31 1/2	2
K-L	43 1/2	2
L-M	55 1/2	2
	(fig. 15-7)	(fig. 15-14)

*Even though fig. 15-14 indicates a 1 1/4-in. size as being adequate, most codes allow only 1 FU on a 1 1/4-in. drain or vent.

†Figure 15-14 table values indicate that a 1 1/2-in. vent is suitable for 24 FU and a branch vent length of 50 ft. However, fig. 15-14 also states (*) that no 6 FU fixture (such as a water closet) may be carried by a 1 1/2-in. vent, so a 2-in. vent is required from the water closets upward and in branch vent section I - J as well. It has also been stated elsewhere herein that a fixture vent must be at least half the size of the fixture drain. Since we are using 4-in. drains from the water closets, their vents must be 2-in. minimum.

using the 50-ft overall branch vent length as one parameter and the FU load of each fixture (or pair of fixtures) as the other parameter. These sizes are all noted in fig. 15-8.

In sizing the soil stack of fig. 15-8, we need only know the total FU load carried at the base of the stack. Notice that the FU load, from the upper floors of the building of fig. 15-8, is 230 FU. This added to the 51 FU and the 6 1/2 FU from the first floor totals a stack load of 287 1/2 FU (230 + 51 + 6 1/2 = 287 1/2).

Referring to the fourth column of fig. 15-11 (for soil and waste stacks more than three stories in height—our building is a five-story building), we see that a 3-in. stack will carry only 72 FU while our load is 287 1/2. We also see that a 4-in. stack will carry a load of 500 FU, which is more than ample. Of course, a 3-in. stack could not be

used since our fixture branch is 4 in. and we would never reduce a pipe size (either drain or vent) as we progress downstream in the direction of flow. Also observe footnote b of fig. 15-11. In our case a 4-in. stack is adequate. It should be 4 in. from bottom to top and should extend with a 4-in. stack vent out through the building roof.

The vent stack should be sized with the use of fig. 15-13. In fig. 15-8, the total load on the vent stack is 285 1/2 FU. This is 2 FU less than the load on the soil stack; this is true because the two floor drains shown are not vented. It is noted in fig. 15-8 that the height of the vent stack from its base to atmosphere is 60 ft. In fig. 15-13 we see that with a 4-in. soil stack and 285 1/2 FU (use the line for 500 FU), a 2 1/2-in. vent stack is adequate if its length is 70 ft or less. Our vent is 60 ft long and the 2 1/2-in. vent stack size is used.

Most plumbing codes specify that if two or more vented soil stacks connect to a building drain, the vent for one of these stacks must be considered to be the main vent for this particular system. Its size should be no less than 3 in., and should be larger if fig. 15-13 so indicates. If the vent stack in fig. 15-8 is not a main vent, the 2 1/2-in. size is acceptable. If it is chosen to be a main vent, its size would need to be increased to 3 in., as a minimum.

15-15 PLUMBING FIXTURES

Most people are thoroughly familiar with various types of plumbing fixtures and their methods of operation. There are, of course, many types of special-purpose fixtures such as hospital and beautician's fixtures which are not generally familiar; these will not be discussed here. We will discuss here only some of the little-known features of the more generally used fixtures.

Water Closets

From the standpoint of general sanitation and protection of public health, the water closet is the most important of all fixtures, and the urinal is second. Some details of the installation of water closets may be seen in figs. 15-9 and 15-10, while fig. 15-15 shows details of their construction. Water closets may be divided into several classifications as follows:

    1 Floor-mounted versus wall-hung
    2 Flush-valve-operated   versus   flush-tank-operated
    3 Round front versus elongated front
    4 Siphon jet versus reverse trap versus washdown
    5 Low profile versus standard profile

1 The first of these classifications is self-explanatory. Floor-mounted and wall-hung closets, within types, are essentially the same, the only differences being the way in which they are mounted and the points at which the effluent leaves—wall-hung closets discharge rearward and floor-mounted downward. As shown in fig. 15-9, wall-hung closets require special chair carrier and fitting combinations; these make a wall-hung installation somewhat more expensive.

2 The second classification (flush valve vs. flush tank) indicates the method by which the

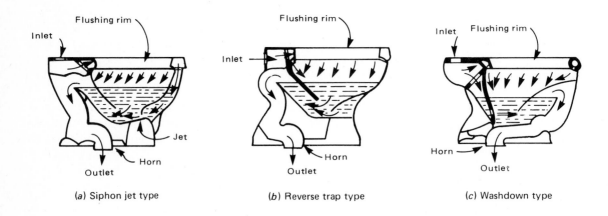

(a) Siphon jet type   (b) Reverse trap type   (c) Washdown type

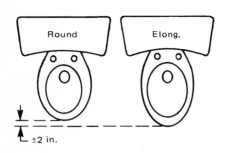

(d) Comparison of round
front and elongated
front types

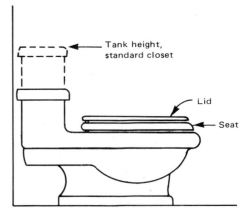

(e) One-piece low-profile tank-
operated type

Figure 15-15 Water closet details.

closet is flushed. Figure 15-10 illustrates a valve-operated closet and fig. 15-15*e* shows a tank-operated type. The tank-type closet of fig. 15-15*e* is a special low-profile, one-piece unit made for best appearance for residential applications. The size of a standard-size flush tank is shown dashed in this detail for comparison.

Because flush valve operators can be operated with less time delay between flushes, and because of their rugged dependability, flush valves are much preferred over flush tanks in public applications. Also, the flush tank, with its removable china lid and vulnerable operating internal parts, is a much greater target for vandalism and mischief.

Where the pipe space behind the water closet is adequate for human access (this requires a 24-in.-wide pipe space), the flush valve may be concealed in the pipe space with only a hand- or foot-operated lever, or floor button, accessible to the user.

3 The third classification (round front vs. elongated front) refers to the actual length of the closet bowl, as shown in fig. 15-15*d*. The elongated bowl is approximately 2 in. longer and provides greater protection for the user because of less chance of making physical contact with the front of the bowl. In a public situation, this is important; and most state plumbing codes require elongated bowls in public buildings. In this case, open-front seats without lids are also used.

4 The fourth classification (siphon jet versus reverse trap versus washdown) refers to the type of flushing action provided by the water closet. All modern water closets utilize the same siphonic action developed by Thomas Crapper in the late 1880s. In this action, dependence is placed on the principle of the siphon. When flushed, the heavy inrush of water into the bowl exceeds the rate of outflow. The water level rises in the bowl, and the trap built into the bowl (see fig. 15-15*a, b,* and *c*) and the descending leg following the trap all fill with water. This fulfills the requirements of a siphon; and all the contents of the bowl are drawn out until the seal is broken, and air rushes in through the bowl to break the vacuum that exists.

When the vacuum drawn by the descending leg of water is broken, the flushing action stops. The flush tank or flush valve continues to trickle water

slowly into the bowl until the water level rises and the trap is filled and well sealed. The bowl is then ready for repeated action.

The siphon jet closet bowl shown in fig. 15-15*a* is considered to provide the best action of all modern bowls. It has a round jet opening at the bottom which by its velocity directed toward the outlet of the bowl starts the siphonic action more quickly and requires less rise of water in the bowl. The flushing action is quieter, and it permits a larger passageway for the waste products, usually 2 1/8 in.; therefore, there is less possibility of clogging. Siphon jet closets are usually somewhat more expensive than the other types; this extra cost is considered to be justifiable. This type of bowl presents the greatest area of exposed water of any modern bowl—usually about 125 in.^{2} of surface.

The reverse trap closet is quite similar to the siphon jet, but its jet is not supplied directly with pressurized water as is true in the siphon jet closet. This closet is moderately noisy but is efficient and is less expensive than the siphon jet closet. Its passageway, capable of passing a 1 1/2-in.-diameter sphere, is somewhat smaller than in the siphon jet closet. The water area is also somewhat less and is usually slightly over 100 in^2.

The washdown closet is the least expensive, the least efficient, and the noisiest. As shown in fig. 15-15*c,* the trap is at the front of the bowl, and because of its longer, more irregular passageway it is more subject to clogging and is not usually made in a wall-hung configuration. As may be seen, the exposed water surface area is quite small, about 85 in.^{2}, so that much of the inside bowl surface is exposed and thus subject to fouling, staining, and contamination.

Urinals

Urinals are available in many types and configurations. As with water closets, different flushing principles are utilized; and again the siphon jet principle is excellent. However, the ordinary wash-out and blowout type of action is also used extensively. The basic problem here is to get a good flushing action over the entire inner surface of the urinal.

Urinals are available in many styles from the floor-mounted full-height stall type to the wall-hung type and the trough type. Urinals save considerable mess and contamination on and around water closets, but much of this is transferred to the floors under and the walls beside and behind the urinals. From a sanitation standpoint, the floor-mounted (recessed into the floor) stall type is probably best, with vitreous china seam covers filling the space between adjacent urinals. However, these are expensive and their installation is quite difficult.

The method of flushing urinals is also a problem deserving much thought and planning. Urinals can and often do waste much water if not intelligently controlled. This waste is experienced when urinals are automatically flushed on a time cycle whether flushing is necessary or not.

Automatic cycling is accomplished by using a time clock to open a solenoid valve a certain number of times per hour to flush all or part of the urinals in a busy toilet room. The rate of cycling can be varied for different times of the day and week according to anticipated rate of usage. Urinals are also often automatically flushed by a flush tank mounted high on the wall in the toilet room above the urinals that it supplies. Usually, though, it is better to conceal the flush tank in the pipe space behind its urinals or in an adjacent janitor's closet.

A urinal flush tank fills with water which is metered through an adjustable orifice to require a certain number of minutes for filling. When the tank is full, a float-operated valve or siphon arrangement operates to cause the tank to empty and flush its urinals. A clock-controlled solenoid would close to prevent flushing during unoccupied hours.

Manual flushing of urinals will save water, but is not as sanitary as automatic flushing—many men are reluctant to operate a flush valve in a public toilet room and will leave without doing so. One suitable but expensive solution to this problem is the flush valve which operates with an invisible beam of light. This beam is reflected into a light

scanner when a user approaches the urinal. Then when the user steps away, the urinal automatically flushes.

Service Sinks

Service sinks are generally available made of vitreous china or enameled cast iron, and the latter are usually enameled only on the sink interior and on the vertical splashback. Since appearance is usually not a matter of concern in a janitor's closet, the less highly finished cast iron sink is more often selected. This type is shown in fig. 15-16. The rim of this type of sink may be 28 in. above the floor, and does represent somewhat of a difficult lift for a janitor carrying a large bucket of mop water.

Some service sinks are very low, and may rest directly on the floor with the rim 12 to 14 in. above the floor. Or a service sink may even be recessed into the floor. The configuration shown in fig. 15-16 seems to be the most popular and involves the least cost. Notice that the trap is a P trap; it is made of heavy cast iron with an adjustable-height floor flange, and can carry the full weight of the sink assembly. In addition, a cast iron or steel wall bracket, as shown, should be used to stabilize the top of the sink; hooks on the splashback engage this bracket.

One danger is present in the use of a service sink. The janitor often needs to use a short length of flexible hose connected to the faucet; the faucet has a threaded end on its spout to which a hose may be secured. As shown in fig. 15-16, this hose often hangs down into the sink with the open end below the level of the water in the sink. Should the water supply system be shut down and drained while this condition exists, the vacuum that is drawn in the supply piping by this draining action will cause contaminated water to be drawn from the sink into the piping system when the faucet is opened. By this means, the water supply piping system can be thoroughly contaminated.

To prevent this, the faucet should always have an integral vacuum breaker which will open and admit room air whenever the water pressure is re-

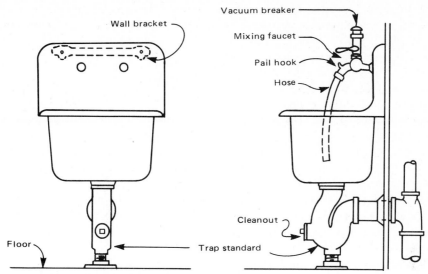

Figure 15-16 Service sink detail.

lieved and there is a tendency for a negative pressure to develop. The faucet will usually have a pail hook cast into the faucet spout for a mop bucket to hang on. Because this bucket is usually large and with water in it may constitute a weight of 30 lb, the faucet may be equipped with an angle brace secured to the faucet and the wall above the sink to relieve the faucet of this load.

15-16 BACKWATER CHECK VALVES

Unfortunately, the public sanitary sewer to which a building's sewer connects may sometimes be overloaded and incapable of carrying satisfactorily the load placed on it. This is often particularly true when some storm water drains are illegally also connected to it. Then during periods of heavy rainfall these sewers are running 100% full and carrying an hydrostatic pressure of as much as 5 to 10 psig.

This hydrostatic pressure not only restricts the flow of sanitary sewage from the buildings that connect to it, but it forces the contents of the public sewer backward into those buildings. This can cause an overflow of this terribly noxious and odorous sewage at low-level plumbing fixtures and floor drains. This must be prevented at all costs. One method of doing this is shown in fig. 15-4.

Here it may seen that a sewage pump has been installed and connected in a special way. Also, a backwater check valve has been installed in the building drain downstream from any stack or fixture branch connection; however, the sewage pump discharge line is connected to the building drain downstream from the backwater check valve.

As the name implies, a *backwater check valve* (sometimes just "backwater valve") is designed to permit the normal flow of sewage from the building but to prevent the backward flow of the same. It has a lightweight flapper valve which is easily pushed open by normal flow, but which is pushed closed by any flow from the public sewer backward into the building. As may be imagined, the seat of such a valve (against which the flapper closes) is covered with the semisolid materials contained in the sewage, and it is difficult for such a valve to close tightly. Often a hand-operated lever or handwheel is made a part of such a valve by means of which the valve may be forced shut. A backwater check valve would not be installed, of course, unless the public sewer was known to be overloaded or subject to storm water penetration.

A backwater valve may be able to protect a building when it is closed by public sewer pressure; however, under that condition sewage may not be able to leave the building. When fixtures on upper floors are flushed, the effluent may overflow through fixtures on lower floors. The answer to this problem is the installation of a sewage lift pump.

In fig. 15-4, the sewage pump was installed primarily to serve basement fixtures below the building sewer. However, this detail also shows connections that would be required when a backwater check valve is needed. Notice that an overflow line is installed between the building drain and the inlet to the sewage pump basin. This line is connected to the top of the building drain so that sewage could only flow to the pump when the building drain is completely full and overflowing. Normally, the building drain would never be more than half full, and overflowing would not occur.

When building sewage does overflow into the pump basin, a rising level of liquid in the basin causes the pump to start and pump the sewage up and into the building drain at a point downstream from the backwater check valve. Now the building is protected from backup from the public sewer; and the building plumbing fixtures can be operated normally. In an important building where the public sewer limitations are severe, a duplex sewage pump unit having two pumps for greater dependability should be installed.

PROBLEMS

15-1   A building has installed in it the following plumbing fixtures:

   20 flush-valve-operated water closets
    8 wall-hung stall-type washout urinals
   16 lavatories

4 bathtubs
4 water coolers (drinking fountains)
8 floor drains (2 in.)
3 service sinks (trap standard type)

Find the total drainage fixture unit load on the plumbing system of this building.

15-2   A horizontal fixture branch has connected to it four flush tank water closets, three wall-hung stall-type washout urinals, four lavatories, and two floor drains. Find the total drainage fixture unit load on this fixture branch and its size.

15-3   What is the maximum number of drainage fixture units that may be connected to a 4-in. soil stack in a two-story building and a 4-in. soil stack in a four-story building?

15-4   The building drain in a building carries away the effluent from a 4-in. soil stack which has a fixture unit load of 300 FU. Can the building drain be of the same 4-in. size as the soil stack?

15-5   A plumbing vent stack in a multistory building serves plumbing fixtures which drain into a 5-in. soil stack and which total 600 fixture units. The total length of this vent stack from its base (where it connects to its soil stack) upward through the building to the stack vent (to which it connects above the highest fixture branch) and then out through the roof to atmosphere is 180 ft. What size should this vent stack be? Would this vent stack be the same size from top to bottom or could it be smaller at the top?

15-6   A branch vent runs horizontally from its vent stack a distance of 60 ft to the farthest fixture that it serves and has a total load of all its fixtures of 70 fixture units. What should be its size where it connects to its vent stack? Would it be this same size for its full length, or would it probably be smaller at its far end?

15-7   When would a backwater check valve be needed and installed in the building drain of a building?

Chapter 16

Storm Drainage

16-1 GENERALITIES

The problems of storm water (rainwater) drainage are all too often ignored or given inadequate consideration. The natural water drainage patterns for a given area are often considerably altered by the construction of a new building, more often than not for the worse. When new patterns are established, the destructive capability of flooding water seeking new flow channels is tremendous.

Building designers must continually hunt for and anticipate the changes which their building projects will cause, and be certain that by one means or another the result of new construction is to improve storm drainage flow patterns. Legally speaking, an adjoining property owner has a full right to expect that his property will not in any way be adversely affected by these changing water flow patterns. Many lawsuits have been instituted with resulting heavy court judgments handed down because the rights of adjoining and other property owners were not always protected.

The construction of a new nonresidential building with perhaps a parking lot and other paved areas, where only vacant land existed before, is almost certain to increase storm water runoff from the site. The storm water runoff from a building roof and paved areas will be 4 to 10 times as great as from a rough, natural sod field. Only if positive provision has been made to channel away this increased runoff properly can the problem be considered to be solved.

The difficulties of disposing of great quantities of storm water runoff are often considerable, and the solution to this problem must be firmly and clearly in mind before site acquisition. In many parts of the world and this nation too, the question is not one of disposition but one of conservation. Often storm water can be delivered into the earth to help maintain a suitable water table. Perhaps a retention pond can be provided which will not only conserve water but beautify the landscape as well.

These considerations are beyond the scope of this text, but building designers must have an appreciation of the overall situation involving proper disposition of excess water or the conservation of it when that is indicated. This text is properly concerned with the estimating of storm water quantities and the drainage fixtures and piping necessary to convey such water away from the building.

Sometimes a public storm sewer or combination storm and sanitary sewer will be nearby and accessible. The problem then is easily solved. Often an existing open drainage ditch will be available; such a ditch, properly designed and maintained, can be an aesthetic asset to an area. It need not be an eyesore, but often is permitted to become choked with small trees and underbrush, and worse yet, is used as a depository for trash.

Too often, little thought is given to the question of where storm water will go. Outside downspouts (storm leaders) are too often hung on a building with splash blocks at their base at grade, and the problem is considered solved if the earth is carefully graded away from the building. Obviously, this is only the first step in the solution to the problem.

The methods of taking this particular step (using outside downspouts) are well established and extensively understood. It is hardly necessary for this text to deal with that subject. This chapter is primarily concerned with the buildings that require inside downspouts (storm leaders) for roof drainage, and area drains and catch basins for paving and lawn areas, and that also require storm drain piping.

16-2 RAINFALL INTENSITIES AND FREQUENCIES

The problem of storm water drainage, of course, begins with rainfall—the amount, intensity, and duration, in minutes, of a heavy rain. Most areas of the United States experience heavy rains frequently, light rains very frequently, and really heavy downpours very infrequently. It is well known that the more severe a rainstorm may be, the less frequently it will occur.

The National Weather Service and the Department of Agriculture have maintained accurate records of the severity and frequency of rainstorms for all weather stations throughout the land. These are readily available, and any building designer should obtain these data for the area of interest. Even though such data may be at hand, the designer still has a decision to make as to the frequency of rainstorm for which he or she should design.

The severity of rainstorms may be referred to according to the frequency with which they occur. For example, a "25-year rain" (one so severe that it would occur only once in 25 years) is much heavier than a "10-year rain." Figure 16-1 shows a chart of frequency curves of rainfall intensities for Springfield, Illinois. In this chart the time duration of rains (on the abscissa) is plotted against rainfall intensities in inches per hour (on the ordinate) for the frequencies of 2, 5, 10, 25, 50, and 100 years. Also shown in fig. 16-2 are similar charts at small scale for 12 other cities strategically located throughout the nation. Figure 16-3 gives national charts showing rainfall intensities for 15-min periods for 2- and 5-year frequencies.

In using figs. 16-1, 16-2, and 16-3, the designer must, of course, make a decision as to the frequency curves to use. Most drainage systems are designed on the basis of 2- or 5-year rains depending on the value of the property in the general area and on the consequences of failure of the drainage system to control flooding. Designers rarely use frequencies greater than a 10-year frequency.

In most areas of the nation there is some public official who has the responsibility of being knowledgeable on the subject of storm frequency in his or her area. This official is often the county engineer, county surveyor, or municipal engineer. This person should always be consulted on the

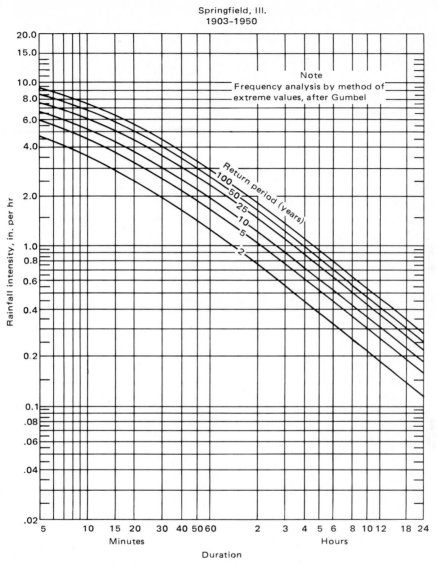

Figure 16-1 Gumbel frequency curves for rainfall intensity. (From Concrete Pipe Handbook, 1959, p. 282, courtesy American Concrete Pipe Association.)

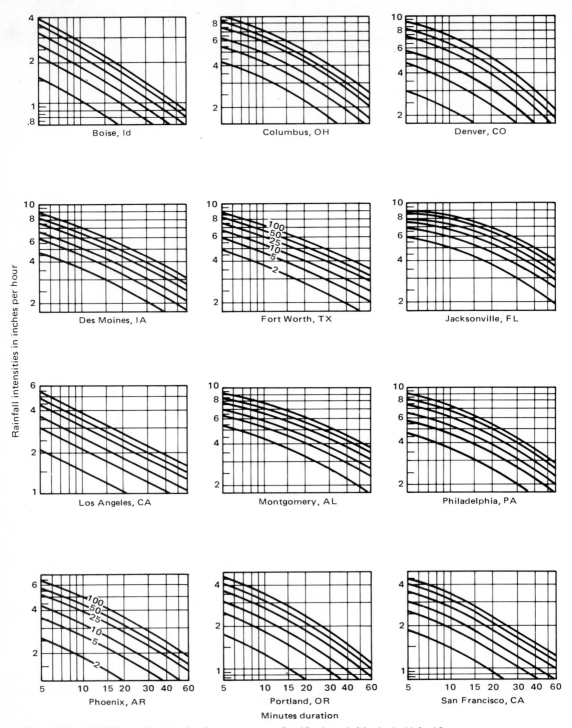

Figure 16-2 Rainfall intensity-duration-frequency curves for 12 selected cities in the United States. (Abstracted from Tech. Paper 25., U.S. Weather Bureau.)

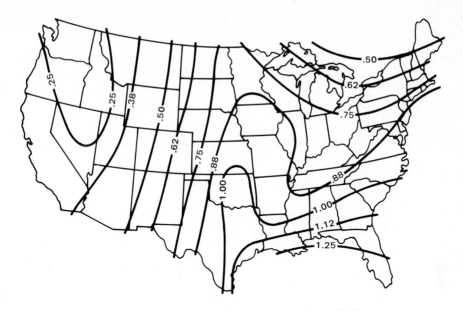

(a) Fifteen-minute rainfall, in inches, to be expected once in 2 years

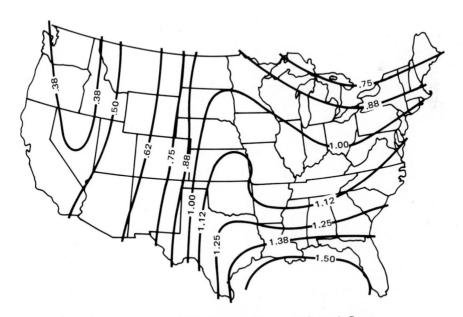

(b) Fifteen-minute rainfall, in inches, to be expected once in 5 years

Figure 16-3 Two-year and 5-year 15-min rains. (From rainfall intensity-frequency data, miscellaneous publications 204, U.S. Dept. of Agriculture.)

subject of rainstorm intensity as well as frequency, and his or her recommendation, obtained in writing, should be a minimum basis for design.

16-3 RAINSTORM DURATION AND CONCENTRATION

At issue, in addition to the rainstorm intensity, is the duration, in minutes, that the storm will last at the rate of intensity chosen. In recorded experience there is an upper limit to the intensity which usually corresponds to a duration time that falls in the range of 5 to 15 min. When designing storm drainage systems, the duration may be safely limited to 15 min, and the charts in fig. 16-3 are drawn on that basis.

Pertinent also to the question of time is the *time of concentration.* This is the time required for water to flow across a lawn, for example, to a catch basin or yard drain, through a branch drain line to a main drain line, and through the main drain line to a ditch or public storm sewer. This could also be the time required for rain falling on a building roof to travel to a roof drain fixture, from the roof drain to a downspout, down the downspout and into the building storm drain, out to the building storm sewer, and through the building storm sewer to a ditch or public storm sewer.

The time of concentration is equal to the average time from all parts of a property for surface water to flow to a point of disposal. The time for water to flow across roof or land surfaces to a drain fitting (roof drain, etc.) may be calculated by use of the formula

$$T_S = R_C \left(\frac{12D}{Si^2} \right)^{1/3} \tag{16-1}$$

where T_S = flow time across a surface, min

R_C = retention coefficient of the surface; this will vary from 1.0 for rough sod fields to 0.5 for smooth roofs and paved surfaces

D = distance water must flow across a surface, ft

S = slope of the surface, in./ft of distance

i = intensity of rainfall, in./hr

To the surface flow time T_S must be added the flow time in the branch drain piping, downspouts, and so on, to the main storm sewer or other point of disposal. The flow time in such piping, T_P, may be estimated on the basis of a velocity of 10 fps in vertical piping and 2 fps in horizontal piping. Thus the time of concentration will be the sum of the surface flow time T_S plus the piping flow time T_P, or

$$T_C = T_S + T_P$$

where T_C is the time of concentration, in minutes.

The time of concentration is quite important; it must be averaged for flow from all points of a property and must be placed in comparison with expected rainfall duration. If T_C is greater than the rainfall duration, the full force of rain will not be felt in the drainage system, and the intensity i may be proportionately reduced for calculation purposes.

It has been well established that high-intensity rains are of short duration—rarely exceeding 15 min. Rains of greater duration are always gentler and of less intensity. It may be concluded that for a given property, the maximum runoff will probably occur when the rain duration and T_C are equal.

16-4 RAINFALL QUANTITIES

Before storm drainage piping can be selected and sized, we must be able to convert rainfall intensities into more manageable terms such as cubic feet per second (cfs) or gallons per minute (gpm). Knowing gpm, for example, and the allowable slope that a drain pipe may have, makes the selection of a pipe size quite simple.

When a rainfall intensity i has been selected from charts such as those in figs. 16-1, 16-2, and 16-3, the duration time (usually 15 min if other information is not available) is compared with T_C, the time of concentration. As mentioned, if T_C is greater than the duration time, a correction to i may be made which, in effect, reduces the magnitude of i. The literature gives little help in the problem of making this reduction, and such correction must be made intuitively.

When the corrected intensity, i, is finalized, the storm water quantity may be calculated in cfs by means of formula (16-2) and in gpm by means of formula (16-3), which is merely a revised form of (16-2).

$$\text{cfs} = C_R iA \qquad (16\text{-}2)$$

$$\text{gpm} = 450\, C_R iA \qquad (16\text{-}3)$$

where cfs = storm water quantity, ft^3/sec

$\quad C_R$ = coefficient of runoff

$\quad\quad i$ = corrected rainfall intensity, in./hr

$\quad A$ = runoff area, acres

gpm = storm water quantity, gal/min

The coefficient of runoff C_R bears a generally reciprocal relationship to the retention coefficient R_C of formula (16-1). C_R is a measure of the char-

acteristics of a surface that permit water to flow from it. R_C is a measure of the ability of a surface to hold or retain water. Figure 16-4 is a table showing coefficients of runoff, C_R, for many types of earth and roof surfaces.

16-5 SIZING A STORM SEWER, EXAMPLE 16-1

Example 16-1 Suppose that a proposed building site has the following characteristics:

1 Area—16 acres.
2 Earth surface—fairly flat with slightly pervious soils with turf.
3 Location—Montgomery, Alabama.
4 Average time of concentration T_C from many calculations using formula (16-1), including proposed building and paved areas, is 22 min.
5 Average coefficient of runoff C_R for turf areas, building roof areas, and paved areas is 0.30.
6 Design for a 15-min rain of 10-year frequency.

Find the size of the storm sewer carrying all the storm drainage from the site if the storm sewer is to be installed with a slope of 2 ft per 100 ft.

Solution The rainfall chart in fig. 16-2 for Montgomery, Alabama, shows a 5.1-in rain for 15-min duration and 10-year frequency. Since T_C is 22 min, which is appreciably greater than the 15-min duration, we can reduce the rainfall intensity somewhat. We can only guess at the amount of reduction possible, but let us be conservative and reduce the 5.1-in. intensity to 3.5 in.

Using formula (16-3), gpm = $450 C_R iA$, we have

$$\text{gpm} = 450 \times 0.30 \times 3.5 \times 16$$
$$= 7560$$

Now turning to fig. 16-5, a chart by which storm sewers and sanitary sewers may be sized when flow rate in cfs or gpm is known, we may select a storm sewer size. The allowable slope was given to be 2 ft per 100 ft, or in other words, an hydraulic gradient of 0.02. The right-hand scale of the chart is expressed in terms of gpm. Finding

Figure 16-4 Coefficients of runoff C_R. (From Concrete Pipe Association, Concrete Pipe Handbook, 1959, p. 281.)

Type of surface	Values of C_R
Impervious surface	0.90–0.95
Steeply sloped barren earth	0.80–0.90
Roofs—flat or nearly flat	0.75–0.95
Asphalt pavement	0.80–0.95
Concrete pavement	0.70–0.90
Rolling barren earth	0.60–0.80
Flat barren earth	0.50–0.70
Rolling meadow	0.40–0.65
Impervious soils, heavy, bare	0.40–0.65*
Deciduous timberland	0.35–0.60
Gravel or rough macadam pavement	0.35–0.70
Impervious soils with turf	0.30–0.55*
Conifer timberland	0.25–0.50
Orchard	0.15–0.40
Gravel surfaces	0.15–0.30
Slightly pervious soils	0.15–0.40*
Rolling farmland	0.15–0.40
Flat farmland	0.10–0.30
Slightly pervious soils with turf	0.10–0.30*
Parks, cultivated land, lawns, etc., depending on slope	0.05–0.30
Moderately pervious soils	0.00–0.20*
Wooded areas	0.01–0.20

*For slopes of 1 to 2%.

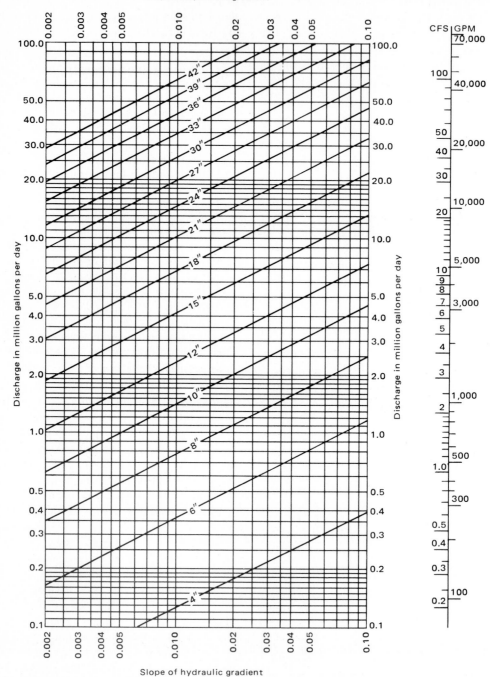

Figure 16-5 Sewer pipe sizing chart. (From Clay Pipe Engineering Manual, 1968, p. 18, courtesy National Clay Pipe Institute.)

the intersection of the vertical 0.02 line and the horizontal projection line for 7560 gpm, let us make a dot on the chart. We can see that this dot is between the 18-in.-diameter and the 21-in.-diameter sewers. The 18-in. pipe would seem to be too small, but not by a great amount. Since the 21-in. pipe would cost 15 to 20% more than an 18-in. pipe, it would be appropriate to try to make some adjustment that would make the 18-in. use possible. Perhaps the slope could be increased to 2.5 ft per 100 ft, in which case the 18-in. size would be adequate.

16-6 BUILDING STORM DRAIN SYSTEMS

The sizing of storm water drain piping in buildings is exceedingly simple after a choice has been made of the proper rainfall intensity for a given location. This intensity does not need to be corrected for time of concentration, and may be carried directly to figs. 16-6, 16-7, and 16-8 for the selection of the sizes of roof drains, downspouts, horizontal storm drains, and gutters. Figure 16-9 and example 16-2 illustrate this simple procedure.

Figure 16-6 Sizing roof drains and downspouts (From Uniform Plumbing Code, 1976, p. 156, courtesy of International Association of Plumbing and Mechanical Officials.)

	Size of drain or leader, in.*					
Rainfall, in.	2	3	4	5	6	8
1	2880	8800	18400	34600	54000	116000
2	1440	4400	9200	17300	27000	58000
3	960	2930	6130	11530	17995	38660
4	720	2200	4600	8650	13500	29000
5	575	1760	3680	6920	10800	23200
6	480	1470	3070	5765	9000	19315
7	410	1260	2630	4945	7715	16570
8	360	1100	2300	4325	6750	14500
9	320	980	2045	3845	6000	12890
10	290	880	1840	3460	5400	11600
11	260	800	1675	3145	4910	10545
12	240	730	1530	2880	4500	9660

	Size of drain or leader, mm*					
Rainfall, mm	50.8	76.2	101.6	127	152.4	203.2
25.4	267.8	818.4	1711.2	3217.8	5022	10788
50.8	133.9	409.2	855.6	1608.9	2511	5394
76.2	89.3	272.5	570.1	1072.3	1673.5	3595.4
101.6	67	204.6	427.8	804.5	1255.5	2697
127	53.5	163.7	342.2	643.6	1004.4	2157.6
152.4	44.6	136.7	285.5	536.1	837	1796.3
177.8	38.1	117.2	244.6	459.9	717.5	1541
203.2	33.5	102.3	213.9	402.2	627.8	1348.5
228.6	29.8	91.1	190.2	357.6	558	1198.8
254	27	81.8	171.1	321.8	502.2	1078.8
279.4	24.2	74.4	155.8	292.5	456.6	980.7
304.8	22.3	67.9	142.3	267.8	418.5	898.4

*Round, square or rectangular rainwater pipe may be used and are considered equivalent when enclosing a scribed circle equivalent to the leader diameter.

Figure 16-7 Sizing chart for horizontal storm drain piping. (From Uniform Plumbing Code, 1976, p. 158, courtesy of International Association of Plumbing and Mechanical Officials.)

Size of pipe, in.	Maximum rainfall, in./hr				
	2 in.	3 in.	4 in.	5 in.	6 in.
1/8-in. slope					
3	1644	1096	822	657	548
4	3760	2506	1880	1504	1253
5	6680	4453	3340	2672	2227
6	10700	7133	5350	4280	3566
8	23000	15330	11500	9200	7600
10	41400	27600	20700	16580	13800
12	66600	44400	33300	26650	22200
15	109000	72800	59500	47600	39650
1/4-in. slope					
3	2320	1546	1160	928	773
4	5300	3533	2650	2120	1766
5	9440	6293	4720	3776	3146
6	15100	10066	7550	6040	5033
8	32600	21733	16300	13040	10866
10	58400	38950	29200	23350	19450
12	94000	62600	47000	37600	31350
15	168000	112000	84000	67250	56000
1/2-in. slope					
3	3288	2295	1644	1310	1096
4	7520	5010	3760	3010	2500
5	13360	8900	6680	5320	4450
6	21400	13700	10700	8580	7140
8	46000	30650	23000	18400	15320
10	82800	55200	41400	33150	27600
12	133200	88800	66600	53200	44400
15	238000	158800	119000	95300	79250

Note: Tabulated values are horizontal projected roof areas in square feet.

Example 16-2 Given the building in fig. 16-9 which has a high roof area of 8360 ft², a low roof area of 3360 ft², a rear driveway area of 3600 ft², and a front drive area of 4800 ft². Total drained area is then 20,120 ft². Also given is the design rainfall intensity of 4 in./hr, and the slope of horizontal drain piping of 1/4 in./ft. Inside downspouts (storm leaders) are to be utilized.

Solution The table in fig. 16-6 is to be used to size roof drains and downspouts. Figure 16-7 is to be used to size all horizontal storm drain piping. Each high roof drain serves 1393 ft² of area (8360 ft² ÷ 6 = 1393.33 ft²). Each low roof drain

serves 1120 ft² of area (3360 ft² ÷ 3 = 1120 ft²). Each rear driveway drain serves 1200 ft² (3600 ft² ÷ 3 = 1200 ft²), and each front driveway drain serves 1600 ft² (4800 ft² ÷ 3 = 1600 ft²). The design steps are:

1 Select size for high roof drains at 1393.33 ft²—use 3 in. (fig. 16-6)

2 Select drain line size for one high roof drain—1393 ft² at 1/4-in./ft slope—use 4 in. (fig. 16-7).

3 Size drain line for two high roof drains—1393 ft² × 2 = 2787 ft² at 1/4 in./ft slope—use

Figure 16-8 Storm water gutter sizing chart. (From Uniform Plumbing Code, 1976, p. 160, courtesy of International Association of Plumbing and Mechanical Officials.)

Diameter of gutter, in.	Maximum rainfall, in./hr				
	2 in.	3 in.	4 in.	5 in.	6 in.
1/16-in. slope					
3	340	226	170	136	113
4	720	480	360	288	240
5	1250	834	625	500	416
6	1920	–	960	768	640
7	2760	1840	1380	1100	918
8	3980	2655	1990	1590	1325
10	7200	4800	3600	2880	2400
1/8-in. slope					
3	480	320	240	192	160
4	1020	681	510	408	340
5	1760	1172	880	704	587
6	2720	1815	1360	1085	905
7	3900	2600	1950	1560	1300
8	5600	3740	2880	2240	1870
10	10200	6800	5100	4080	3400
1/4-in. slope					
3	680	454	340	272	226
4	1440	960	720	576	480
5	2500	1668	1250	1000	834
6	3840	2560	1920	1536	1280
7	5520	3680	2760	2205	1840
8	7960	5310	3980	3180	2655
10	14400	9600	7200	5750	4800
1/2-in. slope					
3	960	640	480	384	320
4	2040	1360	1020	816	680
5	3540	2360	1770	1415	1180
6	5540	3695	2770	2220	1850
7	7800	5200	3900	3120	2600
8	11200	7460	5600	4480	3730
10	20000	13330	10000	8000	6660

Note: Tabulated values are horizontal projected roof areas in square feet.

4 in. (fig. 16-7). This 4 in. is slightly undersized but is the logical choice.

4 Select size for low roof drains—1120 ft^2 each—use 3 in. (from fig. 16-6).

5 Size horizontal drain line from one low roof drain—1120 ft^2 at 1/4 in./ft slope—use 3 in. (fig. 16-7).

6 Size downspout from two high roof drains—2787 ft^2—use 4 in. (fig. 16-6).

7 Size downspout from two high roof drains and one low roof drain—2787 ft^2 + 1120 ft^2 = 3907 ft^2—use 4 in. (fig. 16-6).

8 Same as step 7 but for horizontal drain—3907 ft^2—use 5 in. (fig. 16-7).

9 Size rear drive drain—1200 ft^2 at 1/4 in./ft slope—use 3 in. (fig. 16-7)—also very slightly undersized.

10 Three rear drive drains—3600 ft^2 at 1/4 in./ft slope—use 5 in. (fig. 16-7).

11 Three rear drive drains (3600 ft^2) + four

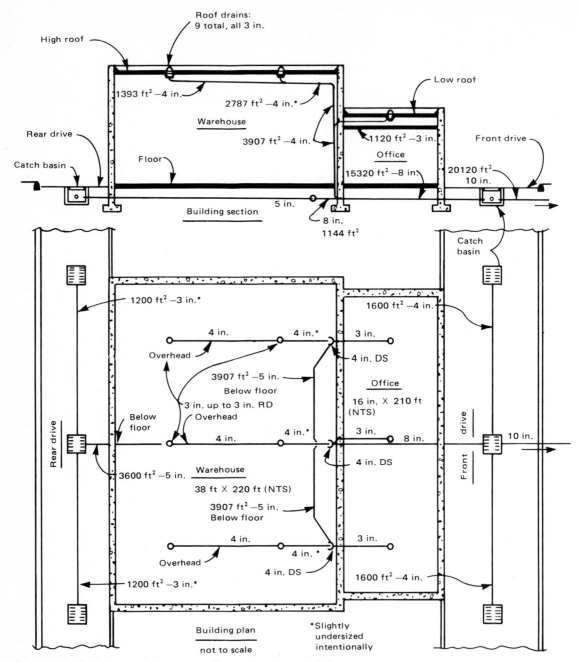

Figure 16-9 Typical storm drain system—office and warehouse building.

high roof drains (1393.33 ft² × 4 = 5573 ft²) + two low roof drains (1120 ft² × 2 = 2240 ft²) = 11,413 ft² —use 8 in. (from fig. 16-7).

12 Same as step 11 (11,413 ft²) + two high roof drains (1393.33 × 2 = 2787 ft²) + one low roof drain (1120 ft²) = 15,320 ft² —use 8 in. (fig. 16-7).

13 Size front drive drain line (1600 ft²) at 1/4 in./ft—use 4 in. (fig. 16-7).

14 Same as step 12 (15,320 ft²) + three front drive drains (1600 ft² × 3 = 4800 ft²) = 20,120 ft² at 1/4 in./ft—use 10 in. (fig. 16-7).

Figure 16-9 shows details of this piping system. Each section of the storm drain piping is noted with the roof area served and the size of the drain pipe required.

The roof drain fixtures would in every case in this example be 3 in. in size with a 3-in. pipe connecting from the drain down through the roof to the 4- or 3-in. drain piping below. Such piping would usually be extra heavy cast iron made up with bell-and-spigot lead and jute joints. However, other types of joints are used, and these may be of threaded type or may be of the *No-Hub* type.

The No-Hub joint uses cast iron pipe with plain ends on each end of each section of pipe; bell ends (or hubs) are not used. In some cases, the plain ends may have a slightly increased diameter. A heavy, rubberlike, neoprene sleeve is slid over the outside of the ends of the two adjacent pipes being joined. A stainless steel draw-band around the outside of the neoprene sleeve is drawn tight with two integral screws which should be tightened with a torque wrench. At the midpoint of the inside of the sleeve is a molded circular ridge against which the adjoining pipes are pushed when assembled into place.

In a No-Hub joint there is no metal-to-metal contact between joining pipes. There is some flexibility in the joint, which is a big advantage if pipe settlement occurs. The outside diameter of such a joint is appreciably less than the bell end of a bell-and-spigot joint. Furred-in downspouts often benefit from this. With the neoprene sleeve, there is less telegraphing of noise from one section of pipe

to the next. A full line of fittings of the No-Hub type is available. The last 15 years have seen a great increase in the use of this type of joint in sanitary as well as storm drain piping.

Galvanized steel and wrought iron and DWV copper have been used in storm drain systems, but galvanized steel and wrought iron are too subject to corrosion and copper is too expensive and fragile. Because of its low cost and comparative incorrodibility, cast iron is still the logical choice for storm drain lines.

As was mentioned in chap. 15, vitrified tile and reinforced concrete tile are eminently suitable for sanitary sewers where not laid under a building or paved area or roadway and where not laid too deeply in the earth. This is equally true of storm drainage piping.

16-7 ROOF DRAINS

The roof drains indicated in the flat, or nearly flat, roof of fig. 16-9 would probably be of the general type shown in fig. 16-10. In the details of fig. 16-10 the roof drain is supported directly by the structural roof deck. An appreciable thickness of rigid-board-type insulation is shown in the interest of energy conservation, as discussed elsewhere in this text. Notice that the insulation is tapered, and the built-up roof membrane is fitted down the slope of the insulation so that the weight of the roof drain and some of the connecting piping can bear on the roof deck and not on the insulation.

However, with some types of rigid board insulation, such as polyurethane or cork or rock cork, the compressive strength may be as high as 50 psi. In this case it may be very satisfactory to extend the insulation with full thickness to the very edge of the hole in the roof deck. Then a 10-gauge steel pan is laid on the insulation and the roof drain is installed in a 12-in.-diameter hole in the center of the pan. The pan should be 18 to 24 in. square and recessed 1/4 in. into the insulation so that the roof membrane that covers it will be slightly lower than on the surrounding roof.

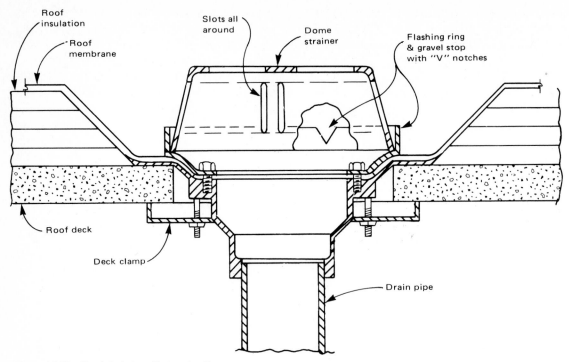

Figure 16-10 Roof drain installation details.

With any method of installation, it is advisable to spray the underside of the roof drain body with a thick coating of self-adhering insulation to prevent condensation in cold weather. In colder climates where snow falls frequently, melting snow on a roof causes a small flow of ice cold water to trickle through the roof drain and the connecting piping. It is good practice to insulate the horizontal portions of such drain piping with 1/2 in. of pipe insulation having a conductivity k of 0.30 or better to prevent condensation and dripping.

16-8 CATCH BASINS AND AREA DRAINS

Storm drainage systems must carry great quantities of water that fall on the earth's surface and flow across that surface. The water that is absorbed and held by the earth is usually not a problem to a storm drainage system. The rain that falls on impervious surfaces and cannot be absorbed by the earth does pose a problem, however. This problem can be minimized if we can intercept the surface flow at many points scattered over a given area, and prevent water from large areas from gathering and forming a concentrated stream. Such a surface stream of swiftly moving water can do an amazing amount of damage.

To prevent this concentration, area drains and catch basins are strategically located on a building site to receive surface flow and carry it underground in storm drain piping in a controlled manner. Area drains, or yard drains, are cast iron fixtures much like a roof drain but with a flat or slightly arched cast iron grating flush with the earth surface. Surrounding earth should, of course, be sloped to the drain.

Area drains are often fitted with a sediment bucket below the drain grating to catch leaves, pebbles, and other debris, generally called detritus. From the area drains, storm water flows into larger drainage structures called *catch basins*. As shown in fig. 16-11, catch basins incorporate a large storage chamber at the bottom to receive and hold mud and other detritus until it can be cleaned out and removed. The size of such catch basins depends on the amount of detritus expected and the frequency with which they will be cleaned. A popular size is 36 in. X 36 in. (grating size), and the depth depends on the depths at which the entering and leaving drain lines must be buried.

As noted in fig. 16-11, the outlet opening is 8 in. below the overflow level, or liquid level, in the basin so that floating debris cannot enter the outlet opening. Also noted is the depth required below the outlet opening of 15 in. in which detritus can collect. The construction of catch basins is usually of reinforced concrete, but the walls may be of brick or concrete block.

If catch basins are located in driveways or roadways or other places where heavy-wheeled vehicles can drive over them, the gratings must be designed for such loads. Steel or cast iron, heavily ribbed beneath, can be found that has adequate strength. Sometimes catch basins are long and narrow, perhaps only 1 ft wide, to minimize the problem of grating strength.

16-9 COMBINATION STORM AND SANITARY SEWERS

In many cases, a municipality may have public sewers that carry both storm and sanitary drainage. The building sanitary sewer and the building

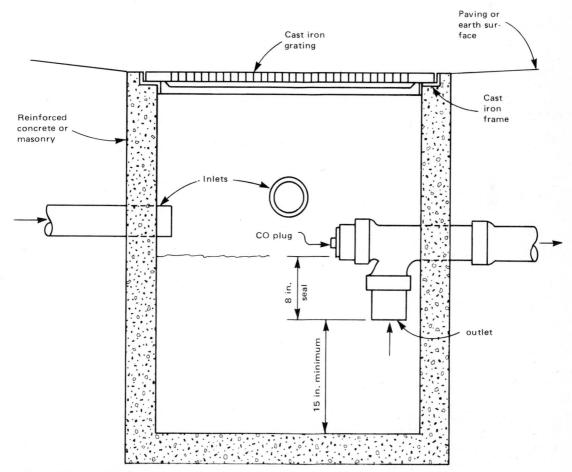

Figure 16-11 Catch basin detail.

Figure 16-12 Combination sewer sizing. (Excerpted from the 1968 Indiana State Plumbing Rules and Regulations.)

Fixture unit load of sanitary drainage system	Equivalent storm drain area to be added per fixture unit
2	41
5	38
10	33
30	29
50	25
80	22
100	20
160	18
250	16
350	14
500	12
1000	10
2000	9
3700	8

storm sewer will then connect together outside the building to make a combination building sewer. This sewer then extends to and connects to the public combination sewer as a single line. However, the two building sewers may connect separately if it is expedient to do so.

When these are combined, the question arises as to the size of such a combination building sewer. The size is based on the area of surface on which storm water can fall, plus an extra equivalent area which is based on the number of fixture units of the sanitary drainage system involved.

Figure 16-12 presents a table on the basis of which the transition from drainage fixture units to storm drain area may be made. Example 16-3 will demonstrate the use of fig. 16-12.

Example 16-3 The building and driveways of fig. 16-9 include a total storm drain area of 20,120 ft^2 (see example 16-2) which on the basis of a 4-in./hr rain and a storm sewer slope of 1/4 in./ft requires a 10-in. sewer (see also fig. 16-7). If this building has plumbing fixtures installed with a total of 250 fixture units, what size combination sewer will be required?

Solution Figure 16-12 shows that for 250 FU, 16 ft^2 of storm drain area must be added for each FU of sanitary load. Total additive area is then 4000 ft^2 (250 FU × 16 ft^2/FU = 4000 ft^2). Then adding the 4000 ft^2 to the 20,120-ft^2 storm drain area, we reach a new total storm drain area of 24,120 ft^2. Figure 16-7 shows that a 10-in. sewer on a 4-in./hr rain has a capacity of 29,200 ft^2. Therefore, the 10-in. sewer, which is now a combination sewer, has ample capacity to carry the new load of 24,120 ft^2.

PROBLEMS

16-1 For rainfall durations of 15 min, what would be the rainfall intensities, in inches per hour, for 2- and 10-year frequencies in Springfield, Illinois? Which is greater?

16-2 For a 10-year rainfall frequency in Phoenix, Arizona, what would be the design rainfall intensity in in./hr for 15- and 30-min durations? Which is greater?

16-3 A level 5-acre building site is developed with a building having 50,000 ft^2 of flat roof and 20,000 ft^2 of level asphalt-paved parking area. If the building is located in Fort Worth, Texas, if drainage of storm water is based on a 10-year rain of 15-min duration, and if the main storm sewer on the site can be sloped at a rate of 2.2 ft per 100 ft of run, what size sewer will be required? Unpaved area around the building will be in well-maintained lawn. (*Note:* 1 acre = 43,560 ft^2.)

16-4 A building roof contains 12,000 ft^2 of horizontal projected area. If design is based on a 4-in./hr rainfall intensity, how many 3-in. roof drains would be required?

16-5 In prob. 16-4, what size horizontal storm drain would be required if it slopes at 1/8 in./ft and if it slopes at 1/4 in./ft?

16-6 A certain building has a roof area of 52,000 ft^2, and also has plumbing fixtures in it which total 750 fixture units. What size combination building sewer should this building have if its slope is 1/4 in./ft and design rainfall intensity is 3 in./hr?

Chapter 17

Private Sewage Treatment and Disposition

17-1 GENERALITIES

Basically, this chapter is devoted to the subject of the treatment and disposition of the sewage effluent from nonresidential buildings. However, most of the information presented in this chapter is also applicable to the residential problem. The sewage treatment systems for private residences are often designed on the basis of a certain amount of system capacity per bedroom. This illogical and imprecise method of design has yielded in this chapter to the more logical methods of nonresidential construction.

There are several methods available for the private treatment of sewage, none of which are applicable in all cases. The type of system to be used should be selected in consideration of the many variable factors that usually attend each building site. Of course, if an approved public sewerage system and treatment plant is available to a certain location, this should always be utilized. However, if such is not available, one of the following systems may be used:

1 Septic tank with disposal field
2 Aeration unit with local stream disposal
3 Aeration unit with sewage lagoon or retention pond
4 Septic tank with sand filter and with or without a rotary distributor
5 Cesspools or leaching pits

All these systems have disadvantages and pose a threat to the purity of both surface water resources and subsurface water supplies. The selection should always be made with the assistance, advice, and approval of local health authorities. It is their responsibility to protect the health of the public, and a private sewage disposal system if incorrectly selected and applied can pose a very serious threat. If the local water table (the level of the water in the earth) is too high, if there is no suitable all-weather creek or river available, and if there is not enough area for a sewage lagoon, it may be that none of the available systems would be suitable. This should, of course, be determined before site acquisition.

Sewage treatment systems, as listed above, all operate on one of two basic processes. First, the sewage is held for a period of time, usually 24 to 36 hr, in a storage chamber, called a *septic tank,* where primary treatment is given by anaerobic (without air) bacterial action. A level of bacterial life is established in such a tank so that the fecal matter and other contaminants can be consumed and digested by such bacteria. In this first process the sewage is given secondary treatment by leaching it into and through the earth in extensive disposal field fingers incorporating large areas of absorptive earth.

In the second process, the sewage is *aerated,* or *oxygenated,* in a mechanical device which rolls and churns and tumbles the sewage by powerful jets of air. This is the same action which is given by a creek or river which, running not too deep, rolls and tumbles over boulders on the stream bed. Such a stream can very quickly give good treatment to sewage. A stream or lake which is deep and quiet and calm cannot do this. A shallow pond or lagoon to which the wind has good access and which as a result has good movement and wave action can also give sewage treatment.

In the second process, secondary treatment is given in a settling chamber where the sewage is held quietly while any solid matter settles out and falls as sludge to the bottom. This sludge must be pumped out and hauled away periodically; it does have some commercial use. Usually, the sewage, or what remains of it, is given a tertiary treatment in which it passes through a chlorination chamber where for a minimum time of 15 min or so it is in contact with a source of chlorine.

The manufacturers of aeration units using this second process claim that the effluent is suitable for human consumption, although one never sees

the claim put to the test. At least, in many cases local boards of health will permit such effluent to be discharged into an all-weather stream if such is available. In many cases, the board of health will require that the effluent pass through a 7-day retention pond before it is permitted to overflow into an all-weather stream. This is good insurance if the pond is shallow and subject to good wind and wave action.

When the first process, involving a septic tank, is to be used on a building site that has a high water table or unabsorptive earth so that a disposal field is not possible, a *sand filter* may be utilized. In such a filter an upper horizontal network of perforated piping is laid near the top of a bed of sand, and a similar network of perforated underdrain piping is laid near the bottom of the bed of sand. A vertical distance of 3 ft or more should separate the two layers of piping, and it is helpful if such a filter can be laid on sloping ground so that the effluent can flow by gravity into an all-weather stream. Without such a stream a sand filter cannot be used.

The effluent from a sand filter should in every case be chlorinated for purity before it enters a stream. It may be necessary in some cases for the effluent to be pumped a considerable distance horizontally and upward to reach a suitable stream.

Some sand filters are made with only the bottom layer of piping underdrains installed. The liquid effluent from a primary treatment device such as a septic tank is distributed over the surface of the sand by a rotary distributor. This distributor consists of an assembly of four perforated pipe arms which rotate in a horizontal plane 2 to 3 ft above the surface of the sand. As the sewage flows from the rotating pipe arms there is some aeration of the sewage. It is evenly distributed over the open surface of the filter, which itself is open to the atmosphere and the sunshine.

Obviously, an open sand filter is a source of odor and is an attractive nuisance to children. It must be securely fenced. A closed sand filter (covered with earth) is obviously better from this standpoint, but does present much more of a maintenance problem. The sand must be cleaned and sometimes replaced, and the removal of 12 to 18 in. of earth cover is an expensive operation. The use of 18 in. of straw cover is a compromise solution to this problem.

With both sand filters and subsurface disposal fields it is always a good idea to utilize the principle of *dosing*. Dosing is accomplished with the use of a collection chamber in which the sewage effluent from a septic tank is held for a period of 3 to 6 hr. When this chamber is full it is pumped out or drawn out with a *dosing siphon* and charged at high rate into the disposal field or the sand filter (see figs. 17-6 and 17-7). One benefit of this is that the entire field or filter is flooded and entirely utilized. Otherwise, only a small part of the field or filter may be utilized when the sewage slowly trickles into it. The portion that is thus used excessively can load up with solid matter (sludge, etc.) and become inoperative.

Cesspools and *seepage pits* are also sometimes utilized in sewage treatment and disposition. These are vertical cylindrical masonry devices 4 to 6 ft in diameter with perforated walls. They are buried with their closed tops a foot or so below the earth's surface and extend to a depth of 10 ft or so below the inlet pipe. They are usually at least 14 to 15 ft deep. As a cesspool, the sewage is discharged directly into the device without preliminary treatment. As a seepage pit, the sewage is given preliminary treatment in a septic tank. Where necessary, more than one pit is used when the sewage load is too great for one pit.

It is this author's recommendation that such devices as cesspools and seepage pits never be used. If there is a legitimate use for such it is in areas where the water table is always 25 ft or more below the surface, and where land is so scarce that not enough is available for a disposal field. In the heavily occupied areas of the United States and the world, the water table is rarely this low consistently. Obviously, a cesspool or seepage pit could contaminate the earth's water-bearing strata over a very great area, and the risk of this is just too great to be tolerated.

Garbage grinders or disposers in kitchens pose somewhat of a problem for private sewage disposal systems. In a residential system where the disposer load is light and from a single kitchen, the usual answer to the problem is to make the septic tank 50% larger than it otherwise would need to be. Except in buildings such as rural schools with large, active kitchens, the problem of garbage disposers in nonresidential buildings is not of consequence.

In the rural school, an effort should be made to dispose of food wastes and other kitchen wastes by means other than the sewage disposal system—unless an aeration-type sewage treatment machine is installed. With an aeration aerobic sewage treatment system, the volume of sludge production will be appreciably greater when large volumes of food wastes are included in the sewage. This will require more frequent pumping of the sludge from the treatment unit, but it would usually be less of a problem than would be the special care required to keep kitchen wastes separate. In a septic tank system, the kitchen wastes should be kept separate if possible.

Sewage disposal systems universally carry a threat to public health. The design of private sewage systems should always be closely controlled to ascertain that adequate clearances are maintained from buildings, streams, wells, adjacent properties, and water lines. For all the problems posed in this article, further discussion will be provided in the following articles.

17-2 SEWAGE FLOW VOLUME

The design of any private sewage disposal system must of necessity begin with an estimate of flow rate in gallons per day to be expected. As mentioned in chap. 14, there is close correlation between the volume of water consumed and the volume of sewage produced in a 24-hr period. The table given in fig. 17-1 shows typical sewage flow rates from various types of buildings. This figure shows sewage flow rates expressed in terms of gpd per person; however, there are many exceptions

Figure 17-1 Sewage flows according to type of establishment. [From the National Standard Plumbing Code, ASA–A40.8–1955. Note: This is an out-of-date document. Both ANSI and ASME have withdrawn their approval of it as a valid document (taken as a whole). But data in this figure coincide well with data from other current sources of information.]

Type of establishment	Gallons per day per person[a]
Schools (toilet and lavatories only)	15
Schools (with above plus cafeteria)	25
Schools (with above plus cafeteria and showers)	35
Day workers at schools and offices	15
Day camps	25
Trailer parks or tourist camps (with built-in bath)	50
Trailer parks or tourist camps (with central bathhouse)	35
Work or construction camps	50
Public picnic parks (toilet wastes, only)	5
Public picnic parks (bathhouse, showers, and flush toilets)	10
Swimming pools and beaches	10
Country clubs	25 gal/locker
Luxury residences and estates	150
Rooming houses	40
Boarding houses	50
Hotels (with connecting baths)	50
Hotels (with private baths-two persons per room)	100
Boarding schools	100
Factories (gallons per person per shift—exclusive of industrial wastes)	25
Nursing homes	75
General hospitals	150
Public institutions (other than hospitals)	100
Restaurants (toilet and kitchen wastes per unit of serving capacity)	25
Kitchen wastes from hotels, camps, boarding houses, etc.	
Serving three meals per day	10
Motels	50 gal/bed space
Motels with bath, toilet, and kitchen wastes	60 gal/bed space
Drive-in theaters	5 gal/car space
Stores	400 gal/toilet room
Service stations	10 gal/vehicle served
Airports	3–5 gal/passenger
Assembly halls	2 gal/seat
Bowling alleys	75 gal/lane
Churches (small)	3–5 gal/sanctuary seat
Churches (large with kitchens)	5–7 gal/sanctuary seat
Dance halls	2
Laundries (coin operated)	400 gal/machine
Service stations	1000 gal (first bay)
	500 gal (each add. bay)
Subdivisions or individual homes	75
Marinas—flush toilets	36 gal/fixture/hr
Urinals	10 gal/fixture/hr
Wash basins	15 gal/fixture/hr
Showers	150 gal/fixture/hr

[a]Unless otherwise indicated.

to this and these should be carefully observed. For example, a bowling alley is rated at 75 gpd per bowling lane—not per person occupying the space. There is no diversity factor to be applied here, and a building holding 1000 people would produce twice the volume of sewage as would the same type of building occupied by 500 people.

17-3 SEPTIC TANKS

As mentioned in art. 17-1, septic tanks do not provide complete treatment of sewage, and further treatment outside the tank must be provided. Most septic tanks are made of reinforced concrete or reinforced masonry. In smaller sizes, some tanks made of heavy gauge steel (3/16 in. and more) have found successful use. However, the reinforced concrete tank is by far the most popular, and details of such a tank are found in fig. 17-2.

Here it may be seen that the nominal volume of the tank is not the total internal volume but is only the volume of the tank below the water line shown. Figure 17-2 shows a manhole accessway to the tank with a gastight, gasketed, cast iron ring and cover. This permits easy access for pumping the sludge out of the bottom of the tank when that becomes necessary. However, a manhole, if left open or unbolted by a careless worker, poses a serious threat to children who may be playing nearby. It is probably better to omit the manhole and provide a permanent marker flush with the earth to show where one must dig to excavate down to the access opening in the tank. A small child falling into such a tank would have little chance of survival; the liquid depth would be too great, and there probably would be very little oxygen to breathe.

Figure 17-2 also shows that the influent sewage enters quite close to the liquid level in the tank, and will enter that tank liquid with very little splash and turbulence. It immediately meets a crosswise baffle (or enters through a "tee" fitting turned down) and is forced down into the body of the liquid. It passes through the tank in a very gentle and quiescent manner so that the solid matter can separate from the liquid and settle to the bottom.

Some of the solid, organic matter will settle quickly to the bottom while a colloidal remainder will settle very slowly. Research and field experience has shown that 24 hr is ample for this sedimentation process to be completed. After this the liquid leaves the tank in a comparatively clear form. However, even though it is clear, it is far from innocuous, and must be handled with great care until receiving further treatment.

The solid matter remaining in the tank is subject to anaerobic digestion by anaerobic bacteria, which do not require oxygen. Their action on the sewage constitutes a putrefaction process which results primarily in the production of ammonia, carbon dioxide, hydrogen sulfide, and methane gas. A sludgelike residue remains at the bottom of the septic tank until it is pumped out—in usually 6 months or more.

Since 24 hr is required for this process to take place, the size of the septic tank depends on the amount of daily sewage flow expected. If sewage flow is estimated to be 1000 gal/day (gpd), the effective volume of the tank must be 1000 gal measured from the top of the sludge layer to the top of the liquid. If the sludge layer is allowed to remain too long and collect to too great a thickness, the capacity of the tank is thereby reduced.

This fact is apparently not known to many property owners, and their septic tanks are never pumped out. The sludge layer builds for years until the active volume of the tank is so greatly reduced that sewage passes on out of the tank before the sedimentation process is complete. Solid matter is then carried out to the sand filter, or the disposal field, which becomes clogged with sediment and rendered ineffective thereby.

When the tank size is adequate, the septic tank effluent will, as mentioned, be essentially clear, and the disposal field or sand filter can do its work effectively. This consists essentially of treatment by aerobic bacteria, by oxidation, and by filtration by the sand or the earth.

Since the septic tank process is universally considered to require 24 hr, and since all the

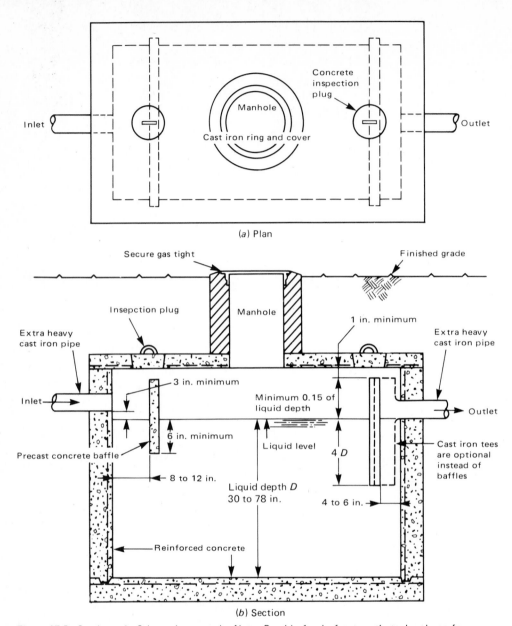

(a) Plan

(b) Section

Figure 17-2 Septic tank. Schematic—no scale. Note: Provide 1 gal of net septic tank volume for each gallon per day of estimated maximum sewage flow rate. (Excerpted from the 1970 Bulletin S.E. 13 of the Indiana State Board of Health Planning Guide.)

sewage that enters a septic tank must receive the full 24-hr treatment, there is little reason to think that with larger flow rates, the tank volume, in gallons per gpd of effluent, may be reduced. Some authorities allow as much as a 50% reduction in tank gallons per gpd when flow rates run as high as 3000 to 4000 gpd. This in effect is saying that with higher daily flow rates, the liquid velocity through the tank may be increased. There is no theoretical basis for this belief.

Therefore, in sizing a septic tank, one must adhere to the practice of setting the effective tank volume equal to the estimated daily flow rate. If a practice is followed of removing the sludge every 6 months, it is considered adequate to base the tank volume on the tank depth from the overflow level all the way to the tank bottom. Extra-conservative designers will assume a sludge depth of 6 in. in calculating effective tank liquid depth.

Usually, a heavy crust of nondigestible material will be found to float on the liquid in the tank. This crust may be 6 in. or more in thickness, but subtracts only a little from the effective depth of the liquid. However, it should be broken up and removed as much as possible when the tank sludge is pumped out.

17-4 DISPOSAL (ABSORPTION) FIELDS

As mentioned, a sewage disposal field gives important final treatment to the septic tank effluent, and provides a means of disposing of the finally clarified water. The use of an absorption field, of course, precludes the necessity of providing surface drainage in a stream or other body of water. However, field absorption can be utilized only when suitably permeable earth is available, when the contours of the site are reasonably favorable, and when the building site is large enough to permit satisfactory horizontal clearance between the various parts of the sewage system and other important features of the developed site.

As shown in fig. 17-3, the disposal field (also called absorption field or finger system) consists of open joint tile or perforated tile laid in trenches in the earth, surrounded by gravel and backfilled over with earth. The tile lines are arranged in usually parallel "fingers" which may be freely extended or may be end-connected as shown in the plan view of fig. 17-3.

When open joint tile lines are used, the tile material is usually 4-in. unglazed clay tile with plain ends (no bell or hub) laid in 12- or 24-in. lengths with a 1/4-in. gap between adjacent tiles. The upper half of the tile at each gap is covered with 8-in. wide pieces of 30- or 40-lb roofing felt or galvanized sheet metal to keep earth out of the tile. Frequently, a 4-in. bituminized fiber or plastic pipe in 8- or 10-ft lengths is used in place of the clay tile; such pipe is perforated on the underside, as laid, and the open joints are not necessary.

The finger tile or pipe is laid on a 6-in. bed of clean, washed gravel, and surrounded and covered with the same. Figure 17-3 shows a layer of building paper (30-lb felt) laid over the gravel before the final earth backfill is placed. Each finger of the system is connected into a distribution box, as shown, which performs the function of distributing the septic tank effluent equally to all fingers. This is usually a reinforced concrete box with one inlet opening and several or many outlet openings. It must be carefully made and even more carefully installed so that even at light flow rates the effluent will be divided up and not be permitted to always flow into the same finger.

Very often a distribution box is not used, and the several fingers are connected to a closed joint vitrified tile main line. Individual fingers often connect to the main line with "double-Y" vitrified tile fittings so that the fingers branch off at a 45° angle. These may be standard double-Y fittings with hubs, but are reversed in position from the usual position of a double-Y fitting.

There is one problem in the design of septic tank and disposal field systems which has never been given an answer on which all designers can agree. This problem is involved with the maximum size that such a system may have. The Indiana State Board of Health has ruled that septic tank liquid capacity shall not exceed 4000 gal. In other words, a building that is expected to generate more than 4000 gpd of sewage effluent may not use a septic tank and disposal field system.

The Uniform Plumbing Code (UPC) published by the International Association of Plumbing and Mechanical Officials (5032 Alhambra Ave., Los Angeles, CA 90032) allows the use of septic tanks as large as 7500 gal if the permeability of the disposal field earth is unusually high—the equivalent of dry sand. In earth that has a percolation rate of about 11 min/in. (see art. 17-9 dealing with percolation tests) and which as a result requires

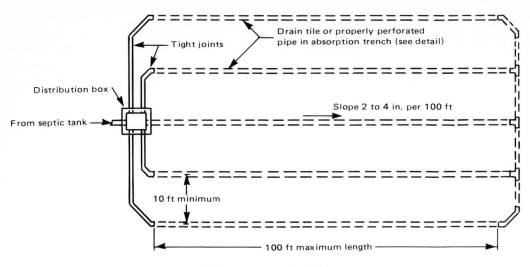

(*a*) Plan of absorption field

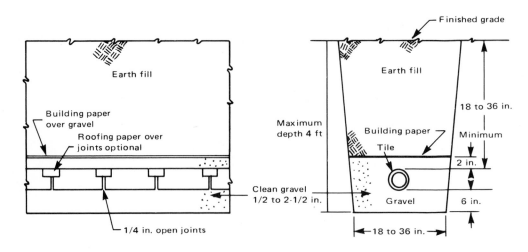

(*b*) Detail of absorption trench

Figure 17-3 Absorption field details. (Schematic—no scale. Excerpted from the 1970 Bulletin S.E. 13 of the Indiana State Board of Health Planning Guide.)

0.6 ft^2 of trench bottom per gpd of sewage effluent, the UPC maximum allowable septic tank size is 3500 gal.

The UPC further lists a maximum tank size of 5000 if the earth is such as to require 0.4 ft^2 of trench bottom per gpd (corresponding to about a 5 min/in. percolation test). It also lists a 3000-gal maximum tank size with earth that requires 0.9 ft^2 of trench bottom per gpd (corresponding approximately to a 19 min/in. percolation test).

The question of maximum tank size is not really concerned with the permeability of the earth in the disposal field. Rather the answer is properly involved with the amount of water coming from sewage which should be allowed to drain into the aquifer (stored earth water) below, as it will probably do, at any one location. Of course, some of the water from the sewage will be drawn to the surface of the disposal field and will evaporate, but most of it will probably descend into the aquifer that exists in most areas. This is not a pleasant thought, and it is recommended here that the

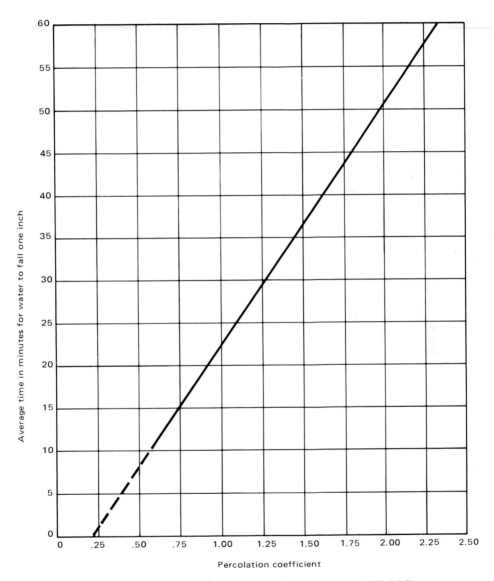

Figure 17-4 Chart for estimating percolation coefficient. (Excerpted from the 1970 Bulletin S.E. 13 of the Indiana State Board of Health Planning Guide.)

4000-gal septic tank limitation be carefully observed, as well as a 4000-gpd limitation on sewage flow.

There are many design rules that should be followed in the design of sewage disposal fields; these are listed as follows:

1 Minimum number of disposal field fingers (or laterals)—two.

2 Minimum spacing of fingers—6 ft.

3 Maximum length of fingers—100 ft.

4 Slope of finger tile lines—4 in. per 100 ft minimum and 6 in. per 100 ft maximum.

5 Total area of finger trench bottom must be based on estimated daily sewage flow and on earth permeability as indicated by percolation tests (see fig. 17-4).

6 Trench bottoms must be held at least 3 ft above the highest water table in wet weather.

7 On rolling or hilly terrain, the fingers must approximately follow the land contour lines.

8 If possible, each separate finger should connect to the distribution box at the septic tank outlet; in hilly areas this will be difficult but should be done.

9 Width of finger trenches—18 in. minimum and 36 in. maximum.

10 Trench depth—30 in. minimum and 48 in. maximum.

11 All parts of the sewage disposal system must be located proper distances from buildings, property lines, wells, water lines, and so on, as shown in fig. 17-5.

12 Whenever daily sewage flow rates equal or exceed 2000 gpd, the disposal field should be dosed with a dosing pump or siphon as shown in figs. 17-6 and 17-7.

13 When the total lineal feet of disposal field finger trench length exceeds 1000 ft, the field

Figure 17-5 Minimum distances between sewage disposal system and site facilities. (From Uniform Plumbing Code, 1976, p. 186, courtesy of International Association of Plumbing and Mechanical Officials.)

Minimum horizontal distance in clear required from:	Location of sewage disposal system			
	Building sewer, ft (m)	Septic tank, ft (m)	Disposal field, ft (m)	Seepage pit or cesspool, ft (m)
Buildings or structures[a]	2 (0.6)	5 (1.5)	8 (2.4)	8 (2.4)
Property line adjoining private property	Clear	5 (1.5)	5 (1.5)	8 (2.4)
Water supply wells[b]	50 (15.2)	50 (15.2)	100 (30.5)	150 (45.7)
Streams	50 (15.2)	50 (15.2)	50 (15.2)	100 (30.5)
Large trees	...	10 (3)	...	10 (3)
Seepage pits or cesspools	...	5 (1.5)	5 (1.5)	12 (3.7)
Disposal field	...	5 (1.5)	4[c] (1.2)	5 (1.5)
Domestic water line	1 (0.3)	5 (1.5)	5 (1.5)	5 (1.5)
Distribution box	...	...	5 (1.5)	5 (1.5)

When disposal fields and/or seepage pits are installed in sloping ground the minimum horizontal distance between any part of the leaching system and ground surface shall be 15 ft (4.6 m).

[a]Including porches and steps, whether covered or uncovered, breezeways, roofed porte-cocheres, roofed patios, car ports, covered walks, covered driveways, and similar structures or appurtenances.

[b]All nonmetallic drainage piping shall clear domestic water supply wells by at least 50 ft (15.2m). This distance may be reduced to not less than 25 ft (7.6 m) when approved type metallic piping is installed. Where special hazards are involved, the distance required shall be increased, as may be directed by the health officer or the administrative authority.

[c]Plus 2 ft (0.6 m) for each additional foot (0.3 m) of depth in excess of 1 ft (0.3 m) below the bottom of the drain line.

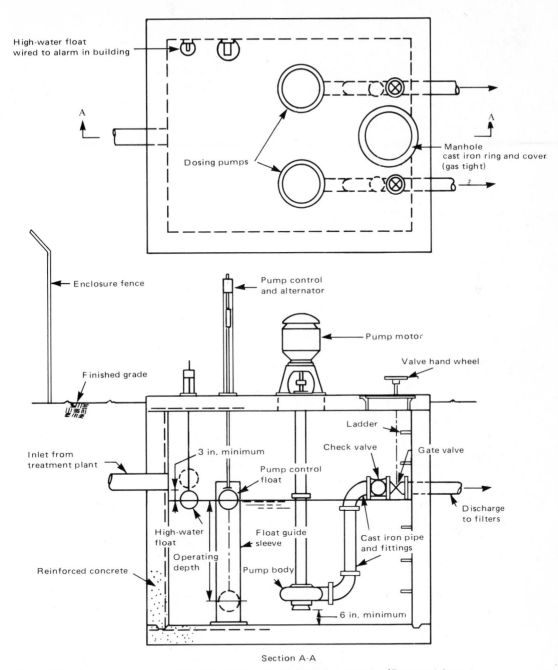

High-water float
wired to alarm in building

A

Dosing pumps

Manhole
cast iron ring and cover
(gas tight)

Enclosure fence

Pump control
and alternator

Pump motor

Valve hand wheel

Finished grade

Ladder

Inlet from
treatment plant

3 in. minimum

Check valve

Gate valve

Pump control
float

Discharge
to filters

High-water
float

Float guide
sleeve

Cast iron pipe
and fittings

Operating
depth

Reinforced concrete

Pump body

6 in. minimum

Section A-A

Figure 17-6 Dosing tank and duplex alternating pumps. Schematic—no scale. (Excerpted from the 1970 Bulletin S.E. 13 of the Indiana State Board of Health Planning Guide.)

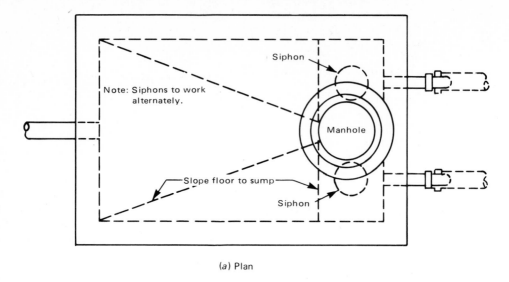

(*a*) Plan

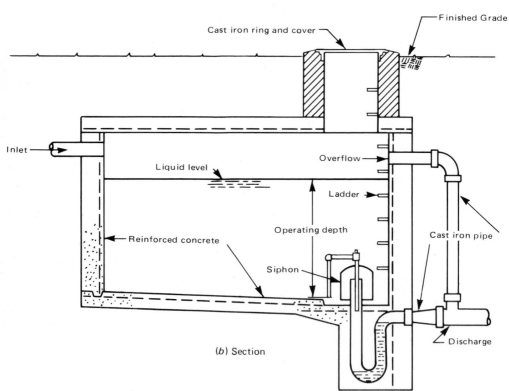

(*b*) Section

Figure 17-7 Dosing tank and siphons. Schematic—no scale. (Excerpted from the 1970 Bulletin S.E. 13 of the Indiana State Board of Health Planning Guide.)

should be divided into two approximately equal halves and dosed with a duplex dosing pump installation; each of the two pumps should serve half the field and should alternate in operation (duplex dosing siphons may also be used in place of pumps).

17-5 DOSING PUMPS

The principle of dosing a sewage disposal field or sand filter is well established and is quite beneficial. Sewage trickling at its own natural rate from a septic tank will rarely distribute itself evenly over the entire field. However, the field has been designed and approved (probably) for a certain rate of application of sewage in gpd per square foot of trench bottom. If most of the sewage trickles into only one finger, for example, that finger will surely be overloaded.

It is of great benefit if the sewage can be supplied into the disposal field in large doses; that is what a dosing pump or dosing siphon can do. Dosing pumps and the tanks in which they are installed should be sized and selected so as to dose a field, or one half of a field, two to six times per day. For example, if a building generates 3000 gpd of sewage and the duplex dosing pump operates in alternating fashion with each pump connected to half of the disposal field, the dosing pump tank would need to have an operating volume of 375 gal. 3000 gpd ÷ 2 = 1500 gpd per pump and 1500 gal in four cycles per day = 375 gal per cycle. The operating volume of the tank would, of course, be the difference between the gallons in the tank at the moment a pump starts (high level) and the gallons in the tank when that pump stops. See the operating depth shown in fig. 17-6.

A duplex dosing pump as shown in fig. 17-6 would have an alternating device which causes first one pump to run and then the other on the next cycle. This alternating action can be achieved mechanically or electrically. It is highly recommended that a valved interconnection between the two pump discharge lines, shown in fig. 17-6, be installed so that either pump can supply the

entire disposal field if one of the pumps becomes inoperative. The high water float shown in fig. 17-6 should be connected to an electric switch and two alarm bells—one at the pump location and one in the building.

17-6 DOSING SIPHONS

A dosing siphon is an ingenious nonelectric device which will cause a sewage disposal field to be dosed in the recommended manner. Figure 17-7 shows a typical detail of a duplex siphon unit with each siphon discharging into a different part of the disposal field. The size of the dosing tank would be calculated in the same manner as shown above for a dosing pump unit.

The heart of such a unit is the siphon, which consists of a dome-shaped cover inverted over the end of the vertical outlet pipe (see fig. 17-7). As the liquid level rises in the dosing tank, the air in the dome is pushed upward in the dome and down the outlet pipe. As the tank liquid level rises higher and higher the liquid in the outlet pipe is pushed, by the air trapped under the dome, farther and farther down until the liquid level in the outlet pipe is down to the dip in the outlet pipe as shown in fig. 17-7. At this point the air in the outlet pipe will escape over into the right-hand leg of the dip (or seal). As the air escapes, liquid rushes in under the dome and fills both legs of the seal and the siphon action begins.

Liquid flow outward with good velocity will then continue until the tank liquid level drops to the bottom end of the small pipe shown to the left of the siphon dome. Air then enters the small pipe, the vacuum in the outlet pipe, caused by the siphon action, is broken, the outward flow stops, and the liquid levels in the outlet pipe seal will equalize at the overflow level.

17-7 SEWAGE AERATION UNITS

As discussed briefly in art. 17-1 and as shown in fig. 17-8, an aeration unit thoroughly mixes the sewage with air from compressed air nozzles. As

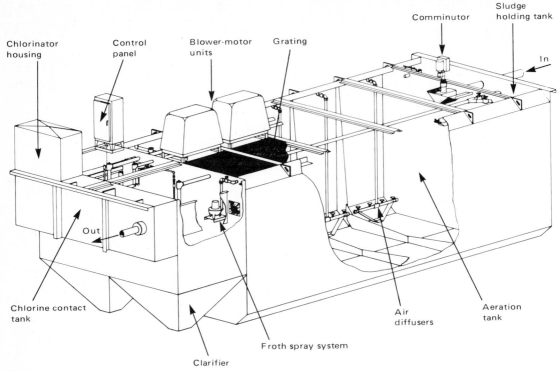

Figure 17-8 Sewage aeration-type treatment plant. (Courtesy of Clow Corporation, Waste Treatment Division, P.O. Box 68, Florence, Ky, 41042, (606) 283–2121.)

opposed to the action in a septic tank, an aeration unit does not use anaerobic bacteria for digestion of the solid matter in the sewage; rather, it uses aerobic bacteria, which require oxygen. An aeration unit maintains sufficient oxygen, mixing, and detention time to allow these microorganisms to decompose the treatable wastes in the sewage into harmless carbon dioxide, water, and an ash residue.

As the sewage first enters the aeration unit it passes through a grinding and pulverizing device, a comminutor, from which the sewage passes through a bar screen into the aeration chamber. After the aeration process is complete, the sewage passes from the heavily agitated aeration chamber into a quiet settling chamber where the solids are permitted to separate and settle to the bottom. The clarified liquid then passes from the final settling chamber and through a chlorination unit before final disposal.

A well-designed, properly functioning aeration unit can render the sewage essentially pure and suitable for discharge into any available natural waterway. Because such units are very complex and depend on the perfect performance of a great number of mechanical and electrical components, malfunction is a distinct possibility. Most local health authorities are thus quite reluctant to permit direct discharge into surface waterways. They often require the effluent to be held temporarily in a sewage lagoon or retention pond.

The aeration process is basically the one used by large municipal sewage treatment plants. Therefore, when used for a single building project, there is no limitation on size, and thus the aeration unit may be the answer to the sewage disposal problem when the 4000-gpd limitation on septic tank systems is too restrictive. The only limitation to the aeration unit is in the problem of disposition of the treated and presumably pure effluent. Sewage lagoons may be of help in this problem.

17-8 SEWAGE LAGOONS

A *sewage lagoon,* often referred to as a *terminal lagoon* or *retention pond,* is a shallow pond into which the treated effluent from a sewage treatment plant flows and is held for a specific number of days. Some sewage lagoons are in use today into which the raw, untreated sewage from a small municipality is discharged. With a shallow depth of 5 ft or less and with a wide-open approach for wind from any direction giving good water motion and wave action, these lagoons are giving good service. In this case the term "sewage lagoon" is very appropriate.

However, the lagoon or pond contemplated here does not receive raw sewage under normal conditions, but it can be easily seen that with such a lagoon, some type of malfunction of an aeration-type treatment plant would not be nearly as serious as if no lagoon were in use. Thus the lagoon, which theoretically should not be required, is a very good safety factor.

Figure 17-9 shows a simple layout plan of an aeration unit and lagoon facility. Notice that the entire area is enclosed with a fence, and this fence should be a high, strong fence topped with barbed wire which will discourage efforts by children and others to climb it. Provision has been made for the addition of a future treatment unit for increased capacity. The area enclosed by the fence is often much smaller than expected. For example, if the facility shown in fig. 17-9 were designed for a present load of 8000 gpd of sewage (well beyond the capacity of a septic tank system) and with plans for this to double in the future to 16,000 gpd, the area enclosed within the fence would probably be about 80 by 100 ft. The lagoon itself would be about 55 ft square, or equivalent.

Lagoons are often required to provide a 7-day retention so that if the daily flow rate is 16,000 gpd, the lagoon volume would need to be 112,000 gal. The inlet and overflow structures must be strategically located so that the entire pond receives circulation. This not only involves the entire pond in the treatment process, but it helps to prevent excessive buildup of ice in winter. The heat of the water entering the pond at 50 to 60°F will, of course, be of benefit here.

In very cold climates, the formation of some ice must be anticipated and the size of the lagoon increased accordingly. In areas as far north as Columbus, Ohio, or Indianapolis, Indiana, the problem of ice will be minimal, but areas farther north or at higher altitudes must face this problem.

Normally, the lagoon is formed with earth embankments on all sides unless a sloping terrain is available. If the local water table is low enough and the flow line of the available stream or other watercourse is low enough, the pond may be fully or partially recessed into the earth. If embankments are required, the slope on such banks should be 1 ft of vertical rise to 3 ft of horizontal if riding-type mowers are to be used for cutting the grass on the banks. With walking-type engine-driven mowers, which are very practical for areas this small, the slope of the embankments may be appreciably greater.

In many cases it may be important to prevent percolation of the liquid into the earth. To provide the benefits of the pond effect, with sunshine, oxygenation from wind, and so on, the liquid must not seep away too quickly. If the lagoon will not hold adequate water, it may be necessary to seal the bottom with a 12-in. thickness of dense clay, or with a commercial sealer such as Bentonite.

The maximum depth of such a pond is 5 ft; less depth will give better wave action but, of course, will require greater surface area. If the natural water table in the earth is quite high, the pond may need to be built from the natural earth grade up; in this case the liquid will have to be pumped up and into the lagoon. This is, of course, to be avoided if possible.

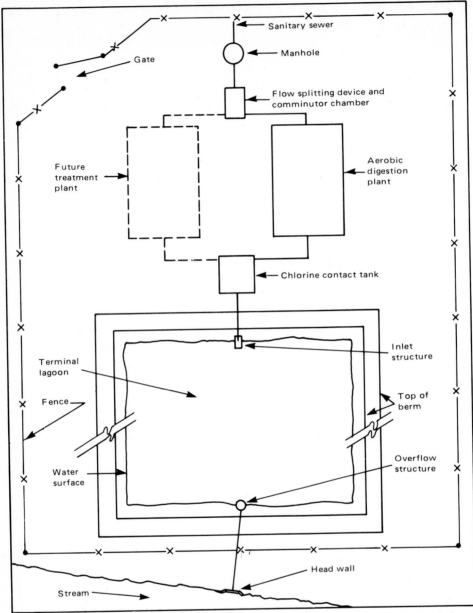

Figure 17-9 Layout plan of aeration unit and sewage lagoon. (Excerpted from the 1970 Bulletin S.E. 13 of the Indiana State Board of Health Planning Guide.)

17-9 PERCOLATION TESTS

As explained in art. 17-4, the trench bottom area of a sewage disposal field must be determined on the basis of the permeability of the earth at the level of the open-joint or perforated tile lines in the trenches. The permeability of the earth can be accurately determined only by conducting percolation tests in the area to be used. One test should be run for each 1000 ft² of disposal field gross area.

The procedure for conducting percolation tests is as follows:

1 Drill or bore a hole in the earth approximately 4 to 6 in. in diameter. This may be done with an auger or a post hole digger. The bottom of this hole should be at the approximate bottom of the proposed disposal trench.

2 Remove any topsoil that may have been carried down and smeared on the inside face of the hole. Clean out all loose soil from the bottom of the hole.

3 Fill the hole with water during the evening of one day.

4 Return early the following morning and refill the hole. Return as often as necessary to refill the hole and keep it more than half full at all times until late in the afternoon of this second day.

5 Allow the water to seep away until about 12 in. remains. Then start taking measurements every 15 to 20 min from the earth surface to the water level, making note of the exact time of each measurement. Continue this until the water level drops 6 in.

6 Refill the hole to 12 in. of water again, and repeat the procedure of step 5.

7 Repeat step 6 so that a total of three sets of measurements are made.

8 From all the readings taken, calculate the average time required for the water in the hole to drop 1 in.

9 Conduct the same test for each of the other test holes required. Find the average value for all test holes.

10 This average value is then taken to the chart of fig. 17-4 to determine the required area of trench bottom per gpd of sewage effluent expected.

This value, multiplied by the total estimated gpd of sewage flow, establishes the total area of trench bottom for the entire disposal field.

17-10 SEPTIC TANK AND DISPOSAL FIELD DESIGN PROBLEM

Example 17-1 A small 20-room hotel with private baths is planned for a rural setting where no public sewer is available. A septic tank and disposal field is contemplated, and a site survey reveals the following information:

1 The water table is 7 ft below the surface on a fairly level site.

2 Percolation tests revealed an average percolation rate of 25 min/in. of fall of water in the test holes.

3 No all-weather stream is available for sewage disposal.

4 With the building, well, and water piping locations contemplated, adequate distance from the sewage system components would be possible.

5 Three large trees standing in the disposal field area would need to be removed or avoided.

Solution Daily sewage flow rate is estimated to be 4000 gpd. (20 rooms × 2 people per room × 100 gpd/person = 4000 gpd.) The 100 gpd/person figure is from fig. 17-1.

The septic tank must have a liquid storage capacity equal to the daily flow rate of 4000 gpd. Use a 4000-gal septic tank.

With a percolation rate of 25 min/in., fig. 17-4 indicates that 1.1 ft² of trench bottom area per gpd of effluent is required. The trench bottom area is then 4000 gpd × 1.1 = 4400 ft².

If a trench bottom width of 30 in. is arbitrarily chosen, the lineal length of finger or trench is 1760 ft (4400 ft² ÷ 2.5 ft = 1760 ft). Let us use 20 fingers, each of which is 90 ft long. Remember that maximum finger length is 100 ft.

Since we need more than 1000 lineal feet of trench, we should definitely use dosing on this 1800-ft field. With the building site as flat as it was surveyed to be, we would have difficulty in using dosing siphons, which require a certain amount of downward slope from the siphon location. Therefore, we should use a duplex dosing pump unit. Each pump would be connected to half the disposal field. Each pump would discharge into a distribution box (see fig. 17-3) from which 10 fingers would carry the sewage out to the field.

With a total effluent flow of 4000 gpd, each pump will handle 2000 gpd. If each pump doses its half of the field four times per day, it must handle 500 gal each pumping cycle with the pumps running in alternate order. Therefore, the dosing tank must have a storage capacity of 500 gal— equal to the amount pumped during each pumping cycle. If each pump is able to deliver 40 gpm, it would require 12-1/2 min to deliver its load of sewage into its 900 lineal feet of trench fingers; this should give good flooding of the entire 900 ft of fingers.

Where the three large trees (mentioned in the site survey) are located, it is recommended that no open joint tile or perforated tile be located within 25 ft of these trees. Where the finger trenches pass within 25 ft of any tree, a closed-joint bell-and-spigot vitrified tile line should be installed.

17-11 SEWAGE DISPOSAL PROBLEM

Example 17-2 In this example, a rural school with cafeteria, but without gym and showers, is to be built for a student body of 750 students. There will also be regularly in the building 30 teachers and other personnel. Calculate the requirements for sewage disposal if a 50% growth in student load is possible.

A site survey revealed that an all-weather stream is located 1/4 mile from the probable location of a sewage disposal unit. The water table is 10 ft below the surface. The site is larger than needed for the school purposes and adequate space is available for a sewage disposal facility. It was realized that the sewage load would be much too great for a septic tank and disposal field; so percolation tests were not conducted.

Solution From fig. 17-1 it may be determined that the sewage effluent from this school may be estimated at 25 gpd per person. Total people will be 750 students + 30 others = 780 people. 780 people × 25 gpd/person = 19,500 gpd of sewage effluent.

It is decided to install a 20,000-gpd aeration sewage treatment plant and to provide space for a second 10,000-gpd plant to be installed when needed in the future. See fig. 17-9 for a typical layout. It is further decided to build a 7-day sewage lagoon based on the future load of 30,000 gpd (20,000 gpd present + 10,000 gpd future). Consultation with the local board of health has indicated that permission to use the all-weather stream will be given when required. Investigation by the school board's attorney has also revealed that easements to extend a sewage pump discharge line underground across intervening property to the stream will be available.

The sewage lagoon may be planned to be excavated into the earth for a depth of 5 ft since the earth's water table is 10 ft below the surface. This leaves a 5-ft barrier of earth between the lagoon bottom and the water table. This is judged to be adequate if the lagoon bottom is properly treated to make it impervious.

The size of the lagoon may be calculated as follows:

Lagoon volume = 30,000 gpd × 7 days = 210,000 gal. 210,000 gal ÷ 7.48 gal/ft^3 = 28,075 ft^3. The average area of the pond with a 5-ft depth = 28,075 ft^3 ÷ 5 ft = 5615 ft^2. A pond 75 ft square would have an area of 5625 ft^2, and this would be suitable. However, it might be necessary to make the lagoon longer and narrower to ensure good movement of the effluent through all parts of the lagoon. To this end also, the water may be drawn out of the pond at several locations.

The pump that delivers water from the lagoon, through 1/4 mile of discharge line and into the all-weather stream, should be a duplex pump for dependability. This pump unit would look very much like the dosing pump of fig. 17-6 and would operate in the same manner. The pump unit would need to handle 30,000 gpd, but since the building is a school building, this volume would probably be delivered to the pump in no more than 8 hr. 30,000 gal in 8 hr = 3750 gal/hr or 62.5 gpm. The pump unit should be selected for 40% running time; therefore, the design pumping capacity should be 62.5 gpm ÷ 0.4 = 156 gpm. Each of the two pumps in this duplex unit should be capable of delivering 78 gpm (156 gpm ÷ 2). If one pump fails, the remaining pump could still carry the full load of 62.5 gpm by itself.

If this pump unit had a water storage capacity of 465 gal, with an influent rate of 62.5 gpm and a pumping rate with one pump running of 78 gpm, the pump basin, or tank, would be pumped out in 30 min [465 gal ÷ (78 gpm - 62.5 gpm) = 30 min]. The refill time would then be 465 gal ÷ 62.5 gpm = 7.44 min. Pump controls should be arranged for alternating operation, and also so that both pumps will run if one pump by itself cannot carry the load. This condition might frequently arise in a school where students are out of class at lunchtime, and other times, and toilet use is heavy. For the same reason, the manufacturer of the sewage aeration units would need to build extra capacity into its equipment, to handle the peak flow rate.

PROBLEMS

17-1 A rural motel has 80 guest rooms each of which has two double beds. What would be the expected rate of sewage flow, in gpd?

17-2 A public picnic park with bathouse, showers, and flush-type toilets is designed to accommodate 500 people. A sewage treatment plant for this facility would need to have how much capacity in gallons per day? Approximately how much water, in gpd, would this facility consume?

17-3 A building discharges 3600 gpd into its septic tank and disposal field. A simplex (one pump) dosing pump unit is sized to dose the disposal field six times per day. What should be the size, in gallons, of the required septic tank, and what should be the operating volume, in gallons, of the dosing pump chamber?

17-4 If the land area available for the disposal field of prob. 17-3 has an average percolation rate of 29 min/in., how much disposal field trench bottom area will be required? Also, if trenches are to be 3 ft wide, how many 75-ft long fingers will be needed?

Chapter 18

Basic Electricity

18-1 GENERALITIES

This is an electric world! What a tremendous metamorphosis has taken place on the face of our world since electricity in all its many forms has become universally available in nations of even modest technological development. How sad it is, indeed, when a person tries to live his or her life today without really knowing the basic facts about the electrical systems with which contact is made daily and even hourly.

Most students and professionals in construction have been exposed at least once, perhaps in high school physics courses, to the basic principles of electricity. Most have some familiarity with terms such as voltage and amperage. However, most high school and even college students seem to have a great capability for quickly dismissing from their consciousness all recollection of the facts and principles presented in such courses. This seems to be especially true of courses in electricity.

Any professional person in the construction business, whether contractor, engineer, architect, or tradesperson, must have a better than casual acquaintance with basic electrical principles and the electrical distribution systems of buildings. How much at a disadvantage is the architect, for example, when in a definitive planning meeting with a prospective building owner-client the subjects of "power factor correction" or "fault current protection" arise and he or she has not the vaguest notion about the meaning of either subject.

Any well-trained architect who has at least one foot on the ground, and who has not spent all of his or her time dreaming about ethereal designs should and will have good, solid understanding of such subjects. The architect will not be expected to be an expert on them, nor does he or she need to be an expert to make an intelligent contribution to such an important discussion and perhaps guide the direction it takes.

It is this author's hope that in this chapter, one more exposure to the basic facts of electricity, tied in with their application to the electrical distribution systems of buildings, may at last fix an understanding in the construction student's consciousness that will carry throughout his or her professional career.

18-2 ELECTRICITY

Electricity is a form of energy which is characterized by a superfluity or buildup of electrons. All matter of which the universe is formed is basically atomic in nature—that is, composed of *atoms.* In its simplest form, the atom consists of a nucleus around which an *electron,* or electrons, revolve in a spherical pattern much as our moon revolves around the earth. The electrons are basically nothing but infinitesimally small charges of electrical energy which we arbitrarily have chosen to describe as being electrically negative.

The *nucleus* is electrically opposite in nature to the electron and is said to be electrically positive. The nucleus is also given the name *proton.* Usually, atoms are electrically neutral in nature with just enough electrons in orbit around the proton/nucleus to exactly balance negative charges against positive charges.

The description above is really quite an oversimplification of reality, but it does build the basic concept on which a theory of electricity may be constructed. In nature, every electron is not neatly attached to a proton, and some atoms are extremely complicated and vary from the description given above. Many materials, such as silver, copper, and aluminum, have a large number of "free" electrons in their makeup, and the number of free electrons varies with each chemical element.

With many materials it is quite easy to remove some of its electrons completely away from the material, and to transport them to a remote location and perhaps store them there. This is exactly what an automobile battery or a flashlight dry cell battery does. They receive electrons that have been removed from their parent material, and they hold or store them until they are needed. When we store electrons in this manner, we are building a pool of electrical energy which has a great "potential" for performing useful work. It is truly *potential energy,* and is described as having *electrical potential.*

Potential energy, it should be remembered, is a static or stationary form of energy which is not performing any work, but has the capability of doing so. When the spring of a wind-up type of clock is wound, potential energy is invested in that spring so that when released it can swing a pendulum for 8 days or 31 days and move the hands of the clock also.

Returning to our storage battery into which electrons are *charged* and in which they are stored, when those electrons are released, they represent a *force* which can turn an electric motor and provide the *motive power* to move an electric train, for example. The stored electrons, we then say, constitute an *electromotive force* (EMF), which has the *electrical potential* of performing useful work.

If we remove a large number of electrons from a material, it is no longer electrically neutral. Because it has lost many of its electrons it is now said to be *positively charged.* In other words, the material may have lost its free electrons, and many of its atoms have given up one or more of their electrons, leaving a great number of unneutralized proton/nuclei. The result is that the material is now electrically positive. The plates in the storage battery on which a large number of electrons are stored are, of course, electrically negative.

If in a piece of copper wire we install some type of switch, and then connect one end of the wire to this positively charged material and the other end to the storage battery, when we close the switch, electrons will flow through the wire and we say that we have an electrical *current.* All materials are not like copper in their ability to provide a course through which electrons can flow. If we connect a narrow strip of rubber, for example, between the positively charged material and the battery plates, nothing happens; no flow occurs. Rubber is not a conductor; it is an electrical insulator.

However, with the copper wire in place, current will flow until the electron deficiency of the positively charged material is restored and then the flow will stop. It is true that with some materials an excess of electrons can exist and the current flow will continue until the material has the same electrical charge as the battery plates.

During the time that the current was flowing from the battery, it flowed in only one direction, of course. Current of this type we say is *direct current* (dc). The reader will undoubtedly remember that we also have electric current which changes its direction with great *frequency,* flowing at one instant in one direction in a conductor, and flowing in the opposite direction in the next instant. A later article will describe the conditions under which we can have such "alternating" current. If this type of current changes direction, or alternates, 60 times per second, we say that we have *alternating current,* (ac), with a frequency of 60 cycles per second [this is universally referred to as 60 hertz (Hz)].

When, as mentioned above, we had our battery plates connected to the positive material with a rubber strip, no flow of electrons occurred, because the electrical *resistance* of the rubber strip was too great. Some materials are good conductors and have low resistance; others, like the rubber strip, are poor conductors, or nonconductors, and have a high resistance. There are also many materials with intermediate-range resistances and are thus semiconductors.

In any discussion of this type, there is a contradiction in the use of our terminology and the way in which we describe basic electricity that often causes confusion in the minds of those who are attempting to achieve an understanding of the subject. This contradiction is involved with the positive and negative concepts of electricity, which we have just discussed, and their relationship to current flow and its directional quality.

A well-established practice in electrical theory is to say that current flows from positive to negative. It is difficult to think, in any flow medium, of flow occurring from a negative value to a positive value. In a pressurized water piping system, the water flow is always from high pressure to locations of low pressure, or from positive pressure to negative pressure.

In an electrical system, flow always occurs from an area where there is an accumulation or superabundance of electrons to another area where there are fewer electrons or a shortage of electrons. We say that this flow is from plus to minus, or from positive to negative. However, we always say that an electron is a negative charge of electricity, a very weak one to be sure, but when we have billions of electrons gathered together, we have a strong charge which is still negative. It is difficult to think of billions of weak, negative electrical charges gathered together to make anything but a stronger negative charge.

The contradiction, then, is involved with the fact that we must say that an accumulation of billions of negative charges constitutes a strong positive charge to comply with the necessary concept that flow in any medium, including the electrical medium, must be from positive pressure to negative pressure. Fortunately, after we accept this contradiction, and decide to live with it, it gives very little difficulty thereafter.

18-3 VOLTAGE

To facilitate our further discussions in electricity it becomes necessary to define and to give specific names and also algebraic symbols to some of the electrical phenomena that we have been thinking about. The first of these is *voltage.*

Voltage is electrical pressure; it is the force that causes current to flow in an electrical circuit. Positive voltage is a superabundance of electrons, and negative voltage is a shortage of electrons or may be a small number of electrons as compared to a common base of reference.

Voltage is the electromotive force (or EMF)

referred to in art. 18-2. Voltage, measured in the units "volts," was given its name in honor of one of the early pioneers in electricity, Alessandro Volta, an Italian physicist. In our algebraic formulas, volts will be represented by the letter E, short for EMF. Voltage may also be referred to as an *electrical potential*. The higher the voltage is, in a given electrical circuit, the greater is its potential for causing current to flow.

18-4 AMPERAGE

Amperage is electrical current, or electron flow. It is the flow that results from the application of voltage to an electrical circuit. It is like water flowing in a pipe in which the flow results from the application of water pressure at one end which is greater than the pressure at the downstream end.

Amperage, which has the units "amperes" (or just "amps"), was given its name in honor of another pioneer physicist, André Marie Ampère. In the early days of electrical experimentation, current was somewhat erroneously referred to as electrical "intensity," and the letter I has been the algebraic symbol in use ever since.

One of the basic laws of electricity is that the amperage in an electrical circuit never changes—does not diminish. It is always the same at the end of a circuit as it is at the beginning. If the circuit divides, as a parallel circuit (to be discussed later) does, the current also divides, but when the circuit is rejoined, as it must be, the current will rejoin and be of exactly the same value as it was at the start.

18-5 RESISTANCE

Resistance is the ability of any material to resist the flow of an electric current. It is the opposition to the flow of electrons. Resistance is a physical quality or property of a material which is dependent on the basic atomic structure of the material. Resistance is measured in units called "ohms,"

again in honor of another electrical pioneer, Georg Simon Ohm, a German physicist. The algebraic symbol for resistance is R and the units "ohms" are expressed by the capital Greek letter omega, Ω.

The resistance of a material is in inverse proportion to the number of free electrons in its atomic structure. The higher the number of free electrons, the lower is its electrical resistance. Materials such as silver, copper, and aluminum have a comparatively large number of free electrons in their makeup; therefore, their resistance is low, and they are called *conductors*. They are used to conduct electric currents, and can do so with very little energy loss.

Other materials, such as rubber, most plastics, and asbestos, have very low free electron counts, their resistances are very high, and they serve us well as electrical *insulators*. Our wiring system conductors are usually made of copper and aluminum and are insulated on their exterior with rubber and thermoplastics. No material has zero resistance or infinitely great resistance; there are no perfect conductors or perfect insulators.

Power is required to push an electric current through a conductor against the opposing effect of its resistance. This loss of power, which may be very slight or very great, is manifested by a loss of voltage and the production of heat. The resistance of a conductor varies in direct proportion to its length and in inverse proportion to its cross-sectional area. For a given amount of current, the greater the conductor diameter, the less is its resistance; and the greater the conductor length, the greater is its resistance. Resistance is also proportional to a conductor's temperature.

The basic resistance of the material of which a conductor is made may be expressed in terms of "ohms per circular mil-foot." For example, the basic electrical resistance of copper is 10.4 Ω/circular mil-foot and of aluminum is 17, at a temperature of 68°F (20°C). A "mil" is a unit of linear measurement equal to 0.001 in., and a circular mil (cmil) is a circle 0.001 in. in diameter. A circular mil-foot in this context refers to a conductor with a cross-sectional area of 1 cmil which is 1 ft long.

The resistance R of a copper conductor may, then, be calculated with the formula

$$R = \frac{10.4 \times length\ (ft)}{cmil} \qquad (18\text{-}1)$$

where R = resistance, ohms
length = length, ft
cmil = cross-sectional area, circular mils

Similarly, the resistance R of an aluminum conductor may be calculated with the formula

$$R = \frac{17 \times length\ (ft)}{cmil} \qquad (18\text{-}2)$$

The cross-sectional area of a conductor in cmil is equal to its diameter in mils, squared. For example, a No. 12 copper or aluminum wire at a temperature of 68° (20°C) has a diameter of 0.08081 in. This is equal to 80.81 mils, and if the 80.81 is squared, we find a cross-sectional area of 6530 cmil. Therefore, the resistance of 100 ft of No. 12 copper wire at 68°F (20°C) is

$$R = \frac{10.4 \times 100\ ft}{6530} = 0.159\ \Omega$$

Most building wiring, which is properly loaded and is not overheated because of overload, will probably operate at a temperature more nearly 86°F (30°C) than at 68°F (20°C). At this higher operating temperature the resistance will be 3.9% higher. The 0.159-Ω resistance shown above will then be $1.039 \times 0.159\ \Omega = 0.165\ \Omega$.

18-6 MAGNETISM

Probably most everyone who reads this book has had experience with magnets of some kind. These include bar magnets, horseshoe magnets, and magnetic catches on cabinet doors and refrigerator doors. Probably everyone has seen how a magnet can attract to it and hold paper clips or other pieces of iron and steel, and how two bar magnets can strongly attract each other or repel each other depending on how they are mutually positioned.

It will surely be remembered that a magnet, such as a bar magnet, has a magnetic field that surrounds it on all sides in an elliptical shape—like a football. A magnetic field is an area of electrical influence attending a magnet of some type which is characterized by lines of force which are distinct and separate from each other and have directional motion. These lines of force are assumed to move from the north pole (N of fig. 18-1a) to the south pole, S, outside the magnet, and then to return from S to N inside the metal of the magnet.

The lines of force that constitute the magnetic field are collectively called *flux*, and the strength or intensity of the field is referred to as its *flux density*. As most everyone knows, the earth is a magnet with a magnetic north pole and a magnetic south pole. The earth is also surrounded by a magnetic field of very low flux density.

A magnetic compass such as is used for navigational purposes also includes a magnet. The compass needle is a very small magnet suspended at its midpoint by a spindle around which the needle can rotate. When immersed in a magnetic field the magnetic needle always aligns itself with the lines of force at the point of immersion. As in fig. 18-1a, the compass needle does not necessarily point to the north pole of the bar magnet, but does align itself with lines of force that lead to the north pole. On earth the lines of force often bend in an unexpected manner; a compass at that location does not point at either magnetic north or true north.

Figure 18-1a simulates the condition often portrayed in a high school physics class. Here a bar magnet is laid on a piece of glass or a very slick piece of paper. Iron filings, little short slivers of iron, are then poured in a thin layer on the glass or paper around the magnet. When the glass or paper is gently vibrated so as to cause the filings to bounce or dance a bit, the filings will align themselves lengthwise with the lines of force and very plainly outline the shape and directional qualities of the magnetic field.

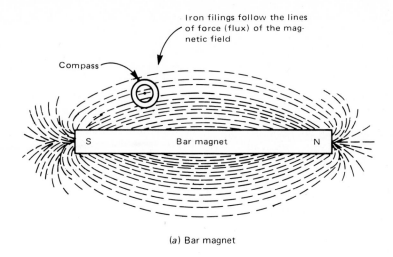

(a) Bar magnet

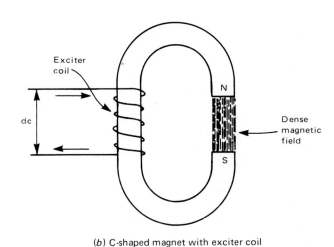

(b) C-shaped magnet with exciter coil

Figure 18-1   Magnets and magnetic fields.

Now, if we take a bar magnet and bend it in the shape of a letter "C," as shown in fig. 18-1b, the N and S poles are brought into fairly close proximity. The magnetic field now exists externally only between the N and S poles, all of the magnetic field is squeezed into this very limited space, and, as a result, the flux density is greatly increased. Then, if we wind a coil of electric conductor wire around the back side of the "C," as shown, so that

it is part of a complete electrical circuit, and impress a dc voltage on the coil, the flux density of the magnetic field is greatly increased even more. As noted, the dc coil is called an *exciter coil.*

The direction of the current in the exciter coil must be such as to enhance the strength and direction of the field rather than to oppose it, as would be the case if the direct current flows the wrong way. It is, of course, necessary to use dc current if we want the direction of the lines of force of the field to be always the same—from the N pole to the S pole.

18-7 ELECTRIC POWER GENERATION

Any study of basic electricity must of necessity impart an understanding of how electric power is generated. Most everyone knows that some type of mechanical prime mover, such as a steam turbine, diesel engine, or hydraulic turbine (in a hydroelectric power plant), is connected to and drives an electric power generator. The prime mover is turned on, the generator starts, and out comes electric power. The energy of steam from coal-fired boilers, or the energy in the diesel fuel, and so on, is fed into the system and converted into electric energy. Unfortunately, as much as 80% of the coal or diesel fuel energy is wasted in the process; only 20% (40% under ideal conditions) of the fuel energy comes out as electric energy.

The question, though, is what happens in that electric generator to enable it to produce electric power. The entire process is based on the one simple fact that if a conductor is passed broadside through a magnetic field, a voltage will be generated in the conductor, and if it is part of a complete circuit a current will flow—while the conductor is passing through the field.

This is *generator theory,* and it is exemplified in fig. 18-2. Here we see the same C-shaped magnet with a dc exciter coil creating a very strong magnetic field between the N and S poles. There also is a conductor poised near the center of the magnet to the left of the magnetic field. If by some means this conductor is moved to the right so that it cuts through the lines of force of the magnetic field, a voltage will be generated in the conductor. That is all we have to do—just move the conductor so as to cut the magnetic field.

Figure 18-2 shows that the ends of the conductor are connected together with another wire so that the original conductor is part of a complete circuit so that current can flow, and its direction will be as indicated by the arrows. In other words, if the conductor is moved to the right, as it cuts the field, voltage will be generated and current will flow upward and to the right in the conductor (as it is drawn).

If we now move the conductor back to the left through the field, lines of force will be cut, a voltage will be generated, and a current will flow. However, this time the current will flow in the opposite direction—downward and to the left in

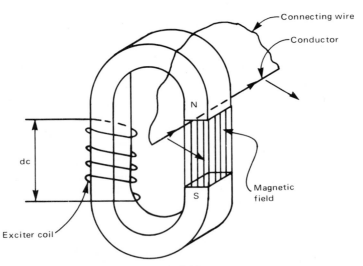

Figure 18-2 Conductor cuts magnetic field.

our original conductor. So the direction of current flow depends on the direction that the conductor moves. It also depends on the direction that the lines of force are moving, but we are holding that constant—downward from N to S.

It is also important to realize here that voltage can also be generated with equal facility if we hold the conductor of fig. 18-2 steady and move the magnet and its magnetic field. Either action will cause the relative motion that is necessary to the generation of electric power. In fact, in almost all commercial power generators it is the field that moves while the conductors are held motionless.

Now consider the simple electric generator of fig. 18-3. Here we see the N pole and the S pole of an electromagnet which is the same as in fig. 18-2. Its magnetic field has high flux density, and it flows from N to S as before. We also see two conductors in the magnetic field which are connected together with wiring to form a loop. However, the loop has extended connections on its right-hand side which extend upward to the right and are soldered to two brass rings called *slip rings*.

These brass rings are secured to round wheel-shaped pieces of insulating material which are mounted on some type of a shaft which provides an axis of rotation. In this simple generator the loop of wire containing the two conductors is supported somehow by the shaft so that the entire assembly can rotate with the two conductors moving in the magnetic field. As the shaft turns, the loop turns with it, as do the two insulator wheels and the brass rings secured to the wheels.

Notice that the wire that extends to the right from conductor A makes an electrical connection to the first brass slip ring, while the wire from conductor D passes through the first insulator wheel and goes on to make electrical contact with the second slip ring. These slip rings are solid continuous circles of brass, which is a good conductor of electricity. As the shaft is turned, then, the loop and the two slip rings turn with it.

Figure 18-3 also includes two carbon brushes which are stationary and are held in close, intimate contact with the slip rings. The carbon brushes are just little blocks of solid carbon shaped to the con-

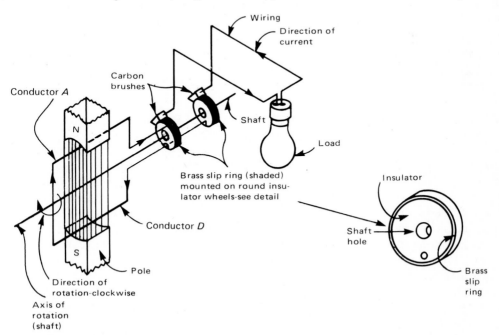

Figure 18-3 Simple ac generator.

tour of the slip rings. Carbon is a good conductor of electricity, and has enough lubricating quality that the stationary brushes can slip easily on the slip rings as they turn. The brushes are wired to a unit of electrical load—in this case, an electric light bulb.

Examination of fig. 18-3 will reveal that as the loop of wire turns, conductors A and D will move in the magnetic field, and cut its lines of force. Therefore, voltage will be generated in both A and D, and since they are part of a complete electrical circuit, current will flow—in the direction shown by the arrows. This current will flow through the slip rings and the carbon brushes to the light bulb which will be lighted.

We are now generating electricity and putting it to good use in lighting the light bulb. Some type of engine will be required to turn the generator shaft. If this is, for example, a small gasoline engine, we would then be converting the chemical, potential energy of the gasoline to the rotative kinetic energy of the engine and the generator, and finally to the electrical energy that produces the light, which is a wave form of energy.

As conductor A moves to the right through the magnetic field and passes the north pole, its current will flow from left to right (actually from lower left to upper right). At the same time, conductor D is moving to the left, and its current is moving from right to left. The two currents supplement each other in causing current flow throughout the entire circuit.

There is one improvement that can be made to the generator of fig. 18-3 to give it much greater capacity. Let us replace the loop that is shown and that has just one conductor at A and one at D and substitute a winding or coil that has exactly the same shape as the loop but has many hundreds of wires at A and also at D. This winding would be closed on the right just as it is on the left (in fig. 18-3) with only the two ends of the winding brought out and connected to the slip rings.

Now we have hundreds of wires at A and hundreds of wires at D all cutting lines of force and generating voltage. With a winding spinning in the magnetic field instead of a single loop of wire, we have a generator of much greater capacity. So from this point on let us think of our generator as having a winding of copper wire with a side A in place of conductor A and side D in place of conductor D.

After the spinning winding has turned 270° from the position shown in fig. 18-3, side A will be off to the left—moving straight up, and side D will be off to the right moving straight down. Both sides will be moving vertically and not cutting any lines of force, and no voltage will be generated at that particular instant. This position is as shown in fig. 18-4.

In fig. 18-4, an inexact section through the generator, an aluminum rotor has been added which is mounted on the generator shaft between the N and S poles, and on which the winding is wound. Sides A and D of the winding are laid in milled slots in the rotor as the winding is wound. One end of the winding connecting the two sides may be seen in fig. 18-4. The vertical lines representing the lines of force of the magnetic field would run from the N pole to the S pole through the rotor, but these have been omitted for clarity.

As mentioned, in the position of fig. 18-4, the sides A and D are moving parallel to the lines of force so that no lines are being cut and no voltage is being generated. As the rotor and winding continues to turn clockwise, side A will reach the top center position with side D at the bottom. In fig. 18-3, side A has current moving from left to right as it passes the north pole. Later, when side A passes the south pole, current will move in it from right to left; this represents a change in current flow direction. Instead of current flowing from side A to the first slip ring, current will be flowing from the first slip ring to side A.

With side D at the top, passing the north pole, current will flow to the right in side D and to the second slip ring. Also, current will then flow from the second slip ring to the load instead of from the load. This represents a change in the direction of current flow, and we now have alternating current. Every time the rotor and its winding makes one complete 360° revolution, the current will pass through one complete cycle with the current flow-

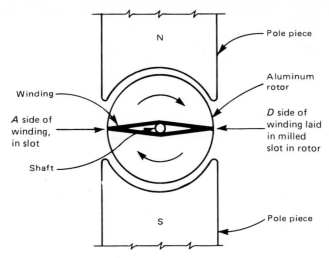

Figure 18-4 Section through generator.

ing first in one direction, then reversing itself, and then returning to the first direction.

If we drive this generator at 3600 rpm, it will turn 60 revolutions per second and we will have 60-cycle ac power (this means 60 cycles per second).

Suppose, again, that in fig. 18-4, side *A* of the winding is at the left and side *D* is at the right as shown. Also, suppose that when *A* passes the north pole and when D passes the south pole, we arbitrarily decide to call that "positive" electricity. Then, of course, when *D* passes the north pole and *A* passes the south pole, the electricity that is being generated will be called "negative."

When the winding of fig. 18-4 is at a 45° angle, and not horizontal or vertical, the wires of the winding will be cutting lines of force because those wires will have a horizontal component to their motion. However, at the 45° position, the wires are not moving horizontally as fast as they will be when the winding reaches the vertical position. This means that at the 45° position, the winding is not cutting lines of force as fast as when at the vertical position, and as a result, not as much voltage is being generated.

Let us now see what the time-voltage and the time-amperage curves will look like. In fig. 18-5 we see time, on the horizontal scale, plotted against voltage and amperage on the vertical scale, with

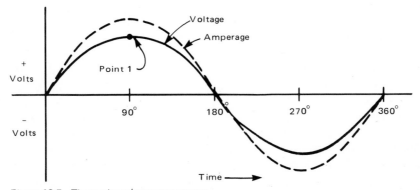

Figure 18-5 Time-voltage/amperage curves.

positive voltage and positive amperage above the horizontal centerline and negative voltage and negative amperage below it.

In the starting position of the winding in fig. 18-4, no lines of force are being cut, and the voltage is zero. In fig. 18-5 at the 0° point, the voltage is zero on the centerline. After 90° of rotation, the winding of fig. 18-4 is now vertical; side A is at the top passing the north pole and side D is at the bottom passing the south pole. We decided before to call the voltage generated in this position positive. Since, at the 90° position, our winding is cutting lines of force at its maximum rate and is positive, we can plot the voltage at point 1 in fig. 18-5. After the winding has turned 180° from the starting position, A is on the right in fig. 18-4, D is on the left, both moving vertically, no lines of force are being cut, and no voltage is being generated. So at the 180° point in fig. 18-5, the voltage is zero. We know from experience that the time-voltage curve for the first 180° of rotation will be a typical sine wave, and it should be easy to see that this is so.

During the last half of the 360° rotation of the winding, side A will pass the south pole and side D will pass the north pole. We said before that we would arbitrarily consider that to be generating negative electricity, because now the current has changed its direction in the circuit. It should be easy to see that from 180 to 360° in fig. 18-5, the voltage curve will be identical to the curve from 0 to 180°, but now the voltage is negative and the curve is below the horizontal centerline. In the circuit of fig. 18-3 the amperage curve is directly proportional to the voltage curve—both being zero at the same time and both reaching maximum positive or maximum negative at the same instant.

We will see later why the two curves of fig. 18-5 are in synchronization with each other, but we now know that when this is true we can say that the voltage and the amperage are *in phase*. This perhaps implies that it is possible for the voltage and the amperage to be *out of phase;* and this is true; they certainly may be out of phase. We will see about that later too.

18-8 THREE-PHASE POWER GENERATION

Most of the readers of this probably know that there is such a thing as single-phase power and also that there is three-phase electric power. Most such readers will have realized by now that the generator of fig. 18-4 is a single-phase generator. If it is driven at 3600 rpm, it will deliver single-phase 60-Hz ac power (60-cycle power).

In fig. 18-6 we see the same generator with three windings on the rotor instead of one. In addition to winding AD, we have added windings BE and CF. All three windings are identical and are equally spaced around the rotor. In discussing fig. 18-4, we said that when the A side of winding AD passed the north pole, we would call its voltage positive, and the direction of the resulting current would also be positive. This was an arbitrary choice.

Following the same line of thought in fig. 18-6, when the A side of winding $AD,$ the B side of winding $BE,$ and the C side of winding CF pass the north pole, the voltage generated is positive. Of course, then, when the A, B, and C sides pass the south pole their voltage is negative, resulting in a direction of current flow opposite to that of the positive voltage. With the one winding of the single-phase generator of fig. 18-3, there are two leads or ends of the winding that are extended out and

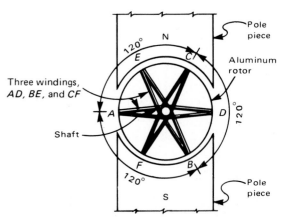

Figure 18-6 Section through three-phase generator.

connected to the slip rings. With three windings there are six leads that must be properly connected, and the way in which they are connected will determine the polarity (whether negative or positive) of each winding. If properly connected as shown a little later herein, the time-voltage curves of the three-phase generator of fig. 18-6 may be shown as in fig. 18-7.

The *A, B,* and *C* sides of the three windings are exactly 120° apart around the rotor in fig. 18-6; therefore, the three resulting pulses of voltage will be equally spaced along the time scale (the horizontal scale) of fig. 18-7. Since the windings do not pass the N and S pole pieces of the stator (the stationary part of the generator) at the same instant, their voltage pulses cannot be coincident; they must be separated. They are separated equally along the time scale by the time of 120° of rotation of the rotor. The rotor is turning 3600 rpm and one revolution then requires 1/60 sec. To turn 120° of rotation requires, then, 1/180 sec, so the voltage pulses of a 60-Hz three-phase ac generator are 1/180 sec apart.

In fig. 18-7, the time frame shown is, as before, one revolution of the rotor, or 1/60 sec. The phase *A* curve of winding *AD* is drawn exactly the same as in fig. 18-5. Amperage curves have been omitted. In fig. 18-6, side *B* of winding *BE* is passing the south pole, so we know that *BE* is generating nega-

tive voltage; its curve must start below the horizontal centerline. We can see in figure 18-6 that the *B* side will reach the bottom center position, where negative voltage is maximum, after it turns 30° from our starting point (the position shown in fig. 18-6). We can really start drawing the phase *B* curve at the maximum voltage and on the 30° vertical line. Incidentally, the amplitude (the distance from the horizontal centerline) of the voltage and amperage curves at the "maximum" points have been arbitrarily chosen and are not drawn to any particular scale.

We also can see that the phase *B* voltage will be zero after the rotor has turned 120° from the starting position, so the phase *B* curve must cross the horizontal centerline (zero voltage lines) at the 120° point. Following this procedure the phase *B* curve may be finished and the phase *C* curve may be drawn. The reader should mentally complete the process herein described.

All of the foregoing should assist in establishing in the reader's mind the theory of how ac electric power, both single-phase and three-phase, is generated. It should make plain the basic differences between single-phase and three-phase power. The reader should realize that single-phase power involves, in a circuit, only one surge of current running out in one of two conductors and returning in the other. However, three-phase power involves

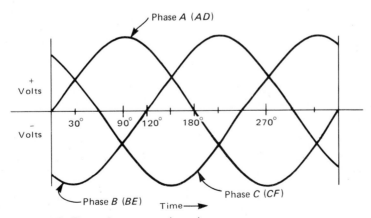

Figure 18-7 Time-voltage curves, three-phase.

three surges of electric current in three conductors with, at one instant, one surge of current running out and two returning, at the next instant two surges running out and one returning, and at yet another instant there may be one surging outward, one returning, and one having zero current.

Figure 18-7, the time-voltage curves, makes it easy to see what is going on at any instant in a three-phase circuit. For example, at the 90° instant in fig. 18-7, we see phase A conductor is carrying positive voltage at maximum value, so current is flowing outward (let's say) at its maximum value. At the same instant, phases B and C conductors are negative and carrying current at much less than maximum rate. An instant later, at the 150° point, phases A and B are positive (outward current) but not maximum, while phase C is negative (returning current) and maximum. We are assuming thus far only an in-phase condition with the amperage maximum and positive when the voltage is maximum and positive, zero when voltage is zero, and so on. However, remember that this is not always true.

The reader may wonder as he or she looks at fig. 18-5, for example, that if the amperage is always changing as shown, what value does an ammeter give as it measures the current flowing in a circuit? An ammeter measures the *root-mean-square* (rms) *current*. The rms current is an average value found by taking amps values, from a curve such as in fig. 18-5, at very small increments of time. These values are each then squared, added together, and divided by the number of such values.

The square root of that value then is the rms value; the ammeter does all this for us automatically.

18-9 CIRCUIT DIAGRAMS: SINGLE-PHASE AND THREE-PHASE

The diagram of the circuit shown in fig. 18-3, which includes a single-phase generator after the loop is replaced with a winding, may be quite simply drawn as shown in fig. 18-8. Here the rotor winding has been opened out, the slip rings and brushes in the wiring are shown, and the load is shown as a zigzag line. We will always show windings this way, and the load will always be schematically shown with the zigzag line no matter what type of load it may be.

In fig. 18-9a, a three-phase generator is similarly diagrammed showing all three rotor windings and other parts. Notice that the load is a three-element load for the three-phase power supply as it always must be. If the three-phase load were a three-phase electric motor, it would of necessity have three motor windings connected as shown. Notice also that the three generator windings are connected together in a special way so that there are only three conductors running to the slip rings and not six. It would be possible to extend the six ends of the three windings to six slip rings and extend six wires to the three-element load; it would perform very well that way. However, the system performs just as well when connected as shown, and, of course, is much simpler and less expensive.

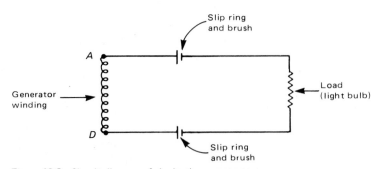

Figure 18-8 Circuit diagram of single-phase generator.

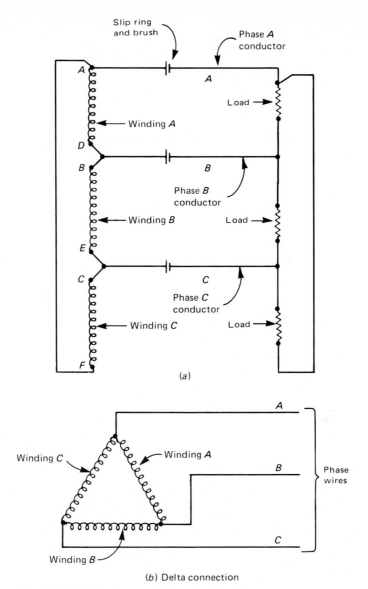

Figure 18-9 Circuit diagram of three-phase generator.

The circuit of fig. 18-9*a* has been redrawn as shown in fig. 18-9*b*. The wiring connections are all exactly the same in both diagrams, but in 18-9*b* the diagram is drawn to show the basic *delta connection,* so-called because it takes the shape of the capital Greek letter delta.

18-10 CROSS-COUNTRY POWER TRANSMISSION

Even though this text is concerned primarily with buildings and the mechanical and electrical systems in and immediately around them, it is pertinent to discuss cross-country power transmission and intracity transmission to the point of connection to a building.

Electric power used in buildings is almost always generated in a commercial power plant capable of generating tremendous quantities of power. The voltage delivered by these huge generators is much higher than we could usually handle in a building, but it is not nearly high enough for cross-country transmission. As the power leaves the commercial generating plant, its voltage is increased by a transformer (discussed later) to an extremely high value —usually somewhere between 100,000 volts [100 kilovolts (kV)] and 500,000 V (500 kV).

As will be shown later, the power lost during transmission is directly proportional to the square of the amount of current flowing. In general, electric power is the product of the voltage times the amperage. If for a given amount of power we raise the voltage to extremely high values, we also decrease the amperage to extremely low values. This permits extremely small power loss and permits the use of smaller conductors, transmission towers, and power poles.

However, these extremely high voltages are not safe for low-level distribution over metropolitan areas, so the cross-country lines must be led to substations at the edges of cities where the voltage is transformed downward to safer levels. The voltage of the power as it leaves the substation may be

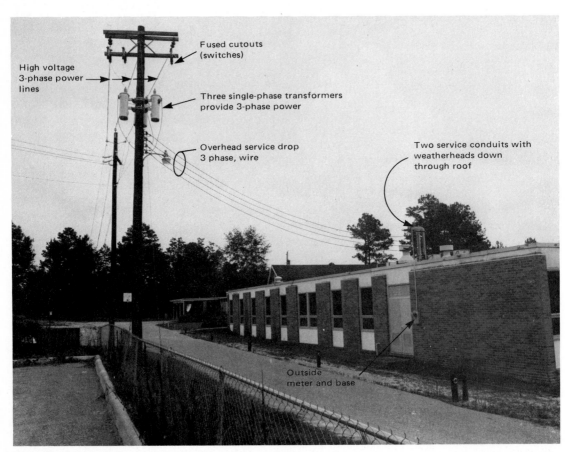

Figure 18-10 Pole-mounted service transformers and overhead service drop.

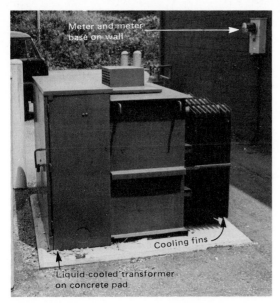

Figure 18-11   Padmount electric service transformers.

of the order of 2400 V, or 4160 V, or as high as 13,800 V, depending on the size of the metropolitan area covered. Power at these levels is then distributed usually on pole lines overhead.

The power then arrives at a particular building location via a pole line and at these still quite high voltages. Of course, most buildings receive power at less than 600 V, so again the voltage must be transformed downward to a value suitable for distribution within the building. Some manufacturing facilities utilize power at very high voltages for their heavy-duty operations and take the power at the full distribution voltages. This text will not be concerned with these unusual situations.

Power is normally delivered into buildings at a few standard voltages; these are 208, 240, and 480 V. Many electric services are dual voltage services such as 120/208, 120/240, 240/480, and 277/480 V. The transformer which reduces the voltage to the required building level is, more often than not, mounted on a utility pole which may or may not also carry the municipal transmission lines. If the electric service runs underground to the building, this transformer may be a "padmount" trans-

former mounted on a concrete pad on the earth's surface near the building. Figure 18-10 shows details of pole-mounted transformers, and fig. 18-11 deals with padmount units.

18-11   OHM'S LAW

As mentioned, the German physicist Georg Ohm enunciated what is now universally known as *Ohm's law.* This law, which establishes the basic relation between voltage, current, and resistance, states: "Current is directly proportional to voltage and inversely proportional to resistance." In other words, if voltage increases, amps increase, and if resistance increases, amps decrease—and vice versa.

This relation can be very simply expressed algebraically by the formula

$$I = \frac{E}{R} \tag{18-3}$$

where I = current, amps
E = voltage (electromotive force), V
R = resistance, ohms

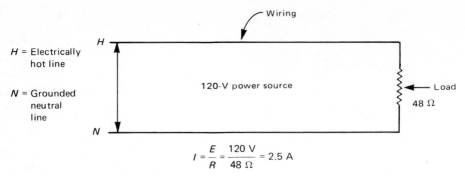

$$I = \frac{E}{R} = \frac{120 \text{ V}}{48 \text{ }\Omega} = 2.5 \text{ A}$$

Figure 18-12 Simple circuit.

Of course, this simple statement leads to other equally simple formulas

$$E = IR \qquad\qquad (18\text{-}4)$$

$$R = \frac{E}{I} \qquad\qquad (18\text{-}5)$$

For example, if in a given electric circuit the voltage is 120 V (see fig. 18-12) and the resistance is 48 Ω, how much current is flowing? The amps are equal to 2.5 A. Using formula (18-3), we have

$$I = \frac{E}{R} = \frac{120}{48} = 2.5 \text{ A}$$

The 48-Ω resistance happens to be that of a 300-watt (W) light bulb; so when a 300-W light bulb is burning, it is drawing 2.5 A when the voltage is 120.

18-12 THE WATT—UNIT OF POWER

Power is the ability to do work, whether it be mechanical power or electric power. Electric power can drive an electric motor and perform great amounts of work, such as in driving an electric locomotive pulling a long heavy train. This is a manifestation of electric power. However, neither voltage alone nor amperage alone can manifest power.

We may have an electric circuit with very high voltage impressed on it, but if the resistance is also very high, very little current can flow and the power of the circuit will be very low. However, amperage alone is not an indication of power. It is possible to have a circuit with very high amps; but if it also has very low resistance, the voltage required to cause the high current to flow may be very slight. In this case, the power will also be slight.

A circuit that has high voltage and low resistance so that current is also high will be a high power circuit, capable of performing much work. We can see, then, that to express power, we must have a proper combination of both volts and amps. This may be expressed algebraically by the formula

$$P = EI \qquad\qquad (18\text{-}6)$$

where P = power, watts
E = voltage
I = amperage

The various electrical units of measurement are such that 1 W = 1 V $\times$ 1 A. If we had an electric circuit with 1-Ω total resistance, and if we impressed a voltage of 1 V on it, the current would be 1 A and the power would be 1 W. The unit "watt" is used in honor of James Watt, who pioneered in the development of the steam engine.

Well, if $P = EI$ and $I = E/R$ as above, then by substitution we can write that $P = E \times E/R = E^2/R$. Therefore, formula (18-7) is

$$P = \frac{E^2}{R} \qquad\qquad (18\text{-}7)$$

where the symbols are as written above. Also since $E = IR$ in formula (18-4), we can write that power, $P = (IR)I = I^2R$. Therefore, formula (18-8) for power is

$$P = I^2R \qquad (18\text{-}8)$$

Formulas (18-3) through (18-8) are all basic formulas that we will use over and over in our study of electrical distribution and utilization in buildings.

18-13 SERIES CIRCUITS

An electrical circuit, as shown in figs. 18-8 and 18-9, consists of a source of power, such as a generator or a battery, an electrical load of some type, the wiring system that connects the load to the power supply, and control devices such as switches to control the operation of the load. In most cases, as in fig. 18-12, the entire circuit will not be shown; the source of power will be omitted, and only the load and connecting wiring and controls will be included.

In fig. 18-13 is portrayed a simple series circuit with only the units of load and the wiring included.

It is a series circuit, because the units of load, R_1 and R_2 and R_3, are connected so that the current that is flowing must pass through each load in series, or sequentially. Most building wiring circuits are not of this type.

In fig. 18-13, the total resistance is, as shown, merely the sum of the component resistances and is 120 Ω. The resistance of the connecting wiring is temporarily ignored here. The amperage of the circuit has been calculated with the use of formula (18-3), $I = E/R$, which gives the value 2 A, as noted.

Knowing the amps, the volts, and the resistance of this circuit, it is easy to calculate the power of the circuit using formulas (18-6), (18-7), and (18-8). As shown in fig. 18-13, they all give the same answer, 480 W.

18-14 VOLTAGE DROP

As previously explained, the amps in a circuit are the same throughout. In fig. 18-13, 2 A are flowing and no matter where a check may be made with a meter (ammeter), the amps will be found to be the same. This is not true of voltage. Voltage is always dropping throughout a circuit, and the magnitude

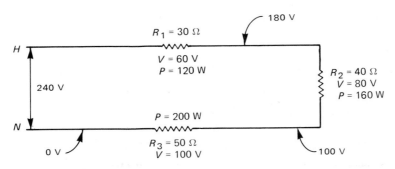

$$R_T = R_1 + R_2 + R_3 = 30\ \Omega + 40\ \Omega + 50\ \Omega = 120\ \Omega \qquad I = \frac{E}{R} = \frac{240\ V}{120\ \Omega} = 2\ A$$

$$P = EI = 240\ V \times 2\ A = 480\ W \qquad P = \frac{E^2}{R} = \frac{\overline{240}^2}{120\ \Omega} = 480\ W$$

$$P = I^2R = \overline{2}^2 \times 120\ \Omega = 480\ W$$
$$V_1 = IR_1 = 2\ A \times 30\ \Omega = 60\ V \qquad V_2 = IR_2 = 2\ A \times 40\ \Omega = 80\ V$$
$$V_3 = IR_3 = 2\ A \times 50\ \Omega = 100\ V \qquad E = V_1 + V_2 + V_3 = 60\ V + 80\ V + 100\ V = 240\ V$$

Figure 18-13 Simple series circuit.

of the drop in a given section of a circuit is directly proportional to the resistance of that section, for a given amount of current. Voltage drop is expressed by the symbol V and is, of course, measured in volts. The symbol V must not be confused with, or used interchangeably with, the symbol E; they do not mean the same thing, even though both are measured in volts.

V is used to indicate the voltage drop of a section of a circuit or a unit of load in a circuit, and the total of all the voltage drops, V, is equal to the original supply voltage, E. Stated differently, we may say that the total of the individual separate voltage drops, V_T, equals E.

$$V_T = V_1 + V_2 + V_3 + \cdots = E$$

In fig. 18-13, $V_1 = I \times R_1 = 2$ A $\times$ 30 Ω = 60 V. Similarly, $V_2 = 80$ V and $V_3 = 100$ V. Then $V_T = 60 + 80 + 100 = 240$ V $= E$. It is not simply happenstance that in this case the sum of the voltage drops equals the supply voltage of 240 V; it will always be so. We have said here that the V of any load or section of a circuit is equal to I times R, in the same way that E for the entire circuit is equal to I times the total resistance R_T. Electrical engineers habitually speak of voltage drop of a unit of load as *IR drop*. The logic of this is obvious.

In fig. 18-13, the power of each unit of load may be calculated in different ways. One way is to use formula (18-8), $P = I^2 R$, so that for the first unit of load $P = 2^2 \times 30$ Ω = 120 W. However, for this 30-Ω load we may also use formulas (18-6) and (18-7) by substituting V for E, so that $P = VI$ and $P = V^2/R$ and so that $P = 60$ V $\times$ 2 A = 120 W or $P = 60^2/30 = 120$ W.

18-15 PARALLEL CIRCUITS

Most building wiring circuits are *parallel circuits,* in which every unit of electrical load (lights, motors, electric heaters, etc.) is connected directly to each of the circuit conductors. Figure 18-14 shows the diagram of such a circuit, and here it

may be seen that each of the three units of load connect directly to each of the two circuit conductors. This is not the case in fig. 18-13, because here the R_2 load has another unit of load between it and the power source. In a series circuit all resistances are added arithmetically to find the total resistance. This may not be done in a parallel circuit.

To find the total resistance of a parallel circuit we first find the reciprocal of each resistance, add the reciprocals together and invert the total. This is shown by the formula

$$\frac{1}{R_T} = \frac{1}{R_1} + \frac{1}{R_2} + \frac{1}{R_3} + \cdots \qquad (18\text{-}9)$$

The truth of this statement may be seen by reviewing Ohm's law and the algebraic expression of that law set forth in art. 18-11. Ohm's law states that current flow is inversely proportional to resistance; as a result, current flow is directly proportional to the reciprocal of resistance. We know that in a parallel circuit, such as is shown in fig. 18-14, the current will divide among the parallel branches, but to find total current, we can simply add currents of the several branches. If we can add currents of the branches arithmetically to find total current, we are allowed to add the reciprocals of the component resistances to find the reciprocal of the total resistance.

The reciprocals of the component resistances are directly proportional to the component currents just as the reciprocal of the total resistance is directly proportional to the total current. An analysis of the parallel circuit of fig. 18-14 is shown in that figure, which uses the preceding logic as a starting point in this analysis. The reader should study through each step of the analysis to be certain of his or her understanding of it.

In fig. 18-14, the total of the reciprocals of the 30-, 40-, and 50-Ω loads equals 0.0783, and when this is inverted, we find that the total resistance of the loads only (this does not include the resistance of the wiring) is equal to 12.77 Ω. Total resistance

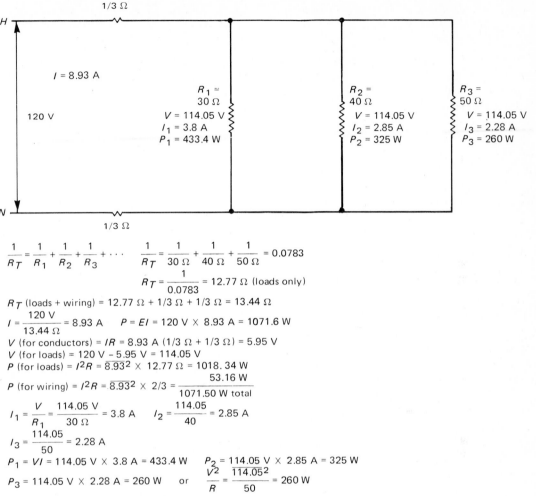

$$\frac{1}{R_T} = \frac{1}{R_1} + \frac{1}{R_2} + \frac{1}{R_3} + \cdots \qquad \frac{1}{R_T} = \frac{1}{30\ \Omega} + \frac{1}{40\ \Omega} + \frac{1}{50\ \Omega} = 0.0783$$

$$R_T = \frac{1}{0.0783} = 12.77\ \Omega \text{ (loads only)}$$

R_T (loads + wiring) = 12.77 Ω + 1/3 Ω + 1/3 Ω = 13.44 Ω

$$I = \frac{120\ \text{V}}{13.44\ \Omega} = 8.93\ \text{A} \qquad P = EI = 120\ \text{V} \times 8.93\ \text{A} = 1071.6\ \text{W}$$

V (for conductors) = IR = 8.93 A (1/3 Ω + 1/3 Ω) = 5.95 V

V (for loads) = 120 V − 5.95 V = 114.05 V

P (for loads) = $I^2R = \overline{8.93}^2 \times 12.77\ \Omega$ = 1018. 34 W

P (for wiring) = $I^2R = \overline{8.93}^2 \times 2/3 = \dfrac{53.16\ \text{W}}{1071.50\ \text{W total}}$

$$I_1 = \frac{V}{R_1} = \frac{114.05\ \text{V}}{30\ \Omega} = 3.8\ \text{A} \qquad I_2 = \frac{114.05}{40} = 2.85\ \text{A}$$

$$I_3 = \frac{114.05}{50} = 2.28\ \text{A}$$

$P_1 = VI$ = 114.05 V × 3.8 A = 433.4 W P_2 = 114.05 V × 2.85 A = 325 W

P_3 = 114.05 V × 2.28 A = 260 W   or $\dfrac{V^2}{R} = \dfrac{\overline{114.05}^2}{50} = 260\ \text{W}$

Figure 18-14   Parallel circuit analysis.

of the entire circuit is the 12.77 Ω of the three loads taken as a unit, plus the 2/3-Ω resistance of the wiring; this is equal to 13.44 Ω.

From this point it is simple to find total current and total power of the circuit. The voltage drop V of the wiring is found to be 5.95 V; and subtracting this from the supply voltage of 120 V, we see that 114.05 V are available to cause current flow through each load. Then using formula (18-3) through (18-8), we find it easy to calculate the current and the power of each unit of load.

18-16   ELECTRIC MOTOR THEORY

Electric motor theory, especially single-phase motor theory, is exceedingly complicated; and the subject could not be properly treated in the space available in a generalized text of this type. However, there is one basic thought concerning electric motors which can be covered here, and which will give some insight into the forces that cause a motor rotor to spin.

First, it must be remembered that an electric

conductor which is carrying current is surrounded by an "electric field" which is just like a magnetic field. It is constituted of lines of force like those of a magnetic field, and they are moving and have direction. These lines of force circle around the conductor, as shown in fig. 18-15 (upper left corner).

If such a conductor is placed in a strong magnetic field, as shown in fig. 18-15, between north and south poles, and a current is passed through the conductor, there will be an immediate interaction between the magnetic field and the electric field of the conductor. In fig. 18-15, the current in the conductor is flowing away from the reader and into the page of this book, and as a result the electric field is circling around the conductor in a clockwise direction.

At the right-hand side of the conductor, all lines of force move in the same direction, the two fields are additive, and the flux density on the

right is very high. However, on the left side of the conductor, the electric field of the conductor and the magnetic field are in direct opposition to one another and cancel each other. The flux density on the left is very low, whereas on the right it is very high.

The high flux density will attempt to equalize this difference and to straighten the lines of force on the right. In the process of doing this, the conductor will be moved to the left until it is completely out of the magnetic field. It will be moved with considerable force so that it can perform a small amount of work.

If this conductor were mounted on the perimeter of a rotor, similar to the rotor of figs. 18-4 and 18-6, it could turn the rotor in its effort to move out of the magnetic field. If that rotor had many hundreds of similar conductors all trying to move from the magnetic field, a very considerable turning force would result, and we would have a motor

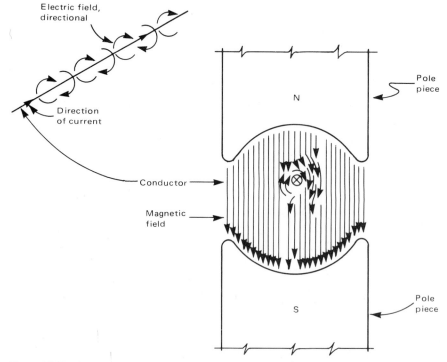

Figure 18-15 Conductor carrying current in a magnetic field. (Electric Motor Theory.)

capable of performing useful work. This is electric motor theory.

18-17 TRANSFORMER THEORY

Transformers serve the purpose of changing the voltage characteristics of an electric power supply. For many purposes the voltages of the electric power that is in or enters a building must be modified to suit local needs. This is done with a transformer.

We have said in art. 18-16 that a conductor carrying a current has an electric field surrounding it as shown in fig. 18-6a. The electric field has directional quality to its lines of force, and these circle the conductor in the same direction that the fingers of the right hand point when the conductor is held in that hand with the thumb pointing outward in the direction of current flow.

If the conductor is carrying direct current, when the dc power is switched on, the field springs up into place and stays there circling the conduc-

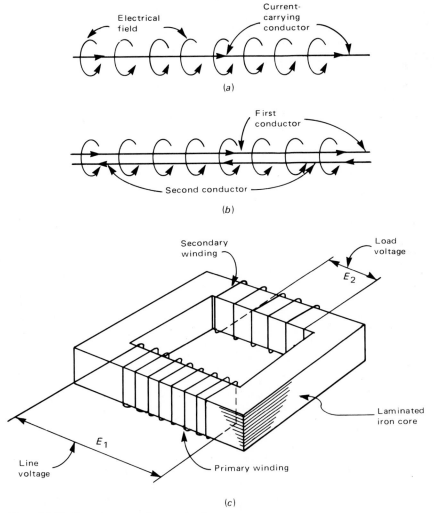

Figure 18-16 Step-down transformer details.

tor. When the dc power is switched off, the electric field collapses and retreats into the conductor. If the conductor of fig. 18-16a is carrying alternating current, the power is, in effect, being turned on and off and reversing its direction with every alternation.

With ac power supplied to the conductor, the electric field is rising and falling continuously, and the lines of force are then continuously moving outward and then back. In other words, with ac power we have a moving field. Now, if we immerse a second conductor, close to the first conductor (as shown in fig. 18-16b) in this moving field, we have lines of force cutting across a conductor. This is all that need be done to generate voltage, and a voltage will be generated in the second conductor. If the second conductor is part of a complete electric circuit, current will flow in it, and the direction of its current will be opposite to that in the first conductor.

This is the basis of transformer theory, and it is utilized effectively in the construction of commercially available transformers. As shown in fig. 18-16c, a transformer usually consists of two windings of electric wire wound on an iron core with the two coils in close proximity. The iron core takes many different shapes and is used to give structural support to the windings, but mainly it is used to enhance the strength of the electromagnetic field of the *primary* winding. Sometimes to gain maximum proximity of the two windings, one winding may be wound on top of the other.

An ac source of power is connected to the primary winding, and as current flows in it a moving electric field is established around it. With the two windings in close proximity, the moving field of the primary passes over and through the other winding, called the *secondary* winding. The secondary is connected to the electric load, whatever it may be.

With the moving field cutting across the loops of wire of the secondary, a voltage is generated in the wire, and when it is part of a complete circuit, current will flow in the secondary and its circuit. Of great importance is the relation between the

number of turns or loops of wire that make up each winding. There is a "direct" relation between the number of turns in a winding and the voltage of that winding. This direct relation may be algebraically expressed as follows:

$$\frac{E_2}{E_1} = \frac{N_2}{N_1} \qquad (18\text{-}10)$$

where E_1 = primary voltage

$\quad E_2$ = secondary voltage

$\quad N_1$ = number of turns or loops of wire in the primary

$\quad N_2$ = number of turns in the secondary

Formula (18-10) expresses direct proportion, which means that the voltage of each winding is in direct porportion to the number of turns of each winding. For example, if a transformer has 2400 turns in its primary and 600 turns in its secondary, we know that the secondary voltage will be one-fourth as great as the primary voltage. This would be a *step-down transformer,* as shown in fig. 18-16c, because the voltage is reduced.

The secondary may have more turns than the primary, and the voltage is stepped up. Also, there may be the same number of turns in both windings and E_1 and E_2 are then the same. This is called an *isolating transformer,* because all it achieves is to isolate the secondary circuit from the remainder of the wiring system. This might be done in a building if an ungrounded circuit is needed, for some reason, and the main building wiring system is grounded—as it surely would be.

Formula (18-10) may, of course, be rewritten to solve for E_2 as in the formula

$$E_2 = E_1 \frac{N_2}{N_1} \qquad (18\text{-}11)$$

As an example, if a building service transformer is supplied with 4160-V power (a standard municipal distribution voltage) and the primary has 8000 turns of wire, and the secondary winding has 400 turns,

$$E_2 = 4160 \ \frac{400}{8000} = 208 \text{ V}$$

Here we can see at a glance that the secondary has 1/20 as many turns as the primary, so its voltage will be 1/20 as great and 1/20 of 4160 V is 208 V.

Most transformers are exceedingly efficient energy transformation units, and we may see as much as 98% of the primary power delivered to the secondary. We can with only a very small error write that $P_1 = P_2$, or that $E_1 I_1 = E_2 I_2$, since, in general, $P = EI$. If, in the example above, E_2 is 1/20 of E_1, then I_2 must be 20 times as great as I_1. Therefore, if I_1 should be 15 A, I_2 would be approximately $20 \times 15 \text{ A} = 300 \text{ A}$.

This tells us that amperage in a transformer is inversely proportional to the ratio of the turns, and we may then write the formula

$$\frac{I_2}{I_1} = \frac{N_1}{N_2} \qquad (18\text{-}12)$$

and from this

$$I_2 = I_1 \frac{N_1}{N_2} \qquad (18\text{-}13)$$

If $I_1 = 15$ A, $N_1 = 8000$ turns, and $N_2 = 400$ turns, we have

$$I_2 = 15 \ \frac{8000}{400} = 300 \text{ A}$$

There are many types of transformers used in the many electrical systems of modern buildings; however, the basic electric power distribution systems mostly involve transformers of only two or three types. First, there are the service transformers which deliver power into buildings with proper characteristics of voltage, phase, and so on. Figures 18-10 and 18-11 show some details of these.

Then there are distribution transformers, shown in fig. 18-17, located throughout a large rambling

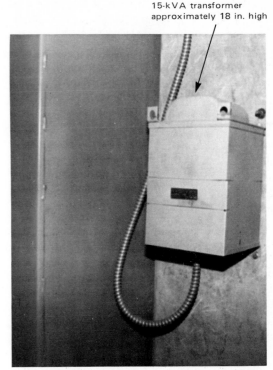

15-kVA transformer approximately 18 in. high

Figure 18-17 Distribution transformer.

building to receive power at a high distribution voltage of perhaps 480 V and to step it down to 120 V for use in lighting systems, small power loads, and receptacle (wall plug) circuits. To a limited extent, isolating transformers may be used for ungrounded circuits, as mentioned.

18-18 INDUCTANCE, INDUCTIVE REACTANCE, AND INDUCTIVE LOADS

More and more the electric distribution systems of modern buildings are carrying *inductive loads—* loads that display inductance and which cause a reaction in those systems called *inductive reactance.* Inductive loads cause problems, and building designers of all types must be familiar with these problems and their solution.

In the word "inductance" may be seen the root word "induce." Inductance is the tendency of, or the ability of, an electric device of some type to induce an "opposing" voltage in an electric circuit. It is algebraically expressed by the symbol L and it is measured in *henrys*. To demonstrate this propensity to any important extent, this device must have a winding with alternating current passing through it. Such devices include transformers, electric motors, and fluorescent light ballasts—anything with a winding.

In a device with a winding, the inductance is 1 henry (H) if the current changing (as alternating current does) at the rate of 1 A/sec induces an opposing voltage of 1 V. We have seen in art. 18-17 that a winding with alternating current flowing in it can induce a voltage in a second coil. It is equally true that such a winding can induce a voltage in itself—sometimes called *back EMF*.

Figure 18-16*b* shows that the moving field of one conductor carrying alternating current can induce a voltage and a current in a second conductor immersed in that moving field, and that the current in the second conductor flows in the opposite direction to that of the first conductor.

When a winding induces by *self-induction* or *auto-induction* an opposing voltage in itself, it tries to make a current flow in the direction opposite to the main current flow. This it cannot do, but in trying, it does reduce the main current flow

somewhat. It is as though a resistor of some type were installed in the circuit.

Here we have a cause-and-effect situation; when we have an inductive-type load in a circuit, its inductance, as a cause, causes a reaction, the effect, which results in a reduction in the current of the circuit. This reaction is called *inductive reactance*; its algebraic symbol is X_L, and it is measured in ohms. Inductive reactance may be expressed by the algebraic relation

$$X_L = 2\pi f L$$

where X_L = inductive reactance, ohms
    f = alternating frequency of the current, usually 60 Hz
    L = inductance, henrys

Of course, when f is 60 Hz, the expression is simplified to $X_L = 377L$.

There is also another very important effect of inductive load in an ac circuit. Inductive load throws the voltage and the current of the circuit out of phase and causes the amps to lag the voltage timewise. In fig. 18-5, the volts and amps are in phase with both peaking simultaneously, reaching zero simultaneously, and so on.

In fig. 18-18, these curves for volts and amps have been redrawn with the amps curve lagging the volts curve by, for example, 30°, as it might

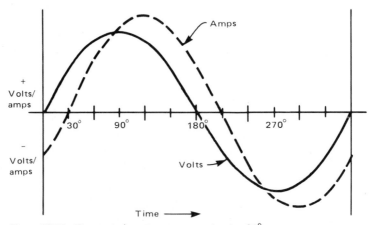

Figure 18-18   Time-volts/amps curves, amps lagging 30°.

really be in a building wiring circuit with a considerable amount of inductive load. If we had a circuit with inductance but with zero resistance (an impossibility, except in imagination) the amps would lag the volts by 90°. With a purely resistive load, with zero inductance, volts and amps are in phase and the angle of lag is zero. It may be seen, then, that in an inductive circuit, having both resistive and inductive load, the angle of lag depends on the relative amounts of resistance and inductance.

The curves in figs. 18-5 and 18-18 are drawn for single-phase circuits, but all that has been said in this article applies equally to three-phase circuits. As will be seen, the fact that current is not in phase with voltage is a matter of great import, placing a severe penalty on circuits and building electrical systems which experience this condition.

In any circuit, power is the product of volts times amperes ($P = E \times I$), but in fig. 18-18 at the 90° point, for example, the voltage is maximum, but the amperage is something less than maximum. At that instant the power is $P = E \times I \times$ PF, where PF is a power factor, always less than unity in an inductive circuit. In a circuit that is heavily loaded, with amperes equal to the maximum allowable value, the circuit is not carrying the power load that it could if its amperes were in phase.

In the circuit pictured in fig. 18-18, where the angle of lag is 30°, the power factor happens to be 0.866, so that the actual power of the circuit is only 86.6% as great as is indicated by $E \times I$. In a building with a poor power factor, the kilowatt-hour meter, which records power consumption, reads only the actual power that the building circuits collectively are receiving. In other words, the power that is actually delivered by the electric power utility to the building in an in-phase condition is discounted by the power factor. The meter readings are then less than they should be, and if the situation is too bad (86.6% power factor is not really bad) the power utility will justifiably add a surcharge to the power bills, and the building owner or operator will have to pay for power that

he or she is not effectively receiving. This is an undesirable situation, but fortunately there is something that can be done about it, as we shall see.

18-19 VECTOR DIAGRAMS

The preceding thoughts about lagging current and power factor can, perhaps, be better illustrated by vector diagrams. In these diagrams the various factors such as voltage, amperage, resistance, and so on, are represented by arrows called *vectors*. The direction and the length of vectors is important, but there is no absolute scale by which the length of an amperage vector, for example, can be placed in meaningful comparison with the length of a voltage vector.

In fig. 18-19, the vector diagrams show volts, amperes, and so on, plotted against time just as figs. 18-5, 18-7, and 18-18 do; however, time is represented by revolutions of the vectors around a central axis of rotation. One 360° revolution counterclockwise represents 1/60 sec or the same time that one revolution of a two-pole 60-Hz generator requires.

Figure 18-19a represents the situation in a single-phase circuit that has only resistive load and no inductive load. Resistive load consists of incandescent lamps, resistance heaters, and so on, which do not include windings of any type. This diagram is an instantaneous picture, like a snapshot, taken at the instant when voltage and amperage are at their maximum and are positive—comparable to the 90° point in the curves of fig. 18-5.

Both the volts and amps vectors begin at the axis of rotation, extend in the same direction, and are coincident. The resistance vector is drawn in direct opposition to the amps vector, indicating that it does oppose the flow of current in a circuit. Since the volts and amps are in phase (coincident in fig. 18-19a), power for this circuit is merely volts multiplied by amperes: $P = EI$.

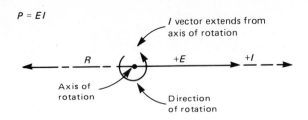

(a) Circuit with resistance
but no inductance

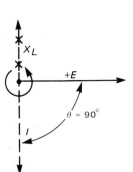

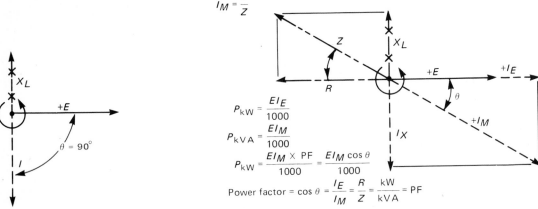

(b) Circuit with inductance
but no resistance

(c) Both resistance and inductance

Figure 18-19 Vector diagrams.

Figure 18-19b shows the vector diagram of an imaginable but impossible circuit in which there is inductive load but no resistance. Again, volts and amps are at maximum, but now the inductance in the circuit throws the current out of phase with the volts and causes it to lag the volts. Since the circuit has zero resistance, the current will lag the voltage by $90°$, as shown by the angle θ. Here the current is opposed by only the inductive reactance X_L, and the X_L vector is drawn directly opposite to the amps vector.

In fig. 18-19c is shown the vector diagram of a circuit of the type normally found in use in building wiring circuits today; it contains both resistive and inductive load. This diagram also represents the situation when voltage is maximum, and is

the $90°$ point of rotation, the same as the $90°$ point on the time scale of fig. 18-18. In fig. 18-19c the amps vector is lagging behind the volts vector by the amount of angle θ. This amps vector is labeled I_M, for actual *measured current* such as would be indicated by an ammeter connected to the circuit.

However, since the current is out of phase, only a portion of the current is effective in producing power. This portion is represented by the vector I_E, *effective current*, which is drawn coincident with the volts vector. Its length is determined by a line drawn perpendicular to the I_E vector through the end of the I_M vector.

Since we have both resistance and inductive reactance in this circuit, the R and X_L vectors are drawn as before straight to the left and straight up. The resistance is drawn in direct opposition to the effective current I_E; and in direct opposition to the inductive reactance vector X_L is drawn the I_X vector for the reactive current. This is usually called the *magnetizing current*. Finally, in direct opposition to the I_M vector is drawn the *impedance vector*, labeled Z.

As may be seen, the impedance vector is the parallelogram resultant of the X_L and R vectors. This quite well defines the term impedance, since it is the resultant that combines the effect of both resistance and inductive reactance. Since they are both expressed in ohms, impedance must also be expressed in ohms. In this type of circuit, it is not accurate to say that $I = E/R$; we must say that $I = E/Z$, or $E = IZ$, or $Z = E/I$.

The power of this circuit may be expressed in two ways—as *true power* in watts or kilowatts, or as *indicated power* in volt-amps or kilovolt-amps. Most people are familiar with the terms watts and kilowatts (kW), but many are not familiar with the terms "volt-amps" (VA) and "kilovolt-amps" (kVA). Kilowatts expresses the true power that the circuit can actually deliver, and $P_{kW} = EI_E/1000$, where I_E, the effective current, is not the full, actual current that is flowing in the circuit. I_E is only a portion of the current whose magnitude depends on the magnitude of angle θ. As θ increases, I_E reduces to zero as a limit. When the angle θ reduces to zero as it is in a purely resistive circuit, I_E increases until it equals I_M.

The *indicated power* is the power that is indicated by the product of measured volts and measured amps, and is expressed as kVA: $P_{kVA} = EI_M/1000$. To convert P_{kVA} to P_{kW} a power factor, PF, must be applied to the P_{kVA}. The PF is always less than unity in an inductive circuit. True power in kW may also be expressed by $P_{kW} = EI_M(PF)/1000$. Of course, in all of this, 1 kW = 1000 W. Power factor, then, may be defined as a numerical factor, always less than unity, which when applied as a multiplier to indicated power will give true power. $P_{kVA} \times PF = P_{kW}$ and $PF = P_{kW}/P_{kVA}$.

We can also say algebraically that

$$PF = \frac{P_{kW}}{P_{kVA}} = \frac{EI_E/1000}{EI_M/1000} = \frac{I_E}{I_M}$$

Well if $PF = I_E/I_M$, we can also see in fig. 18-19c that $PF = R/Z$ by the theorem of proportional triangles.

In trigonometry, the ratio of the side adjacent to the hypotenuse of a right triangle is called the *cosine* of an angle. The cosine of the angle θ is I_E/I_M, so power factor is also the cosine of the angle of lag of the current. Therefore,

$$PF = \cos \theta = \frac{I_E}{I_M} = \frac{R}{Z} = \frac{kW}{kVA}$$

18-20 CAPACITANCE AND CAPACITIVE REACTANCE

Capacitance and capacitive reactance are introduced into an electric circuit when a capacitor is installed in that circuit. A capacitor, sometimes called a condenser, in its simplest form consists of two metal plates brought into proximity to each other, but insulated from each other by some type of electric insulating sheet. In a single-phase ac circuit into which a capacitor is installed, a conductor is connected from one capacitor plate to one side of the circuit, and the second plate is likewise connected to the other side of the circuit, as shown in fig. 18-20a.

A capacitor is not limited to two plates; however, it may consist of a whole stack of plates with alternate plates connected together and to one side of a two-wire single-phase circuit, while the remaining plates are similarly connected together and to the other side of the circuit. For light duty, one popular type of capacitor is the cylindrically shaped one in which two or more thin sheets of metal foil are stacked with insulating sheets separating them. Electrical connections are made to the sheets and the entire stack is rolled up and

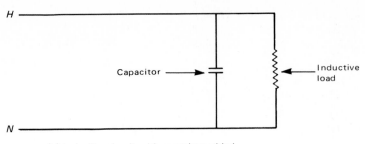

(a) Inductive circuit with capacitor added

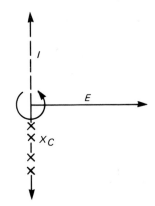

(b) Circuit with capacitance only

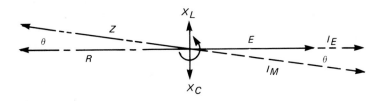

(c) Circuit with resistance,
inductance, and capacitance

Figure 18-20 Vector diagrams—circuits with capacitance.

enclosed in a sheet metal or plastic housing (see fig. 18-21).

Because of the large surface area of the plates or metallic sheets in a capacitor, when a voltage, either positive or negative, is impressed on it a tremendously large number of electrons can be stored. If the power supply is switched off, that charge will remain on the plates or sheets indefinitely. When the power supplied to the capacitor is from an ac circuit, one set of plates will store a charge when the voltage supplied is positive. That charge is quickly returned to the circuit when

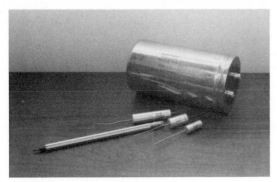

Figure 18-21 Small capacitors.

the ac voltage changes to zero and becomes negative. While the voltage is then negative, the other set of plates in the capacitor will be likewise charged and then discharged.

A capacitor is said to have "capacity" to store a charge of electrons. In so doing, it seems to be striving to maintain the voltage in an ac circuit at one fixed value. When the circuit voltage rises, it receives electrons and to a slight extent does prevent the circuit voltage from rising. When the voltage then falls in the circuit, the capacitor opposes this too by returning its electron charge to the circuit.

Capacitors, then, display a characteristic called *capacitance,* which may be defined as its ability to oppose any change in the voltage of the circuit to which it is connected. Capacitance is algebraically expressed by the symbol C and is measured in farads. The term "farad" is used in honor of a British scientist, Michael Faraday. The capacitance is said to amount to one farad if a change in voltage of one volt causes a change in the stored electric charge of one *coulomb.*

The term "coulomb" is used to express a large quantity of electrons; one coulomb is equal to 6.25×10^{18} electrons. The coulomb is also the number of electrons that passes a point in an electric circuit in one second when the current flow is one ampere. One farad is a very large unit, and capacitance is usually expressed in microfarads, or millionths of a farad.

With capacitance, as with inductance, we again have a cause-and-effect situation. When capacitance is the "cause" in a circuit, the effect is called *capacitive reactance,* which is given the symbol X_C and measured in ohms. The relation between capacitance and capacitive reactance may be expressed algebraically as follows:

$$X_C = \frac{1}{2\pi f C} \tag{18-14}$$

where X_C = capacitive reactance, ohms
  f = power frequency, hertz
  C = capacitance, farads

A more useful expression of this relation may be written as

$$X_C = \frac{2650}{C} \tag{18-15}$$

where C is the capacitance in microfarads and the frequency is 60 Hz.

The antithetical or inverse relation between the capacitive reactance X_C and inductive reactance X_L may be seen by comparing the formula for inductive reactance $(X_L = 2\pi f L)$ with formula (18-14). It will not be surprising, then, to learn that one effect of capacitive reactance in a circuit is to try to make the current "lead" the voltage. As shown in fig. 18-20b, if a circuit had only capacitive reactance and no resistance or inductive reactance, its current would lead its voltage by $90°$.

18-21 POWER FACTOR CORRECTION

We have said that an electric circuit containing a large amount of inductive load will have a seriously lagging current and a very poor power factor. This condition can be corrected by the installation of a capacitor in such a circuit. As noted in art. 18-20, this will introduce a leading effect to the current of the circuit which will offset to a certain extent the lagging effect of the inductive load.

As a result, the angle θ of fig. 18-19 will be reduced, and the power factor will be brought closer to unity. The circuit will then be able to carry more load, and the possibility of surcharges being added to the power bills for a given building will be reduced. Figure 18-20c shows the vector diagram of such a circuit to which capacitive reactance X_C has been added.

The X_C vector is drawn in direct opposition to the inductive reactance vector X_L; the net effect is that angle θ is reduced, and the power factor is increased closer to unity. Normally, in correcting power factor in this manner, no effort is made to achieve complete correction to unity. Most electric utility companies will not complain if the overall power factor of a building at the kilowatt-hour meter is 0.85 or 0.9 or better.

Power factor correction may be applied to an individual circuit as shown in fig. 18-20a, or may be applied to an entire building by applying a single phase (two-wire) or a three-phase (three-wire) capacitor to the wiring at the electrical service entrance location.

In all our discussions in this chapter pertaining to inductance and capacitance and power factor correction we have used illustrations of single-phase two-wire circuits. However, all the principles and ideas offered are completely applicable to three-phase three-wire circuits. A three-phase capacitor has three plates, or sets of plates, or rolled sheets, with three wiring connections made to the three-phase wires of a three-phase circuit or system.

PROBLEMS

18-1   In the simple circuit of fig. 18-12, if voltage is 120 V and amperage is 10 A, what is the circuit resistance, in ohms, and what is the power of the circuit in watts?

18-2   What is the approximate resistance of a 150-W 120-V light bulb? Is this resistance

greater or smaller than the resistance of a 300-W light bulb?

18-3   In the fig. 18-13 series circuit, if the three component resistances are 100 Ω each and the circuit wiring has a resistance of 6 Ω, what is the total circuit resistance? Also, what is the circuit current in amps, and the circuit power, in watts, if voltage is 240 V? What is the voltage drop across each of the 100-Ω loads and also in the wiring?

18-4   In the parallel circuit of fig. 18-14, what is the total circuit resistance, including wiring at 2/3 Ω, if the three loads shown have resistances of 45, 55, and 60 Ω? Find the circuit current and power if voltage is 240 V.

18-5   The service transformer of a building receives power at 4160 V and delivers it into its building at 480 V. What must be the ratio of the number of winding turns in the primary and secondary windings?

18-6   If the transformer of prob. 18-5 must deliver 800 A of current into its building, what must its primary current be?

18-7   If in a service transformer E_1 = 13,800 V, N_1 = 10,000, N_2 = 150, and I_2 = 400 A, find E_2 and the power, in kVA, of this transformer.

18-8   Draw the time-voltage and time-amperage curves for a single-phase ac circuit in which the amperage is leading the voltage by 30°. Draw the same curves if the current is lagging the voltage by 45°.

18-9   In a single-phase ac circuit the voltage is 240 V and the current is measured at 40 A. If the circuit has inductive load in it and the current, as a result, lags the voltage by 30°, find the power of the circuit in kW. (Note: The cosine of 30° is 0.866.)

18-10   A 240-V single-phase circuit has a continuous load of 32 A. A kilowatt-hour meter indicates a true power of the circuit of 6.68 kW. What is the power factor of this circuit?

Chapter 19

Building Electrical Distribution Systems

19-1 GENERALITIES

It is not the intent in this chapter to discuss the intimate details of building wiring systems and electrical equipment to the end that the reader may be rendered qualified to apply for a journeyman electrician's license. The construction professionals to whom this text is directed would have no need of such a license.

Rather it is the hope here that with a basic understanding of the theories of electricity, discussed in chap. 18, enough generalized knowledge on electrical distribution equipment and its installation will be added to those theories to provide the reader with a well-rounded, overall understanding of building electrical systems. This understanding should permit the reader to participate in definitive planning discussions on building concept and design, and to make productive contributions to such discussions.

Further, this chapter should condition readers concerning building electrical systems so that when they visit construction sites they will quickly recognize the electrical system components that they see and understand the part that each component plays in the overall system.

The installation of building electrical systems is closely controlled and regulated in most areas of the United States by electrical codes and governmental agencies that administer and enforce these codes. Most local codes of this type are patterned after the National Electrical Code (NEC) or adopt the NEC in totum. The NEC is concerned primarily with the design and installation of electrical systems that are safe and protect the well-being of people and the buildings that they occupy.

It is important that all construction professionals have a better than nodding acquaintance with the NEC. Of course, those who are deeply involved with detail electrical design or installation must be thoroughly familiar with all its provisions. Those interested in procuring a copy of the NEC may do so by applying to the National Fire Protection Association (NFPA), 470 Atlantic Avenue, Boston, MA 02210, requesting a copy of the latest issue of NFPA No. 70 (American National Standards Institute). The cost of this is quite modest.

Electrical distribution systems for buildings consist of five basic divisions:

1 *Service entrance:* including main disconnecting devices, distribution panelboards, metering equipment, and conduit and wiring.

2 *Feeder system:* a system of heavy-duty conduits and wiring that carries electric power from the service entrance equipment to the various lighting and power panelboards that are strategically located throughout a building.

3 *Lighting and power panelboards:* metal enclosures which house the circuit breakers, fuses, and fused switches to which all branch circuits connect and which give electrical protection to those branch circuits.

4 *Branch circuits:* the wiring circuits that receive power in a controlled manner from the lighting and power panelboards and carry that power to all the many items of electrical equipment that constitute the electrical load of the building. Branch circuits usually extend to and serve all parts of a building. A large building will have hundreds of branch circuits running overhead, under the floors, and in walls, switched and protected as necessary.

5 *Electrical load:* consists of a wide range of electrically operated equipment, including lighting fixtures, electric motors, heaters, signal systems of many types, etc.

19-2 SERVICE ENTRANCE

Figure 19-1 shows a partial section through a building which very briefly pictures the five basic components of the electrical system. At the extreme left may be seen a utility pole, service transformer, service drop, and overhead power transmission lines belonging to the local electric power utility company. These are not part of the

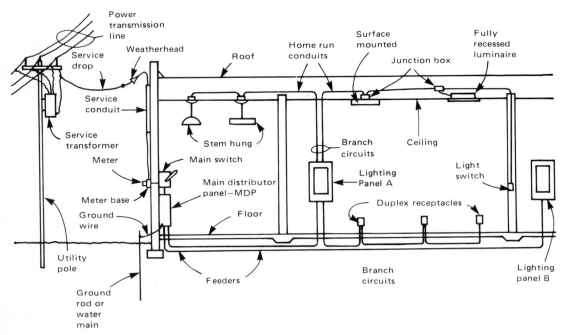

Figure 19-1 Typical building wiring system components.

building system; usually, they are owned by the power utility company.

The building system, with an overhead service drop as shown, begins with the weatherhead on the exterior of the building and the wiring conductors in it. The weatherhead, in smaller services, is usually a round, tapered metal piece which threads onto a metal conduit which is turned downward. The bottom, open end is 4 to 8 in. in diameter, and the electrician, in finishing the installation, leaves 2 to 6 ft of service conductors hanging out of this opening.

Usually, a ceramic or plastic filler piece with three or four holes in it (for the wires to pass through) is used to close this bottom opening. The electric utility workers make the final connection to these hanging wires with the service drop wires which they install. In larger, overhead services the weatherhead may be a larger rectangular sheet metal hood secured to the building. This hood has an open bottom through which the service wires enter.

From the weatherhead a rigid, galvanized steel conduit carries the service conductors down to a meter base and from this cast metal base into the building. The base is provided by the electric utility so as to properly accept their meter, which they also provide and install. Service conductors are again left hanging at this base by the electrician for connection by the utility workers. Such a meter installation, in which all of the power drawn by the building passes through the meter, is usually limited to 200 A capacity. Most nonresidential buildings require more than 200 A much of the time, and a different metering setup is required, as will be shown later.

Inside the building, the entering service conductors and conduit first meet and are connected to a disconnecting device—a fused main switch or a main circuit breaker. This disconnecting device may be one switch or breaker or it may be more—as many as six maximum all at one location. It serves as a means of manually shutting down the power for the entire building, when that becomes necessary, and it also provides overload protection

by opening the line when current flow becomes excessive (see fig. 19-2).

19-3 MAIN DISTRIBUTION PANELS

From the main disconnecting device, the service conductors and conduit extend to some type of distribution panel usually referred to as the *main distribution panel* (MDP). The function of the MDP is to divide the entering power into several or many different streams of power for distribution to various areas of the building.

Usually, the MDP is an integrated, unitized assembly which includes a disconnecting and protective device, such as a *circuit breaker* (C/B) to control each of the various streams of power that spread throughout the building. However, the MDP takes many different forms and may consist of an assembly of fused switches mounted separately on a common mounting panel. See fig. 19-3 for illustrations of a main distribution integrated panelboard.

As will be discussed later in detail, one of the conductors of the electrical service must be *grounded*—connected to the earth (in England they say "earthed" instead of "grounded"). Also, all of the *equipment*, such as panelboard enclosures, switch enclosures, and conduits, must be grounded. This is accomplished by making connection from the equipment and the grounded conductor to a *ground rod*, sometimes called a *grounding electrode*, or to a metallic water main. The ground rod is a copper or brass or copper-coated steel rod driven 8 ft or so into the earth to make contact with moist earth.

Connection to a water main for grounding purposes is usually quite effective, because it runs for great distances in the earth. However, some water service pipes are laid too close to the earth surface, where the earth may be quite dry or of the wrong consistency. In this case, a ground rod may give better grounding. Figure 19-1 shows a ground rod and the ground wire connection from the rod to the MDP.

Welded cover hinges
Provide strong secure
construction.

Visible blades: one glance
tells if the switch is ON or
OFF. When the handle is
down, the switch is OFF
and the blades are
separated from the switch
jaws.

Quick-make, quick-break
action: Spring activated
mechanism linked directly
to the handle.

Dual cover—interlock: Hinged
cover cannot be opened when
the switch is ON, nor can the
switch be turned ON if the
cover is open . . . except when
the interlock is purposely
bypassed.

Multiple lock-off provisions:
For up to three 3/8-in. shank
padlocks in the OFF position.

Fuse clips

Field installable
electrical interlocks
available (not shown)

UL listed with 200,000 ampere
short circuit rating when class J
or class R fuses are used.

Class R fuse kits: Can be
field installed to reject all
except class R fuses.

Field installable
solid neutral assembly:
For addition to switches not
supplied with factory installed
solid neutral assemply.

Figure 19-2 Main disconnect switch. (Courtesy of The Square D. Co.) Fuse clips hold cartridge
fuses top and bottom. Switch shown is a three-pole, three-fuse, solid neutral, 30-A size (30 amp/3P/
3F/SN).

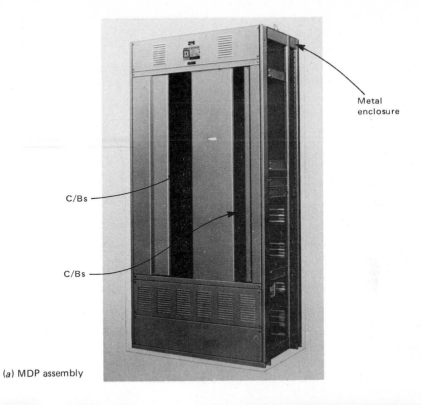

Metal
enclosure

C/Bs

C/Bs

(a) MDP assembly

Conductors

Conduits

(b) Feeder conduits and
conductors

(c) C/Bs being installed
in MDP

Figure 19-3 Main distribution panel (MDP) details. (Courtesy of The Square D. Co.)

19-4 FEEDERS

Feeders are the heavy-duty wiring facilities that carry the power from the MDP out to the various lighting and power panels (panelboards) which are located throughout the building. Feeders consist of heavy-duty copper or aluminum insulated conductors enclosed in galvanized steel or plastic conduits. Feeders connect to the several C/Bs in the MDP and to copper bus bars in the panelboards.

Feeders are often run below floors, buried in the earth as shown in fig. 19-1, or through crawl spaces; or they may be run above ceilings or other places where they can be given protection from mechanical damage. Of course, when buried, feeder conduits and conductors must be capable of resisting the wet, corrosive conditions that may prevail there.

Sometimes heavy-duty power loads and even lighting loads are fed directly from the MDP to the loads, especially when those loads are in the same equipment room or boiler room as the MDP. In this case, the MDP also serves as a panelboard, and the conductors that carry power from the MDP to a heavy motor, for example, are also called a *feeder*. So the term "feeder" is not limited to those conductors carrying power to remote panelboards, although that may be the most frequent use of the word.

19-5 PANELBOARDS

Depending on the types of load placed on them, panelboards are called *lighting panels*, or *power panels*, or combination lighting and power panels. To a certain extent, the MDP is a panelboard, at least in the smaller sizes. The panels out in the building away from the service entrance location, almost always in modern buildings, are circuit breaker (C/B) panels. As shown in fig. 19-4,

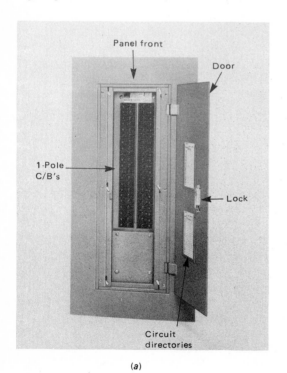

(a)

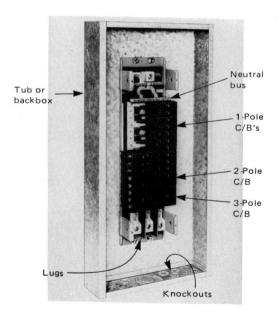

(b)

Figure 19-4 Panelboard details. (Courtesy of the Square D. Co.)

they consist of steel *backboxes* (sometimes called *tubs*) into which copper bus bars and C/Bs are mounted.

The *bus bars* are just plain bars of solid copper mounted vertically near the center of the backbox and, of course, are very carefully insulated from the metal of the box. A circuit breaker is installed in the box for each branch circuit that receives power from the panel. The C/Bs provide a means of disconnecting each branch circuit (switching them on and off), and at the same time provide protection from excessive current flow.

Panelboards may utilize *fuses* instead of C/Bs, and fuse panels are often found in small load centers in low-cost housing. The fuses provide overcurrent protection, and by removing the fuse for a certain circuit that circuit is disconnected from the power supply. Fuses may be of the screw-in plug type or of the cartridge type. Cartridge-type fuses are cylindrical in shape with a copper or brass cap on each end where electrical contact is made.

Cartridge fuses are usually mounted on Bakelite or plastic blocks, either one, two, or three fuses per block, with a handle on the block by means of which the block and its fuses may be withdrawn and its circuit disconnected. Details of C/Bs and fuses are shown in figs. 19-5 and 19-6.

As mentioned, a panelboard is supplied with power by a feeder extending outward from an MDP. Feeder conduits usually contain three or four conductors, and each of these conductors is connected securely to a copper bus bar in the panel. Therefore, panels will usually contain three or four bus bars arranged so that the individual C/Bs can make electrical contact with one, two, or three of them. One of the bus bars is usually a neutral bus and is usually grounded—more about this later.

The panel backbox, or tub, is punched on all sides and the back by punch press dies that do not cut completely through the box metal. This provides round disks of metal of different sizes that may be easily punched out with hammer and chisel to leave openings where conduits may be

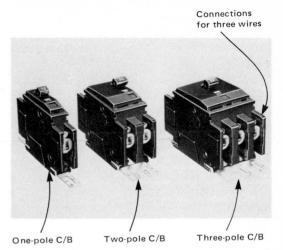

Connections for three wires

One-pole C/B   Two-pole C/B   Three-pole C/B

Figure 19-5 Molded case circuit breakers. (Courtesy of The Square D. Co.)

connected. The feeder conduit and all branch circuit conduits connect with specially designed connectors to these openings in the box.

When a panelboard is located in an equipment room or boiler room or other space where good appearance is not important, it should always be surface mounted on a wall or partition and not recessed into the wall or partition. When it is surface mounted, all connecting conduits are fully exposed to view and are accessible for service. Further, the panel tub is fully exposed, and the installation of new conduits and branch circuits in the future is easily accomplished.

However, this construction is not acceptable in well-finished areas where good appearance is important. Here the panels must be fully recessed into a wall with only the removable front exposed to view and flush with the surface of the wall. In this case, all connecting conduits are concealed in the wall. With recessed panels the installation of new conduits at a later date is very difficult, and extensive cutting and patching of the wall is necessary. To minimize this difficulty, it is highly recommended that for each recessed panelboard a few extra empty conduits be run upward and perhaps downward to points where future accessibility will be easy. When the building has sus-

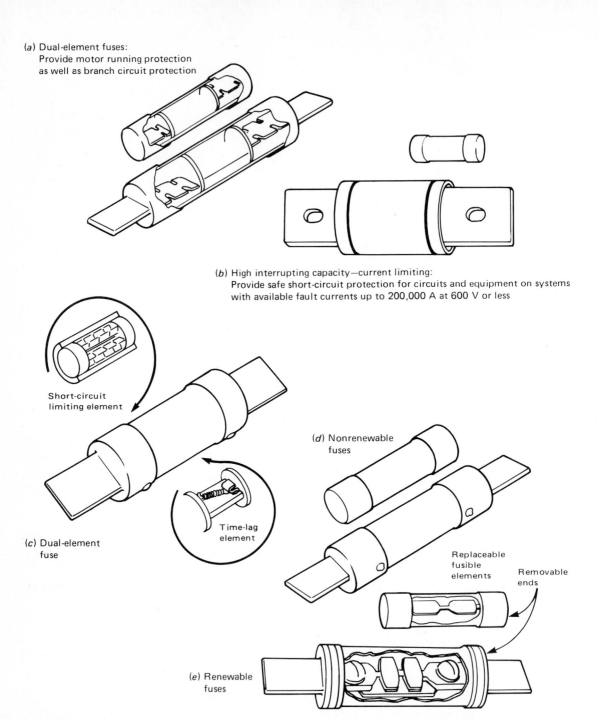

(a) Dual-element fuses:
   Provide motor running protection
   as well as branch circuit protection

(b) High interrupting capacity—current limiting:
   Provide safe short-circuit protection for circuits and equipment on systems
   with available fault currents up to 200,000 A at 600 V or less

Short-circuit
limiting element

(d) Nonrenewable
   fuses

(c) Dual-element
   fuse

Time-lag
element

Replaceable
fusible
elements

Removable
ends

(e) Renewable
   fuses

Figure 19-6 Fuses; various types.

pended acoustic ceilings with easily removable ceiling panels, these future conduits need run only 3 to 5 ft—a very small cost concession to the problem of future expansion.

As shown in fig. 19-4, the panel front has a small, lockable, hinged door mounted in it. Opening this door exposes the operating handles of the C/Bs and exposes the fuses, but with the panel front in place, none of the dangerous, electrical parts, terminals, or exposed wires inside the panel are accessible.

Mounted on the inside of the panel front door is a removable circuit directory card behind a clear plastic protector. This card is provided for the purpose of showing what load each circuit breaker controls, and should give the room location of such load. As anyone who has worked with electricians knows, it is exceedingly difficult to get these circuit directories intelligently, neatly, and completely executed. Each C/B in a panel has a number that establishes the branch circuit number. The directory card is similarly numbered, and for each number, space for the circuit load description is provided.

The circuit description should show room location by room number, and the load should be described as lights, duplex receptacles, exhaust fan, and so on. In defense of the installing electrician, it is often true that the final room numbers ascribed by the building owner or occupant are different from those shown on the electrical drawings with which the electrician worked during construction. If all the electrician knows is the room numbers on the drawings, that is all he or she can enter on the directory card. So often, though, the card entries are made by hand with a dull pencil and are barely legible. It must be insisted that these cards be carefully typed.

Most lighting and power panels do not have a main C/B controlling the entering power; however, when for some reason it is expected that it will often be necessary to disconnect all power supply from the panel for emergency or routine purposes, a main C/B may be supplied with the panel by its manufacturer. This main C/B can open the circuit in all hot phase wires leading to the panel. If the feeder includes a grounded neutral wire, this would bypass the main C/B.

When a main C/B is not required, the feeder conductors connect directly to the panel bus bars by means of built-in devices called *lugs*. Lugs provide sockets into which the bare ends of the heavy feeder conductors may be inserted. They also have *set screws*, which can be screwed down tightly onto the bare end of the wire to hold it securely in place and make good electrical connection. A panel that has no main C/B to which the feeder wires can connect provides a connecting lug for each wire. Such a panel is described by the letters MLO, meaning *main lugs only*. In fig. 19-1, the schematic drawing shows two lighting panels, A and B.

Lighting and power panels as well as the C/Bs that fit into them are available in standard voltage and amp ratings. However, the standardization is not complete, and between manufacturers there will be some variation from the schedule set forth below. This schedule is concerned only with molded case C/B panelboards.

Lighting and Power Panelboards

1 Available for single-phase two-wire, single-phase three-wire, three-phase three-wire, and three-phase four-wire electrical systems.
2 Available with main C/B or "lugs only" (MLO).
3 Designed for 240, 480, or 600 V maximum.
4 Available with *branch* C/Bs, fuses, or fused switches.
5 Accommodate one-, two-, or three-phase C/Bs or fuse blocks.
6 C/Bs or fuses make connection to panel bus bars which are fed by panel *feeders*.
7 One bus bar required for each feeder *phase wire* and for the neutral wire; no neutral bus required in three-phase three-wire panels.
8 Panels sized for 42 poles maximum.
9 Standard panel sizes (varies somewhat among manufacturers)
   a 240-V panels—lugs only—60, 100, 125, 225, 400, and 600 A. With main C/B—60, 100, 225, and 400 A.
   b 480- and 600-V panels—lugs only—125,

225, 400, 600, 800, and 1200 A. With main C/B–100, 225, 400, 600, 800, and 1200 A.

10 Branch C/B sizes–120, 240, 277, 480, and 600 V ratings.

    a 100-A frame–15, 20, 30, 40, 50, 60, 70, 80, 90, and 100 A.

    b 225-A frame–70, 100, 125, 150, 175, 200, and 225 A.

    c 400-A frame–225, 250, 300, 350, and 400 A.

    d Also 400, 1000, 1200, 2000, and 2500 A in heavier frame sizes.

19-6 BRANCH CIRCUITS AND LOADS

Branch circuits are those portions of the electrical distribution system that extend beyond the last circuit protective devices (C/Bs and fuses). Branch circuits, as shown in fig. 19-1, extend from the panelboards outward to all elements of electrical load in the building. In nonresidential buildings, branch circuit wires are enclosed in metallic conduits; three such conduits are shown in fig. 19-1, each carrying one branch circuit—one duplex receptable circuit and two lighting circuits.

An effort has been made in fig. 19-1 to indicate schematically lighting circuits with different types of lighting fixtures. Two of these fixtures are stem-hung from the ceilings—one rounded dome incandescent and one long narrow fluorescent fixture. The other two fixtures are also fluorescent, one being surface mounted and one recessed into the ceiling. Notice that the last two fixtures are controlled by a wall-mounted light switch. The first two fixtures are not so switched, and would be controlled by the circuit breaker in lighting panel A (LPA).

The remaining branch circuit shown is a duplex receptacle (wall plug) circuit with the three receptacles shown. These receptacles are connected to a branch circuit conduit which extends downward from the LPA tub to below the floor. Notice how the conduit connections to the receptacle boxes are made. It is not necessary to limit a branch circuit conduit to one branch circuit, and usually each such conduit will carry two, three, or four branch circuits.

19-7 ELECTRIC SERVICE: 120/240-V/ SINGLE-PHASE/60-HZ/THREE-WIRE TYPE

We must now go back to the subject of electrical services and examine the various types of services in common use and the electrical characteristics of each. The first of these is the simplest and least expensive and is a dual-voltage single-phase three-wire service. There is really one lighter-weight service, a 120-V single-phase two-wire service, but its use is limited to very small structures, such as a small lake cottage. It would not be suitable for a normal residence and certainly has no place in the nonresidential field.

Figure 19-7 schematically shows the components of a 120/240-V single-phase three-wire service. All services and systems that we will discuss are for 60-Hz (cycle) power and that fact will not be repeated each time. At the left in fig. 19-7 we see the three conductors of an overhead, three-phase power distribution system hung on utility poles. All municipal distribution systems will not always be a three-wire three-phase system, as shown. Sometimes in residential areas of a city, three-phase power is not needed, and the pole line will be only a single-phase line.

However, in fig. 19-7 it is three-phase, and to obtain single-phase service for a particular building, connection to only two of the three pole-line conductors is made—by the utility company. These two connections are extended to the primary winding of the service transformer as shown. This service transformer is provided and mounted by the electric utility and is, of course, a step-down unit. The primary voltage will be some very high value suitable for transmitting power for long distances; in fig. 19-7 it is shown to be 4160 V.

The secondary winding of the transformer is designed for 240 V and has a small number of winding *turns* compared to the turns in the primary winding. The ratio of the winding turns is equal to the ratio of the primary and secondary

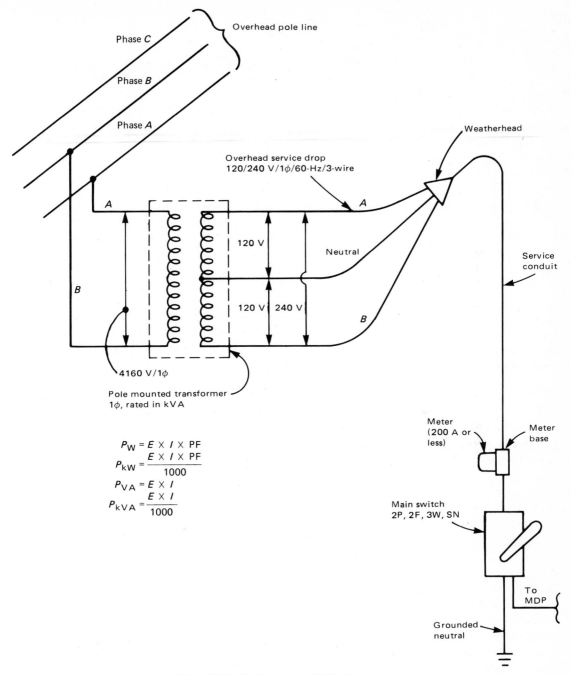

Phase C

Phase B

Phase A

Overhead pole line

Weatherhead

Overhead service drop
120/240 V/1φ/60-Hz/3-wire

A

A

120 V

Neutral

B

120 V 240 V

B

Service
conduit

4160 V/1φ

Pole mounted transformer
1φ, rated in kVA

$$P_W = E \times I \times PF$$
$$P_{kW} = \frac{E \times I \times PF}{1000}$$
$$P_{VA} = E \times I$$
$$P_{kVA} = \frac{E \times I}{1000}$$

Meter
(200 A or
less)

Meter
base

Main switch
2P, 2F, 3W, SN

To
MDP

Grounded
neutral

Figure 19-7 Electric service to a building: 120/240V/single phase/60Hz/3-wire.

voltages, or $4160 \div 240 = 17.33$. The primary has 17.33 times as many winding turns as does the secondary. Figure 19-7 shows that the secondary winding has a center tap. That is, an electrical connection is made to the exact midpoint of the secondary, and a lead is brought out to the exterior of the transformer.

This center tap divides the secondary winding into two 120-V windings, and the ratio of turns with the primary is $4160 \div 120 = 34.67$. So, in effect, we have two 120-V secondary windings connected together in series to make one 240-V secondary. As shown, there are three connections to the secondary winding, and the three service drop wires are connected thereto.

Our three-wire service drop consists, then, of three wires, two of which are indirect extensions of the high-voltage pole lines—phases A and B—while the third is an extension of the center tap. These three wires extend overhead, or perhaps underground, to the meter base and to the main disconnecting device, whatever it may be. A manual, fused switch is shown.

Of the three wires, the one that is connected to the transformer center tap is grounded by means of a connection from it to a grounding rod or water pipe. This wire is called the neutral wire, and as a result of being grounded is at earth potential, or zero voltage. This grounding connection is usually made somewhere near the main switch. As mentioned previously, the "equipment" (switch enclosure, conduit, etc.) is usually grounded here also.

As noted by abbreviations, the main switch is a two-pole two-fuse, three-wire solid neutral switch. By "two-pole" we mean that there are two terminals for incoming power lines and two terminals for outgoing power lines; and these lines are the phase A and phase B conductors whose continuity is broken when the switch is opened. There are two fuses because phases A and B conductors are the only ones that need fuse protection. The third conductor, the neutral, is never fused and this conductor must pass right through the switch with complete continuity. Hence, the

"SN" notation means solid neutral, or unbroken continuity.

As mentioned before, when the size of this service is 200 A or less, all the incoming power will pass through the meter. If the service is larger than 200 A, as it very well may be, other provisions must be made, as discussed later. Notice that because of the design of the service transformer secondary winding, the voltage between phase wires A and B is 240 V, and between the neutral wire N and either phase wire the voltage is 120 V.

These three wires extend from the service entrance equipment through the MDP, the feeders, and the panel boards to all parts of the building. Wherever 240-V single-phase power is needed by some piece of equipment (load), it is connected to phase A and phase B conductors. Wherever a load requires 120-V single-phase power it is connected to the neutral N and to either the phase A or phase B conductors. In most buildings there is a great amount of 120-V single-phase load items, and it is the electrician's responsibility to "balance" this load by connecting equal amounts to phases A and B.

In fig. 19-7 are listed the formulas for calculating power in this system, where P_W = power in watts, P_{kW} = power in kilowatts, P_{VA} = power in volt-amperes, P_{kVA} = power in kilovolt-amperes, E = voltage, I = measured current, and PF = power factor. In the vector diagrams of chap. 18, we included vectors for I_E, effective current, and I_M, measured current. In all of our discussions before and after the vector diagram discussion, when we use the symbol I, we mean measured current, the current that is actually flowing whether in phase or out of phase. We will not have use for effective current I_E in our future discussions; I will always mean measured current.

19-8 ELECTRIC SERVICE: 240-V/THREE-PHASE/THREE-WIRE

The second type of service to be examined here is the 240-V three-phase three-wire service. It very well might also be a voltage other than 240 V; it

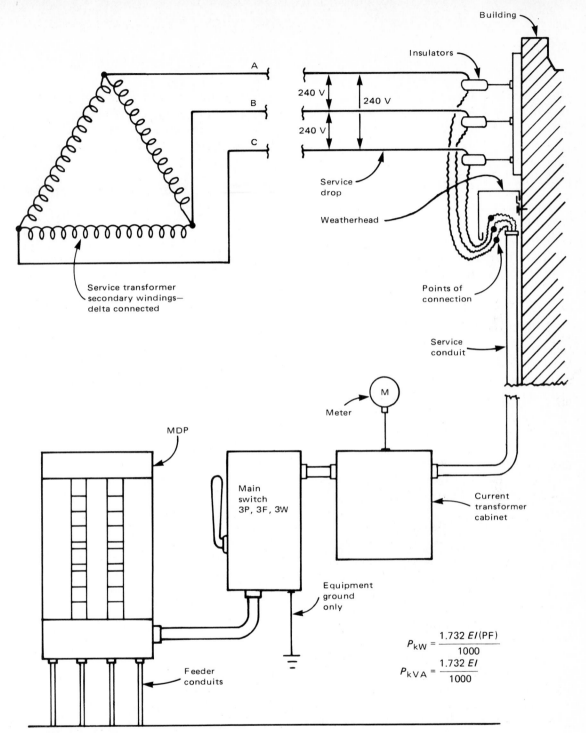

Figure 19-8 240-V/three-phase/three-wire service.

Building

Insulators

240 V

240 V

240 V

Service
drop

Weatherhead

Points of
connection

Service
conduit

A

B

C

Service transformer
secondary windings—
delta connected

Meter

M

MDP

Main
switch
3P, 3F, 3W

Current
transformer
cabinet

Equipment
ground
only

Feeder
conduits

$$P_{kW} = \frac{1.732\ EI(PF)}{1000}$$

$$P_{kVA} = \frac{1.732\ EI}{1000}$$

might be 208 or 480 V. This is a service that is electrically ungrounded and should be used for three-phase load only.

This service might be used in an existing building which has a light-duty, single-phase power system, but which experiences an extensive change in use making a heavy-duty, three-phase power system necessary. This happens occasionally when a warehouse type of building is put to use for heavy manufacturing activities. As a warehouse, it probably had only a lighting and duplex receptacle system. With the change, many large three-phase motors, electric heaters, and so on, are now in use, and a three-phase power system is needed. A service such as that shown in fig. 19-8 would be added while the original single-phase system remained in use.

In fig. 19-8, the service transformer is a three-phase unit, pole-mounted or pad-mounted (see figs. 18-10 and 18-11). Transformers for power entrance service are also detailed in fig. 19-9; these are liquid filled, and the cooling system radiators (pipes, etc.) may be seen.

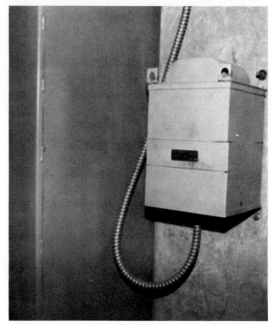

Figure 19-10 Dry type distribution transformer, wall mounted.

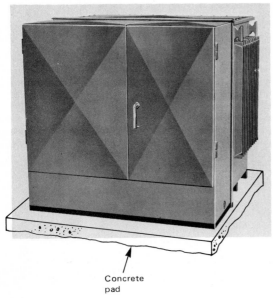

Concrete
pad

Figure 19-9 Liquid-filled, padmount transformer. (Courtesy of The Square D. Co.)

Notice that the transformer in fig. 19-8 has three windings, and that those windings are connected in the familiar "delta" configuration. These are the secondary windings only; the primary windings are not shown.

In this service there is no neutral conductor, and all three conductors in the service drop are hot. If the secondary voltage is 240 V, as shown, a voltmeter would read 240 V between any two of the three service conductors. The service conductors extend from the transformer to the building weatherhead, where the electric utility company workers make connection to the service conductors left hanging by the building electrician. A different type of weatherhead is shown in fig. 19-8, and the unsightly points of connection are well concealed inside it.

This type of power service will usually supply appreciably more than 200 A of current, and the type of metering shown in fig. 19-7 is not adequate. For sizes of service over approximately 200 A, current transformers must be used. These are enclosed in a locked and sealed steel cabinet called a *current transformer* (CT) cabinet. The CT cabinet is located inside the building and the service conduit connects to it.

As shown in fig. 19-11, current transformers are generally doughnut-shaped; in fact, they are often referred to as "doughnuts." They consist of a coil of wire wound on an iron core. In a three-phase service, three doughnuts would be mounted in the CT cabinet and the three service conductors would pass through the holes of the doughnuts. The lines of force of the electrical field surrounding each conductor cut across the loops of the windings and a small voltage is generated. A small current will then flow through the windings and through the kilowatt-hour (kWh) meter that is wired to the three doughnuts. The current that flows through the meter is only a small fraction of the current flowing in the service. Very often the actual current to the kWh meter is about 5 A.

Of course, the kWh meter is calibrated to read the power that is actually flowing in the service conductors. One of the CTs shown in fig. 19-11 is an assembly of three CTs with three holes through which the service conductors pass; this provides a more compact and easier-to-mount CT unit. Figure 19-8 shows the kWh meter connected to the CT cabinet; the meter may be mounted remotely at any point of convenience and may be mounted outdoors so that the electric utility's meter reader does not need to enter the building.

From the CT cabinet the service conductors pass through the main switch or circuit breaker. If a switch, it would be a three-pole three-fuse three-wire switch without provision for a neutral wire, of course (see fig. 19-2). If this main disconnect device is a C/B, it would be as shown in fig. 19-12 and would be enclosed in a steel enclosure with provisions for conduit and wiring connections. Somewhere in this area, an equipment ground connection would be made from this service equipment to a grounding electrode or buried water pipe.

(a) Individual CTs for one wire— various sizes

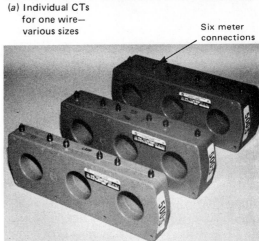

Six meter connections

(b) Three-phase CTs for three wires— three different size CTs

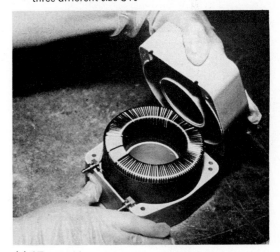

(c) CT assembly

Figure 19-11 Current transformers. (Courtesy of The Square D. Co.)

(a) 600 to 2000 A capacity

(b) 125 to 1000 A capacity

(c) 600 to 1200 A capacity

Figure 19-12   Heavy duty, molded case, three-pole circuit breakers. (Courtesy of The Square D. Co.)

From the main disconnect device, the service conductors extend to the main distribution panel, MDP. Figure 19-3 shows an MDP with C/Bs, and also shows a view of an electrician installing the C/Bs in such a panelboard. The feeder conduits shown in fig. 19-8 carry the conductors that feed power to the various lighting and power panelboards located throughout the building. One of the details in fig. 19-3 shows conduits of this type entering the enclosure of an MDP unit that stands on the floor; this detail also shows some of the feeder wires connecting to C/Bs.

Figure 19-8 includes the formulas that should be used to calculate power in either kW or kVA. These formulas are not quite the same as we have discussed thus far for single-phase power and incorporate an additional factor, 1.732, the square root of 3 ($\sqrt{3} = 1.732$). Otherwise, these formulas are no different.

It would not be beneficial to take the space here to develop the mathematical justification for including this 1.732 factor. However, it should not be difficult for the reader to realize that a three-phase three-wire circuit with all wires hot will carry more power than a two-wire single-phase circuit with the same size conductors. At a superficial glance, it might seem that three wires could carry 1.5 times as much power as two wires; however, this is not the case here, and the 1.732 factor is correct.

The reader should take steps to remember that in every case, without exception, a three-phase power calculation *must* include this 1.732 factor. Failure to do so will, of course, introduce very substantial errors in power calculations. To reinforce this understanding, fig. 19-13 is included here, which lists useful formulas for many uses in dc and single- and three-phase electrical systems. Notice that in every three-phase formula, the 1.732 factor is included, but it is not included in any of the others.

In fig. 19-8, the three phase wires A, B, and C deliver three-phase power into the building. Extensions and branches of these three wires deliver power throughout the building to wherever three-

Figure 19-13 Useful electrical formulas for determining amperes, horsepower, kilowatts, and KVA.

To find:	Direct current	Alternating current	
		Single-phase	Three-phase
Amperes when horsepower is known	$\dfrac{hp \times 746}{E \times \% \text{ efficiency}}$	$\dfrac{hp \times 746}{E \times \% \text{ efficiency} \times PF}$	$\dfrac{hp \times 746}{1.732 \times E \times \% \text{ efficiency} \times PF}$
Amperes when kilowatts is known	$\dfrac{kW \times 1000}{E}$	$\dfrac{kW \times 1000}{E \times PF}$	$\dfrac{kW \times 1000}{1.732 \times E \times PF}$
Amperes when kVA is known		$\dfrac{kVA \times 1000}{E}$	$\dfrac{kVA \times 1000}{1.732 \times E}$
Power in kilowatts	$\dfrac{I \times E}{1000}$	$\dfrac{I \times E \times PF}{1000}$	$\dfrac{I \times E \times 1.732 \times PF}{1000}$
Power in kVA		$\dfrac{I \times E}{1000}$	$\dfrac{I \times E \times 1.732}{1000}$
Horsepower (output)	$\dfrac{I \times E \times \% \text{ efficiency}}{746}$	$\dfrac{I \times E \times \% \text{ efficiency} \times PF}{746}$	$\dfrac{I \times E \times 1.732 \times \% \text{ efficiency} \times PF}{746}$

phase power is needed. All three phase wires are represented in all branch circuits and feeders so that three-phase power is available. It would be possible to make electrical connection to two of the three conductors, and 240-V single-phase power would be delivered in that connection. However, normally that should not be done, because that would unbalance the load on the three phase conductors; whereas three-phase load applies load equally on all phase conductors. The power utility company would probably require that all load be three-phase in nature.

19-9 ELECTRIC SERVICE: 120/240-V/THREE-PHASE/FOUR-WIRE

Another method of delivering electric power into a building is by means of the dual-voltage, 60-Hz service that may be described as 120/240-V/three-phase/four-wire. This service would be installed when a building is new and is capable of meeting the building needs for 120-V single-phase power,

240-V single-phase power, and 240-V three-phase power.

As shown in fig. 19-14, the service equipment is basically the same as in fig. 19-8, the three-phase three-wire service. The weatherhead, CT cabinet, main switch, MDP, and metering are basically the same. However, the transformer, the service conductors, and the grounding are quite different, and the service is much more versatile.

The service transformer secondary windings are 240-V windings and are again connected in the familiar delta connection, so that between any two of the three phase wires (A, B, and C) we measure 240 V. One big difference in the transformer is that one of the three windings has a center tap connection, and a fourth wire, the neutral wire (N), is connected thereto. The N wire is grounded so that it is essentially at earth potential at all points, and runs throughout the building along with the phase wires.

Since the N wire connects to the center tap of a 240-V secondary winding, it divides that winding

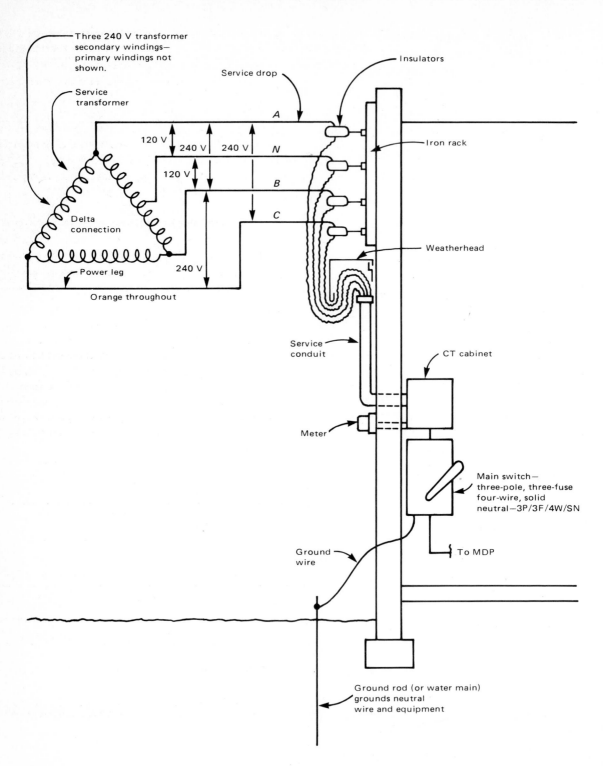

Three 240 V transformer secondary windings— primary windings not shown.

Service transformer

Service drop

Insulators

Iron rack

A

120 V

240 V 240 V

N

120 V

B

C

Delta connection

Power leg

240 V

Orange throughout

Weatherhead

Service conduit

CT cabinet

Meter

Main switch— three-pole, three-fuse four-wire, solid neutral—3P/3F/4W/SN

To MDP

Ground wire

Ground rod (or water main) grounds neutral wire and equipment into two 120-V windings connected in series, and the voltage between the N wire and either phase A wire or phase B wire is 120 V. Therefore, any circuit in the building that is connected to phase A and the neutral N or to phase B and N receives 120-V single-phase power, used extensively, of course, for lighting load, receptacle load, small motors, heaters, and so on.

However, 120-V single-phase load must never be connected to N and phase C. The voltage between N and C is neither 120 nor 240 V; it is an odd voltage not suitable for this type of load. Because of this difference, phase C conductor is called the "power leg" or the "high leg" and must be colored orange at all points of accessibility for ready recognizability. The power leg C, then, is only usable for a 240-V three-phase power load, or a 240-V single-phase load—never for a 120-V load.

Since most modern buildings have a very great amount of 120-V load in them, none of which may be connected to phase C, it is evident that phases A and B will carry much more load than C. In other words, the load in the building cannot be properly balanced on all phase wires. This unbalancing effect carries right on through the service transformer into the electric utility's high-voltage distribution system and unbalances it.

The utility company engineers will not like this, because now they must attempt to balance their distribution system load, so as to fully utilize all wiring, by balancing one power customer against other customers. If one customer has light load on phase C, they must arrange for other customers to use phases A and B for their power legs. This is a very difficult task, and the utility engineers may, as a general policy, refuse to supply power to

this type of service. However, in many areas it is available.

In this type of service, as well as the two services previously discussed, it is possible to utilize "primary metering" instead of the secondary metering shown in all three service diagrams. With primary metering, the power flowing in the primary windings of the service transformer is metered.

With primary metering, since the voltage in the primary is very high, 2400, 4160, 12,470 or 13,800 V, the amperage as a result is very low. In fact, the amperage is so low that current transformers are often not needed for a very large building. When primary metering is used, the electric utility provides and installs the entire metering setup.

If the high-voltage distribution lines are run overhead on utility poles, the utility will extend a conduit with high-voltage conductors down a pole, near the building, to a level that permits easy meter reading. The meter is usually enclosed in a weatherproof, steel enclosure with a small glass window near the meter dial. The enclosure is locked and sealed to prevent tampering by unauthorized people.

If the utility's power distribution wiring is run underground, the service transformer will probably be a padmount unit, as shown in fig. 19-9, mounted on a concrete pad on grade. In this case, the metering equipment will probably be enclosed in the transformer enclosure.

It is obvious that primary metering increases the electric utility's installation costs; for this reason, utility companies are often reluctant to provide primary metering. However, it is usually of

---

Figure 19-14 120/240V/three-phase/four-wire service. Notes: (1) Primary metering may be available—secondary metering shown. (2) Single-phase load must not be connected to the power leg so load is unbalanced. (3) Ratio of voltages is 2 to 1 (240/120 = 2). (4) Three-phase load is connected to phase wires *A, B,* and *C* but not *N*. (5) Single-phase, 240-V load may be connected to any two phase wires (A, B, or C). (6) $P_{kW}(3\phi) = (1.732 \times 240V \times I \times PF)/1000$. (7) $P_{kVA}(3\phi) = (1.732 \times 240V \times I)/1000$. (8) $P_W(1\phi) = 120V \times I \times PF$ or $240V \times I \times PF$. (9) $P_{VA}(1\phi) = 120V \times I$ or $240V \times I$. (10) Electric utility company may refuse this service. (11) Ratio of voltages is 2 to 1 (240V/120V = 2).

appreciable benefit to the building owner, and often primary metering can be provided if the owner agrees to have an installation surcharge added to his or her monthly power bills until the extra cost to the utility is recovered.

In any event, a main disconnecting switch or C/B will be required in the building, and in this service, this would need to be a three-pole, three-fuse, four-wire, solid neutral (3P/3F/4W/SN) switch or a 3P/4W/SN circuit breaker. At this location a grounding electrode or buried water line would be used for grounding the neutral wire N of the system, and for grounding the electrical equipment.

Figure 19-14 shows four formulas for electrical power in kW, kVA, watts, and VA—both three-phase and single-phase. Notice that the three-phase formulas include the 1.732 factor, and the single-phase formulas do not. Notice also that the formulas for watts and kW include a power factor term, whereas those for kVA and VA do not.

19-10   ELECTRIC SERVICE: 120/208-V/ THREE-PHASE/FOUR-WIRE

The 120/208-V/three-phase/four-wire service has in the last 40 years become the most popular of all services for buildings other than the very large and the very small. For the vast midrange sizes of buildings, this service has become the national standard. It is a dual-voltage three-phase service which when extended throughout a building can meet the needs for 120-V single-phase power, 208-V single-phase power, and 208-V three-phase power.

This same service is also very popular in large rambling buildings when the voltages are 277/ 480 V instead of 120/208 V. Notice in each case the ratio of the two voltages available is 1.732:1. Remember that in the service of art. 19-9 and fig. 19-14, the ratio of voltages is 2:1.

$$\frac{208 \text{ V}}{120 \text{ V}} = 1.732 \qquad \frac{480 \text{ V}}{277 \text{ V}} = 1.732 \qquad \frac{240 \text{ V}}{120 \text{ V}} = 2$$

It may be seen in fig. 19-15 that the secondary windings of the service transformer are much different from those in fig. 19-14. Here each secondary winding is designed for 120 V instead of the 240 V of fig. 19-14. Also, the secondary windings here are connected not in the delta configuration, but in a different configuration called a *star* or *wye*.

In fig. 19-14 one of the 240-V windings consists, in effect, of two 120-V windings connected in series. Here the two 120-V values may be added to get 240 V total, because the two smaller windings are in phase with each other. The voltage that one 120-V winding generates is received and further increased by the other 120-V winding. However, in fig. 19-15 this is not the case.

It is true that any two of the three windings seem to be connected in series, but it must be remembered that the power surges of these three windings are not in phase. When the voltage of one winding is maximum and positive, the voltage of the other two windings will be negative, but less than maximum. This may be seen in the three-phase, time-voltage curves presented in chap. 18. In fig. 19-15, the net result is that the voltage in the service conductors is 208 V between any two of the three conductors as shown.

Since the neutral wire N is connected at the center point so that there is only a 120-V winding between N and any phase wire, the voltage difference between N and phase A or B or C must be 120 V. Therefore, in the building wiring, any 120-V single-phase load may be connected to N and to any of the three phase wires A, B, and C. Also 208-V single-phase circuits may be connected to any two of the three phase wires, and any three-phase circuit must be connected to all three of the phase wires.

Unlike the delta system of fig. 19-14, all single-phase load may be equally loaded onto the three main phase conductors, and the load will be balanced. Maximum use will be made of the three phase conductors of the building, as well as the electric utility's high-voltage conductors outside the building. This is a big advantage, and this service will find great application in future buildings.

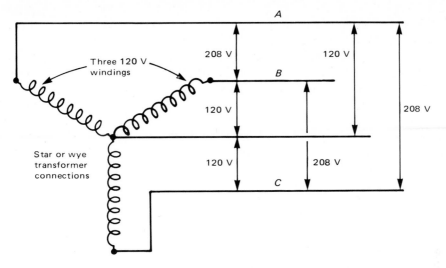

Figure 19-15 120/108V/three-phase/four-wire service. Service equipment same as that in fig. 19-14. Notes: (1) 120V, single-phase load can be balanced. (2) Primary metering often available. (3) National standard. (4) May also be 277/480V three-phase, four-wire. (5) Ratio of voltages is 1.732 to 1: 208V/120V = 1.732 or 480V/277V = 1.732. (6) $P_{kW} = (1.732 \times 208 \times I \times PF)/1000$, three-phase. (7) $P_{kVA} = (1.732 \times 208 \times I)/1000$, three-phase. (8) $P_W = 120V \times I \times PF$ or $P_W = 208V \times I \times PF$, single-phase; (9) $P_{VA} = 120V \times I$ or $P_{VA} = 208V \times I$, single-phase. (10) Main switch is 3P/3F/4W/SN.

If by varying the number of turns of wire in the secondary windings, the three windings of fig. 19-15 are made to deliver 277 V instead of 120 V, we obtain a power service which is also gaining in popularity. Now, the voltage between phase wires is 480 V instead of 208 V. The ratio of the voltages is 1.732, as before.

It is very advantageous to distribute electric power over a large building at 480 V instead of at 208 or 240 V. Remember, as the voltage is increased for a given amount of power, the amperage is decreased in proportion; distribution wiring can be much smaller and/or line losses reduced. Electric motor manufacturers regularly make motors designed for 480-V power, and because they carry less amperage, these motors are lighter and less troublesome.

There are many good reasons for distributing power at 480 V, but with the wye-type transformer connections, we are then left with a lower

distribution voltage of 277 V. This may seem to be an odd, useless value, but the construction industry is rapidly adapting to it. The National Electric Code (NEC) has for many years approved the use of voltages up to 300 V in industrial and commercial lighting systems where:

1 Qualified personnel in general will perform all maintenance.

2 Branch lighting circuits supply only the ballasts for permanently installed electric-discharge lamp fixtures (such as fluorescents, etc.).

3 Lamp holders of the screw-shell type (such as for incandescent lamps) are to be mounted not less than 8 ft above the floor.

4 Integral lighting switches, if used, are not readily accessible.

We find many 277-V lighting systems in use today; so the 277/480-V system of power distribution is very practical. However, all buildings still

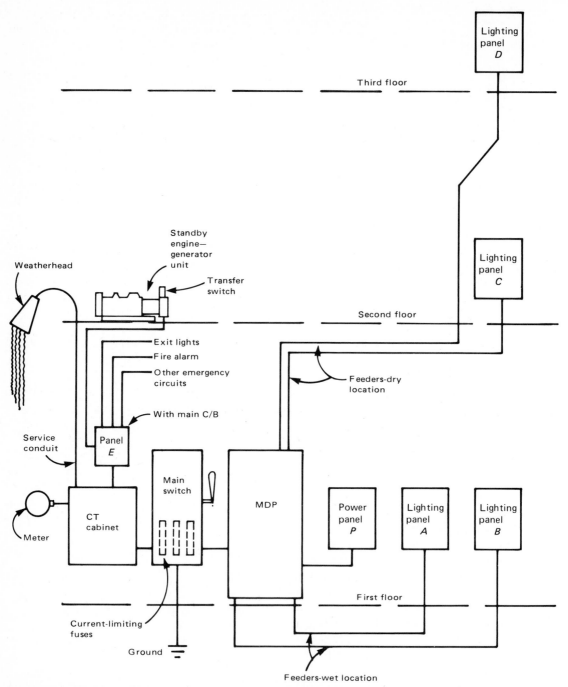

Figure 19-16 Distribution diagram (or one-line diagram or riser diagram).

have an extensive use for 120-V single-phase power, and this must be made available. For this purpose, step-down distribution transformers must be provided. Accordingly, at strategic points throughout a large, rambling, or tall building such transformers, reducing the voltage from 480 V to 120 V, are provided.

Of course, such transformers and appurtenances represent an appreciable cost; however, their cost is more than repaid by the resultant reduction in distribution system costs and reduced operating costs. These transformers are very often small enough to permit mounting high on the wall in an equipment room or other such space where their appearance is acceptable. They are usually dry-type units rather than the oil-filled type, and their maintenance requirements are minimal (see fig. 19-10).

In fig. 19-15, four formulas are listed for calculating three-phase and single-phase power in kW, kVA, watts, and VA. These formulas are identical to those shown in fig. 19-14. It should also be noted that in fig. 19-15 the service equipment, such as the weatherhead, main switch, and MDP, has been omitted since it would be identical to the equipment shown in fig. 19-14.

19-11   DISTRIBUTION DIAGRAMS

The *distribution diagram* appears as part of the electrical layout in the electrical drawings which are a part of the plans that are drawn for a new building. This diagram, which is also sometimes called *one-line diagram* or *riser diagram,* is drawn to give, at a glance, an overall view of the power distribution system in the entire building; however, no branch circuits are shown.

In fig. 19-16, the diagram is divided vertically to show the distribution equipment on each floor of the building. It could also be divided horizontally if the building were to be divided into sections or wings. Figure 19-16 shows that power enters the system at a weather-head, indicating an overhead service drop, and that is passes through the service conduit to a CT cabinet where sec-

ondary metering takes place. From there the power flows through a main switch, an MDP, and through the feeders to four lighting panels and one power panel.

Further, fig. 19-16 shows that part of the entering power flows to an *emergency panel* E, which has its own main C/B for disconnecting purposes, and which supplies emergency circuits such as exit light circuits, fire alarm circuits, and other emergency circuits. It may be seen that if a serious fault occurs in the main electrical system and the fuses in the main switch burn out and interrupt the power, power will still flow to panel E, and the emergency circuits will remain active.

Figure 19-16 also shows that the building will have an emergency standby engine-generator unit with an automatic transfer switch. This unit would be equipped with a diesel or gas engine driving a generator such as is shown in fig. 19-17. If a general power failure occurred because of a storm, the engine-generator would automatically start, and the automatic transfer switch would connect its power to emergency panel E.

Whether or not a standby generator is needed depends on the use of the building. A hospital has great need for one or more units to supply power to its surgical suite, an elevator or two, corridor lighting, refrigeration for food and drugs, and some cooking facilities. A busy metropolitan airport needs standby power for its control tower and runway lighting. A radio or television station needs standby power to transmit messages during times of catastrophe. If such is required and planned for a building, the distribution diagram will quickly show this fact, as does fig. 19-16.

19-12   BUILDING LOAD CONNECTIONS AND CURRENT FLOW PATTERNS

Almost all building wiring circuits are parallel circuits; that is, electrical loads are connected in parallel, as shown in chap. 18, and very few series circuits are used. Figure 19-18 shows a parallel circuit in a 120/240-V/single-phase/three-wire system. Included in the diagram are the service trans-

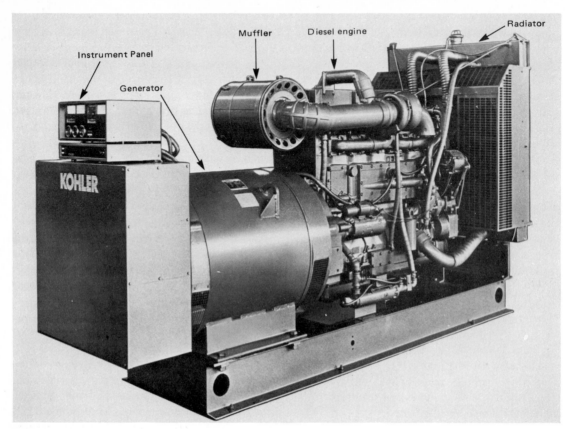

Figure 19-17 Standby engine-generator unit. (Photo courtesy of Kohler Co.)

former secondary windings, the two-pole/two-fuse/three-wire solid neutral main switch, and the three conductors, consisting of phase wires A and B and the neutral wire N.

Figure 19-18a shows a balanced load connected to the wiring. Of these loads, two are 80-A 120-V single-phase loads with one load connected between phase A and the neutral, and the other connected between phase B and N. The remaining load is a 20-A 240-V single-phase load; and to receive proper power it is connected between phase wires A and B.

When the switch of fig. 19-18a is closed and the system is energized and the three loads are turned on, current will flow at one instant in the direction shown by the arrows. One half cycle, or 1/120 sec later (with 60-Hz power), every one of the arrows

would reverse itself and point in the opposite direction. As shown in part a, current is flowing left to right in phase B, downward in the center load (80 A), upward in the left-hand load (80 A), upward in the 20-A load, and right to left in phase A. Also notice that in a short length of N, an 80-A current is flowing, but N is mostly without current. The current in N is zero because the loads are balanced on phases A and B; each phase wire carries 100 A.

Now, if one of the 80-A loads is switched off, the load will no longer be balanced, and N will carry 80 A of current. In fig. 19-18a, with the loads shown, 80 A is the most current that could flow in N, so N may be sized for 80 A while phase wires A and B must be sized for 100 A. Notice that the 240-V load causes no unbalance because it

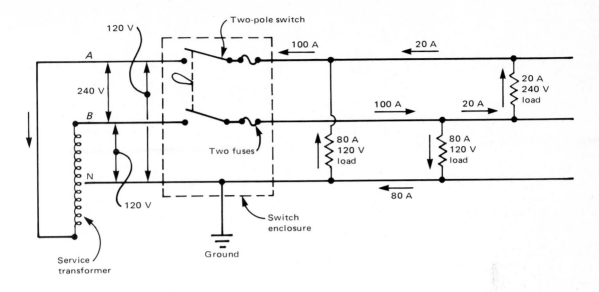

(a) Balanced load

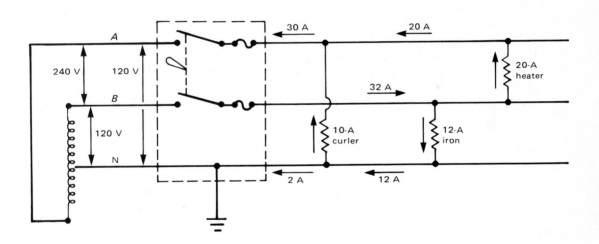

(b) Unbalanced load

Figure 19-18 Current flow patterns in a 120/240V single-phase three-wire system.

equally utilizes both A and B; only the 120-V loads can cause unbalance.

Of course, in a real building situation there would be dozens or hundreds or thousands of units of load, and it is the responsibility of the

electrician to determine that equal amounts of 120-V load are connected to phase wires A and B. No one can say, of course, how those 120-V loads will actually be used. It is possible, although unlikely, that all of the many units of load connected to phase A will be switched off, while those on phase B remain switched on. This would represent the condition of maximum unbalance, and as mentioned, the resulting current in N determines its size.

The NEC stipulates that N shall be sized on maximum unbalanced current up to 200 A, but only 70% added for any excess over 200. For example, if maximum unbalanced current is calculated to be 300 A, N would be sized for 270 A [200 + (300 − 200)0.7 = 270 A] .

Figure 19-18*b* shows the same system as in part *a*, except the loads are revised and are now unequal. The 20-A load is a 240-V electric heater; for example, the 12-A load might be a 120-V electric iron, while the 10-A load might be a 120-V electric hair curler. When all loads are switched on, the directions and magnitudes of the currents are, for an instant, as shown. For most of its length the neutral N carries 2 A, and the most it could ever carry would be 12 A, when the hair curler is switched off or unplugged from its receptacle.

In fig. 19-18*a*, it might seem at first glance that the total power of the system, based on the loads shown, is calculated using 180 A (80 + 80 + 20) for current *I*. This is wrong, though, because the 80-A loads together cause only 80 A to flow in phase wires A and B at a voltage of 240 V. The power of the system is

$$P = (80 \text{ A} + 20 \text{ A})240 \text{ V} = 24{,}000 \text{ W or } 24 \text{ kW}$$

or

$$P = [(80 \text{ A} + 80 \text{ A})120 \text{ V}] + (20 \text{ A} \times 240 \text{ V})$$
$$= 24{,}000 \text{ W}$$

The power of a circuit or an entire system of this type is usually calculated by multiplying the current capacity of the phase wires in amps by the higher of the two voltages (in this case, 240 V) and by the power factor:

$$P = EI(\text{PF})$$

In the circuit of fig. 19-18, all load is purely resistive in nature, and the power factor is 1.0 and was not included in the foregoing calculations. Also since this circuit is single-phase only, the 1.732 multiplier was not used.

Figure 19-19 also gives more information concerning the method of making load connections to a three-phase four-wire system. In this figure the three service transformer secondary windings are shown in the wye-type connection with the grounded neutral conductor N connected at the midpoint similar to the connections in fig. 19-15. In fig. 19-19 the loads that are connected are shown to be a 120-V single-phase lighting circuit, a 120-V single-phase receptacle (wall plug) circuit, a 120-V single-phase motor, a 208-V three-phase motor, and a 208-V single-phase electric heater.

Notice that to obtain 120-V single-phase power from this system, connection must be made from N to one of the phase wires A, B, or C. The lighting circuit, the receptacle circuit, and the single-phase motor all make this type of connection. Also to obtain 208-V three-phase power for the three-phase motor, connection must be made to all three of the phase wires, but not to N. The outer frame of this motor would usually be grounded to the equipment grounding system of the building (which is not shown), but no connection is made to the neutral wire N.

Notice further that to obtain 208-V single-phase power, as for the electric heater, connection must be made to any two of the three phase wires. Again, no connection is made to N, although the metal frame of the heater would usually be grounded. Figure 19-19, however, is only schematic and connection is not actually made *directly* to phase wires A, B, and C and to N. Connections are made *indirectly* through circuit breakers or fuses located in lighting panels and power panels. Branch circuit conductors are connected directly to the C/Bs in the panels, which connect directly to the heavy copper bus bars in the panels, which connect directly to the feeder conductors which represent the phase wires and the neutral.

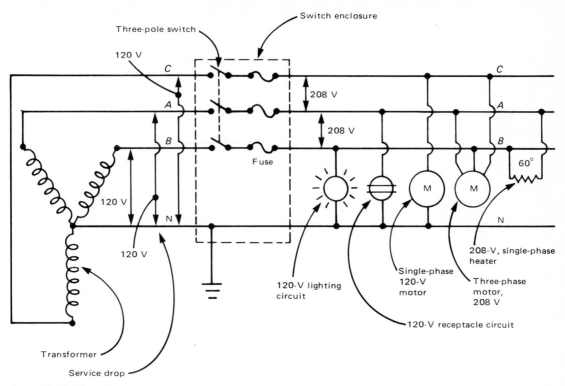

Figure 19-19 Typical load connections in a 120/208V three-phase, four-wire system.

Figure 19-20a shows how typical wiring connections would be made to an MDP in this type of electrical system—a 120/208-V/three-phase/four-wire system. While the panel shown is an MDP, the branch circuit connections are exactly the same as they would be in a lighting panel or a power panel. Also shown are connections of the main power conductors coming from the main disconnect switch or C/B, as well as the connections of a feeder which carries power out to a lighting panel.

In the center of the panel are the three bus bars (shown in fig. 19-3) to which the main service conductors (phase wires A, B, and C), running from the main switch, connect. Also with the main switch located nearby, no main breaker is needed for this panel, so it is an MLO (main lugs only) type. Lined up on each side of the bus bars are the individual C/Bs which make electrical contact with the bus bars. As noted, these are one-, two-, and

three-pole C/Bs as required by the load connected to, and supplied by, this MDP.

At the top of the panel is a neutral bus bar to which the main neutral (N) service conductor is connected, and to which the N conductor of any branch circuit or feeder also connects. All the bus bars and C/Bs are contained within a heavy metal enclosure, part of which, as shown, is the tub or backbox. Except in residential construction, connections to such a panel are made with metal conduit using a conduit connector consisting of a bushing and a locknut. After the conduit installation is complete, the electrician pulls all conductors in place through the conduits.

Figure 19-20a shows how the wiring connections are made in the panel, and this should give reinforcement to the discussions herein with reference to figs. 19-18 and 19-19. Figure 19-20a shows that any 120-V single-phase circuit connects

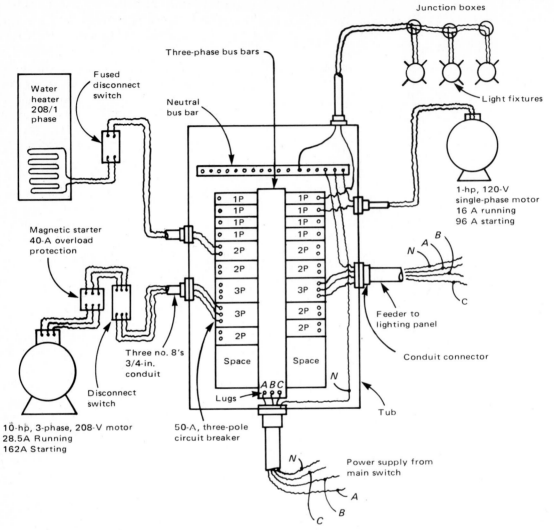

Figure 19-20A Power and distribution (MDP) panel—120/208V, 3-phase, four wire.

to a one-pole C/B and to the N bus. See the schematic representation of the lighting circuit and the 1-hp motor for examples of this.

Also, any 208-V single-phase circuit, such as the water heater shown, connects to a two-pole C/B in the panel. In this way, the water heater is connected to two of the three hot bus bars (which are connected in turn to the three main service phase conductors A, B, and C). This connection is equivalent to the connection of the 208-V single-phase heater of fig. 19-19. The C/Bs, then, make the connection, for the circuit involved, to the phase conductors A, B, and C.

Also as shown, any three-phase load, such as the 10-hp motor of fig. 19-20a, makes connections to a three-pole C/B which also makes electrical

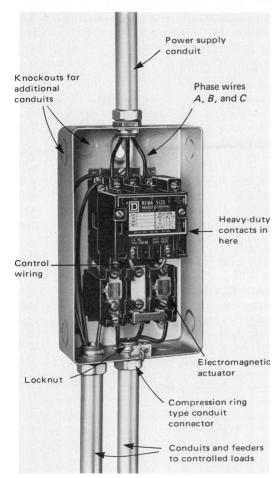

Figure 19-20B Magnetic contactor or starter. (Courtesy of Square D. Co.)

connection to the phase conductors A, B, and C. See the comparable wiring connections of the three-phase motor of fig. 19-19.

The lighting panel feeder that connects to the righthand side of this panel is a 120/208-V/three-phase/four-wire feeder; therefore, it must connect to a three-pole C/B and to the N bus bar in this MDP. Included in the connections for the 10-hp three-phase motor and the water heater are the usual auxiliary control devices required. For the motor is shown a disconnect switch and a magnetic starter; the three-pole C/B in the panel gives overcurrent protection to the wiring of the circuit,

and the magnetic starter has overload, overcurrent devices which protect the motor. The water heater is controlled and protected by a fused disconnect switch.

The magnetic starter shown in fig. 19-20A to control the 10-hp motor is an electromagnetic device by means of which power can be quickly and positively applied to the motor terminals. A similar device is shown in fig. 19-20B; this is a magnetic contactor which can be used like a magnetic starter to apply electric power to some type of heavy-duty electric load under the control of a time clock or thermostat or other automatic control device. A magnetic starter for motor control is identical to a contactor except that the starter has overload devices by means of which power can be disconnected if current flow to the motor or other controlled device becomes excessive.

19-13 FAULT CURRENT PROTECTION

One important fact which every building designer or construction professional, especially architects and contractors, must fully understand is that in any electrical distribution system, the possibility of a serious fault with drastic consequences exists. Serious faults have occurred in the past and will again; there has been loss of life and building destruction in these occurrences. A serious fault, as contemplated here, might be a *dead short* of two very heavy conductors fairly close to the service entrance location in a building. If two heavy conductors with opposite polarity lose their insulation and then come into intimate contact, a terrible flash of power can result, with great damage to the surroundings.

The magnitude of the release of power and the resulting damage will depend upon the *fault current potential,* or capability, of the electrical system that supplies power to the point where the fault occurs. In the downtown area of a large city, or in a heavy industrial area where electric power consumption is tremendously high, the fault current potential will also be tremendously high—perhaps 100,000 to 200,000 A. With this amount of energy pouring into a low-resistance fault and being released there, the resulting damage can be catastrophic.

On the other hand, if the location of the fault is in a building located remotely from heavily concentrated areas, in a suburban or rural location, the fault current potential may be very low. Only the local electric utility can answer the question as to the magnitude of the fault current potential, but the main point here is that the question must be asked. The design professional must remember on every building project to check to see that the question has been asked and that the building electrical system design is based on the answer.

If there is proper capability of interrupting whatever fault current could flow, nothing will happen if such a fault should occur—except that a fuse will burn or a circuit breaker will trip, and the building will be without power. But no life will be lost, and no building damage will result.

Fault current protection can take the form of current-limiting fuses or current-limiting C/Bs. Of course, all fuses and C/Bs are current-limiting devices, but these are very special fuses and C/Bs and can give very special protection. Most fuses and C/Bs are designed to act comparatively slowly and to permit an overload to exist momentarily before opening a circuit. In fig. 19-20a, for example, the 10-hp three-phase 208-V motor is shown to have a normal full-load running current of 28.5 A; however, while it is starting and coming up to normal running speed, its starting current will be 162 A.

This motor's overload protector in its magnetic starter and the three-pole C/B in the MDP must permit the starting current to flow for an instant while the motor comes up to speed, but if the motor cannot start or starts too slowly for some reason (indicating some type of equipment failure) the motor starter or the C/B must trip to protect the motor and its circuit.

Current limiting fuses and C/Bs, however, are designed to act quickly, and to open the circuit (that supplies power to the fault) in a half-cycle or less when the high value of the fault current occurs. With 60-Hz power, a half-cycle is 1/120

sec; if the excessive fault current is interrupted in 1/120 sec or less, usually no damage will result. In fig. 19-16, current-limiting fuses are shown in the enclosure of the main switch. Very often current-limiting fuses and C/Bs will be installed in a separate enclosure and located as close to the source of incoming power as possible.

Recognition must also be given to the fact that even with adequate fault current protection, some of the other current-carrying devices near the service entrance location, such as the C/Bs in the MDP, will probably carry a very heavy current for an instant. The manufacturer of C/Bs will give his C/Bs two ratings, such as 225 A and 10,000 A, for example. The 225-A rating is its normal interrupting rating, and the 10,000 A rating indicates that for a very brief instant the C/B can carry 10,000 A without damage; that is its fault current rating. Some manufacturers also report that their current-limiting C/Bs can interrupt a heavy fault current in 0.01 sec or less.

19-14   CONDUCTORS: TYPES

For building wiring systems, electrical conductors are in general limited to the use of copper and aluminum. There are other good conductor materials, such as silver, tungsten, iron, and nickel, but silver is too expensive, even though it is a slightly better conductor than copper, and the other materials have resistances that are too high. All copper and aluminum conductors are round, except, of course, bus bars, which are wide and flat. In art. 18-5, the subject of calculating the cross-sectional area of a round conductor in cmil (circular mils) was discussed and perhaps should be reviewed now.

There is one strange characteristic of solid conductors which affects the construction of building wire and cables. This characteristic is called the *skin effect*. When ac current flows in a conductor, the current is not evenly distributed throughout the cross-sectional area of the conductor. The current density is greater in the outer portions of the conductor than in the center core. The center core material is thus not fully utilized. In a very fine wire this effect is negligible, and we find that smaller conductors, of size No. 8 and smaller, are solid copper or aluminum. However, in sizes larger than No. 8, conductors are usually made of a large number of small wires stranded and twisted together to make one larger cable. In this way the entire conductor is made to carry current effectively.

Figure 19-21 shows in tabular form some of the physical properties of copper and aluminum conductors. Column 1 is headed "Conductor size— AWG or MCM." AWG stands for *American wire gage*, a standard widely accepted schedule of conductor sizes or wire of any type, whether steel fence wire or copper electrical wire. In fig. 19-21, No. 18 wire is the smallest listed, although the AWG schedule includes wires as small as No. 40 having only 9.89 cmil cross-sectional (CS) area. The largest in the AWG schedule is No. 0000, often written 4/0 and pronounced "quad-naught." Conductor sizes larger than 4/0 are not AWG sizes and are expressed in accordance with their circular mil CS area in thousands and written in units of MCM (thousands of circular mils). For example,

Figure 19-21 Properties of copper and aluminum conductors. (Data from 1978 National Electric Code, with permission.)

Conductor size, AWG or MCM (1)	CS‡ area, cmils (2)	Diameter, in.* (3)	Diameter, mm (4)	AC resistance† copper (5)	AC resistance† aluminum (6)
18	1,620	0.0403	1.02	6.51	10.70
16	2,580	0.0508	1.29	4.10	6.72
14	4,110	0.0641	1.63	2.57	4.22
12	6,530	0.0808	2.05	1.62	2.66
10	10,380	0.1019	2.59	1.018	1.67
8	16,510	0.1285	3.26	0.640	1.05
6	26,240	0.184	4.67	0.410	0.674
4	41,740	0.232	5.89	0.259	0.424
3	52,620	0.260	6.60	0.205	0.336
2	66,360	0.292	7.42	0.164	0.266
1	83,690	0.332	8.43	0.130	0.211
0	105,600	0.373	9.47	0.104	0.168
00	133,100	0.418	10.62	0.0835	0.133
000	167,800	0.470	11.94	0.0668	0.106
0000	211,600	0.528	13.41	0.0534	0.0844
250	250,000	0.575	14.61	0.0457	0.0722
300	300,000	0.630	16.00	0.0385	0.060
350	350,000	0.681	17.30	0.0333	0.052
400	400,000	0.728	18.49	0.0297	0.046
500	500,000	0.813	20.65	0.0244	0.0375
600	600,000	0.893	22.68	0.0209	0.0319
700	700,000	0.964	24.48	0.0183	0.0281
750	750,000	0.998	25.35	0.0174	0.0264
800	800,000	1.031	26.18	0.0165	0.0252
900	900,000	1.093	27.76	0.015	0.0231
1000	1,000,000	1.152	29.26	0.014	0.0211

*Conductors No. 6 and larger are stranded.
†Alternating current resistance in ohms per 1000 ft at 77°F (25°C) in metallic conduit.
‡CS area is cross-sectional area.

Figure 19-22 Allowable ampacities of insulated conductors rated 0 to 2000 V, 60 to 90°C. Not more than three conductors in raceway or cable or earth (directly buried), based on ambient temperature of 30°C (86°F). (Excerpted from tthe National Electric Code, with permission.)

Temperature rating of conductor, see Table 310-13 in the NEC

	60°C (140°F)	75°C (167°F)	85°C (185°F)	90°C (194°F)	60°C (140°F)	75°C (167°F)	85°C (185°F)	90°C (194°F)	
Size	Types	Types	Types	Types	Types	Types	Types	Types	Size
AWG MCM	†RUW, †T †TW, †UF	†FEPW, †RH, †RHW, †RUH, †THW, †THWN, †XHHW, †USE, †ZW	V, MI	TA, TBS, SA, AVB, SIS, †FEP, †FEPB, †RHH †THHN, †XHHW*	†RUW, †T, †TW, †UF	†RH, †RHW, †RUH, †THW †THWN, †XHHW, †USE	V, MI	TA, TBS, SA, AVB, SIS, †RHH, †THHN, †XHHW*	AWG MCM
	Copper				Aluminum or copper-clad aluminum				
18	—	—	—	14	—	—	—	—	—
16	—	—	18	18	—	—	—	—	—
14	20†	20†	25	25†	—	—	—	—	—
12	25†	25†	30	30†	20†	20†	25	25†	12
10	30†	35†	40	40†	25†	30†	30	35†	10
8	40	50	55	55	30	40	40	45	8
6	55	65	70	75	40	50	55	60	6
4	70	85	95	95	55	65	75	75	4
3	85	100	110	110	65	75	85	85	3
2	95	115	125	130	75	90	100	100	2
1	110	130	145	150	85	100	110	115	1
0	125	150	165	170	100	120	130	135	0
00	145	175	190	195	115	135	145	150	00
000	165	200	215	225	130	155	170	175	000
0000	195	230	250	260	150	180	195	205	0000
250	215	255	275	290	170	205	220	230	250
300	240	285	310	320	190	230	250	255	300
350	260	310	340	350	210	250	270	280	350
400	280	335	365	380	225	270	295	305	400
500	320	380	415	430	260	310	335	350	500
600	355	420	460	475	285	340	370	385	600
700	385	460	500	520	310	375	405	420	700
750	400	475	515	535	320	385	420	435	750
800	410	490	535	555	330	395	430	450	800
900	435	520	565	585	355	425	465	480	900
1000	455	545	590	615	375	445	485	500	1000
1250	495	590	640	665	405	485	525	545	1250
1500	520	625	680	705	435	520	565	585	1500
1750	545	650	705	735	455	545	595	615	1750
2000	560	665	725	750	470	560	610	630	2000

Correction factors

Ambient temperature °C	For ambient temperatures over 30°C, multiply the ampacities shown above by the appropriate correction factor to determine the maximum allowable load current							Ambient temperature °F
31-40	0.82	0.88	0.90	0.91	0.82	0.88	0.90	0.91	86-104
41-45	0.71	0.82	0.85	0.87	0.71	0.82	0.85	0.87	105-113
46-50	0.58	0.75	0.80	0.82	0.58	0.75	0.80	0.82	114-122
51-60	—	0.58	0.67	0.71	—	0.58	0.67	0.71	123-141
61-70	—	0.35	0.52	0.58	—	0.35	0.52	0.58	142-158
71-80	—	—	0.30	0.41	—	—	0.30	0.41	159-176

†The load current rating and the overcurrent protection for conductor types marked with an obelisk (†) shall not exceed 15 amperes for 14 AWG, 20 amperes for 12 AWG, and 30 amperes for 10 AWG copper, or 15 amperes for 12 AWG and 25 amperes for 10 AWG aluminum and copper-clad aluminum.

*For dry locations only. See 75°C column for wet locations.

Figure 19-22 *(Cont.)*
More Than 3 Conductors in a Raceway or Cable.

Number of conductors	Percent of values in Tables 310-16 and 310-18
4–6	80
7–24	70
25–42	60
43 and above	50

Where the number of conductors in a raceway or cable exceed three, the maximum allowable load current of each conductor shall be reduced as shown in the table.

Where single conductors or multiconductor cables are stacked or bundled without maintaining spacing and are not installed in raceways, the maximum allowable load current of each conductor shall be reduced as shown in the above table.

the next size larger than a 4/0 is a 250-MCM conductor having a CS area of 250,000 cmil.

In this text we will not be dealing with the subject of dc electricity, so that the electrical resistances shown in columns 5 and 6 of fig. 19-21 are ac resistances in ohms per thousand feet at 77°F. Usually, these resistances are listed as dc resistance and a correction must be made for ac practices. In international practices, col. 4, which expresses wire sizes in terms of diameter in millimeters, will be useful. Column 3 gives wire diameter in inches, and it should be realized that for a given CS area, a stranded wire will be slightly larger than a solid wire. Diameters shown for wire sizes No. 6 and larger are for stranded wire, and for No. 8 and smaller are solid. This is the way that building wire is usually manufactured.

In building wiring systems, No. 14 AWG is the smallest size approved for use by the NEC. The smaller No. 16 and 18 sizes will be used by manufacturers of building electrical products, such as lighting fixtures, but the electrician's work will always involve No. 14 and larger sizes.

Figure 19-22 shows a table setting forth the allowable "ampacities" of insulated copper, aluminum, or copper-clad aluminum conductors when they are enclosed in a raceway (conduit, duct, etc.), or made up into a "cable" or buried directly in the earth. The word "ampacity," of course, means "amps capacity" or current-carrying capacity. The word "cable" represents a manufactured product, usually UL (Underwriters Laboratory) approved, consisting of two or more insulated conductors assembled together and enclosed in some type of metallic or nonmetallic jacketing.

Notice that the table in fig. 19-22 shows ampacities when there are not more than three conductors assembled together. Well, we routinely run conduits with more than three conductors in them; in this case, we must make a correction to the allowable ampacities and reduce them in accordance with the correction table included in fig. 19-22. For example, if there are four, five, or six conductors in a conduit, the ampacities of fig. 19-22 must be reduced to 80% of the tabulated values. A No. 3 type TW conductor, in that case, cannot carry 85 A of load as the table shows, but only 80% of 85 A or 68 A.

Notice also in fig. 19-22 that there are many different "types" of conductors listed. In all types of conductors, the copper or aluminum of which the conductor is made does not change. It is the insulation on the exterior of the conductor that dictates the "type" designation. Figure 19-23 lists the various types of conductors, their letter designators (type RH, for example), their maximum operating temperatures, and the type of application

Figure **19-23** Conductor application and insulations. (Excerpted from the National Electric Code, with permission.)

Trade name	Type letter	Maximum operating temperature	Application provisions	Insulation	AWG or MCM	Thickness of insulation (mils)	Outer covering
Heat-resistant rubber	RH	75°C 167°F	Dry locations	Heat-resistant rubber	14-12† / 10 / 8-2 / 1-4/0 / 213-500 / 501-1000 / 1001-2000	30 / 45 / 60 / 80 / 95 / 110 / 125	Moisture-resistant, flame-retardant, non-metallic covering*
Heat-resistant rubber	RHH	90°C 194°F	Dry locations				
Moisture and heat-resistant rubber	RHW	75°C 167°F	Dry and wet locations. For over 2000-V insulation shall be ozone-resistant	Moisture and heat-resistant rubber	14-10 / 8-2 / 1-4/0 / 213-500 / 501-1000 / 1001-2000	45 / 60 / 80 / 95 / 110 / 125	
Heat-resistant latex rubber	RUH	75°C 167°F	Dry locations	90% un-milled, grainless rubber	14-10 / 8-2	18 / 25	
Moisture-resistant latex rubber	RUW	60°C 140°F	Dry and wet locations	90% un-milled, grainless rubber	14-10 / 8-2	18 / 25	
Thermoplastic	T	60°C 140°F	Dry locations	Flame-retardant, thermoplastic compound	14-10 / 8 / 6-2 / 1-4/0 / 213-500 / 501-1000 / 1001-2000	30 / 45 / 60 / 80 / 95 / 110 / 125	None

Trade Name	Type Letter	Max. Operating Temperature	Application Provisions	Insulation	AWG or kcmil	Thickness of Insulation (mils)	Outer Covering
Moisture-resistant thermoplastic	TW	60°C 140°F	Dry and wet locations	Flame-retardant, moisture-resistant thermoplastic	14-10 8 6-2 1-4/0 213-500 501-1000 1001-2000	30 45 60 80 95 110 125	None
Heat-resistant thermoplastic	THHN	90°C 194°F	Dry locations	Flame-retardant, heat-resistant thermoplastic	14-12 10 8-6 4-2 1-4/0 250-500 501-1000	15 20 30 40 50 60 70	Nylon jacket or equivalent
Moisture- and heat-resistant thermoplastic	THW	75°C 167°F 90°C 194°F	Dry and wet locations Special applications within electric discharge lighting equipment. Limited to 1000 open-circuit volts or less.	Flame-retardant, moisture- and heat-resistant thermoplastic	14-10 8-2 1-4/0 213-500 501-1000 1001-2000	45 60 80 95 110 125	None
Moisture- and heat-resistant thermoplastic	THWN	75°C 167°F	Dry and wet locations	Flame-retardant, moisture- and heat-resistant thermoplastic	14-12 10 8-6 4-2 1-4/0 250-500 501-1000	15 20 30 40 50 60 70	Nylon jacket or equivalent
Moisture- and heat-resistant cross-linked synthetic polymer	XHHW	90°C 194°F 75°C 167°F	Dry locations Wet locations	Flame-retardant cross-linked synthetic polymer	14-10 8-2 1-4/0 213-500 501-1000 1001-2000	30 45 55 65 80 95	None

*Outer covering shall not be required over rubber insulations which have been specifically approved for the purpose.

†For 14-12 sizes RHH shall be 45 mils thickness in insulation.

For insulated aluminum and copper-clad aluminum conductors, the minimum size shall be no. 12.

for which they have been designed. Of the many types shown, for general building wiring, the thermoplastics are by far the most frequently used; these include types T, TW, THW, THWN, and THHN.

19-15 RACEWAYS

The NEC makes very frequent reference to *raceways,* and we should therefore give consideration to the definition of the term in the NEC. It states that a raceway is "a channel designed expressly for holding wires, cables, or bus bars, with additional functions as permitted in this code. Raceways may be of metal or insulating material, and the term includes rigid metal conduit, rigid nonmetallic conduit, intermediate metal conduit, liquidtight flexible metal conduit, flexible metallic tubing, flexible metal conduit, electrical metallic tubing, underfloor raceways, cellular concrete floor raceways, cellular metal floor raceways, surface raceways, wireways and busways.

Of the raceways noted above, most are round conduits; however, there are some, such as surface raceways, wireways, cable ducts, and busways, which are square or rectangular with one or more sides removable for access. Some raceways use passageways that are built into the building for structural or mechanical reasons, and that only incidentally provide space for installation and protection of electrical conductors. Cellular concrete or cellular metal floor structures do present these raceways and are frequently utilized. Sometimes a circulating air duct in an HVAC system may be used as a wireway in special circumstances; a special high-temperature Teflon-insulated UL listed and classified conductor (made for example by Hitemp Wires, Inc., Hauppage, NY 11787) is now available for this service.

In addition to the protection that raceways give to conductors against physical, chemical, and other attack, metallic raceways are routinely used to provide grounding continuity for all the electrical equipment of the system. All equipment connecting to or enclosing electrical conductors must be maintained at earth potential (voltage) so that no one can suffer an electrical shock by coming into contact with it.

When nonmetallic conduits or parts of a building are used as raceways, grounding must be accomplished by an extra conductor enclosed in the raceway and connected to all equipment for grounding purposes.

Sometimes a metallic raceway can become involved electrically with the conductors that it encloses. It will be remembered that a conductor carrying an alternating current has a moving electric field that surrounds it. The lines of force of this field move over the metallic raceway as though it were another conductor, and a voltage and a current can be induced in the raceway. If only one such conductor were in the raceway, this definitely would happen; a voltage drop would result, and there would be some heating of the raceway.

If the raceway contained two conductors, each carrying the same amount of current in opposite directions (the usual case), there is no resulting current in, or heating of, the conduit. With current equal and in opposite directions, the opposing currents induced in the raceway cancel each other. Even with more than two conductors, as long as the total current in each direction is equal, the heating effect is zero. Of course, if the raceway is made of nonmetallic material and is a poor conductor, current and heating in the conduit is not a problem.

19-16 NONFLEXIBLE CONDUITS

Round, pipelike raceways are called conduits which are used much more than any other type of raceway in nonresidential buildings. Conduits have historically been made of metal, mostly steel and some aluminum, but plastic conduits are gaining rapidly in popularity.

However, steel conduits still predominate, and these are available in three different weights and with four different finishes. According to weight, steel conduits are classified as:

1 Rigid steel conduit, type RS
2 Intermediate metallic conduit, type IMC
3 Electrical metallic tube (or thin wall), type EMT

Steel conduits are given the following types of finishes:

1 Hot-dip galvanized
2 Enameled with a tough corrosion-resistant enamel
3 Plastic coated
4. Sheradized (zinc coated)

Until recently, the rigid, galvanized steel conduit was predominant, especially in larger sizes. However, with the formal adoption of the 1978 NEC on May 19, 1977, the IMC conduit was approved for use under all conditions and occupancies. Since then, the use of rigid conduit has fallen until now some electrical warehouses do not even stock it. The intermediate-weight IMC has supplanted the rigid, except in 5- and 6-in. sizes—the IMC being generally available in sizes only up to 4 in. and approved by the NEC only in sizes up to and including 4 in.

Electrical metallic tubing (EMT), often called thin-wall conduit, does have a thinner, lighter wall and is too thin to permit threading. Connections are made with EMT connectors that secure the EMT with compression rings or set screws (see fig. 19-20b). EMT is approved for use under certain conditions in sizes up to 4 in. EMT is, on average, about 43% lighter than IMC, while IMC is about 29% lighter in weight than rigid conduit.

EMT may be buried in concrete and built into masonry walls if proper connecting fittings are used. However, it must not be used where it is subject to continuous moisture attack. Many building designers will not accept EMT in masonry walls and concrete floors even though the NEC permits those uses.

Aluminum conduits have enjoyed much popularity through the years, but the use of aluminum in recent years is decreasing. Its major advantages of course, are its lightness and, in many situations, its comparative incorrodibility. It is 15% lighter in weight than thin wall (EMT) and is about 50% lighter than IMC. Aluminum is basically more expensive than steel, but often the labor savings in the use of aluminum conduit will more than offset the extra material cost. Aluminum is nonmagnetic and nonsparking, and where conduit must be painted, aluminum will take and hold a coat of paint much better than will galvanized steel. Often, aluminum conduit may be left unpainted in a situation where steel conduit would require painting. Aluminum conduit should probably not be buried in the earth, because of the chemical attack of some earths on aluminum. Threaded joints in aluminum conduits are very difficult to disconnect whenever that becomes necessary.

Nonflexible conduits are often made of nonmetallic materials such as plastics, asphalt-impregnated bituminous fiber, and cement-asbestos. Of these, the plastic conduits are finding much greater use than the others; these are mostly PVC (polyvinyl chloride) conduits, although high-density polyethylene and other plastics are also used. These rigid, nonmetallic conduits are finding very extensive use for underground application, and in time should entirely supplant metal conduits here.

For above ground use, plastic conduits have achieved very limited use because of their susceptibility to physical damage and failure under fire or high-temperature conditions. As mentioned, the conduit cannot be used as a grounding conductor for equipment grounding and a separate grounding wire must be added.

The NEC is very specific as to the number of conductors that may be included in a conduit of a given size. Installations of nonflexible conduit are usually completed with all fittings, pull boxes, junction boxes, panelboards, and so on, in place before conductors are installed. Conductors are pulled into and through the conduits by various techniques. A tough spring-steel wire called a *fish-tape* is pushed through a conduit; the conductors that are to be installed are connected to the fish-tape. As the fish-tape is withdrawn, by hand or by machine, the conductors are pulled into

Figure 19-24 Maximum number of conductors in trade sizes of conduit or tubing. (Excerpted from the National Electric Code, with permission.)

Type letters	Conductor size AWG, MCM	Conduit trade size, in.												
		1/2	3/4	1	1 1/4	1 1/2	2	2 1/2	3	3 1/2	4	4 1/2	5	6
TW, T, RUH, RUW, XHHW (14 through 8)	14	9	15	25	44	60	99	142	171					
	12	7	12	19	35	47	78	111	131	176				
	10	5	9	15	26	36	60	85						
	8	2	4	7	12	17	28	40	62	84	108			
RHW and RHH (without outer covering), THW	14	6	10	16	29	40	65	93	143	192				
	12	4	8	13	24	32	53	76	117	157				
	10	4	6	11	19	26	43	61	95	127	163			
	8	1	3	5	10	13	22	32	49	66	85	106	133	
TW, T, THW, RUH (6 through 2), RUW (6 through 2)	6	1	2	4	7	10	16	23	36	48	62	78	97	141
	4	1	1	3	5	7	12	17	27	36	47	58	73	106
	3	1	1	2	4	6	10	15	23	31	40	50	63	91
	2	1	1	2	4	5	9	13	20	27	34	43	54	78
	1		1	1	3	4	6	9	14	19	25	31	39	57
FEPB (6 through 2), RHW and RHH (without outer covering)	0		1	1	2	3	5	8	12	16	21	27	33	49
	00		1	1	1	3	5	7	10	14	18	23	29	41
	000		1	1	1	2	4	6	9	12	15	19	24	35
	0000			1	1	1	3	5	7	10	13	16	20	29
	250			1	1	1	2	4	6	8	10	13	16	23
	300			1	1	1	2	3	5	7	9	11	14	20
	350					1	1	3	4	6	8	10	12	18
	400					1	1	2	4	5	7	9	11	16
	500					1	1	1	3	4	6	7	9	14
	600						1	1	3	4	5	6	7	11
	700						1	1	2	3	4	5	7	10
	750						1	1	2	3	4	5	6	9
THWN,	14	13	24	39	69	94	154	164	160	106	136			
	12	10	18	29	51	70	114							
	10	6	11	18	32	44	73							
	8	3	5	9	16	22	36							
THHN, FEP (14 through 2), FEPB (14 through 8), PFA (14 through 4/0), PFAH (14 through 4/0), Z (14 through 4/0)	6	1	4	6	11	15	26	37	57	76	98	125	154	
	4	1	2	4	7	9	16	22	35	47	60	75	94	137
	3	1	1	3	6	8	13	19	29	39	51	64	80	116
	2	1	1	3	5	7	11	16	25	33	43	54	67	97
	1		1	1	3	5	8	12	18	25	32	40	50	72

XHHW (4 through 500MCM)	0		1	1	3	4	7	10	15	21	27	33	42	61
	00		1	1	2	3	6	8	13	17	22	28	35	51
	000		1	1	1	3	5	7	11	14	18	23	29	42
	0000		1	1	1	2	4	6	9	12	15	19	24	35
	250			1	1	1	3	4	7	10	12	16	20	28
	300			1	1	1	3	4	6	8	11	13	17	24
	350			1	1	1	2	3	5	7	9	12	15	21
	400				1	1	1	3	5	6	8	10	13	19
	500				1	1	1	2	4	5	7	9	11	16
	600				1	1	1	1	3	4	5	7	9	13
	700					1	1	1	3	4	5	6	8	11
	750					1	1	1	2	3	4	6	7	11
XHHW	6	1	3	5	9	13	21	30	47	63	81	102	128	185
	600				1	1	1	1	3	4	5	7	9	13
	700					1	1	1	3	4	5	6	7	11
	750					1	1	1	2	3	4	6	7	10
	14	3	6	10	18	25	41	58	90	121	155			
RHW,	12	3	5	9	15	21	35	50	77	103	132			
	10	2	4	7	13	18	29	41	64	86	110	138		
	8	1	2	4	7	9	16	22	35	47	60	75	94	137
	6	1	1	2	5	6	11	15	24	32	41	51	64	93
RHH (with outer covering)	4	1	1	1	3	5	8	12	18	24	31	39	50	72
	3	1	1	1	3	4	7	10	16	22	28	35	44	63
	2		1	1	3	4	6	9	14	19	24	31	38	56
	1		1	1	1	3	5	7	11	14	18	23	29	42
	0		1	1	1	2	4	6	9	12	16	20	25	37
	00			1	1	1	3	5	8	11	14	18	22	32
	000			1	1	1	3	4	7	9	12	15	19	28
	0000			1	1	1	2	4	6	8	10	13	16	24
	250				1	1	1	3	5	6	8	11	13	19
	300				1	1	1	3	4	5	7	9	11	17
	350				1	1	1	2	4	5	6	8	10	15
	400				1	1	1	1	3	4	6	7	9	14
	500				1	1	1	1	3	4	5	6	8	11
	600					1	1	1	2	3	4	5	6	9
	700					1	1	1	1	3	3	4	6	8
	750						1	1	1	3	3	4	5	8

place in the conduit with loose ends left hanging at each end for wiring connections.

To make this pulling action possible, a conduit may not be too tightly filled with conductors. Obviously, the inner surfaces of conduits and all fittings must be smooth and free of burrs, in order that the conductor insulation is not damaged during pulling. It should be obvious that careful reaming of all conduit ends during installation is mandatory.

With regard to the amount of free space left in a conduit when its conductors are in place, the NEC specifies that of the cross-sectional area of a conduit, the conductors may occupy the following percentages (for all conductors except lead-covered conductors): one conductor, 53%; two conductors, 31%; three conductors and over, 40%.

Figure 19-24 translates the preceding percentages into the specific number of conductors of various types that may be included in standard sizes of commercially available conduits when the conductors are all of the same size. For example, four No. 2 THW conductors would require a 1 1/4-

in. conduit to contain them with the conduit not more than 40% full.

With lead-covered conductors, the permissible percentage of fill is slightly different. This fact shows up in the table of fig. 19-25, which shows the area in square inches that conductors of all types may occupy in various circumstances. With this information and the cross-sectional area of various sizes and types of conductors given in fig. 19-26, it is a simple matter to select a conduit size when the number and sizes of conductors is known.

Example 19-1 A feeder containing three No. 4/0 THWN conductors and one No. 2/0 THWN neutral conductor requires a 2-in. conduit, as follows: three No. 4/0 THWNs have 0.3278 in^2 area $\times$ 3 = 0.9834 in^2 from column 7 of fig. 19-26, one No. 2/0 THWN area = 0.2265 in^2 (also from column 7, fig. 19-26). 0.9834 in^2 + 0.2265 in^2 = 1.2099 in^2 total conductor area. Figure 19-25, fifth column, shows that with more than two conductors, not lead-covered, a 2-in. conduit can contain conductors having a total area of as much as

Figure 19-25 Dimensions and percent area of conduit and of tubing. Areas of conduit or tubing for the combinations of wires permitted in Table 1, Chapter 9, NEC. (Excerpted from the National Electric Code, with permission.)

			Area, in.^{2}							
			Not lead covered			Lead covered				
Trade size	Internal diameter in.	Total 100%	Two con-ductors 31%	Over Two con-ductors 40%	One con-ductor 53%	One con-ductor 55%	Two con-ductors 30%	Three con-ductors 40%	Four con-ductors 38%	Over four con-ductors 35%
1/2	.622	.30	.09	.12	.16	.17	.09	.12	.11	.11
3/4	.824	.53	.16	.21	.28	.29	.16	.21	.20	.19
1	1.049	.86	.27	.34	.46	.47	.26	.34	.33	.30
1 1/4	1.380	1.50	.47	.60	.80	.83	.45	.60	.57	.53
1 1/2	1.610	2.04	.63	.82	1.08	1.12	.61	.82	.78	.71
2	2.067	3.36	1.04	1.34	1.78	1.85	1.01	1.34	1.28	1.18
2 1/2	2.469	4.79	1.48	1.92	2.54	2.63	1.44	1.92	1.82	1.68
3	3.068	7.38	2.29	2.95	3.91	4.06	2.21	2.95	2.80	2.58
3 1/2	3.548	9.90	3.07	3.96	5.25	5.44	2.97	3.96	3.76	3.47
4	4.026	12.72	3.94	5.09	6.74	7.00	3.82	5.09	4.83	4.45
4 1/2	4.506	15.94	4.94	6.38	8.45	8.77	4.78	6.38	6.06	5.56
5	5.047	20.00	6.20	8.00	10.60	11.00	6.00	8.00	7.60	7.00
6	6.065	28.89	8.96	11.56	15.31	15.89	8.67	11.56	10.98	10.11

Figure 19-26 Dimensions of rubber-covered and thermoplastic-covered conductors. (Excerpted from the National Electric Code with permission.)

Size AWG MCM (1)	Types RFH-2, RH, RHH[d], RHW[d], SF-2 — Approx. diameter, in. (2)	Approx. area, in.² (3)	Types TF, T, THW[c], TW, RUH[b], RUW[b] — Approx. diameter, in. (4)	Approx. area, in.² (5)	Types TFN, THHN, THWN — Approx. diameter, in. (6)	Approx. area, in.² (7)	Types FEP, FEPB, FEPW, TFE, PF, PFA, PFAH, PGF, PTF, Z, ZF, ZFF[e] — Approx. diameter, in. (8)	Approx. area, in.² (9)	Type XHHW, ZW[f] — Approx. diameter, in. (10)	Approx. area, in.² (11)	Types KF-1, KF-2, KFF-1, KFF-2 — Approx. diameter, in. (12)	Approx. area, in.² (13)
18	0.146	0.0167	0.106	0.0088	0.089	0.0064	0.081	0.0052	...	...	0.065	0.0033
16	0.158	0.0196	0.118	0.0109	0.100	0.0079	0.092	0.0066	...	...	0.070	0.0038
14 (30 mils)	0.171	0.0230	0.131	0.0135								
14 (45 mils)	0.204[a]	0.0327[a]	0.162[c]	0.0206[c]								
14			0.148	0.0172	0.105	0.0087	0.105	0.0087	0.129	0.0131	0.083	0.0054
12 (30 mils)	0.188	0.0278	0.179[c]	0.0251[c]								
12 (45 mils)	0.221[a]	0.0384[a]	0.168	0.0224								
12			0.199[c]	0.0311[c]	0.122	0.0117	0.121	0.0115	0.146	0.0167	0.102	0.0082
10	0.242	0.0460	0.245	0.0471	0.153	0.0184	0.142	0.0159	0.166	0.0216	0.124	0.0121
8	0.328	0.0854	0.276[c]	0.0598[c]	0.218	0.0373	0.206, 0.186	0.0333, 0.0272	0.241	0.0456		
6	0.397	0.1238	0.323	0.0819	0.257	0.0519	0.244, 0.302	0.0467, 0.0716	0.282	0.0625		
4	0.452	0.1605	0.372	0.1087	0.328	0.0845	0.292, 0.350	0.0669, 0.0962	0.328	0.0845		
3	0.481	0.1817	0.401	0.1263	0.356	0.0995	0.320, 0.378	0.0803, 0.1122	0.356	0.0995		
2	0.513	0.2067	0.433	0.1473	0.388	0.1182	0.352, 0.410	0.0973, 0.1316	0.388	0.1182		
1	0.588	0.2715	0.508	0.2027	0.450	0.1590	0.420	0.1385	0.450	0.1590		
0	0.629	0.3107	0.549	0.2367	0.491	0.1893	0.462	0.1676	0.491	0.1893		
00	0.675	0.3578	0.595	0.2781	0.537	0.2265	0.498	0.1974	0.537	0.2265		
000	0.727	0.4151	0.647	0.3288	0.588	0.2715	0.560	0.2463	0.588	0.2715		
0000	0.785	0.4840	0.705	0.3904	0.646	0.3278	0.618	0.2999	0.646	0.3278		

Figure 19-26 *(Cont.)*

Size AWG MCM	Types RFH-2; RH, RHH,[d] RHW,[d] SF-2 Approximate diameter, in.	Approximate area, in.^{2}	Types TF, T, THW,[c] TW, RUH,[b] RUW[b] Approximate diameter, in.	Approximate area, in.^{2}	Types TFN, THHN, THWN Approximate diameter, in.	Approximate area, in.^{2}	Types[e] FEP, FEPB, FEPW, TFE, PF, PFA, PFAH, PGF, PTF, Z, ZF, ZFF Approximate diameter, in.	Approximate area, in.^{2}	Type XHHW, ZW[f] Approximate diameter, in.	Approximate area, in.^{2}
(1)	(2)	(3)	(4)	(5)	(6)	(7)	(8)	(9)	(10)	(11)
250	0.868	0.5917	0.788	0.4877	0.716	0.4026	...	...	0.716	0.4026
300	0.933	0.6837	0.843	0.5581	0.771	0.4669	...	...	0.771	0.4669
350	0.985	0.7620	0.895	0.6291	0.822	0.5307	...	...	0.822	0.5307
400	1.032	0.8365	0.942	0.6969	0.869	0.5931	...	...	0.869	0.5931
500	1.119	0.9834	1.029	0.8316	0.955	0.7163	...	...	0.955	0.7163
600	1.233	1 1940	1.143	1.0261	1.058	0.8792	...	...	1.073	0.9043
700	1.304	1 3355	1.214	1.1575	1.129	1.0011	...	...	1.145	1.0297
750	1.339	1.4082	1.249	1.2252	1.163	1.0623	...	...	1.180	1.0936
800	1.372	1 4784	1.282	1.2908	1.196	1.1234	...	...	1.210	1.1499
900	1.435	1 6173	1.345	1.4208	1.259	1.2449	...	...	1.270	1.2668
1000	1.494	1 7531	1.404	1.5482	1.317	1.3623	...	...	1.330	1.3893
1250	1.676	2.2062	1.577	1.9532	...	...	...	...	1.500	1.7672
1500	1.801	2.5475	1.702	2.2748	...	...	...	...	1.620	2.0612
1750	1.916	2.8895	1.817	2.5930	...	...	...	...	1.740	2.3779
2000	2.021	3.2079	1.922	2.9013	...	...	...	...	1.840	2.6590

[a]The dimensions of types RHH and RHW.
[b]No. 14 to no. 2.
[c]Dimensions of THW in sizes 14 to 8. No. 6 THW and larger is the same dimension as T.
[d]Dimensions of RHH and RHW without outer covering are the same as THW No. 18 to No. 10. solid; no. 8 and larger, stranded.
[e]In columns 8 and 9 the values shown for sizes no. 1 thru 0000 are for TFE and Z only. The right-hand values in columns 8 and 9 are for FEPB, Z, ZF, and ZFF only.
[f]No. 14 to no. 2.

624

1.34 in^2. This is more than the 1.2099-in^2 area required, but a 1 1/2-in. conduit, at 0.82 in^2, is much too small. The 2-in. size should be used.

19-17 FLEXIBLE METAL CONDUITS

This type of conduit consists of a galvanized steel or aluminum strip which is spirally wound with interlocking edges to form an enclosure that is light and flexible. It is generally available in sizes of 3/8 to 4 in. diameter, although it is also made by at least one manufacturer in 5/16-in. diameter.

In the trade, this conduit is referred to as *greenfield*. In sizes smaller than 1/2 in. its use is limited by the NEC to lengths of 6 ft or less when part of an approved assembly, or for lighting fixtures, or when the conduit is used as a means of grounding equipment. It finds extensive use for enclosing the leads to electric motors or other vibrating equipment. In recent years, the use of *flex* has been greatly expanded for wiring lighting and receptacle circuits in sizes 1/2 in. and larger. Such wiring systems have generally been called *soft* wiring systems, as contrasted with the conventional *hard* systems of rigid conduits.

Soft wiring systems are light in weight, may be installed very quickly, and usually result in appreciable cost savings over hard wiring systems. One of their greatest benefits results from their great flexibility in use and ease of remodeling. Figure 19-27 shows details of a soft wiring system using flexible greenfield conduit for all branch circuits.

One special form of flexible metal conduit is *liquidtight* conduit, which is essentially the same as greenfield but has an outer, liquid-impervious, nonmetallic covering which is also resistant to sunlight attack, and the attack of many chemicals. It is often known in the electrical trade by the name *sealtight* and is generally available in sizes from 3/8 to 4 in., but the 3/8-in. size is limited, as described above for limitations on greenfield.

Sealtight may be used as a grounding conductor where connecting fittings are the proper type. Its

greatest use seems to be in making flexible connections, of 6 ft or less, to rotating or vibrating equipment exposed to the weather. It may be filled with conductors to the same percentages as set forth in art. 19-16.

19-18 METAL-CLAD AND ARMORED CABLE

As mentioned previously, cables are complete assemblies consisting of conductors and their enclosing raceway manufactured as a unit. The raceway may be metallic or nonmetallic, but in metal-clad and armored cable, the raceway is of spirally wound galvanized steel similar to greenfield. The raceway is wound tightly around the conductors, so that the raceway is 100% full.

Type AC armored cable, sometimes called BX, is made for small loads and light duty and is available with wire sizes as small as No. 14. It is available with two or three conductors, and except for type ACL (lead covered), must have an internal bonding (grounding) wire or strip of copper or aluminum in intimate contact with the armor for its entire length. The conductors must have a surrounding moisture-resistant and fire-retardant fibrous covering.

For heavier duty, type MC metal-clad cable is used. The NEC permits its construction with conductors as small as No. 18 copper or No. 12 aluminum or copper-clad aluminum. However, its greatest use is in larger sizes for heavier loads. Type MC cable may be installed with the outer metal covering serving as an equipment ground.

Both types AC and MC may be installed in wet locations when the metallic covering is impervious to moisture or when a smooth, continuous lead sheath is provided inside the metallic covering. The use of these cables is subject to many NEC limitations, especially type AC cables; and NEC articles 333 and 334 should be reviewed before being planned for use.

One important recent development in the use of metal-clad cables is in *modular* wiring systems.

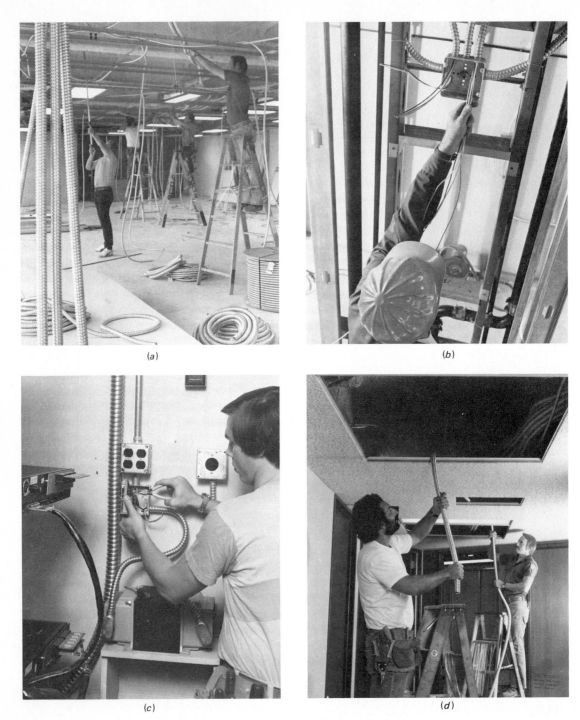

(a)

(b)

(c)

(d)

Figure 19-27 Soft wiring installations. (Courtesy of Alflex Corp., Long Beach, Ca.)

Here most of the branch circuit wiring is run with factory-assembled modules of varying lengths which are complete with metal-clad cables and plug-type connectors at each end. The prefabricated cable sets are ordered by the electrical contractor according to the lighting and power circuits shown on the electrical layout drawings. These cable sets are then merely plugged into matching receptacles during construction.

With these modular systems, job-site labor requirements are greatly reduced, overall cost is appreciably lower, and time during construction is also much less. Of course, maximum flexibility in use is achieved and remodeling in the future is easily accomplished. Figure 19-28 shows details of this construction.

19-19 NONMETALLIC SHEATHED CABLE

This type of cable consists of two or three conductors encased in a nonmetallic jacket of reinforced fabric or plastic that is moisture-resistant and flame-retardant. It is approved by the NEC as types NM and NMC with wire sizes No. 14 through No. 2 in copper and Nos. 12 through 2 in aluminum. It is available with or without a bonding wire for equipment grounding; when included, this bonding wire is either bare or insulated with green insulation.

In general, nonmetallic sheathed cable is approved for use in wiring single- or multifamily dwellings and other structures not exceeding three stories in height above grade. It should not be used for service entrance cable, should not be embedded in concrete, and should not be used in hazardous locations such as commercial garages, theaters, or storage-battery rooms.

This cable is frequently called *Romex,* and a complete complement of fittings, connectors, junction boxes, and switch boxes is made to facilitate its use. Romex is very light and flexible and easy and inexpensive to install. It is easily damaged, however, and its jacket can be easily penetrated by

a carpenter's nail or even the rounded end of a supporting staple that is driven in too far.

19-20 METAL DUCTS

Plain metal ducts, or wireways, are sheet metal troughs with removable covers into which a large number of conductors may be laid in a busy location such as a service entrance location, where a 4 in. × 4 in. or 6 in. × 6 in. duct can replace a large number of conduits and greatly simplify an installation. In this type of application, the duct is exposed and accessible for wiring repair or extension. The sides and bottom of such a duct are supplied with many knockout openings for conduit connections.

19-21 BUS-DUCTS

Other metal ducts, called bus-ducts, are frequently used in manufacturing plants where heavy power demands and frequent revisions must be accommodated. Bus-ducts usually consist of long lengths of three or four heavy copper bus bars enclosed in a heavy sheet steel housing. It is manufactured in sections which are bolted together to form a power supply source hundreds of feet long, mounted overhead, and fully exposed and accessible.

Bus-duct construction is such that at almost any point along its length a fused or nonfused switch may be plugged in to make good electrical contact with the bus bars. Some type of feeder or branch circuit is then extended from this switch. Figure 19-29 shows a small section of such a bus-duct with a disconnect switch mounted in place. For very heavy power distribution, the voltage impressed on the bus bars may be very high to reduce bus-bar size and minimize power loss in the bus bars. Voltages may be as high as 600 V for low-voltage systems, but in industrial applications may be much higher than that.

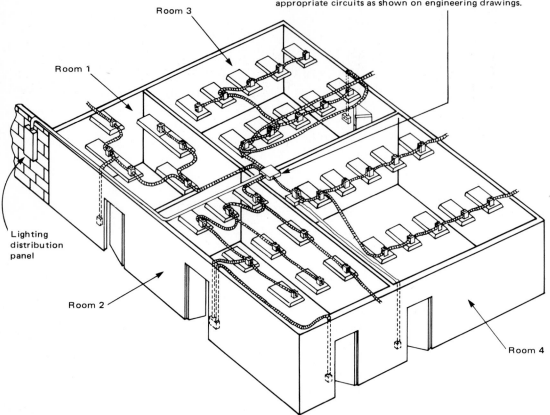

The usual modular wiring system begins at the ceiling distribution box (CDB). The system is "hard-wired" by the electrical contractor to this point. CDB connectors are installed in standard half-inch knockouts and wired to the appropriate circuits as shown on engineering drawings.

Room 3

Room 1

Lighting distribution panel

Room 2

Room 4

Figure 19-28 Modular wiring system details. Room 1: Local switching of six fixtures is accomplished with modular wiring by first plugging an A cable assembly into the CDB and plugging the opposite five-face connector end into a fixture. From this first fixture, B-cable assemblies will be plugged into the remaining five fixtures. From any one of these six fixtures, a plug connection may be made from the switch face to the local switch location. To connect another group of fixtures to this same circuit, an A cable assembly is plugged into the output face in the last fixture in the chain. This breaks the switching circuit for room 1 and allows other local switching functions to be introduced in the circuit. Room 2: Three-way switching of nine fixtures is accomplished with modular wiring by first plugging an A cable assembly into the CDB and plugging the opposite five-face connector end into the fixture. From the first fixture, B-cable assemblies will be plugged into the remaining fixtures. From any of these fixtures, a plug connection may be made from the switch face to one of the three-way switching locations. Three-way switches are interconnected with modular wiring cable set. To connect another group of fixtures to this same circuit, an A cable assembly is plugged into the output face of the last fixture in the chain. This breaks the switching circuit for room 2 and allows other local switching functions to be introduced to the circuit. Room 3: Local switching of alternate fixtures is accomplished with modular wiring by plugging a C cable assembly into the CDB and plugging the opposite five-face connector end into a fixture. From the first fixture, B-cable assemblies will be plugged into the remaining fixtures. A switch cable assembly is installed from the switch face of the C cable assembly to local switch loca-

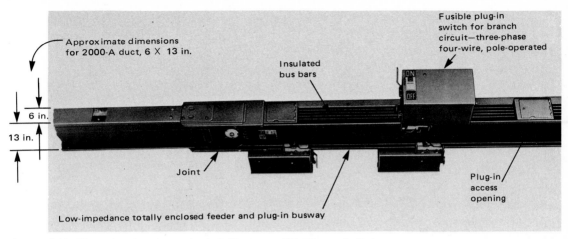

Figure 19-29 Three-phase bus duct and switch (Courtesy of The Square D. Co.)

19-22 UNDERFLOOR RACEWAYS

Underfloor raceways consist of proprietary, manufactured systems of metal ducts laid below concrete floors on concrete forms or compacted fill before concrete is poured. As shown in figs. 19-30 and 19-31, these raceways consist of parallel ducts for electric power and for telephone and signal systems. On top of the ducts, extending up to within 1/4 in. or so of the finished concrete floor, are cylindrical inserts. These inserts are welded to the ducts on a spacing of 24 in. or more.

When an insert is to be used, the thin layer of concrete above the insert is broken away and the dish-shaped cover of the insert is removed. This provides access to the interior of the duct so that wires can be fished through and out the insert for whatever use is necessary.

As also shown in fig. 19-32, other configurations of underfloor wireways are useful; this illustration shows details of a *trench duct* installation. In this photograph, the main trench and all connecting laterals are mounted on a prepoured concrete floor; a concrete topping slab is to be poured flush with the top of the main trench duct. A space remains at each side of the trench duct; this will be filled with concrete later, with a very accurate allowance made for the thickness of the finished floor tile.

tions. Alternate switching is accomplished by selecting either the U or S face of the five-face connector. An A cable assembly is plugged into the X face of the C cable assembly. This breaks the switching circuit for room 3 and allows other local switching functions to be introduced in the circuit. Room 4: Low voltage switching of 10 fixtures is accomplished with modular wiring by plugging an A cable assembly into the CDB and plugging the opposite five-face connector into the low voltage switch-in assembly (LVM). From the output faces of this five-face connector, B-type cable assemblies will be plugged into the fixtures. A low-voltage control pair is run from the LVM to the local switching location. To connect another group of fixtures to this same circuit, an A cable assembly is plugged into the output face of the last fixture in the chain. This breaks the switching circuit for room 4 and allows other switching functions to be introduced in the circuit. (Dual-Lite Inc., Wiring Products Division, Dallas, Texas, 75247.)

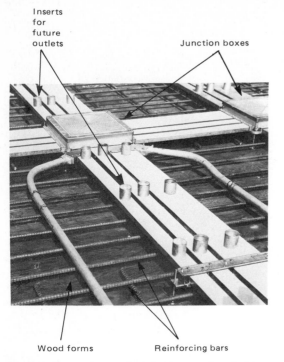

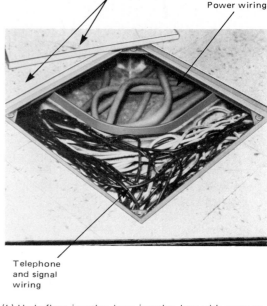

(a) Underfloor raceway: single-level system installed in a flat slab; shown in a three-duct system—two standard ducts and one super, using single-level junction boxes

(b) Underfloor junction box: junction box with cover removed, showing telephone and power lines in their separate compartments

Figure 19-30 Underfloor raceway and junction box. (Courtesy of The Square D. Co.)

19-23 BRANCH CIRCUITS

As previously defined, branch circuits are those parts of the electrical distribution system that extend beyond the last overcurrent protective devices and make final connection to the various items of electrical load. A branch circuit begins at the lighting or power panelboard from which it draws power; it includes its fuse or circuit breaker in the panel, and it includes the conductors and raceways that extend outward to the area of the building that it serves.

The standard sizes of branch circuits have evolved through the years of the last century to meet three requirements:

1 C/Bs or fuses should be *small* enough to be able to give power interruption if an electrical fault (e.g., a short circuit) occurs in a single appliance or its wiring. With a very large C/B, a fixture might suffer a fault and burn itself and the building and never trip the C/B.

2 Branch circuits and their C/Bs and fuses should be *small* enough that the area that they serve will be only a small percent of the total building. Thus a circuit failure will affect only a small part of a building.

3 Branch circuits and their C/Bs and fuses should be *large* enough to make a practical, economical system. Going to the extreme, we might provide a separate circuit for each lighting fixture in a building; this would give wonderful protection

(a) Underfloor raceway: standard power duct and super telephone duct integrated into a flat slab

but would be completely impractical and horribly expensive.

The NEC has standardized on five sizes of branch circuits: 15, 20, 30, 40, and 50 A. It is the size of the C/B or fuse that determines the amperage rating of a branch circuit; other characteristics, such as wire size and lamp holders, must be in proper proportion. Figure 19-33 sets forth in tabular form the requirements of the five standard sizes of branch circuits.

In connection with the use of the ampacity table of fig. 19-22, a few extra provisos should be recognized and understood.

1 The ampere rating of any portable (connected by cord and plug) appliance should not exceed 80% of the branch circuit rating in amps.

2 The ampere rating of any fixed (permanently wired in place) appliance should not exceed 50% of the branch circuit rating in amps, where lighting units or portable appliances or both are also supplied.

3 A 30-, 40-, or 50-A branch circuit may be used to supply fixed lighting circuits in nonresidential buildings but not in residential buildings.

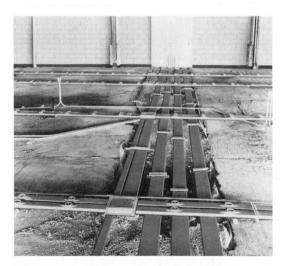

(b) Two-level underfloor raceway: feeder beam area of a two-level underfloor raceway system on grade

Figure 19-31 Underfloor raceway. (Courtesy of The Square D. Co.)

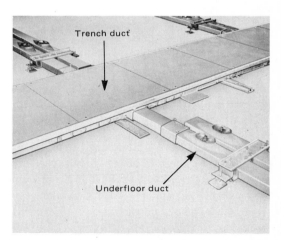

Trench fed underfloor raceway system; the underfloor raceway connects to the side of the trench

Figure 19-32 Trench duct. (Courtesy of The Square D. Co.)

Figure 19-33 Summary of branch-circuit requirements. (Type FEP, FEPB, RUW, SA, T, TW, RH, RUH, RHW, RHH, THHN, THW, THWN, and XHHW conductors in raceway or cable.) (Excerpted from the National Electric Code with permission.)

	Circuit rating, amps				
	15	20	30	40	50
Conductors: (minimum size)					
Circuit wires*	14	12	10	8	6
Taps	14	14	14	12	12
Fixture wires and cords					

	Overcurrent protection, amps				
	15	20	30	40	50
Outlet devices:					
Lampholders permitted	Any type	Any type	Heavy duty	Heavy duty	Heavy duty
Receptacle rating†	15 maximum amperes	15 or 20 A	30 A	40 or 50 A	50 A

	Maximum load, amps				
	15	20	30	40	50
Permissible load	Refer to Sec. 210-23(a) in NEC	Refer to Sec. 210-23(a) in NEC	Refer to Sec. 210-23(b) in NEC	Refer to Sec. 210-23(c) in NEC	Refer to Sec. 210-23(c) in NEC

*These ampacities are for copper conductors where derating is not required. See fig. 19-22.

†For receptacle rating of cord-connected electric discharge lighting fixtures, see Sec. 410-30(c) in NEC.

4 A 30-A branch circuit may be used to supply appliance loads in any type of occupancy, including residential.

5 A 40- or 50-A branch circuit may be used to supply fixed cooking appliances that are fastened in place in any type of occupancy.

For general 120-V lighting and receptacle circuits, the 15- and 20-A branch circuits predominate, and of those two, the 20-A circuit is easily predominant. According to the 80% limitation recommended above in proviso 1, a 15-A circuit should not carry more than 12 A (80% of 15 A = 12 A), a 20-A circuit is limited to 16 A, and so on. Therefore, a 15-A circuit should not carry more load than 1440 VA (15 A × 120 V × 0.8 = 1440 VA), and a 20-A circuit is limited to 1920 VA at 120 V, and so on.

A 30-A circuit at 208 V single-phase should be limited to a load of 4992 VA (30 × 208 × 0.8 = 4992 VA). In like manner a 30-A 208-V three-phase circuit should not carry a load in excess of 8646 VA (30 × 208 × 1.732 × 0.8 = 8646 VA) In actuality, when an electrical designer is assigning the electrical load of a building to the various branch circuits that are planned, he or she should never load a branch circuit up to 80% of its nominal capacity. The original design should plan for branch circuits that are 50 to 60% loaded; accordingly, a 20-A 120-V circuit should not originally carry connected load in excess of 1200 to 1440 VA.

One problem in assigning electrical load to various circuits (this is called "circuiting" the load) is in determining the number of 120-V duplex receptacles (wall plugs) to be carried by a circuit.

Such duplex receptacles will carry an unknown load, and it is suggested that each duplex receptacle be estimated as carrying 180 VA of load. It is further suggested that no more than six duplex receptacles be connected to a 15- or 20-A circuit. Such circuits would then be tabulated on a panelboard load tabulation sheet at 1080 VA per circuit.

Figure 19-33 refers to *taps* and the allowable minimum size of them for various sizes of branch circuits. A tap is merely a branch connection to the main circuit wires. In a 20-A circuit, for example, if the electrician makes connections to the No. 12 circuit wires to extend power to a lighting fixture, those wires (there would be two) running to the fixture should not be smaller than No. 14 wires. Also fig. 19-33, with reference to "permissible load," refers the reader to section 210-23 in the NEC; the recommendations of section 210-23 are essentially as set forth in items 1 through 5 listed above. The reader may wish to further review section 210-23 in the latest NEC for further branch circuit recommendations.

19-24 BRANCH CIRCUIT LAYOUT

Any student or professional person active in construction must be able to read and interpret the electrical drawings that are part of a complete set of plans for a given building. Many drafting conventions are followed in presenting a layout of the electrical load and wiring of a building, and these conventional techniques must be carefully learned by students of construction. However, many electrical draftsmen have their own special techniques of presentation; sometimes these are not self-explanatory and make the reading of such drawings difficult. It would be helpful if we could achieve complete standardization in this respect; that is not likely, but it certainly is not unreasonable to ask all draftsmen to add explanatory notes to their drawings explaining their methods when they are not standardized. Figure 19-34 shows one suggested set of standard drafting symbols.

Figure 19-35 shows a typical layout in a small part of a school building including two classrooms, offices, and other rooms. Here the floor plan of the building has been reproduced with very little detail of the building showing except walls, partitions, and doors. The electrical load, consisting of lighting fixtures and duplex receptacles, has been drawn on this blank plan.

First, all lighting fixtures are drawn in proper location and to proper shape and approximate scale. Four types of fixtures are shown in fig. 19-35—types A, B, C, and D, as noted. Types A and B are 2 ft wide × 4 ft long fluorescent fixtures, and type C is a 1 ft × 4 ft fluorescent fixture. An effort has been made to show them drawn to scale. The type D fixture in the storage room is a round incandescent fixture. Usually, a very complete schedule of fixtures, fully describing each type of fixture, is shown on the plans or in the project specifications.

In fig. 19-35 a capital-letter designator has been shown for each fixture either inside the fixture outline or just beside it. Also shown beside each fixture is an alphanumeric designator, consisting of a letter and a number; for example, No. A12 in classroom 1, which shows the branch circuit to which the load is connected. Designator A12 indicates that the branch circuit is the twelfth circuit supplied by lighting panel A.

Notice that panels A, B, and X are located in an equipment room in the upper left-hand corner of the sheet. All three panelboards are surface mounted on the walls, not recessed into the walls. All connecting conduits are thus exposed and accessible; in an unfinished equipment room this would be satisfactory in appearance.

Type A lighting fixtures are either mounted below the ceiling on stem supports or are surface mounted exposed against the ceiling. In both cases, a junction box is necessary for termination of the conduits that run to each fixture. In office 3, for example, a small circle indicates a 3- or 4-in.-diameter junction box above each pair of type A fixtures.

The conduits that connect to these J (junction) boxes would be installed above the ceiling and are shown as a single, solid line. The type D fixture in the storage room also has a J box. In office 3, the

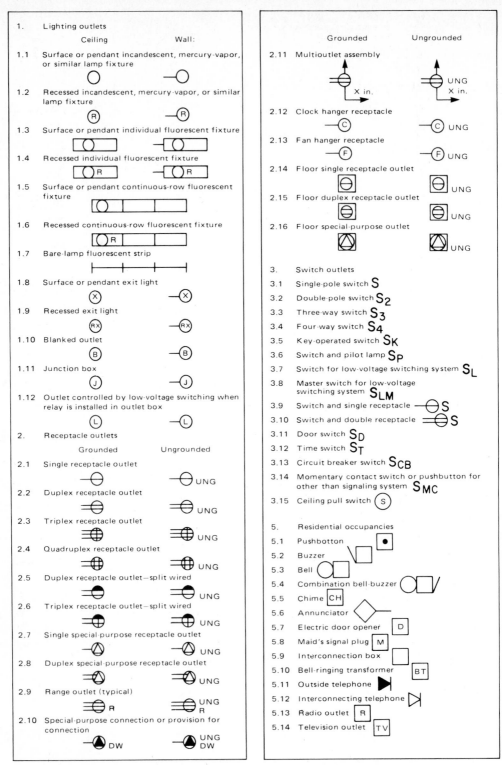

Figure 19-34 Electrical drafting symbols. (Suggested by the American National Standards Institute, Inc.—standard Y32.9–1972 as formulated and published by the Institute of Electrical and Electronics Engineers.)

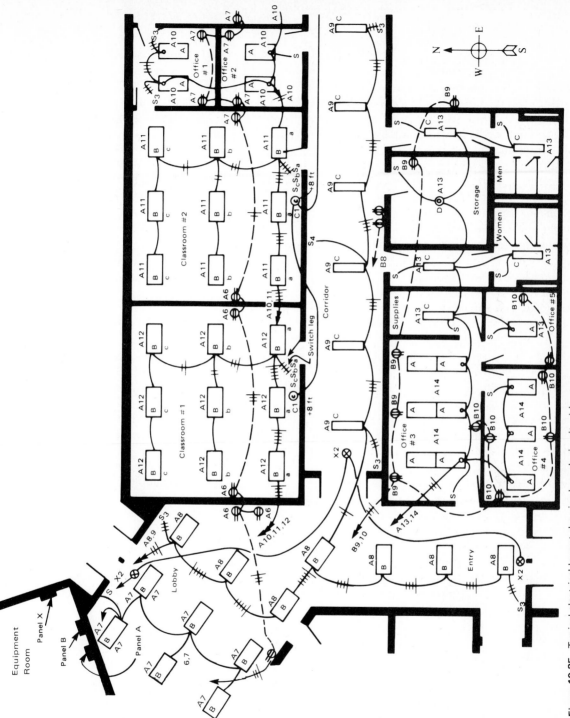

Figure 19-35 Typical electrical layout showing branch circuit wiring.

wiring would extend from the J boxes mentioned down the supporting stems, if used, and into the wireways built into the fixtures. The wiring can extend from the first fixture to the second fixture, of the two in a row, without use of conduit. The conductors extend through the wireways built into the fixture bodies.

Types B and C fixtures are fully recessed into the ceilings, with the bottom surface flush with the ceiling surface and the bodies of the fixtures extending up into the furred space above the ceiling. With this construction, J boxes are not needed for conduit termination; conduits may be connected directly to the bodies of such fixtures, and the J boxes omitted.

Figure 19-35 is based on the use of hard wiring using IMC and EMT conduits; no flexible conduits are shown. However, soft wiring could very well be used and probably would be less expensive. Figures 19-27 and 19-28 show details of soft wiring system installations.

In fig. 19-35, some of the conduit runs are shown with broken lines; these represent conduit runs installed in or below the floor. The solid conduit lines represent conduits that run above the floor—in walls and above the ceilings. In many sets of electrical drawings, the lighting system and its wiring is shown on one floor plan while the power system and its wiring is shown on a separate drawing. In fig. 19-35, both are shown on the same sheet, and this should always be done when the resulting drawing will not be too crowded and cluttered. The power system and its wiring, in general, consists of duplex receptacles (drawn as small circles with two lines through them), motor loads, heater loads, and so on.

Duplex receptacles are usually located 12 to 18 in. above the floor in walls, and their wiring is usually in or below the floor. The conduits that carry power from the panelboards to the locations of branch circuits are called *home run* conduits. They connect to the panelboard tub and to the nearest fixtures or J boxes in the area of the branch circuit. Home run conduits are not limited to carrying one branch circuit only, and they routinely carry two, three, or four branch circuits with appreciable saving in conduit cost.

Home run conduits are not drawn on the plans all the way to the panel; instead, a home run arrow is drawn pointing to the panel it runs to. Omitting the long conduit lines on the drawing saves considerable clutter, especially in the area of the panels. A home run arrow of this type is shown originating at a duplex receptacle in the northwest (see the north arrow of fig. 19-35) corner of office 3. This arrow is labeled "B9,10," indicating that it carries the conductors for circuits B9 and B10 to panel B.

This arrow has two arrowheads, one for each circuit, is dashed to indicate that it is in or below the concrete floor slab, and is drawn with three *hash marks* or *tics* (cross-marks) to indicate that there are three conductors in the conduit. Of these three wires, two must be "hot," one for each circuit, while the third wire is a neutral wire which would serve as the neutral for both circuits. If a home run conduit has three circuits in it, a single neutral wire could serve all three circuits; however, if four circuits are included, two neutral wires should be provided, each neutral serving two circuits. It is usually wise to not carry more than four 20-A circuits in a single home run conduit.

In fig. 19-35 it should be further noted that light switches are indicated by a letter S to show the point where lights in a given room are to be controlled. These are usually located beside the entrance to the room on the lock side of the door—opposite the hinge side. Often, more than one switch will be required so that lights can be switched in rows or in groups. In classroom 1, the nine light fixtures are switched in two rows of three fixtures, and each row has its own switch.

A small lowercase letter has been noted beside each fixture to show which switch is to control which fixture and also to show which fixtures are to be included in a particular group. In classroom 1, the three fixtures adjacent to the outside wall are to be switched together as group c by switch S_c, since a letter "c" appears beside each of those three fixtures. The other two rows are to be controlled by switches S_a and S_b. During daylight hours, if there are windows in the outside wall, the area near these windows may not need artificial light and switch S_c could be turned off.

Often a room such as office 1 has two entrances; it is convenient to have a light switch at each door. This may be done with the use of three-way

switches which will permit the lights to be switched either on or off at each of two locations. A three-way switch is a single-pole double-throw switch, as shown in fig. 19-36. It has a common terminal which may be connected by the switch action to either of two other terminals. The wiring of fig. 19-36 may be easily traced through to prove that

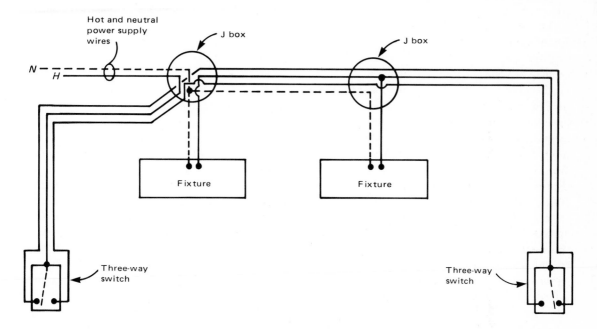

(a) Three-way switches in office 1

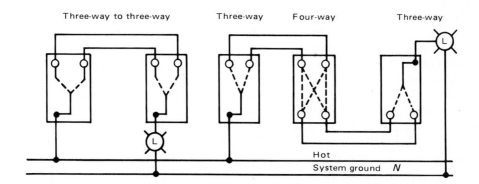

(b) Three-way and four-way switches

Figure 19-36 Three-way and four-way switch diagrams.

whether the lights are on or off depends on the positioning of the two switches.

The lights in a room may also be controlled by more than two switch locations, as shown in the corridor of fig. 19-35. Here the lights are controlled by three switches—two three-way switches and one four-way switch. When more than two switches are involved, the first two switches must always be three-way switches; any other switches beyond the first two must be four-way switches. Therefore, if four switch locations are needed, two of these switches must be three-way, and the remaining two must be four-way switches.

As shown in fig. 19-35, the cross-marks on the conduits are often drawn at two different lengths; the shorter marks indicate hot wires, and the longer marks indicate grounded neutral wires. When a conduit contains only two wires the cross-marks are often omitted, so a conduit without cross-marks has two conductors in it (see fig. 19-35).

In a wiring plan, it is also true that sizes of conduits and the wires in them are carefully noted. However, if a conduit is 1/2 in. in size and the conductors in it are No. 12 AWG, no notation is given; only conduit sizes other than 1/2 in. and wire sizes other than No. 12 are noted. In fig. 19-35 all conduits are 1/2 in. and all wires are No. 12, so no notations of size are necessary.

In the interest of economy, the electrician should always run circuit conductors through conduits that are also needed for other purposes and, in effect, make those conduits perform double or triple duty. An example of this is demonstrated in fig. 19-35. Here branch circuit No. A10 serves offices 1 and 2, and the two home run conductors must extend back to panel A. Those two conductors are not installed in a separate home run conduit which runs back to panel A; they run through other conduits and the wireways of six lighting fixtures which happen to be in their path.

Notice that the home run for circuit A10 begins in the southwest corner of office 2, where it is labeled with one arrowhead and the A10 designation. This circuit continues through three type B

lighting fixtures in classroom 2, and leaves that room at the southwest corner in a conduit which also carries the home run conductors for circuit A11 and which is marked "A10, 11." It has two arrowheads to indicate that it contains the home run conductors for two circuits. These two circuit home runs continue in similar fashion through the fixtures and conduits of classroom 1, where they are joined by the home run conductors of circuit A12. All three circuits then continue in the same 1/2-in. home run conduit back to panel A, and the home run arrow has three arrowheads and is labeled "A10, 11, 12." This home run conduit would be installed above the ceiling.

Figure 19-35 also shows three exit lights designated by a circle with an X in it. These exit lights, of course, are located so as to indicate by their presence the most expeditious path from the building when an emergency of some type, such as a fire, exists. The branch circuit, X2, is an emergency circuit and is connected to panel X, an emergency panel. As mentioned previously, emergency panels are frequently designated panel E as well as panel X. Emergency circuits of all types should not be run in conduits which also contain nonemergency circuits; they should have their own separate conduits.

Sometimes it is a complicated problem to determine the number of conductors that a certain conduit will contain. In classroom 1, for example, the hot wire for circuit A12 runs from panel A to the southeast lighting fixture in classroom 1 and from there to the switch location, where we find switches S_c, S_b, and S_a. The conduit from that southeast fixture to the switch location runs down inside the wall to a "three-gang" switch box—a metal or plastic box which contains the three switches and space for wiring connections to them; this conduit is called the *switch leg* and is so labeled.

The switch leg conduit contains the hot wire of circuit A12, which delivers power to the three light switches. There is also, then, a hot wire from each switch running in the switch leg conduit and on to the three rows of light fixtures in this room.

Therefore, the switch leg conduit contains four hot wires and the drawing shows four cross-marks (hash marks or tics) on this conduit.

Further, notice that in classroom 1, the conduits that run between the fixtures in the south row of fixtures have five cross-marks—four short and one long, indicating four hot wires and one grounded neutral wire. The four hot wires include one for each of the three circuits A10, A11, and A12, plus one hot wire running from light switch S_a to the three fixtures—a total of four hot wires. The one neutral wire is needed for grounding these three circuits.

Both classrooms 1 and 2 have clock outlets located 8 ft above the floor in the south wall. The clock symbol is a circle with a C in it, or it may be a circle with two radial lines to indicate the hands of a clock. These two clock outlets are merely recessed junction boxes with hooks on which electric clocks may be hung after the cord of the clock is plugged into a receptacle in the box. Both clock outlets are on circuit C1, which probably extends back to a master clock located in the main office of this school.

19-25 FEEDERS

As previously defined, feeders are those parts of an electrical distribution system that deliver power from the main distribution panel (MDP), to the various lighting and power panelboards. Feeders consist of conduits or ducts of some type with heavy-duty conductors within. Feeder conductors must be sized so as to be able to deliver as much power to its panelboard as will be demanded by the panelboard while keeping the voltage drop in the feeder to a reasonable minimum.

Feeder conductors must first be selected on the basis of the current that can be expected to flow. Then before conductor sizes can be finalized, the voltage drop V must be checked on the basis of the actual length of the feeder and the voltage drop that can be allowed. If V is too great, the wire size must, of course, be increased.

It is not an easy matter to determine what the maximum demand in amps will be. In most buildings, it is not logical to assume that all connected load will be in fully loaded operation at one time. To reach that condition, every light in the building would need to be lit, every receptacle circuit would be loaded, every electric motor would need to be running at full load, and so on. This condition is approached in some buildings, such as busy office buildings, but 100% load is probably never reached in any building. In many, many buildings, the actual maximum demand is only a small fraction of the connected load.

The NEC attempts to give guidance in the selection of a demand factor which applied to the connected load will give a reasonable approximation of the actual maximum load that will be experienced:

$$\text{Demand factor} = \frac{\text{actual power demand}}{\text{connected load}}$$

Most of the assistance given by the NEC applies to residential buildings, which are not a concern in this text. The designer is largely left to his own judgment to determine the demand factor for large nonresidential buildings.

Figure 19-37 presents a NEC table which gives demand factors for lighting systems in a few nonresidential buildings, and it may be seen that these factors for hospitals, hotels, motels, and warehouses are generally less than 0.5 (50%). Figure 19-37 states that for all buildings not listed in the table a lighting demand factor of 1.0 (100%) should be used. This is probably satisfactory for a busy office building, as mentioned, but in many buildings, such as a university classroom and office building, for example, a factor of 1.0 is not realistic.

To determine what is realistic for a given structure, the designer must carefully analyze all the elements of the anticipated connected load to determine the operational characteristics of each. For example, if a large number of electric heating units are to heat a building, it is highly unlikely that every one of 100 units will be on at maximum capacity at one time. Such units might be sized to

Figure 19-37 Lighting load feeder demand factors. (Excerpted from the National Electric Code with permission.)

Type of occupancy	Portion of lighting load to which demand factor applies, wattage	Demand factor percent
Dwelling units	First 3000 or less at	100
	Next 3001 to 120,000 at	35
	Remainder over 120,000 at	25
Hospitals*	First 50,000 or less at	40
	Remainder over 50,000 at	20
Hotels and motels*—including apartment houses without provision for cooking by tenants	First 20,000 or less at	50
	Next 20,001 to 100,000 at	40
	Remainder over 100,000 at	30
Warehouses (storage)	First 12,500 or less at	100
	Remainder over 12,500 at	50
All others	Total wattage	100

*The demand factors of this table shall not apply to the computed load of feeders to areas in hospitals, hotels, and motels where the entire lighting is likely to be used at one time; as in operating rooms, ballrooms, or dining rooms.

heat the structure at night when lights are not lit and when appliances are inactive. During occupied hours, lights and appliances would be fully or partially in use; their activity would help heat the building, and the electric heaters would not need to be 100% active. This is the type of analysis that would be required, and only after such a complete study can demand factors be applied to feeder loads and to electrical service loads.

It is not possible to be specific about demand factors (DFs) in a text of this type, and only a few generalizations can be made:

1 Building air conditioning systems use a DF of 1.0.
2 Duplex receptacle circuits: 1 to 6 circuits, DF = 1.0; 7 to 15 circuits, DF = 0.7; 16 to 25 circuits, DF = 0.5; over 25 circuits, DF = 0.4.
3 Commercial kitchens: first 25 kW of cooking equipment, DF = 1.0; next 12.5 kW, DF = 0.7; next 12.5 kW, DF = 0.5; remaining load, DF = 0.4.

Another problem that arises in connection with the determination of feeder loads is the problem of future load increases. Experience has shown

that electrical loads in existing nonresidential buildings have consistently increased at the rate of 3 to 10% per year. With the emphasis now being placed on the curtailment of energy use, this rate of growth may change, but even so it would be foolish to ignore the problem of increased power demands in future years.

This problem may be resolved by several different methods:

1 By estimating future growth and providing service and feeder conduits and conductors, and entrance equipment and panelboards capable of meeting the ultimate load.
2 By sizing all service and feeder conductors on original load (plus a small growth allowance) but providing oversized conduits, panelboards, and so on, to permit the installation of larger conductors in the future.
3 By providing spare, empty conduits in strategic locations that will permit future power demand increases without expensive alterations or cutting of the building structure.
4 By making positive provision in the building structure for the future addition of feeder conduits, panelboards, and so on; this might include

the use of demountable ceilings where they would normally be of a permanent type, the sleeving of beams and slabs to permit future conduit installation, the installation of accessible pipe chases, and so on.

Solution 1 is, of course, the most expensive and would be utilized to only a very limited extent. Which of the other three solutions to use can be decided only after a study of the plans of a specific building; no one solution to this problem will always be the best. This study will require input from more persons than the electrical designer; the owner, the architect, the mechanical designer, and the electrical contractor should all contribute to this study.

In the sample problems included in this chapter, a percentage growth factor will be included to give the problem realism; however, the reader must not accept these percentages as recommended values for the reader's use in his or her own designs. They will be values that are arbitrarily and randomly chosen and not based on any logical process.

19-26 FEEDER SIZING

The sizing of feeders to lighting panels, power panels, and combination lighting and power panels must start with a tabulation of the connected load-listed branch circuit by branch circuit. Before this can be done, all of the original load items of all types must be drawn on the building plans at the proper locations. As mentioned previously, the entire building may then be "circuited" and the original, connected load on each circuit may be totaled. A panelboard load tabulation sheet will be shown and discussed later.

With the connected load established for the panel, a study must now be made as to how the anticipated future load is to be handled—as discussed above. The future load will usually be expressed as a percent of connected load. This figure must now be translated into branch circuits to be added in the future, and bus bar capacity and space in the panels provided.

Some of the future load can surely be accommodated by addition to the original branch circuits. Remember that in the original design, each branch circuit will be only 50 to 60% loaded. In every case *spare* C/Bs and *space* for more C/Bs in the panel must be provided. The number of spares and spaces to be included in the panel will depend to a certain extent on which of the four solutions (listed in art. 19-25) to the problem of the future is chosen. In any case, it would be extremely shortsighted not to provide spare capacity in the panel itself. Extra space in a panelboard and extra capacity in the panel bus bars can be obtained at very low unit cost, and is a very good bargain.

Feeder wires can usually be removed and replaced with heavier ones in the future, but it is not practical to attempt to increase panel bus bar capacity. Therefore, our original design should include a certain number of spares (spare C/Bs) and a certain number of spaces where more C/Bs can be installed. This will automatically procure spare bus bar capacity and spare panel space. No matter how future load is to be handled, the capacity of the spares and spaces should equal *at least* 40 to 50% of connected load.

When spare C/Bs are to be included, a decision must be made as to whether these should be one-, two-, or three-pole or some of each, This decision can be made in consideration of the connected C/Bs in the panel and the types that they are. In general, if the panel is made by a manufacturer of long standing which does a good job of making spare parts for its old products, more than 10 years old, and from whom spare C/Bs can be readily procured, it is probably best to provide more spaces and fewer spares. This too is a matter of judgment.

When, at last, the total panel load is finalized, a "demand factor" is applied, and the feeder is designed on the resulting value. This process is summarized as follows:

1 Start with the total connected load in volt-amps.
2 Add the load that could be connected to the

spare C/Bs. This should usually be at least 20% of connected load or the equivalent of four to six single-pole C/Bs at 1400 VA each.

3 Add the load that could be connected in the "spaces" at the rate of 1400 VA per one-pole space. This should usually be at least 25 to 30% of connected load.

4 Total load = item 1 + item 2 + item 3.

5 Feeder design load = total load × demand factor.

19-27 SINGLE-PHASE FEEDER SIZING

Example 19-2 In an office building, lighting panel B serves 6000 ft² of floor area, and has a connected load of 28,000 VA; this consists of twenty 20-A branch lighting and receptacle circuits which are each controlled and protected by 20-A one-pole C/Bs. In the foreseeable future, a growth in connected load of 80% is anticipated, and feeder and panel capacity is to be installed now to handle one-half of this growth. Provision will be made to run another feeder and set another panel when this capacity is exceeded. The electrical system is to be a 120/240-V/single-phase three-wire system, and the feeder is to use type TW copper conductors.

Find the size of the feeder conductors and conduit, the nominal size of the panel, and the size and type of C/B needed in the MDP to protect this feeder.

Solution

1. Connected load	28,000 VA
2. Add four one-pole spare C/Bs with expected future load of 1400 VA each. 4 × 1400 VA	5,600 VA
3. Add six one-pole spaces with expected future load of 1400 VA each. 6 × 1400 VA	8,400 VA
4. Total load	42,000 VA

The provision for future load must equal one-half of 80% of the connected load, or 28,000 VA × 80% × 1/2 = 11,200 VA. Items 2 and 3 above total 5600 VA + 8400 VA = 14,000 VA for future

load. This is somewhat more than required, but for this size panel (28 to 30 poles) four spares should be the minimum. The six spaces could be reduced to four spaces, but very little cost reduction would result, so let us settle on four spares and six spaces and a total load of 42,000 VA.

Since our building is an office building, the lights may very well be 100% on at times; but the receptacles and other miscellaneous loads (coffee urns, water coolers, computers, copy machines, etc.) will not reach anywhere near 100% usage; let us assume a demand factor of 90%. Feeder design load is then 42,000 VA × 0.9 = 37,800 VA. Feeder amperage is then equal to

$$I = \frac{37,800 \text{ VA}}{240 \text{ V}} = 157.5 \text{ A}$$

In fig. 19-22 we see that a No. 3/0 TW conductor has a capacity of 165 A. The next size smaller, No. 2/0 TW wire, has capacity of 145 A. This is too small, and a No. 3/0 size should be used. There are only three conductors in this feeder, so the tabular values in fig. 19-22 may be used without derating. The feeder conduit size may now be selected from fig. 19-24. This table shows that a 1 1/2-in. conduit can hold only two No. 3/0 TW conductors, and since we will have three such wires, a 2-in. conduit must be used; it can hold four No. 3/0 TW conductors. Therefore, our feeder may be described as three No. 3/0 TWs in a 2-in. conduit, and it should be so noted on the electrical layout drawing, but not until the voltage drop in this feeder is calculated and found to be satisfactory. We will deal with voltage drop calculations a little later.

Another check that must be made before finalizing the result in example 19-2 is for compliance with the concept of "unit lighting loads" as set forth in article 220 of the NEC. This article specifies that for lighting purposes a certain amount of power capability must be provided as a minimum, whether planned to be used or not. Figure 19-38 provides a table of the unit lighting loads required for various types of occupancies.

Figure 19-38 General lighting loads by occupancies. (Excerpted from the National Electric Code with permission.)

Type of occupancy	Unit load per ft² (Watts)	
Armories and auditoriums	1	
Banks	3 1/2†	
Barber shops and beauty parlors	3	
Churches	1	
Clubs	2	
Courtrooms	2	
*Dwelling units	3	
Garages—commercial (storage)		1/2
Hospitals	2	
*Hotels and motels including apartment houses without provisions for cooking by tenants	2	
Industrial commercial (loft) buildings	2	
Lodge rooms	1 1/2	
Office buildings	3 1/2†	
Restaurants	2	
Schools	3	
Stores	3	
Warehouses (storage)		1/4
In any of the above occupancies except one-family dwellings and individual dwelling units of multifamily dwellings:		
Assembly halls and auditoriums	1	
Halls, corridors, closets		1/2
Storage spaces		1/4

*All receptacle outlets of 20 A or less rating in one-family and multifamily dwellings and in guest rooms of hotels and motels [except those connected to the receptacle circuits specified in NEC section 220-3(b)] shall be considered as outlets for general illumination, and no additional load calculations shall be required for such outlets.

†In addition, a unit load of 1 W/ft² shall be included for general-purpose receptacle outlets when the actual number of general-purpose receptacle outlets is unknown.

Notice that a footnote to this table advises that in residential dwellings (except in kitchen and laundry areas) and in hotel and motel guest rooms, the load of receptacle outlets is included in the unit lighting loads. In other words, no extra load for receptacle outlets need be added above and beyond the 3 W/ft² for residences and 2 W/ft² for hotels and motels.

By implication, then, for the other types of buildings listed in fig. 19-38, receptacle load and

other special load must be additive beyond the unit lighting load shown. In example 19-2, the floor area served by this particular feeder is given to be 6000 ft². For office buildings, fig. 19-38 lists a unit load of 3.5 W/ft² of floor. 6000 ft² × 3.5 = 21,000 W as the minimum amount of power to be provided for lighting; receptacle load must be in addition to that.

Our preliminary selection of feeder conductors was No. 3/0 conductors with an ampacity of 165 A. 165 A × 240 V = 39,600 VA of power capability. This might be adequate or not; it is impossible to say without an actual load layout to study to see the extent of the receptacle load. Remember also that here we are comparing "volt-amperes" capacity with "watts" of load. We do not know the nature of the lighting load, but if it is mostly fluorescent fixture load, which is largely inductive in nature, the power factor may be 0.9 or less. If it were 0.9, the feeder capacity in watts would be 165 A × 240 V × 0.9 PF = 35,640 W. This might very well be inadequate with receptacle load included, and the next larger size feeder conductors (No. 4/0 TW with 195 A ampacity) would be required.

19-28 THREE-PHASE FEEDER SIZING

Example 19-3 In a high school building, a feeder is to supply power to a section of the building having 10,000 ft² of floor area. The electrical system and this particular feeder is designed to be a 120/208-V/three-phase/four-wire system. Total connected load consists of 32,000 VA of lighting load and 8000 VA of receptacle outlet load—total 40,000 VA. After a study, it is decided to add 35% for future growth. Use type THW wires.

Total design load = 40,000 VA + 35% = 54,000 VA.

$$\text{Feeder amps} = \frac{54,000 \text{ VA}}{208 \text{ V} \times 1.732} = 149.89 \text{ A}$$

Let us assume a 100% demand factor.

Notice that since this is a three-phase feeder, we must involve the constant 1.732 in the calculation. This was done as shown above. This feeder is also a four-wire feeder, and we have more than three wires in the feeder conduit, but fig. 19-22 notes that ampacities shown are for not more than three wires in the raceway. It would seem that we should derate the tabulated ampacities according to a footnote to fig. 19-22; however, this is not correct. The NEC states that where the fourth wire is a grounded neutral wire which carries only unbalanced current from the three phase wires, it may be ignored in the count of the number of conductors. So derating is not necessary in this case.

Figure 19-22 shows the ampacity of a No. 1/0 THW conductor to be 150 A. Figure 19-38 shows the unit lighting load for a school to be 3 W/ft^2 of floor. We have 10,000 ft^2 involved; 10,000 ft^2 × 3 W/ft^2 = 30,000 W. Our capacity, as calculated above, is well beyond the minimum, and no increase in capacity is needed. In sizing the conduit for this feeder, we must count the neutral wire, of course, and select a conduit to hold four No. 1/0 THW conductors.

Figure 19-24 shows that for four No. 1/0 THW conductors a 2-in. conduit is required. A 1 1/2-in. conduit can hold only three No. 1/0 THWs. Since a 2-in. conduit is somewhat larger than necessary for the usual 40% fill with conductors, we should check to see just how much wiring capacity could be installed in the 2-in. conduit in future years. Figure 19-24 shows that in the future, the No. 1/0 THW conductors could be replaced with four No. 4/0 THWN conductors. Number 4/0 THWNs can carry 230 A; this is a very substantial increase above the 150-A ampacity of the No. 1/0 THWs.

19-29　FEEDER VOLTAGE DROP

The NEC in general permits a voltage drop in branch circuits of 3% of the supply voltage (3% of 240 V = 7.2 V) and permits a 5% drop in the feeder and the branch circuit taken together. A 5% loss in the voltage represents a very substantial loss in energy, and we should really do better than this. This voltage loss is transformed into heat in the wiring which is dissipated into the building. In the winter, when heat may be needed in the building, much of this heat may be beneficial and some may not. At any rate, it is a very expensive way to heat a building (with electric resistance heating). In summer, when the building is being mechanically cooled, this heat is a dead loss, and more energy must be expended to remove it. Let us try to design our electrical systems for a 1% voltage drop in our feeders and 2% in our branch circuits—a total voltage drop of 3%.

In example 19-2, the length of the feeder was not given; let us assume this length to be 125 ft from the MDP to the panelboard. The two-way round-trip distance is then 2 × 125 ft = 250 ft of wire (excluding the neutral wire) in the feeder. Figure 19-21 gives the alternating current resistance of No. 3/0 wire (selected in example 19-2) to be 0.0668 Ω per 1000 ft of length. Then 250 ft of feeder wire has a resistance of 0.0668 V × 250 ft/1000 ft = 0.0167 ohms. Since we have said before that voltage drop V equals IR, the voltage drop in this feeder, when the current as calculated is 157.5 A, is equal to 157.5 A × 0.0167 Ω = 2.63 V. 2.63 ÷ 240 V supply voltage = 0.01096, or 1.096%; this is slightly over 1% but should be quite satisfactory. The No. 3/0 conductors are adequate if the one-way feeder length does not exceed 125 ft.

In example 19-3 we have a three-phase feeder of No. 1/0 wires carrying 148.89 A. A three-phase feeder has a somewhat different situation from a single-phase feeder. When one of the three wires is carrying maximum current, the other two wires are carrying much less current at that instant, and their voltage drop is then much less. The design resistance of a three-phase feeder or circuit may be based on 1.732 times its one-way distance. Figure 19-21 gives the ac resistance of No. 1/0 copper wire as 0.104 Ω per 1000 ft. At 80 ft long, for example, this feeder in example 19-3 has a resistance of

$$\frac{80 \text{ ft} \times 1.732}{1000 \text{ ft}} \times 0.104 = 0.0144 \ \Omega$$

The voltage drop V is then equal to 149.89 A $\times$ 0.0144 Ω = 2.16 V drop in the feeder. This is 1.04% (2.16 V/208 V = 0.0104), which again is slightly more than 1% but should be satisfactory.

19-30 PANELBOARDS FOR EXAMPLES 19-2 AND 19-3

In example 19-2 we have a 120 V/240-V/single-phase/three-wire system which is designed to carry a total load of 42,000 VA, derated by a 90% demand factor to 37,800 VA. The design current is 157.5. A. In art. 19-5 we see in the panelboard data that panels are designed for 240, 480, and 600 V; in this problem we need a 240-V panel.

Also from the panel data we should select a 225-A panel, which is somewhat oversized for our 157.5-A load, but the next smaller standard size is 125 A, which is too small. We probably would not need a main C/B in this panel, but if one were required for some reason, we must choose between a 225-A frame C/B which is calibrated for a 175-A trip rating, or the same frame size with a 200-A trip rating.

Some disconnecting equipment, such as C/Bs and fused switches, is designed to continuously carry current right up to its nominal rating. Other equipment is not so designed, and may not carry more than 80% of its nominal rating continuously or for several hours at a time. If such disconnecting equipment is designed for continuous duty, it must be permanently labeled with a statement such as "suitable for 100% continuous duty."

In example 19-2, a 200-A unlabeled C/B would be suitable (200 A $\times$ 0.8 = 160 A), or a 175-A labeled C/B would be suitable, because it could continuously carry our load of 157.5 A. Including the main C/B, the panel for example 19-2 would be described as a "225-A/120/240-V/single-phase three-wire panel with a 200-A (if unlabeled) two-pole main C/B." It would also require further

description, giving the depth of the tub (or back-box), the width of the wiring channels, and the quantity, size, and arrangement of all the branch circuit C/Bs to be included.

In example 19-3, the maximum voltage is 208 V, the continuous current load is 149.89 A, and the system is a three-phase four-wire system. Therefore, the panel description would be: 225-A/120/208-V/three-phase/four-wire panel with a 175-A/three-pole labeled main C/B (or a 200-A/three-pole unlabeled C/B).

As mentioned, most panelboards do not have main C/Bs, and these two would probably not either; in this case this last mentioned panel would be described as a 225-A/120/208-V/three-phase/four-wire/MLO panel. The letters MLO (main lugs only) indicate that no main C/B is required.

Each of the two feeders described above would need to be protected from overcurrent and under-voltage conditions by a fuse or fused switch or C/B located in the MDP at the service entrance location. If C/Bs are used for this protection, they would have the same description as set forth above for main C/Bs in the panels. In addition, all such C/Bs would need to have an additional rating showing its fault current handling capacity. As mentioned before, such ratings are extremely high, and may be from 10,000 A to as much as 100,000 A. The fault current capacity required would depend on the fault current potential of the particular location of the building. See art. 19-13 for further discussion of fault current protection.

19-31 PANELBOARD LOAD TABULATIONS AND CIRCUITING

As described previously, when all items of electrical load of all types are drawn and noted on the floor plans of a building, it can then be circuited. That is, all load can be assigned to a branch circuit of proper size and description. These branch circuits originate at one of the lighting and/or power panels.

Most of the branch circuits are either 15 or 20

A, with 20 A being the most frequent choice. There are, of course, many branch circuits of special nature that service only one particular piece of equipment, such as a motor-compressor unit, an electronic computer, or an air conditioning unit. The circuits that feed such equipment are tailor-made to its specific needs, and do not necessarily involve one of the standard sizes of branch circuits.

Before circuiting a system, decisions must be made as to the amperage and voltage that will be used. If the building being circuited is of modest dimensions, a 120/208-V/three-phase/four-wire system will probably be used throughout. Lighting and receptacle circuits will mostly be 120-V single-phase 20-A circuits, and power circuits will mostly be 208-V three-phase and 208-V single-phase. If the building is very large, the system will probably be a 277/480-V/three-phase/four-wire system with distribution transformers strategically located throughout the building to step the 480-V power down to 120-V single-phase for use in lighting and receptacle circuits.

In the 277/480-V/three-phase/four-wire system, all electric motors of 3/4 hp size and larger will be wound for 480-V, three-phase power. For lighting purposes, 277-V single-phase power will be extensively used.

In any system, the locations of lighting and power panels should be selected very carefully. In general, the building should be divided into areas to be served by one panel. The size of this area should be such that the branch circuits and the home runs do not involve a one-way distance of more than 50 to 80 ft. To keep branch circuit lengths within this limitation, panelboards should be located as near as possible at the exact center of the area it serves, never off to the side or perimeter of its area. Only in this way can reasonable panel area coverage be achieved with branch circuit voltage drop limited to 2% of the supply voltage.

Panelboards should also be located at some point of good accessibility, so that anyone needing quickly to "kill" a certain circuit in an emergency can find the panel, get the hinged door open easily and find the correct C/B without delay. The panel that is located in a janitor's closet behind a locked closet door, with a locked panel-front door, and with C/Bs that are not properly identified has little excuse for existence.

Panelboards are not things of beauty, but with a little imagination and resourcefulness, they can be somewhat concealed and yet readily accessible and located in the geographic center of its service area.

To the extent possible, branch circuit loads should be expressed and tabulated in terms of volt-amps, not watts. It is often convenient to tabulate a few special circuits, such as motor circuits, in amps. Then, after the main bulk of the load is tabulated in volt-amps and converted to amps, these special circuits may be added in amps.

In tabulating panel loads, the following approximations may be helpful:

1 Include all 40-W fluorescent lamps at 50 VA each.
2 Include all 75-W fluorescent lamps at 100 VA each.
3 Include all fractional horsepower electric motors at 1500 VA/hp; for example, a 1/2-hp motor should be tabulated at $1/2 \times 1500$ VA = 750 VA.
4 To find volt-amperes for any larger 208-V three-phase induction motors, use the following formula:

$$VA = \frac{800 \times hp}{eff}$$

where VA = volt-amperes
  hp = motor horsepower
  eff = motor efficiency

The 800 constant in item 4 was estimated by multiplying the full-load amps (FLA) of a motor (e.g., 84 A for a 30-hp 208-V three-phase motor) by 208 and by 1.732 to get tabulated VA for a 208-V three-phase motor:

$$84 \text{ A} \times 208 \text{ V} \times 1.732 = 30,261.5 \text{ VA}$$

Then multiplying this by eff (80%) and dividing by hp (30) we get 806.97. This was roughed off at 800.

We need a VA value for tabulating, which when divided by 208 V and by 1.732 equals the proper full-load amps. If FLA is known, it should be used directly.

Motor efficiencies may be selected from the following schedule of efficiencies:

$$1 \text{ hp} = 65\%$$
$$5 \text{ hp} = 70\%$$
$$10 \text{ to } 50 \text{ hp} = 80\%$$
$$60 \text{ hp and above} = 85\%$$

In the formula above, the power factor has been assumed to be 85%; for other known power factors, a correction can easily be made (as PF increases, volt-amperes decrease).

Figure 19-39 shows a typical load tabulation sheet for one combination lighting and power panelboard. The information at the top of the sheet shows that this is to be panel A located at the west end of the first floor of a proposed new country club. It is to be a 120/208-V/three-phase/four-wire panel receiving that type of power from the MDP (main distribution panel) and delivering, to the area that it serves, 120-V single-phase power, 208-V single-phase power, and 208-V three-phase power.

This panel is not to be equipped with a main C/B, but is to have main lugs only (MLO) to which the feeder wires can connect. It is to be a 32-pole panel with 14 single-pole 20-A C/Bs connected (circuits 1 through 14), four single-pole 20-A spare C/Bs (circuits 15 through 18), five single-pole spaces (circuits 19 through 23), one three-pole 125-A C/B (for the 30-hp motor), one three-pole 30-A C/B (for the 5-hp motor), and one three-pole 40-A C/B (for the 12-kW water heater).

There are then in this panel:

23 single-pole C/Bs and spaces	23	
3 three-pole C/Bs	9	
Total	32 poles	

Remember that the NEC does not permit more than 42 poles in one panel, and in this case we are well short of the maximum.

Notice that in fig. 19-39 the second column (Item) gives a description of the type of load connected to each circuit. In circuit 1, for example, seven type A lighting fixtures constitute the load of that circuit. The last column (Remarks) shows that circuit 1 is located in room 101. This information is very important. Also shown is information regarding the branch circuit breakers to be used, giving for each circuit the number of poles, the C/B trip setting, and the C/B frame size.

In the fifth column, the load in volt-amps for each circuit is listed, except the last three circuits, where it is easier to list the load directly in amps. However, it would be satisfactory if the motor running currents were not known to list the load of circuits 24, 25, and 26 in the fifth column in volt-amps. The formula given in item 4 of this article will be of help in approximating the VA to be entered for 208-V three-phase motors.

In other columns of fig. 19-39, the amps load of each circuit and the wire and conduit sizes are listed; however, the conduit size shown is not the home run conduit size; that will be developed on the wiring layout plan. Voltage drop for each circuit is also estimated from the amps flowing, the circuit wire size, and the one-way length of each branch circuit. The percentages of voltage drop were calculated by the methods shown in art. 19-29.

19-32 GROUNDING AND GROUND FAULT INTERRUPTERS

As discussed previously in art. 19-3, there are two grounding systems required in building electrical systems. One is called the *system ground* and the other is the *equipment ground*. The system ground is merely the neutral wire N, which begins at the service transformer and extends throughout the electrical distribution system of the building. It is grounded, electrically connected to the earth, at

Job Name: NEW COUNTRY CLUB   Job No: 8206   Panel Designation: LIGHTING & POWER PANEL "A"   Date: JAN. 21, 1982

Voltage: 120/208/3PH/4W   Location: 1ST FLOOR, WEST END   Mains: MLO   Poles: 32   Sheet: 1 of 1

Ckt no.	Item	Poles & trip	Frame	Load volt-amps	HP	Amps	Wire & conduit size	1-way run, ft.	% drop	Remarks
1	7 TYPE A	1-20	100	1400		11.67	#12-½"	45	1.4	ROOM 101
2	7 TYPE A			1400		11.67		55	1.73	ROOM 102
3	12 TYPE B			1200		10		55	1.48	RM 103 & 104
4	3 Ds & 4 Fs			1050		8.75		50	1.18	RM 120
5	3 Ds & 4 Fs			1050		8.75		60	1.40	RM 121
6	6 As & 1 G			1350		11.25		65	1.96	RM 124
7	12 Bs			1200		10		60	1.62	RM 122
8	6 As & 1 G			1350		11.25		70	2.12	RM 123
9	6 DUP. RECEP.			1080		9		50	1.22	RMS 101, 102 & 119
10	6 DUP. RECEP.			1080		9		55	1.34	RMS 103, 104 & 105
11	6 DUP. RECEP.			1080		9		65	1.58	RMS 120, 121 & 124
12	7 DUP. RECEP.			1260		10.5		65	1.84	RMS 122 & 123
13	6 DUP. RECEP.			1080		9		60	1.46	RMS 119 & 125
14	6 DUP. RECEP.			1080		9		50	1.22	RMS 117 & 118
15	SPARE			1400						
16	SPARE			1400						
17	SPARE			1400						
18	SPARE			1400						
19-23	SPACES			7000						
24	30 H.P. MOTOR	3-125	225		30	84	#2 THW, 1"	65	.74	AIR COND. #1 COMPRESSOR
25	5 H.P. MOTOR	3-30	100		5	16	#12 THW, ½"	65	1.40	AIR COND. FAN, 3-PH
26	12 KW WAT. HEATER	3-40	100	7000		33.3	#8 THW, ¾"	55	.98	3-PH

TOTAL VOLT-AMPS = 29,260   (AT 120 VOLTS, 1-PHASE)

$$\frac{29,260}{208 \times 1.732} = 81.2A \quad \text{(AT 208 VOLTS, 3 PHASE)}$$

TOTAL AMPS AT 208V, 3 PHASE
= 81.2A + 84A (30 H.P. MOTOR) + 16A (5 H.P. MOTOR) + 33.3A (WATER HEATER)
= 214.5 AMPS

Figure 19.39   Typical load tabulation sheet.

the service entrance location, so that the neutral wire is at, or within, a few volts of earth potential at all points throughout the system.

The equipment ground system is a complicated assembly of equipment which includes metal conduit, junction boxes, pull boxes, metal ducts, bus ducts, cable trays, switch enclosures, panelboard enclosures, CT cabinets, and all the metal parts of the electrical system except the hot wires and neutral wires themselves. Where nonmetallic conduit and cable sheathing is used, a grounding wire is enclosed to maintain the continuity of the grounding system. These grounding conductors must be carefully secured electrically to any metallic parts that precede or follow sections of these nonmetallic sheathings or raceways.

The equipment grounding system must be carefully connected to any metallic cabinets, frames, enclosures, and so on, of all electrically operated appliance equipment with which people can make physical contact. If all such appliances (this term is used in a very broad sense) are well and properly grounded and at earth potential, no person can suffer a serious electrical shock.

In fig. 19-40a a fault has occurred, and the metal cabinet of the appliance is electrically connected to the hot wire of the branch circuit that supplies electrical power. If the electrical connection to the metal cabinet is a good one with very low electrical resistance, enough current will flow to trip the C/B that protects the branch circuit. By this process the appliance becomes inoperative, and it is soon learned that a fault exists which is then repaired. This process would take place quickly and no person would be injured.

However, if the fault is not a complete one, we have a different problem. Suppose that some of the insulation was inadvertently damaged on the hot wire where it enters the appliance cabinet, but the hot wire is making a poor contact with the cabinet, and the resistance to current flow into the cabinet is quite high. Perhaps only 18 A is flowing into the cabinet, but this is not enough to trip the 20-A C/B. Now the cabinet is electrically charged, and if someone should put one hand on this cabinet and one hand on the metal pipe adjacent to it, the person could get an electrical shock—probably a mild one.

The problem above can be solved with the use of a *ground fault interrupter* (GFI). A GFI is a device that takes many forms, but all are designed to do one thing—to open a circuit when the current flow in the circuit conductors is unequal. In a normal circuit, single-phase or three-phase, the current flow in one direction is always the same as the flow in the other direction. If, in a given circuit with a GFI installed, the current flow in each direction is unequal, the GFI will interrupt the current and shut down the circuit.

In fig. 19-40a, if because of the fault described, current flows in the "hot" wire, through the fault, and back through the ground wire, there will be more current flowing in the hot wire than in the neutral wire. A GFI would sense this condition and shut the circuit down immediately. No one would get even a mild shock. Even very small differences in current flow will activate the GFI.

A GFI operates on the current-transformer principle. A coil of wire surrounds the circuit conductors, not including any ground wire. A very slight difference in current flow in the circuit conductors will induce a small current in the GFI coil. This small current is amplified or put through a relay. The relay causes a second and heavier current to flow which activates a magnetic device which opens the circuit.

Some GFIs are built into a panelboard C/B (see fig. 19-40c) which trips the circuit when unequal currents flow. The GFI-type C/B has the built-in coil mentioned above; this may be seen in fig. 19-40b.

GFIs are available in many types from the heavy-duty type, monitoring the entire building service, to one isolated branch circuit, to one outlet on a branch circuit. One frequently used device is the GFI-protected weatherproof receptacle for plugging in a heavy-duty extension cord used for temporary power on a construction project. GFIs are available as one-, two-, or three-pole devices.

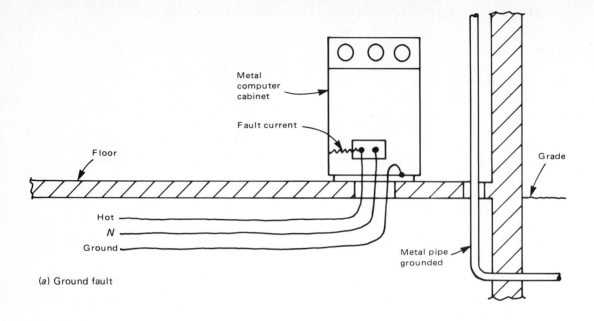

Metal
computer
cabinet

Fault current

Floor

Grade

Hot

N

Ground

Metal pipe
grounded

(a) Ground fault

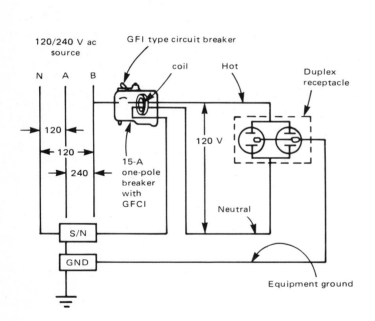

120/240 V ac
source

GFI type circuit breaker

coil

Hot

Duplex
receptacle

N   A   B

120

120

240

120 V

15-A
one-pole
breaker
with
GFCI

Neutral

S/N

GND

Equipment ground

(b) Ground fault interrupter

(c) Ground fault
interrupter C/B

ON

OFF

PUSH
TO
TEST

Figure 19-40 Grounding problem details. (Courtesy of The Square D. Co.)

PROBLEMS

19-1 A 375-kVA three-phase service transformer delivers electrical power into its building at 240 V. How much current will flow in the three-phase service conductors when rated load is carried?

19-2 What is the power of the service in prob. 19-1, in kW, if the system power factor is 0.9?

19-3 What is the rated amps of a 150-kVA single-phase 240-V electric service?

19-4 What is the ratio of the two voltages in a dual-voltage three-phase delta-connected electric service, and what is the same ratio for a three-phase Y-connected electric service?

19-5 In a building served with the electric service of fig. 19-14, may a 120-V single-phase load be connected between the neutral (N) wire and the phase A wire, between N and the phase B wire, and between N and the phase C wire?

19-6 In the 120/240-V/three-phase/four wire, delta electric power service of a building, the service conductors are capable of carrying 340 A. Find the maximum power capacity of this service in kVA.

19-7 Using cryptic notation, how would you describe the system switch shown in fig. 19-18a?

19-8 In a main distribution panel (MDP) of a building 120/208-V/three-phase/four-wire electrical system, to what would the following connect:

a A 120/208-V/three-phase/four-wire feeder to a lighting panel

b A 208-V three-phase electric motor

c A 208-V single-phase branch circuit

d A 120-V single-phase branch circuit

19-9 A conduit has seven power conductors in it. If all conductors are No. 250 MCM type THW copper, what size conduit would be required to contain them?

19-10 A lighting and power panel feeder that must carry a load of 260 A is to be made of type THHN copper conductors in a metallic raceway. If this is a three-phase four-wire feeder, what size conductors and conduit are required?

19-11 A conduit must carry six No. 3/0 TW conductors and two No. 1/0 TW conductors. What size conduit is required to legally contain these eight conductors?

19-12 A certain room has in it lighting fixtures which are controlled from three locations in the room. What types of wall-mounted light switches, and how many of each type, would be required?

19-13 A certain feeder in a building electrical system extends 220 ft from its MDP to its lighting and small power panelboard. The connected load on this panel is 36,000 VA, and the feeder is a 120/208-V/three-phase/ four-wire feeder. For future expansion, 40% of the connected load is to be added and the voltage drop is not to exceed 1.5% of the supply voltage after the future load is added. The demand factor is assumed to be 70%. Ambient temperature is assumed to rise as high as 100°F frequently. Find the sizes of the conductors and the conduit if type TW conductors are to be used. Also, give the description of the required lighting/power panel if no main C/B is needed.

Lighting

20-1 GENERALITIES

Today's modern buildings, of course, need modern lighting systems. To be modern a lighting system must do more than provide adequate illumination; it must do so with the least possible consumption of energy. To be economical a system must maximize the use of the most efficient lamps (a lamp is a source of light, such as a light bulb or a fluorescent tube) installed in luminaires (lighting fixtures) capable of comfortably, effectively, and with good appearance directing a high percent of the lamp light to the points or area where it is needed.

Further, the lighting system must be able to do this quietly and with very little maintenance cost. In some systems there is objectionable noise, and in some systems the maintenance cost of cleaning luminaires and replacing worn-out lamps is exces-

sive. The problem of selecting and designing a lighting system that will effectively meet all these requirements is a difficult problem. Its proper solution requires diligent effort by a person who is completely trained in the many complicated aspects of lighting problems.

Unfortunately, there are not nearly enough persons with adequate training to solve all of the design problems that occur every day all over the nation where buildings are being designed. Really capable practicing lighting designers are exceedingly scarce; it is the rare city of a half million population that has even one such person. If a city of one million people has more than two, or possibly three, it is very unusual. Probably not more than 1% of the plans for new buildings includes lighting layouts designed by top-notch, highly qualified lighting experts.

Rare indeed is the university curriculum that

includes courses in lighting design taught by fully trained and experienced lighting designers. Rare indeed is the architectural firm that has such a person on its staff. The question must then be asked: "Well, who is designing the new lighting systems that are being installed every day?" In most cases, the answer must be: "Really, nobody is designing them; they just happen." There is a chance that such systems will happen to be good in all the many necessary aspects; but it is not likely.

Only as a result of the intelligent, experienced evaluation of all the many, many aspects of a lighting design can the final result be as good as a building owner has a right to expect. Such designs do not just happen. Of course, the full responsibility for lighting design rests squarely on the shoulders of the architect, and with some notable exceptions, architects have abdicated this responsibility. Yet what is more important to a building's aesthetic design and function than its lighting system?

The architect will spend many months in polishing the physical form of a building; will spend weeks and weeks in selecting interior finishes in the form of fabrics, carpeting, and furnishings; will spend days in preparing sample boards with samples of finishes and their colors; and will then turn over to an electrical engineer the problem of designing a lighting system. Well, the electrical engineer is by definition anything but a lighting expert, so he or she turns the problem over to a draftsman, who out of necessity has had to learn a little about lighting —not much, but a little. Unfortunately, in too many cases, this is where lighting systems evolve.

It is hoped that this text and others like it will, in the simplest terms, inspire this fairly uneducated draftsman to accept the challenge of digging deeper, studying harder, and learning more about the intricacies and ramifications of lighting design. Our future buildings will greatly benefit, but of course, the proper solution to the problem is for every school of architecture to require its graduates to be well trained in all principles of lighting design. Then, with the consulting assistance of the few real lighting experts that exist,

the architect can integrate the lighting design of a building with all its other aesthetic and functional aspects.

Lighting design must begin with an evaluation of the needs of a proposed building. This evaluation must consist of much more than just selecting recommended lighting levels from the *Illuminating Engineers Society* (IES) *Handbook*. Many other factors, as listed below, must be considered:

1 The control of fixtures (switching) to provide maximum flexibility
2 The use of dimmers to establish proper illumination levels
3 The types of lamps to use
4 The types of fixtures and their location
5 The possible use of emphasis lighting with spotlights, floodlights, wall-wash lights, downlights, up-lights, and so on.
6 The possible use of the high-efficiency lamps that are now available even though their color may not be optimum
7 The possible use of contrasting bright and dark areas and resulting shadows
8 The possible use of colored light for emphasis and psychological effect
9 The minimization of maintenance expense, including lamp-life expectations

Once the building needs are well established, the qualified designer can begin to meet those needs with his knowledge of the vast array of equipment that is available. Of course, today he must always balance every decision against the need to save energy.

20-2 BASIC CONCEPTS AND DEFINITIONS

Before we can fluently discuss lighting practices, there are a few terms peculiar to these practices that must be fully understood.

20-3 CANDLEPOWER

Candlepower is a term which, in lighting practices, is being eliminated; however, it is useful in establishing a basic concept of light and light measurement. It merely means the power or luminous intensity of a *standard candle*—also called *international candle*. The standard candle is a sperm oil candle about 7/8 in. in diameter with a standard-size wick. When a standard candle is burning and being consumed at the rate of 120 grains/hr, it is producing one candlepower, or one *candela*.

20-4 CANDELA

The candela (pronounced can-DEL-a) is the unit of luminous intensity of a light source and is defined as 1/60 of the intensity of a square centimeter of a blackbody radiator which is operating at a temperature of 2047° Kelvin, or 1774°F, which is the fusing temperature of platinum. The terms "candela" and "candlepower" do not express light quantity but do express light intensity or light brightness.

20-5 LUMEN

The term *lumen* is used to express light quantity, or the luminous output, or the light-producing capacity of a lamp or a lighting fixture. By defini-

tion, a standard candle burning at the center of a sphere with 1 ft radius (see fig. 20-1) will cause one lumen of light to fall on each square foot of interior surface of the sphere. Since a sphere of 1 ft radius has a surface area of 12.566 ft², the standard international candle must produce light at the rate of 12.566 lumens (lm).

20-6 FOOTCANDLE

The term *footcandle* is used to express the level of illumination on a surface; it is measured in terms of lumens per square foot. If light is falling on a surface at the quantity rate of one lumen per square foot, the level of illumination at that surface is one footcandle. This is our standard unit of measurement of illumination, and it is usually related to some surface, called the *work surface* or *work plane* where a seeing task is being performed.

In fig. 20-1, since one lumen is falling on each square foot of interior surface, the level of illumination at the surface is one footcandle. If the sphere of fig. 20-1 had a radius of 2 ft, the interior area of the sphere would be four times greater ($A = \pi d^2 = (\pi)(4 \text{ ft}^2) = 50.265 \text{ ft}^2$; 50.265/12.566 = 4). The same amount of light falling on an area

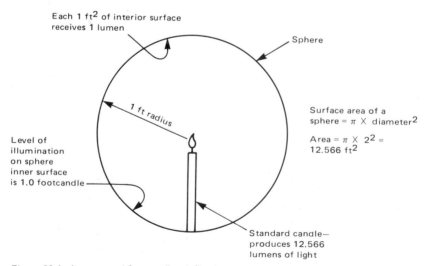

Figure 20-1 Lumens and footcandles defined.

four times greater would give a level of illumination one-fourth as great, or 1/4 footcandle (fc). This expresses the "inverse square" relationship.

If the radius of the sphere in fig. 20-1 were 1 meter instead of 1 foot, the level of illumination would be one *lux,* which is the international unit used to express level of illumination. The lux, then, is a much smaller unit of measurement than the footcandle; one footcandle is equal to 10.8 lux (lx).

20-7 FOOTLAMBERT

The term *footcandle* is used to express the amount of light falling on a surface; this is called *incident light.* The term *footlambert* is used to express *reflected light* or the light coming from a surface that is lit with incident light. If a surface is a perfect reflector, the incident light and the reflected light are equal, and footcandles and footlamberts are also equal. Footlamberts are then used to measure the brightness of a surface, which is a function of the footcandles of light falling on the surface and the reflecting ability of the surface. When a person reads a book, his or her eyes are perceiving light which may be measured in footlamberts.

20-8 REFLECTANCE

Reflectance is a reflection factor which gives a measure of the ability of a surface to reflect incident light. Obviously, the reflectances of the various surfaces in a room have a profound effect on the seeing conditions that prevail in a room.

The opposite of reflectance (reflection factor) is called *absorption factor.* If a surface absorbs 40% of the light that falls on it, its absorption factor is 0.4 and its reflectance is 0.6. Figure 20-2 gives a rough approximation of the reflectances of various types of surfaces both painted or stained and natural. The reflectances of painted surfaces vary considerably with the texture of the paint, whether flat or glossy, and with the age and the thickness of the paint coating.

Figure 20-2 Typical surface reflectances.

	Percent
White plaster	90–92
White terra cotta	65–80
Limestone, light color	35–65
Light marble	70–85
Concrete, stucco, light brick	45–70
Medium-color stone (limestone and sandstone), tan and gray (rough)	20–45
Wood finishes	
Light birch	42
Dark oak	13
Light oak	34
Dark mahogany and walnut	8
Wallpaper, white	80
Wallpaper, medium color	50
Wallpaper, dark color	25
Paint finishes	
Gloss white	84
Flat white	82
Eggshell white	81
Ivory white	80
Caen stone	76
Primrose	78
Pearl gray	72
Ivory	71
Very light gray	70
Cream	70
Bright sage and ivory tan	48
Medium gray	44
Buff stone	41
French gray	40
Pale azure	40
Buff stone and pale azure	39
Bronze	38
Sky blue	37
Tan	35
Aluminum	65
Buff	64
Lichen gray	63
Ivory tan	63
Light gray	60
Satin green	56
Pale azure and white	55
Shell pink	54
Silver gray and caen stone	52
Dark gray	28
Olive green	21
Forest green	20
Cardinal red	20
Very dark gray	19
Cocoanut brown	19

Considerable judgment is required in the use of reflectance factors which can only come after extensive experience. Lacking this experiential judgment, a designer should be quite conservative in the selection of reflectance factors to be used in lighting design problems. He or she should realize that when room surfaces are new and clean, their reflectances are appreciably higher than they will be years later.

20-9   HUMAN NEEDS IN SEEING

The mission of a lighting system in a building must be to satisfy the physical and psychological needs of the human beings who use the building. The lighting system must make it possible for people to be able to see to perform their work, play, or tasks in general. But in addition to that, the system must play a part in causing people to react or respond favorably and positively to the building environment and be contented therein. A lighting system can make a big contribution in the latter responsibility.

There are several specific things that a good lighting system should do:

1 Provide adequate illumination at the *work plane* (WP) where seeing tasks are being performed; the work plane, for example, could be a desk top or drafting table.

2 Provide adequate ambient illumination in the areas that surround those who are performing seeing tasks; too great a contrast between light levels at the work plane and on surrounding areas can be very uncomfortable.

3 Provide adequate illumination at the work plane with minimum glare or veiling reflections.

4 Provide good illumination with a minimum of bright spots in the lighting fixtures, and with no beams of light directed into the eyes of room occupants.

5 Provide flexibility or controllability so that the lighting system can be easily modified to everyday changes in requirements—for example, to modify light supply in accordance with changing patterns of sunlight.

6 Provide efficient operation with low maintenance so that energy is conserved and operating cost is minimized.

20-10   CONTRAST AND CONTRAST RENDITION FACTOR

Seeing in general, and the performance of close seeing tasks, is extensively affected by the *contrast* between the work viewed and its background (e.g., between printing on a book page and the page itself). Contrast and visibility resulting from good or bad contrast depends on the size of the details of the task and the *specularity* of the task and its background.

"Specularity" refers to the shinyness or the dullness of a surface. A mirror has high specularity; a burlap-covered wall has low specularity. A specular surface is, in general, a shiny surface. With a given task of certain types of characters on a certain background, contrast depends further on the lighting layout, the candlepower distribution of the luminaires, the polarization of the light (how the light waves vibrate in various planes approaching the task), the specularity of the light sources, and the viewing angle in relation to the light sources.

The object of a seeing task (e.g., a printed page) has its own inherent, built-in contrast characteristics, but the lighting system under which it is viewed can have a marked effect on the manner in which the basic contrast characteristics are rendered perceivable or are lost.

The *contrast rendition factor* (CRF) is a numerical index of how well a lighting system produces contrast rendition. Richard Blackwell has made contrast rendition measurements using an instrument called a *Visual Task Photometer* (reported in *Architectural Record,* October 1971). Using Blackwell's methods, the contrast rendition for the same task is determined when it is covered by a hemispherical enclosure and similarly illuminated. The CRF is then calculated by dividing the first reading (actual) by the second (sphere enclosed) reading.

The illumination in a uniformly lit sphere may not be the very best possible in all respects, but it is excellent and does serve as a basis for comparison.

20-11 EQUIVALENT SPHERE ILLUMINATION AND LIGHTING EFFECTIVENESS FACTOR

As mentioned in the preceding paragraph, the illumination of the subject of a seeing task located at the center of a uniformly lit sphere is essentially free of glare and is uniform. A person working on a table outdoors in an open field at midday when the sky is cloudy-bright has a seeing condition which is very close to *spherical illumination.* The extent to which a lighting system in a closed room, with equal footcandles of light falling on the work plane, can equal or duplicate this condition is its *equivalent spherical illumination* (ESI).

Some of the light falling on a particular work plane in an artificially illuminated room will be spherical and some will not. The amount of spherical illumination divided by total illumination gives an ESI *index.* This may be applied to total illumination to obtain ESI expressed in footcandles. This ESI index, spherical footcandles divided by total raw footcandles, is usually known as the *lighting effectiveness factor* (LEF).

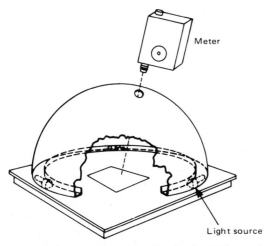

Meter

Light source

Figure 20-3 Equivalent sphere illumination testing equipment. (Courtesy of General Electric Company.)

While ESI and CRF considerations are valuable in designing lighting systems, at the present moment, this calculation, or other determination of ESI and CRF specific values, is not practical outside the laboratory. Calculations of ESI and CRF require a computer and proper programs along with much judgment in the use of same. Figure 20-3 is representative of the type of equipment used in the laboratory for measuring ESI. Here the inner surface of the hemisphere is evenly lit by many peripheral light sources, so that the task is illuminated by light approaching from all directions.

20-12 GLARE AND VEILING REFLECTIONS

Glare, in lighting work, is considered to be light that comes directly into an observer's eyes from lighting fixtures, windows, mirrors, or any shiny surface. The human eye has a wide range of peripheral vision, and with normal head and eye movements we see a great amount of our surroundings. Even though this is true, the primary direct glare zone is considered to fall within the angle between the horizontal and 45° above the horizontal (see fig. 20-4). Glare is distracting and contributes to visual discomfort.

Most sources of glare are not harsh, blinding sources, but are rather subtle and give the viewer a general feeling of excessive illumination in the room. At the same time, the "task" may not be particularly well lit, and the viewer may not realize that ambient glare is causing trouble. The problem is that the viewer has poor light "quality." The answer to this problem is usually found by providing shielding in the 0 to 45° (above horizontal) direct glare zone.

The lighting system itself can do nothing to minimize glare from ambient sources such as windows, but one important source of glare that can be controlled is the glare from light fixtures themselves. Figure 20-5 shows a striking comparison of the brightness of two different lighting systems which provide about equal illumination.

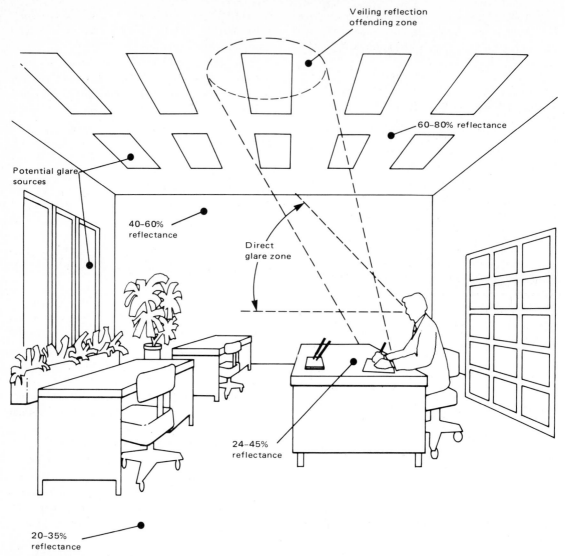

Figure 20-4 Depiction of direct glare zone and veiling reflection offending zone. (Courtesy of General Electric Company.)

The drafting room of fig. 20-5 is illuminated to a level of 200 fc at the work plane, and the ceiling fixtures are equipped with *parabolic wedge* plastic louvers. These louvers are quite expensive, but their performance is excellent. Notice the excessive glare from the fixtures in the conference room.

Glare or brightness of room surfaces within an observer's field of vision should be controlled by the architect to make seeing easier and to minimize the problems of the lighting system. In general, it is recommended that the background be slightly darker than the task. Often a desk top will be 10 times darker than a white paper placed on it; this

(a) Conference room illuminated with high-brightness recessed fluorescent fixture

(b) Parabolic wedge louvers on a semirecessed fixture produce 200 footcandles of exceptionally low brightness illumination

Figure 20-5 Comparison of high brightness and low brightness illumination systems. (Courtesy of General Electric Co.)

can cause fatigue and discomfort, which can result in errors and unhappiness on the part of a person working for long hours at the desk.

Figure 20-4 shows a *veiling reflection offending zone,* which, with respect to the person shown, is the area from which light emanating and falling on the work plane can cause a type of glare known as *veiling reflections.* In fig. 20-4, the light from the veiling reflection zone approaches the work plane at such an angle that the light reflected from the task is directed squarely into the worker's eyes. Such light, as everyone knows only too well, can obscure the characters on the task with an aura of light—a veiling reflection. The worker may strain to see through this veil, or he or she may be able to change the position of the task or the position of his or her head. Such adjustments are themselves wearying.

The worker can confirm the presence of these veiling reflections by placing a mirror flat on the work plane; if any of the overhead luminaires are visible in the mirror, veiling reflections will be a problem. Assuming that luminaires cannot be moved, the obvious answer to this problem is for the work plane surface (desk, etc.) to be relocated, or for the worker to change his or her position at the surface.

When a room is lit by rows of luminaires, the best position for minimum veiling reflections is between rows, with the worker facing in a direction that is parallel to the rows. Figure 20-6 shows an ideal fixture arrangement when two fluorescent-type fixtures can be utilized; these fixtures should be placed slightly behind the worker rather than ahead of him or her on each side.

In the original design of a new building, much can be done to minimize glare and veiling reflections and to maximize contrast and ESI values. One technique that should be explored is the use of nonuniform lighting fixture and work-station layouts. Figure 20-7 shows how ESI can be improved by optimum placement of 2 ft × 4 ft fluorescent luminaires relative to the desks in an office. Here the numbers in parentheses are ESI values in spherical footcandles.

Figure 20-6 Lighting for minimum glare and veiling reflections. (Courtesy of General Electric Company.)

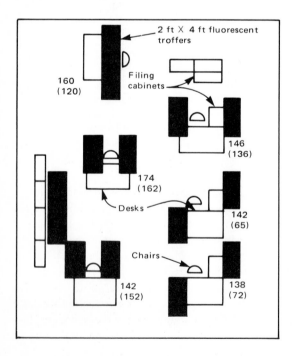

Figure 20-7 Effect on ESI of location of office desks relative to fixture locations. (General Electric Company.) A nonuniform layout of four-lamp 2 × 4 ft fluorescent troffers is shown for an office. The numbers shown are footcandles, with ESI values in parentheses.

20-13   VISUAL COMFORT PROBABILITY

Visual comfort, and as a result, visual efficiency is greatly influenced, as we have said, by glare and veiling reflections. An index of visual comfort called *visual comfort probability* (VCP), based on extensive research, can be calculated by means of a series of complicated, computerized calculations. VCPs take into account fixture brightness at different viewing angles and fixture size for an assumed set of conditions, which includes room size, mounting height of fixtures, level of room illumination, and room surface reflectances.

Figure 20-8 Typical tabulation of VCPs for a particular luminaire. (Courtesy of General Electric Company.)

100 FC room		Reflectances 80/50/20							
		Luminaires lengthwise				Luminaires crosswise			
W	L	8.5*	10.0*	13.0*	16.0*	8.5*	10.0*	13.0*	16.0*
20	20	71	74	79	82	68	71	74	78
20	30	66	68	72	75	64	66	67	70
20	40	64	65	68	70	63	64	64	65
20	60	62	64	65	66	62	62	62	63
30	20	72	75	79	81	70	73	76	79
30	30	66	68	72	74	65	67	68	70
30	40	63	65	67	69	63	64	64	65
30	60	61	62	63	65	61	62	61	62
30	80	60	61	62	63	60	61	61	61
40	20	73	76	80	81	72	74	78	80
40	30	67	69	73	74	66	68	70	71
40	40	63	65	67	69	63	64	65	66
40	60	61	62	63	64	62	62	62	62
40	80	59	61	61	62	61	61	60	60
40	100	59	60	60	61	61	61	60	60
60	30	68	70	73	75	67	69	70	73
60	40	64	65	67	69	64	65	65	67
60	60	61	62	62	64	62	62	62	62
60	80	60	61	60	61	61	61	60	60
60	100	59	60	59	60	61	61	59	59
100	40	67	68	69	71	67	68	68	69
100	60	64	64	64	65	65	64	63	64
100	80	62	62	61	62	63	63	61	62
100	100	61	61	60	60	62	62	60	60

The visual comfort probability system produces ratings for lighting equipment according to a fixture's potential for producing glare. A fixture will ordinarily not be a problem in a room where it has a VCP of 70 or greater.

*Fixture mounting height in feet.

Fixture manufacturers make these calculations and present tables of VCPs for their various fluorescent fixtures. Thus the system designer makes no such calculations, but merely selects the values from the appropriate tabulations. Figure 20-8 shows such a tabulation for a particular luminaire for a room level of illumination of 100 fc when ceiling reflectance is 80%, wall reflectance is 50%, floor reflectance is 20%, and when fixture mounting heights are 8, 10, 13, and 16 ft. It is assumed that a VCP of 70 or higher will give satisfactory results.

20-14 LIGHT DISTRIBUTION CURVES

The light distribution, or candlepower distribution, curve for certain luminaires equipped with certain lamps can give at one glance a very good idea of the type of performance that may be expected. An understanding of what such a curve is can best be achieved by learning how such a curve is drawn.

Figure 20-9 shows the test rig that might be used to obtain the data of fixture performance needed to plot a distribution curve. Figure 20-9 shows a vertical support post on to which a swing

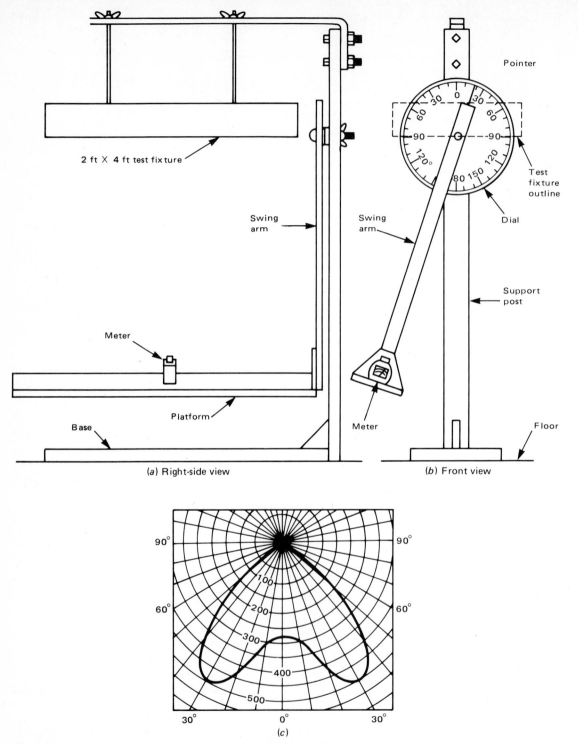

(a) Right-side view

2 ft × 4 ft test fixture

Swing arm

Meter

Platform

Base

(b) Front view

Pointer

Test fixture outline

Dial

Swing arm

Support post

Meter

Floor

(c)

Figure 20-9 Light distribution curve and testing rig for plotting same.

arm is mounted. The swing arm is pivoted around a pivot point in the center of the dial shown. The swing arm supports a small platform onto which is secured a light meter. The lighting fixture (luminaire) to be tested is hung, as shown, above the meter and centered in line with the post support. It may be hung in the position shown or rotated in a horizontal plane through 90° or any other angle desired. The meter may be mounted at any point on the platform.

The swing arm is positioned at all angles and meter readings taken at each position. The foot-candle readings of the meter are then transposed into candle power values and plotted on the polar coordinate chart, also shown in fig. 20-9. So the distribution curve shows quickly and easily the magnitude of the light that emanates from a luminaire in all directions.

A rectangular fixture such as the 2 ft × 4 ft fluorescent fixture shown does not cast a symmetrical pattern of light in all directions, and the fixture would need to be tested in different positions, although lengthwise (as shown) and crosswise curves would be all that would normally be published.

20-15 LAMPS

The lamps which are used bare and enclosed, fully or partially, in luminaires are available in many, many types which with all their modifications and configurations are too numerous to list here. However, the primary categories of available lamps may be listed as follows.

Incandescent Lamps

Incandescent lamps consist of a coil of tungsten wire, or filament, supported in the effective center of a spherical or tubular glass enclosure, which filament becomes heated to incandescence (white hot) when an electric current passes through it. So that this filament will not oxidize and disintegrate, all air and other gases are exhausted from the enclosing glass bulb, which is then in most lamps filled with an inert gas. This gas is usually a mixture of nitrogen and argon. Incandescent lamps are available in many shapes, sizes, finishes, colors, capacities, and voltages:

1 Standard bulb (e.g., type A) (see fig. 20-10)
2 Reflector (R)
3 Parabolic (PAR)
4 Spot
5 Flood
6 Shapes: candles, tubular, spheres, etc. (see fig. 20-10)
7 Finishes: clear, frosted enameled, colored, plastic coated, etc.
8 Bases: medium, admedium, mogul, medium skirted, medium prefocus, mogul prefocus, candelabra, mini-can, candelabra prefocus, bayonet, ferrule, medium bipost, mogul bipost, mogul end prong, etc. (see fig. 20-11)
9 Voltages: from 6 to 300 V in many odd and unusual voltages
10 Wattages: from 2 to 10,000 W

Fluorescent Lamps

The fluorescent lamp consists basically of a glass tube with an electrode assembly mounted in each end, upon which a voltage is impressed. Facilitated by a filling of gas, an arc is struck between the two electrodes. A small amount of mercury placed inside the tube vaporizes with the heat of the arc and a great amount of ultraviolet light is produced as the current of the arc passes through the mercury vapor. The tube is internally coated with phosphorescent material which fluoresces as the ultraviolet light strikes it and is transformed in wavelength to visible light. Some details of types of fluorescent lamps follow:

1 Preheat type (for use with starters)
2 Rapid start
3 Slimline instant start
4 High output and very high output (HO and VHO) power groove
5 Nominal tube lengths: 5, 6, 9, 12, 15, 18, 21, 24, 26, 28, 33, 36, 48, and 60 in.
6 Tube shapes: straight, U-shaped, and circular (see fig. 20-10)

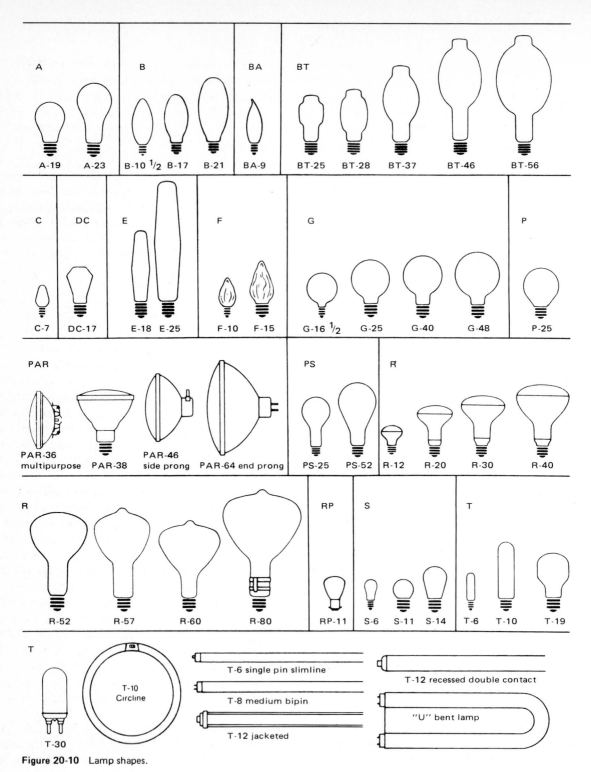

Figure 20-10 Lamp shapes.

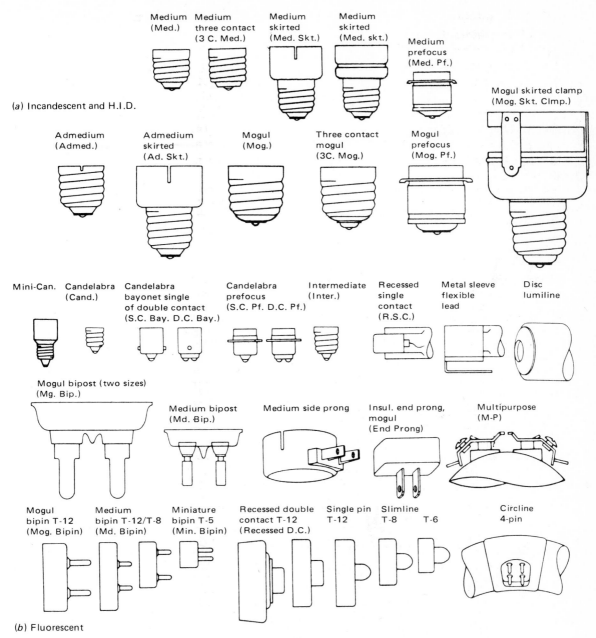

(a) Incandescent and H.I.D.

Medium (Med.)
Medium three contact (3 C. Med.)
Medium skirted (Med. Skt.)
Medium skirted (Med. skt.)
Medium prefocus (Med. Pf.)
Mogul skirted clamp (Mog. Skt. Clmp.)

Admedium (Admed.)
Admedium skirted (Ad. Skt.)
Mogul (Mog.)
Three contact mogul (3C. Mog.)
Mogul prefocus (Mog. Pf.)

Mini-Can.
Candelabra (Cand.)
Candelabra bayonet single of double contact (S.C. Bay. D.C. Bay.)
Candelabra prefocus (S.C. Pf. D.C. Pf.)
Intermediate (Inter.)
Recessed single contact (R.S.C.)
Metal sleeve flexible lead
Disc lumiline

Mogul bipost (two sizes) (Mg. Bip.)
Medium bipost (Md. Bip.)
Medium side prong
Insul. end prong, mogul (End Prong)
Multipurpose (M-P)

Mogul bipin T-12 (Mog. Bipin)
Medium bipin T-12/T-8 (Md. Bipin)
Miniature bipin T-5 (Min. Bipin)
Recessed double contact T-12 (Recessed D.C.)
Single pin T-12
Slimline T-8   T-6
Circline 4-pin

(b) Fluorescent

Figure 20-11 Lamp mounting bases (not actual size.) Base types and designations with abbreviations.

7 Tube diameters: 1/2, 5/8, 3/4, 1, 1 1/8, 1 1/4, 1 1/2, and 2 1/8 in.

8 Colors: cool white, warm white, deluxe cool white, deluxe warm white, daylight, black light, black light blue, soft white, natural, red, blue, green, gold, pink, and cool green

9 Mounting bases: Single pin, miniature bipin, medium bipin, mogul bipin, four pin, and recessed double contact (see fig. 20-11)

10 Voltages: as required by lamp ballasts—118, 120, 208, 220, 236, 260, 265, 277, 464, and 480 standard nominal voltages

11 Wattages: from 4 to 220 W

For more on fluorescent lamps, see arts. 20-17 through 20-20.

Tungsten Halogen Lamps

The tungsten halogen lamp is a form of incandescent lamp which incorporates the halogen regenerative cycle. Into this incandescent lamp is charged a small amount of a gas of the halogen family (iodine, bromine, chlorine, fluorine, and cyanogen); usually iodine or bromine are used. As any incandescent lamp burns, molecules of the tungsten filament are emitted and fly off the filament to settle on the surface of the glass bulb. This causes a darkening of the bulb with consequent loss of light, and causes the filament to gradually disintegrate until failure occurs.

In the tungsten halogen lamp, the free molecules of tungsten combine with molecules of the halogen gas and recirculate in the bulb and are deposited back on the filament. The filament structure is thus maintained, the bulb does not blacken, and the life of the lamp is greatly extended. Some details of tungsten halogen lamps follow:

1 *Lamp shapes:* tubular, PAR, and PS bulb

2 *Tubular contacts:* single or double end

3 *PAR shaped* (parabolic aluminized reflector type)

4 *Tube diameters* (tubular type): 5/16 to 3 in. but mostly 3/8 to 1 in.

5 *Type bases:* screw base (mini-can, medium skirted, and mogul), recessed single contact, two-pin prefocus, bayonet, mogul end prong, medium two-pin, medium prefocus, medium bipost, mogul bipost

6 *Voltages:* 7, 25, 28, 120, 125–130, 130, 185, 208, 220, 240, 277, and 480 V

7 *Wattages:* 75, 100, 150, 200, 250, 300, 400, 500, 750, 800, 1000, 1250, 1500, 2000, 5000, 6000, and 10,000 W

8 *Tube finishes:* clear and outside frosted

9 *Par finish:* clear

10 *PS bulb finish:* inside frosted

11 *PAR light patterns:* very narrow spot, narrow spot, medium flood, wide flood

High-Intensity-Discharge Lamps

All high-intensity-discharge (HID) lamps include a glass bulb or tube which is mounted on some type of screw base (or other type base), and which encloses an *arc tube*. The arc tube is a short quartz glass tube 2 to 5 in. long which has electrodes at each end, and a starting gas which is easily ionized when a high voltage is impressed on the electrodes. The arc tube also contains some type of *arc metal* which can be vaporized and ionized when an electric arc is established between the arc tube electrodes (see figs. 20-20, 20-24, and 20-26).

When switched on, the ionization of the starting gas (mercury vapor lamp) enables a current to flow between electrodes. As current flows, temperature rises and the arc metal begins to vaporize and fill the arc tube until current flow is adequately high to strike an arc. When this occurs, a tremendous number of collisions take place among the ions and electrons in the arc tube. These collisions result in energy addition to the atoms so struck, and an orbital shift in the outer ring of electrons occurs. As this added energy is then lost, the electrons shift back to their original orbits, and as this occurs radiation is produced.

High-intensity-discharge lamps are available in three varieties: mercury vapor, metal halide, and high-pressure sodium. They may be described further as follows:

Mercury Vapor Lamps (see fig. 20-20)

1 *Lamp shapes:* arbitrary (typical light bulb shape), tubular, elliptical, PAR, reflector, and bulged tubular (tubular with center of tube enlarged)

2 *Types of bases:* medium screwed, admedium screwed, mogul screwed, admedium skirted, and medium side prong

3 *Overall length:* arbitrary—5 7/16 in.; elliptical—5 1/8, 7 1/2, and 8 1/4 in.; tubular—5 5/8 and 11 in.; PAR—4 11/32 and 5 7/16 in; reflector type—7, 7 1/2, 10 1/8, 11 3/4, and 13 7/8 in.; bulged tubular—11 5/16, 14 5/16, and 15 1/16 in.

4 *Diameter:* arbitrary—2 7/8 in.; elliptical—2 1/8, 2 15/16, 3 1/2, and 4 5/8 in.; tubular—1 1/4 and 2 in.; PAR type—4 3/4 in.; reflector type—5, 6 1/2, 7 1/2, and 10 in.; bulged tubular—4 5/8, 5 3/4, and 7 in.

5 *Voltages:* require ballasts which are available in all standard voltages

6 *Wattages:* 40, 50, 75, 85, 100, 175, 250, 400, 700, and 1000 W plus self-ballasted types in sizes 160, 300, 450, and 750 W

7 *Finishes:* clear (predominantly blue-green color), deluxe white, and warm deluxe white

See also art. 20-22 for more on MV lamps.

Metal Halide Lamps

Metal halide (MH) lamps are basically similar to the mercury vapor lamps described above except that metallic compounds are added in the arc tubes to improve color and other radiation characteristics as well as efficiency. These metals are added in the form of their halide salts, usually iodides of sodium, thallium, indium, and scandium as well as mercury. The result is lamps with 50% gain in efficacy, over mercury vapor lamps, improved optical control due to a smaller light source, and an acceptable white light which gives much improved color rendition compared to clear mercury vapor lamps.

1 *Lamp shapes:* elliptical and bulged tube
2 *Types of bases:* mogul screwed only
3 *Overall lengths:* 8 1/4, 11 5/16, and 15 1/16 in.
4 *Diameter:* 3 1/2, 4 5/8, and 7 in.
5 *Voltages:* require ballasts which are available in all standard voltages
6 *Wattages:* 175, 250, 400, 1000, and 1500 W
7 *Finishes:* clear and phosphor coated

See also art. 20-23 for more on MH lamps.

High-Pressure Sodium Lamps

The high-pressure sodium (HPS) lamp is quite different from the mercury vapor and metal halide types and has a much smaller, ceramic arc tube which has 92% transparency. This arc tube contains the rare gas xenon and a solid amalgam of mercury and sodium. A starting voltage of 2500 V ionizes the xenon, and the arc is struck. As the mercury and sodium are vaporized and ionized, the color of the light resolves into a golden value that is somewhat warmer than a warm white fluorescent. The efficacy is extremely high—as much as 140 lm/W.

1 *Lamp shapes:* elliptical only
2 *Types of bases:* mogul screwed only
3 *Overall lengths:* 7 3/4, 9, 9 3/4, 11 5/16, and 15 1/16 in.
4 *Diameters:* 2 1/4, 2 15/16, 3 1/8, 3 1/2, and 4 5/8 in.
5 *Voltages:* require ballasts which are available in all standard voltages
6 *Wattages:* 50, 70, 100, 150, 200, 215, 250, 310, 360, 400, 880, and 1000 W
7 *Finishes:* clear and diffuse coated

See also art. 20-24 for more on HPS lamps.

20-16 MORE ON INCANDESCENT LAMPS

The "Incandescent Lamps" section of art. 20-15 gives some generalized information concerning incandescent lamps. More specific data on these are covered here.

As shown in Fig. 20-10, the glass enclosures for incandescent lamps take many shapes and have identifying letter designators. Some of these letter designators are abbreviations of the names given to the shape shown: C = candle; F = flame; G = globular; PAR = parabolic aluminized reflector; R = reflector; T = tubular; ER = elliptical reflector. Other abbreviations, such as A and B, are strictly arbitrary choices and give no direct indication.

The lamp bases of all types are sketched in fig. 20-11; these sketches do give a good indication of relative size within types but otherwise are not to scale. Figure 20-12 gives a specific tabulation of

pertinent data for a wide range of incandescent lamps, including initial lumens and lumens per watt for most lamps.

20-17 MORE ON FLUORESCENT LAMPS

Figures 20-13 and 20-14 show photographs and some construction details of fluorescent lamps. Let us now examine some of the specific characteristics of the several types of fluorescent lamps in common use. See also art. 20-15 for generalized information on lamps.

Figure 20-12 Incandescent lamp data. (Courtesy of General Electric Company.)

Watts	Bulb size	Volts	Amperes	Approximate initial lumens	Rated initial lumens per watt	Rated average life hours	Filament diameter, in.	Type base
6[b]	S-6	120	.050	44	7.4	1500	0.00045	Candle
10[b]	S-14	120	.083	80	8.0	1500	0.00064	Medium
25[b]	A-19	120	.21	235	9.4	2500	0.0012	Medium
40	A-19	120	.34	455	11.4	1500	0.0013	Medium
60[c]	A-19	120	.50	870	14.5	1000	0.0018	Medium
75[c]	A-19	120	.63	1,190	15.9	750	0.0021	Medium
100[a]	A-19	120	.83	1,750	17.5	750	0.0025	Medium
100	A-21	230	.43	1,280	13.0	1000	0.0016	Medium
100	A-23	34	3.12	2,160	21.6	1000	0.0061	Medium
100 (Proj.)[c]	T-8 1/2	120	.83	1,920	19.2	50	0.0024	Medium
150[a]	A-21	120	1.25	2,880	19.2	750	0.0033	Medium
200[a]	A-23	120	1.67	4,010	20.1	750	0.0040	Medium
200	PS-30	120	1.67	3,710	18.5	750	0.0038	Medium
300	PS-30	120	2.50	6,110	20.4	750	0.0050	Medium
300	PS-35	120	2.50	5,820	19.4	1000	0.0051	Mogul
500[a]	PS-35	120	4.17	10,850	21.7	1000	0.0071	Mogul
500	T-3	120	4.17	10,950	21.9	2000	0.0073	
1000[a]	PS-52	120	8.3	23,740	23.7	1000	0.0110	Mogul
1000	PS-52	250	4.3	17,700	17.7	2000	0.0075	Mogul
1000	T-20	120	8.3	22,000	22.0	500	0.0107	Mog. Bipost
1000 (Spot)	G-40	120	8.3	25,000	25.0	200	0.0114	Mog. Prefocus
1500	PS-52	120	12.5	34,400	22.9	1000	0.015	Mogul
1500	T-3	240	6.25	35,800	23.9	2000	0.0093	
2000	G-48	120	16.7	58,000	29.0	200	0.018	Mog. Bipost
5000	G-64	120	41.7	145,000	29.0	150	0.029	Mog. Bipost
10,000	G-96	120	83.3	335,000	33.5	75	0.046	Mog. Bipost

[a]Vertical coiled-coil filament

[b]Vacuum

[c]Coiled-coil filament

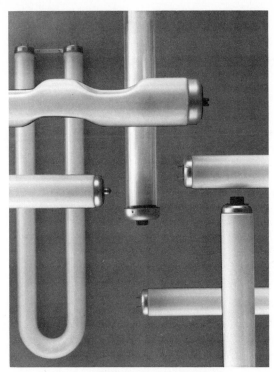

Figure 20-13 Typical fluorescent lamps. (Courtesy of General Electric Company.)

Preheat Lamps (for use with starters)

The earliest fluorescent lamps were all of the preheat type, and even though more favorable types have since been developed we still use preheat lamps in great quantities. These lamps require starters which are automatic switching devices designed to preheat the electrodes for starting purposes. The preheating of the electrodes by current flow through them causes the electrodes to emit a stream of electrons through the glass tube, thus ionizing the gas in the tube. This ionization causes the gas to be more conductive and enables the electrodes to strike an electric arc between the electrodes. The starter automatically turns the preheat process off after a few seconds and applies the voltage to the main electrodes and the lamp lights.

Preheat (starter type) lamps always have bipin (two-pin) mounting bases. They are available in

wattages ranging from 4 to 90 W and in lengths from 6 in. to 5 ft. However, the 20-W, 24-in.-long preheat lamp is by far the most popular. As is true with almost all fluorescent lamps, preheat lamps are available in all the popular colors, listed with their standard abbreviations:

> Cool white, CW
> Soft white, SW
> Warm white, WW
> Deluxe cool white, CWX
> Deluxe warm white, WWX
> Daylight, D
> Natural, N
> Red, R
> Blue, B
> Green, G
> Gold, GO
> Pink, PK
> Plant light, PL (for plant growth)
> Black light, BL
> Black light blue, BLB
> Chroma 50, C50

Preheat, starter-type lamps are identified by the same type of code number system that other fluorescent types use. This code consists, in standard sequence, of "F" for fluorescent, the wattage (or length), "T" for tubular shape, the diameter in eighths of an inch, and the lamp color as abbreviated above. Thus the ordering code number for a 20-W, cool white, preheat, starter-type lamp may be written as F20T12CW. Here the T12 tells us that this lamp is tubular and is 12 eighths of an inch, or 1 1/2 in., in diameter.

Rapid Start Fluorescent Lamps

The rapid start circuit, introduced to the lighting market in 1952, is a combination of the features of the preheat and the instant start types. Both of those types preceded the rapid start lamp. No starter is required to preheat the electrodes of the rapid start lamp; the ballasts which are required have separate windings which heat the cathodes continuously.

Rapid start (RS) lamps may be successfully

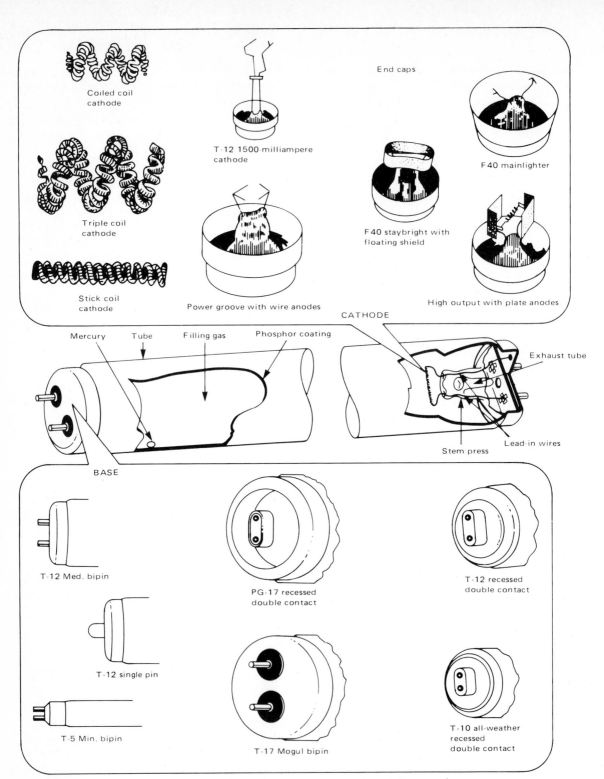

Coiled coil cathode

Triple coil cathode

Stick coil cathode

T-12 1500-milliampere cathode

Power groove with wire anodes

End caps

F40 staybright with floating shield

F40 mainlighter

High output with plate anodes

Mercury   Tube   Filling gas   Phosphor coating

CATHODE

Exhaust tube

Stem press   Lead-in wires

BASE

T-12 Med. bipin

T-12 single pin

T-5 Min. bipin

PG-17 recessed double contact

T-17 Mogul bipin

T-12 recessed double contact

T-10 all-weather recessed double contact

Figure 20-14 Fluorescent lamp construction details. (Courtesy of General Electric Company.)

dimmed or operated in a flashing manner. The RS lamp is used in the vast majority of new fluorescent lighting installations today and has for many years. Type HO (high output), Power Groove or type VHO (very high output) or type SHO (super high output), Circline, and all-weather lamps all utilize the RS-type circuit.

When two lamps are operated together, series start capacitors are used in the ballast assemblies. These capacitors cause one lamp to lead or to start first and the other lamp then has nearly the entire ballast voltage across the connections to the second lamp to aid in quick, reliable starting.

The rapid start circuit made it possible to develop fluorescent lamps with power loading beyond the previous limit of about 10 W per foot of tube length, which had been achieved with a lamp current of 430 milliamperes (mA; 0.43 A). Lamp currents of 800 and 1500 mA are now common in the high output and very high output (power groove) lamps. RS lamps are available in all the colors listed above for preheat, starter-type lamps, and with a few exceptions the ordering code (e.g., F40T12CW/RS) is similar.

Rapid start, 430-mA lamps are made in 25 and 30 W sizes, 36 in. long, and in 35 and 40 W sizes, 48 in. long. High-output, 800-mA, RS lamps are available in 12 sizes, ranging from 25 to 110 W and in lengths ranging from 18 to 96 in. Very high output Power Groove 1500-mA RS lamps are available in capacities ranging from 38 to 215 W (38, 55, 115, 135, 160, 195, and 215 W) and in lengths from 18 to 96 in. The high output and very high output (HO and VHO) lamps have a somewhat different ordering code in that the number following the "F" is the lamp length in inches instead of the wattage. For example, a 160-W 72-in.-long very high output Power Groove, 1 1/2-in.-diameter cool white lamp bears the designator F72T12/CW/VHO.

Instant Start (Slimline) Lamps

Instant start (IS) lamps were introduced to the lighting marketplace in 1944 and have enjoyed great success and popularity ever since. IS lamps

ignite as soon as they are switched on and do not need starters. IS lamp ballasts supply adequate voltage across the electrodes at each end of the lamps to strike the necessary arcs. The arc heats the electrodes quickly so that they begin to emit electrons to sustain the arc.

As with types HO and VHO rapid start lamps, the ordering code designator uses the lamp length rather than the lamp wattage for the number that follows the letter "F." IS lamps usually have a single-pin base at each end and may be easily distinguished by this. However, some IS lamps have two pins even though the circuitry is identical; in this case, the two pins are connected together inside the end caps.

T6 (3/4 in.) and T8 (1 in.) type IS lamps are usually operated at 200 mA current flow rate, while T12 (1 1/2 in.) IS lamps are operated at 425 mA. At higher currents these lamps do emit more light, but efficiency is slightly reduced and at lower currents the opposite is true. Minimum current is about 120 mA; at less than this, lamp life is seriously curtailed. Dimming of IS lamps is not practical, although an IS lamp may be operated at different output levels by providing separate ballasts for each level.

In the past IS two-lamp circuits were connected with the lamps in a "lead-lag" parallel arrangement. One lamp was connected with a capacitor to give capacitive reactance and a leading power factor, while the other without a capacitor had a lagging power factor. The net result was a power factor very near unity. Today the two lamps are connected in series with sequence starting of the lamps and with an overall power factor which is slightly leading. The reader may wish to review at this time the discussions in chap. 18 dealing with inductive reactance, capacitive reactance, power factor, and the use of capacitors for power factor correction. The use of "series-sequence" ballasts for IS lamps has provided considerable benefit from the standpoint of reduced ballast cost, operating noise level, and size.

Instant start (slimline) lamps are available in essentially all of the colors listed above for preheat lamps except some of the more unusual ones such as black light. The ordering code number, as mentioned, is based on the lamp length instead of wattage, and available lengths are 24, 36, 42, 48, 60, 72, 84, and 96 in. Available wattages are 20, 25, 30, 35, 40, 50, 55, 60, 65, and 75 W.

20-18 COLOR FROM FLUORESCENT LAMPS

One of the greatest advantages of fluorescent lamps is the opportunities they present for the use of light in wide range of colors. As listed above in the section on preheat-type lamps, fluorescent lamps come in many colors. The inside of a fluorescent lamp is coated with a mixture of fluorescent phosphor materials which are able to receive the ultraviolet light that the mercury arc in the tube emits, and convert that light to visible light. Different phosphors produce different colors of visible light.

In other words, the phosphors receive light of one wavelength, that of ultraviolet, which wavelength is much too short for the eye to perceive, and transform that light into visible light of a greater wavelength to which the eye is sensitive. Light wavelength is measured in nanometers; one nanometer (nm) is one billionth of a meter (10^{-9} meter). Light was previously measured in angstroms; an angstrom is 1/10 of a nanometer. The range of visible light extends from about 380 nm to about 750 nm. Ultraviolet light has a wavelength that ranges from about 10 nm to 380 nm.

The composition of the lamp phosphors is varied according to the color purpose of the lamp, since

Figure 20-15 Lamp phosphors and their sensitivities. (Courtesy of General Electric Company.)

Phosphor	Lamp color	Wavelength, nanometers			
		Exciting range	Sensitivity peak	Emitted range	Emitted peak
Barium silicate	Black light	180–280	200–240	310–400	346
Barium-strontium- magnesium silicate	Black light	180–280	200–250	310–450	360
Cadmium borate	Pink	220–360	250	520–750	615
Calcium halophosphate	White	180–320	250	350–750	580
Calcium tungstate	Blue	220–300	272	310–700	440
Magnesium tungstate	Blue-white	220–320	285	360–720	480
Strontium halophosphate	Greenish-blue	180–300	230	400–700	500
Strontium ortho phosphate	Orange	180–320	210	450–750	610
Yttrium oxide	Orange	180–300	220–280	550–650	611
Zinc silicate	Green	220–296	253.7	460–640	525

Conversion Table For Frequently Used Wavelength Units

Unit	Equals	Exponential notation
1 millimeter (mm)	one thousandth of a meter	10^{-3}
1 micrometer (µm)	one millionth of a meter	10^{-6}
1 nanometer (nm)	one billionth of a meter	10^{-9}

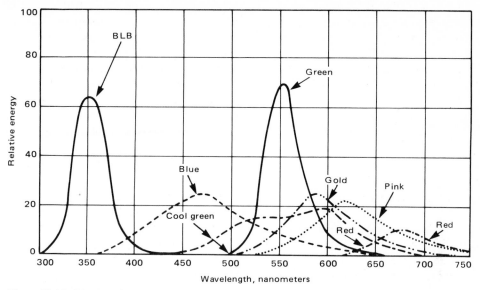

Figure 20-16 Wavelength curves for various colors of light. These curves show the relative energy outputs from colored fluorescent lamps of equal wattage. They represent only the energy transferred by phosphor conversion. Some energy generated by the mercury arc source is originally in the visible region. This direct generation of light represents less than 10 percent of the lumen output but does influence phosphor composition for final result. This applies to all but the gold and red lamps, in which the colored coatings inside the bulb absorb not only the directly radiated mercury wavelengths, but also the shorter wavelengths emitted by the phosphors. (Courtesy of General Electric Company.)

different phosphors produce varying colors, as shown in fig. 20-15. This table shows the sensitivities of the various phosphors to ultraviolet light and the range of wavelengths of visible light produced. Figure 20-16 shows the wavelength curves of various light colors plotted against the relative energy or intensity of each. These curves show the relative energy outputs of colored fluorescent lamps of equal wattages.

Figure 20-17 shows wavelength curves for six of the more popular fluorescent lamps. These curves should be compared with the curves of fig. 20-16 to see what light components constitute the resultant output of each of the six lamps. In fig. 20-17, the heavy smooth curves show only the light produced by transformation in the phosphor coatings. The mercury arc in each lamp produces some visible light directly, and this light is indicated by the vertical bars that appear on each graph.

The appearance of the light from a given lamp, as it is perceived by the human eye, is not a good indication of how lighted objects and room surfaces will appear. In many situations, accurate color rendition is very important, as in a retail store where clothing and other color-important products are on display. Many fluorescent light sources render an entirely different color quality than does daylight or incandescent lamp light.

Incidentally, incandescent lamps produce light which is considered by many to be quite favorable in color rendition, especially on human skin tones. In selecting fluorescent lamps, three considerations are most important:

1 Luminous efficacy, or the rate of lumen production per watt of electric power consumed

2 Color rendition, the accuracy of true color representation

3 Whiteness

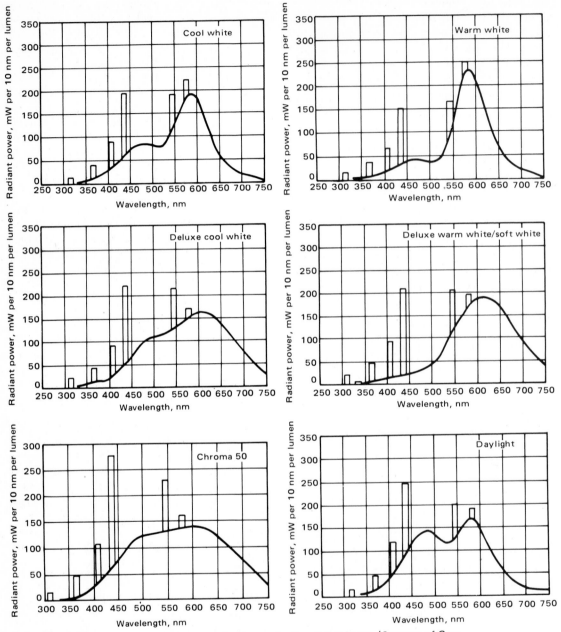

Figure 20-17 Light output wavelength curves for six popular fluorescent lamps. (Courtesy of General Electric Company.)

Optimum color rendition is always achieved at the expense of some loss in luminous efficacy. Deluxe lamps which give better color rendition produce about 30% less lumens than standard cool white or warm white lamps, but the increased vividness of colors offsets to a considerable extent the loss of lumens, and the same number of lamps may often be used for a given lighting installation.

Notice in fig. 20-17 how the deluxe cool white and deluxe warm white lamps are stronger in the red wavelengths of 600 to 750 nm than are the cool white and warm white lamps. Also notice that cool white lamps produce more blue light than do warm white lamps, and that the daylight lamp is very strong in the blue range.

One lamp manufacturer (General Electric Company) produces lamps trade-named Chroma 50 and Chroma 75, which perform exceptionally well where color rendition is unusually important. In clothing stores, printing establishments, hospital patient rooms and examining rooms, and museums, for example, precise color rendition is the foremost consideration. For best color rendition, many experts feel that a light source should be as close as possible to natural daylight and, of course, produce excellent color rendition. Figure 20-17 shows the curve for the Chroma 50 lamp and also the curve for daylight at noontime, sunny conditions. Notice the similarity of the two curves and how well each covers the full color spectrum.

20-19 SPECIAL FLUORESCENT LAMPS

Space does not nearly permit a full coverage of all the special lamps, designed for special purposes, and their reasons for being, that are available, but a brief mention of some of these follows (see fig. 20-18):

1 *Circline lamps.* These lamps are bent into a perfect circle with outside diameters of 6 1/2, 8 1/4, 10, 12, and 16 in. Tube diameter is 1 1/8 in., and wattages are 20, 22, 32, 40, and 44 W. They are usually RS type and are designed to produce seven of the most popular colors; cool white, warm white, and so on. Circline lamps lose efficacy when they are bent into a circle and their average

rated life is reduced; however, compared to incandescent lamps, which they often replace, their general performance is very favorable. The 44-W Circline lamp is made integral with its ballast, which is circular and fitted with a medium screw base so that it can be screwed directly into a medium screw-shell socket from which an incandescent lamp has been removed.

2 *Power saver lamps.* These lamps include the General Electric Watt-Miser, Westinghouse Econowatt, and Sylvania Supersaver lamps. These lamps are designed for extra low power consumption with little or no reduction in lumen output during their effective life. System efficiency is increased as much as 24%, and wattage is reduced up to 19%. Part of this efficiency increase resulted from the use of krypton gas in the lamp in place of argon; the higher molecular weight of krypton reduced voltage drop across the lamp, thereby reducing power consumption. Part of the efficiency increase also resulted from redesigned ballasts particularly suitable for the power saver lamps.

The power saver lamps are available in most of the popular lengths and colors and in a wide range of wattages from 25 to 185. With the emphasis on energy conservation that exists today, it is difficult to see how standard fluorescent lamps can be justified when these power saver lamps are available.

3 *U-shaped lamps.* These lamps, which are of 24 in. nominal length, are made to be used for 24-in.-long fixtures instead of the 24-in.-long straight tube lamp. Two such lamps would thus be used with one ballast and four lamp holders instead of four 24-in. straight lamps requiring two ballasts and eight lamp holders. Using standard life-cycle costing comparisons, two 40-W U-shaped lamps provide more illumination at 30% less cost per footcandle than four 20 W lamps.

U-shaped lamps are available with center-to-center distance between tubes of 3 5/8 and 6 in.; of these the 3 5/8-in. spacing is more popular with fixture manufacturers. They are of rapid start design, and are available in cool white, warm white, deluxe cool and warm white, and white colors. They are 40-W lamps. Lamp life is somewhat less than 48-in. straight tube lamps, but is appreciably greater than 24-in. straight tube lamps (see fig. 20-19).

Nominal lamp watts	Bulb	Nominal outside diameter, in.	Base	Lamp ordering code	Standard packing quantity	Description	Rated life, three or more burning hours per start	Approximate initial lumens	Approximate lumens at 40% rated average life
T-9 1 1/8 in. diameter									
20	T-9	6 1/2 in. Diameter	Four-Pin	FC6T9/CW	12	Cool white	12000	800	590
				FC6T9/WWX	12	DeLuxe warm white	12000	630	370
				FC6T9/WW	12	Warm white	12000	825	610
22		8 1/4 in. Diameter		FC8T9/CW	12	Cool white	12000	1050	775
				FC8T9/SW	12	Soft white	12000	800	590
				FC8T9/CWX	12	DeLuxe cool white	12000	850	630
				FC8T9/WWX	12	DeLuxe warm white	12000	800	590
				FC8T9/WW	12	Warm white	12000	1000	740
				FC8T9/D	12	Daylight	12000	850	630
32		12 in. Diameter		FC12T9/CW	12	Cool white	12000	1900	1445
				FC12T9/SW	12	Soft white	12000	1300	960
				FC12T9/CWX	12	DeLuxe cool white	12000	1400	1120
				FC12T9/WWX	12	DeLuxe warm white	12000	1300	960
				FC12T9/WW	12	Warm white	12000	1800	1495
				FC12T9/D	12	Daylight	12000	1500	1245
				FC12T9/BL	12	Black light	12000	. . .	. . .
40		16 in. Diameter		FC16T9/CW	12	Cool white	12000	2600	2055
				FC16T9/SW	12	Soft white	12000	1900	1520
				FC16T9/CWX	12	DeLuxe cool white	12000	2000	1600
				FC16T9/WWX	12	DeLuxe warm white	12000	1900	1520
				FC16T9/WW	12	Warm white	12000	2500	1850

(*a*) Circline fluorescent lamp data

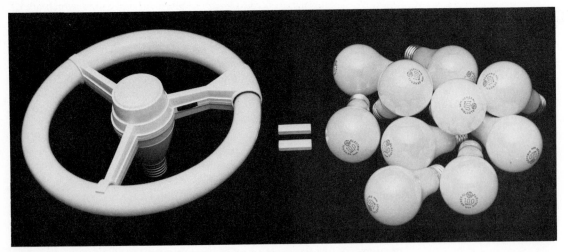

(*b*) Circlite lamp for incandescent lamp replacement

Figure 20-18 Special fluorescent lamps. (Courtesy of General Electric Company.)

(The example used here compares performance data of lamps on standard ballasts in a typical four-lamp recessed troffer operated at 77°F ambient temperature.)	Standard GE F40CW	Watt-miser GE F40CW/RS/WM	Watt-miser II GE F40LW/RS/WM	
Watts (two lamps plus ballast)	88	78	78	
Relative light, %	100	91	98	
Relative light per watt, %	100	103	110	
Comparative performance data				
Nominal lamp watts	40	35	35	
Approximate initial lumens	3150	2850	3050	
Average rated life* @ three or more hours per start	20,000	20,000	20,000	

*Life ratings are estimated, based on engineering design evaluations.

(c) Power saver lamps

Figure 20-18 *(Cont.)*

Nominal lamp watts	Bulb	Nominal length, in.	Base	Lamp ordering code	Standard packing quantity	Description	Average rated life, three hr per start*	Approximate initial lumens	Approximate lumens at 40% rated average life
T-12 1 1/2 in. Diameter—3 5/8 in. leg spacing									
40	T-12 U-shape	24	Medium Bipin	F40CW/U/3	12	Cool white—Mod-U-Line; 3 5/8 in. leg spacing	12000	2900	2525
				F40CW/U/3 360-PALLET	360	Cool white—Mod-U-Line; 3 5/8 in. leg spacing; palletized—360 lamps	12000	2900	2525
				F40CWX/U/3	12	DeLuxe cool white— Mod-U-Line; 3 5/8 in. leg spacing	12000	2020	1675
				F40WWX/U/3	12	DeLuxe warm white— Mod-U-Line; 3 5/8 in. leg spacing	12000	1980	1645

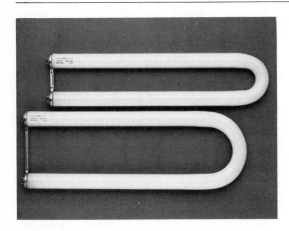

*At 12 hours per start, average rated life is 18,000 hours.

(d) Mod-U-Line U-shaped fluorescent lamps (rapid start)

Reflector lamps

Several sizes of fluorescent lamps are available with an internal white reflector on part of the inner surface of the tube to provide built-in light control. The unreflectorized portion of the tube is called "the window". Intensity of the light emitted through the window is significantly increased; however, total light output is reduced. Except in applications with special requirements, regular lamps in efficient luminaires will usually perform better.

Aperture lamps

For certain applications, special fluorescent lamps are made with both the reflector and the phosphor coating removed from the window aperture. These are known as aperture lamps.

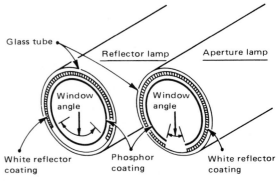

(e) Reflector and aperture fluorescent lamps

Figure 20-18 *(Cont.)*

Figure 20-19 Approximate fluorescent lamp data. (See explanatory notes in art. 20-20.)

Nominal	Ordering code	Diameter, in.	Length, in.	Current, mA	Watts, approximate	Life, hr	Lumens, approximate	At 40% life	Initial efficacy
				Preheat lamps					
15	F15T8/CW	1	18	425	23	7,500	870	765	38
20	F20T12/CW	1 1/2	24	425	30	9,000	1,250	1,110	42
30	F30T8/CW	1	36	425	37.5	7,500	2,200	2,000	59
40	F40T12/CW or WW	1 1/2	48	425	46	6,000	3,150	2,770	68
				Rapid-start lamps					
30	F30T12/CW	1 1/2	36	425	37.5	18,000	2,300	1,955	61
30	F30T12/WW	1 1/2	36	425	37.5	18,000	2,360	2,005	63
30	F30T12/CWX	1 1/2	36	425	37.5	18,000	1,530	1,285	41
40	F40T12/CW	1 1/2	48	425	46	20,000	3,150	2,770	68
40	F40T12/CWX	1 1/2	48	425	46	20,000	2,200	1,825	48
40	F40T12/WW	1 1/2	48	425	46	20,000	3,150	2,770	68
40	F40T12/D	1 1/2	48	425	46	20,000	2,600	2,290	57
40	F40T12/C50	1 1/2	48	425	46	20,000	2,200	1,890	48
40	F40T12/CW/U	1 1/2	24	425	46	12,000	2,900	2,525	63
				Rapid-start, high output (HO) lamps					
25	F18T12/CW/HO	1 1/2	18	800	38	9,000	1,060	880	28
35	F24T12/CW/HO	1 1/2	24	800	48	9,000	1,700	1,410	35
45	F36T12/CW/HO	1 1/2	36	800	58	9,000	2,850	2,480	49
60	F48T12/CW/HO	1 1/2	48	800	72.5	12,000	4,300	3,740	59
75	F60T12/CW/HO	1 1/2	60	800	90.0	12,000	5,400	4,700	60
85	F72T12/CW/HO	1 1/2	72	800	98	12,000	6,650	5,785	68
100	F84T12/CW/HO	1 1/2	84	800	114	12,000	7,800	6,785	68
110	F96T12/CW/HO	1 1/2	96	800	124	12,000	9,200	8,005	74
60	F48T12/CWX/HO	1 1/2	48	800	72.5	12,000	3,050	2,560	42
60	F48T12/WW/HO	1 1/2	48	800	72.5	12,000	4,300	3,740	59

Figure 20-19 (Cont.)

Nominal	Ordering code	Diameter, in.	Length, in.	Current, mA	Watts, approximate	Life, hr	Lumens, approximate	At 40% life	Initial efficacy
	Rapid-start, very high output (VHO), super-high output (SHO), and power groove (PG)								
110	F48T12/CW/SHO	1 1/2	48	1,500	115	12,000	6,900	5,240	60
135	F60T12/CW/VHO	1 1/2	60	1,500	140	10,000	9,000	7,020	64
165	F72T12/CW(GE)	1 1/2	72	1,500	170	10,000	9,900	7,720	58
215	F96T12/CW(GE)	1 1/2	96	1,500	225	10,000	14,500	11,310	64
110	F48PG17/CW(GE)	2 1/8	48	1,500	115	12,000	7,450	5,510	65
165	F72PG17/CW(GE)	2 1/8	72	1,500	170	12,000	11,500	8,510	68
215	F96PG17/CW(GE)	2 1/8	96	1,500	225	12,000	16,000	12,160	71
215	F96PG17/CWX(GE)	2 1/8	96	1,500	225	12,000	11,000	7,370	49
	Instant-start slimline lamps								
20	F24T12/CW	1 1/2	24	425	34	7,500	1,150	1,035	34
25	F42T6/CW	3/4	42	200	38	7,500	1,750	1,490	46
35	F42T12/CW	1 1/2	42	425	48	7,500	2,300	2,070	48
40	F48T12/CW	1 1/2	48	425	53	9,000	3,000	2,760	57
50	F64T12/CW	1 1/2	64	425	64	12,000	3,850	3,505	60
55	F72T12/CW	1 1/2	72	425	68	12,000	4,600	4,185	68
65	F84T12/CW	1 1/2	84	425	78	12,000	5,400	4,915	69
75	F96T12/CW	1 1/2	96	425	88	12,000	6,300	5,800	72
40	F48T12/CWX	1 1/2	48	425	53	9,000	2,050	1,825	39
	Power-saver lamps—GE Watt-miser, Westinghouse Econowatt, and Sylvania Supersaver								
25	F30T12/CW/WM	1 1/2	36	425	34	18,000	2,000	1,700	59
35	F40CW/RS/WM II	1 1/2	48	425	39.5	20,000	3,050	2,685	77
60	F96T12/CW/WM II	1 1/2	96	425	73	12,000	6,000	5,620	82
95	F96T12/CW/HO/WM II	1 1/2	96	800	109	12,000	9,100	7,915	83
185	F96PG17/CW/WM II	2 1/8	96	1,500	198	12,000	14,900	11,325	75

20-20 FLUORESCENT LAMP TABLE

Figure 20-19 presents a tabulation of the most important data concerning the most popular sizes of fluorescent lamps of the various types. In this table the abbreviations used have the following meanings:

CW—cool white
WW—warm white
CWX—deluxe cool white
WWX—deluxe warm white
D—daylight
U—U shaped
PG—Power Groove (General Electric trade name)
HO—high output
VHO—very high output (Westinghouse designator)
SHO—super high output (Sylvania designator)
T—tubular
F—fluorescent
C50—Chroma 50 (General Electric trade name)
C75—Chroma 75 (General Electric trade name)
RS—rapid start
IS—instant start
MA—milliamps
LPW—lumens per watt
SW—soft white
W—white
WM—Watt-Miser (General Electric power saver lamps)
N—natural

The following explanatory notes also apply to the table in fig. 20-19:

1 Lamp-life figures assume 3-hr burning time per start.
2 Initial lamp output in lumens is the rating after lamps have burned 100 hr.
3 LPW-lumens per watt is based on total wattage, including ballast.
4 Power saver lamps include the General Electric Watt-Miser, Westinghouse Econ-o-watt, and Sylvania Super Saver.
5 Total watts include lamps and ballasts.
6 Lamp current is in milliamps (mA) (e.g., 425 mA = 0.425 A).

7 Data in fig. 20-19 were taken from lamp manufacturers' catalogs; however, not all data were available and some are estimated. For use on an actual, large-scale project, all data should be confirmed before design use.
8 Cool white (CW) lamps are the basic lamps for comparison purposes in fig. 20-19. Some deluxe cool white (CWX) lamps have been included to show the appreciable reduction in lumens per watt compared to cool white lamps. In general, warm white (WW) lamps are equal to or slightly higher in LPW than cool white lamps. Deluxe warm white lamps (WWX) are appreciably lower in LPW efficacy than are CW or WW lamps.
9 Total watts shown include lamps and ballasts and are for two-lamp circuits; ballast wattage varies somewhat from manufacturer to manufacturer.

20-21 MORE ON HIGH-INTENSITY-DISCHARGE LAMPS

As outlined previously, HID lamps include several radiation sources—the mercury vapor lamp, the metal halide lamp, and the sodium vapor lamp (see art. 20-15). All are characterized by arc tubes which operate at a pressure and current density sufficient to strike and maintain an arc of exceedingly high intensity.

In 1934 the production and generalized use of the first high-pressure mercury vapor lamps began. This was a 400-W lamp consisting of an arc tube inside a glass chamber approximately 7 in. long, which was enclosed in another glass bulb. The HID mercury vapor lamp of 1934 had a luminous efficacy nearly twice that of available incandescent lamps. It also produced relatively great quantities of light from a light source that was physically small enough to permit good control of its light and to permit easy maintenance.

Today, HID lamps have been so extensively developed that our urgent need to save energy makes mandatory the consideration and use of HID lamps wherever possible. Luminous efficacy has been vastly increased from the early days when streets were lighted with carbon arc lamps that required almost constant maintenance. The following gives an idea of the improvement that has taken place in lamp efficacy:

1 Carbon arc lamps produced 4 lumens per watt (LPW).
2 Incandescent—up to 35 LPW.
3 Mercury vapor—now range from 30 to 63 LPW.
4 Fluorescent—now range from 30 to 83 LPW.
5 Metal halide—now range from 85 to 100 LPW.
6 Sodium vapor—95 to 140 LPW.

All high-intensity arc-discharge lamps, if connected to an unregulated electric power source, will draw an unlimited amount of current immediately and will self-destruct. To prevent this, a current-limiting device called a *ballast* is interposed between the power source and the lamp. So the ballast performs the following functions:

1 Limits current flow to the lamp to safe values
2 Transforms supply voltage if necessary to the voltage required to fire the arc
3 Regulates supply voltage to permit stable operation after ignition
4 Prevents any feedback of current or voltage disturbances from the arc into the power supply circuit
5 Compensates for the low power factor characteristics of the arc with the use of capacitance

All HID lamps require the use of ballasts.

20-22 MORE ON MERCURY VAPOR LAMPS

Figure 20-20 shows a typical mercury vapor (MV) HID lamp enclosed in the popular elliptical glass enclosure. However, mercury lamps are available in many configurations, as shown in fig. 20-21. This illustration also shows the wattage ratings available for each bulb shape as well as the types of bases utilized and the designator number—E17, for example. As with other types of

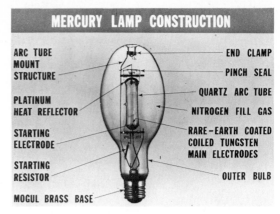

Figure 20-20 Typical mercury vapor lamp. (Courtesy of General Electric Company.)

lamps, the lamp designator is an alphanumeric one consisting of one or more letters and a number. The letters indicate bulb shapes as follows:

A—arbitrary designator (not symbolic)
BT—bulged tubular
E—elliptical
PAR—parabolic aluminized reflector
R—reflector
T—tubular

The number in the designator indicates the diameter of the bulb in eighths of an inch. Therefore, an E17 designator indicates an elliptically shaped bulb which is 2 1/8 in. in diameter (17 eighths) at the largest part of the lamp.

Mercury vapor lamps provide a great improvement in lighting efficacy compared with incandescent lamps which they often replace. A 300-W incandescent lamp can emit, when new, 6360 lm, or 21.2 LPW, while a 250-W standard mercury lamp, which with its ballast consumes 275 W, can produce 12,100 lm, or 44 LPW. This represents a dramatic improvement; however, the MV lamp loses some of its luster when compared with the 250-W metal halide lamp at 74.5 LPW, or the 250-W sodium vapor lamp at 90 LPW.

The arc in the arc tube of a MV lamp radiates ultraviolet light in many wave lengths; however, the heat-resistant glass of the outer bulb absorbs

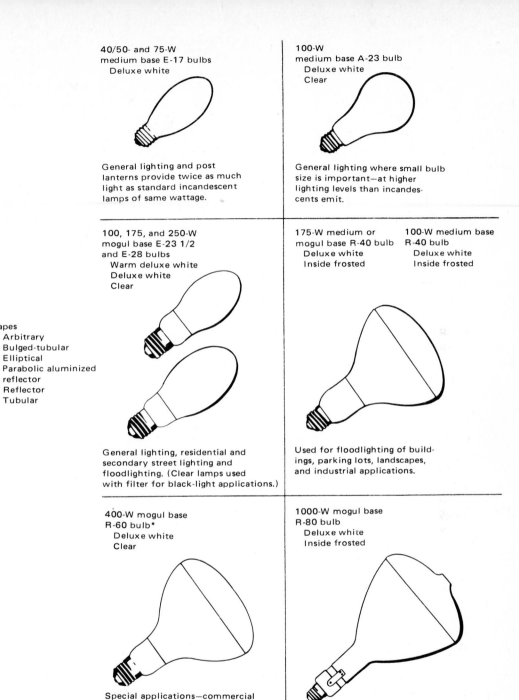

40/50- and 75-W
medium base E-17 bulbs
  Deluxe white

General lighting and post
lanterns provide twice as much
light as standard incandescent
lamps of same wattage.

100-W
medium base A-23 bulb
  Deluxe white
  Clear

General lighting where small bulb
size is important—at higher
lighting levels than incandescents emit.

100, 175, and 250-W
mogul base E-23 1/2
and E-28 bulbs
  Warm deluxe white
  Deluxe white
  Clear

Bulb shapes
A   Arbitrary
BT   Bulged-tubular
E   Elliptical
PAR   Parabolic aluminized
       reflector
R   Reflector
T   Tubular

General lighting, residential and
secondary street lighting and
floodlighting. (Clear lamps used
with filter for black-light applications.)

175-W medium or
mogul base R-40 bulb
  Deluxe white
  Inside frosted

100-W medium base
R-40 bulb
  Deluxe white
  Inside frosted

Used for floodlighting of buildings, parking lots, landscapes,
and industrial applications.

400-W mogul base
R-60 bulb*
  Deluxe white
  Clear

Special applications—commercial
and industrial floodlighting.
Two beam shapes available.
*Recommended minimum
mounting height in work
areas: 18 ft.

1000-W mogul base
R-80 bulb
  Deluxe white
  Inside frosted

Special applications—high bay
industrial lighting. Three beam
shapes available.

Figure 20-21 Mercury vapor lamp shapes and sizes.

683

85- and 100-W medium
base T-10 bulb
    Clear
    UV transmitting

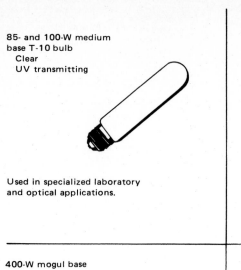

Used in specialized laboratory
and optical applications.

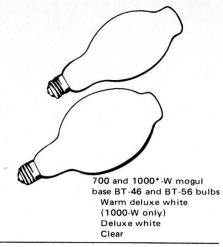

700 and 1000*-W mogul
base BT-46 and BT-56 bulbs
    Warm deluxe white
    (1000-W only)
    Deluxe white
    Clear

400-W mogul base
E-37 bulb
    Warm deluxe white
    Deluxe white
    Clear

General lighting—widely used
lamp for industrial, street, and
floodlighting. (Also available in
BT-37 shape.)

100-W admedium
base PAR-38 bulb
    Clear

Used for building and landscape
floodlighting, and with ultraviolet
filter for black-light applications.
Available with either
flood distribution.

400-W mogul base
R-52 bulb
    Deluxe white
    Inside frosted

General lighting—high mounting
industrial applications.

Figure 20-21 *(Cont.)*

much of this and limits the range of frequencies to those provided by the sun. MV lamps are also available with internal coatings of phosphors which convert much of the ultraviolet light to visible light much of which is in the red portion of the visible spectrum. The total light output is then essentially white, and both deluxe white (DX) and warm deluxe white (WDX) lamps are available.

When a MV lamp is turned off momentarily, or if a brief power failure occurs, it will not relight immediately when power is restored. A period of 3 to 6 min is required for the arc tube to cool and for internal pressure to fall until the arc can be struck again. This is a disadvantage that incandescent and fluorescent lamps do not have and is a factor that must be carefully considered. Every location experiences power failures, and some supplementary incandescent or fluorescent lamps must be installed with the MV lamps to prevent plunging a space into total darkness for as much as 6 min when power is momentarily curtailed.

MV lamps can be installed in any position; however, initial light output, as well as lumen maintenance, is slightly greater (3 to 4%) in the vertical position. All lamps experience a deprecia-tion in their light output during their entire life. After 24,000 hr of operation, the luminosity of MV lamps will range from 33 to 75% of original luminosity. Clear MV lamps have a slightly greater lumen maintenance than do those to which phosphors have been added. Figure 20-22 shows lumen characteristics for MV lamps with clear lamps falling in the upper portion of the shaded area, deluxe white lamps falling in the upper center portion of the shaded area, and warm de-luxe lamps in the lower portion. Of course, lamp lumen depreciation at various stages of life must be considered when luminaires are selected for installation.

MV lamp ballasts are, in general, of four types:

1 *Inductive ballasts.* This is a reactor type which is simple and inexpensive and when equipped with an across-the-line capacitor gives a high power factor.

2 *Lag ballasts.* This type consists of an auto-transformer plus a reactor, and is used where power factor correction is not required; it is some-what more expensive than other types.

3 *Regulator ballasts.* This ballast consists of an isolating transformer with a capacitor in the cir-cuit between the transformer secondary winding and the lamp. It gives a good power factor, about

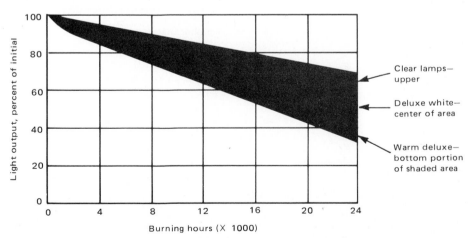

Figure 20-22 Mercury vapor lamp life maintenance characteristics. Shaded area shows compara-tive luminosity at various points of lamp life. (Courtesy of General Electric Company.)

95%, is easily applied to most any type of circuit, and gives very good voltage regulation. However, it is comparatively expensive.

4 *Autoregulator ballasts.* This is basically an autotransformer type with a capacitor in series with the lamp. It is the most popular ballast for new installations and is a compromise between the regulator type and the lag type. It gives low cost, low size and weight, and fairly good lamp wattage stability.

One factor that should be carefully examined in selecting a MV lamp system or fixture is the anticipated power factor. To be good, a PF should be 90% or higher. Most ballasts which are considered to be of normal or usual design will have a PF of 50% or so. This means that a normal PF ballast system will draw 80% more current than a high PF system; efficiency is much lower and the wiring system must be heavier.

When two lamps are used together, frequently a two-lamp ballast will be used. This is lighter, more compact, and less expensive than the use of two ballasts. Two-lamp ballasts are available for series or parallel connection of the lamps; the series connection is more popular, and is more compact and less expensive. With a series connection, if one lamp burns out, both lamps go out, and the good lamp is not damaged. With a parallel

Figure 20-23 Mercury vapor lamp performance data and mortality curve. (Courtesy of General Electric Company.)

Watts	ANSI code	Bulb	Base	MOL* in.	Average rated life (hours)	Approximate lumens for vertical operation		LPW* including ballast
						Initial	Mean	
Clear lamps—producing light having the characteristic blue-green color of the mercury spectrum								
100	H38HT-100	E-23 1/2	Mogul	7 1/2	24,000+	3,850	3,120	34
	H38LL-100	A-23	Medium	5 7/16	18,000	3,700	3,000	32
175	H39KB-175	E-28	Mogul	8 1/4	24,000+	7,950	7,470	41
250	H37KB-250	E-28	Mogul	8 1/4	24,000+	11,200	10,300	38
400	H33CD-400	E-37	Mogul	11 5/16	24,000+	21,000	19,100	48
1000	H36GV-1000	BT-56	Mogul	15 1/16	24,000+	57,000	48,400	52
	H34GV-1000	BT-56	Mogul	15 1/16	16,000+	56,000	48,700	51
Deluxe white lamps—phosphor coated								
40	H45AY-40/50/DX	E-17	Medium	5 7/16	16,000	1,140	910	23
50	H45AY-40/50/DX	E-17	Medium	5 7/16	16,000	1,575	1,260	26
75	H43AV-75/DX	E-17	Medium	5 7/16	16,000	2,800	2,250	32
100	H38JA-100/DX	E-23 1/2	Mogul	7 1/2	24,000+	4,200	3,530	35
	H38MP-100/DX	A-23	Medium	5 7/16	18,000	4,000	3,040	37
175	H39KC-175/DX	E-28	Mogul	8 1/4	24,000+	8,600	7,650	44
250	H37KC-250/DX	E-28	Mogul	8 1/4	24,000+	12,100	10,400	42
400	H33GL-400/DX	E-37	Mogul	11 5/16	24,000+	22,500	19,100	51
1000	H36GW-1000/DX	BT-56	Mogul	15 1/16	24,000+	63,000	47,500	57
	H34GW-1000/DX	BT-56	Mogul	15 1/16	16,000+	62,000	47,700	56
Warm deluxe white lamps—phosphor coated								
175	H39KC-175/WDX	E-28	Mogul	8 1/4	24,000+	6,500	5,760	34
250	H37KC-250/WDX	E-28	Mogul	8 1/4	24,000+	9,500	7,600	33
400	H33GL-400/WDX	E-37	Mogul	11 5/16	24,000+	20,000	16,400	46
1000	H36GW-1000/WDX	BT-56	Mogul	15 1/16	24,000+	58,000	39,440	52

*MOL = maximum overall length; LPW = lumens per watt

connection, when one lamp fails the other lamp continues and with proper connections is not damaged.

One popular parallel circuit connection for two lamps is the *lead-lag circuit*. Here, one of the two lamps is connected in series with a capacitor; this results in a high power factor.

Figure 20-23 presents a table of MV lamp performance data. In this table the second column lists ANSI code numbers suggested by the American National Standards Institute; these numbers are not the same as those given by lamp manufacturers, but lamps may be ordered from any manufacturer by using the ANSI code numbers. The column headed "MOL" gives the maximum overall length in inches. The right-hand column, approximate mean lumens of light production, shows the lumen output when a third of a lamp's average rated life in hours remains—for example, at the 16,000-hr point of a 24,000-hr rating.

In the mercury vapor type of lamp, a great amount of ultraviolet (UV) radiation is produced which is dangerous to the health of human beings. Fortunately, the outer bulb of a MV lamp prevents the passage of the UV radiation and no health hazard exists. However, if the outer bulb is broken away, the arc tube can continue to fire and the UV radiation may then be a threat to room occupants. Responsible people who regularly occupy a given building should watch for this hazard and take remedial action whenever necessary.

Some sizes of MV lamps (175, 250, and 400 W) are available in a special safety design in which the lamp is automatically turned off whenever the outer bulb is lost. Protection from UV radiation is thus assured. Mercury vapor lamps, in addition to those shown in fig. 20-23, are available in the PAR (parabolic aluminized reflector) configuration at 75 and 100 W, and also the reflector, "R," configuration at 175 W, R40, and 1000 W, R80.

20-23 MORE ON METAL HALIDE LAMPS

Figure 20-24 shows a typical metal halide lamp enclosed in an elliptical glass bulb. MH lamps are also available in the bulged tubular type of bulb

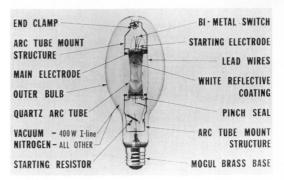

Figure 20-24 Metal halide (MH) lamp details. (Courtesy of General Electric Company.)

configuration in the 1000- and 1500-W sizes. As mentioned earlier, MH lamps are available with only the mogul screwed base and are available in 175-, 250-, 400-, 1000-, and 1500-W sizes.

Figure 20-25 gives performance data for MH lamps (General Electric Multi-Vapor). Here it may be seen that the LPW (lumens per watt), which is for the lamp only, not including the ballast, is much higher than for a mercury vapor lamp. For example, a 1000-W metal halide lamp produces 100 to 150 LPW. From fig. 20-23 it may be seen that a 1000-W MV lamp produces a maximum of 63,000 initial lumens (lm), or 63 LPW—appreciably less than the MH lamp.

The metal halide lamp, as mentioned, is basically a mercury vapor lamp with halides of metals such as scandium, sodium, indium, and thallium added to the arc tube. This addition causes the MH lamp to radiate light in colors that are different and generally more favorable than the basic color of the MV lamp. However, a comparison of figs. 20-23 and 20-25 shows that the life of MH lamps has been considerably shortened by the addition of these metal halide compounds.

Where color rendition is very important, as in most indoor applications, the MH bulb has a phosphor coating added to obtain this. For exterior applications, the clear MH lamp is usually utilized. With the phosphor coating, the MH lamp is now finding very extensive use in indoor applications in offices, commercial applications, and in schools and other institutional buildings.

Figure 20-25 Metal halide lamp performance data. (Courtesy of General Electric Company.)

Watts	Bulb	Base	General Electric lamp-ordering code	Lamp description (use lamps only on ballasts and in positions as described below)	MOL, in.[a]	Average rated life, hr (vertical)[b]	Ballast type[d]	Average lumens for vertical operation[g]		LPW, lamp only
								Initial	Mean[b]	
				Standard multivapor lamps[a]						
175	E-28	Mogul	MXR175/C/U	General lighting; any burning position; enclosed fixtures only	8 1/4	15,000	M-H M57	17,500	13,125	100
250	E-28	Mogul	MV250/U	Clear and phosphor-coated; general lighting; any burning position; use in enclosed fixtures only	8 1/4	10,000	M-H M58	20,500	17,000 (horizontal) 14,000	82 78
			MV250/C/U (phosphor-coated)					20,500	16,000 (horizontal) 13,500	82 78
400	E-37	Mogul	MV400/U	General lighting; any burning position; when within ±15° of vertical, may be used in open or enclosed fixtures; in all other positions, use in enclosed fixtures only	11 5/16	20,000[c]	M-H M59	34,000 32,000	25,600 (horizontal) 23,600	85 80
			MV400/C/U (phosphor-coated)					34,000 32,000	24,600 (horizontal) 22,600	85 80
1000	BT-56	Mogul	MV1000/U	General lighting; any burning position; when within ±15° of vertical may be used in open or enclosed fixtures; in all other positions, use in enclosed fixtures only	15 1/16	10,000[c]	M-H[e] M47	110,000 107,800	88,000 (horizontal) 86,240	110 108
			MV1000/C/U (phosphor-coated)					105,000 100,000	83,000 (horizontal) 79,000	105 100

Watts	Bulb	Base	Designation	Description	Max. length (in.)	Rated life (hr)	Ballast	Initial lumens	Mean lumens	Lumens per watt
1500	BT-56	Mogul	MV1500/HBU/E	Clear-special; burn base up to base 15° below horizontal; enclosed fixtures only	15 1/16	3,000	M-H[e] M48	155,000 150,000	140,000 (horizontal) 135,000	103 100
1500	BT-56	Mogul	MV1500/HBD/E	Clear-special; burn base down to base 15° above horizontal; enclosed fixtures only	15 1/16	3,000	M-H[e] M48	155,000 150,000	140,000 (horizontal) 135,000	103 100

I-line multivapor lamps[a]

Watts	Bulb	Base	Designation	Description	Max. length (in.)	Rated life (hr)	Ballast	Initial lumens	Mean lumens	Lumens per watt
400	E-37	Mogul	MV400/BU/I (base up)	Clear-general lighting; burning position; vertical base up to ±15° of vertical base up; open or enclosed fixtures	11 5/16	15,000	M-H or Lag CW/CWA[f] M59	34,000	26,500	85
400	E-37	Mogul	MV400/BD/I (base down)	Clear-general lighting; burning position; vertical base down to ±15° of vertical base down; open or enclosed fixtures	11 5/16	15,000	M-H or Lag CW/CWA M59	34,000	26,500	85
1000	BT-56	Mogul	MV1000/BU/I (base up) MV1000/BD/I (base down)	Clear-general or street lighting; burn vertical to ±15° of vertical; open or enclosed fixtures.	15 1/16	10,000	M-H M47	115,000	92,000	115

[a] Metal halide lamps normally exhibit some color variations from lamp to lamp, and gradual change in color throughout life. Operating conditions such as burning position and normal voltage variations can also affect the color of these lamps. All multivapor lamps have bulbs made of heat-resistant glass and are supplied with date-coded brass bases.

[b] Life and mean lumen ratings are for 10 hr per start operation, except the 1500-W lamp ratings which are for 5 hr per start.

[c] 6000 hr average rated life where operated in burning positions other than vertical ±30°.

[d] Ballast designations: M-H = metal halide; lag = mercury reactor or auto transformer type; CW/CWA = constant wattage or constant wattage auto transformer regulator type.

[e] Mercury-lag type ballasts can be used, providing a minimum 440 V rms, down to 0°F for the 1,000-W lamp and down to –20°F for the 1500-W lamp.

[f] Mercury lag or CW/CWA ballasts are suitable if they contain no peaking capacitor and are not two lamp series type.

[g] See current lamp specification bulletin for off-vertical lumens of lamps designed for angular burning.

The MH lamp is quite sensitive to fluctuations in supply voltage. If voltage is too low, less sodium in the arc tube is vaporized and a loss of yellow and red colors results. Excess line voltage has the opposite effect, with more yellows and reds produced. Because of this voltage sensitivity, special ballasts with better voltage regulation are usually required. Even then there will be some color variation from lamp to lamp, but with the standard MH lamp this is not usually an insuperable problem. Many MH lamps may be used with standard mercury vapor lamp ballasts.

Figure 20-25 gives specific information as to the burning position of the various MH lamps, and usually a vertical position is necessary. Often also, MH lamps are required to be enclosed in a fixture, and this fact is shown in fig. 20-25. In the MH lamp, the time required to strike the arc is less than in the MV lamp, and is about 2 to 3 min. However, the restrike time is longer and may be as much as 10 min.

Figure 20-25 mentions the trade name "Multi-Vapor"; this is used by the General Electric Company. Other trade names in use are Metalarc by Sylvania, and Metal Halide by Westinghouse. The I-Line, Multi-Vapor lamp, manufactured by General Electric and shown in fig. 20-25, has a somewhat different combination of metal halide compounds in the arc tube. It may be used exposed to view in open fixtures and has the additional advantage of often being interchangeable with mercury vapor lamps, using the same ballast.

20-24 MORE ON HIGH-PRESSURE SODIUM LAMPS

The HPS lamp is quite different in many respects than other HID lamps. The arc tube is much smaller, and it is made of an aluminum oxide ceramic of high transparency (92%) instead of the quartz glass of other HID lamps. This ceramic arc tube will withstand very high operating temperatures of 2300 to 2400°F (1300°C) compared to 1800°F for the glass arc tubes. The intensity of HPS lamps is thus exceedingly high, and HPS

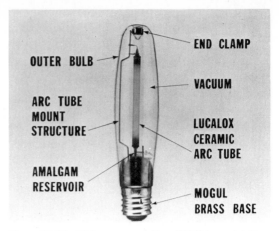

Figure 20-26 High-pressure sodium (HPS) lamp details. (Courtesy of General Electric Company.)

lamps should be enclosed in a fixture. However, the HPS "coated" lamp (see fig. 20-27) may be used in fixtures with open bottoms, or where glare is a problem, or where a wider pattern of light distribution is needed. See fig. 20-26 for a photograph and schematic diagram of a HPS lamp.

Ballasts for HPS lamps are much different than those for MV and MH lamps, because of the very high ignition voltage required. Also, because a lamp stabilizing voltage is required, the ballast must be able to control wattage within a narrow range. All HPS ballasts must include a "starting aid" which supplies a low-energy, high-voltage pulse of 2500 V for the smaller sizes of lamps and 3000 V for the 1000-W lamp.

Mercury vapor lamp ballasts are not suitable for standard HPS lamps, and this precludes the possibility of replacing MV lamps with HPS lamps to obtain the greater efficacy that would result. However, all three major lamp manufacturers have now made available special HPS lamps that can be used in MV lamp systems that are equipped with lag-type autotransformer ballasts or 240- or 277-V reactor ballasts. These lamps are the General Electric E-Z Lux, the Sylvania, Unalux and the Westinghouse Econolux lamps. They are available in 150-, 215-, 360-, and 880-W sizes to replace the 150-, 250-, 400-, and 1000-W mercury vapor

Figure 20-27 High-pressure sodium (HPS) lamp performance data.

Clear (CL coated, (CO) Watts	ANSI code	Bulb type	Maximum overall length	Approximate ballast, Watts	Average* rated hours	Approximate lumens		Initial lumen/W including ballast
						Initial	Mean	
Standard HPS lamps; require special ballasts; any burning position								
50 CL	S68MS–50	E 23 1/2	7 3/4		24,000	3,300	2,970	
50 CO	S68MT–50	E 23 1/2	7 3/4		24,000	3,150	2,835	
70 CL	S62ME–70	E 23 1/2	7 3/4	30	24,000	5,800	5,220	58
70 CO	S62MF–70	E 23 1/2	7 3/4	30	24,000	5,400	4,860	54
100 CL	S54SB–100	E 23 1/2	7 3/4	44	24,000	9,500	8,550	66
100 CO	S54MC–100	E 23 1/2	7 3/4	44	24,000	8,800	7,920	61
150 CL	S55SC–150	E 23 1/2	7 3/4	52.5	24,000	16,000	14,400	79
150 CO	S55MD–150	E 23 1/2	7 3/4	52.5	24,000	15,000	13,500	74
200 CL	S66MN–200	E 18	9 3/4		24,000	22,000	19,800	
250 CL	S50VA–250	E 18	9 3/4	55.5	24,000	27,500	24,750	90
250 CO	S50VC–250	E 28	9	55.5	24,000	26,000	23,400	85
310 CL	S67MR–310	E 18	9 3/4		24,000	37,000	33,300	
400 CL	S51WA–400	E 18	9 3/4	81	24,000	50,000	45,000	104
400 CO	S51WB–400	E 37	11 5/16	81	24,000	47,500	42,750	99
1000 CL	S52XB–1000	E 25	15 1/16	129	24,000	140,000	126,000	124
Replacement (for mercury vapor) HPS lamps using MV-type H ballasts; burning position: type BU—base up to base 5° below horizontal and type BD—base down to base 5° above horizontal, or as noted								
150 CL	S63MG–150 BU	E 28	9	36	12,000	12,000	10,800	65
150 CO	S63MH–150 BU	E 28	9	36	12,000	11,000	9,900	59
150 CL	S63MG–150 BD	E 28	9	36	12,000	12,000	10,800	65
150 CO	S63MH–150 BD	E 28	9	36	12,000	11,000	9,900	59
215 CL	S65ML–215 BD or BU	E 28	9		12,000	19,000	17,100	
215 CO	S65MM–215 BD or BU	E 28	9		12,000	18,000	16,200	
360 CL	S64MJ–360 any position	BT 37	11 1/2	49	16,000	38,000	34,200	93
360 CO	S64MJ–360 any position	BT 37	11 1/2	49	16,000	36,000	32,400	88
880 CL	any position	E 25	15 1/16		12,000	102,000	91,800	

*Based on 10 hr minimum per start and with proper auxiliary equipment.

lamps. These HPS lamps provide the high LPW efficacy of the sodium vapor lamp which delivers 50% more light with 14% less power consumption than the lamps they were designed to replace. In fact, the 150-W HPS replacement lamp produces as much light as, or slightly more light than, the 250-W standard MV lamp.

The golden color of the light from both the clear and the diffuse coated HPS lamps is finding extensive acceptance in many applications where accurate color rendition is not mandatory. School classrooms are a good example of this. Where the golden light is only slightly unacceptable, their use may be made possible by mixing with it the white light from lamps such as metal halide lamps. A very efficient lighting system can result.

HPS lamp performance data are summarized in fig. 20-27. The reader should also refer to art. 20-15 herein for other generalized data on HPS lamps.

20-25 LOW-PRESSURE SODIUM LAMPS

Because of its characteristic deep yellow color of light, the LPS lamp is not considered to be suitable for building lighting purposes even though its lighting efficacy is extremely high. Efficacy in lumens per watt with ballasts included may exceed the 140 LPW of the best HPS lamp without ballast watts included. Lamp life is not quite as high as standard HPS lamps, but lumen maintenance is much higher—nearly 100%. If in some special application, the color of the LPS lamp is acceptable, it should certainly be considered.

20-26 COLOR IN LIGHTING

The color of the light produced by the many light sources available is, of course, exceedingly important. No architect should attempt to finalize the color selections of room finishes of a building without integrating into the process the color of the light sources to be used and the effect that they will have on the room finishes selected.

The color of a source of light may be made specific in one way by listing its temperature in degrees Kelvin (°K). On the Kelvin temperature scale, zero is what we usually call "absolute zero," 273°K is the temperature at which water freezes (0°C or 32°F), 293°K is usual wintertime room temperature (20°C or 68°F), and 373°K is the boiling point of water (100°C or 212°F).

All objects will emit light if they are heated to a high enough temperature, and the hotter the object becomes, the more intense and brighter it becomes as a source of light. As a blacksmith heats a horseshoe, it starts out as dull black steel. As its temperature increases, it soon becomes a dull red at about 500°K and bright red at 800°K. If it could be heated further, at 3000°K it would be yellow, white at 5000°K, pale blue at 8000°K, and brilliant blue at 60,000°K. Figure 20-28 includes a table, one column of which gives °K temperature of various sources of light.

Figure 20-28 also includes a column for the *color rendering index,* (CRI). CRI is a measure of the extent to which colors of surfaces and objects observed under a given source of light appear the same as those same surfaces and objects appear under a "standard" source of light. The standard source of light is usually daylight at the same temperature in °K. The color temperature of daylight varies considerably under varying sky conditions, and two sources of light can only be compared, on the basis of CRI, when their color temperatures are within 100 to 300°K of each other.

When an observer is in a demonstration room with surfaces and objects having a wide variety of colors, it is amazing how the appearance of these surfaces and objects can change as the room is illuminated with different types of light sources in sequence.

Lamps such as the Chroma 50 and Chroma 75 (by General Electric) have exceedingly high color rendering accuracy and have color rendering indices in the 90s. Where color matching of printed material, yarn, fabrics, and so on, to an "original" of some type must be accurately done, these Chroma lamps are unsurpassed. The Chroma 50 lamps simulate closely the type of direct daylight normally produced at noon. The Chroma 50 lamps have a color temperature of 5000°K and combine the coolness of skylight with the warmth in red tones of noon sunlight. They can be found to be most effective commercially in such establishments as clothing stores, cosmetic areas, art galleries, fabric shops, and fur salons.

The Chroma 75 lamp, which has a higher color temperature of 7500°K, and which has a cooler light than the Chorma 50, is found to be most useful in printing establishments and in studios where close simulation to north skylight is important.

Figure 20-28 includes a table that lists the color characteristics of various sources of light (lamps). This figure should be of help in selecting lamps where color rendering qualities are particularly important. This table is concerned with fluorescent, incandescent, and HID lamps. The Chroma 50 and 75 lamps mentioned above were not included by those who gathered the information for

Figure 20-28 Color characteristics of various light sources. (Courtesy of General Electric Co.)

Type of lamp	Color temperature, °K	Efficacy, LPW	Lamp appearance effect on neutral surfaces	Effect on "atmosphere"	Colors strengthened	Colors grayed	Effect on complexions	CRI[c]	Remarks
Fluorescent lamps									
Cool[a] white, CW	4350	High	White	Neutral to moderately cool	Orange, yellow, blue	Red	Pale pink	67	Blends with natural daylight—good color acceptance
Deluxe[a] cool white, CWX		Medium	White	Neutral to moderately cool	All nearly equal	None appreciably	Most natural		Best overall color rendition; simulates natural daylight
Warm[b] white, WW	3100	High	Yellowish white	Warm	Orange, yellow	Red, green, blue	Sallow	55	Blends with incandescent light—poor color acceptance
Deluxe[b] warm white, WWX	3020	Medium	Yellowish white	Warm	Red, orange, yellow, green	Blue	Ruddy	77	Good color rendition; simulates incandescent light
Daylight	6600	Medium-high	Bluish white	Very cool	Green, blue	Red, orange	Grayed	75	Usually replaceable with CW
White		High	Pale yellowish white	Moderately warm	Orange, yellow	Red, green blue	Pale		Usually replaceable with CW or WW
Soft white/natural		Medium	Purplish white	Warm pinkish	Red, orange	Green, blue	Ruddy pink		Tinted source usually replaceable with CWX or WWX
Incandescent lamps, tungsten halogen									
Incandescent filament	2850	Low	Yellowish white	Warm	Red, orange, yellow	Blue	Ruddiest	97	Good color rendering

693

Figure 20-28 *(Cont.)*

Type of lamp	Color temperature, °K	Efficacy, LPW	Lamp appearance effect on neutral surfaces	Effect on "atmosphere"	Colors strengthened	Colors grayed	Effect on complexions	CRI[c]	Remarks
				High-intensity discharge lamps					
Clear mercury	5900	Medium	Greenish blue-white	Very cool, greenish	Yellow blue, green	Red, orange	Greenish	22	Very poor color rendering
White mercury	4200	Medium	Greenish white	Moderately cool, greenish	Yellow, green, blue	Red, orange	Very pale	45	Moderate color rendering
Deluxe white[a] mercury	4000	Medium	Purplish white	Warm, purplish	Red, blue, yellow	Green	Ruddy	43	Color acceptance similar to CW fluorescent
Metal halide[a], clear	5200	High	Greenish white	Moderately cool, greenish	Yellow, green, blue	Red	Grayed	55	Color acceptance similar to CW fluorescent
High-pressure sodium[b]	2250	High	Yellowish	Warm, yellowish	Yellow green, orange	Red, blue	Yellowish	25	Color acceptance approaches that of WW fluorescent

[a]Greater preference at higher levels.
[b]Greater preference at lower levels.
[c]Color rendering index.

fig. 20-28. However, they would be most like the deluxe cool white fluorescent lamp, but would have a somewhat higher CRI. Color temperatures and CRIs are included for most of the lamps included in fig. 20-28.

20-27 LIGHTING FIXTURES: LUMINAIRES

The range of types of luminaires in use today in modern nonresidential lighting systems is indeed great. To cover them all accurately and adequately would require a text half the size of this text; this amount of space in a multidisciplinary book such as this one is, of course, not available. Therefore, we will limit our luminaire discussions to general types and generalized discussions of them. Unfortunately, some types cannot be mentioned at all. However, once initiated into the procedures of planning and selecting luminaires, the reader can, if interested, extend study beyond this book to all those missing types.

In recent years the grinding weight of the energy shortage has compounded the difficulties of effective luminaire selection. With reduced lighting levels, an old enemy of past years has reappeared— that of shadows or shadowy areas. With our past higher levels of illumination, these shadows have been burned away even though our luminaire selection and placement was not the best. Now, we will need to be more careful.

However, we must be careful about reducing illumination levels too far. Another of the great problems of this nation is productivity, which has been in serious decline for many years. Adequate lighting and productivity go hand in hand; the answer we must seek is not in less light, although we have certainly indulged in excesses of light in the past, but in greater efficiency of light production and utilization. "Proper choice" of luminaires and their installation, use, and maintenance holds the key to the solution of our lighting problems.

Proper choice of a luminaire involves many factors, all of which must be placed in proper perspective and given weighted consideration.

Some of these factors are:

1 *Efficiency.* This is a ratio of the amount of light that a fixture emits to the amount of light produced by its lamps. Some of the lumens generated within a fixture will be absorbed by the fixture and converted into heat; this is a measure of its inefficiency.

2 *Coefficient of utilization (CU).* This is the ratio of the quantity of light that reaches the plane where seeing tasks are being performed (desks, work benches, etc.) to the quantity of light produced by the lamps in a fixture—more about CU later.

3 *Visual comfort probability (VCP).* As previously mentioned in this chapter, VCP is a measure of the percentage of a room's occupants that would consider the lighting system to be visually comfortable. VCP is involved with reducing direct glare from the fixtures directly into the eyes of room occupants. Among other considerations, this involves low brightness fixtures and the light cutoff effect of any lamp shielding. VCP is mathematically determined by fixture manufacturers, and is now extensively published with fixture performance data. A VCP of 70 is considered to be minimum for rooms such as offices and classrooms.

4 *Reflected glare.* Some fixtures may be very good with respect to glare that enters directly into room occupants' eyes, and yet be very uncomfortable because of this propensity for bouncing light off the shiny surfaces of desks into room occupants' eyes. The light distribution curve shown in fig. 20-9 is called a "bat-wing" curve. A fixture producing such a pattern of light gives a minimum of reflected glare because of the angle with which most of its light leaves the fixture and strikes shiny horizontal surfaces below it.

5 *Efficacy, fixture cost, etc.* There are other factors, too, that must be considered before a final choice is made. Of course, the efficacy, in lamp lumens per watt, of the lamps for which the fixture is designed is all-important. The uninstalled cost, cost of installation, flexibility in use, cost to clean and maintain, ESI rating, contrast rendition, color rendition, and other factors must all be evaluated. Only a small percent of those who regularly select and specify luminaires are qualified to make such an evaluation. What a shame this is!

The reader is referred to an article entitled "Choosing Lighting Fixtures for Efficiency and Visual Comfort," written by Gordon D. Rowe of General Electric Company. This was presented at an annual meeting of the IES (Illuminating Engineering Society) and published in the February 1976 issue of *Lighting Design and Application,* the official monthly publication of the IES. In this article, Rowe presents a process by which a logical selection may be made from the dozens of possibilities presented by manufacturers. In the article Rowe uses four-lamp, recessed troffer fixtures, but the same procedure may be applied to any type of fixture for which sufficient rating data are available. Emphasis is placed on fixture VCP, efficiency, and CU. He assumes a standard room size of 60 ft × 60 ft with a 10-ft ceiling, ceiling reflectance of 80%, wall reflectance of 50%, floor reflectance of 20%, and a level of illumination of 100 footcandles.

Figure 20-29 Summary data for selecting lighting fixtures for efficiency and VCP. (CU = coefficient of utilization; VCP = visual comfort probability. (Courtesy of General Electric Co.)

| | | CU for RCR | | | Visual comfort probability | | | | | |
| | | | | | Lengthwise | | | Crosswise | | |
Enclosure	EFF	1	5	10	High	Low	60× 60	High	Low	60× 60
A White metal louver	41	44	30	19	82	72	74	83	71	73
B Parabolic louver	43	48	34	22	99	99	99	99	99	99
C Pigmented acrylic lens*	50	55	37	23	85	75	77	85	75	77
D Plastic louver	53	56	37	23	72	56	58	72	57	58
E Clear glass lens	58	62	39	23	72	58	60	72	60	62
F Translucent diffuser	59	61	37	21	61	37	41	61	37	41
G Clear acrylic lens	63	67	45	27	75	59	62	75	60	62

*For 9 troffers: the first three heavily-pigmented lenses (Troffers 25, 27 and 29) were omitted to preclude inordinate weighing of averages.

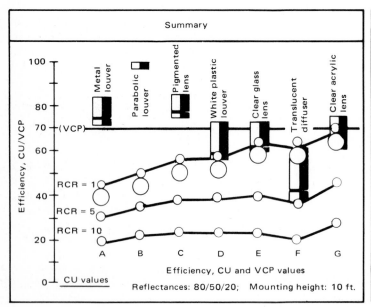

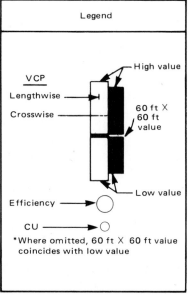

Rowe tabulates data that include efficiencies, VCPs, and CUs for room cavity ratios (RCR) of 1, 5, and 10. RCR will be explained later, but, in general, it is an index of the room proportions, weighting wall area against ceiling area. Performance data from 67 different fixtures equipped with seven different types of bottom closures were tabulated, averaged, and plotted on graphs. From each graph individual fixtures were selected for (1) maximum efficiency, (2) maximum VCP, and (3) best combination of high efficiency and high VCP.

Information from the four tables and four graphs of this article were then summarized in the table and the graph in fig. 20-29. This figure shows how such an extensive evaluation process can be brought to a conclusion, and one particular fixture selected. From the graph it may be seen that for maximum efficiency, a type G fixture with a clear acrylic lens was best; for highest VCP, type B with a plastic parabolic louver was best, and the best combination of high efficiency and high VCP was represented by a type C fixture with a pigmented acrylic lens.

There is a widespread belief that high VCP can be obtained only at the expense of efficiency. This particular investigation shows the error of this belief.

20-28 INCANDESCENT FIXTURES

The incandescent lamp lends itself beautifully to varying the design of the lighting fixture to house it. The incandescent lamp itself comes in many shapes and a wide range of sizes, so that the range of fixture shapes and their uses seems to be without limit. For the nonresidential building this wide range of fixture shapes seems to concentrate itself into a fairly short, limited list. This list contains the following:

1 Recessed downlights—round and square
2 Surface-mounted cylinder or "can" lights
3 Weatherproof bracket lights—such as those used at building entrances
4 Spotlights
5 Floodlights
6 Decorative lights—such as pendant and bracket type spheres, and squares used for appearance and not for illumination

A long list of incandescent fixtures used in the past for general illumination have yielded to the fluorescent, mercury vapor, metal halide, and sodium vapor types of fixtures. The latter types can provide general illumination so much more efficiently that the use of incandescent fixtures can hardly be justified.

Since decorativeness and not performance is, and will continue to be, the criterion for the selection of incandescent fixtures, the architect or interior designer who is fully trained in aesthetic considerations needs no assistance from a text of this type. He or she is perfectly capable of surveying the range of decorative incandescent fixtures available and making proper selection. However, the tables of coefficients of utilization (CUs) presented later in this chapter will provide some information concerning incandescent fixtures.

20-29 FLUORESCENT FIXTURES

Although fluorescent fixtures are beginning to lose popularity to the more efficacious HID lamps, the main burden of general illumination is still being carried by the fluorescent fixture. This picture may slowly change somewhat as greater acceptance of HPS lamps and their golden color occurs. However, 10 years from now the fluorescent fixture should still be easily predominant. The fluorescent fixture represents an excellent compromise between the primary factors of installed cost, power cost, lamp life, color selectivity, flexibility in use, and external appearance (brightness, glare, etc.).

The CU tables presented in fig. 20-36 give very extensive information concerning fluorescent fixtures. One fluorescent fixture that deserves special discussion is the parabolic louver type detailed in fig. 20-30. This fixture is characterized by very

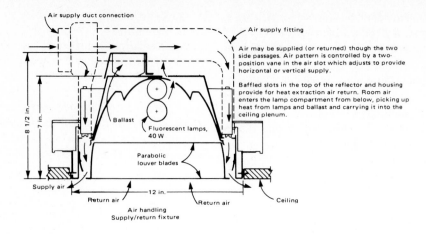

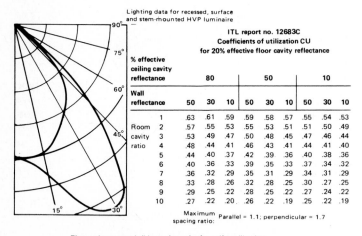

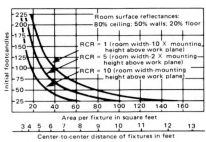

The maximum permissible spacing ratios for uniform illumination were computed in accordance with standard IES practice. However, to minimize veiling reflections, it is recommended that a spacing ratio of 1.0 be used for both parallel and perpendicular directions.

Figure 20-30 Details of parabolic louver type fluorescent fixture with performance data. Parabolic louver blades of semispecular aluminum give low brightness and high VCP. Batwing light distribution curve (see fig. 20-9 and below) gives good control of veiling reflections.

low brightness which contributes to a VCP of 95 when viewed both lengthwise and crosswise, and when installed in the IES standard 60 ft × 60 ft × 10 ft room illuminated to 100 footcandles. This fixture is represented by the reference letter "B" in fig. 20-29, where it may be seen that the VCP is extremely high while the efficiency and CU ratings are also very good.

Figure 20-30 also shows details of how HVAC system air may be supplied and returned through the fluorescent fixture. As noted, the return air

passing up through the fixture and out through the furred space above the ceiling carries the heat of the lamps and ballast away before it can enter the conditioned room below. This appreciably reduces the requirement for supply air into the room and reduces, somewhat, the load on the HVAC system.

One other very important feature of the fixture of fig. 20-30 is the highly desirable "bat-wing" light distribution curve, which, as previously mentioned, gives excellent control of veiling reflections.

This fixture, although not lowest in cost, has a reasonable cost, and since it provides better visibility, a lower level of illumination may be used, and fewer fixtures with less power consumption results. The louver assembly is easily removed for cleaning and other maintenance, so that maintenance costs are quite low.

Figure 20-30 also shows typical performance data for this excellent fluorescent fixture as well as the light distribution curves in both crosswise and lengthwise directions. A table of CUs and a quick calculator chart is also included; these will be discussed later.

With fluorescent troffer fixtures, performance is dependent on the type of bottom closure or shielding that is used. Many factors influence the decision as to which type of shielding to use—such as fire rating, ease of cleaning, code requirements, module size, type of ceiling, veiling reflections, and durability. However, there are three factors which are most often evaluated when selecting troffer shielding—for 2 ft × 4 ft fluorescent troffers, for example. These are VCP, efficiency, and cost. Various types of shielding are listed below, together with an approximate value or rating for each type in these three important factors:

Visual Comfort (VCP)		Comparative Typical Cost, 2 ft × 4 ft (1979)	
Parabolic louver	99	Parabolic louver	$20–25
Dark metal louver	70–90	Polarizer	$15–24
Toned lens	70–85	Toned lens	$10–25
White metal louver	70	Dark metal louver	$10–20
Polarizer	65	White metal louver	$8–15
Clear lens	60–80	Plastic louver	$8–10
Plastic louver	60	Diffuser	$6–15
Diffuser	45	Clear lens	$5–20

Efficiency (%)			
Clear lens	45–70	Parabolic louver	35–45
Polarizer	55–60	Toned lens	30–65
Diffuser	40–60	Dark metal louver	25–40
Plastic louver	45–55		
White metal louver	35–45		

The VCPs shown here are calculated for a large room such as 30 ft × 30 ft or 60 ft × 60 ft; VCP ratings should be 70 or better. All values are presented by courtesy of General Electric Company.

20-30 GENERAL FIXTURE TYPES

There are, in general, six categories of lighting fixtures, and all fixtures can be placed in one of these. Many fixtures are intentionally designed to utilize the ceiling of a room by bouncing light off the ceiling and in that process achieving beneficial results. The various categories may be thought of as varying in the extent to which they use the ceiling by directing all or part of their light upward. The six general categories are as follows:

1 *Indirect fixtures.* These direct nearly 100% of their light upward. A solid metallic bowl-type fixture with a wide-open top, or a fluorescent cove light or valance light with open top and closed bottom are examples of this—see fixture 50 in fig. 20-36.

2 *Semi-indirect fixtures.* These send approximately 60 to 90% of their light upward and 10 to 40% downward. A translucent glass or plastic bowl type of fixture with open top, a cove, or valance-type fluorescent fixture with open top and partially open bottom, or a stem-hung fluorescent troffer with open top and translucent bottom are examples of this type.

3 *General diffuse fixtures.* These transmit their light outward in all directions with equal intensity. A pendant (or stem-hung) opal sphere is the best example of this type. See fixture 1 in fig. 20-36.

4 *Direct-indirect fixtures.* These transmit approximately equal amounts of light upward and downward. A stem-hung, pendant fluorescent troffer with open top, open or louvered bottom, and either solid or translucent sides, or a cove or valance-type fixture with wide-open top and bottom are examples of this category.

5 *Semi-direct fixtures.* These transmit only 10 to 40% of their light upward and the remainder downward. As with the preceding types, this type can benefit greatly from the use of light-colored

ceilings with 80% reflectance and light or medium-colored walls with 50% or more reflectance. The opal glass ceiling-surface-mounted drum-shaped or spherical or square fixture which extends 6 to 10 in. down from the ceiling is this type. The cove or valance-type "wall-wash" fixture with only a small opening on top is this type. And the stem-hung fluorescent troffer with translucent sides and bottom, or louvered bottom, and with closed or partially open top is this type. See fixtures 4 and 27 in fig. 20-36.

6 *Direct fixtures.* This type embraces a wide range of fixtures, all of which transmit all of their light downward. All fully recessed troffers, recessed down-lights, round or square surface-mounted square or round cylinder (can) lights, as well as a wide range of stem-hung or wall-mounted fixtures with closed tops and sides are all of the direct type. See fixtures 3, 6 to 16, and 42 and 44 in fig. 20-36.

20-31 MAINTENANCE OF ATMOSPHERE

A lighting system does much more than efficiently distribute light to permit seeing. The lighting system can create an atmosphere of quiet serenity, of restful beauty, of dynamic activity, or of cheerfulness. Cheerfulness with a positive human response is probably the atmosphere most often sought. The lighting system alone has difficulty in doing this, but it can give strong support to a room decor in which the architect has imaginatively integrated room finish colors and textures with the shape, pattern, and color of the illumination.

In the architect's efforts to provide an energy conservative lighting system, he or she may wish to specify and employ the high efficacy of high-pressure sodium lamps, but finds the golden color somewhat objectionable. Progressive thought today does permit the mixing of light from different types of lamps. Following this example further, the architect might then mix the golden light of HPS with the white light of metal halide (MH) lamps. However, this is something that the architect or interior designer must do; it should

not be left to the electrical engineer. It is not an engineering problem; it is art in one of its highest forms.

What a shame it is, however, when after such imaginative, creative design has reached fruition, the major benefit is quickly lost through poor maintenance. Can a building owner really afford to invest the kind of money required for good maintenance? You bet! The owner cannot afford not to. Assuming that a good lighting system and building decor were necessary and justifiable in the original design, good maintenance, like building insulation, does not cost; it pays.

Permitting dirt and other soil to accumulate and permitting lamps to burn until they burn out is just plain foolish. The economics of the situation are irrefutable; if good lighting for accurate seeing is important to a building user or owner, good maintenance will pay high dividends and result in a net economic advantage. Almost every lighting system, as well as the building that houses it, should have a well-planned, well-scheduled, continuing maintenance program. The result will be more light per dollar of overall cost, better appearance, greater efficiency from building occupants, and fewer mistakes and accidents—all vitally important considerations.

There are three principal factors that cause loss of light; they are:

1 Dirt on lamps and luminaires
2 Soiling of room surfaces, especially ceilings, that are depended on for good light reflectance
3 Reduction in lamp lumen output

Of these three causative factors, the greatest is usually the first one listed—soiling of lamps and fixtures. A 30% loss of initial light output is not at all unusual. The rate of soil accumulation varies greatly, of course, with the type of use of a building. In a machine shop where cutting-oil vapors fill the air, fixtures will collect soil much more rapidly than in an automobile salesroom. But because of the precision required of machining operations, the machine shop is one place where the best illumination is required, and the best maintenance

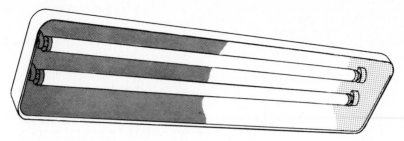

Dramatic example of how much dirt a fluorescent fixture without the open-top design will collect in factory area in a few months.

Figure 20-31 Dirt collection in a fluorescent fixture.

is mandatory. Figure 20-31 shows how much soil a fluorescent fixture can collect in only a few months in a dirty location.

The design and construction of a lighting fixture has much to do with the rate at which it will collect soil. Luminaires that have openings in their tops so that air may circulate upward through them will be appreciably easier to keep clean. With a well-ventilated fixture, the heat generated within it will induce air movement upward through it which will carry soiling agents right on past the lamps and fixture surfaces. Figure 20-32

presents a chart with curves that compare the soiling rate of ventilated and unventilated mercury vapor fixtures of the general type shown.

The two fixtures shown were installed in the same "high-bay" location; one had ventilating holes in it whereas the other did not. The unventilated fixture lost 38% efficiency whereas the ventilated one lost only 6% efficiency in a 12-month period. Figure 20-33 demonstrates the same principle applied to three fluorescent troffer luminaires, two of which are ventilated.

A ventilated troffer will usually permit appre-

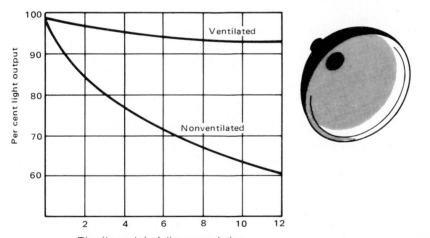

Depreciation of light output caused by dirt accumulation for the filament or mercury-lamp type reflectors. Note that in 12 months the nonventilated design dropped in efficiency 38% while the ventilated one only decreased 6%.

Dirt collected by two types of high-bay reflectors installed in a typical manufacturing area for 12 months. The reflector on the left has no ventilating holes while the one on the right is ventilated.

Figure 20-32 Comparison of soiling in ventilated and unventilated fixtures.

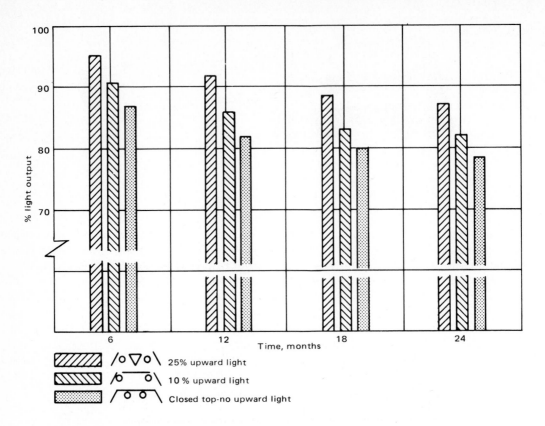

25% upward light

10 % upward light

Closed top-no upward light

Depreciation in light output average conditions caused by
accumulation of dust and dirt on three types of industrial
fluorescent luminaires. Ventilated top fixtures not only
collect less dirt but also light the ceiling areas.

Figure 20-33 Comparative soiling rates in three types of industrial fluorescent fixtures. (Courtesy
of General Electric Co.)

ciable quantities of its light to transmit upward
as well as downward, and where ceilings are clean
and light in color, a better VCP is achieved than
is possible with unventilated troffers. Of course,
if fixtures must be mounted against the ceiling and
not suspended below it, the problem of ventilation is greatly increased. However, even when
mounted against the ceiling 2 to 3 in. of space
between the fixture and the ceiling should be
maintained for fire safety reasons. Even this small
space will permit some ventilation.

A lighting system maintenance program must
embrace the question of lamp replacement.

Should lamps be replaced on a group relamping
schedule based on probable lamp life, or should
lamps be left to burn until burnout? The cost of
labor for relamping is much, much greater if a
maintenance worker must, for *each lamp*, make
a trip to procure a ladder, carry the ladder and a
new lamp to the burn-out location, replace the
lamp while interrupting the workers in that location, and then return the ladder and dispose of the
burned-out lamp.

Compare this process with a group relamping
process in which all the lamps in a certain room
are replaced at one time, after working hours.

Group relamping obviously makes good sense for several reasons:

1 Relamping labor will be only 10 to 20% as much as with individual replacement.

2 Group relamping permits purchasing lamps in large-quantity palletized shipments at a reduced cost per lamp. This can partially or fully offset the extra cost attendant to a somewhat shorter lamp life.

3 Since lamps are not permitted to burn as long, their average lumen production is greater than that of lamps which are permitted to burn until burn-out.

4 There will be very few interruptions of the activities of building occupants if relamping is done during unoccupied hours.

5 Some types of fluorescent fixtures can be damaged if permitted to operate with the power on after lamp failure; this is true of instant start lamps, for example. Group relamping can almost completely eliminate ballast and other equipment failure.

6 Where fluorescent lamps are exposed to view, group relamping can minimize the poor appearance that results from operating a lamp until blackened ends develop and color and brightness variations result from the mixing of old and new lamps.

There is more than one method of operating a group relamping program, but the one with greatest overall merit works like this. The fixtures in a given space are group relamped at 50 to 80% of average life. Of the lamps removed, a certain number of the best-appearing lamps are stored for use in replacing lamps that burn out early, before planned life is attained. When this stock of used lamps is depleted, it is probably time for another group relamping. The percentage of average life to use for a relamping schedule and the number of used lamps to retain for replacement purposes will depend on the type of lamps installed and the manner in which they are operated. Actual experience with a given lighting system and guidance from the manufacturers involved will aid in establishing a satisfactory schedule.

20-32 COEFFICIENTS OF UTILIZATION

As previously defined, the coefficient of utilization (CU) is the ratio of lumens of light, in a given room, that reaches the work plane, to the lumens of light that are produced by the lamps in the fixtures. The work plane is the level in the room at which seeing tasks are being performed. For example, in an office, the work plane is at the height of the desk tops—30 in. above the floor—and is as long and as wide as the room itself.

$$CU = \frac{\text{lumens falling on the work plane}}{\text{lumens per lamp} \times \text{lamps}}$$

If a room is illuminated with 50 footcandles at the work plane (WP), it will have 50 lumens of light falling on each square foot of the work plane area. If the room is 40 ft long and 25 ft wide, its 1000 ft² of WP area would receive 50,000 lm (1000 ft² × 50). If the lighting fixtures in this room will hold 30 lamps, each of which produce 3150 lm of light, the CU in this room would need to be

$$CU = \frac{1000 \text{ ft}^2 \times 50 \text{ fc}}{3150 \text{ lm/lamp} \times 30 \text{ lamps}} = 0.53$$

The CU of a contemplated installation is sometimes rather difficult to predict; it is based on five different considerations, some of which we have not yet defined or discussed:

1 Type of fixture to be used
2 Type of lamps to be used in the fixtures
3 Reflectance of the "ceiling cavity"
4 Reflectance of room walls
5 "Room cavity" ratio

We have discussed previously the term *reflectance*; typical room reflectances are shown in fig. 20-2. Reflectance is usually expressed with an algebraic symbol, the Greek letter ρ. However, in the list above the terms "ceiling cavity" and "room cavity ratio" have not been previously defined and must now be discussed. In fig. 20-34 a cross section of a room is drawn, and the room is divided into three separate volumes, which are called *cavities*. The volume of the room that extends, for the full length of the room, from the lighting fixtures up to the ceiling is called the *ceiling cavity*. The volume of the room from the lighting fixtures down to the work plane (the level of the desk tops, tabletops, etc.) is called the *room cavity*, and the volume from the work plane down to the floor is, not surprisingly, called the *floor cavity*.

To establish the overall effective reflectance of a ceiling cavity, for example, when ceiling and wall reflectances are known, we must take into consideration the relative areas of the walls and the ceiling. It has been found to be effective in establishing this relationship to divide mathematically the ceiling area, floor area, or work plane area into a value equal to 2.5 times the wall area. Thus, the *ceiling cavity ratio* (CCR) may be expressed as

$$CCR = \frac{2.5 \times \text{ceiling cavity wall area}}{\text{ceiling area}}$$

Similarly, the *floor cavity ratio* (FCR) and the *room cavity ratio* (RCR) may be expressed as

$$FCR = \frac{2.5 \times \text{floor cavity wall area}}{\text{floor area}}$$

and

$$RCR = \frac{2.5 \times \text{room cavity wall area}}{\text{work plane area}}$$

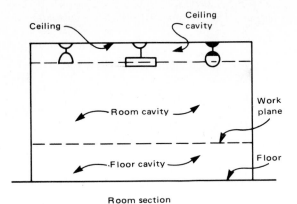

Room section

Figure 20-34   Ceiling, floor, and room cavities.

In all our deliberations herein, we will assume that all room walls are vertical, and that ceiling area, floor area, and work plane area are exactly equal. They are almost never different.

To determine the ceiling cavity reflectance ρ_{cc}, item 3 above, we must use the table of fig. 20-35. Knowing the ceiling reflectance ρ_c, the wall reflectance ρ_w, and the ceiling cavity ratio CCR, we can then enter fig. 20-35 and select the ρ_{cc} directly. When the lighting fixtures are fully recessed into the ceiling, as is often the case, the height of the ceiling cavity is zero. There is no ceiling cavity, and the room cavity extends all the way up to the ceiling. In this case, the ceiling cavity wall area is zero, the CCR is zero, and the ceiling cavity reflectance ρ_{cc} is exactly the same as the ceiling reflectance ρ_c. If $\rho_c = 80\%$, then ρ_{cc} is also 80%.

Now, armed with the five required bits of information, we may enter the tables of fig. 20-36 and select the proper CU. Having reached this point, we are well along in the procedure of lighting design for a given room. Of course, before fig. 20-36 can be used to select a CU value, a final or at least a tentative choice of luminaires and their lamps must be made. It should be realized that the values for CU shown in fig. 20-36 are based on the assumption that the floor cavity reflectance ρ_{fc}, is 20%.

Figure 20-35 Cavity reflectances. (Reprinted with permission from IES, IES Lighting Handbook, 5th ed, 1972.)

Percent effective ceiling or floor cavity reflectances for various reflectance combinations

Percent base* reflectance, reading left to right in blocks of ten columns: **90** (columns 1–10), **80** (11–20), **70** (21–30), **50** (31–40), **30** (41–50). Within each base‑reflectance block the ten columns are the **percent wall reflectance**: 90, 80, 70, 60, 50, 40, 30, 20, 10, 0.

Cavity ratio	90·90	90·80	90·70	90·60	90·50	90·40	90·30	90·20	90·10	90·0	80·90	80·80	80·70	80·60	80·50	80·40	80·30	80·20	80·10	80·0	70·90	70·80	70·70	70·60	70·50	70·40	70·30	70·20	70·10	70·0	50·90	50·80	50·70	50·60	50·50	50·40	50·30	50·20	50·10	50·0	30·90	30·80	30·70	30·60	30·50	30·40	30·30	30·20	30·10	30·0
0.2	89	88	88	87	86	86	85	85	84	84	79	79	78	78	77	77	76	76	76	75	70	69	69	68	68	67	67	66	65	64	50	50	50	50	50	50	50	50	50	50	31	31	31	30	30	29	29	28	28	27
0.4	88	87	86	85	84	84	83	81	80	79	79	77	76	75	74	73	72	71	70	68	69	68	67	66	65	64	63	62	61	58	50	50	49	49	48	48	47	47	46	44	31	31	31	30	29	28	28	26	26	25
0.6	87	86	84	82	81	79	77	76	74	73	78	76	75	73	71	70	68	66	65	63	69	67	65	64	63	61	59	58	57	54	50	49	48	47	46	46	45	44	43	41	32	31	30	29	28	27	26	25	23	23
0.8	87	85	82	80	77	75	73	71	69	67	78	75	73	71	69	67	65	63	61	57	68	66	64	62	60	58	56	54	53	50	50	49	47	46	45	44	43	41	40	37	32	31	30	29	28	26	25	23	22	22
1.0	86	83	80	77	75	72	69	66	64	62	77	74	72	69	67	65	62	60	57	55	68	65	62	60	58	55	53	51	50	47	50	48	46	44	43	42	40	38	36	34	33	32	31	29	27	25	23	22	20	20
1.2	85	82	78	75	72	69	66	63	60	57	76	73	70	67	64	61	58	55	53	51	67	64	61	59	57	54	50	48	46	44	50	47	45	43	41	39	37	35	33	32	33	32	30	29	26	24	22	20	19	19
1.4	85	80	77	73	69	65	62	59	57	52	76	72	68	65	62	59	55	53	50	48	67	63	59	57	54	51	47	45	45	44	50	47	44	42	40	37	35	33	31	30	34	33	30	28	24	22	20	19	18	18
1.6	84	79	75	71	67	63	59	56	53	50	75	71	67	63	60	57	53	50	47	44	67	62	59	56	53	49	47	44	43	38	50	46	43	40	38	36	33	30	30	28	35	33	30	27	23	21	18	17	16	17
1.8	83	78	73	69	64	60	56	53	50	47	75	70	66	62	58	54	50	47	44	41	66	61	58	54	51	48	46	43	41	35	50	46	42	40	37	34	32	29	28	26	35	33	29	26	22	20	17	16	15	16
2.0	83	77	72	67	62	58	53	50	47	43	74	69	64	60	56	52	48	45	41	38	66	60	56	52	49	45	45	42	40	33	50	45	42	39	36	33	31	28	26	24	36	33	29	25	22	19	16	15	14	14
2.2	82	76	70	65	59	54	50	47	44	40	74	68	63	58	54	50	45	42	38	35	66	60	55	51	48	44	42	38	36	32	50	45	41	38	35	32	30	27	25	22	36	32	29	24	21	18	16	14	13	13
2.4	82	75	69	64	58	53	48	45	41	37	73	67	61	56	52	47	43	40	36	33	65	59	54	50	46	43	41	37	35	30	50	44	40	37	34	31	29	26	23	21	36	32	29	24	21	18	15	13	12	12
2.6	81	74	67	62	56	51	46	42	38	35	73	66	60	55	50	45	41	38	34	31	65	59	54	49	45	40	40	37	34	28	50	44	40	37	33	30	28	25	22	20	36	33	28	23	20	17	14	13	11	12
2.8	81	73	66	60	54	49	44	40	36	34	73	65	59	53	48	43	39	36	32	29	65	59	53	48	43	38	38	33	32	26	50	44	39	36	33	30	27	24	21	19	37	33	29	23	20	16	14	12	11	11
3.0	80	72	64	58	52	47	42	38	34	30	72	65	58	52	47	42	37	34	30	27	64	58	52	47	42	37	37	31	30	24	50	44	39	35	32	29	26	24	20	17	37	33	29	23	19	16	13	11	10	10
3.2	79	71	63	56	50	45	40	36	32	28	72	65	57	51	45	40	35	33	28	25	64	58	51	46	40	36	31	28	25	23	50	43	38	35	31	28	25	23	20	16	37	33	29	23	19	15	13	11	10	10
3.4	79	70	62	54	48	43	38	34	30	27	71	64	56	49	44	39	34	32	27	24	64	57	50	45	39	35	29	25	24	22	50	43	38	34	31	27	24	22	19	15	37	33	29	22	18	15	12	10	09	09
3.6	78	69	61	53	47	42	36	32	28	25	71	63	54	48	43	38	32	31	25	23	63	56	49	44	38	33	28	24	22	21	50	43	37	34	30	27	24	21	18	14	38	33	29	22	18	14	12	10	09	09
3.8	78	69	60	51	45	40	35	31	27	23	70	62	53	47	41	36	31	28	24	22	63	56	49	43	37	32	27	23	21	19	50	43	37	33	29	26	23	20	17	13	38	33	28	22	17	14	11	09	08	08
4.0	77	69	58	51	44	39	33	29	25	22	70	61	53	46	40	35	30	26	22	20	63	55	48	42	36	31	26	22	20	17	50	43	36	32	28	25	22	20	17	12	38	33	28	21	17	13	11	09	08	07
4.2	77	60	52	45	39	34	29	25	21	18	69	60	52	45	39	34	29	25	21	18	62	55	47	41	35	30	25	22	19	16	50	43	35	32	28	24	22	19	15	12	38	33	28	21	16	13	10	08	07	07
4.4	76	61	56	49	42	36	31	27	21	18	69	60	51	44	38	33	28	24	20	17	62	54	46	40	34	29	24	21	18	15	50	43	35	31	27	24	21	18	15	11	39	33	28	20	15	12	10	08	07	06
4.6	76	60	55	47	40	35	30	26	22	15	69	59	50	43	37	32	27	23	19	15	62	53	45	39	33	28	24	20	17	14	50	43	35	31	26	23	21	18	15	10	39	33	27	19	15	12	09	08	06	06
4.8	75	59	54	46	39	34	28	25	21	18	68	58	49	42	36	31	26	22	18	14	62	53	45	38	32	27	23	20	16	13	50	43	34	30	26	22	20	17	14	09	39	33	27	19	14	11	09	07	06	05
5.0	75	59	53	45	38	33	28	24	20	16	68	58	48	41	35	30	25	21	18	14	61	52	44	38	31	26	22	19	16	12	50	42	34	30	25	22	19	17	14	09	39	33	27	19	14	11	09	07	06	05
6.0	73	56	50	43	37	32	27	23	20	16	66	55	44	38	31	27	22	19	15	10	60	51	41	35	28	24	19	16	13	09	50	42	32	27	22	18	17	14	12	06	39	33	26	18	13	10	07	06	05	04
7.0	70	45	38	30	27	21	18	14	08	11	64	53	41	35	28	24	19	16	13	08	58	48	38	33	26	22	17	14	11	06	49	41	30	25	20	17	14	11	09	05	39	32	24	17	12	09	06	05	04	03
8.0	68	42	35	27	23	18	15	12	06	06	62	50	38	32	25	21	17	14	11	05	57	46	35	29	23	19	15	13	10	05	49	40	29	23	19	15	13	10	08	04	40	33	23	16	11	08	05	04	03	02
9.0	66	36	30	27	21	16	14	11	09	04	61	49	36	30	23	19	15	13	10	04	56	45	33	27	21	18	14	11	08	04	48	39	27	21	16	13	12	10	07	03	40	33	22	15	10	07	04	03	02	02
10.0	65	36	29	22	19	15	11	09	04	04	59	46	33	27	21	18	14	11	08	03	55	43	31	25	19	16	12	10	08	03	47	37	25	19	15	12	10	08	06	01	40	32	20	14	09	06	04	03	02	01

*Ceiling, floor, or floor of cavity.

Figure 20-36 Coefficients of utilization.

Typical Luminaire	Typical Intensity Distribution and Per Cent Lamp Lumens		Maint Cat	SC	RCR ↓	ρcc → 80			70			50			30			10			0
						ρw → 50	30	10	50	30	10	50	30	10	50	30	10	50	30	10	0
						Coefficients of Utilization for 20 Per Cent Effective Floor Cavity Reflectance (ρfc = 20)															
1 Pendant diffusing sphere with incandescent lamp	35%↑ 45%↓		V	1.5	0	87	87	87	81	81	81	70	70	70	59	59	59	49	49	49	45
					1	71	67	63	66	62	59	56	53	50	47	45	42	38	37	35	31
					2	60	54	49	56	50	45	47	43	39	39	36	33	32	29	27	23
					3	52	45	39	48	42	37	41	36	31	34	30	26	27	24	22	18
					4	46	38	33	42	36	30	36	30	26	30	26	22	24	21	18	15
					5	40	33	27	37	30	25	31	26	22	26	22	18	21	18	15	12
					6	36	28	23	33	26	21	28	23	19	23	19	16	19	15	13	10
					7	32	25	20	29	23	18	25	20	16	21	16	13	17	13	11	09
					8	29	22	17	26	20	16	23	17	14	19	15	12	15	12	09	07
					9	26	19	15	24	18	14	20	15	12	17	13	10	14	11	08	06
					10	23	17	13	22	16	12	19	14	10	16	12	09	13	09	07	05
3 Porcelain-enameled ventilated standard dome with incandescent lamp	0%↑ 83%↓		IV	1.3	0	99	99	99	97	97	97	93	93	93	89	89	89	85	85	85	83
					1	88	85	82	86	83	81	83	80	78	79	78	76	77	75	73	72
					2	78	73	68	76	72	67	73	69	66	71	67	64	68	65	63	61
					3	69	62	57	67	61	57	65	60	56	63	58	55	61	57	54	52
					4	61	54	49	60	53	48	58	52	48	56	51	47	54	50	46	45
					5	54	47	41	53	46	41	51	45	41	50	44	40	48	43	40	38
					6	48	41	35	47	40	35	46	39	35	44	39	34	43	38	34	32
					7	43	35	30	42	35	30	41	34	30	40	34	29	38	33	29	28
					8	38	31	26	38	31	26	37	30	26	36	30	26	35	30	26	24
					9	35	28	23	34	27	23	33	27	23	32	27	23	31	26	22	21
					10	31	25	20	31	24	20	30	24	20	29	24	20	29	23	20	18
4 Prismatic square surface drum	18½%↑ 60½%↓		V	1.3	0	89	89	89	85	85	85	77	77	77	70	70	70	63	63	63	60
					1	78	75	72	74	72	69	68	66	64	62	60	58	56	55	54	51
					2	69	65	61	66	62	58	61	57	54	56	53	50	51	49	47	44
					3	62	57	52	60	55	50	55	51	47	50	47	44	46	43	41	39
					4	56	50	46	54	49	44	50	45	42	46	42	39	42	39	37	35
					5	51	45	40	49	43	39	45	41	37	42	38	35	39	36	33	31
					6	46	40	36	45	39	35	42	37	33	39	35	31	36	32	30	28
					7	42	36	32	41	35	31	38	33	29	35	31	28	33	29	27	25
					8	38	32	28	37	32	28	35	30	26	32	28	25	30	27	24	22
					9	35	29	25	34	29	25	32	27	24	30	26	23	28	24	22	20
					10	32	27	23	31	26	22	29	25	21	27	23	20	26	22	20	18
6 R-40 flood with specular anodized reflector skirt; 45° cutoff	0%↑ 85%↓		IV	0.7	0	1.01	1.01	1.01	99	99	99	94	94	94	90	90	90	87	87	87	85
					1	96	94	92	94	92	91	90	89	88	87	86	85	84	84	83	82
					2	91	88	86	90	87	85	87	85	83	84	83	82	82	81	80	79
					3	87	84	81	86	83	81	84	81	79	82	80	78	80	78	77	76
					4	83	80	77	82	79	77	81	78	76	79	77	75	78	76	74	73
					5	79	76	73	79	75	73	77	74	72	76	73	71	75	73	71	70
					6	76	73	70	76	72	70	75	72	69	74	71	69	73	70	68	67
					7	73	69	66	73	69	66	72	68	66	71	68	66	70	67	65	64
					8	70	66	63	70	66	63	69	65	63	68	65	63	67	65	63	62
					9	67	63	60	67	63	60	66	62	60	65	62	60	65	62	60	59
					10	64	60	58	64	60	58	63	60	58	63	60	57	62	59	57	56
8 Medium distribution unit with lens plate and inside frost lamp	0%↑ 54½%↓		V	1.0	0	65	65	65	63	63	63	60	60	60	58	58	58	55	55	55	54
					1	60	58	57	58	57	56	56	55	54	54	53	52	52	52	51	50
					2	55	53	51	54	52	50	52	50	49	51	49	48	49	48	47	46
					3	51	48	46	50	47	45	49	46	44	47	45	44	46	44	43	42
					4	47	44	41	47	44	41	45	43	41	44	42	40	43	41	40	39
					5	44	40	38	43	40	38	42	39	37	41	39	37	40	38	37	36
					6	41	37	35	40	37	35	39	36	34	39	36	34	38	36	34	33
					7	38	34	32	37	34	32	37	33	32	36	33	31	35	33	31	30
					8	35	32	29	35	31	29	34	31	29	34	31	29	33	30	29	28
					9	33	29	27	32	29	27	32	29	26	31	28	26	31	28	26	25
					10	30	27	25	30	27	24	30	27	24	29	26	24	29	26	24	23
9 Recessed baffled downlight, 140 mm (5 ½") diameter aperture—150-PAR/FL lamp	0%↑ 68%↓		IV	0.5	0	82	82	82	80	80	80	76	76	76	73	73	73	70	70	70	69
					1	78	77	76	77	76	75	74	74	73	72	71	71	69	69	69	68
					2	76	74	73	75	73	72	73	71	70	71	70	69	69	68	67	67
					3	74	72	70	73	71	70	71	70	69	70	69	68	68	67	67	66
					4	72	70	68	71	69	68	70	68	67	69	67	66	67	66	65	65
					5	70	68	66	69	67	66	68	67	65	67	66	65	67	65	64	64
					6	69	66	65	68	66	65	67	66	64	67	65	64	66	65	64	63
					7	67	65	63	67	65	63	66	64	63	65	64	63	65	64	62	62
					8	66	64	62	65	63	62	65	63	62	64	63	62	64	62	61	61
					9	65	63	61	64	62	61	64	62	61	63	62	61	63	62	61	60
					10	63	61	60	63	61	60	63	61	60	62	61	60	62	61	60	59

NOTES: ρ_{cc} = ceiling cavity reflectance, ρ_w = wall reflectance, RCR = room cavity ratio, SC = luminaire spacing criterion = luminaire horizontal spacing (feet) ÷ height above work plane (feet), luminaire reference numbers are those used in the I.E.S. Lighting Handbook. Please see this handbook for a complete listing of luminaires. Above data excerpted with permission from the Illuminating Engineering Society Handbook, 1981 Reference Volume.

Figure 20-36 *(Cont.)*

Typical Luminaire	Typical Intensity Distribution and Per Cent Lamp Lumens		ρcc →	80			70			50			30			10			0
	Maint Cat / SC		ρw →	50	30	10	50	30	10	50	30	10	50	30	10	50	30	10	0
		RCR ↓		Coefficients of Utilization for 20 Per Cent Effective Floor Cavity Reflectance (ρfc = 20)															

13 — Bilateral batwing distribution—clear HID with dropped prismatic lens
Maint Cat V, SC N.A., 2½↑, 71½↓

RCR	50	30	10	50	30	10	50	30	10	50	30	10	50	30	10	0
0	87	87	87	85	85	85	80	80	80	76	76	76	73	73	73	71
1	76	73	70	74	71	69	71	68	66	67	65	64	64	63	61	60
2	67	62	58	66	61	57	63	59	56	60	57	54	57	55	53	51
3	59	54	49	58	53	48	56	51	47	53	49	46	51	48	45	43
4	53	47	42	52	46	42	50	45	41	48	44	40	46	42	39	38
5	47	41	36	46	40	36	44	39	35	43	38	35	41	37	34	32
6	42	36	31	41	35	31	40	34	30	38	33	30	37	33	29	28
7	37	31	26	37	31	26	35	30	26	34	29	25	33	28	25	24
8	34	27	23	33	27	23	32	26	22	31	26	22	30	25	22	20
9	30	24	20	29	24	20	28	23	19	27	23	19	27	22	19	17
10	27	21	17	27	21	17	26	20	17	25	20	17	24	19	16	15

16 — "High bay" narrow distribution ventilated reflector with clear HID lamp
Maint Cat III, SC 0.7, 1½↑, 77½↓

RCR	50	30	10	50	30	10	50	30	10	50	30	10	50	30	10	0
0	93	93	93	90	90	90	86	86	86	82	82	82	78	78	78	77
1	87	85	83	85	83	82	81	80	79	78	77	76	75	75	74	72
2	81	79	76	80	77	75	77	75	73	75	73	72	72	71	70	69
3	77	73	71	76	72	70	73	71	69	71	69	67	70	68	66	65
4	73	69	66	72	68	65	70	67	64	68	66	64	67	65	63	62
5	69	65	62	68	64	61	66	63	61	65	62	60	64	61	59	58
6	65	61	58	64	61	58	63	60	57	62	59	57	61	58	56	55
7	62	57	54	61	57	54	60	56	54	59	56	53	58	55	53	52
8	58	54	51	58	54	51	57	53	51	56	53	51	55	52	50	49
9	55	51	48	55	51	48	54	50	48	53	50	48	53	50	48	47
10	53	49	46	52	48	46	52	48	46	51	48	45	50	47	45	44

20 — "High bay" wide distribution ventilated reflector with phosphor coated HID lamp
Maint Cat III, SC 1.5, 12↑, 69↓

RCR	50	30	10	50	30	10	50	30	10	50	30	10	50	30	10	0
0	93	93	93	90	90	90	83	83	83	77	77	77	72	72	72	69
1	85	83	81	82	80	78	77	75	74	72	71	69	67	66	65	63
2	78	74	71	76	72	69	71	68	66	67	65	63	63	61	60	58
3	71	67	63	69	65	62	65	62	59	62	59	57	58	56	54	53
4	65	60	56	64	59	55	60	56	53	57	54	51	54	52	50	48
5	60	54	50	58	53	49	55	51	48	53	49	46	50	47	45	43
6	54	49	45	53	48	44	51	46	43	48	45	42	46	43	40	39
7	49	44	40	48	43	39	46	41	38	44	40	37	42	39	36	34
8	45	39	35	44	38	35	42	37	34	40	36	33	38	35	32	31
9	41	35	31	40	34	31	38	33	30	36	32	29	35	31	28	27
10	37	31	27	36	31	27	34	30	27	33	29	26	32	28	25	24

26 — Diffuse aluminum reflector with 35°CW shielding
Maint Cat II, SC 1.5/1.3, 17↑, 66↓

RCR	50	30	10	50	30	10	50	30	10	50	30	10	50	30	10	0
0	95	95	95	91	91	91	83	83	83	76	76	76	69	69	69	66
1	85	82	80	82	79	77	75	73	72	69	68	66	64	63	62	59
2	76	72	68	74	70	66	68	65	62	63	61	58	58	56	55	52
3	69	63	59	66	61	57	62	58	54	57	54	51	53	51	48	46
4	62	56	51	60	54	50	56	51	47	52	48	45	48	45	43	41
5	55	49	44	53	48	43	50	45	41	47	43	39	44	40	38	36
6	50	43	39	48	42	38	45	40	36	42	38	35	40	36	33	31
7	45	38	34	43	37	33	41	36	32	38	34	30	36	32	29	27
8	40	34	29	39	33	29	37	31	28	35	30	27	33	29	26	24
9	36	30	25	35	29	25	33	28	24	31	26	23	29	25	22	21
10	33	26	22	32	26	22	30	25	21	28	23	20	26	22	19	18

27 — Porcelain-enameled reflector with 30°CW × 30°LW shielding
Maint Cat II, SC 1.0, 23½↑, 57↓

RCR	50	30	10	50	30	10	50	30	10	50	30	10	50	30	10	0
0	91	91	91	86	86	86	77	77	77	68	68	68	61	61	61	57
1	81	78	76	77	74	72	69	67	66	62	61	59	56	55	54	51
2	72	68	64	69	65	61	62	59	57	56	54	52	51	49	47	45
3	65	59	55	62	57	53	56	52	49	51	48	45	46	44	42	39
4	58	52	48	56	50	46	51	46	43	46	43	40	42	39	37	35
5	52	46	41	50	44	40	46	41	37	42	38	35	38	35	33	30
6	47	41	36	45	39	35	41	37	33	38	34	31	35	31	29	27
7	43	36	32	41	35	31	38	33	30	34	30	27	32	28	26	24
8	38	32	28	37	31	27	34	29	26	31	27	24	29	25	23	21
9	35	29	24	33	28	24	31	26	22	28	24	21	26	22	20	18
10	32	26	22	30	25	21	28	23	20	26	22	19	24	20	18	16

32 — 2 lamp, surface mounted, bare lamp unit—Photometry with 460 mm (18") wide panel above luminaire (lamps on 150 mm (6") centers)
Maint Cat I, SC 1.3, 9½↑, 78↓

RCR	50	30	10	50	30	10	50	30	10	50	30	10	50	30	10	0
0	1.02	1.02	1.02	99	99	99	92	92	92	86	86	86	81	81	81	78
1	86	82	78	83	79	75	78	74	71	73	70	67	68	66	64	61
2	74	67	61	71	65	60	66	61	57	62	58	54	58	55	52	49
3	64	56	50	62	55	49	58	52	47	54	49	45	51	47	43	41
4	56	48	42	55	47	41	52	45	39	48	42	38	45	40	36	34
5	49	41	35	48	40	34	45	38	33	42	36	32	39	34	30	28
6	44	36	30	43	35	29	40	33	28	38	32	27	35	30	26	24
7	39	31	25	38	30	25	36	29	24	34	28	23	32	27	23	21
8	35	27	22	34	27	22	32	26	21	30	24	20	29	23	19	18
9	32	24	19	31	23	18	29	22	18	27	21	17	26	20	17	15
10	29	21	17	28	21	16	26	20	16	25	19	15	23	18	15	13

Figure 20-36 *(Cont.)*

Typical Luminaire	Typical Intensity Distribution and Per Cent Lamp Lumens		ρcc →	80			70			50			30			10			0
	Maint Cat	SC	ρw →	50	30	10	50	30	10	50	30	10	50	30	10	50	30	10	0
			RCR ↓	Coefficients of Utilization for 20 Per Cent Effective Floor Cavity Reflectance (ρfc = 20)															
36 — 2 lamp prismatic wraparound — see note 7	V	1.2	0	82	82	82	77	77	77	69	69	69	61	61	61	53	53	53	50
			1	71	68	65	67	65	62	60	58	56	53	51	50	47	45	44	41
			2	63	58	54	59	55	52	53	50	47	47	45	42	42	40	38	35
			3	56	50	46	53	48	44	47	44	40	42	39	37	38	35	33	31
			4	50	44	40	48	42	38	43	39	35	38	35	32	34	32	29	27
			5	45	39	34	43	37	33	38	34	31	35	31	28	31	28	26	24
			6	41	35	30	39	33	29	35	30	27	32	28	25	28	25	23	21
			7	37	31	27	35	30	26	32	27	24	29	25	22	26	23	20	19
			8	33	27	23	32	26	23	29	24	21	26	22	20	23	20	18	16
			9	30	24	20	29	23	20	26	22	19	24	20	17	21	18	16	14
			10	27	22	18	26	21	18	24	19	16	22	18	15	19	16	14	13
42 — Fluorescent unit with flat prismatic lens, 4 lamp 610 mm (2') wide — see note 7	V	1.4/1.2	0	75	75	75	73	73	73	70	70	70	67	67	67	64	64	64	63
			1	67	65	63	66	64	62	63	62	60	61	60	58	59	58	57	55
			2	60	57	54	59	56	53	57	54	52	55	53	51	53	51	50	49
			3	54	50	47	53	49	46	52	48	45	50	47	45	48	46	44	43
			4	49	44	40	48	44	40	47	43	40	45	42	39	44	41	39	37
			5	44	39	35	43	38	35	42	38	34	41	37	34	40	36	34	33
			6	40	34	31	39	34	31	38	34	30	37	33	30	36	32	30	29
			7	36	30	27	35	30	27	34	30	27	33	29	26	32	29	26	25
			8	32	27	23	32	27	23	31	26	23	30	26	23	29	26	23	22
			9	29	24	20	28	23	20	28	23	20	27	23	20	26	23	20	19
			10	26	21	18	26	21	18	25	21	18	24	20	18	24	20	18	16
44 — Bilateral batwing distribution — louvered fluorescent unit	IV	N A	0	71	71	71	70	70	70	66	66	66	64	64	64	61	61	61	60
			1	65	63	61	63	62	60	61	59	58	59	57	56	57	56	55	54
			2	59	55	53	58	55	52	55	53	51	54	52	50	52	50	49	48
			3	53	49	46	52	48	45	50	47	45	49	46	44	47	45	43	42
			4	47	43	40	47	43	40	45	42	39	44	41	39	43	40	38	37
			5	42	38	34	42	37	34	41	37	34	40	36	34	39	36	33	32
			6	38	33	30	38	33	30	37	33	30	36	32	29	35	32	29	28
			7	34	29	26	33	29	26	33	28	25	32	28	25	31	28	25	24
			8	30	25	22	30	25	22	29	25	22	28	24	22	27	24	21	20
			9	27	22	18	26	22	18	26	21	18	25	21	18	24	21	18	17
			10	24	19	16	24	19	16	23	19	16	22	19	16	22	18	16	15

Typical Luminaires	ρcc →	80			70			50			30			10			0
	ρw →	50	30	10	50	30	10	50	30	10	50	30	10	50	30	10	0
	RCR ↓	Coefficients of utilization for 20 Per Cent Effective Floor Cavity Reflectance, ρfc															
50 — Single row fluorescent lamp cove without reflector, mult. by 0.93 for 2 rows and by 0.85 for 3 rows	1	42	40	39	36	35	33	25	24	23	Coves are not recommended for lighting areas having low reflectances.						
	2	37	34	32	32	29	27	22	20	19							
	3	32	29	26	28	25	23	19	17	16							
	4	29	25	22	25	22	19	17	15	13							
	5	25	21	18	22	19	16	15	13	11							
	6	23	19	16	20	16	14	14	12	10							
	7	20	17	14	17	14	12	12	10	09							
	8	18	15	12	16	13	10	11	09	08							
	9	17	13	10	15	11	09	10	08	07							
	10	15	12	09	13	10	08	09	07	06							
52 — Prismatic plastic or glass. 1) Ceiling efficiency ~67%, prismatic transmittance ~72%, prismatic reflectance ~18%. Cavity with minimum obstructions and painted with 80% reflectance paint — use ρc = 70. 2) For lower reflectance paint or obstructions — use ρc = 50. ρcc from below ~60%	1				71	68	66	67	66	65	65	64	62				
	2				63	60	57	61	58	55	59	56	54				
	3				57	53	49	55	52	48	54	50	47				
	4				52	47	43	50	45	42	48	44	42				
	5				46	41	37	44	40	37	43	40	36				
	6				42	37	33	41	36	32	40	35	32				
	7				38	32	29	37	31	28	36	31	28				
	8				34	28	25	33	28	25	32	28	25				
	9				30	25	22	30	25	21	29	25	21				
	10				27	23	19	27	22	19	26	22	19				

The assumption of a 20% $ρ_{fc}$ is almost always a good assumption. It is a midrange value and is sometimes used even when a light-colored shiny floor finish is contemplated. So often a floor finish is changed — darker-colored carpeting added, for example. However, fig. 20-37 provides correction factors which, if necessary, may be used when $ρ_{fc}$ is other than 20%. The factors in fig. 20-37 serve as multipliers that are to be applied to the CU values selected from fig. 20-36. For example, if a CU of 0.54 has been selected from fig. 20-36, and a correction factor of 1.037 is selected from

Figure 20-37 Multiplying factors for other than 20 percent effective floor cavity reflectance. (Reprinted with permission from IES, IES Lighting Handbook, 5th ed., 1972.)

Multiplying factors for other than 20 percent effective floor cavity reflectance

Percent effective ceiling cavity reflectance, ρ_{cc}

For 30 percent effective floor cavity reflectance (20 percent = 1.00)

Room cavity ratio	ρ_{cc} = 80				ρ_{cc} = 70				ρ_{cc} = 50			ρ_{cc} = 30			ρ_{cc} = 10		
ρ_w →	70	50	30	10	70	50	30	10	50	30	10	50	30	10	50	30	10
1	1.092	1.082	1.075	1.068	1.077	1.070	1.064	1.059	1.049	1.044	1.040	1.028	1.026	1.023	1.012	1.010	1.008
2	1.079	1.066	1.055	1.047	1.068	1.057	1.048	1.039	1.041	1.033	1.027	1.026	1.021	1.017	1.013	1.010	1.006
3	1.070	1.054	1.042	1.033	1.061	1.048	1.037	1.028	1.034	1.027	1.020	1.024	1.017	1.012	1.014	1.009	1.005
4	1.062	1.045	1.033	1.024	1.055	1.040	1.029	1.021	1.030	1.022	1.015	1.022	1.015	1.010	1.014	1.009	1.004
5	1.056	1.038	1.026	1.018	1.050	1.034	1.024	1.015	1.027	1.018	1.012	1.020	1.013	1.008	1.014	1.009	1.004
6	1.052	1.033	1.021	1.014	1.047	1.030	1.020	1.012	1.024	1.015	1.009	1.019	1.012	1.006	1.014	1.008	1.003
7	1.047	1.029	1.018	1.011	1.043	1.026	1.017	1.009	1.022	1.013	1.007	1.018	1.010	1.005	1.014	1.008	1.003
8	1.044	1.026	1.015	1.009	1.040	1.024	1.015	1.007	1.020	1.012	1.006	1.017	1.009	1.004	1.013	1.007	1.003
9	1.040	1.024	1.014	1.007	1.037	1.022	1.014	1.006	1.019	1.011	1.005	1.016	1.009	1.004	1.013	1.007	1.002
10	1.037	1.022	1.012	1.006	1.034	1.020	1.012	1.005	1.017	1.010	1.004	1.015	1.009	1.003	1.013	1.007	1.002

For 10 percent effective floor cavity reflectance (20 percent = 1.00)

Room cavity ratio	ρ_{cc} = 80				ρ_{cc} = 70				ρ_{cc} = 50			ρ_{cc} = 30			ρ_{cc} = 10		
ρ_w →	70	50	30	10	70	50	30	10	50	30	10	50	30	10	50	30	10
1	.923	.929	.935	.940	.933	.939	.943	.948	.956	.960	.963	.973	.976	.979	.989	.991	.995
2	.931	.942	.950	.958	.940	.949	.957	.963	.962	.968	.974	.976	.980	.985	.988	.991	.995
3	.939	.951	.961	.969	.945	.957	.966	.973	.967	.975	.981	.978	.983	.988	.988	.992	.996
4	.944	.958	.969	.978	.950	.963	.973	.980	.972	.980	.986	.980	.986	.991	.987	.992	.996
5	.949	.964	.976	.983	.954	.968	.978	.985	.975	.983	.989	.981	.988	.993	.987	.992	.997
6	.953	.969	.980	.986	.958	.972	.982	.989	.977	.985	.992	.982	.989	.995	.987	.993	.997
7	.957	.973	.983	.991	.961	.975	.985	.991	.979	.987	.994	.983	.990	.996	.987	.993	.998
8	.960	.976	.986	.993	.963	.977	.987	.993	.981	.988	.995	.984	.991	.997	.987	.994	.998
9	.963	.978	.987	.994	.965	.979	.989	.994	.983	.990	.996	.985	.992	.998	.988	.994	.999
10	.965	.980	.989	.995	.967	.981	.990	.995	.984	.991	.997	.986	.993	.998	.988	.994	.999

Figure 20-37 (Cont.)

Multiplying factors for other than 20 percent effective floor cavity reflectance

Percent effective ceiling cavity reflectance, ρ_{cc}

For 30 percent effective floor cavity reflectance (20 percent = 1.00)

For 0 percent effective floor cavity reflectance (20 percent = 1.00)

Room cavity ratio	80				70				50			30			10		
Percent wall reflectance, ρ_w	70	50	30	10	70	50	30	10	50	30	10	50	30	10	50	30	10
1	.859	.870	.879	.886	.873	.884	.893	.901	.916	.923	.929	.948	.954	.960	.979	.983	.987
2	.871	.887	.903	.919	.886	.902	.916	.928	.926	.938	.949	.954	.963	.971	.978	.983	.991
3	.882	.904	.915	.942	.898	.918	.934	.947	.936	.950	.964	.958	.969	.979	.976	.984	.993
4	.893	.919	.941	.958	.908	.930	.948	.961	.945	.961	.974	.961	.974	.984	.975	.985	.994
5	.903	.931	.953	.969	.914	.939	.958	.970	.951	.967	.980	.964	.977	.988	.975	.985	.995
6	.911	.940	.961	.976	.920	.945	.965	.977	.955	.972	.985	.966	.979	.991	.975	.986	.996
7	.917	.947	.967	.981	.924	.950	.970	.982	.959	.975	.988	.968	.981	.993	.975	.987	.997
8	.922	.953	.971	.985	.929	.955	.975	.986	.963	.978	.991	.970	.983	.995	.976	.988	.998
9	.928	.958	.975	.988	.933	.959	.980	.989	.966	.980	.993	.971	.985	.996	.976	.988	.998
10	.933	.962	.979	.991	.937	.963	.983	.992	.969	.982	.995	.973	.987	.997	.977	.989	.999

fig. 20-37, the resultant CU would be 0.54 × 1.037 = 0.56.

20-33 LAMPS REQUIRED

In most lighting system designs, many preliminary decisions must be made before the final lighting design calculations can be made. Of course, decisions are now required as to the general lighting level desired, the types of luminaires and lamps to be used, the placement of luminaires, and so on. After these decisions have been made and the CU has been determined as set forth in the preceding article, a fairly simple calculation will determine the number of lamps and their luminaires that will be needed. The formula for this calculation is

$$\text{lamps required} = \frac{\text{fc} \times \text{floor area}}{\text{lumens/lamp} \times \text{CU}}$$

where fc = footcandles of illumination required at the work plane
CU = coefficient of utilization

In this calculation, the value of lumens per lamp that is usually used is the "initial" lumen output when lamps are new. Therefore, the formula above will tell us how many lamps will be required to provide the desired level of illumination at the work plane when both lamps and fixtures are new and sparkling clean. As discussed in art. 20-31, lamps, fixtures and room finishes do not stay sparkling clean very long, and a *maintenance factor* must be added into the denominator of the formula above. This maintenance factor is always less than unity, ranging from 0.6 to 0.8, which when included in the formula has the effect of increasing the number of lamps required. The formula then becomes

$$\text{Lamps required} = \frac{\text{fc} \times \text{floor area}}{\text{lumens/lamp} \times \text{CU} \times \text{MF}}$$

where MF is the maintenance factor.

The inclusion of a maintenance factor in the formula above is necessary for two reasons:

1 Lamps and fixtures, as previously discussed, get dirty and luminosity is diminished; the factor that measures this effect is called the *luminaire dirt depreciation* (LDD) *factor.*
2 With usage all lamps lose some of their lumen output; the factor that measures this effect is called the *lamp lumen depreciation* (LLD) *factor.*

These two factors multiplied together constitute the *maintenance factor* (MF).

$$\text{MF} = \text{LDD} \times \text{LLD}$$

The magnitude of the LDD and LLD factors is a matter of judgment and depends on the maintenance considerations discussed in art. 20-31. The LDD factor is concerned extensively with the degree to which a fixture is ventilated; remember that a well-ventilated fixture stays clean much longer and suffers much less dirt depreciation than a poorly ventilated one.

LDD factors may be selected from the curves of fig. 20-38. In fig. 20-38, the designer must select a factor from families of curves ranging from "very clean" fixtures to "very dirty" fixtures, representing very good to very poor maintenance. In fig. 20-38, fixtures are categorized from category I to category VI in accordance with their construction and their tendency to stay clean or to collect dirt rapidly. Each of the fixtures in the CU table of fig. 20-36 is given a category number. Category numbers for fixtures not listed in fig. 20-36 may be obtained from the published literature of their manufacturer.

The lamp lumen depreciation (LLD) factor is a very elusive one, and is difficult to resolve into a definite and limited value. LLD values are sometimes taken as *mean luminosity,* or luminosity at 50% of effective life, or at 70% of effective life, or at some specific point such as at 16,000 hr in a rated 24,000-hr life. Between lamps of a given size in a given type there is considerable variation, so it is futile to attempt to reduce LLD values to specific

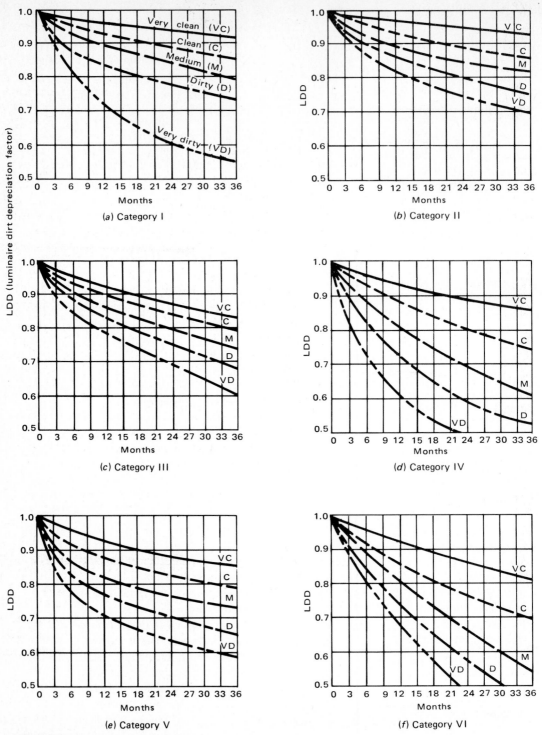

Figure 20-38 Luminaire dirt depreciation factors. (Reprinted with permission from IES, IES Lighting Handbook, 5th ed., 1972.)

Figure 20-39 LLD factors for various types of lamps.

Incandescent	0.88-0.94
Tungsten halogen	0.94-0.98
Fluorescent, 430 or 425 mA	0.85-0.90
Fluorescent, 800 mA (HO)	0.81-0.85
Fluorescent, 1500 mA (VHO)	0.71-0.75
Mercury vapor (MV)	0.76-0.80
Metal halide (MH)	0.75-0.80
High-pressure sodium (HPS)	0.88-0.92

figures. Figure 20-39 presents a table of approximate LLDs for various types of lamps.

20-34 PLACEMENT OF LUMINAIRES IN A ROOM

An endless variety of patterns is available for arranging lighting fixtures in a room. More often than not fixtures are located at the ceiling, either stem hung (suspended) below the ceiling, surface mounted against the ceiling, or fully recessed into the ceiling. Ceiling fixtures are usually arranged in parallel rows, although there are many deviations from this. So often a ceiling, either acoustic or otherwise, is suspended on metal framing members —exposed T-bars or concealed runner channels and furring channels. The grid pattern of these framing members will have an extensive effect on fixture locations when fixtures are to be recessed.

Cove lighting, similar to fixture 50 in fig. 20-36, is located on room walls and arranged to cast light either upward or downward, or both. Where room width is not too great, not over 15 to 18 ft, cove lights on all walls can do a fine job of providing good, comfortable illumination, although the CU may be lower than desired.

Some lighting systems have been quite effective in employing the *task-ambient principle,* in which a fairly low level of general illumination, perhaps 40 fc, is provided from the ceiling with localized task lighting provided at the specific location where a seeing task is being performed. Task-ambient lighting can result in very good visibility with very low power consumption. In a drafting room, for example, the task lighting may consist of fluorescent or incandescent fixtures mounted on drafting boards, or chain suspended a few feet above board level at the left and the right of the draftsman.

As previously discussed, luminaire location, or the location of people relative to luminaires, is exceedingly important in establishing satisfactory conditions of visual comfort probability (VCP), minimal veiling reflections, contrast rendition factor (CRF), and equivalent sphere illumination (ESI).

In arranging rows of fixtures, such as fluorescent fixtures, a few rules should be followed to the extent possible.

1 Rows should be equally spaced with the distance between outer rows and the side walls equal to one-half the row spacing. This means that row spacing S, the distance from centerline to centerline of adjacent rows, should equal the room width divided by the number of rows.

$$S = \frac{\text{room width in feet}}{\text{number of rows of fixtures}}$$

where S is the row centerline spacing in feet. Then the distance from the centerline of the outer rows of fixtures to the side walls should be $1/2S$.

2 Rows of fixtures should, as much as possible, be run parallel to an outside wall having windows in it. This will permit switching off one or two rows nearest the windows when daylight from the windows provides enough illumination.

3 Rows of fixtures may extend, if necessary, to within an inch or so of the end walls of a room. Only enough space is required for expansion as fixtures heat up during operation. The maximum space between end walls and ends of rows of fixtures depends somewhat on the *cutoff angle* of the fixtures, but in general should not exceed 3 ft or perhaps 4 ft. The cutoff angle of a fixture is the angle, measured from the vertical to the line of sight from a person to the fixture, when that person standing to the side or the end of the fixture can just see the lamps through any louvers or shielding in the bottom of the fixture below the lamps. This cutoff angle is usually between 30 and 45°.

The proximity of the fixtures to the end wall

and the cutoff angle will determine the height of the light pattern cast on the wall by the fixtures. In some cases, a number of rows of fixtures, such as fluorescent fixtures, will cast a scalloped pattern of light on an end wall; this may or may not be objectionable, but that possibility should be considered.

4 Most fixture manufacturers publish information as to the maximum spacing between fixtures, or rows of fixtures, that should not be exceeded if a continuous, unvarying level of illumination at the work plane is to be achieved. The maximum spacing is, of course, involved with the height of the fixtures above the work plane. The maximum spacing then is expressed as a ratio of the horizontal spacing to the fixture mounting height *above the work plane.* Figure 20-36 includes this information, for most of the fixtures listed, in the column of the table with the heading "SC" (maximum *spacing coefficient,* or spacing ratio)."

Fixture 36 in fig. 20-36 lists a maximum SC ratio of 1.2. This means that if No. 36 fixtures are mounted 6 ft above the work plane, spacing between fixtures or rows of fixtures should not exceed 7.2 ft (6 ft × 1.2 = 7.2 ft). In some cases, fig. 20-36 lists two values of SC ratios; see fixture 42, which lists the values "1.4/1.2." The first value (1.4) indicates maximum lateral spacing, and the second value (1.2) indicates maximum end spacing in a row of fixtures.

In some situations it may be desirable to increase the light level near the side walls of a room above the general level throughout the room. This may be easily accomplished by reducing the side wall spacing to less than half the general row spacing in the center of the room.

20-35　SELECTING FLUORESCENT FIXTURES

Example 20-1 Select fluorescent fixtures and show their location in a business office as described below.

Given:

1 *Office dimensions:* 30 ft long, 15 ft wide, and 9 ft high. Work plane height, 30 in.

2 *Reflectances:* ceiling 80%, walls 50%, and floor cavity 20%.

3 *Level of illumination:* 70 footcandles maintained.

4 *Maintenance:* lamps will be replaced on a 24-month schedule and cleanliness of lamps and fixtures will be "medium."

Find the number of lamps and fixtures required and their arrangement in the room for overall even illumination.

Solution Use fixture 36 (see fig. 20-36), which is a two-lamp prismatic wraparound type. Use 40-W, cool white, T12, 430 mA, rapid start lamps, F40T12CW. Mount fixtures 8 ft above the floor. Figure 20-19 lists lamp lumens for F40T12CW lamps at 3150 lumens.

To find CU, first determine RCR, CCR, and ρ_{cc}. With fixtures mounted 8 ft above the floor, they are 1 ft below the ceiling. Ceiling cavity height is then 1 ft. Fixtures are also 5.5 ft above the 30-in. work plane; therefore, the room cavity is 5.5 ft high.

$$RCR = \frac{2.5 \times \text{room cavity wall area}}{\text{floor area}}$$

$$= \frac{2.5 \ [(30 \text{ ft} + 15 \text{ ft})2] \times 5.5 \text{ ft}}{30 \text{ ft} \times 15 \text{ ft}} = 2.75$$

$$CCR = \frac{2.5 \ [(30 \text{ ft} + 15 \text{ ft})2] \times 1 \text{ ft}}{30 \text{ ft} \times 15 \text{ ft}} = 0.5$$

Find ceiling cavity reflectance ρ_{cc} in fig. 20-35. In the 50% wall reflectance column under 80% ceiling (base) reflectance, and in the 0.5 horizontal line for cavity ratio (CCR), find a value of 72.5%. Interpolate between the lines for 0.4 and 0.6 cavity ratios.

Select CU from fig. 20-36 for fixture 36. Enter the ρ_{cc} column nearest our ρ_{cc} of 72.5%, which is 70%. In the 50% ρ_w column under 70%, follow down to the section belonging to fixture 36 and read a CU value of 0.545 for an RCR of 2.75. Again, interpolate between CU values for RCRs of 2 and 3.

Notice also in fig. 20-36 that fixture 36 is listed as belonging in maintenance category V, and that the S/MH guide ratio is 1.2 maximum. We may now select the luminaire dirt depreciation (LDD) factor from fig. 20-38 in the category V graph at the intersection of the medium dirty, "M," curve and the vertical line for a 24-month relamping schedule. LDD may be read at approximately 0.77.

From fig. 20-39 the lamp lumen depreciation (LLD) factor for a 430-mA fluorescent lamp falls in the range 0.85 to 0.90. Let us use an LLD of 0.87.

Our maintenance factor may now be calculated as

$$MF = LDD \times LLD = 0.77 \times 0.87 = 0.67$$

We may now calculate the number of lamps required (see art. 20-32):

$$\text{Lamps required} = \frac{FC \times \text{floor area}}{\text{lumens/lamp} \times CU \times MF}$$

$$= \frac{70 \times 30 \text{ ft} \times 15 \text{ ft}}{3150 \times 0.545 \times 0.67}$$

$$= 27.4 \text{ lamps}$$

Lamps required = 27 or 28 lamps; 28 lamps would require 14 two-lamp fixtures. The 14 fixtures must be properly arranged in the room for even light distribution.

Before we do that, let us see how many lamps and fixtures would be required if we choose to use four-lamp fixtures instead of two-lamp fixtures. With four lamps in a fixture, the CU is usually only 90 to 95 percent of that for a two-lamp fixture. This means that our 0.545 CU previously selected will be reduced somewhat if four-lamp fixtures are to be used. The CU would by 0.545 × 0.95 = 0.518; use 0.52, if we use 95 percent.

Using a 0.52 value for CU, the number of lamps required becomes:

$$\text{Lamps required} = \frac{70 \times 30 \text{ ft} \times 15 \text{ ft}}{3150 \times 0.52 \times 0.67}$$

$$= 28.7 \text{ lamps}$$

We could still use 28 lamps in 7 four-lamp fixtures.

In arranging the 14 two-lamp fixtures in our 30 ft × 15 ft room, our first thought is to arrange the 14 fixtures in two continuous rows of 7 fixtures each. Each row of 7 fixtures would be 28 ft long, since our F40T12CW lamps have a nominal length of 48 in. and fit into a 4-ft-long fixture. The 28-ft-long rows fit beautifully into the 30-ft-long room, and everything seems fine except for one problem. Fixture 36 allows a maximum SC spacing ratio of 1.2. Since our mounting height (MH) is 5.5 ft, our maximum allowable spacing is 5.5 ft × 1.2 = 6.6 ft.

This is not enough. If we mount the two rows at 6.6 ft apart, the spacing between the rows and the side walls will be 4.2 ft. This is too much since 4.2 ft is much more than one-half of 6.6 ft. We would not have adequate illumination at the side walls. If less light at the side walls is satisfactory, two rows are fine.

We might run the rows crosswise in the room and use five rows of three fixtures each. The row spacing would be 6 ft (30 ft/5 rows = 6 ft), which would satisfy our SC requirement of 6.6 ft maximum. If we had windows in the 15-ft wall this would be a good answer to the problem, but if there were windows in the longer 30-ft wall or in both a 30-ft wall and a 15-ft wall, it would be better to run the rows lengthwise.

One can see at a glance that seven four-lamp fixtures would not suffice at all, since the same SC limitation still prevails. Many factors apply to this problem that we do not know about, but probably our best fixture arrangement will involve 15 two-lamp fixtures hung in three rows of five each. Since a row of five fixtures is only 20 ft

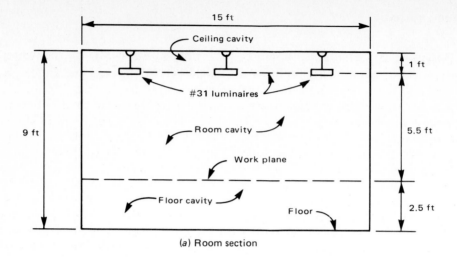

(a) Room section

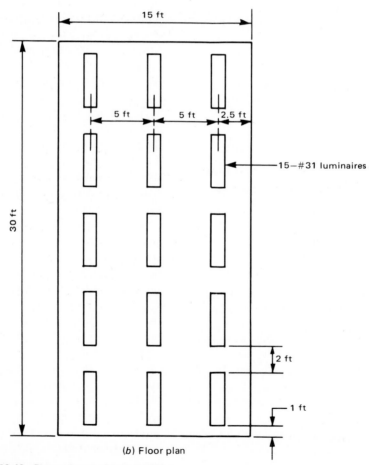

(b) Floor plan

Figure 20-40 Fixture layout, Example #20-1.

long, we would have an end spacing of 5 ft in the 30-ft-long room. This is too much, and we will need to break the rows up as shown in fig. 20-40.

There is a shortcut method available for selecting the required number of fixtures in a room. This involves the use of "quick calculator charts" that are published by fixture manufacturers together with the photometric data for a given fixture. Such a chart is included in fig. 20-30 for the fluorescent fixture detailed there.

In example 20-1, 70 FC of maintained illumination are required. As shown the maintenance factor (MF) is 0.67. Therefore, initial illumination will be 70 FC ÷ 0.67 = 104.4 FC. The RCR of example 20-1 is also 2.75, and room reflectances are ρ_c = 80%, ρ_w = 50%, and ρ_{fc} = 20%. Entering the quick calculator chart of fig. 20-30 with these data, we can read that if we use that particular fixture, we will need one fixture for each 32 ft^2 of floor. The number of fixtures required would then be

$$\frac{30 \text{ ft} \times 15 \text{ ft (floor area)}}{32} = 14.06 \text{ fixtures}$$

This method is perhaps not as accurate as the longer method, but is extensively used.

20-36 LIGHT DIMMING FOR ENERGY SAVINGS

Most lamps can be dimmed so as to modify the level of illumination in a room as desired by room occupants. In many nonresidential buildings the ability to reduce lighting levels is of great benefit. Some of the uses of dimming is in theaters, restaurants, museums, and churches. In past years, dimming left much to be desired. It was jerky, nonlinear, difficult to control, and usually consumed as much power while dimmed as when bright. The art of dimming has come a long way since those early days, of course, and the need to save energy has raised the possibility of the use of dimming in many applications where not previously considered.

Incandescent, fluorescent, and HID lamps can all be dimmed, although in some cases special dimming ballasts are required. Because of this it is highly recommended that where extensive dimming is to be used, the entire system of dimmers, ballasts, meters and controls, and perhaps lamps should be acquired as an integrated package. In this way radio-frequency interference, noise, overheating of equipment, and loss of equipment life can be minimized.

With the use of solid-state electronic equipment, smooth dimming control down to nearly 5% of maximum light can be obtained. Fortunately power demand is now almost exactly in proportion to light output in a linear fashion. This presents many opportunities for building owners and operators to save energy by reducing light levels, very often at increased comfort levels, when close-seeing tasks are not being performed.

One very interesting recent development in this field is the use of photosensitive, ceiling-mounted light sensors which measure the amount of daylight entering a room and automatically reduce the amount of artificial light delivered by the lighting system. In this way a constant level of light can be maintained at all times while minimizing the use of artificial light. Substantial amounts of energy can be saved.

At the same time, manual control of light levels is easily achieved to obtain further energy savings. Another major benefit of such an automatic dimming system results from the fact that nearly all lighting systems are designed to maintain a certain level of light when fixtures and lamps are soiled and after lamp luminosity has depreciated. In example 20-1, a maintenance factor of 0.67 was entered in the calculation to assure a lighting level of 70 footcandles after dirt depreciation and lamp lumen depreciation have occurred. However, when fixtures and lamps are new and clean, the lighting level will be as much as 104 fc instead of 70 (70 fc ÷ .67 = 104).

In example 20-1, with a 24-month relamping period, for most of these 24 months light levels will be well above 70 fc. With an automatic dim-

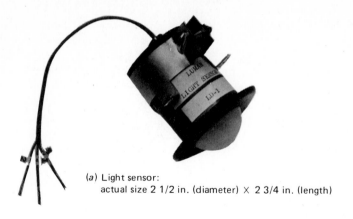

(a) Light sensor:
    actual size 2 1/2 in. (diameter) × 2 3/4 in. (length)

(b) High-frequency ballast

(c) Power control module:
    actual size 12 5/8 in. (height) × 9 5/8 in. (width) × 4 1/2 in. (diameter)

Figure 20-41 Automatic dimming system details. (Courtesy of Lutron Electronics Co., Inc.)

(*d*) Electrical and wiring information

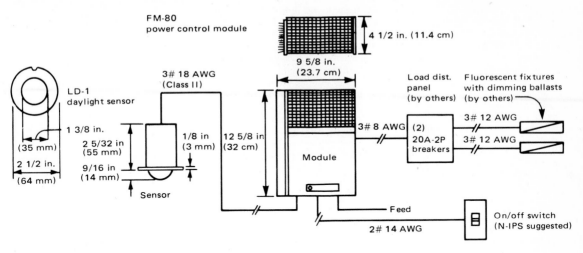

Figure 20-41 *(Cont.)*

ming system the light-sensitive controller will reduce power input until light levels are held steady at 70 fc. Very considerable amounts of power can thus be saved. As fixture and lamp luminosity gradually depreciate, more power is automatically supplied to maintain the desired light level. Another benefit of the system described is that the basic control module includes a frequency inverter which supplies comparatively high frequency power to fluorescent lamp ballasts and fluorescent lamps. At the higher frequencies, fluorescent systems operate much more efficiently; for example, one manufacturer estimates that an F40T12, 40-W fluorescent lamp which with its ballast consumes 46 to 48 W at 60-Hz frequency, will consume only 36 W—a reduction of 22 to 25%, at a higher frequency.

Yet another benefit is the savings in energy required to operate a building cooling system. For every 1000 W of lighting power saved in mechanically cooled rooms, another 300 to 400 W will be saved in HVAC operating cost. The sum total of all the energy savings described above can easily amount to 25 to 50% of the power that an undimmed system would require.

These energy savings, coupled with the "Investment and Energy Tax Credits" that are possible make a 2- to 5-year payoff of the dimming system cost a distinct possibility. There are some additional benefits to be derived from installing such a system in a new building; however, the retrofit possibilities in an existing building are also great. Figure 20-41 shows details of equipment and a schematic wiring diagram of a typical dimming system.

20-37 RECOMMENDED LIGHTING LEVELS

The Illuminating Engineering Society (IES) has been the source of recommendations as to the amount of light that may be required in various types of rooms in various types of buildings. The energy shortage has caused many authorities to begin a process of reevaluating these recommendations to determine whether values that have been automatically accepted in the past can be, on any basis, revised downward. Until this process is complete, the table in fig. 20-42 should be used with a questioning judgment.

Figure 20-42 Currently recommended illuminance categories and illuminance values for lighting design—target. The tabulation is a consolidated listing of the IES current illuminance recommendations. It is intended to guide the lighting designer in selecting an appropriate illuminance for design and evaluation of lighting systems. Guidance is provided in parts I and II as an illuminance category, representing a range of illuminances. Illuminance categories are represented by letter designations A through I. Illuminance values are given in lux, with an approximate equivalence in footcandles and as such are intended as target (nominal) values with deviations expected. These target values also represent maintained values. Part I provides a listing of both illuminance categories and illuminance values for generic types of interior activities. It is normally to be used when illuminance categories for a specific area of activity cannot be found in part II. In all cases, the recommendations in this table are based on the assumption that the lighting will be properly designed to take into account the visual characteristics of the task. (All information has been excerpted with permission from the *IES Handbook,* 1981 Reference volume.)

I. Illuminance categories and illuminance values for generic types of activities in interiors

Type of activity	Illumi-nance Category	Ranges of illuminances		Reference work-plane
		Lux	Footcandles	
Public spaces with dark surroundings	A	20–30–50	2–3–5	
Simple orientation for short temporary visits	B	50–75–100	5–7.5–10	General lighting throughout spaces
Working spaces where visual tasks are only occasionally performed	C	100–150–200	10–15–20	
Performance of visual tasks of high contrast or large size	D	200–300–500	20–30–50	
Performance of visual tasks of medium contrast or small size	E	500–750–1000	50–75–100	Illuminance on task
Performance of visual tasks of low contrast or very small size	F	1000–1500–2000	100–150–200	
Performance of visual tasks of low contrast and very small size over a prolonged period	G	2000–3000–5000	200–300–500	
Performance of very prolonged and exacting visual tasks	H	5000–7500–10000	500–750–1000	Illuminance on task obtained by a combination of general and local (supplementary lighting)
Performance of very special visual tasks of extremely low contrast and small size	I	10000–15000–20000	1000–1500–2000	

II. Commercial institutional, residential, and public assembly interiors

Area or activity	Illuminance category	Area or activity	Illuminance category
Air terminals (see Transportation terminals)		Art galleries (see Museums)	
		Auditoriums	
		Assembly	C[a]
Armories	C[a]	Social activity	B

Figure 20-42 *(Cont.)*

II. Commercial institutional, residential, and public assembly interiors

Area or activity	Illuminance category	Area or activity	Illuminance category
Banks (also see Reading)		Cafeterias (see Food service facilities)	
Lobby		Dormitories	
General	C	Exhibition halls	C[a]
Writing area	D		
Tellers' stations	E[b]	Food service facilities	
		Dining areas	
Conference rooms		Cashier	D
Conferring		Cleaning	C
Critical seeing (refer to individual task)	D	Dining	B[d]
		Food displays (see Merchandising	
Court rooms		spaces)	
Seating area	C	Kitchen	E
Court activity area	E[b]	Health care facilities	
		Corridors[e]	
Drafting		Nursing areas—day	C
Mylar		Nursing areas—night	B
High contrast media; India ink,		Operating areas, delivery, recovery,	
plastic leads, soft graphite leads	E[b]	and laboratory suites and service	E
Low contrast media; hard graphite		Critical care areas[e]	
leads	F[b]	General	C
Vellum		Examination	E
High contrast	E[b]	Handwashing	F
Low contrast	F[b]	Elevators	C
Tracing paper		EKG and specimen room[e]	
High contrast	E[b]	General	B
Low contrast	F[b]	On equipment	C
Overlays[c]		Emergency outpatient[e]	
Light table	C	General	E
Prints		Local	F
Blue line	E	Examination and treatment rooms[e]	
Blueprints	E	General	D
Sepia prints	F	Local	E
		Lobby	C
Educational facilities		Locker rooms	C
Classrooms		Medical records	E
General (see Reading)		Nursing stations[e]	
Drafting (see Drafting)		General	D
Home economics		Desk	E
Science laboratories	E	Corridors, day	C
Lecture rooms		Corridors, night	A
Audience (see Reading)		Patients' rooms[e]	
Demonstration	F	General[f]	B
Music rooms (see Reading)		Observation	A
Shops (see Part III. Industrial Group)		Critical examination	E
Sight saving rooms	F	Reading	D
Study halls (see Reading)		Toilets	D
Typing (see Reading)			
Sports facilities			

Figure 20-42 *(Cont.)*

Area or activity	Illuminance category	Area or activity	Illuminance category
Pharmacy[e]		Municipal buildings—fire and police	
General	E	Police	
Physical therapy departments		Identification records	F
Gymnasiums	D	Jail cells and interrogation rooms	D
Tank rooms	D	Fire hall	D
Treatment cubicles	D		
Radiological suite[e]		Museums	
Diagnostic section		Displays of non-sensitive materials	D
General[f]	A	Lobbies, general gallery areas, corridors	C
Waiting area	A	Restoration or conservation shops and	
Radiation therapy section		laboratories	E
General[f]	B		
Waiting area	B	Nursing homes (see Health care facilities)	
Solarium			
General	C	Offices	
Local for reading	D	Accounting (see Reading)	
Stairways	C	Conference areas (see Conference rooms)	
Toilets	C	Drafting (see Drafting)	
Utility room	D	General and private offices (see Reading)	
Waiting areas[e]		Libraries (see Libraries)	
General	C	Lobbies, lounges and reception areas	C
Local for reading	D	Mail sorting	E
		Off-set printing and duplicating area	D
Hospitals (see Health care facilities)			
		Post offices (see Offices)	
Hotels			
Bedrooms, for reading	D	Reading	
Corridors, elevators and stairs	C	Copied tasks	
Lobby		Ditto copy	E[b]
General lighting	C	Micro-fiche reader	B[g,h]
Reading and working areas	D	Mimeograph	D
		Photographs, moderate detail	E[h]
Kitchens (see Food service facilities)		Thermal copy, poor copy	F[b]
		Handwritten tasks	
Libraries		#3 pencil and softer leads	E[b]
Reading areas (see Reading)		#4 pencil and harder leads	F[b]
Book stacks (vertical 760 millimeters		Ball-point pen	D[b]
(30 inches) above floor)		Felt-tip pen	D
Active stacks	D	Handwritten carbon copies	E
Inactive stacks	B	Non photographically reproducible	
Cataloging	D[b]	colors	F
Card files	E	Chalkboards	E[b]
Circulation desks	D	Printed tasks	
		6 point type	E[b]
Locker rooms	C	8 and 10 point type	D[b]
		Glossy magazines	D[h]
Merchandising spaces		Maps	E
Stock rooms	D	Newsprint	D
Wrapping and packaging	D	Typed originals	D
Sales transaction area	E	Typed 2nd carbon and later	E
		Telephone books	E
Motels (see Hotels)			

Figure 20-42 *(Cont.)*

Area or activity	Illuminance category	Area or activity	Illuminance category
Restaurants (see Food service facilities)		Transportation terminals	
		Waiting room and lounge	C
Schools (see Educational facilities)		Ticket counters	E
Service spaces		Baggage checking	D
Stairways, corridors	C	Rest rooms	C
Elevators, freight and passenger	C	Concourse	B
Toilets and wash rooms	C	Boarding area	C
Toilets and washrooms	C		

[a] Include provisions for higher levels for exhibitions.

[b] Task subject to veiling reflections. Illuminance listed is not an ESI value. Currently, insufficient experience in the use of ESI target values precludes the direct use of Equivalent Sphere Illumination in the present consensus approach to recommend illuminance values. Equivalent Sphere Illumination may be used as a tool in determining the effectiveness of controlling veiling reflections and as a part of the evaluation of lighting systems.

[c] Degradation factors: Overlays—add 1 weighting factor for each overlay; Used material—estimate additional factors.

[d] Provide higher level over food service or selection areas.

[e] Good to high color rendering capability should be considered in these areas. As lamps of higher luminous efficacy and higher color rendering capability become available and economically feasible, they should be applied in all areas of health care facilities.

[f] Variable (dimming or switching).

[g] Veiling reflections may be produced on glass surfaces. It may be necessary to treat plus weighting factors as minus in order to obtain proper illuminance.

[h] Especially subject to veiling reflections. It may be necessary to shield the task or to reorient it.

For more detailed description and guidance on determining the illuminance within the ranges shown, please consult the IES *Lighting Handbooks* 1981 Reference and Application Volumes. These handbooks provide extensive additional information and recommendations on commercial, institutional, residential, public and industrial buildings as well as outdoor facilities, sports and recreational facilities, and transportation vehicles.

All information in Figure 20.42 has been excerpted with permission from the I.E.S. Handbook, 1981 Reference Volume.

PROBLEMS

20-1 What percent of original luminosity does a deluxe white mercury vapor lamp retain at the 50% point of its life?

20-2 What is the initial lumen output of a 40-W F40/T12 cool white rapid start fluorescent lamp? What is its anticipated life in operating hours? What is its luminosity when 60% of its life is gone and only 40% remains?

20-3 How does the efficacy of an F40T12 cool white rapid start lamp compare with that of an F40T12 deluxe cool white lamp?

20-4 Approximately how much more light, if any, would be obtained in a given room if existing 250-W phosphor-coated deluxe white mercury vapor lamps (H37KC-250/DX) were replaced with 175-W standard multivapor metal halide lamps (MXR 175/C/U)? Use initial luminosities for comparison. What size incandescent lamps would be required to produce the same amount of light as these 175-W MH lamps?

20-5 What would be the CU of the parabolic louver fluorescent fixtures described in fig. 20-30 in a room where the ceiling cavity reflectance is 75%, the wall reflectance is 50%, and the room cavity ratio is 5? Also, how many such fixtures would be required in that room if initial footcandles required is 75 and the room is 40 ft wide and 60 ft long?

20-6 A given office is 40 ft wide and 60 ft long and has a lighting level of 66 fc. It is illuminated by 43 lighting fixtures each of which has two fluorescent lamps which emit 3000 lm. What is the CU in this office?

20-7 An office is 40 ft wide, 60 ft long, and 10 ft high. It is lit by luminaires which are 9 ft above the floor. The work plane is 3 ft above the floor. Find the CCR and the RCR.

20-8 In a certain room in a building the ceiling has recently been painted eggshell white, the walls are medium gray (new and clean), and the ceiling cavity ratio is 1.4. Find the ceiling cavity reflectance.

20-9 The lobby of a theater building is lit with pendant diffusing spheres equipped with 150-W incandescent lamps. The ceiling reflectance of this lobby is 50% and the wall reflectance is 30%. The CCR is 0.8, the RCR = 4, luminaires are maintained "clean," and lamps are replaced every 3 months. How many of these luminaires will be required to light this lobby to 20 fc if the floor area is 2000 ft^2?

20-10 If the theater lobby of prob. 20-9 is to be lit with fluorescent lamps, how many 75-W instant start slimline cool white F96T12/CW lamps mounted in single-row fluorescent cove luminaires would be required? These lamps will burn 56 hr per week, will be replaced every 3 years, and will be maintained in "clean" condition; they are category II luminaires.

Answers to Selected Problems

3-1 Sensible heat increase.

3-2 Latent heat decrease.

3-3 All will change except DP and specific humidity.

3-4 DB temperature will not change.

3-5 WB and TH will not change.

3-6 Upward and to the left.

3-7 90%.

3-8 Increase.

3-9 Decrease.

3-10 DB = 82.25°F, TH = 33.55 Btu/lb., WB = 69.3°F, specific humidity = 87 grains/lb., DP = 63.3°F, RH = 53%, specific volume = 13.9 ft³/lb.

DB = (0.25 × 95°F) + (0.75 × 78°F) = 82.25°F.

TH = (0.25 × 40.6 Btu/lb) + (0.75 × 31.2 Btu/lb) = 33.55 Btu/lb. MA – WB is 69.3°.

Plot this point and read: specific humidity

= 87 grains/lb, DP = 63.3°F, RH = 53%, specific volume = 13.9 ft³/lb.

4-1 $R = x/k = 2.5/5.5 = 0.45; R = 0.45.$

4-2 $R = 1/c = 1/0.6 = 1.67.$

4-3 $U = 1/4.5$
   $= 0.22.$

4-4 BH = 700 × 0.22(66° – 15°) = 7854.

4-5 $R_R = 1/0.25 = 4$; ins. $R_I = 4/0.2, = 20.$
   $R_T = 4 + 20 = 24; U = 1/24 = 0.042.$

4-6 $C = 0.90; R = 1/0.90 = 1.11.$

4-7 $U_W = 0.39$ (fig. 4-4b); BH = 300 × 0.39 × 80 = 9360.

4-8 $U_D = 0.31.$

4-9 BH = (5000 × 3) + (7000 × 6) = 57,000 (fig. 4-4d).

4-10 0.61/15 = 0.04067; 0.04067 × 62° Δt = 2.52°; 67° – 2.52 = 64.48°F. 0.61/25 = 0.0244; 0.0244 × 62° Δt = 1.51°; 67 – 1.51 = 65.49°F.

4-11 $CFH = 0.70 \times 6 \times 32$ ft $\times 30$ CFH/ft = 4032 maximum; eastwind CFH $= 3 \times 32$ ft $\times 30$ CFH/ft = 2880.

4-12 BH $= 4032 \times 0.02 \times 55°F = 4435$;   BH $= 2880 \times 0.02 \times 55°F = 3168$.

5-1 50 people $\times$ 510 bh (total) = 25,500 BH
        2500 W of light $\times 3.42 =$ 8,550
        Coffee brewers $2 \times 1000 =$ 2,000
        Water cooler (1500 W/4) $\times$
                  $3.42 \times 0.6 =$ 770
        Typewriters 16×65 W $\times$
                  $0.45 \times 3.42 = \underline{\ \ 1,600}$
                        38,420 BH =
                        3.2 tons

5-2 120 ft $\times$ 75 ft = 9000 ft^2; 9000/6 ft^2/person = 1500 people seated at rest.
    Sensible heat load = 1500
        $\times$ 210 = 315,000 BHS = 26.25 tons
    Latent heat load = 1500
        $\times$ 140 = 210,000 BHL = $\underline{17.50}$
           Total load = 43.75 tons

5-3 No, the air movement is downward in summertime.

5-4 The floor structure at each floor level should extend through such enclosed shafts with sleeved openings in the floor for duct and pipe passage. The spaces around such ducts and pipes should be well caulked with resilient material.

5-5 OA should be at least 7% of the 80,000 cfm. $0.07 \times 80,000 = 5600$ cfm.

5-6 BH = 5600 cfm $\times 1.08(68° - 10°) =$ 350,784 BH = 350.784 MBH.

5-7 BHL = 5600 cfm(109.5 grains/lb $- 56$)0.68 = 203728.

5-8 Conduction gain $= 5 \times 4$ ft $\times 5$ ft $\times 0.94$ (fig. 4-4b) $(97° - 76°) = 1974$ BH.
    Solar gain at 16:00 o'clock.
    South $= 3 \times 4$ ft $\times 5$ ft $\times$
        0.8 $\times$ 25 (fig. 5-9)
        $= 1200$ BH $\times 0.69$
           (fig. 5-10) =   828 BH
    West $= 2 \times 4$ ft $\times 5$ ft $\times$
        0.8 $\times$ 178 (fig. 5-9)
        $= 5696$ BH $\times 0.69 = \underline{3930}$
           Solar total = 4758
    Conduction gain from
           above = $\underline{1974}$
           Total = 6732 BH

5-9 (4758 (prob. 5-8)/0.69) $\times$ 0.21 (fig. 5-11) = 1448 BH + 1974 BH conduction = 3422 BH.

5-10 Approximately 50%, or slightly less, of the window will be sunlit.

5-11
       R_o Brick   Air   Shtg   Air
  $R_T = 0.333 + 0.444 + 0.91 + 2.06 + 0.91$
    Insulation   Plaster R_i
  $+ (2\text{-in}/0.25) + 0.149 + 0.685 = 13.491$
  $U_W = 0.074$ p. 5-53; group E wall at 17:00
  ETD $= 34° \times 0.65$ color correction $= 22.1°$
  $ETD_c = 22.1° + (78° - 76°) + (97° - 18/2$
  $- 85) = 27.1°$
  BH $= (630 - 130)0.074 \times 27.1° = 1003$.

6-1 Condensing unit: compressor, compressor motor, condenser, mounting base and service valves; water chiller: compressor, compressor motor, condenser, water cooler, refrigerant piping, control panel, valves and accessories.

6-2 Eight zones; may be different.

6-3 That area of a building supplied with air by one zone duct from a multizone HVAC unit. All rooms or spaces in a zone have similar load characteristics.

6-4 40 hp $\times$ 2540 BH = 101,600 BH. This heat is delivered by the motor to the fan, then to the circulating air, into the supply duct system, to the rooms being supplied with air, from the room to the exterior (in winter) or through the return duct system to the cooling coil in the HVAC unit (in summer), from the cooling coil through the refrigerant (or chilled water) to the refrigerating machine, through the refrigerating machine to the outdoors.

6-5 Only a little of it; most of it (80 to 90%) is absorbed by the cooling (in summer) coil and delivered by the refrigerating system to the outdoors.

6-6 (400 ft/100) ft $\times$ .1-in. wg/100 ft = 0.4 in. wg.

6-7 Check that duct air velocities are not excessive.

6-8 1300 fpm maximum velocity, 40 in. $\times$ 19 in. or 34 in. $\times$ 22 in. etc., and 30-in. diameter.

6-9 3000 fpm (see fig. 6-30).

6-10 (15 in./12) π X 1200 rpm = 4712 fpm tip speed; maximum allowable commercial TS = 5000 fpm; 4712 fpm is not excessive.

6-11 Because acoustic terminals are used which provide noise reduction.

6-12 hp = (42,000 cfm X 2.2 in. X 69.33)/ (13.33 X 33,000 X .87) = 16.74. This is too much for a 15-hp motor; use a 20-hp motor.

6-13 Area = 6-ft girth X 92-ft length = 552 ft². U from fig. 6-39 = 0.20; Δt = 110° – 38° = 72°F; BH = A X U X Δt = 552 X 0.20 X 72 = 7949.

7-1 When air is overcooled for dehumidification purposes, it must then be reheated so that it will not overcool the controlled space.

7-2 One that uses OA for building cooling. The enthalpy controller is necessary to prevent the introduction of air with too high a wet bulb temperature into a building.

7-3 Normally open to help prevent the introduction of freezing air into a building.

8-1 gpm = BH/(500 X Δt) = 20,000,000/[500 (380° – 250°)] = 307.7.

8-2 The system is self-balancing.

8-3 100°F + [2(65°F – 20°F)] = 190°F.

8-4 From fig. 8-22, pressure drop is 1.5 feet of head per 100 ft of length. Drop = (210 ft/ 100 ft) X 1.5 = 3.15 ft head. Heating capacity = 80 gpm X 500 X 20° Δt = 800,000 BH = 800 MBH.

8-5 From fig. 8-22 velocity = 34 ft/sec. at 80 gpm in 3-in. iron pipe. 3.15-ft head (prob. 8-4) = 37.8-in. head X 1000 = 37,800 milinches.

8-6
Elbows, eight at 5.4 ft (fig. 8-24) =	43.20 ft
Tees, two at 50% to branch = 0.6 ells X 2 = 1.2 ells X 5.4 ft =	6.48 ft
Tees, six at ±10% to branch = 6 X 0.1 ell = 0.6 X 5.4 ft =	3.24 ft
Tees, one at ±50% to branch (air conditioning unit) = 0.6 X 1 = 0.6 X 5.4 ft =	3.24 ft
Tee fitting at air vent near boiler = 2 elbows (given) X 5.4 ft =	10.80 ft
Six radiators and venturis at 20 ft = 120 ft of pipe =	120.00 ft
Total =	186.96 ft

30 gpm in 2-in. copper pipe = 220 milinches/ ft pipe

= 0.22 in./ft X 186.96 ft = 41.13 in. of head = 3.43-ft head piping = 3.43-ft head

Air conditioning unit and venturi fitting =	5.0-ft head
(given)	
Boiler =	4.0 ft
Five gate valves—open = 5 X 0.7 ft =	3.5 ft
Total pumping resistance =	15.93-ft head
of water	

8-7 R = (1 in./0.26) + 0.68 = 4.53; U = 1/4.53 = 0.22; OD of covering = 3.5 in. + 1 in. + 1 in. = 5.5 in. (5.5 ÷ 12)π = 1.44 perimeter X 360 ft = 518.4 ft²; BH = $A U \Delta t$ = 518.4 X 0.22(215° – 65°) = 17,107 BH.

9-1 In a vacuum heating system only the condensate return piping is continuously maintained at a negative pressure (vacuum). In a vapor system both the steam supply and condensate return systems may fall into a vacuum, and at times they may both carry a positive pressure.

9-2 Because a head or height of water above the boiler water line is necessary to force the returning condensate into the boiler which is at a slightly higher pressure than the return main.

9-3 With face-and-bypass dampers temperature control is achieved by bypassing some or all of the air around the coil, while the coil is kept full of steam and thus hot at all times.

9-4 From fig. 9-7 a 3-in. pipe size is selected and velocity is 6000 fpm at zero psig. From fig. 9-8, the corrected steam velocity is 5300 fpm.

9-5
Five elbows at 6.5 ft =	32.5 ft
One tee =	13.0 ft
One angle valve =	34.0 ft
Actual length =	40.5 ft
	120.0 ft

9-6 Capacity is 42 lb/hr from fig. 9-10. Note c of fig. 9-10 indicates that runouts longer than 8 ft must be oversized one pipe size.

10-1 COP = 1750/[2544/(6 × 0.6)] = 2.48.

10-2 (42 × 12,000)/53,000 = 9.5 EER. Probably could not be improved appreciably.

10-3 41.0 psig = 41 + 14.7 = 55.7 psia. Figure 10-1 shows a saturation temperature of approximately 18°F. This is also the boiling point (temperature) and the condensing temperature.

10-4 84.82 psia from fig. 10-2.

10-5 Yes, it is subcooled 142°F (212° − 70° = 142°).

10-6 It is saturated because both liquid and vapor are present.

10-7 (a) Causes refrigerant circulation.
(b) Removes vapor from the evaporator.
(c) Compresses the vapor until its temperature is higher than that of the available condenser cooling medium (outside air in fig. 10-5).

11-1 The CV system holds cfm constant and varies air temperature; the VAV system varies air volume with essentially constant supply air temperature.

11-2 To relieve excessive building air pressure which results from the introduction of OA at the OA intake louvre, reference 15.

11-3 SHR = 20,000/(20,000 + 5000) = 0.8; ADP from chart is 52.5°F.

11-4 4 ft × 2 ft = 8 ft² face area; 3200 cfm/8 ft² = 400 fpm face velocity which gives 0.10 bypass factor or 10% of the air passes through unconditioned. At 4000 cfm 11% bypasses (see fig. 11-4).

11-5 DTD = (78° − 52°)(0.8) = 20.8°; LA = 78° − 20.8° = 57.2°;   cfm = 120,000/(1.08 × 20.8) = 5342.

11-6 With frequency inverter−30%; with throttling damper−102%; with inlet vanes−76%.

11-7 Yes, it is likely; and yes, it could.

11-8 Blow-through; and yes it can.

11-9 Same but in 2 air conditioning unit has zone-mixing dampers, and in 3 mixing dampers are out in the ducts. In 2, air conditioning unit may be either double or triple deck; but in 3 it may be only double deck.

11-10 Use rejected heat from the refrigerating machine condenser for reheat purposes.

11-11 By "transferring" heat from one part of a building where heat is in excess to other parts where heat is needed.

13-1 Room occupants = [(70 ft × 40 ft)/1000] × 150 = 420 people; OA = 420 × 10 cfm/occupant = 4200 cfm; total air = 420 occupants × 30 cfm/occupant = 12,600 cfm, or total air = (70 ft × 40 ft × 10 ft × 8)/60 = 3733 cfm; total air must be 12,600 cfm; 7% of 12,600 cfm = 882 cfm of OA which is less than the 4200 cfm above.

13-2 Room occupants = [(70 × 40)/1000] × 15 = 42 people; OA = 42 × 7.5 = 315 cfm; total air = (70 ft × 40 ft × 10 ft × 4)/60 = 1867 cfm or total air = 42 people × 20 cfm/person = 840 cfm; total air must be 1867 cfm; 5% of 1867 cfm = 93 cfm, which is less than the 315 cfm above, which governs.

13-3 20 ft × 30 ft = 600 ft² floor area × 2 (from art. 13-3) = 1200 cfm exhaust volume; (20 ft × 30 ft × 9 ft × 6)/60 = 540 cfm exhaust for six air changes per hour. The smaller amount governs (540 cfm).

14-1 400 × 1.8 = 720 people (from fig. 14-4); 720 people × 50 gpd each = 36,000 gpd total demand.

14-2 150 closets (flush tank) × 3 = 450 FU
150 tubs × 2   = 300
150 lavs × 1   = 150
                    Total = 900 FU

14-3 150 tubs × 1.5 = 225 FU
150 lavs × 0.75 = 112.5
                    Total = 337.5 FU

14-4 150 closets × 3 = 450 FU
150 tubs × 1.5 = 225
150 lavs × 0.75 = 112.5
                    Total = 787.5 FU

14-5 prob. 14-2−900 FU = 193 gpm (use curve 2, fig. 14-7)
prob. 14-3−337.5 FU = 94 gpm (use curve, fig. 14-7)
prob. 14-4−787.5 FU = 175 gpm (use curve, fig. 14-7)

14-6 prob. 14-2−3-in. pipe (use fig. 14.9)
prob. 14-3−2 1/2-in. pipe
prob. 14-4−3-in. pipe

14-7 From fig. 14-26, 90% of 0.4 gph/person = 0.36; storage tank delivery capacity (from 14-26) = 0.125 gal/person; 0.36 × 1200 people = 432 gph heater recovery; 0.125 × 1200 = 150-gal delivery capy; 150 ÷ 0.7 = 214-gal tank size.

15-1 (20 × 6 = 120) + (8 × 4 = 32) + (16 × 1 = 16) + (4 × 2 = 8) + (4 × 1/2 = 2) + (8 × 1 = 8) + (3 × 3 = 9) = 195 FU.

15-2 (4 × 4 = 16) + (3 × 4 = 12) + (4 × 1 = 4) + (2 × 1 = 2) = 34 FU; Size is 4 in. from fig. 15-11.

15-3 Two-story = 240 FU; four-story = 500 FU.

15-4 No, it must be 5 in. (fig. 15-12).

15-5 4 in. (fig. 15-13), same size top to bottom.

15-6 2 1/2 in. (fig. 15-14), would get smaller.

15-7 When the public sewer is overloaded and frequently backs up sewage into connecting buildings.

16-1 2 year = 2.9 in./hr; 10 year = 4.2 in./hr; the 10-year rain intensity is greater.

16-2 15 min. = 2.75 in./hr; 30 min. = 1.7 in./hr; the 15-min. rain is greater.

16-3 i = 4.5 in. (fig. 16-2); C_R = 0.05 for lawns; C_R = 0.80 for paved areas; C_R = 0.75 for flat-roof area; C_R = [(50,000 × 0.75) + (20,000 × 0.80) + (147,800 × 0.05)]/ 217,800 = 0.28; runoff gpm = 450 $C_R iA$ = 450 × 0.28 × 4.5 × 5 = 2835 gpm; 15-in. storm sewer required. If midrange values of C_R are used (0.85 for roofs, 0.875 for paving, and 0.175 for lawns) the runoff gpm = 450{[(50,000 × 0.85) + (20,000 × 0.875) + (147,800 × 0.175)]/217,800}4.5 × 5 = 3992 gpm and 15-in. storm sewer is still OK.

16-4 12000 ft^2/2200 (fig. 16-6) = 5.45; use six drains.

16-5 At 1/8 in./ft use 10 in. and at 1/4 in./ft use 8 in. (fig. 16-7).

16-6 750 FU = 11 (fig. 16-12) × 750 = 8250 ft^3 drainage area; 52,000 + 8250 = 60,250 ft.^{2} Combination sewer is 12 in. from fig. 16-7.

17-1 80 rooms × 4 bed spaces = 320 bed spaces; 320 × 50 gpd = 16,000 gpd.

17-2 500 people × 10 gpd/person = 5000 gpd both sewage and water consumption.

17-3 Septic tank = 3600 gal., dosing pump chamber operating volume = 3600 ÷ 6 = 600 gal.

17-4 3600 gpd × 1.25 (fig. 17-4) = 4500 ft^2 trench bottom; 4500 ÷ 3 ft wide = 1500 ft length; 1500 ft ÷ 75 ft = 20 fingers needed

18-1 $R = E/I$ = 120 V/10 A = 12 Ω.
$P = E × I$ = 120 V × 10 A = 1200 W.

18-2 $P = E^2/R$; $R = E^2/P = \overline{120^2}/150$ = 96 Ω (more than a 300-W light bulb—which is 48 Ω).

18-3 100 + 100 + 100 + 6 = 306 Ω; $I = E/R$ = 240/306 = 0.7843 A; $P = EI$ = 240 × 0.7843 = 188.2 W; V for each load = (240 (100/306) = 78.43 V; V in wiring = (6 Ω/ 306 Ω) × 240 = 4.7 V.

18-4 $1/R_T$ = (1/45) + (1/55) + (1/60) = 0.05707 R_T = 17.522 + 0.666 = 18.188 Ω; $I = E/R$ = 240/18.188 = 13.195 A; $P = I^2R$ = 13.195^2 × 18.188 Ω = 3166.9 W.

18-5 Ratio of turns must be 4160 V/480 V = 8.666.

18-6 $I_1 = I_2/8.666$ = 800/8.666 = 92.3 A.

18-7 E_2 = 13800 V (150/10,000) = 207 V; P = (400 A × 207 V)/1000 = 82.8 kVA.

18-9 $P_{kW} = (E × I_M × \cos\theta)/1000$ = (240 × 40 × .866)/1000 = 8.3 kW.

18-10 PF = kW/kVA = 6.68/[(240 × 32)/1000] = 0.87; PF = 87%.

19-1 I = (kVA × 1000)/(1.732 × E) = (375 × 1000)/(1.732 × 240) = 902 A.

19-2 $P_{kW} = P_{kVA} × $ PF = 375 × 0.9 = 337.5 kW.

19-3 I = (kVA × 1000) ÷ E = 150,000 ÷ 240 = 625 A.

19-4 Delta-connected ratio = 2 to 1 and in a Y connected service the ratio is 1.732 to 1.

19-5 Between N and A, and N and B yes, but not between N and C.

19-6 P_{kVA} = (1.732 × 240 × 340)/1000 = 256.35 kVA.

19-7 100 A/2P/2F/3W/SN.

19-8 (a) To a three-pole CB and the neutral bus bar.
(b) To a three-pole CB.
(c) To a two-pole CB.
(d) To a single-pole CB and the neutral bus bar.

19-9 From fig. 19-24, 7-#250 MCM THW's require a 3 1/2-in. conduit.

19-10 Derating is not required and fig. 19-2? indicates that #250 MCM conductor are needed; fig. 19-24 indicates that

2 1/2-in. conduit is required for 4-THHN conductors.

1 3/0 TW's have 0.3288-in.^{2} area and 1/0 TW's have 0.2367-in.^{2} area. From fig. 19-26, col. 5. $(6 \times 0.3288) + (2 \times 0.2367) = 2.4462$ in.^{2}. From fig. 19-25, fifth column, a 3-in. conduit is required.

.2 Three switches required: two three-way switches and one four-way switch.

3 36,000 VA connected load + 40% for future = 50,400 VA; 50,400 $\times$ 0.7 demand factor = 35,280 VA; 35,280/(208 V $\times$ 1.732) = 97.93 A. For 100°F ambient, correction factor = 0.82; from fig. 19-22, 97.93/0.82 = 119.43 A corrected. Fig. 19-22 indicates 1/0 TW's required; A/C resistance = 0.104 Ω/1000 ft (fig. 19-21) (0.104 $\times$ 220 ft $\times$ 1.732)/1000 ft = 0.0396 Ω in 220 ft; 0.0396 Ω $\times$ 97.93 A = 3.88-V drop. 3.88 V/208 V = 0.0186 or 1.86% voltage drop—too much. Use 2/0 TW's in 2-in. conduit (fig. 19-24). The panelboard will be a 125 A/120 V/208 V/ three-phase/four-wire/MLO panel. A 100-A panelboard could be used if necessary to save cost.

·1 From fig. 20-22, approximately 72% remains.

·2 3150 lumens from fig. 20-19; 20,000 hours life; 2770 lumens output at 40% life.

20-3 The cool white (CW) is higher at 68 LPW than the deluxe cool white (CWX) at 48 LPW.

20-4 17,500 lumens/12,100 lumens = 1.45, approximately 45% more; see figs. 20-23 and 20-25; 1000-W incandescents required, see fig. 20-12.

20-5 CU = .44 and fixtures required = (40 ft $\times$ 60 ft)/38 = 63
38 ft^2/fixture from fig. 20-30.

20-6 CU = (40 ft $\times$ 60 ft $\times$ 66 FC)/(3000 $\times$ 43 $\times$ 2) = 0.614.

20-7 CCR = [2.5(40 ft + 40 ft + 60 ft + 60 ft)]/ (40 ft $\times$ 60 ft) = 0.208; RCR = [2.5(40 ft + 40 ft + 60 ft + 60 ft)(9 ft – 3 ft)]/(40 ft $\times$ 60 ft) = 1.25.

20-8 From fig. 20-2, ρ_C = 0.81 and ρ_W = 0.44; from fig. 20-35, ρ_{CC} = 0.61 approximately.

20-9 Lamp lumens = 2880 (fig. 20-12), ρ_{CC} = 0.4 (fig. 20-35), CU = 0.28 (fig. 20-36— interpolating), LLD = 0.91 (fig. 20-39), LDD = 0.94 (fig. 20-38); lamps = (2000 ft^2 $\times$ 20 FC)/(2880 $\times$ 0.28 $\times$ 0.91 $\times$ 0.94) = 60; use 60 single lamp fixtures.

20-10 Lamp lumens = 6300 (fig. 20-19), ρ_{CC} = 0.4 (fig. 20-35); CU = 0.15 (fig. 20-36), LDD = 0.87 (fig. 20-38), LDD = 0.875 (fig. 20-39 for 425 MA lamps); lamps = (2000 ft^2 $\times$ 20 FC)/(6300 $\times$ 0.15 $\times$ 0.87 $\times$ 0.875) = 55.6; use 56 lamps.

Index

LV	low velocity
lx	lux
m	meters, length
MA	mixed air
mA	milliamps current flow
MBH	Btu per hour in thousands (1 MBH = 1000 BH)
MDP	main distribution panel
MF	maintenance factor (of lighting fixtures)
MH	metal halide, lamps
MLO	main lugs only, lighting and power panels
MOL	maximum overall length, lamps
mph	miles per hour
MRT	mean radiant temperature
MV	mercury vapor, lamps
N	neutral wire
NEC	national electric code
nm	nanometer, one-billionth meter
OA	outside air
OD	outside diameter
P	poles, electrical equipment
P-E	pressure-enthalpy (chart)
ph	electrical phases
psi	pressure, lb/in^2
psia	absolute pressure, lb/in^2
psig	gauge pressure, lb/in^2
RA	room air or return air (usually are the same)
RCR	room cavity ratio
RH	relative humidity
rpm	revolutions per minute
RS	rapid start, lamps
S	electric switch, with subscripts S_2 etc.
S_3	electric switch, three-pole
S_4	electric switch, four-pole
SA	supply air
SC	shading coefficient
SC	maximum spacing coefficient, lighting fixtures
SEER	seasonal energy efficiency ratio
SHG	solar heat gain
SI	International System (Système International)
SN	solid neutral, electrical
SP	static pressure
Sp. hum.	specific humidity, usually in grains/lb of air
Sp. vol.	specific volume, ft^3/lb
TEL	total equivalent length
ton	cooling rate, 12,000 BH
TXV	thermostatic expansion value
V	volts
VA	volt-amps
VAV	variable air volume
VCP	visual comfort probability
VHO	very high output, lamps
W	watts
WB	wet bulb temperature
WG	pressure expressed in inches or feet of water (gauge pressure)
WP	work plane, lighting
ρ_c	ceiling reflectance
ρ_{cc}	ceiling cavity reflectance
ρ_{fc}	floor cavity reflectance
ρ_w	wall reflectance